# Krause - Minkus
# STANDARD CATALOG OF
# U.S. STAMPS

## 1999 EDITION • LISTINGS 1845 - DATE

### Fred Baumann & George Cuhaj – Editors
### Robert Wilhite – Market Analyst

### Wayne Youngblood
### Publisher, Philatelics Division, Krause Publications

### Special Contributors

Steve Crippe • Albert Curulli • Stephen G. Esrati • Denis J. Norrington • Robert A. Lacey • Joann Lenz • Robert L. Markovits
Frank Marrelli • Charles & Janice McFarlane • Irving Miller • Ján Ozábal • J. Eric Stone • Marios Theodossiou

A fully illustrated catalog for the postage stamps of the United States with stories of the men, women, places and events that have made America's history.

© 1999 by
Krause Publications, Inc.

Published by

**krause
publications**

700 E. State Street • Iola, WI 54990-0001
Telephone: 715/445-2214


Please call or write for our free catalog.
Our toll-free number to place an order or obtain a free catalog is 800-258-0929
or please use our regular business telephone 715-445-2214
for editorial comment and further information.


Library of Congress Catalog Number: 98-84099
ISBN: 0-87341-682-1


Printed in the United States of America

# Contents

# A note from the Publisher

Welcome, collector, to the revised and expanded second edition of the *Krause-Minkus Standard Catalog of U.S. Stamps*!

As you may know, the Minkus catalog that served as the nucleus of the volume you now hold was developed by and named for pioneering U.S. stamp dealer Jacques Minkus.

Minkus, who operated the largest chain of stamp stores in the nation, started his stamp division in 1931 in Gimbel's Department Store in New York City. It grew over the years into one of the most respected lines of catalogs and stamp albums during the following decades. After passing through several owners, the Minkus name and line of albums, supplements and catalogs was acquired in July 1997 by Krause Publications, the world's largest hobby publisher.

It is our intention, with the reintroduction and the ongoing, continuous improvement of the *Krause-Minkus Standard Catalog of U.S. Stamps*, to restore Minkus to its rightful place as a reference every collector of United States stamps will be proud to own and use (The usual sales hype is to say "It belongs on every collector's bookshelf," but, frankly, we hope it will spend more time open on your lap or in use on the desk of your stamp den!).

Of course, stamp catalogs have been part of the hobby since its inception, dating back at least as far as the mid-1860s. U.S. catalogs were certainly already well established when Minkus was in his heyday. But Jacques felt that there was something lacking in most of them. Stated succinctly in the first line of his notes on how to use his U.S. catalog 23 years ago, he wished "to emphasize that this catalog has been compiled with the aim to give the collectors of United States Stamps more *fun and knowledge*." (That original emphasis is his and it is mine as well!)

Or, as Jacques put it in the introduction to that same work, "The collecting of postage stamps is possibly the most fascinating hobby ever discovered. The collecting of United States stamps is a particularly enjoyable branch of that hobby. The goal of this book is to further that enjoyment." As a guiding principle in creating a stamp catalog, that objective, *to further your enjoyment of the hobby,* is hard to improve upon, but all too easy to overlook. We have tried to make it our guiding star.

What's new in this second, revised edition?

On the pages that follow, you'll discover more than 3,500 newer, crisper, clearer photographs of United States stamps. We replaced many of the photographs, knowing the better illustrations will make the catalog more useful to you.

- The entire format of the text has been redesigned for convenience, to make it a more user-friendly reference. We've even overhauled the typeface to make it easier to read and use.
- You'll also find vastly expanded listings of some of the most avidly followed and widely collected U.S. back-of-the-book specialties. Listings of 1865-97 U.S. newspaper and periodical stamps have been restored to their rightful place.

- Another big feature in this catalog is a special eight-page section listing and pricing postage currency, encased postage and postage stamp envelopes of the Civil War.
- In addition, this second, revised edition offers illustrated, priced listings for many of the most popular revenue stamps, including the classic first through third issues of the 1860s, documentary stamps, stock transfer stamps, playing card stamps, proprietary stamps, wine stamps and more. And we've restored the listings for stamps from popular United States possessions, including Hawaii, Canal Zone, Ryukyu Islands, Cuba and Danish West Indies.

In all, you'll find more than 575 pages of copiously illustrated, priced listings, with easy-to-understand descriptions and all the information about the individual issues that you just won't find in any other United States stamp catalog, domestic or foreign. But then, that's what Jacques Minkus had in mind from the beginning. We think he'd approve *and we hope that you will, too.*

And don't forget, by purchasing this catalog, you are entitled to a free copy of our Minkus/Scott number cross reference. Simply return the postcard found opposite the inside back cover.

Wayne L. Youngblood

# The NEW Centurion Stock Sheets

- All plastic 8½x11" stock sheets
- Two-sided **Jet-Black Back** pages - or -
- **All-Clear** pages (to view both sides)
- 100% free of chemical softeners
- Fits standard 3-Ring (or 4-Ring) Binders

- Sizes 1-8 rows plus special sizes
- Mix singles, covers, plate blocks, booklets, miniature sheets, etc. all in the same album
- Pages always lie perfectly flat
- Deluxe padded 3-Ring Binder with Dustcase

## BONUS 1 Free pkg. with each 5 pkgs. purchased.

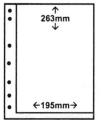

**263mm** ↕ **←195mm→**

1 Pocket  Black Back 1S
All-Clear 1C

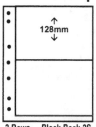

**128mm** ↕

2 Rows  Black Back 2S
All-Clear 2C

**84mm**

3 Rows  Black Back 3S
All-Clear 3C

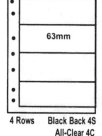

**63mm**

4 Rows  Black Back 4S
All-Clear 4C

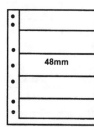

**48mm**

5 Rows  Black Back 5S
All-Clear 5C

**39mm**

6 Rows  Black Back 6S
All-Clear 6C

**33mm**

*AS LOW AS 49¢ PER PAGE*

7 Rows  Black Back 7S
All-Clear 7C

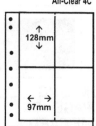

**29mm**

8 Rows  Black Back 8S
All-Clear 8C

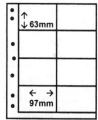

**128mm** ↕  **← →ᴺ 97mm**

4 Pocket  Black Back 2SP

**↕ 63mm  ← → 97mm**

2 Pocket  Clear 4VC8

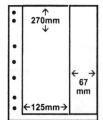

**270mm** ↕  **←125mm→  ← → 67 mm**

2 Vert. Rows  Black Back 2VDS

**270mm** ↕  **← → 97mm**

2 Vert. Rows  All-Clear 2VC

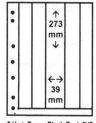

**273 mm** ↕  **← → 61mm**

3 Vert. Rows  All-Clear 3VC

**273 mm** ↕  **← → 39 mm**

5 Vert. Rows  Black Back 5VS

Standard
8½x11"
Page Size

Centurion Interleaving
Black Only          Z

## G&K CENTURION STOCK SHEETS

Sold in pkgs. of 5 pages per size   **GK-CEN** ____ (Fill in code) **"S"** Black pages, **"C"** All-Clear pages
$3.95, **SALE $3.15** ea. pkg., 10-49 pkgs. **$3.00** ea. pkg., 50 or more pkgs. **$2.90** ea. pkg.

Interleaving, pkg. of 5 **GK-CENZ** $2.95, **SALE $2.35**

| Buy 5 pkgs. - Get 1 FREE | Buy 10 pkgs. - Get 2 FREE | Buy 50 pkgs. - Get 10 FREE | Buy 100 pkgs. - Get 20 FREE |
|---|---|---|---|

## G&K DELUXE 3-RING BINDER AND DUSTCASE

**THE PRINCE:** Beautiful binder and matching dustcase with a deep grained vinyl covering. Softly padded with gold embossed binder spine. Colors: **BL, RD, GR, BK, BR**.........**GK-PR** $34.95, **SALE $26.95**, 4 or more **$25.95** ea.

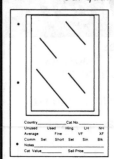 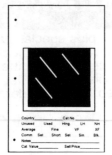  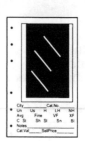 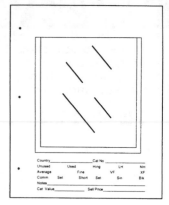
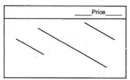 

# Catalog Introduction

While such factors as age, quantity issued, scarcity and especially demand all have a bearing on the value of a given stamp or cover, the fundamental determinants of value for any given stamp are its grade and its condition. In general, the scarcer and more valuable the basic stamp, the greater the importance of grade or centering in determining its market value.

**Grade** is a rough measure of the relationship between the printed design of the stamp and its edges or margins, a characteristic that also is often referred to as a stamp's *centering.*

Generally speaking, the more nearly equal in width all margins of a stamp are and the farther those equal margins are from the printed design, the more desirable the stamp will be to collectors. A stamp with unusually broad margins of identical width on all sides may sell for as much as 100 times the price of an otherwise identical stamp with unbalanced margins and perforations or, in the case of imperforate stamps, a copy with a straightedge cutting the printed design.

**Condition** refers to the overall appearance and quality of the stamp -- the state of its health, so to speak -- which can enhance or detract from the desirability (and hence the demand and value) of a stamp.

# Stamp Grade

Values shown in this catalog reflect the prices that you may expect to pay for a listed stamp in a grade between **fine** (visibly off-center on two sides, with margins or perforations either just touching or barely clear of the printed design on one side) and **very fine** (barely off-center on one side, with all margins or perforations almost equally distant and well clear of the printed stamp design).

This intermediate grade, which has been the predominant grade in which stamps have been collected for more than a century, is referred to as **fine-to-very-fine**, often abbreviated as "**f-vf**." To define the term more explicitly, fine-to-very-fine stamps may be perceptibly off-center to one side, or very slightly off-center on two sides, with the stamp design printed clear of all sides and untouched by any of the margins. (Imperforate stamps graded f-vf will have at least two and usually three margins clear of the printed design.)

Stamps of grades lower than fine-to-very-fine (such as **very good** and **fine**) will usually sell for less than the f-vf copies that are priced here, whereas stamps of grades higher than fine-to-very fine (including **very fine** and the elusive **extremely fine** or **superb**) will sell for more than the stamps that are priced here.

## *Unused United States stamps in a grade of fine-to-very-fine*

# Stamp Condition

Values shown in this catalog reflect the prices that you may expect to pay for a listed stamp in fault-free condition, clear of any detectable defects.

Defects of condition on stamps include (but are not necessarily limited to) tears, scrapes, thins (places where some of the paper is missing from the back of a stamp, often due to inept removal of a hinge), stains, foxing and so-called tropical toning (brown spots on the gum or perforation tips), absence of original gum, the presence of substantial hinge remnantsinclusions (pieces of foreign matter accidentally embedded in the stamp paper during manufacture), heavy, smeared or otherwise disfiguring cancellations or postal markings, pulled, torn or clipped perforations, creases, pinholes, missing corners, and faded, bleached or oxidated pigments and other color changelings (wherein the color of the stamp has changed after it was produced). Extremely defective stamps, with pieces missing , the design unrecognizable due to strains or postmarks and other serious shortcomings, may be virtually uncollectible and unsalable at any price, even if sound, well-centered examples of the same stamp have a high catalog value. The actual, nominal value of stamps in such poor condition has no relationship whatsoever to the values listed in this or any other catalog.

Stamps that have been repaired or altered (with filled thins, regumming, reperforation, repaired tears, bleaching to remove soiling or lighten a cancel, hand-printed notes on the back of the stamp) also are generally regarded as defective and valued accordingly. Repaired stamps may be quite presentable and collectible, but they will generally have only a fraction of the value of a comparable, sound example of the same stamp. Knowingly attempting to represent and sell a repaired copy of a damaged stamp as a sound copy in original condition is fraud.

Just as defects and other undesirable traits detract from a stamp's condition, thereby diminishing its value, exceptionally desirable aspects of a stamp's condition can enhance that value, sometimes substantially.

Positive attributes to a stamp's condition can include unusually wide margins on all sides, exceptionally fresh-looking paper and ink color and sharpness of the printing, unusually crisp, sharp and regular perforations (especially on older stamps), the presence of margin selvage (especially with a plate number or other marginal printing of significance) and, on 19th-century stamps, most or all of the original gum.

# Minkus Catalog Values

Values in the price columns reflect either unused, original-gum fine-very fine stamps (UnFVF) or canceled fine-very fine stamps (UseFVF). For stamps issued since 1940, the price grades reflect mint never-hinged very fine (MNHVF) and canceled very fine (UseVF) stamps. Most unused stamps since 1940 are collected in mint, never-hinged condition, with full, undisturbed and unblemished original gum on the back.

Where a stamp or other catalog-listed item is seldom sold publicly or frequently, values appear in italics. Where adequate pricing information for a specific item has proven to be currently unobtainable (as in the case of a recently discovered error or, more prosaically, a common plate block in used condition) in the place of a value a line appears (−).

Every reasonable effort has been made to make the values in this catalog as accurate, realistic and up-to-date as possible. Sources for pricing information may include (but are not necessarily limited to) dealers' published retail price lists and advertisements, auction catalogs with published prices realized, and prices solicited from selected dealers, individuals and collector organizations. This information may have been reviewed for accuracy and consistency by individual specialists-collectors and specialist-dealers.

The minimum stamp value in this catalog (20¢) represents the cost to a retail stamp dealer to maintain in inventory and supply to a collector on demand a single copy of even the most common stamp in fault-free condition and a grade of fine-to-very-fine. The comparable minimum for a first day cover is $1. These figures more accurately reflect a dealer's cost of doing business than the scarcity of a given stamp or FDC.

Values in this catalog do not reflect the generally much lower cost of stamps acquired in mixtures, collections, bulk lots or other large-quantity purchases, nor stamps sold at unusually advantageous prices to attract additional business or offered as approvals, premiums, and so forth. In addition, some stamps can be acquired at lower prices through public auctions and mail-bid sales in which the collector may sometimes secure a lot at an uncontested minimum bid or reserve price.

The publishers of this catalog neither buy or sell stamps.

# Minkus Catalog Listings

Shown nearby is a typical listing from the catalog , displaying most of the kinds of information that this catalog can provide.

**1987. LOVE STAMP ISSUE** *Gravure, perforated 11 1/2 x 11.*

CM1212 *Love*

| CM1212 | | | MNHVF | UseVF |
|---|---|---|---|---|
| 22¢ | **multicolored,** tagged *(811,560,000)* | | .35 | .20 |
| | Plate block of 4 | | 2.75 | |
| | FDC *(Jan. 30, 1987)* | | | 1.00 |

**A. Year of Issue**

**B. Title of Issue** often as assigned by the U.S. Post Office Department or the U.S. Postal Service.

**C. Description of Issue** a brief synopsis of the person, place or thing depicted on or commemorated by the issue, with information on any special characteristics or significance and any series of which it is a part.

**D. Printing** details of the type of printing, printer(s) and gauge of the perforations or rouletting.

**E. Minkus Catalog Number** appears adjacent to the image of the stamp and also at the beginning of the corresponding priced listing for stamps in a grade of fine-to-very-fine. Collectors can use the Minkus catalog numbers to organize their collections, and to identify stamps when buying, selling or exchanging stamps for their collections. Minkus catalog numbers also are used in Minkus stamp albums and supplements.

Each Minkus catalog number refers to a specific stamp. Varieties of that stamp are identified by suffixes appended to the basic catalog number (see item N). Where stamps that are similar in appearance are regarded as distinct issues, collectors are referred to the other issue or issues in a footnote (see item O).

With but few exceptions, and unlike other catalogs, Minkus catalog numbers are assigned in strict chronological sequence, and definitive issues (stamps that may go back to press for additional printings at any time to furnish new stocks) are listed separately from commemorative issues (typically printed in a single, much smaller run than their definitive counterparts). Definitive series that extend over many years are identified by series name, but are listed in the order and at the intervals at which they were released by the U.S. Postal Service. This avoids the confusing situation clumps of stamps from an ongoing series being listed at random and arbitrary intervals throughout the catalog, and the necessity of introducing additional subnumbers (e.g., 123B, 123C, 123D) due to a miscalculation of the number of stamps in a given set or series. The stamps are organized into their natural sets in Minkus stamp albums and supplements.

Minkus catalog numbers consist of numerals only for regular definitive issues (e.g., Minkus 123, which refers to the Continental Bank Note Co. 5c Prussian blue Zachary Taylor definitive released in 1875). Other types of postage and revenue stamps listed in this catalog are indicated by a suffix. "CM" indicates commemorative stamps (e.g. Minkus CM123, which refers to the 3c blue Byrd Antarctic Expedition II commemorative of 1933), "A" indicates airmail stamps (e.g. Minkus A123, which refers to the 45c multicolored Hypersonic Airliner stamp in the se-tenant block of four from the Future Mail Transportation issue of 1989), and so on.

**G. Description of Image** sometimes but not invariably the same as item B, this is intended to represent the design title by which collectors refer to the individual stamp. In practice, many stamps are readily recognized both ways. For example, Minkus CM24 is well-known to stamp collectors both as the $1 denomination from the Trans-Mississippi commemoratives of 1898 (the title of the issue) and as the $1 black Cattle in a Storm commemorative (the description of the image).

**H. Denomination** is the numeric value of the stamp (or in the case of a lettered value issue or an un-valued issue, the equated value at time of issue.

**I. Color(s)** when a single color or up to three distinct colors are used they are listed, else the term multicolor is used.

**J. Tagging** where relevant, on selected U.S. stamps beginning in the 1960s, refers to the presence of a special ink on the face of the stamp visible only under ultraviolet light, used to position the envelope on which the stamp is affixed correctly so that the cancellation will be applied in automated facing-canceling equipment.

**K. Quantity Printed** is recorded, where available, typically for U.S. commemorative and airmail issues. For U.S. definitives, which may go back to press many times in the course of their working life, accurate figures are rarely available. Quantities include accurate counts and approximate estimates made by the U.S. Post Office Department and Postal Service, counts of quantities shipped but not including stamps returned, unused or destroyed when the issue was taken off sale and, in some cases, accurate counts of copies sold.

**L. Catalog Values** are expressed in U.S. dollars for unused stamps (UnFVF) and used stamps (UseFVF) in **fine-to-very-fine** condition for issues prior to 1940, and for mint never-hinged (MNH) and used (Use F-VF) for post 1940 releases. Unused stamps refer to those that have not been canceled with most of their original gum (for 19th century issues) or full original gum, lightly hinged (for early 20th century stamps). Stamps issued without gun are identified in the listings. Used stamps refer to those that have been canceled correctly in the course of performing their intended function.

**M. Date of Issue** is displayed, in most cases on the same line as that used for the basic first day cover listing.

**N. Additional Varieties** includes (where relevant) plate blocks, se-tenant configurations, paper type, gum type, tagging presence and type, perforation varieties, major errors, plate flaws and varieties.

**O. Footnotes** convey additional important information about the stamp and related varieties or issues.

# Introduction to Stamps

The ability to accurately identify a stamp is indispensible to your full enjoyment of and participation in the stamp hobby. Differences in printing, gum, paper, watermark, ink, perforation, luminescence and design — variations that may be slight, but which are readily apparent to the trained eye — can be the key to getting the most out of the time you spend with your collection. They also can be the difference between a common stamp that is worth a handful of pennies and a rarity that is valued at thousands of dollars.

There is no substitute for the knowledge that you can gain from the experience of closely examining and working with stamps, not only those in your own collection, but also those that you can read about in philatelic literature, and see on display at stamp shows and, if you are fortunate, in the albums of friends at the local stamp club.

The following text is intended to familiarize you with the basic considerations of collecting stamps and the terminology and jargon of the stamp hobby. Inquiries, suggestions and requests for additional clariffications may be addressed to Editor, Krause-Minkus Stamp Catalog, Krause Publications, 700 East State Street, Iola, WI 54990-0001. (www.krause.com)

# Stamp Printing

All stamps may be characterized by the technique or techniques by which they are printed. Although others exist, five primary printing technologies have been used, alone or in combination, on virtually all United States postal paper: intaglio; lithography; gravure; letterpress; and embossing. (Since 1989, holography also has been used to print the special foil patches that have served as stamped images on several U.S. stamped envelopes.)

**Intaglio** (also known as Line-Engraving, Engraving, Etching)

The first step in the intaglio process is creating a **master die**, a small, flat block of soft steel upon which the stamp design is recessed engraved in reverse. The original art intended for use on the stamp is photographically reduced to the appropriate size, and will serve as a tracing guide for the initial outline of the design on steel.

The highly skilled and detailed work of creating the master die is done by an engraver, who lightly traces the design on the steel, then slowly develops the fully detailed engraving, using gravers, burins and other small chisel-like tools to carve a fine pattern of precisely positioned grooves that collectively form the finished image.

At various points during the engraving process, the engraver hand-inks the dies and makes an impression to check his progress, thereby creating incomplete images what will become the finished design, known as **progressive die proofs**.

After the engraving is complete, the soft steel of the master die is hardened greatly through various processes so that it will be able to withstand the stress and pressure of the subsequent operations that are needed to convert it into an intaglio printing plate.

Next, a **transfer roll** is prepared, consaisting of a roll of soft steel mounted on a mandrel which, as the name implies, is used to transfer the engraved subject from the master die to the intaglio printing plate. A blank roll of soft steel, mounted at the center of a mandrel, which is a metal axle of lesser diameter. The mandrel is placed in a transfer press, in which it rotates freely, and the highly polished soft steel of the transfer roll is brought into contact with the hardened master die in the bed of the press.

The bed of the transfer press is slowly rocked back and forth under increasing pressure, forcing or "rocking in" the soft steel of the transfer roll in every finely engraved line of the hard master die, and eventually transferring the complete engraved image. The resulting design on the transfer roll, now positive in appearances (with its design components as they are intended to appear on the printed stamp), is referred to as a **relief transfer**, because the lines of engraving that were carved into the master die stand out on the completed roll. The soft steel of the transfer roll is hardened, as was the master die before it, after the number of relief transfers that are required have been created.

Because the relief is what is used to create the intaglio printing plate, any imperfections during the creation of the relief transfer may result in flaws that will appear on the finished stamps. A small fleck of foreign material present during the rocking-in process may leave a mark on the relief transfer. Similarly, imperfections in the steel of the transfer roll may cause the loss of part of the design from the master die. These flaws are known as **relief breaks**, which appear as small, uninked areas on the finished stamp. Reliefs also may be deliberately modified to minimize or rectify such flaws, resulting in what is referred to as an **altered relief**, the characteristics of which again will be expressed on the finished stamp.

When the transfer roll has been completed and hardened, it is used to rock in the design to a large plate of polished, soft steel, where it again appears in reversed form as on the original master die. Layout lines or position dots are placed to precisely locate the transfer roll over the plate, and may sometimes later appear on stamps if they are not burnished away during final plate preparation.

It is during this process that double transfers, shifted transfers and dropped transfers occur.

A **shifted transfer** on a plate is one that shows doubling of part ot or all the design (typically one edge or corner of the design), usually because the relief transfer shifted slightly while the design was being rocked into the printing plate.

A similar effect also can be achieved on the plate when a defective transfer is incompletely removed, and a second transfer is rocked in over it. Any place where the engraving of the original transfer remains and is not covered by the second transfer is likely to appear on the printed stamp as a **double transfer** (or, in cases where traces of two previous transfers exist, a **triple transfer**). Sometimes the printers need to delete the original transfer from a plate and enter it from scratch again. Should this completed transfer show some traces of the original, impression, it is referred to as a **partial double transfer**.

A **dropped transfer** is one that is made normally but is misaligned with respect to the other designs on the plate. A stamp printed from such a dropped transfer will be noticably out of alignment with the stamps around it in the final sheet.

Failure to center the transfer roll correctly on the plate will result in the failure of the relief transfer to completely record all portions of the master die, resulting in the loss of the edge of the engraved design on the finished stamp. This is known as a **short transfer**,

The impressions of the transfer roll on the plate often are referred to as **subjects**, and as many of these subjects are transferred as are required for the final plate (typically 200 or 400 subjects on most plates up to the 1950s and 1960s).

When all the subjects have been put in place, all position dots, layout lines and any other minor scratches, burrs or imperfections are removed from the printing surface. With the addition of marginal and other sheet markings including guide lines, arrows and plate numbers, a **plate proof** is printed to confirm that the plate is rerady to produce stamps. (**Trial color proofs** may also be printed in a variety of colors other than those eventually selected for the finished stamps, to test the clarity and appearance of the finished print in different hues.) When these impressions are approved, the **printing plate** is machined for fitting onto a press, hardened and sent off to the plate vault, ready to be used.

On the press, the intaglio plate is inked and its smooth surface is wiped clean, leaving ink only in the lines created by the relief transfer. Paper is then forced under pressure into the engraved recessed lines, the ink of which is transferred to the surface of the stamp paper. When dry, the lines of raised ink on the intaglio stamp are slightly raised, giving such stamps their characteristic crisply ridged feel, and slight depressions (known as debossing) on the back of the stamp show where therse inked lines appear on the front.

For the first century or so of U.S. intaglio stamp production, prior to the advent of modern, high-speed presses, paper used in intaglio stamp production often was moistened to facilitate the transfer of the ink, known as a **wet printing**. However, this sometimes led to uneven shrinkage by the time the stamps were perforated, resulting in improperly perforated stamps, or misperfs. More modern presses that supplantred early models do not require the use of moistened paper, thus giving rise to stamps that exist in both **wet print** and **dry print** versions.

Dry Printing

Wet Printing

Until 1915, only **flat press plates** were used to print engraved United States stamps. **Rotary press** printing was introduced in that year and slowly spread to account for an ever larger share of U.S. stamp production. Older **rotary press plates** require additional machining , and are curved under pressure to fit the press cylinder. The stretching of the plate during the curving process distorts the subjects on it, with the result that stamps printed from rotary press plates usually are longer or wider than the same stamps printed from flat plate presses. The two basic versions of the Harding Memorial Issue (Minkus CM60 and CM62) provide a good example of this frequently encountered phenomenon. With the exception of the 1919 coil waste issues (Minkus 410-12), all rotary press issues up to 1953 have between one and four **gum breaker ridges** per stamp, impressed on the gum to break its even surface across thebeack of the stamp during manufacture to inhibit the natural tendency of rotary press-printed stamps to curl.

In the early days of intaglio flat-plate printing, heavily worn plates were sometimes spruced up to give additional service by re-entering their designs, reapplying the transfer roll to the old plate to sharpen worn-down designs. However, if the registration between the transfer roll and the engraving on the worn plate is not exact, or if the original transfer is not completely burnished flat before the design is rocked in again, the result is often a **re-entry**. In a **re-entry**, another sort of **double transfer** can be created, which will appear on stamps printed from such a subject as a design with portions of the previous, worn design still visible.

If the alignment is exact and the placement of the transfer roll is true, a skillful re-entry may be all but undetectable.

Other, slightly less radical techniques of rendering a worn plate fit for continued use usually require that the plate be softened by having its temper drawn (generally by the precise application of heat and cooling) for retooliong by hand. Among the techniques involved are **retouching** (the deepening or modification of lines by etching), and **recutting** (the deepening or alteration of lines with an engraving tool). If the resulting inked impression varies slightly from the original, it is referred to as a **re-engraved** stamp.

The intricate line patterns of intaglio printing are an excellent safeguard against would-be counterfeiters, but additional techniques also have been used to make intaglio stamps even more difficult to forge. One of these that was especially popular in the early days of U.S. stamp production was the incorporation of **lathework** and other **engine-turned designs** into the backgrounds and frames of various issues -- complicated and precisely repeated designs produced on a mechanical device called an engraving engine. Examples of such patters can clearly be seen in the frame and spandrels of the 1851 3c Washington stamps (Minkus 10-11) and the complex frame of the 1860 24c Washington (40).

**Bicolored** engraved stamps, such as the high values of the 1869 Pictorial issue (92-96), the 1901 Pan-American commemoratives (CM26-31) and the 24c Jenny airmail stamp of 1918 (A3), are created by passing the printing sheet through a flat-bed press two times, once with a plate to print the frame, and a second time, with a second plate inked in a different color, to print the vignette at the center of the design. Performing either of these operations with the sheet incorrectly oriented would result in one part of the stamp beiung printed upside-down in relation to the rest  of the design, creeating the category of major error referred to as inverted-center (or inverted-frame) errors, or **inverts**, in common parlance.

Except for such bicolored issues, all other engraved U.S. stamps for more than a century were single-color designs until the advent of the **Giori Press** at the Bureau of Engraving and Printing in 1957. The Giori Press, capable of intaglio printing in two or three colors simultaneously, made its philatelic debut with the 4c 48-Star Flag commemorative (CM406) on July 4, 1957, and soon made a distictive mark on U.S. postage stamps, including the multicolored high values of the Champions of Liberty series, the Conservation series and the American Credo series.

Another innovation in intaglio printing was the **Huck Multicolor Press**, first used in 1969 to print the first multicolored U.S. coil stamp, the 6c Flag and White House coil (650), followed by the 6c Angel Gabriel stamp from the 1969 Christmas issue (649). The Huck Press not only  printed in as many as nine colors and applied phosphorescent taggant to stamps, but also gummed

and perforated them all at the same time.

**Lithography** (also Photolithography, Offset Lithography, Stone Lithography, Dilitho, Planography, Collotype)

Lithography uses the principle that oil and water do not mix to produce a printed design. The design is produced from original artwork and transferred in an oily or greasy ink onto the printing surface, originally a prepared surface of stone (from which lithography takes its name) but now more frequently a metal surface. This greasy design can attract and hold the ink for transfer onto the surface to be printed, while the rest of the plate is moistened with an acidic fluid that repels such ink, corresponding to the uninked portions of the design. To create a plate, special transfer paper is used to make duplicates of the desired design from the original lithographic stone or plate, which are in turn assembled to create the final lithographic printing plate.

In a well-crafted lithographic stamp, the design may have fine and sharply printed lines as in an intaglio stamp, but its design also will have distinct, solidly inked areas that are not to be seen either on intaglio or on gravure issues. Also, unlike either intaglio printing (where lines of ink are raised on the surface of the stamp) or letterpress printing (where the inked areas are impressed into the paper, leaving a debossed surface on the back of the stamp), both sides of a stamp printed by lithography are completely flat.

**Offset Lithography**, also known as offset printing refers to a refinement of the basic lithographic technique, whereby a greasy ink impression on a rubber blanket transfers the lithographic image from the printing surface to the paper. The first use of offset lithography on regular United States postage stamps took place with the Washington-Franklin definitives of 1918-20 (Minkus 403-09), when the technique was introduced due to manpower and material restrictions on intaglio printing caused by World War I. Offset lithography and intaglio were used together in printing the 5c Homemakers commemorative of 1964 (CM538) and the 1976 Bicentennial souvenir sheets (CM839-42), which showcased the ability of lithography to convey subtle textures, tints and tones.

Because of its greater ease of use and range of applications, offset lithography has largely replaced lithography today, and is now frequently (but actually erroneously) referred to simply as "offset."

**Gravure** (including such variants as Photogravure, Rotogravure, Heliogravure)

The preparation of stamps for printing by gravure begins with the photographing of the intended design through a fine mesh, referred to as a dot-matrix screen, which renders it onto a metal plate as a pattern of tiny dots. A chemical process etches this fine dot or halftone pattern onto the plate, where it is converted into a multitude of shallow pits or depressions, known as cells, which hold the ink during the printing process.

In the gravure printing process, the paper pressed against the gravure plate lifts the ink out of the **cells** to produce the intended design. Deeper, larger cells produce the more heavily inked and frequently darker portions of the printed design, with shallow, small cells producing more lightly inking and often lightly colored areas on the stamp.

The chief use of gravure is in producing multi-colored stamps. Using only the primary colors red, yellow and cyan (blue), along with black, gravure's dot pattern can be combined and recombined tro furnish almost any color that might be required. These overlapping patterns of dots, clearly visible under magnification, are they key characteristic by which gravure stamps may be easily identified.

The first gravure U.S. stamps were printed by private firms: the 1967 5c Thomas Eakins commemorative (Minkus CM585), printed by Photogravure & Color Co. of Moonachie, N.J.; and the 1968 6c Walt Disney issue (CM602), printed by the Achrovure Division of Union-Camp Corp. in Englewood, N.J. In 1970, Guilford Gravure Inc. of Guilford, Conn., produced both the se-tenant Anti-Pollution issue (CM643-46) and all the Christmas stamps (655-59) for the Bureau of Engraving and Printing.

The following year, the BEP acquired the multicolor Andreotti Press, and began printing its own gravure stamps, the first of these being the 8c Missouri Statehood issue (CM654).

**Letterpress** (also known as Typography, Surface Printing, Flexography, Dry Offset, High Etch)

Essentially the oppositeof intaglio printing, in letterpress printing it is the raised rather than the incised areas of the printing plate that are inked to print the finished design. In fact, the process of creating the printing plate is an inversion of the intaglio process as well, with an additional step in which the design is transferred to another surface before the creation of the transfer roll. This results in the transfer roll having a recessed rather than a relief design, which means that the final plate will have the areas that are to be inked raised above rather than carved into the surface, similar to a rubber handstamp.

Reproducing a letterpress transfer electromechanically is referred to as **electrotype** or **stereotype** production, and these are then gathered together in the desired configuration to form the plate from which stamps are produced. A plate for letterpress printing made using the assembled electrotypes is referred to as an **electroplate**.

The first postage stamps for nationwide use to make use of letterpress printing were the first newspaper and periodical issues of 1865 (Minkus N1-4), which was printed by the National Bank Note Co. in combination with embossing and an engine-turned engraved design to create an almost forgery-proof set. The American Bank Note Co. also combined offset vignettes showing the flags with engraved frames in 1943-44 to produce the Overrun Countries series (CM251-63). More typically (and less dramatically), letterpress was used to create the Molly Pitcher and Hawaii Sesquicentennial overprints of 1928 (CM79-81), the Kansas-Nebraska overprints of 1929 (495-516) and the many different Bureau precancels used over the years.

As with a piece of paper printed using a handstamp or a typewriter, paper printed by letterpress will show a slight depression (debossing) in the printed portion of the printed side of the paper, and a slight elevation (embossing) on the reverse side of the paper. This is characteristic of this printing method.

**Embossing** (also Colorless Embossing, Blind Embossing, Relief Printing)

Not truly a printing technique (since, technically, ink need not be involved), embossing is, however, an important security technique used on U.S. postal paper (chiefly stamped envelopes). In embossing, a design is carved into a die, which is reproduced to yield a shallow, three-dimensional sculpture from which additional embossing dies are made. A similar back plate, or platen, mirroring the design is created, and the two sides are pressed together to create the embossed image (often with ink on the inside of the die in front, producing the inscribed, denominated printed collar around the embossed portrait or image).

Embossing also has been used on some U.S. stamps, including the first issue newspaper and periodical stamps of 1865.

## Stamp Components and Characteristics

If a stamp's image is derived in large measure from its printing (and the techniques used), the rest of the characteristics that define it have to do with the materials used in the stamp's creation -- ink, gum, paper and separation technique -- and some of the key obserevable characteristics of these materials, including the watermark, the method of stamp separation and the gauge of its perforations or rouletting,, as well as the presence or absence of luminscence.

Examples may be found of otherwise identical stamps that differ in only one or two subtle respects, creating, at the least, two interesting varieties to seek out for your album and, at the most, an opportunity for the obwservant stamp collector to pick out a gem amid a pile of perfectly common postage. Few of us may ever have such an experience, to be sure, but fortune favors those who have prepared. Contrarily, collectors who are unaware that a rarity exists will never find it.

## Ink and Color

Ink is the basic stuff of printing, typically consisting of a finely powdered admixture or suspension of mineral, natural organic or synthetic organic pigment in a liquid solvent or base.

Ink is directly related to color. Many of the inks used in printing 19th-century stamps were mixed by hand to the closely guarded specifications of the private printing firms that did the work, and often varied perceptibly from batch to batch. This gave rise to at least some of the many collectible shades and hues found on a number of classic U.S. issues, such as the 24c Washington definitives (Minkus 54-56) of 1861-63.

This wealth of color varieties continued briefly even after the Bureau of Engraving and Printing assumed responsibility for printing virtually all U.S. stamps in 1894, best reflected in the manmy shades of the 2c issues of 1894 (170-74) and 1895-988 (189-92). Thereafter, inks became coinsiderably more standardized and the number and variety of color varieties decreased consieriably. Still, there are some highly collectible exceptions to this rule, such as the 1922 11c Hayes definitive (430).

One consequence of the arrival of single-press-run multicolor printing in the 1950s and 1960s was that minor variations in the individual colors on a stamp became harder to clearly discern, and in time came to be largely ignored, except on monochrome engraved stamps where such varieties remained easy to see. At the same time, however, there slowly developed a considerable increase in the number of color-omitted errors -- errors that could never have taken place on monochrome intaglio stamps.

An important transition in inks took place in the 1970s under federal health regulations, when solvent-based inks used at the BEP were screened for potential toxicity and adverse health and environmental effects, and replaced with new, safer water-based inks of similar color. As a result, different shades can be seen on the versions of some values of the Prominent Americans and Americana definitives printed both before and after this period.

In fact, ink is not the only variable that determines the color of a stamp. The quantity of ink, the pressure with which it is applied, the type of paper and its moisture content at the time that the printing takes place and the type of base that carries the pigment in the ink all can affect the apparent color.

Of special concern to collectors are stamps printed in **fugitive ink**, which is soluble and tends to run or dissolve when the stamp is immersed in such otherwise innocuous liquids as water or watermark fluid. Fugitive inks include synthetic organic pigments produced as derivatives of nitrobenzene (aniline inks) and some photogravure stamps as well. Some modern U.S. commeoratives printed in purple can suffer ink damage when immersed in watermark fluid, including the 1963 5c Eleanor Roosevelt (CM522), 1964 5c Amateur Radio (CM541) and the 1980 15c Edith Wharton (CM953).

Stamps that have had their color altered after they were printed, intentionally or accidentally, are referred to as **color changelings**.

Generally such changelings occur as the result of a photochemical reaction (such as prolonged exposure to sunlight or artificial light) or chemical activity (such as the useof a cleaning agent or solvent to remove soiling or lighten a heavy cancel).

One especially notorious kind of accidental color changeling is often seen on 19th-century and early 20th-century yellow, orange and red U.S. stamps in which the oxidation of sulfur compounds in the pigment turns the image a deep brown shade,occasionally approaching black. The immersion of one of these affected stamps in a mild solution of hydrogen peroxide frequently will reverse the effects of such oxidation, though it may not return the stamp precisely tro its original color.

While many collectors retain color changelings as curios, they are in fact nothing more than stamps in which the ink has been irreversibly damaged (much as the paper or perforations might be damaged). Color changelings have no place in an authentic collection of the production varieties of U.S. stamps.

## Gum

Stamp gum is known in a wide range of textures, shades and degrees of reflectivity. In addition, the gum arabic usedon many 19th-century and early 20th-century U.S. stamps was applied to the stamps in two formulations -- a harder mixture intended to remain dry in storage even during months of relatively high seasonal heat and humidity (summer gum), and a softer gum that was used on stamps produced for use in the drier, cooler months (winter gum). Most stamp gums today use dextrine or polyvinyl alcohol as a base.

Shiny and matt gum varieties are cataloged separately in those instances where both are known to be found on the same U.S. definitive stamps, even though such stamps may not be distinguishable in used condition or used on cover.

The gum on unused stamps encountered by collectors exists in a variety of conditions, which are listed, abbreviated and defined here in decreasing order of desirability:

**Mint Never Hinged (MNH)** stamps have pristine gum just as originally acquired from the post office, without a blemish, fingerprint or mark of any kind. Mint prices in this catalog for stamps issued since 1945 refer to stamps in this condition.

**Lightly Hinged (LH)** stamps have 50 percent to 100 percent of their original gum, but show a minor disturbance on the back, such as traces where a stamp hinge was previously located, so-called disturbed gum or a fingerprint. Mint prices in this catalog for stamps issued prior to 1945 are for stamps in this condition, although in practice many earlier 19th-century stamps are less likely to have much of their original gum still intact.

**Heavily Hinged (HH)** stamps have less than 50 percent of their original gum and/or remnants of older non-peelable paper hinges still affixed to the back of the stamp.

All three of the preceding types of unused stamps are sometimes referred to as **original gum** stamps, their desirability and value increasing according to the the quantity and quality of the gum. However, not all unused stamps have original gum.

**No Gum (NG)** stamps are stamps from which the original gum has been removed. For purposes of saving the stamp, it may sometimes be advisable to soak off an especially heavy hinge remnant, which may otherwise cause a stamp to warp, buckle or even tear internally. Stamps issued without gum, such as the Farley issues (CM142-61) and the Continental Bank

Note Co. special printing of the 1875 newspaper and periodical stamps (SPN5-28), are for all practical purposes regarded as mint, never-hinged in that state.

**Regummed (R, RG** or **RE)** stamps are stamp from which the original gum has been removed and other gum has been added later. When it is clearly identified as such, there is nothing objectionable about a regummed stamp, and auction catalog realizations often seem to suggest that collectors are willing to pay a bit more for an expertly regummed stamp than for its NG counterpart.

However, it is fraud to knowingly represent and sell regummed stamps as original-gum copies, which is often attempted to obtain the considerably higher price that such OG stamps typically command Similarly, it is fraudulent to chemically or otherwise remove a light cancellation from a stamp and offer it as unused. Both regumming and removal of cancellations have some skilled practiners, which is why expertization is recommended for valuable mint stamps.

## Paper

Paper, the medium for all printing, consists of dried sheets of processed vegetable fiber laid down on a fine screen from a water suspension. The two basic broad classifications of paper are **laid paper** in which the lines left by the screen during the papermaking process are still visible in transmittefd light, and **wove paper**, which has no such visible grain or lines. Papers also may be categorized as thin or thick, soft or hard, and according to its naturally occurring color (as in the listings for some U.S. stamped envelopes).

A very thin, hard translucent paper known as **pelure** also has occasionally been used for U.S. stamps, including the 1847 5c and 10c St. Louis postmaster provisionals (Minkus PM28-29). **India paper**, refers both to a softer, thin translucent paper used for pulling intaglio die and plate proofs and to a tougher, opaque thin paper, rarely but occasionally used in U.S. stamp printing, including varieties of the 1851 3c and 12c Washington (10p, 17p).

In addition, **colored paper** has been deliberately selected for use in specific issues, as in the orange paper of the 1956 3c Nassau Hall issue (CM395), the light Venetian red paper used for the 1965 5c Dante issue (CM549) and the tan paper of the 1976 Telephone Centennial commemorative (CM836).

**Ribbed paper**, which has actual ridges on the front or back side of the stamp, or both, was used for some of the Continental Bank Note Co. issues of 1873 (119-30). The ribs are parallel and typically run horizontally across the stamp, although vertical ribbed paper is known as well on stamps including the CBNC 15c Daniel Webster (128).

**Double paper** has two very different meanings. On the previously mentioned 1873 CBNC issues (119-30), it refers to a security paper patented by Charles F. Steel, in which a thin, weak surface paper and a thicker, stronger backing paper were bonded before printing. This produced a two-layer stamp, the printed design of which would be ruined if any attempt were made to clean a cancel after the stamp had been used.

The second meaning of double paper is in reference to the rotary presses that began producing U.S. stamps in 1915. Rotary presses print stamps on a continuous roll of paper, and when one roll of paper ends, the beginning of a new roll is spliced to the end of it so that production will not be interrupted. Stamps printed on the splice, where paper of the old and new rolls overlaps, is typically marked, cut out and discarded when the stamps are separated into sheets and panes. However, stamps printed across the splice do occasionally escape detection and survive to reach collectors, and these are known as **rotary press double paper** varieties.

**Paper with silk fibers** also was used in printing 1873 CNBC issues (119-30). As the name implies, this is paper with one or several long colored silk threads embedded in it. In this it differs from some early U.S. revenue stamps printed on so-called "silk paper," in which more numerous short, colored fibers are impressed during the papermaking process. Although it has rarely been used on U.S. stamps, a third silk-related paper is **granite paper** of the sort found on the 1967 5c Lions International issue (CM576), in which the grayish paper is shot through with short red and blue silk fibers, mimicing the veins in the rock for which it is named.

In an effort to better control uneven paper shrinkage during stamp manufacturing, in 1909 the Bureau of Engraving and Printing tried using high rag-content paper in place of the wood fiber paper then chiefly used to print stamps. This experimental stock, used for some 1c to 15c definitives and a small part of the printing of the 1909 2c Lincoln Memorial commemorative (CM42), is referred to as **bluish paper**, although many people describe it as actually more gray in color, best seem in comparing the back of the stamp to others of the same period. See the note preceding Minkus 263-72. Unscrupulous fakers have sometime attempted to simulate these pricey varieties of otherwise relatively inexpensive stamps by tinting them, so competent expertizing is recommended.

A very small number of the definitives of this same periofd were printed on a grayish, thick, hard stock known as **China Clay paper**, said to have mineral content of 5 percent to 20 percent rather than the 2 percent that was the standard at the time (although recent research conducted on paper from long-authenticated copies of these stamps failed to confirmed the presence of such clay). These China Clay paper varieties, which appear even darker than the bluish paper varieties and also are known on the 1c to 15c definitives, are cataloged here as subvarieties of the 1908-09 definitives (237p-46p).

For information about Hi-Brite paper, fluorescent papers, phosphor-tagged and pre-phosphored papers, and other papers characterized by their response to ultraviolet light, please refer to the section of this introduction on luminescence.

## Watermarks

A watermark is a pattern laid down on paper during manufacturing. Shallow designs in metal, called bits, are woven into the screen on which the pulp is formed and drained. When the paper is dry and light is transmitted through it, the impression of the designs of these bits shows as a bright pattern in the paper, which is slightly thinner where the bits were positioned.

On most stamps, watermarks also may best be seen by immersing them in **watermark fluid**, a non-aqueous fluid that will not moisten gum on mint stamps. The fluid increases the transparency of the paper, to make watermarks show more clearly as dark patterns when the stamp is placed face-down in the fluid. (Look under Ink for fugitive inks, which notes U.S. stamps printed with inks that are soluble in watermark fluid.)

The widest range of U.S. watermarks on postal paper consists of those on U.S. postal stationery, including 1873-75 postal cards (PC1-3), Official Mail envelopes of 1991 (PDEN82-83) and a wide range of watermarks on stamped envelopes of 1853-1968 (EN1-855).

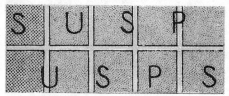

Single line USPS watermark

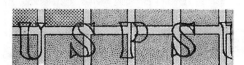

Double line USPS watermark

U.S. postage stamps are known with three watermarks: the double-line watermark "USPS" (for "U.S. Postage Stamp") used on the definitives of 1895-98 (187-210) and the single-line "USPS" watermark used on paper for the 1910-15 Washington-Franklin definitives (273-347); and the watermark "USIR" (for "U.S. Internal Revenue") intended for use on U.S. revenue stamps but used in error in a 1951 printing of the $1 Woodrow Wilson stamp from the 1938 Presidential definitive series (553w).

## Perforation Errors

In addition to plate manufacturing errors, which include double impressions in the engraving, and printing errors, which include missing or inverted colors, and folding of the paper in the press, the widest variety of errors occur in the perforation process. To aid with the explaination of these errors, we have the following illustrations. However, none of these errors occur on the stamp illustrated.

Horizontal Pair, Imperforate-between

Horizontal Pair, Imperforate Vertically

Horizontal Pair, Imperforate

Vertically Pair, Imperforate-between

Vertical Pair, Imperforate Horizontally

Vertical Pair, Imperforate

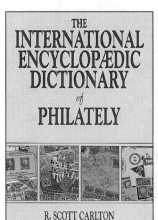

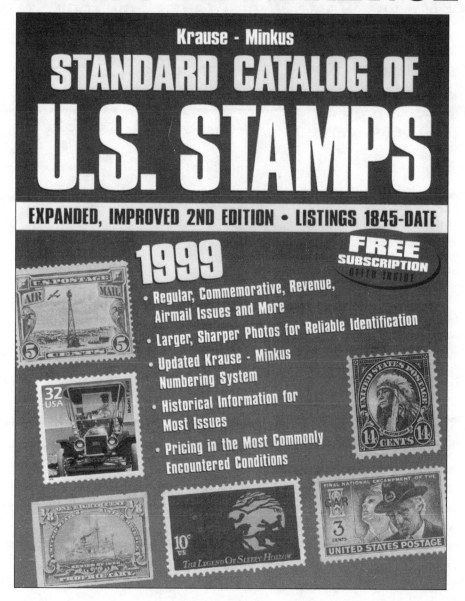

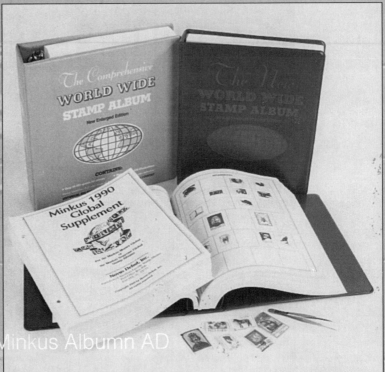

# Postmasters Provisionals

Although the first government-issued adhesive stamps did not appear until 1847, the postmaster at New York City began using his own adhesives in July 1845, immediately after the Congressional act establishing the new postal rates. He was followed by a number of postmasters in other cities, who used either handstamps or adhesives of their own design.

## 1846. ALEXANDRIA, VA. ISSUE
Postmaster Daniel Bryan issued *typset and imperforate* stamps without gum. Known copies of stamps are cut to shape. The circle of the 5¢ black-on-buff is found with 39 (Type I) or 40 asterisks (Type II).

PM1-PM2

| PM1 | | UnFVF | UseFVF |
|---|---|---|---|
| 5¢ | black on buff paper, Type I | — | — |
| | v. Type II | — | 78000. |

| PM2 | | UnFVF | UseFVF |
|---|---|---|---|
| 5¢ | blue on buff paper, Type I, on cover | — | — |

## 1846. ANNAPOLIS, MD. ISSUE
Postmaster Martin E. Revell issued red stamps printed onto the upper right corner of white envelopes. Envelopes with circular design and figure "2" hand stamped are known and believed to be locals. Blue circular designs without numeral or "PAID" were used as postmarks.

PM3

| PM3 | | UnFVF | UseFVF |
|---|---|---|---|
| 5¢ | carmine red | | 175000. |

## 1845. BALTIMORE, MD ISSUE
Envelopes in various shades of paper with the signature of the postmaster, James M. Buchanan, printed in black, blue or red. colors listed below are those of the "PAID", numeral, and oval.

PM4-PM5

| PM4 | | UnFVF | UseFVF |
|---|---|---|---|
| 5¢ | blue | — | 5000. |

| PM5 | | UnFVF | UseFVF |
|---|---|---|---|
| 5¢ | red | — | 8500. |

| PM6 | | UnFVF | UseFVF |
|---|---|---|---|
| 5¢ | black | — | 18000. |

| PM7 | | UnFVF | UseFVF |
|---|---|---|---|
| 5¢ | blue +5¢ blue | — | — |

| PM8 | | UnFVF | UseFVF |
|---|---|---|---|
| 10¢ | red | — | 17500. |

| PM9 | | UnFVF | UseFVF |
|---|---|---|---|
| 10¢ | blue | — | 15000. |

| PM10 | | UnFVF | UseFVF |
|---|---|---|---|
| 10¢ | black | — | — |

## 1846. ADHESIVE STAMP ISSUE
Adhesive stamps *printed by intaglio on white or bluish papers, and imperforate.* Eleven varieties of the 5¢ and five varieties of the 10¢ stamps are known.

PM11

| PM11 | | UnFVF | UseFVF |
|---|---|---|---|
| 5¢ | black, on white paper | — | 7500. |
| | p. Bluish paper | 25000. | 7500. |

| PM12 | | UnFVF | UseFVF |
|---|---|---|---|
| 10¢ | black, on white paper | — | 55000. |
| | p. Bluish paper | — | 60000. |

## 1846. BOSCAWEN, NH ISSUE
Postmaster Worcester Webster issued a *typset, imperforate* stamp of which only one copy is known.

PM13

| PM13 | | UnFVF | UseFVF |
|---|---|---|---|
| 5¢ | dull blue | — | 180000. |

## 1846. BRATTLEBORO, VT ISSUE
Postmaster Frederick N. Palmer issued *intaglio, imperforate* stamps printed from plates of 10 separately engraved subjects. The imprint "Eng'd by Thos. Chubbuck, Bratto," appears below the middle stamp of the bottom row. Eleven varieties are known.

PM14

| PM14 | | UnFVF | UseFVF |
|---|---|---|---|
| 5¢ | black on buff paper | — | 6000. |
| | On cover | — | 15000. |

## 1846. LOCKPORT, NY ISSUE
Postmaster Hezekiah W. Scovell issued adhesive labels with double-lined oval handstamped in red, "PAID" in black, and a hand written "5."

PM 15

| PM15 | | UnFVF | UseFVF |
|---|---|---|---|
| 5¢ | red on buff paper, on cover | — | 150000. |

## 1846. MILLBURY, MASS. ISSUE
Postmaster Asa H. Waters issued imperforate stamps printed singly from a *woodcut on a hand press.*

PM16 *George Washington*

| **PM16** | | UnFVF | UseFVF |
|---|---|---|---|
| **5¢** | **black on bluish paper** | 135000. | 25000. |
| | On cover | — | 85000. |

**1846. NEW HAVEN CONN. ISSUE** Postmaster Edward A. Mitchell used a brass hand stamp to impress envelopes with his provisional stamp as the envelopes were brought to the post office. The postmaster's signature was added to prevent forgery. Reprints are known having been made at various times between 1871 and 1932.

 PM17-18

| **PM17** | | UnFVF | UseFVF |
|---|---|---|---|
| **5¢** | **red** | — | 75000. |

| **PM18** | | UnFVF | UseFVF |
|---|---|---|---|
| **5¢** | **blue,** on buff paper | — | 75000. |

**1845. GEORGE WASHINGTON ISSUE** Robert H. Morris was the first postmaster to issue adhesive stamps in July 1845, and featured George Washington's portrait, adapted from the then-current banknotes. The New York provisionals were also used by postmasters at Albany, Boston, Philadelphia, Washington, and probably other cities with a view of testing the practical usage of adhesive stamps. Reprints in black, blue, green, red, and brown were struck from a new plate.

The original stamps were *printed by intaglio* from plates of 40 by Rawdon, Wright & Hatch. They were *imperforate* and usually initialed "A.C.M." (Alonzo Castle Monson, a clerk in the post office) before sale.

 PM19 *George Washington*

| **PM19** | | UnFVF | UseFVF |
|---|---|---|---|
| **5¢** | **black on bluish paper** | 625. | 350. |
| | On cover | — | 500. |
| | Pair | 1600. | 850. |
| | a. Signed "R.H.M." | 12500. | 2500. |
| | b. without signature | 1200. | 550. |
| | p. blue paper | 6000. | 1400. |
| | p1. Gray paper | 5000. | 1400. |

**1846. PROVIDENCE R.I. ISSUE** Postmaster Welcome B. Sayles issued *intaglio-printed, imperforate* stamps produced from copper plates containing 12 subjects. The stamps were engraved directly onto the plate.

| **PM20** | | UnFVF | UseFVF |
|---|---|---|---|
| **5¢** | **black** | 200. | 1250. |

| **PM21** | | UnFVF | UseFVF |
|---|---|---|---|
| **10¢** | **black** | 1000. | |
| | Pair, 1 each 5¢ & 10¢ | 1400. | — |

*Reprints with initials on the back were made in 1898.*

**1845-46. ST. LOUIS, MO. ISSUE** Postmaster John M. Wimer isued *imperforate* stamps printed from copper plates of six subjects. Varieties of each stamp are known. *Wove paper.*

   PM22-PM29 *Missouri coat of arms.*

| **PM22** | | UnFVF | UseFVF |
|---|---|---|---|
| **5¢** | **black on greenish paper** | 5000. | 2500. |

| **PM23** | | UnFVF | UseFVF |
|---|---|---|---|
| **10¢** | **black on greenish paper** | 4500. | 2500. |

| **PM24** | | UnFVF | UseFVF |
|---|---|---|---|
| **20¢** | **black on greenish paper** | — | 20000. |

**1846. ST. LOUIS MO. ISSUE** Previous stamps in new paper color. Varieties exist.

| **PM25** | | UnFVF | UseFVF |
|---|---|---|---|
| **5¢** | **black on gray lilac paper** | — | 4500. |

| **PM26** | | UnFVF | UseFVF |
|---|---|---|---|
| **10¢** | **black on gray lilac paper** | 4500. | 2250. |

| **PM27** | | UnFVF | UseFVF |
|---|---|---|---|
| **20¢** | **black on gray lilac paper** | — | 11000. |

**1847. ST. LOUIS MO. ISSUE** Previous stamp designs on pelure paper.

| **PM28** | | UnFVF | UseFVF |
|---|---|---|---|
| **5¢** | **black on bluish paper** | — | 6500. |

| **PM29** | | UnFVF | UseFVF |
|---|---|---|---|
| **10¢** | **black on bluish paper** | — | 5500. |

# Regular Postal Issues

The First Government stamps were put into use early in July 1847. They superseded Postmaster's Provisionals and other stamps which were thereafter not tolerated by the Postmaster General. The 5¢ stamp paid for carrying an ordinary letter up to 300 miles, and the 10¢ value was used for letters requiring higher postage.

Rawdon, Wright, Hatch & Edson of New York engraved the stamps and printed them in sheets of 200 that were cut into panes of 100 before distribution to the post offices. *The stamps were printed on thin, bluish wove paper. They were unwatermarked and imperforate, Intaglio.*

## 1847. BENJAMIN FRANKLIN ISSUE

1 *Benjamin Franklin, after painting by James R. Longacre*

**1**

| 5¢ | | UnFVF | UseFVF |
|---|---|---|---|
| | **red brown** | 4500. | 500. |
| | orange brown | 4500. | 600. |
| | black brown | 4500. | 525. |
| | bright orange brown | 5000. | 600. |
| | bright reddish brown | — | — |
| | brown orange | — | 1100. |
| | dark brown | 4500. | 475. |
| | dark brown orange | — | — |
| | dark olive brown | — | — |
| | gray brown | 4500. | 450. |
| | orange | — | — |
| | reddish brown | — | — |
| | On cover, numeral *5* cancel | | 600. |
| | Mark in "S" at upper right | 5000. | 550. |
| | Double impression | — | — |
| | Double transfer, top frame line | — | 550. |
| | Double transfer, top and bottom frame lines | — | 550. |
| | Double transfer, bottom and lower part of left frame line | — | — |
| | Double transfer, top, bottom, left frame lines | — | 1000. |
| | Double transfer. "U," "POST OFFICE," and left numeral | — | — |
| | Double transfer, top and upper part of side frame lines, "U" "POST OFFICE" | — | — |
| | FDC *(July 1, 1847)* | | |

## 1847. GEORGE WASHINGTON ISSUE

2 *George Washington, after painting by Gilbert Stuart, Boston Museum of Fine Arts.*

**2**

| 10¢ | | UnFVF | UseFVF |
|---|---|---|---|
| | **black** | 17500. | 1250. |
| | gray black | 17500. | 1150. |
| | greenish black | — | 1150. |
| | On cover | | 1800. |
| | Mark across lips | — | 1800. |

**2**

| | UnFVF | UseFVF |
|---|---|---|
| Mark in necktie | — | 1800. |
| Short transfer at top | 18000. | 1250. |
| Vertical line through second "F" of "OFFICE" | — | 1400. |
| Double transfer, left and bottom frame line | — | 1800. |
| Double transfer, "POST OFFICE" | — | 1800. |
| Double transfer, "X" at lower right | — | 1800. |
| v. Diagonal bisect on cover | | 10000. |
| v1. Horizontal bisect on cover | | — |
| v2. Vertical bisect on cover | | — |

*Government imitations of the 5¢ (in blue) and 10¢ (in Venetian red) were printed in 1947 and are listed as CM290 in the commemorative stamp section.*

## 1875. BENJAMIN FRANKLIN SPECIAL PRINTING ISSUE

**Special Printing of the 1847 Regular Issue.** New dies were engraved and the stamps were printed by the Bureau of Engraving and Printing on *gray-blue paper. They are imperforate, without gum and both shorter and wider than the originals. Intaglio.* Reproductions on laid paper are known. Not valid for postage.

1 *Original (1847): The top edge of Franklin's shirt touches the frame on a level with the top of the "F" of "FIVE".*

SP1 *Reproduction (1875): The top of the shirt is on a level with the top of the figure "5".*

*2 Original (1847): The left and right vertical outlines of the coat point at the "T" of "TEN" and between the respectively.*

*SP2 Reproduction (1875): Above lines point to the right edge of "X" and to the center of the "S" of "CENTS".*

| SP1 | | UnFVF | UseFVF |
|---|---|---|---|
| 5¢ | **red brown** *(4,779 copies sold)* | 800. | |
| | brown | 800. | |
| | dark brown | 800. | |

## 1875. GEORGE WASHINGTON SPECIAL PRINTING ISSUE

| SP2 | | UnFVF | UseFVF |
|---|---|---|---|
| 10¢ | **black** *(3,883 copies sold)* | 950. | |
| | gray black | 950. | |

**1851. BENJAMIN FRANKLIN ISSUE** The 1851-57 Regular Issue Series consisted of 1¢, 3¢, 5¢, 10¢, and 12¢ denominations, issued to cover the needs of a rapidly expanding postal service.

While the production methods of the day were excellent, they were not of uniform consistancy. As a result, more than one type of some of the stamps are recognized by collectors. It will add to your pleasure to determine the correct types of your stamps through the use of illustrations in this catalog.

Toppan, Carpenter, Casilear & Co. printed the stamps on *unwatermarked* paper. *Intaglio, imperforate.*

*3, 18 Benjamin Franklin, after bust by Jean Antoine Houdon. For detailed descriptions of Types I-V, see Nos. 3-9 and 18-24.*

*3 Type I is the most complete design of the various types of this stamp. It shows the full scroll work at the top and bottom of the design. The ornaments in the upper right corner are "doubled".*

| 3 | | UnFVF | UseFVF |
|---|---|---|---|
| 1¢ | **blue,** Type I | 175000. | 15000. |
| | dark blue | — | — |
| | pale blue | — | — |
| | On cover | | 20000. |
| | Pair, one each Type I and Type II | — | 25000. |
| | FDC (July 1, 1851) | | |

## 1857. BENJAMIN FRANKLIN TYPE IA REGULAR ISSUE

*4, 19 Type Ia has the design complete at the bottom but imcomplete at the top.*

| 4 | | UnFVF | UseFVF |
|---|---|---|---|
| 1¢ | **blue,** Type Ia | 25000. | 6500. |
| | On cover | | 7000. |
| | Curl on "C" | 26000. | 7000. |
| | Curl on shoulder | 26000. | 6500. |
| | *Earliest documented cover:* (April 19, 1857) | | |

## 1851. BENJAMIN FRANKLIN TYPE IB ISSUE

*5 Type Ib has the design at the top complete and the design at the bottom nearly complete. Type Ib is often mistaken for Type I.*

| 5 | | UnFVF | UseFVF |
|---|---|---|---|
| 1¢ | **blue,** Type Ib | 9000. | 3500. |
| | dark blue | 9000. | 3000. |
| | pale blue | 9000. | 3000. |
| | On cover | | 3500. |
| | FDC *(July 1, 1851)* | | 130000. |

*Catalog prices for the above stamp are for nice examples of the type. Stamps with a slightly less complete design at the bottom are worth about one-fourth of the above prices.*

## 1857. BENJAMIN FRANKLIN TYPE II ISSUE

*6, 20 Type II has the top line always complete, the top ornaments complete or may be partially cut away. The bottom line is always complete, while the little balls of the bottom scrolls and the bottom of the lower plume ornaments are missing. 1/3 to 1/2 of the listed value.*

| 6 | | UnFVF | UseFVF |
|---|---|---|---|
| 1¢ | **blue,** (Plate 1) Type II | 500. | 95.00 |
| | dark blue | 500. | 95.00 |
| | pale blue | 500. | 95.00 |
| | On cover | | 100. |
| | Double transfer | 500. | 100. |
| | Plate 2 *(Dec. 5, 1855)* | 500. | 95.00 |
| | Cracked plate | 675. | 225. |
| | Double transfer | 500. | 95.00 |
| | Triple transfer | 800. | 250. |
| | Plate 3 *(May 6, 1856)* | — | 325. |
| | Double transfer | — | 350. |
| | Plate 4 | | |
| | *(April 19, 1857)* | 2000. | 500. |
| | Curl in hair | — | 650. |
| | FDC *July 1, 1851)* | | 17500. |

## 1851. George Washington Issue

7, 21 *Type III has both the top and bottom lines broken. It should be noted particularly that the side ornaments are complete. If they are not, the stamp has been cut out of a perforated stamp of Type V (No. 24.) The finest examples of No. 7 are found in position 99R2, which is why that item is listed separately.*

| 7 | | UnFVF | UseFVF |
|---|---|---|---|
| 5¢ | **blue,** Type III | 7500. | 1600. |
| | On cover | | 1800. |
| | Position 99R2 | 12000. | 3250. |

## 1851. Benjamin Franklin Type IIIa Issue

8, 22 Type IIIa has the outer line broken at the top or bottom of the stamp but both lines are not broken on the same stamp.

| 8 | | UnFVF | UseFVF |
|---|---|---|---|
| 1¢ | **blue,** (Plate 1E), Type IIIa | 2400. | 550. |
| | Dark blue | 2400. | 550. |
| | pale blue | 2400. | 550. |
| | On cover | | 750. |
| | Double transfer, 1 inverted (blue) | 2800. | 700. |
| | Double transfer, 1 inverted (dark blue) | 2800. | 700. |
| | Double transfer, 1 inverted (pale blue) | 2800. | 700. |
| | Plate 2 | — | — |
| | Plate 4 | — | 800. |
| | FDC *(July 1, 1851)* | | |

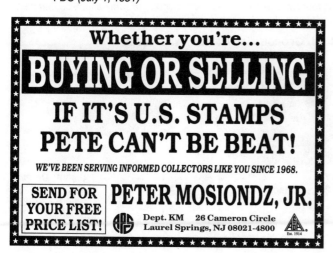
## 1852. Benjamin Franklin Type IV Issue

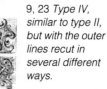

9, 23 *Type IV, similar to type II, but with the outer lines recut in several different ways.*

| 9 | | UnFVF | UseFVF |
|---|---|---|---|
| 1¢ | **blue,** Type IV (recut Type IV (recut once at top & once at bottom) | 400. | 85.00 |
| | On cover | | 95.00 |
| | Plate block of 8, w/imprint | — | |
| | Bottom frame line broken | — | 200. |
| | Cracked plate | 475. | 125. |
| | Double transfer | 425. | 90.00 |
| | Triple transfer, 1 inverted | 475. | 125. |
| | t.   Recut once at top | 425. | 85.00 |
| | t1. Recut once at top and twice at bottom | 425. | 90.00 |
| | t2. Recut twice at bottom | 450. | 95.00 |
| | t3. Recut once at bottom | 475. | 110. |
| | t4. Recut once at bottom & twice at top | 475. | 110. |
| | t5. Recut once at top & twice at bottom | 550. | 150. |
| | t6. Printed both sides | — | — |
| | t7. Double impression | — | — |
| | v.   Perforated 12 1/2 (unofficial) | — | 3000. |
| | v1. Diagonal bisect on cover | | — |
| | v2. Vertical bisect on cover | | — |
| | *Earliest documented cover:* June 18, 1852 | | |

## 1851. George Washington Issue

10, 11, 25 *George Washington after bust by J.W. Houdon, Mount Vernon, Pa. Type I with outer frame lines at top and bottom. For descriptions of Types II and III, see Nos. 26 and 27.*

| 10 | | UnFVF | UseFVF |
|---|---|---|---|
| 3¢ | **orange brown,** Type I | 1700. | 50.00 |
| | deep orange brown | 1700. | 50.00 |
| | copper brown | 1850. | 75.00 |
| | On cover | | — |
| | Mark on lower right diamond | — | 80.00 |
| | Nick on shoulder | — | 50.00 |
| | Double transfer | — | 60.00 |
| | Triple transfer | — | 200. |
| | p.   Thin, India-like paper | — | 250. |
| | t.   Printed both sides | — | — |
| | FDC *(July 1, 1851)* | | 12000. |

## 1851. George Washington Issue

| 11 | | UnFVF | UseFVF |
|---|---|---|---|
| 3¢ | **Venetian red,** Type I | 120. | 7.00 |
| | claret | 150. | 10.00 |
| | bright brown carmine | 135. | 8.50 |
| | brown carmine | 135. | 8.50 |
| | dark brown carmine | 135. | 8.50 |
| | dark violet | 135. | 8.50 |
| | dull brown carmine | 135. | 8.50 |
| | dull carmine red | 175. | 13.50 |
| | dull orange red | 120. | 7.00 |
| | dull rose carmine | 120. | 7.00 |
| | Plate block of 8 | — | |
| | Mark on lower right diamond | 165. | 20.00 |

**11**

| | UnFVF | UseFVF |
|---|---|---|
| Nick on shoulder | 135. | 7.50 |
| Cracked plate | 375. | 55.00 |
| Worn plate | 125. | 7.00 |
| Double transfer in "CENTS" | 190. | 25.00 |
| Double transfer in "THREE CENTS" | 150. | 8.00 |
| Double transfer in "THREE CENTS" & rosettes double | 215. | 35.00 |
| Triple transfer | 190. | 25.00 |
| t. Double impression | — | — |
| v. Perforated 12 1/2 (unofficial) | 1500. | — |

*Earliest documented cover:* Oct. 4, 1851

### 1856. THOMAS JEFFERSON ISSUE

12. 28-30 *Thomas Jefferson, after painting by Gilbert Stuart. Type I, with full projections at top and bottom as well as the sides. Copies that do not have these complete projections at top and bottom are trimmed from perforated varieties issued at a later date. For a description of Type II see Nos. 31 and 32.*

**12**

| 5¢ | | UnFVF | UseFVF |
|---|---|---|---|
| | **red brown,** Type I | 8500. | 900. |
| | dark red brown | 8500. | 900. |
| | Double transfer | — | 1150. |

*Earliest documented cover:* March 24, 1856

### 1855. GEORGE WASHINGTON TYPE I ISSUE

13, 33 *George Washington, after painting by Gilbert Stuart. Type I. For description of Types II-IV, see Nos. 14-16 and 34-37.*

13, 33 *Type I has the "shells" at the lower corners almost complete. The line below "TEN CENTS" is very nearly complete. The outer lines above the middle of the stamp and over the "X" in each upper corner are broken. There are three small circles on each side opposite the words "TEN CENTS".*

**13**

| 10¢ | | UnFVF | UseFVF |
|---|---|---|---|
| | **green,** Type I | 11000. | 585. |
| | dark green | 11000. | 585. |
| | yellow green | 11000. | 585. |
| | On cover | | 645. |
| | Curl in left "X" | 11500. | 660. |
| | Double transfer | 11500. | 660. |
| | FDC *(May 1855)* | | |

### 1855. GEORGE WASHINGTON TYPE II ISSUE

14, 34 *Type II has the outer line at the bottom broken in the middle, the "shells" are partially cut away, and the design is complete at the top. There are three small circles on each side.*

**14**

| 10¢ | | UnFVF | UseFVF |
|---|---|---|---|
| | **green,** Type II | 1900. | 200. |
| | dark green | 1900. | 200. |
| | yellow green | 1900. | 200. |
| | On cover | | 260. |
| | Curl opposite left "X" | 1950. | 290. |
| | Double transfer | 1950. | 270. |

*Earliest documented cover:* May 12, 1855

### 1855. GEORGE WASHINGTON TYPE III ISSUE

15, 35 *Type III has outer lines broken above the top label that contains words "U.S. POSTAGE" and the lines are broken above the "X" numerals. The shells and outer line at the bottom are partially cut away. There are three small circles on each side.*

**15**

| 10¢ | | UnFVF | UseFVF |
|---|---|---|---|
| | **green,** Type III | 1900. | 200. |
| | dark green | 1900. | 200. |
| | yellow green | 1900. | 200. |
| | On cover | | 260. |
| | Curl on forehead | 2000. | 265. |
| | Curl to right of left "X" | 2000. | 265. |
| | Double transfer at top and bottom | — | — |

*Earliest documented cover:* May 23, 1855

### 1856. GEORGE WASHINGTON TYPE IV ISSUE

16, 36 Type IV has had the outer lines at the top or bottom of the stamp, or at both places, recut. There are three small circles on each side.

**16**

| 10¢ | | UnFVF | UseFVF |
|---|---|---|---|
| | **green,** Type IV (outer line recut at top only) | 12500. | 1200. |
| | dark green | 12500. | 1200. |
| | yellow green | 12500. | 1200. |
| | On cover | | 1450. |
| | t. Outer line recut at bottom only | 12500. | 1200. |
| | t1. Outer line recut at top and bottom | 14000. | 1300. |

*All four types of the 10¢ stamp occur on the same sheet, so that pairs and blocks showing combination of these types exist.*

### 1851. GEORGE WASHINGTON TYPE I ISSUE

17, 38 *George Washington, Type I, with complete frame lines. For Type II see No. 39.*

**17**

| 12¢ | | UnFVF | UseFVF |
|---|---|---|---|
| | **black,** Type I | 2600. | 225. |
| | deep black | 2600. | 225. |
| | gray black | 2600. | 225. |
| | On cover | | 1250. |
| | Double transfer | 2700. | 250. |

**17**

| | | UnFVF | UseFVF |
|---|---|---|---|
| | Recut in lower left corner | 2800. | 275. |
| | Triple transfer | 2900. | 300. |
| p. | Thin, India-like paper | — | 550. |
| t. | Printed on both sides | — | 5500. |
| y. | Diagonal bisect on cover | | 2500. |
| | On "Via Nicaragua" cover | | 5500. |
| y2. | Vertical bisect on cover | | 8500. |
| y1. | Quarter on cover | | — |
| | FDC *(July 1, 1851)* | | |

**1861. BENJAMIN FRANKLIN TYPE I ISSUE** Regular Issue Series, printed by Toppan, Carpenter & Co., had the same designs and types as the preceding issue, with some further types and values being noted. Three new values, the 24¢, 30¢, and 90¢ stamps, were added to this issue.

This issue marked a great milestone in postal service progress. Due to a pressing need for a faster stamp dispensing methold, the stamps were machine perforated and were now easily and quickly separated, instead of being cut apart by scissors. *Intaglio, perforated 15.*

While No. 18 has the complete design like the imperforate stamp No. 3, it does not have the "doubled" ornaments in the upper right corners.

**18**

| | | UnFVF | UseFVF |
|---|---|---|---|
| 1¢ | **blue,** Type I | 725. | 325. |
| | On cover | | 450. |
| | Cracked plate | — | 500. |
| | Double transfer | 775. | 400. |
| | *Earliest documented cover: Jan. 15, 1861* | | |

*The normal setting of the perforating machine was such that perforations cut the design on almost every stamp. Prices quoted are for such copies. Where the perforations do not cut the design No. 18 stamps command very high premiums.*

**1857. BENJAMIN FRANKLIN TYPE IA ISSUE**

**19**

| | | UnFVF | UseFVF |
|---|---|---|---|
| 1¢ | **blue,** Type Ia | 12000. | 3250. |
| | On cover | | 4000. |
| | Curl on shoulder | 12500. | 3500. |
| | *Earliest documented cover: Nov. 2, 1857* | | |

**1857. BENJAMIN FRANKLIN TYPE II ISSUE**

**20**

| | | UnFVF | UseFVF |
|---|---|---|---|
| 1¢ | **blue** (Plate 2), Type II | 475. | 135. |
| | On cover | | 160. |
| | Cracked plate | 700. | 325. |
| | Double transfer | 525. | 150. |
| | Plate 4 | — | 750. |
| | Curl in hair | — | 650. |
| | Double transfer | — | 1000. |
| | Plate 11 | 600. | 175. |
| | Double transfer | — | — |
| | Plate 12 | 475. | 135. |
| | *Earliest documented cover: July 26, 1857* | | |

**1857. BENJAMIN FRANKLIN TYPE III ISSUE**

**21**

| | | UnFVF | UseFVF |
|---|---|---|---|
| 1¢ | **blue,** Type III | 5000. | 1150. |
| | On cover | | 1500. |
| | Position 99R2 | — | 7500. |
| | *Earliest documented cover: Nov. 20, 1857* | | |

*The finest examples of No. 21 are found in position 99R2, which is why that item is listed separately.*

**1857. BENJAMIN FRANKLIN TYPE IIIA ISSUE**

**22**

| | | UnFVF | UseFVF |
|---|---|---|---|
| 1¢ | **blue** (Plate 4), Type IIIa | 800. | 260. |
| | On cover | | 290. |
| | Double transfer | 850. | 290. |
| v. | Horizontal pair, imperforate between | — | 4750. |
| | Plate 11 | 900. | 290. |
| | Double transfer | 950. | 320. |
| | Triple transfer | — | — |
| | Plate 12 | 900. | 290. |
| | Double transfer | 950. | 320. |
| | *Earliest documented cover: July 26, 1857* | | |

**1857. BENJAMIN FRANKLIN TYPE IV ISSUE**

**23**

| | | UnFVF | UseFVF |
|---|---|---|---|
| 1¢ | **blue,** Type IV. recut top and once at bottom | 3000. | 325. |
| | Cracked plate | 3500. | 425. |
| | On cover | | 340. |
| | Double transfer | 3250. | 350. |
| | Triple transfer, 1 inverted | | |
| t. | Recut once at top | | |
| t1. | Recut once at top and twice at bottom | 3250. | 350. |
| t2. | Recut twice at bottom | 3500. | 375. |
| t3. | Recut once at bottom | 3250. | 360. |
| t4. | Recut once at bottom and twice at top | 3250. | 375. |
| t5. | Recut twice at top and twice at bottom | 3250. | 410. |
| | *Earliest documented cover: July 25, 1857* | | |

**1857. BENJAMIN FRANKLIN TYPE V ISSUE**

*24 Type V occurs only on the perforated stamps. The top and bottom lines are broken and the sides of the design have been partially cut away. Trimmed copies of this stamp often are offered as Type III imperforate. They easily can be detected since Type III, and all other types that come imperforate, have the complete design at the sides.*

**24**

| | | UnFVF | UseFVF |
|---|---|---|---|
| 1¢ | **blue,** Type V | 120. | 24.00 |
| | On cover | | 30.00 |
| | Plate block of 8, w/imprint | 3250. | |
| | Curl in hair | 160. | 33.00 |
| | Curl on shoulder | 160. | 33.00 |
| | Curl over "C" of "CENT" | 170. | 38.00 |
| | Curl over "E" of "CENT" | 180. | 47.00 |
| | Horizontal dash in hair | 200. | 48.00 |
| | "Ring" below ear | 210. | 55.00 |
| | Double curl in hair | 190. | 45.00 |
| | Double transfer, at bottom | 195. | 55.00 |
| | Double transfer, at top | 160. | 50.00 |
| | Plate 5 | 315. | 75.00 |
| | Curl in "O" of "ONE" | — | — |
| | Curl on shoulder | — | — |
| p. | Laid paper | — | — |
| v. | Vertical strip of 5, imperforate horizontally | — | — |
| | *Earliest documented cover: Nov. 17, 1857* | | |

**1857. GEORGE WASHINGTON TYPE I ISSUE**

**25**

| | | UnFVF | UseFVF |
|---|---|---|---|
| 3¢ | **rose,** Type I | 900. | 30.00 |
| | brownish carmine | 900. | 30.00 |
| | dull red | 900. | 30.00 |
| | On cover | | 35.00 |
| | Gash on shoulder | 925. | 35.00 |
| | Cracked plate | 1200. | 100. |
| | Double transfer | 975. | 45.00 |
| | Double transfer, "GENTS" | — | 250. |
| | Triple transfer | — | 300. |
| | Worn plate | 850. | 30.00 |
| v. | Horizontal pair, imperforate vertically | — | — |
| v1. | Vertical pair, imperforate horizontally | — | 10000. |
| | *Earliest documented cover: Feb. 28, 1857* | | |

*Fakes are known of the Horizontal pair, imperforate vertically.*

**1857. GEORGE WASHINGTON TYPE II ISSUE**

*26, Type II has the outer frame removed at the top and bottom of the design. The side frame lines were recut to form continuous lines from the top to the bottom of the plate so they extend beyond the design of the stamp.*

| 26 | | UnFVF | UseFVF |
|---|---|---|---|
| 3¢ | **Venetian red,** Type II | 45.00 | 3.50 |
| | bright carmine | — | — |
| | brown carmine | 52.00 | 4.00 |
| | dull red | 45.00 | 3.50 |
| | dull rose brown | 45.00 | 3.50 |
| | orange brown | — | — |
| | On cover | | 4.00 |
| | Cracked plate | 425. | 130. |
| | Double transfer | 65.00 | 11.00 |
| | Double transfer in rosettes, line through "POSTAGE" | — | 65.00 |
| | Left frame line double | 65.00 | 9.00 |
| | Right frame line double | 65.00 | 9.00 |
| | Transfer damage above lower left rosette | 50.00 | 4.50 |
| | Transfer damage, retouched | 55.00 | 5.00 |
| | Transfer damage, retouched /w 2 vertical lines | 65.00 | 6.00 |
| | Worn plate | 50.00 | 3.50 |
| | t. Double impression | — | — |
| | v. Horizontal pair, imperforate between | — | — |
| | v1. Horizontal pair, imperforate vertically | — | 8000. |
| | v2. Vertical pair, imperforate horizontally | — | — |
| | *Earliest documented cover: Sept. 15, 1857* | | |

### 1857. GEORGE WASHINGTON TYPE III ISSUE

*27, Type III has the outer frame lines removed at the top and bottom of the design. The side frame lines extend only to the top and bottom of the stamp design.*

| 27 | | UnFVF | UseFVF |
|---|---|---|---|
| 3¢ | **Venetian red,** Type III | 110. | 20.00 |
| | brownish carmine | 110. | 20.00 |
| | dull red | 110. | 20.00 |
| | claret | 120. | 24.00 |
| | On cover | | 75.00 |
| | Damaged transfer, above lower left rosette | 120. | 21.00 |
| | Damaged transfer, retouched | 125. | 23.00 |
| | Double transfer | 175. | 32.00 |
| | Double transfer, bottom part of stamp & rosettes | — | 75.00 |
| | Triple transfer | — | 100. |
| | Worn plate | 110. | 20.00 |
| | *Earliest documented cover: July 11, 1857* | | |

### 1857. THOMAS JEFFERSON TYPE I ISSUE

| 28 | | UnFVF | UseFVF |
|---|---|---|---|
| 5¢ | **red brown,** Type I | 1350. | 260. |
| | bright red brown | 1350. | 260. |
| | pale red brown | 1350. | 260. |
| | henna brown (Indian red) | 1900. | 400. |
| | On cover | | 400. |
| | *Earliest documented cover: Aug. 22, 1857* | | |

### 1858. THOMAS JEFFERSON TYPE I ISSUE

| 29 | | UnFVF | UseFVF |
|---|---|---|---|
| 5¢ | **brick red,** Type I | 9000. | 600. |
| | On cover | — | 1000. |
| | *Earliest documented cover:* Oct. 6, 1858 | | |

### 1859. THOMAS JEFFERSON TYPE I ISSUE

| 30 | | UnFVF | UseFVF |
|---|---|---|---|
| 5¢ | **brown,** Type I | 950. | 250. |
| | dark brown | 950. | 250. |
| | pale brown | 950. | 250. |
| | yellow brown | 950. | 250. |
| | On cover | — | 300. |
| | *Earliest documented cover: April 4, 1859* | | |

### 1860. THOMAS JEFFERSON TYPE II ISSUE

31, 32 *Type II does not have full projections at the top and bottom. These projections have been partially or completely cut away.*

*Partiall cut*        *Completely cut*

| 31 | | UnFVF | UseFVF |
|---|---|---|---|
| 5¢ | **brown,** Type II | 500. | 175. |
| | dark brown | 500. | 175. |
| | yellow brown | 500. | 175. |
| | On cover | | 230. |
| | Cracked plate | — | — |
| | Printed on both sides | 3800. | 4000. |
| | *Earliest documented cover:* May 14, 1860 | | |

### 1861. THOMAS JEFFERSON TYPE II ISSUE

| 32 | | UnFVF | UseFVF |
|---|---|---|---|
| 5¢ | **orange brown,** Type II | 800. | 1100. |
| | dark orange brown | 800. | 1100. |
| | On cover | | 2300. |
| | *Earliest documented cover: (May 8, 1861)* | | |

### 1857. GEORGE WASHINGTON TYPE I ISSUE

| 33 | | UnFVF | UseFVF |
|---|---|---|---|
| 10¢ | **green,** Type I | 8250. | 500. |
| | bluish green | 8250. | 500. |
| | dark green | 8250. | 500. |
| | yellowish green | 8250. | 500. |
| | On cover | | 825. |
| | Curl in left "X" | 8250. | 600. |
| | Double transfer | 8250. | 600. |
| | Vertical pair, imperforate horizontally | | 6600. |
| | *Earliest documented cover: (Oct. 29, 1857)* | | |

### 1857. GEORGE WASHINGTON TYPE I ISSUE

| 34 | | UnFVF | UseFVF |
|---|---|---|---|
| 10¢ | **green,** Type II | 2500. | 200. |
| | bluish green | 2500. | 200. |
| | dark green | 2500. | 200. |
| | yellowish green | 2500. | 200. |
| | On cover | | 225. |
| | Curl opposite left "X" | — | 240. |
| | Double transfer | 2600. | 210. |
| | *Earliest documented cover: July 27, 1857* | | |

### 1857. GEORGE WASHINGTON TYPE III ISSUE

| 35 | | UnFVF | UseFVF |
|---|---|---|---|
| 10¢ | **green,** Type III | 2600. | 200. |
| | bluish green | 2600. | 200. |
| | dark green | 2600. | 200. |
| | yellowish green | 2600. | 200. |
| | On cover | | 225. |
| | Curl in left "X" | — | 260. |
| | Curl on forehead | — | 260. |
| | Double transfer | — | — |
| | *Earliest documented cover: (July 25, 1857)* | | |

### 1857. GEORGE WASHINGTON TYPE IV ISSUE

| 36 | | UnFVF | UseFVF |
|---|---|---|---|
| 10¢ | **green,** Type IV, recut at top | 17500. | 1500. |
| | bluish green | 17500. | 1500. |
| | dark green | 17500. | 1500. |
| | yellowish green | 17500. | 1500. |
| | On cover | | 1900. |
| | t. Recut once at bottom | 18000. | 1500. |
| | t1. Recut at top and bottom | 18500. | 1600. |
| | *Earliest documented cover: (July 25, 1857)* | | |

## 1859. GEORGE WASHINGTON TYPE V ISSUE

37 *Type V had the side ornaments partially cut away. In no case do three small circles remain on each side of the stamp. There usually is one small circle at each side, but some copies show two or three small circles on the right side. The outer lines at the top are complete except over the right "X". Trimmed copies of this stamp are offered as imperforates. If an imperforate does not have three circles at each side it is a trimmed fake.*

| 37 | | UnFVF | UseFVF |
|---|---|---|---|
| 10¢ | **green,** Type V | 200. | 60.00 |
| | bluish green | 200. | 60.00 |
| | dark green | 200. | 60.00 |
| | yellowish green | 200. | 60.00 |
| | On cover | | 70.00 |
| | Plate block of 8, /w imprint | — | 9000. |
| | Curl in "E" of "CENTS" | 250. | 80.00 |
| | Curl in "T" of "CENT" | 250. | 80.00 |
| | Curl (small) on forehead | 240. | 70.00 |
| | Double transfer at bottom | 250. | 80.00 |
| | Cracked plate | — | — |

*Earliest documented cover: (April 29, 1859)*

## 1957. GEORGE WASHINGTON TYPE I ISSUE

| 38 | | UnFVF | UseFVF |
|---|---|---|---|
| 12¢ | **black,** Type I | 380. | 100. |
| | gray black | 380. | 100. |
| | On cover | | 485. |
| | Double transfer | 430. | 110. |
| | Triple transfer | 525. | — |
| | v. Diagonal bisect on cover | | 17500. |
| | v1. Horizontal pair, imperforate between | — | — |

*Earliest documented cover: (July 39, 1857)*

## 1859. GEORGE WASHINGTON TYPE II ISSUE

39 *Type II has the frame line broken or missing on one or both sides.*

| 39 | | UnFVF | UseFVF |
|---|---|---|---|
| 12¢ | **black,** Type II | 360. | 115. |
| | deep black | 360. | 115. |
| | On cover | | 575. |
| | Double transfer, frame line at left | 390. | 125. |
| | Double transfer, frame line at right | 390. | 125. |
| | Vertical line through rosette | 460. | 160. |

*Earliest documented cover: (Dec. 9, 1859)*

## 1851. GEORGE WASHINGTON ISSUE

40 *George Washington*

| 40 | | UnFVF | UseFVF |
|---|---|---|---|
| 24¢ | **gray lilac** | 725. | 210. |
| | gray | 725. | 210. |
| | lilac | 725. | 210. |
| | On cover | | 750. |
| | Plate block of 12, w/ imprint | 32000. | |
| | v. Imperforate single | 1250. | |
| | v1. Pair, imperforate | 16000. | |

*Earliest documented cover: (July 7, 1860)*

## 1860. BENJAMIN FRANKLIN ISSUE

41 *Benjamin Franklin*

| 41 | | UnFVF | UseFVF |
|---|---|---|---|
| 30¢ | **orange** | 850. | 300. |
| | reddish orange | 850. | 300. |
| | yellow orange | 850. | 300. |
| | On cover | | 1250. |
| | Cracked plate | — | — |
| | Double transfer | 950. | 350. |
| | Recut at bottom | 1000. | 450. |
| | v. Imperforate single | 2500. | |
| | v1. Pair, imperforate | 7500. | 1250. |

*Earliest documented cover: (Aug. 8, 1860)*

## 1860. GEORGE WASHINGTON ISSUE

42 *Gen. George Washington, after a painting by John Trumbull, Yale University.*

| 42 | | UnFVF | UseFVF |
|---|---|---|---|
| 90¢ | **deep blue** | 1300. | 5500. |
| | blue | 1300. | 5500. |
| | On cover | | 4500. |
| | Double transfer at bottom | 1400. | — |
| | Double transfer at top | 1400. | — |
| | Short transfer at bottom, left and right | 1350. | — |
| | v. Imperforate single | 3000. | |
| | v1. Pair, imperforate | — | — |

*Earliest documented cover: (Sept. 11, 1860)*

*Many fake cancellations exist on this stamp.*

## 1875. BENJAMIN FRANKLIN SPECIAL PRINTING ISSUE

Special Printing of the 1857-61 Regular Issue. The original dies were intact, but new plates were made of the 1¢, 3¢, 10¢ and 12¢ values. Since these were perforated 12, while the originals were 15, they are quite easy to distinguish from the originals. The issue is very bright in color, *printed on white paper, issued without gum.* Printed by the Continental Bank Note Co. Not valid for postal use. *Intaglio.*

| SP3 | | UnFVF | UseFVF |
|---|---|---|---|
| 1¢ | **brilliant blue** *(3,846 copies sold)* | 500. | |
| | Cracked plate | 600. | |
| | Double transfer | 600. | |

## 1875. GEORGE WASHINGTON SPECIAL PRINTING ISSUE

| SP4 | | UnFVF | UseFVF |
|---|---|---|---|
| 3¢ | **bright vermillion** *(479 copies)* | 2000. | |

## 1875. THOMAS JEFFERSON SPECIAL PRINTING ISSUE

| SP5 | | UnFVF | UseFVF |
|---|---|---|---|
| 5¢ | **bright orange brown** *(878 copies)* | 950. | |
| | Margin strip of 4, w/plate number | 10000. | |

**1875. George Washington Special Printing Issue**

| SP6 | | UnFVF | UseFVF |
|---|---|---|---|
| 10¢ | **bluish green** *(516 copies)* | 1750. | |

**1875. George Washington Special Printing Issue**

| SP7 | | UnFVF | UseFVF |
|---|---|---|---|
| 12¢ | **greenish black** *(489 copies)* | 2000. | |

**1875. George Washington Special Printing Issue**

| SP8 | | UnFVF | UseFVF |
|---|---|---|---|
| 24¢ | **dark violet black** *(479 copies)* | 2000. | |

**1875. Benjamin Franklin Special Printing Issue**

| SP9 | | UnFVF | UseFVF |
|---|---|---|---|
| 30¢ | **yellow orange** *(480 copies)* | 2000. | |

**1875. George Washington Special Printing Issue**

| SP10 | | UnFVF | UseFVF |
|---|---|---|---|
| 90¢ | **indigo** *(454 copies)* | 3300. | |

*This set is known imperforate.*

**1861. National Banknote Issue** Upon the outbreak of the War Between the States in 1861, the postal authorities in Washington found it advisable to demonetize all U.S. postage stamps issued up to that time in order to prevent possible use in the Confederate States. It is interesting to note that due to the scarcity of metal coins during this period, stamps - encased in small containers - often were pressed into use as small change.

The National Bank Note Co. obtained the engraving and printing contract and prepared a set of eight essay designs in the form of finished 1¢, 3¢, 5¢, 10¢, 12¢, 24¢, 30¢ and 90¢ stamps, and evidently submitted them for approval prior to August 1. At least six of these miscalled "August" designs were not approved. Beginning August 17, postage stamps were issued from new plates of 1¢, 3¢, 5¢, 10¢, 12¢ and 90¢ made from altered designs. The set was completed by regular printings from the 24¢ and 90¢ essay plates after possible alterations on them. A second printing from the 10¢ essay plate was issued and is known used in September 1861.

The second set of designs, regulary issued, are listed here, as well as two denominations, 2¢ and 15¢, added in 1863 and 1866 respectively. The essays as well as the issued stamps are on *unwatermarked* paper and are *Intaglio and perforated 12.*

43 *Benjamin Franklin, after bust by Jean Caffert, Pennsylvania Academy of Fine Arts.*

*Unissued design: There is no dash under the tip of the ornaments at the right of the numeral in the upper left corner.*

43 *A dash has been added under the tip of the ornament at the right of the numeral in the upper left corner.*

| 43 | | UnFVF | UseFVF |
|---|---|---|---|
| 1¢ | **blue** | 150. | 16.00 |
| | bright blue | 150. | 16.00 |
| | pale blue | 150. | 16.00 |
| | ultramarine | 360. | 45.00 |
| | dark blue | 300. | 25.00 |
| | indigo | 300. | 25.00 |
| | On cover | — | 21.00 |
| | Plate block of 8, w/imprint | 2450. | — |
| | Dot on "U" | 160. | 18.00 |
| | Double transfer | — | 24.00 |
| | t.  Printed on both sides | — | 2500. |
| | p.  Laid paper | — | — |
| | v.  Vertical pair, imperforate horizontally | — | — |
| | FDC *(Aug. 17, 1861)* | | |

**1863. Andrew Jackson Issue**

44 *Andrew Jackson, after miniature by John Wood Dodge.*

| 44 | | UnFVF | UseFVF |
|---|---|---|---|
| 2¢ | **black** | 175. | 24.00 |
| | deep black | 175. | 24.00 |
| | gray black | 175. | 24.00 |
| | On cover | | 42.00 |
| | Plate block of 8, w/imprint | 8000. | |
| | Cracked plate | — | — |
| | Double transfer | 200. | 27.00 |
| | Double transfer of top left corner & "POSTAGE" ("Atherton shift") | 6000. | — |
| | Double transfer of right side ("Preston shift") | — | — |
| | Short transfer | 190. | 25.00 |
| | Triple transfer | — | — |
| | p.  Laid paper | — | — |
| | t.  Printed on both sides | — | 5000. |
| | y.  Diagonal bisect on cover | — | 1250. |
| | y1. Horizontal bisect on cover | — | — |
| | y2. Vertical bisect on cover | — | 1250. |
| | *Earliest documented cover: (July 6, 1863)* | | |

**1861. George Washington Issue**

45 *George Washington, after bust by J. A. Houdon.*

*Unissued Design: The ornaments forming the corners of the design are plain.*

45 *A ball has been added to each corner of the design and the ornaments have been enlarged.*

**45**

| | | UnFVF | UseFVF |
|---|---|---|---|
| **3¢** | **pink** | 4500. | 450. |
| | On cover | | 500. |
| | FDC *(Aug. 17, 1861)* | | 25000. |
| | a. rose pink | 70.00 | 1.75 |
| | On cover | | 2.00 |
| | av. Vertical pair, imperforate horizontally | 2500. | 750. |
| | b. pigeon blood pink | 2700. | — |
| | On cover | | 4000. |

*It is almost impossible to describe a "pink" in words, but it should be kept in mind that the inking on a "pink" is rather heavy, and the lines of the design do not stand out as sharply as on the other shades. The color, while not as outstanding as a dull pink ribbon, is nevertheless on that order. It is not any of the shades of brown, dull red, rose red, or brown red so often mistaken for the real pink.*

## 1861. GEORGE WASHINGTON ISSUE

**46**

| | | UnFVF | UseFVF |
|---|---|---|---|
| **3¢** | **brown carmine** | 625. | — |
| | dull brown red | 625. | — |
| | dull red | 625. | — |
| | pale carmine red | 625. | — |
| | dark brown red | 625. | — |
| | On cover | | — |
| | Plate block of 8, w/imprint | 19000. | |
| | Cracked plate | — | — |
| | Double impression | 2900. | |
| | Double transfer | — | — |
| | p. Laid paper | — | — |
| | t. Printed on both sides | — | — |
| | v. Vertical pair, imperforate horizontally | 2500. | 750. |

## 1861. THOMAS JEFFERSON ISSUE

*47 Thomas Jefferson. Unissued Design (left): No leaflets project from the corner ornaments. Issued design (right): A leaflet projects from each corner ornament.*

**47**

| | | UnFVF | UseFVF |
|---|---|---|---|
| **5¢** | **buff** | 9000. | 425. |
| | brown yellow | 9000. | 425. |
| | olive yellow | 9000. | 425. |
| | On cover | | 725. |
| | *Earliest documented cover: (Aug. 18, 1861)* | | |

## 1862. THOMAS JEFFERSON ISSUE

**48**

| | | UnFVF | UseFVF |
|---|---|---|---|
| **5¢** | **red brown** | 2000. | 225. |
| | dark red brown | 2000. | 225. |
| | On cover | — | 475. |
| | Double transfer | 2300. | 250. |
| | *Earliest documented cover: (Jan. 2, 1862)* | | |

## 1863. THOMAS JEFFERSON ISSUE

**49**

| | | UnFVF | UseFVF |
|---|---|---|---|
| **5¢** | **brown** | — | — |
| | dark brown | — | — |
| | pale brown | — | — |
| | black brown | — | — |
| | On cover | — | — |
| | Double transfer, bottom frame line | — | — |
| | Double transfer, bottom & top frame lines | — | — |
| | Double transfer, top frame line | — | — |
| | p. Laid paper | — | — |
| | *Earliest documented cover: (Feb. 3, 1863)* | | |

## 1861. GEORGE WASHINGTON TYPE I ISSUE

*50, 51 George Washington*

*50 Type I does not have a heavy curved line cut below the stars, and the ornament directly over the center star at the top has only one outer line. This stamp is found only on thin, semi-transparent paper.*

**50**

| | | UnFVF | UseFVF |
|---|---|---|---|
| **10¢** | **green,** Type I | 4500. | 550. |
| | dark yellow green | 4500. | 550. |
| | On cover | | 900. |
| | Double transfer | — | — |
| | FDC *(Sept. 17, 1861)* | | — |

## 1861. GEORGE WASHINGTON TYPE II ISSUE

*51 Type II has a heavey curved line cut below the stars. The ornament directly over the center star at the top has a double outer line.*

**51**

| | | UnFVF | UseFVF |
|---|---|---|---|
| **10¢** | **green,** Type II | 325. | 30.00 |
| | dark green | 350. | 32.00 |
| | yellow green | 325. | 30.00 |
| | blue green | 325. | 35.00 |
| | On cover | | 45.00 |
| | Plate block of 8, w/imprint | 5000. | |
| | Double transfer | 375. | 40.00 |
| | v. Vertical pair, imperforate horizontally | — | 3500. |

## 1861. GEORGE WASHINGTON ISSUE

*52 George Washington*

*Unissued Design. The four corners of the design are rounded.*

*52 The four corners of the design have had ovals and scrolls added to form "square corners."*

**52**

| | | UnFVF | UseFVF |
|---|---|---|---|
| 12¢ | **black** | 625. | 55.00 |
| | gray black | 625. | 55.00 |
| | On cover | | 85.00 |
| | Double transfer of bottom frame line | 650. | 65.00 |
| | Double transfer of top frame line | 650. | 65.00 |
| | Double transfer of top & bottom frame lines | 675. | 75.00 |
| | FDC (Aug. 17, 1861) | | — |

### 1866. ABRAHAM LINCOLN ISSUE

53 Abraham Lincoln

**53**

| | | UnFVF | UseFVF |
|---|---|---|---|
| 15¢ | **black** | 650. | 72.00 |
| | On cover | | 125. |
| | Plate block of 8, w/imprint | — | |
| | Cracked plate | — | — |
| | Double transfer | 600. | 80.00 |
| | FDC (Apr. 14, 1866) | | |

### 1861. GEORGE WASHINGTON ISSUE

54-56 George Washington

**54**

| | | UnFVF | UseFVF |
|---|---|---|---|
| 24¢ | **violet** | 6500. | 575. |
| | gray violet | 1400. | 350. |

*No. 54 is found only on thin, semi-transparent paper, while Nos. 55 and 56 are on a thicker and more opaque paper.*

### 1861. GEORGE WASHINGTON ISSUE

**55**

| | | UnFVF | UseFVF |
|---|---|---|---|
| 24¢ | **red lilac** | 800. | 80.00 |
| | brown lilac | 750. | 80.00 |
| | steel blue | 5000. | 325. |
| | blackish violet | 800. | 80.00 |
| | violet, on thin paper (Aug. 17, 1861) | — | — |
| | grayish lilac, on thin paper | — | — |
| | On cover | | 135. |
| | Scratch under "A" of "POSTAGE" | — | — |
| | Earliest documented cover: (Oct. 4, 1861) | | |

### 1862. GEORGE WASHINGTON ISSUE

**56**

| | | UnFVF | UseFVF |
|---|---|---|---|
| 24¢ | **lilac** | 400. | 55.00 |
| | gray lilac | 400. | 55.00 |
| | gray | 400. | 55.00 |
| | dark lilac | 12500. | 1200. |
| | On cover | | 125. |
| | Scratch under "A" of "POSTAGE" | — | — |
| | p. Printed on both sides | — | 3500. |
| | v. Pair, imperforate | — | — |
| | Earliest documented cover: (Oct. 29, 1862) | | |

### 1861. BENJAMIN FRANKLIN ISSUE

57 Benjamin Franklin

**57**

| | | UnFVF | UseFVF |
|---|---|---|---|
| 30¢ | **orange** | 650. | 75.00 |
| | deep orange | 650. | 75.00 |
| | On cover | | 350. |
| | p. Printed on both sides | — | — |
| | FDC (Aug. 17, 1861) | | |

### 1861. GEORGE WASHINGTON ISSUE

58 George Washington

Unissued design. There is no spot of color in the apex of the lower line of the angle at the top of the design. No row of dashes appear between the lines of the angle, and the lines in the leaf at the left of the "U" at the lower left of the design run at an angle.

58 *There is a spot of color in the apex of the lower line of the angle at the top of the design. A row of small dashes appear between the lines of the angle, and the lines in the leaf at the lower left corner of the stamp are nearly vertical.*

**58**

| | | UnFVF | UseFVF |
|---|---|---|---|
| 90¢ | **blue** | 1500. | 250. |
| | dark blue | 1650. | 300. |
| | pale blue | 1500. | 250. |
| | dull blue | 1500. | 250. |
| | On cover | | 13500. |
| | FDC (Aug. 17, 1861) | | |

**1875. SPECIAL PRINTING ISSUE** Again the dies were available and new plates were made of the 1¢, 2¢, 10¢ and 12 ¢ values. Printed on hard, extremely white paper, absolutely white gum and without grill. They can be distinguished by their color shades, which are very deep and clear, and the white paper (compared to the slightly yellowish of the originals). *Intagalio* by the National Bank Note Co. and *perforated 12.* Used copies are seldom found.

### 1875. BENJAMIN FRANKLIN SPECIAL PRINTING ISSUE

**SP11**

| | | UnFVF | UseFVF |
|---|---|---|---|
| 1¢ | **dark ultramarine** (3,195 copies) | 500. | 800. |

### 1875. ANDREW JACKSON SPECIAL PRINTING ISSUE

**SP12**

| | | UnFVF | UseFVF |
|---|---|---|---|
| 2¢ | **jet black** (979 copies) | 2300. | 4000. |

### 1875. GEORGE WASHINGTON SPECIAL PRINTING ISSUE

**SP13**

| | | UnFVF | UseFVF |
|---|---|---|---|
| 3¢ | **brown red** (465 copies) | 2500. | 4300. |

### 1875. THOMAS JEFFERSON SPECIAL PRINTING ISSUE

**SP14**

| | | UnFVF | UseFVF |
|---|---|---|---|
| 5¢ | **light yellow brown** (672 copies) | 1850. | 2300. |

### 1875. GEORGE WASHINGTON SPECIAL PRINTING ISSUE

**SP15**

| | | UnFVF | UseFVF |
|---|---|---|---|
| 10¢ | **bluish green** (451 copies) | 2000. | 3750. |

### 1875. GEORGE WASHINGTON SPECIAL PRINTING ISSUE

**SP16**

| | | UnFVF | UseFVF |
|---|---|---|---|
| 12¢ | **deep black** (389 copies) | 2800. | 4500. |

### 1875. ABRAHAM LINCOLN SPECIAL PRINTING ISSUE

**SP17**

| | | UnFVF | UseFVF |
|---|---|---|---|
| 15¢ | **deep black** (397 copies) | 2250. | 4800. |

**1875. GEORGE WASHINGTON SPECIAL PRINTING ISSUE**

| SP18 | | UnFVF | UseFVF |
|---|---|---|---|
| 24¢ | **deep brown violet** *(346 copies)* | 3250. | 6000. |

**1875. BENJAMIN FRANKLIN SPECIAL PRINTING ISSUE**

| SP19 | | UnFVF | UseFVF |
|---|---|---|---|
| 30¢ | **brown orange** *(346 copies)* | 3500. | 6000. |

**1875. GEORGE WASHINGTON SPECIAL PRINTING ISSUE**

| SP20 | | UnFVF | UseFVF |
|---|---|---|---|
| 90¢ | **dark blue** *(317 copies)* | 4800. | 20000. |

**1867. GEORGE WASHINGTON W/GRILL ISSUE** Stamps of 1861-66, impressed with grills of various sizes. The grills were adopted in order to prevent the removal of cancellations from used stamps. They were impressed into the stamps in the form of small pyramids arranged in parallel rows as noted for each type of grill listed.

**Grills with points projecting upward from face of the stamp.**

*Grill A. Grill covers the entire stamp and appears as small mounds that have small breaks in their tops. An essay grill is similar, but paper breaks appear on only a few, if any, of each of the individual mounds that make up the entire grill.*

| 59 | | UnFVF | UseFVF |
|---|---|---|---|
| 3¢ | **rose,** grill A | 2200. | 475. |
| | On cover | | 675. |
| | a. Printed on both sides | 11000. | — |
| | v. Imperforate pair | 1750. | |
| | *Earliest documented cover: Aug. 13, 1867* | | 25000. |

**1867. THOMAS JEFFERSON GRILL A ISSUE**

| 60 | | UnFVF | UseFVF |
|---|---|---|---|
| 5¢ | **brown,** grill A | 42000. | — |
| | dark brown | — | 45000. |

**1867. BENJAMIN FRANKLIN GRILL A ISSUE**

| 61 | | UnFVF | UseFVF |
|---|---|---|---|
| 30¢ | **orange,** grill A | — | 32500. |

**1868. GEORGE WASHINGTON GRILL B ISSUE Grill B.** *This grill, about 18 x 15mm in size, containing 22 x 18 rows of points projecting unpward from the face of the stamp, exists on one copy of the 3¢ rose. The grill points differ from any other issued grill. A variety of Grill C, No. 62, often is mistaken for this item.*

| 61A | | UnFVF | UseFVF |
|---|---|---|---|
| 3¢ | **rose,** grill B | — | 45000. |
| | *Earliest documented cover: (Feb. 1868)* | | |

**1867. GEORGE WASHINGTON GRILL C ISSUE**

*Grill C. The grill was produced by the same grill roller as Grill A, after the roller had been machined to "erase" portions of the grill so that it now formed groups of grill points on each stamp rather than grilling all over the stamps. This grill is about 13 x 16mm with 16 to 17 by 18 to 21 points projecting upward from the face of the stamp.*

| 62 | | UnFVF | UseFVF |
|---|---|---|---|
| 3¢ | **rose,** grill C | 3000. | 650. |
| | On cover | | 575. |
| | Double grill | 4200. | 1500. |
| | Grill with points down | 3750. | 650. |
| | v. Imperforte pair | 1750. | |
| | *Earliest documented cover: (Nov. 26, 1867)* | | |

*No. 62 shows rows of grill points, not as heavily impressed as the normal grill, forming a grill whose total area is about 18 x 15mm. Caused by a failure to cut deep enough into the grill roller when it was being machined, which left a few areas on the roller only "partially erased."*

**1868. ANDREW JACKSON W/GRILL D ISSUE** Grill with points projecting downward.

*Grill D. The tips of the grill points form vertical ridges. This grill is about 12 x 14mm, always has 15 points in each horizontal row, with 17 to 18 points in each vertical row.*

 *Detail of Grill D*

| 63 | | UnFVF | UseFVF |
|---|---|---|---|
| 2¢ | **black,** grill D | 9500. | 1500. |
| | On cover | | 1750. |
| | Double transfer | — | — |
| | Split grill | — | 1600. |
| | *Earliest documented cover: (Feb. 15, 1868)* | | |

**1868. GEORGE WASHINGTON GRILL D ISSUE**

| 64 | | UnFVF | UseFVF |
|---|---|---|---|
| 3¢ | **rose,** grill D | 3000. | 475. |
| | On cover | | 600. |
| | Double grill | — | — |
| | Split grill | — | 525. |
| | *Earliest documented cover: (Feb. 2, 1868)* | | |

**1868. BENJAMIN FRANKLIN GRILL Z ISSUE Grill Z:** *When originally discovered by William L. Stevenson, this then unknown grill was given the algebraic "unknown" symbol of "Z" and it has thus remained. It is very easy to distinguish from other pyramid grills as the tip of the pyramids are horizontal ridges, all through the entire area of the grill, while on the D, E and F grills these ridges are vertical. The grill is about 11 x 14mm, with 13 to 14 by 17 to 18 points.*

*Detail of Grill Z*
Grill Z

| 65 | | UnFVF | UseFVF |
|---|---|---|---|
| 1¢ | **blue,** grill Z | — | — |

**1868. ANDREW JACKSON GRILL Z ISSUE**

| 66 | | UnFVF | UseFVF |
|---|---|---|---|
| 2¢ | **black,** grill Z | 3000. | 400. |
| | On cover | | 550. |
| | Double grill | — | — |
| | Double transfer | 3100. | 450. |
| | *Earliest documented cover: (March 13, 1868)* | | |

**1868. GEORGE WASHINGTON GRILL Z ISSUE**

| 67 | | UnFVF | UseFVF |
|---|---|---|---|
| 3¢ | **rose,** grill Z | 5000. | 1200. |
| | On cover | | 1600. |
| | Double grill | 6000. | — |
| | *Earliest documented cover: (Feb. 19, 1868)* | | |

**1868. GEORGE WASHINGTON GRILL Z ISSUE**

| 68 | | UnFVF | UseFVF |
|---|---|---|---|
| 10¢ | **green,** grill Z | 47500. | — |

**1868. GEORGE WASHINGTON GRILL Z ISSUE**

| 69 | | UnFVF | UseFVF |
|---|---|---|---|
| 12¢ | **black,** grill Z | 4000. | 600. |
| | Double transfer of top frame line | — | 675. |
| | On cover | | 1000. |

**1868. ABRAHAM LINCOLN GRILL Z ISSUE**

| 69A | | UnFVF | UseFVF |
|---|---|---|---|
| 15¢ | **black,** grill Z | 100000. | — |

**1868. BENJAMIN FRANKLIN GRILL E ISSUE** Grill E. *This grill is about 11 x 13mm and has 14 by 15 to 17 points.*

| 70 | | UnFVF | UseFVF |
|---|---|---|---|
| 1¢ | **blue,** grill E | 1100. | 275. |
| | dull blue | 1000. | 250. |
| | On cover | | 325. |
| | Split grill | 1100. | 275. |
| | Double grill | — | 375. |

*Earliest documented cover: (March 9, 1868)*

**1868. ANDREW JACKSON GRILL E ISSUE**

| 71 | | UnFVF | UseFVF |
|---|---|---|---|
| 2¢ | **black,** grill E | 525. | 75.00 |
| | gray black | 525. | 75.00 |
| | intense black | 560. | 80.00 |
| | On cover | | 110. |
| | Grill with points up | — | — |
| | Split grill | 575. | 85.00 |
| | Double grill | 560. | 80.00 |
| | Double transfer | 550. | 80.00 |
| | Triple grill | — | — |
| | v.  Diagonal or Vertical Bisect on cover | | 2000. |

*Earliest documented cover: (March 11, 1868)*

**1868. GEORGE WASHINGTON GRILL E ISSUE**

| 72 | | UnFVF | UseFVF |
|---|---|---|---|
| 3¢ | **rose,** grill E | 375. | 10.00 |
| | pale red | 375. | 10.00 |
| | pale rose | 375. | 10.00 |
| | lake red | 475. | 13.00 |
| | On cover | | 14.00 |
| | Split grill | 450. | 12.00 |
| | Double grill | — | — |
| | Triple grill | — | — |
| | p.  Very thin paper | 500. | 12.00 |

*Earliest documented cover: (May 23, 1868)*

**1868. GEORGE WASHINGTON GRILL E ISSUE**

| 73 | | UnFVF | UseFVF |
|---|---|---|---|
| 10¢ | **green,** grill E | 2000. | 175. |
| | blue green | 2000. | 175. |
| | dark green | 2000. | 175. |
| | On cover | | 275. |
| | Double transfer | — | 225. |
| | Split grill | 2100. | 190. |
| | Double grill | 2900. | 300. |
| | p.  Very thin paper | 2100. | 190. |

*Earliest documented cover: (May 6, 1868)*

**1868. GEORGE WASHINGTON GRILL E ISSUE**

| 74 | | UnFVF | UseFVF |
|---|---|---|---|
| 12¢ | **black,** grill E | 2250. | 210. |
| | gray black | 2250. | 210. |
| | On cover | | 340. |
| | Double transfer of bottom frame line | 2350. | 225. |
| | Double transfer of top frame line | 2350. | 225. |
| | Double transfer of top & bottom frame line | 2500. | 260. |
| | Split grill | 2400. | 225. |

*Earliest documented cover: (March 3, 1868)*

**1868. ABRAHAM LINCOLN GRILL E ISSUE**

| 75 | | UnFVF | UseFVF |
|---|---|---|---|
| 15¢ | **black,** grill E | 4750. | 460. |
| | gray black | 4750. | 460. |
| | On cover | | 750. |
| | Split grill | — | 550. |
| | Double grill | — | 750. |

*Earliest documented cover: (June 25, 1868)*

**1868. BENJAMIN FRANKLIN GRILL F ISSUE** Grill F. *This grill is about 9 x 13mm and has 11 to 12 by 15 to 17 points.*

| 76 | | UnFVF | UseFVF |
|---|---|---|---|
| 1¢ | **blue,** grill F | 500. | 100. |
| | dark blue | 500. | 100. |
| | pale blue | 500. | 100. |
| | On cover | | 130. |
| | Split grill | 525. | 120. |
| | Double grill | — | 200. |
| | Double transfer | 525. | 125. |
| | p.  Very thin paper | 525. | 110. |

*Earliest documented cover: (March 19, 1868)*

**1868. ANDREW JACKSON GRILL F ISSUE**

| 77 | | UnFVF | UseFVF |
|---|---|---|---|
| 2¢ | **black,** grill F | 200. | 35.00 |
| | gray black | 200. | 35.00 |
| | On cover | | 45.00 |
| | Plate block of 8, w/imprint | — | |
| | Split grill | 220. | 40.00 |
| | Double grill | — | 125. |
| | Double transfer | 220. | 40.00 |
| | v.  Bisect (any) on cover | | 1300. |

*Earliest documented cover: March 27, 1868.*

**1868. GEORGE WASHINGTON GRILL F ISSUE**

| 78 | | UnFVF | UseFVF |
|---|---|---|---|
| 3¢ | **rose,** grill F | 175. | 3.50 |
| | a.  rose red | 175. | 3.50 |
| | On cover | | 3.75 |
| | Plate block of 8, w/imprint | 2500. | |
| | Double transfer | 200. | 5.50 |
| | Grill with points up | | |
| | Split grill | 185. | 4.00 |
| | Quadruple split grill | 325. | 85.00 |
| | Double grill | — | — |
| | Triple grill | — | 100. |
| | p.  Very thin paper | 185. | 4.00 |
| | t.  Printed on both sides | 1100. | — |
| | v.  Imperforate pair | 1000. | — |
| | v1. Vertical pair, imperforate horizontally | — | — |

*Earliest documented cover: (May 28, 1868)*

**1868. THOMAS JEFFERSON GRILL F ISSUE**

| 79 | | UnFVF | UseFVF |
|---|---|---|---|
| 5¢ | **brown,** grill F | 1500. | 225. |
| | black brown | 1600. | 250. |
| | On cover | | 350. |
| | Double transfer of top frame line | — | — |
| | Split grill | 1600. | 250. |
| | Double grill | — | — |
| | p.  Very thin paper | 1600. | 250. |

*Earliest documented cover: (Dec. 2, 1868)*

**1868. GEORGE WASHINGTON GRILL F ISSUE**

| 80 | | UnFVF | UseFVF |
|---|---|---|---|
| 10¢ | **yellow green,** grill F | 1200. | 120. |
| | blue green | 1200. | 120. |
| | dark green | 1200. | 120. |
| | green | 1200. | 120. |
| | On cover | | 145. |
| | Double transfer | — | — |
| | Split grill | 1300. | 125. |
| | Quadruple split grill | — | 350. |
| | Double grill | — | 210. |
| | p.  Very thin paper | 1250. | 130. |

*Earliest documented cover: (Oct. 1, 1868)*

**1868. GEORGE WASHINGTON GRILL F ISSUE**

| 81 | | UnFVF | UseFVF |
|---|---|---|---|
| 12¢ | **black,** grill F | 1500. | 125. |
| | gray black | 1500. | 135. |
| | On cover | | 150. |
| | Split grill | 1600. | 145. |

**81**

| | | UnFVF | UseFVF |
|---|---|---|---|
| | Double grill | — | 270. |
| | Double transfer of bottom frame line | 1600. | 135. |
| | Double transfer of top frame line | 1600. | 135. |
| | Double transfer of top & bottom frame lines | — | 165. |
| | Triple grill | — | — |
| | p. Very thin paper | 1550. | 130. |

*Earliest documented cover: (May 27, 1868)*

### 1868. ABRAHAM LINCOLN GRILL F ISSUE

**82**

| | | | UnFVF | UseFVF |
|---|---|---|---|---|
| **15¢** | **black,** grill F | | 1500. | 140. |
| | gray black | | 1500. | 135. |
| | On cover | | | 150. |
| | Plate block of 8, w/imprint | | 25000. | |
| | Double transfer of upper right corner | | — | — |
| | Split grill | | 1600. | 150. |
| | Quadruple split grill | | 2250. | 350. |
| | Double grill | | — | 250. |
| | p. Very thin paper | | 1500. | 140. |

*Earliest documented cover: (May 4, 1868)*

### 1869. GEORGE WASHINGTON GRILL F ISSUE

**83**

| | | | UnFVF | UseFVF |
|---|---|---|---|---|
| **24¢** | **gray lilac,** grill F | | 2100. | 450. |
| | gray | | 2100. | 450. |
| | On cover | | | 900. |
| | Plate block of 8, w/imprint | | 30000. | |
| | Scratch under "A" in "POSTAGE" | | — | — |
| | Split grill | | 2200. | 475. |
| | Double grill | | 2700. | 800. |

*Earliest documented cover: (March 5, 1868)*

### 1868. BENJAMIN FRANKLIN GRILL F ISSUE

**84**

| | | | UnFVF | UseFVF |
|---|---|---|---|---|
| **30¢** | **orange,** grill F | | 2750. | 400. |
| | deep orange | | 2750. | 400. |
| | On cover | | | 1200. |
| | Split grill | | 2750. | 450. |
| | Double grill | | 3250. | 750. |
| | Double grill, one split | | — | — |

*Earliest documented cover: (Nov. 21, 1868)*

### 1869. GEORGE WASHINGTON GRILL F ISSUE

**85**

| | | | UnFVF | UseFVF |
|---|---|---|---|---|
| **90¢** | **blue,** grill F | | 5000. | 850. |
| | dark blue | | 5000. | 850. |
| | On cover | | | — |
| | Split grill | | 5250. | 950. |
| | Double grill | | 7000. | — |

*Earliest documented cover: (May 8, 1869)*

**NOTE:** *Most of the stamps that bear grills can be found with double grills, triple grills, split grills and quadruple split grills. Double grills are two impressions of the grill on the same stamp, triple grills are three impressions of the grill on the same stamp, split grills are those with about half of a normal grill on each end or on each side of the stamp and quadruple split grills are those that show just a small portion of the grill on each corner of the stamp. The split grill varieties were caused by misplacing the stamps under the grill roller so that the grills were not properly placed on the stamps. Fake grills exist.*

## 1869 National Bank Note Co. Pictorial Series

This series of stamps was printed by the National Bank Note Co. The stamps are square in design. For some reason, now difficult for us to understand, this series was not popular and was replaced with a new series in about a year. The stamps were grilled with a new size of grill, Grill G, 9 1/1 x 9 1/2mm in size. The stamps were *printed in intaglio on hard wove paper, unwatermarked and were perforated 12.*

Three denominations of these stamps are known with inverted centers and are extremely scarce. This was the first time an error of this type was issued and was due to carelessness when printing the bi-colored stamps.

### 1869. BENJAMIN FRANKLIN ISSUE

*86 Benjamin Franklin*

**86**

| | | UnFVF | UseFVF |
|---|---|---|---|
| **1¢** | **buff** | 275. | 65.00 |
| | brown orange | 275. | 65.00 |
| | dark brown orange | 275. | 65.00 |
| | On cover | | 135. |
| | Plate block of 10, w/imprint | — | |
| | Margin block of 4, w/arrow | 1400. | |
| | Double transfer | — | — |
| | Split grill | 300. | 75.00 |
| | Double grill | 450. | 150. |
| | Double grill, 1 split | — | — |
| | Grill omitted, original gum | 775. | |

*Earliest documented cover: (May 2, 1869)*

### 1869. PONY EXPRESS ISSUE

*87 Pony Express*

**87**

| | | UnFVF | UseFVF |
|---|---|---|---|
| **2¢** | **brown** | 225. | 28.00 |
| | dark brown | 225. | 28.00 |
| | pale brown | 225. | 28.00 |
| | yellow brown | 225. | 28.00 |
| | On cover | | 70.00 |
| | Plate block of 10, w/imprint | — | |
| | Margin block of 4, w/arrow | 975. | |
| | Double transfer | — | 40.00 |
| | Split grill | 250. | 40.00 |
| | Quadruple split grill | — | 225. |
| | Double grill | — | 150. |
| | Grill omitted, original gum | 600. | |
| | p. Printed on both sides | — | — |
| | v. Bisect (any) on cover | — | — |

*Earliest documented cover: (March 20, 1869)*

### 1869. EARLY LOCOMOTIVE ISSUE

*88 Early Locomotive*

**88**

| | | UnFVF | UseFVF |
|---|---|---|---|
| **3¢** | **ultramarine** | 175. | 8.00 |
| | blue | 175. | 8.00 |
| | dark blue | 175. | 8.00 |
| | dark untramarine | 175. | 8.00 |
| | pale ultramarine | 175. | 8.00 |
| | On cover | | 14.00 |
| | Plate block of 10, w/imprint | 7000. | |
| | Margin block of 4, w/arrow | 900. | |
| | Double transfer | 190. | 9.00 |
| | Split grill | 185. | 9.00 |
| | Quadruple split grill | 400. | 65.00 |
| | Double grill | 350. | 45.00 |
| | Triple grill | — | — |
| | Grill omitted | 600. | — |
| | t. Double impression | — | — |

*Earliest documented cover: (March 27, 1869)*

## 1869. GEORGE WASHINGTON ISSUE

89 *George Washington*

| 89 | | UnFVF | UseFVF |
|---|---|---|---|
| 6¢ | **ultramarine** | 950. | 100. |
| | pale ultramarine | 950. | 100. |
| | On cover | | 300. |
| | Margin block of 4, w/arrow | 5000. | |
| | Double transfer | — | 120. |
| | Split grill | 1025. | 120. |
| | Quadruple split grill | — | 400. |
| | Double grill | — | 300. |
| | v. Vertical bisect on cover | | — |

*Earliest documented cover: (April 26, 1869)*

## 1869. SHIELD AND EAGLE ISSUE

90 *Shield and Eagle*

| 90 | | UnFVF | UseFVF |
|---|---|---|---|
| 10¢ | **yellow** | 1000. | 90.00 |
| | yellowish orange | 1000. | 90.00 |
| | On cover | | 335. |
| | Margin block of 4, w/arrow | 5300. | |
| | Split grill | 1050. | 110. |
| | Double grill | — | 275. |

*Earliest documented cover: (April 1, 1869)*

## 1869. STEAMSHIP ADRIATIC ISSUE

91 *Steamship Adriatic*

| 91 | | UnFVF | UseFVF |
|---|---|---|---|
| 12¢ | **green** | 975. | 100. |
| | bluish green | 975. | 100. |
| | dark green | 975. | 100. |
| | yellowish green | 975. | 100. |
| | On cover | | 375. |
| | Margin block of 4, w/arrow | 5000. | |
| | Split grill | 1025. | 125. |
| | Double grill | — | 300. |

*Earliest documented cover: (April 1, 1869)*

## 1869. LANDING OF COLUMBUS TYPE I ISSUE

92 *Landing of Columbus. Type I has a white area coming to an apex under the "T" of "POSTAGE." It is also known as the 'unframed picture."*

| 92 | | UnFVF | UseFVF |
|---|---|---|---|
| 15¢ | **brown and blue,** Type I | 2500. | 350. |
| | dark brown & blue | 2800. | 350. |
| | pale brown & blue | 2800. | 350. |
| | On cover | | 1000. |
| | Split grill | 3000. | 380. |
| | Double grill | — | 550. |
| | Grill omitted | 4000. | — |

*Earliest documented cover: (April 2, 1869)*

## 1869. LANDING OF COLUMBUS TYPE II ISSUE

93t *Inverted center*

93 *Landing of Columbus. Type II has a diamond ornament under the "T" of "POSTAGE," a line has been drawn around the circumference of the central design so that picture appears to be framed. Some diagonal shading lines have been drawn around the base of the picture.*

| 93 | | UnFVF | UseFVF |
|---|---|---|---|
| 15¢ | **brown & blue,** Type II | 1200. | 160. |
| | dark brown & blue | 1200. | 160. |
| | On cover | | 800. |
| | Plate block of 8, w/imprint | 20000. | |
| | Double transfer | — | — |
| | Split grill | 1300. | 180. |
| | Double grill | 2100. | 295. |
| | v. Center inverted | — | 14500. |
| | v1. Center doubled, 1 inverted | — | — |
| | v2. Imperforate, horizontally | 2750. | |

*Earliest documented cover: (May 23, 1869)*

## 1869. SIGNING OF THE DECLARATION OF INDEPENDENCE ISSUE

94 *Declaration of Independence*

94t *Inverted Center*

| 94 | | UnFVF | UseFVF |
|---|---|---|---|
| 24¢ | **green and violet** | 3100. | 550. |
| | bluish green & violet | 3100. | 550. |
| | On cover | | 10000. |
| | Split grill | 3100. | 550. |
| | Double grill | — | 1000. |
| | Grill omitted | 5600. | — |
| | v. Center inverted (83 known) | 160000. | 17500. |
| | On cover | | 110000. |
| | *Earliest documented cover: (April 7, 1869)* | | |

## 1869. SHIELD, EAGLE AND FLAGS ISSUE

95 *Shield, Eagle and Flags*

| 95 | | UnFVF | UseFVF |
|---|---|---|---|
| 30¢ | **blue and carmine** | 3100. | 350. |
| | dull blue & dark carmine | 3100. | 350. |
| | On cover | | 16000. |
| | Split grill | 3200. | 300. |
| | Double grill | — | 650. |
| | Grill omitted | 4500. | — |
| | Double paper, grill omitted | 3800. | — |
| | v. Flags inverted (46 known) | 200000. | 57000. |
| | *Earliest documented cover: (May 22, 1869)* | | |

## 1869. ABRAHAM LINCOLN ISSUE

96 *Abraham Lincoln*

| 96 | | UnFVF | UseFVF |
|---|---|---|---|
| 90¢ | **carmine & black** | 6000. | 1800. |
| | carmine rose & black | 6000. | 1250. |
| | On cover | — | — |
| | Split grill | — | — |
| | Grill omitted | 11000. | — |
| | *Earliest documented cover: (May 10, 1869)* | | |

## 1875. BENJAMIN FRANKLIN SPECIAL PRINTING PICTORIAL ISSUE

Again the dies were available, and a new plate was made for the 1¢ and for the frame of the 15¢. The frame is similar to the Type I of the 1869 issue except that it is without the fringe of brown shading lines around the central vignette. *Printed by the National Bank Note Co., without grill, printed in intaglio on hard white paper, with white crackly gum and perforated 12.*

| SP21 | | UnFVF | UseFVF |
|---|---|---|---|
| 1¢ | **buff** (approx. 2,750 copies sold) | 335. | 230. |

## 1875. PONY EXPRESS SPECIAL PRINTING PICTORIAL ISSUE

| SP22 | | UnFVF | UseFVF |
|---|---|---|---|
| 2¢ | **brown** *(4,755 copies)* | 385. | 330. |

## 1875. EARLY LOCOMOTIVE SPECIAL PRINTING PICTORIAL ISSUE

| SP23 | | UnFVF | UseFVF |
|---|---|---|---|
| 3¢ | **ultramarine** *(1,406 copies)* | 3000. | 10000. |

## 1875. GEORGE WASHINGTON SPECIAL PICTORIAL ISSUE

| SP24 | | UnFVF | UseFVF |
|---|---|---|---|
| 6¢ | **ultramarine** *(2,226 copies)* | 900. | 600. |

## 1875. SHIELD AND EAGLE SPECIAL PRINTING PICTORIAL ISSUE

| SP25 | | UnFVF | UseFVF |
|---|---|---|---|
| 10¢ | **yellow** *(1,947 copies)* | 1400. | 1200. |

## 1875. STEAMSHIP ADRIATIC SPECIAL PRINTING PICTORIAL ISSUE

| SP26 | | UnFVF | UseFVF |
|---|---|---|---|
| 12¢ | **bright green** *(1,584 copies)* | 1500. | 1250. |

## 1875. LANDING OF COLUMBUS SPECIAL PRINTING PICTORIAL ISSUE

| SP27 | | UnFVF | UseFVF |
|---|---|---|---|
| 15¢ | **brown and blue** Type III *(1,981 copies)* | 1400. | 600. |
| | a. Imperforate horizontally (single stamp) | 1650. | |

## 1875. DECLARATION OF INDEPENDENCE SPECIAL PRINTING PICTORIAL ISSUE

| SP28 | | UnFVF | UseFVF |
|---|---|---|---|
| 24¢ | **deep green and violet** *(2,091)* | 1300. | 600. |

## 1875. SHIELD, EAGLE AND FLAGS SPECIAL PRINTING PICTORIAL ISSUE

| SP29 | | UnFVF | UseFVF |
|---|---|---|---|
| 30¢ | **bright blue and carmine** *(1,356)* | 1750. | 1000. |

## 1875. ABRAHAM LINCOLN SPECIAL PRINTING PICTORIAL ISSUE

| SP30 | | UnFVF | UseFVF |
|---|---|---|---|
| 90¢ | **carmine and black** *(1,356)* | 3800. | 4300. |

## 1880. GEORGE WASHINGTON SPECIAL PRINTING PICTORIAL ISSUE on soft porus paper, without grill. Perforated 12. Printed by the American Bank Note Co.

| SP31 | | UnFVF | UseFVF |
|---|---|---|---|
| 1¢ | **buff,** without gum (approx. 2,500) | 210. | 190. |
| | Plate block of 10, w/imprint | 18000. | |
| | brown orange, without gum (approx 3,000 copies) | 180. | 125. |

## 1870 National Bank Note Co. Portrait Series

The short-lived pictorial issue of 1869 was replaced by a series of new portraits, produced by the National Bank Note Company. The new stamps were issued both with and without grills. The grilled stamps are listed as Nos. 97-107 and the ungrilled stamps are Nos. 108-118. The grills are of two sizes, *Grill H,* about 10 x 12mm with sharp tips on the grill points, and *Grill I,* about 8 1/2 x 10mm having rather blunt tips on the grill points. Grill H was used on all values while Grill I was used only on the 1¢ through 7¢ values. *Intaglio on thin to medium thick white wove paper, unwatermarked and perforated 12.*

## 1870. BENJAMIN FRANKLIN ISSUE

97, 108 *Benjamin Franklin after bust by Rubricht. The pearl at the left of the numeral "1" is clear.*

**97**

| | | UnFVF | UseFVF |
|---|---|---|---|
| **1¢** | **ultramarine,** grill H | 850. | 65.00 |
| | dark untramarine | 850. | 65.00 |
| | dull ultramarine | 850. | 65.00 |
| | On cover | | 90.00 |
| | Double transfer | 900. | 70.00 |
| | Split grill | 925. | 75.00 |
| | Quadruple split grill | — | 225. |
| | Double grill | — | 130. |
| | v. Grill I | — | — |
| | *Earliest documented cover: (April 9, 1870)* | | |

## 1870. ANDREW JACKSON ISSUE

98, 109 *Andrew Jackson after bust by Hiram Powers.*

*In the notch formed underneath the semi-circular ornament to the left of the "S" of "U.S." the lines forming the notch do not quite join at the apex of the notch. This stamp is always of a red brown shade.*

**98**

| | | UnFVF | UseFVF |
|---|---|---|---|
| **2¢** | **red brown,** grill H | 480. | 38.00 |
| | dark red brown | 480. | 38.00 |
| | dull red brown | 480. | 38.00 |
| | On cover | | 57.00 |
| | Split grill | 525. | 50.00 |
| | Quadruple split grill | 1200. | 125. |
| | Double grill | 650. | 80.00 |
| | v. Diagonal bisect on cover | | — |
| | v1. Grill I | — | — |
| | *Earliest documented cover: (Sept. 1, 1870)* | | |

## 1870. GEORGE WASHINGTON ISSUE

99, 110 *George Washington. Under the word "THREE," the long tail of the ribbon is lightly shaded along its lower edge.*

**99**

| | | UnFVF | UseFVF |
|---|---|---|---|
| **3¢** | **green,** grill H | 370. | 10.00 |
| | deep green | 370. | 10.00 |
| | pale green | 370. | 10.00 |
| | yellow green | 370. | 10.00 |
| | On cover | | 15.00 |
| | Plate block of 10, w/imprint | 5500. | |
| | Plate block of 12, w/imprint | 6500. | |
| | Cracked plate | — | 50.00 |
| | Double transfer | — | 12.00 |
| | Split grill | 400. | 12.00 |
| | Quadruple split grill | — | 75.00 |
| | Double grill | 550. | 40.00 |
| | v. Grill I | — | — |
| | v1. Printed on both sides | — | — |
| | v2. Imperforate pair | 1250. | |
| | *Earliest documented cover: (March 25, 1870)* | | |

## 1870. ABRAHAM LINCOLN ISSUE

100, 111 *Abraham Lincoln after bust by Leonard Volk. The first four vertical lines of the shading in the lower part of the left ribbon, to the left and downward from the "S" of "SIX," are of normal strength.*

**100**

| | | UnFVF | UseFVF |
|---|---|---|---|
| **6¢** | **carmine,** grill H | 2000. | 300. |
| | carmine rose | 2000. | 300. |
| | dull carmine | 2000. | 300. |
| | On cover | | 500. |
| | Split grill | 2200. | 375. |
| | Quadruple split grill | — | 570. |
| | Double grill | — | 500. |
| | v. Grill I | — | — |
| | *Earliest documented cover: (Aug. 1870)* | | |

## 1871. EDWIN STANTON ISSUE

101, 112 *Edwin Stanton. Edwin M. Stanton, Attorney General under Buchanan and Secretary of War under Lincoln and Johnson, actively opposed the latter's Reconstruction policies. An attempt to dismiss him served as the pretext for Johnson's impeachment in 1868. Appointed to the Supreme Court in 1869, Stanton died before he could take office.*

There are no semi-circles around the ends of the lines forming the ball in the lower right corner.

**101**

| | | UnFVF | UseFVF |
|---|---|---|---|
| **7¢** | **vermillion,** grill H | 1325. | 275. |
| | On cover | | 450. |
| | Split grill | 1400. | 300. |
| | Quadruple split grill | — | 500. |
| | Double grill | — | 450. |
| | v. Grill I | — | — |
| | *Earliest documented cover: (Feb. 12, 1871)* | | |

## 1871. THOMAS JEFFERSON ISSUE

102, 113, 138 *Thomas Jefferson after bust by Hiram Powers. The scroll ornament at the right end of the upper label, below the letter "E" of "POSTAGE," is clear.*

**102**

| | | UnFVF | UseFVF |
|---|---|---|---|
| **10¢** | **brown** | 1800. | 450. |
| | dark brown | 1800. | 450. |
| | yellow brown | 1800. | 450. |
| | On cover | | 750. |
| | Split grill | 1900. | 500. |
| | Double grill | — | 800. |
| | *Earliest documented cover: (June 11, 1871)* | | |

## 1872. Henry Clay Issue

103, 114 *Henry Clay after bust by Joel T. Hart. Clay was the first prominent Speaker of the House and "The Great Pacificator" of the Senate, where he effected compromises between slavery and anti-slavery forces. Twice a candidate for President, in 1824 he threw his electoral votes to John Quincy Adams, defeating Jackson, and served as Adams' Secretary of State.*

*The "2" in the figure "12" has balls nearly round in shape at the upper and lower portion of the figure.*

| 103 | | UnFVF | UseFVF |
|---|---|---|---|
| 12¢ | **pale violet** | 14000. | 1750. |
| | On cover | | 4700. |
| | Split grill | — | 1850. |
| | *Earliest documented cover: (Feb. 9, 1872)* | | |

## 1870. Daniel Webster Portrait Issue

104, 115 *Daniel Webster after bust by S. V. Clevenger. (For Webster's biography, see CM115). The thin lines shading the triangles, and below the letters "U.S. POSTAGE" are fine but of normal color and strength.*

PU
page 21

| 104 | | UnFVF | UseFVF |
|---|---|---|---|
| 15¢ | **orange** | 2600. | 750. |
| | bright orange | 2600. | 750. |
| | dark orange | 2600. | 750. |
| | On cover | | 1350. |
| | Split grill | 2500. | 820. |
| | Double grill | — | — |
| | *Earliest documented cover: (Oct. 29, 1870)* | | |

## 1870. Gen. Winfield Scott Issue

105, 116, 129 *Gen. Winfield Scott after bust by Coffee. (For Scott biography, see CM173).*

| 105 | | UnFVF | UseFVF |
|---|---|---|---|
| 24¢ | **purple** | — | 10000. |
| | dull purple | — | 10000. |
| | On cover | | — |
| | Split grill | — | — |

## 1870. Alexander Hamilton Issue

106, 117 *Alexander Hamilton was Washington's aide and secretary during the Revolution and commanded troops at Yorktown. One of the drafters of the Constitution, he advocated extremely strong central government. As first Secretary of the Treasury, "the Hamiltonian system" established the fiscal policy, strengthened federal government and the public credit, promoted*

*industrialization as opposed to Jefferson's concept of an agricultural economy, and aroused factionalism which led to the developement of political parties in America. Thwarting Aaron Burr's election as President in 1800 and as governor of New York in 1804, he was killed by the latter in a pistol duel.*

| 106 | | UnFVF | UseFVF |
|---|---|---|---|
| 30¢ | **black** | 3750. | 550. |
| | Deep black | 3750. | 550. |
| | On cover | | 2100. |
| | Double grill | — | |
| | *Earliest documented cover: (Aug. 1870)* | | |

## 1870. Oliver Perry Issue

| 107 | | UnFVF | UseFVF |
|---|---|---|---|
| 90¢ | **carmine** | 4250. | 550. |
| | Dark carmine | 4250. | 550. |
| | On cover | — | |
| | Double grill | — | |
| | Split grill | | 1100. |
| | FDC *(April 12, 1870)* | | |

## 1870. Benjamin Franklin Issue

| 108 | | UnFVF | UseFVF |
|---|---|---|---|
| 1¢ | **ultramarine** | 120. | 5.00 |
| | dark ultramarine | 120. | 5.00 |
| | gray blue | 120. | 5.00 |
| | pale ultramarine | 120. | 5.00 |
| | On cover | | — |
| | Double transfer | — | 15.00 |
| | Worn Plate | 300. | 10.00 |
| | *Earliest documented cover: (July 18, 1870 )* | | |

## 1870. Andrew Jackson Issue

| 109 | | UnFVF | UseFVF |
|---|---|---|---|
| 2¢ | **red brown** | 90.00 | 3.50 |
| | dark red brown | 90.00 | 3.50 |
| | orange brown | 90.00 | 3.50 |
| | pale red brown | 90.00 | 3.50 |
| | On cover | | 7.50 |
| | Bisect (any) on cover | | — |
| | Double transfer | — | 8.00 |
| | v. Double impression | — | — |
| | *Earliest documented cover: (June 11, 1870)* | | |

## 1870. George Washington Issue

| 110 | | UnFVF | UseFVF |
|---|---|---|---|
| 3¢ | **green** | 90.00 | .50 |
| | dark green | 90.00 | .50 |
| | pale green | 90.00 | .50 |
| | yellow green | 90.00 | .50 |
| | On cover | | 1.50 |
| | Plate block of 10, w/imprint | 1750. | |
| | Double transfer | — | 8.00 |
| | Cracked plate | — | 4.50 |
| | Worn plate | 225. | 1.00 |
| | v. Double impression | — | 1000. |
| | v1. Printed both sides | — | 1500. |
| | *Earliest documented cover: (March 13, 1870)* | | |

## 1870. Abraham Lincoln Issue

| 111 | | UnFVF | UseFVF |
|---|---|---|---|
| 6¢ | **carmine** | 175. | 7.50 |
| | brown carmine | 175. | 7.50 |
| | dark carmine | 175. | 7.50 |
| | rose | 175. | 7.50 |
| | violet carmine | 175. | 7.50 |
| | On cover | | 135. |
| | Vertical bisect on cover | | — |
| | Double paper | — | |
| | Double transfer | — | — |
| | v. Double impression | — | 1250. |
| | *Earliest documented cover: (March 28, 1870)* | | |

## 1871. EDWIN STANTON ISSUE

| 112 | | UnFVF | UseFVF |
|---|---|---|---|
| 7¢ | vermilion | 200. | 30.00 |
| | deep vermilion | 200. | 30.00 |
| | On cover | | 140. |
| | Cracked plate | — | — |
| | Double transfer | — | |

*Earliest documented cover: (May 11, 1871)*

## 1870. THOMAS JEFFERSON ISSUE

| 113 | | UnFVF | UseFVF |
|---|---|---|---|
| 10¢ | brown | 185. | 9.00 |
| | dark brown | 185. | 9.00 |
| | yellow brown | 185. | 9.00 |
| | On cover | | 30.00 |
| | Double transfer | — | 60.00 |

*Earliest documented cover: (May 1870)*

## 1870. HENRY CLAY ISSUE

| 114 | | UnFVF | UseFVF |
|---|---|---|---|
| 12¢ | pale violet | 400. | 40.00 |
| | dark violet | 400. | 40.00 |
| | violet | 400. | 40.00 |
| | On cover | | 350. |

*Earliest documented cover: (July 9, 1870)*

## 1870. DANIEL WEBSTER ISSUE

| 115 | | UnFVF | UseFVF |
|---|---|---|---|
| 15¢ | orange | 400. | 50.00 |
| | deep orange | 400. | 50.00 |
| | On cover | | 225. |
| | v. Double impression | — | |

*Earliest documented cover: (Sept. 24, 1870)*

## 1870. GEN. WINFIELD SCOTT ISSUE

| 116 | | UnFVF | UseFVF |
|---|---|---|---|
| 24¢ | purple | 400. | 50.00 |
| | bright purple | 400. | 50.00 |
| | dark purple | 400. | 50.00 |
| | dull purple | 400. | 50.00 |
| | On cover | | 1250. |
| | Double paper | — | — |

*Earliest documented cover: (Nov. 18, 1870)*

## 1871. ALEXANDER HAMILTON ISSUE

| 117 | | UnFVF | UseFVF |
|---|---|---|---|
| 30¢ | black | 950. | 75.00 |
| | On cover | | 675. |

*Earliest documented cover: (Jan. 31, 1871)*

## 1872. OLIVER PERRY ISSUE

| 118 | | UnFVF | UseFVF |
|---|---|---|---|
| 90¢ | carmine | 950. | 100. |
| | dark carmine | 950. | 100. |
| | On cover | | — |

*Earliest documented cover: (Sept. 1, 1872)*

## 1873 Continental Bank Note Co. Portrait Series

The Continental Bank Note Company was awarded the printing contract for the period of May 1, 1873, through April 30, 1877. This contract later was extended until this company was consolidated with the American Bank Note Company on February 4, 1879. When Continental took over the printing contract, it took over some of the plates and the dies used by National in the production of the stamps of 1970-71. While the designs of the stamps printed by Continental are similar or identical to those printed by National, the 1¢ through 12¢ easily may be identified because the Continental stamps had so-called "secret marks." The 15¢ can be distinguished by plate wear and some shade variation, and the 30¢ and 90¢ can be distinguished by slight shade differences. The stamps were printed on hard, white wove paper, varing from thin to thick, that generally is difficult or impossible to differentiate from the paper used by National. *The paper is unwatermarked and the stamps are printed by intaglio and perforated 12.*

## 1873. BENJAMIN FRANKLIN ISSUE

*119, 132 Benjamin Franklin. In the pearl at the left of the numeral "1" there is a small dash of color.*

| 119 | | UnFVF | UseFVF |
|---|---|---|---|
| 1¢ | ultramarine | 70.00 | 1.25 |
| | blue | 70.00 | 1.25 |
| | dark ultramarine | 70.00 | 1.25 |
| | dull ultramarine | 70.00 | 1.25 |
| | gray blue | 70.00 | 1.25 |
| | On cover | | 3.25 |
| | Plate block of 12, w/imprint | 2500. | |
| | "Cogwheel" punch cut in paper | 275. | |
| | Cracked plate | — | |
| | Double paper | — | |
| | Double transfer | 2.00 | 5.00 |
| | p. Paper with silk fibers | — | 17.50 |
| | p1. Ribbed paper | 175. | 3.25 |
| | v. With grill | 1500. | |
| | v1. Pair, imperforate | 1150. | 6.00 |

*Earliest documented cover: Aug. 22, 1873.*

## 1873. ANDREW JACKSON ISSUE

*120, 121, 133 Andrew Jackson. In the notch formed underneath the semi-circular ornament immediately to the left of the "S" of "U.S." the lines forming the apex of the notch join in a small point of color.*

| 120 | | UnFVF | UseFVF |
|---|---|---|---|
| 2¢ | brown | 115. | 7.00 |
| | dark brown | 115. | 7.00 |
| | dark red brown | 115. | 7.00 |
| | yellow brown | 115. | 7.00 |
| | On cover | | 17.50 |
| | Vertical bisect on cover | | — |
| | Cracked plate | — | — |
| | Double paper | 400. | 25.00 |
| | Double transfer | — | 17.50 |
| | W/secret mark | 325. | 14.00 |
| | p. Ribbed paper | 300. | 14.00 |
| | v. Double impression | — | — |
| | v1. With grill | 1300. | 550. |

*Earliest documented cover: (July 12, 1873)*

## 1875. ANDREW JACKSON ISSUE

| 121 | | UnFVF | UseFVF |
|---|---|---|---|
| 2¢ | vermilion | 115. | 3.50 |
| | On cover | | 8.50 |
| | Plate block of 12, w/imprint | — | |
| | Double paper | — | — |
| | Double transfer | — | — |
| | p. Paper with silk fibers | 325. | 9.00 |
| | p1. Ribbed paper | — | — |
| | p2. With grill | 350. | |
| | v. Imperforate pair | 650. | |

*Earliest documented cover: (July 15, 1875)*

## 1873. GEORGE WASHINGTON ISSUE

*122, 134 George Washington. Under the word "THREE," the long tail of the ribbon is heavily shaded along its lower edge.*

**122**

| 3¢ | | UnFVF | UseFVF |
|---|---|---|---|
| | **green** | 40.00 | .20 |
| | bluish green | 40.00 | .20 |
| | dark green | 40.00 | .20 |
| | yellow green | 40.00 | .20 |
| | dark yellow green | 40.00 | .20 |
| | olive green | 40.00 | .20 |
| | On cover | | 40.00 |
| | Plate block of 10, w/imprint | 1500. | |
| | Plate block of 12, w/imprint | 2250. | |
| | Plate strip of 5, w/imprint | 600. | |
| | Plate strip of 6, w/imrpint | 675. | |
| | "Cogwheel" punch cut in paper | 200. | 150. |
| | Cracked plate | — | 30.00 |
| | Double transfer | — | 4.50 |
| | Double paper | 150. | 5.00 |
| | Short transfer | — | 12.50 |
| | p. Ribbed paper | 75.00 | 1.50 |
| | p1. Paper with silk fibers | — | 4.50 |
| | p2. With grill | 200. | |
| | v. Double impression | — | 1100. |
| | v1. Printed on both sides | — | |
| | v2. Imperforate pair | 850. | |
| | v3. Horizontal pair, imperforate between | — | |
| | v4. Horizontal pair, imperforate vertically | — | |

*Earliest documented cover: (July 9, 1873)*

### 1875. ZACHARY TAYLOR ISSUE

123, 136 *Zachary Taylor. This is an historically interesting stamp for it marked the inauguration of the Universal Postal Union, setting a 5¢ rate for mail abroad and the blue color which was generally adhered to after 1898. Also a standing almost unique in changing world is the fact the 5¢ rate for a letter to Europe stood for 78 years, until November 1, 1953, when the rate was changed to 8¢.*

**123**

| 5¢ | | UnFVF | UseFVF |
|---|---|---|---|
| | **Prussian blue** | 145. | 5.50 |
| | bright blue | 145. | 5.50 |
| | dark blue | 145. | 5.50 |
| | greenish blue | 145. | 5.50 |
| | pale blue | 145. | 5.50 |
| | On cover | | 30.00 |
| | Cracked plate | — | 390. |
| | Double paper | 500. | — |
| | Double transfer | — | 75.00 |
| | p. Paper with silk fibers | — | 100. |
| | p1. Ribbed paper | — | 100. |
| | p2. With grill | 700. | |

*Earliest documented cover: (July 12, 1875)*

### 1873. ABRAHAM LINCOLN ISSUE

124, 137 *Abraham Lincoln. The first four vertical lines of the shading in the lower part of the left ribbon, to the left and downward from the "S" in "SIX" have been made heavier.*

**124**

| 6¢ | | UnFVF | UseFVF |
|---|---|---|---|
| | **dull Venetian red** | 140. | 7.00 |
| | brown rose | 140. | 7.00 |
| | rose | 140. | 7.00 |
| | On cover | | 37.50 |
| | Plate block of 12, w/imprint | 11000. | |
| | Double paper | — | |
| | p. Paper with silk fibers | — | 32.50 |
| | p1. Ribbed paper | — | 14.00 |
| | p2. With grill | 1250. | |

*Earliest documented cover: (July 24, 1873)*

### 1873. EDWIN STANTON ISSUE

125 *Edwin Stanton. A small semi-circle has been drawn around each end of the two lines that outline the ball in the lower right corner.*

**125**

| 7¢ | | UnFVF | UseFVF |
|---|---|---|---|
| | **vermilion** | 300. | 30.00 |
| | dark vermilion | 300. | 30.00 |
| | On cover | | 150. |
| | Plate block of 12, w/imprint | — | |
| | Double paper | — | — |
| | Double transfer of "SEVEN CENTS" | — | 175. |
| | Double transfer in lower left corner | — | 75.00 |
| | p. Paper with silk fibers | — | 100. |
| | p1. Ribbed paper | — | 75.00 |
| | p2. With grill | 1750. | |

*Earliest documented cover: (Oct. 5, 1873)*

### 1873. THOMAS JEFFERSON ISSUE

126, 139 *Thomas Jefferson. The scroll ornament at the right end of the upper label, below the letter "E" of "POSTAGE," has a small crescent of color within it.*

**126**

| 10¢ | | UnFVF | UseFVF |
|---|---|---|---|
| | **brown** | 200. | 8.00 |
| | dark brown | 200. | 8.00 |
| | yellow brown | 200. | 8.00 |
| | On cover | | 25.00 |
| | Plate block of 10, w/imprint | 8750. | |
| | Plate block of 12, w/imprint | 9250. | |
| | Double paper | 550. | |
| | Double transfer | — | |
| | p. Paper with silk fibers | — | 25.00 |
| | p1. Ribbed paper | — | 22.50 |
| | p2. With grill | 2250. | |
| | v. Imperforate pair | — | 2750. |
| | v1. Horizontal pair, imperforate between | — | 3500. |

*Earliest documented cover: (Aug. 2, 1873)*

### 1874. HENRY CLAY ISSUE

127 *Henry Clay. The balls of the figure "2" are crescent shaped instead of nearly round.*

**127**

| 12¢ | | UnFVF | UseFVF |
|---|---|---|---|
| | **blackish violet** | 500. | 40.00 |
| | On cover | | 300. |
| | p. Ribbed paper | — | 75.00 |
| | p1. With grill | 3500. | |

*Earliest documented cover: (Jan. 3, 1874)*

### 1873. DANIEL WEBSTER ISSUE

128, 140 *Daniel Webster. The thin lines shading the triangles and below the letter "U.S. POSTAGE" are worn. These areas show less color and therefore appear more white than the 15¢ National Printing.*

| 128 | | UnFVF | UseFVF |
|---|---|---|---|
| 15¢ | yellow orange | 475. | 37.50 |
| | dull orange | 475. | 37.50 |
| | red orange | 475. | 37.50 |
| | On cover | | 250. |
| | Double paper | — | |
| | p. Paper with silk fibers | 1250. | 80.00 |
| | p1. Paper with vertical ribs | 1100. | 75.00 |
| | p2. With grill | 3500. | |

*Earliest documented cover: (July 22, 1873)*

**1874. GEN. WINFIELD SCOTT ISSUE** The 24¢ Continental has been the subject of much controversy. It is known that 365,000 copies of this stamp were printed and delivered to the Stamp Agent, but there is no proof that any of them were issued to post offices. In 1885, 364,950 copies of the 24¢ stamps were destroyed, for they were no longer needed to make up the then-existing postage rates. It is not known whether or not these were all Continentals. Some experts think that unused examples can be distinguished by their gum, with the Continentals bearing a thinner and lighter colored gum than the Nationals. Another possible means of identification lies in the paper. The Continental 24¢ was printed from the same plate as the National 24¢, so they are identical in design. The Philatelic Foundation issued a certificate of genuineness to a 24¢ on vertically ribbed paper; experts believe that only Continental used such paper. The listing below is based on that single item.

| 129 | | UnFVF | UseFVF |
|---|---|---|---|
| 24¢ | light purple | — | — |

**1874. ALEXANDER HAMILTON ISSUE**

| 130 | | UnFVF | UseFVF |
|---|---|---|---|
| 30¢ | gray black | 600. | 37.50 |
| | greenish black | 600. | 37.50 |
| | On cover | | 625. |
| | Double paper | — | 85.00 |
| | Double transfer | — | 625. |
| | p. Paper with silk fibers | — | |
| | p1. Ribbed paper | 1250. | 75.00 |
| | p2. With grill | 3500. | |

*Earliest documented cover: (Oct. 30, 1874)*

*The 30¢ Continental and 30¢ National are identical except in shade.*

**1874. OLIVER PERRY ISSUE**

| 131 | | UnFVF | UseFVF |
|---|---|---|---|
| 90¢ | rose carmine | 1100. | 105. |
| | dull rose carmine | 1100. | 105. |
| | On cover | | 5500. |

*The 90¢ Continental and the 90¢ National are identical except in shade.*

**1875. BENJAMIN FRANKLIN SPECIAL PRINTING PICTORIAL ISSUE** which was still in use. Printed by the Continental Bank Note Co. by intaglio on hard white wove paper, perforated 12, and issued without gum. For some reason, these stamps usually were cut apart with scissors so that the perforations generally are mutilated. The special printing can be identified by the color shades and by the very white paper (instead of the yellowish of the original issue). Numbers sold are not known. Some estimate can be made by studying the table that follow SP57.

| SP32 | | UnFVF | UseFVF |
|---|---|---|---|
| 1¢ | bright ultramarine | 7250. | |

**1875. ANDREW JACKSON SPECIAL PRINTING PICTORIAL ISSUE**

| SP33 | | UnFVF | UseFVF |
|---|---|---|---|
| 2¢ | blackish brown | 3000. | |

**1875. ANDREW JACKSON SPECIAL PRINTING PICTORIAL ISSUE**

| SP34 | | UnFVF | UseFVF |
|---|---|---|---|
| 2¢ | carmine vermilion | 20000. | |

**1875. GEORGE WASHINGTON SPECIAL PICTORIAL ISSUE**

| SP35 | | UnFVF | UseFVF |
|---|---|---|---|
| 3¢ | bluish green | 9250. | |

**1875. ZACHARY TAYLOR SPECIAL PRINTING PICTORIAL ISSUE**

| SP36 | | UnFVF | UseFVF |
|---|---|---|---|
| 5¢ | bright blue | 27500. | |

**1875. ABRAHAM LINCOLN SPECIAL PRINTING PICTORIAL ISSUE**

| SP37 | | UnFVF | UseFVF |
|---|---|---|---|
| 6¢ | pale rose | 8000. | |

**1875. EDWIN STANTON SPECIAL PRINTING PICTORIAL ISSUE**

| SP38 | | UnFVF | UseFVF |
|---|---|---|---|
| 7¢ | scarlet vermilion | 1500. | |

**1875. THOMAS JEFFERSON SPECIAL PRINTING PICTORIAL ISSUE**

| SP39 | | UnFVF | UseFVF |
|---|---|---|---|
| 10¢ | yellow brown | 8000. | |

**1875. HENRY CLAY SPECIAL PRINTING PICTORIAL ISSUE**

| SP40 | | UnFVF | UseFVF |
|---|---|---|---|
| 12¢ | black violet | 2750. | |

**1875. DANIEL WEBSTER SPECIAL PRINTING PICTORIAL ISSUE**

| SP41 | | UnFVF | UseFVF |
|---|---|---|---|
| 15¢ | bright orange | 8000. | |

**1875. GEN. WINFIELD SCOTT SPECIAL PRINTING PICTORIAL ISSUE**

| SP42 | | UnFVF | UseFVF |
|---|---|---|---|
| 24¢ | dull purple | 1750. | |

**1875. ALEXANDER HAMILTON SPECIAL PRINTING PICTORIAL ISSUE**

| SP43 | | UnFVF | UseFVF |
|---|---|---|---|
| 30¢ | greenish black | 5750. | |

**1875. OLIVER PERRY SPECIAL PRINTING PICTORIAL ISSUE**

| SP44 | | UnFVF | UseFVF |
|---|---|---|---|
| 90¢ | violet carmine | 7500. | |

## 1879 American Bank Note Co. Portrait Series

The American Bank Note Co. absorbed the Continental Bank Note Co. on February 4, 1879, and continued to print postage, department and newspaper stamps. American used many of the plates bearing the Continental imprints, so the imprint does not always accurately indicate the producing firm. The American Bank Note Co. printed stamps on unwatermarked soft porous paper instead of the hard paper used by National and Continental. With the exception of one type of the 10¢, all the stamps from 1¢ through the 12¢ carry the same "secret marks" as the Continentals. With the exception of the color changes on the 3¢, 30¢ and 90¢ that were issued later, these stamps were issued in 1879. *All were printed by intaglio and perforated 12.*

**1879. BENJAMIN FRANKLIN ISSUE**

| 132 | | UnFVF | UseFVF |
|---|---|---|---|
| 1¢ | dark ultramarine | 75.00 | 1.00 |
| | blue | 75.00 | 1.00 |
| | gray blue | 75.00 | 1.00 |
| | On cover | | 2.25 |
| | Plate block of 10, w/imprint | 3000. | |
| | Double transfer | — | 6.00 |

*Earliest documented cover: (April 25, 1879)*

**1879. ANDREW JACKSON ISSUE**

| 133 | | UnFVF | UseFVF |
|---|---|---|---|
| 2¢ | vermilion | 45.00 | 1.00 |
| | orange vermilion | 45.00 | 1.00 |
| | On cover | | 2.25 |
| | Plate block of 10, w/imprint | 1250. | |
| | Plate block of 12, w/imprint | 1750. | |
| | Double transfer | — | |
| | Double impression | — | 400. |
| | FDC (Feb. 4, 1879) | | 500. |

## 1879. GEORGE WASHINGTON ISSUE

| 134 | | UnFVF | UseFVF |
|---|---|---|---|
| 3¢ | **green** | 35.00 | .25 |
| | dark green | 35.00 | .25 |
| | dull green | 35.00 | .25 |
| | On cover | | .50 |
| | Plate block of 10, w/imprint | 800. | |
| | Plate block of 12, w/imprint | 1000. | |
| | Plate block of 14, w/imprint | 1300. | |
| | Double transfer | — | 4.00 |
| | Short transfer | — | 5.00 |
| | Double impression | — | — |
| | v. Imperforate pair | 550. | |

*Earliest documented cover: (Feb. 7, 1879)*

## 1887. GEORGE WASHINGTON ISSUE

| 135 | | UnFVF | UseFVF |
|---|---|---|---|
| 3¢ | **vermilion** | 45.00 | 20.00 |
| | On cover | | 75.00 |
| | Plate block of 10, w/imprint | 900. | |
| | Plate block of 12, w/imprint | 1100. | |
| | Plate strip of 5, w/imprint | 350. | |
| | Plate strip of 6, w/imprint | 400. | |

*Earliest documented cover: (Oct. 18. 1887)*

## 1879. ZACHARY TAYLOR ISSUE

| 136 | | UnFVF | UseFVF |
|---|---|---|---|
| 5¢ | **blue** | 145. | 6.00 |
| | bright blue | 145. | 6.00 |
| | dark blue | 145. | 6.00 |
| | dull blue | 145. | 6.00 |
| | On cover | | 17.50 |
| | Plate block of 12, w/imprint | 7000. | |

*Earliest documented cover: (May 12, 1879)*

## 1879. ABRAHAM LINCOLN ISSUE

| 137 | | UnFVF | UseFVF |
|---|---|---|---|
| 6¢ | **dull pink** | 257. | 8.50 |
| | brown pink | 257. | 8.50 |
| | pink | 257. | 8.50 |
| | On cover | | 32.50 |

*Earliest documented cover: (July 1, 1879)*

## 1879. THOMAS JEFFERSON ISSUE

| 138 | | UnFVF | UseFVF |
|---|---|---|---|
| 10¢ | **brown,** like No. 102, but no secret mark | 550. | 12.50 |
| | yellow brown | 550. | 12.50 |
| | On cover | | 35.00 |
| | Double transfer | — | 30.00 |

*Earliest documented cover: (Sept. 5, 1879)*

## 1879. THOMAS JEFFERSON ISSUE

| 139 | | UnFVF | UseFVF |
|---|---|---|---|
| 10¢ | **brown,** like No. 126, with secret mark | 425. | 12.50 |
| | black brown | 425. | 12.50 |
| | yellow brown | 425. | 12.50 |
| | On cover | | 32.50 |
| | Cracked plate | — | — |
| | Double transfer | — | 35.00 |
| | Pair, 1 each Nos. 138, 139 | — | 200. |
| | v. Vertical pair, imperforate between | — | — |

*Earliest documented cover: (Feb. 21, 1879)*

## 1879. DANIEL WEBSTER ISSUE

| 140 | | UnFVF | UseFVF |
|---|---|---|---|
| 15¢ | **orange** | | |
| | red orange | 100. | 11.00 |
| | yellow orange | 100. | 11.00 |
| | On cover | | 75.00 |
| | Plate block of 12, w/imprint | 5750. | |

*Earliest documented cover: (Jan. 20, 1879)*

## 1882. ALEXANDER HAMILTON ISSUE

| 141 | | UnFVF | UseFVF |
|---|---|---|---|
| 30¢ | **black** | 300. | 22.50 |
| | greenish black | 300. | 22.50 |
| | On cover | | 375. |
| | Plate block of 10, w/imprint | 8500. | |

*Earliest documented cover: (Nov. 13, 1882)*

## 1888. HAMILTON ALEXANDER ISSUE

| 142 | | UnFVF | UseFVF |
|---|---|---|---|
| 30¢ | **orange brown** | 325. | 40.00 |
| | dark orange brown | 325. | 40.00 |
| | On cover | | 1200. |
| | Plate block of 10, w/imprint | 6000. | |
| | Plate block of 12, w/imprint | — | |
| | Plate strip of 5, w/imprint | 2200. | |

*Earliest documented cover: (Sept. 22, 1888)*

## 1880. OLIVER PERRY ISSUE

| 143 | | UnFVF | UseFVF |
|---|---|---|---|
| 90¢ | **carmine** | 725. | 95.00 |
| | carmine rose | 725. | 95.00 |
| | rose | 725. | 95.00 |
| | On cover | | 4000. |
| | Double paper | — | — |

*Earliest documented cover: (June 17, 1880)*

## 1880. OLIVER PERRY ISSUE

| 144 | | UnFVF | UseFVF |
|---|---|---|---|
| 90¢ | **dark red violet** | 750. | 85.00 |
| | bright purple | 750. | 85.00 |
| | On cover | | 6500. |
| | Plate block of 10, w/imprint | 18500. | |
| | Plate block of 12, w/imprint | — | |
| | Plate strip of 5, w/imprint | 5000. | |
| | v. Imperforate pair | 2250. | |

**1880. SPECIAL PRINTING OF THE 1879-88 ISSUE OF 1879.** By the American Bank Note Co. Designs on *soft porous paper, printed by intaglio, perforated 12.*

| SP45 | | UnFVF | UseFVF |
|---|---|---|---|
| 1¢ | **deep ultramarine** | | |
| SP46 | | UnFVF | UseFVF |
| 2¢ | **blackish brown** | 5750. | |
| SP47 | | UnFVF | UseFVF |
| 2¢ | **scarlet vermillion** | 13500. | |
| SP48 | | UnFVF | UseFVF |
| 3¢ | **bluish green** | 11000. | |
| SP49 | | UnFVF | UseFVF |
| 5¢ | **deep blue** | 2000. | |
| SP50 | | UnFVF | UseFVF |
| 6¢ | **pale rose** | 9500. | |
| SP51 | | UnFVF | UseFVF |
| 7¢ | **scarlet vermillion** | 3500. | |
| SP52 | | UnFVF | UseFVF |
| 10¢ | **deep brown** | 11250. | |
| SP53 | | UnFVF | UseFVF |
| 12¢ | **black purple** | 3500. | |
| SP54 | | UnFVF | UseFVF |
| 15¢ | **orange** | 7500. | |
| SP55 | | UnFVF | UseFVF |
| 24¢ | **blackish violet** | 8750. | |
| SP56 | | UnFVF | UseFVF |
| 30¢ | **greenish black** | 18500. | |
| SP57 | | UnFVF | UseFVF |
| 90¢ | **pale carmine** | 30000. | |

**1881-82. RE-ENGRAVED DESIGNS OF 1873 ISSUE** for the 1¢, 3¢, 6¢, and 10¢ denominations. They were printed by the American Bank Note Co. by *Intaglio on soft porous, unwatermarked paper and were perforated 12.*

145 *The vertical lines forming the background in the upper part of the stamp have been made much heavier and the background now appears to be almost solid. Lines of shading also have been added to the curving ornaments in the upper corners of the stamp.*

*1879 Design*

145. *1881 Design, re-engraved*

| 145 | | UnFVF | UseFVF |
|---|---|---|---|
| 1¢ | **ultramarine** | 22.50 | .35 |
| | bright ultramarine | 22.50 | .35 |
| | dull blue | 22.50 | .35 |
| | gray blue | 22.50 | .35 |
| | On cover | | 1.00 |
| | Plate block of 10, /wimprint | 900. | |
| | Plate block of 12, /wimprint | 1000. | |
| | Plate strip of 5, /wimprint | 300. | |
| | Plate strip of 6, w/imprint | 350. | |
| | "Cogwheel" punch cut in paper | 125. | |
| | Double transfer | 65.00 | 3.50 |

*Earliest documented cover: (Dec. 5, 1881)*

### 1881. GEORGE WASHINGTON ISSUE

146 *1879 Design.*

The shading at the sides of the large central oval is only about half the previous thickness. A short horizontal dash has been added just below the "TS" of "CENTS".

*1881 Design, Re-engraved.*

| 146 | | UnFVF | UseFVF |
|---|---|---|---|
| 3¢ | **blue green** | 27.50 | .20 |
| | green | 27.50 | .20 |
| | yellow green | 27.50 | .20 |
| | On cover | | .75 |
| | Plate block of 10, /wimprint | 1100. | |
| | Plate strip of 5, w/imprint | 350. | |
| | Cracked plate | — | |
| | Double transfer | — | 7.00 |
| | Punched w/8 small holes in a circle | 150. | |
| | v1. Plate block of 10, w/imprint | 2000. | |
| | v2. Double impression | — | — |

*Earliest documented cover: (Oct. 24, 1881)*

### 1882. ABRAHAM LINCOLN ISSUE

147 *There are only three vertical lines from the outside of the panel to the outside of the stamps. The preceding issue had four lines.*

| 147 | | UnFVF | UseFVF |
|---|---|---|---|
| 6¢ | **rose** | 150. | 27.50 |
| | dull rose | 150. | 27.50 |
| | brown red | 125. | 30.00 |
| | On cover | | 125. |
| | Double transfer | 450. | 65.00 |
| | Block of 4 | 1600. | |

*Earliest documented cover: (Sept. 27, 1882)*

### 1882. THOMAS JEFFERSON ISSUE

148 *There are only four vertical lines between the left side of the oval and the edge of the shield while the* preceding issues had five lines. The lines of the background have been made heavier so that these stamps appear much more heavily inked than their predecessors.

| 148 | | UnFVF | UseFVF |
|---|---|---|---|
| 10¢ | **brown** | 50.00 | 1.50 |
| | olive brown | 50.00 | 1.50 |
| | orange brown | 50.00 | 1.50 |
| | purple brown | 50.00 | 1.50 |
| | yellow brown | 50.00 | 1.50 |
| | black brown | 100. | 9.00 |
| | On cover | | 7.00 |
| | Plate block of 10 w/imprint | 1500. | |
| | Plate block of 12, w/imprint | 1800. | |
| | Plate strip of 5, w/imprint | 650. | |
| | Plate strip of 6, w/imprint | 750. | |
| | v. Double impression | — | |

*Earliest documented cover: (May 11, 1882)*

## 1882-88 American Banknote Co. Portrait Series

New designs. *Intaglio, unwatermarked soft porous paper, perforated 12.*

### 1887. BENJAMIN FRANKLIN ISSUE

149 *Benjamin Franklin*

| 149 | | UnFVF | UseFVF |
|---|---|---|---|
| 1¢ | **ultramarine** | 32.50 | .65 |
| | bright ultramarine | 32.50 | .65 |
| | On cover | | 1.50 |
| | Plate block of 10, w/imprint | 1000. | |
| | Plate block of 12, w/imprint | 1250. | |
| | Plate strip of 5, w/imprint | 450. | |
| | Plate strip of 6, w/imprint | 550. | |
| | Double transfer | — | |
| | v. Imperforate pair | 1000. | 525. |

*Earliest documented cover: (July 28, 1887)*

## 1883. GEORGE WASHINGTON ISSUE

150, 151 *George Washington. This stamp was issued to pay the reduced rate for first class letters as provided by an Act of Congress approved March 3, 1883, and effective October 1, 1883.*

| 150 | | UnFVF | UseFVF |
|---|---|---|---|
| 2¢ | **red brown** | 20.00 | .20 |
| | dark red brown | 20.00 | .20 |
| | orange brown | 20.00 | .20 |
| | On cover | | .50 |
| | Plate block of 10, w/imprint | 750. | |
| | Plate block of 12, w/imprint | 1000. | |
| | Plate strip of 5, w/imprint | 225. | |
| | Plate strip of 6, w/imprint | 375. | |
| | Double transfer | 40.00 | 1.25 |
| | v. Imperforate pair | — | |
| | v1. Horizontal pair, imperforate between | 2000. | — |
| | FDC *(Oct. 1, 1883)* | | 2000. |

## 1887. GEORGE WASHINGTON ISSUE

| 151 | | UnFVF | UseFVF |
|---|---|---|---|
| 2¢ | **green** | 15.00 | .20 |
| | bright green | 15.00 | .20 |
| | dark green | 15.00 | .20 |
| | On cover | | .75 |
| | Plate block of 10, w/imprint | 650. | |
| | Plate block of 12, w/imprint | 750. | |
| | Plate strip of 5, w/imprint | 175. | |
| | Plate strip of 6, w/imprint | 240. | |
| | Double transfer | — | 2.50 |
| | v. Printed on both sides | — | — |
| | Imperforate pair | 1000. | 1000. |
| | *Earliest documented cover: (Sept. 21, 1887)* | | |

## 1883. ANDREW JACKSON ISSUE

152, 153 *Andrew Jackson. This denomination was issued to take care of the rate on first class letters of double weight.*

| 152 | | UnFVF | UseFVF |
|---|---|---|---|
| 4¢ | **deep bluish green** | 80.00 | 4.00 |
| | blue green | 80.00 | 4.00 |
| | On cover | | 32.50 |
| | Plate block of 12, w/imprint | 3500. | |
| | Plate block of 6, w/imprint | 1200. | |
| | Cracked plate | — | |
| | Double transfer | — | |
| | v. Imperforate pair | — | |
| | v1. Horizontal pair, imperforate between | — | |
| | FDC *(Oct. 1, 1883)* | | 40000. |

**1883. SPECIAL PRINTING ISSUE** of the 2¢ and 4¢ stamps of 1883. Printed by the American Bank Note Co. *by intaglio on soft porous paper, the 2¢ with gum and the 4¢ without gum, both perforated 12.* Quantities are not known.

| SP59 | | UnFVF | UseFVF |
|---|---|---|---|
| 2¢ | **red brown** | 600. | |
| | v. Horizontal pair, imperforate between | 1800. | |

**1883. SPECIAL PRINTING ISSUE**

| SP60 | | UnFVF | UseFVF |
|---|---|---|---|
| 4¢ | **blue green** | 14500. | |

## 1889. ANDREW JACKSON ISSUE

| 153 | | UnFVF | UseFVF |
|---|---|---|---|
| 4¢ | **carmine** | 75.00 | 7.50 |
| | dull rose | 75.00 | 7.50 |
| | rose carmine | 75.00 | 7.50 |
| | On cover | | 50.00 |
| | Plate block of 10, w/imprint | 3000. | |
| | Plate block of 12, w/imprint | 3850. | |
| | Plate strip of 6, w/imprint | 1000. | |
| | Plate strip of 6, w/imprint | 1100. | |
| | Double transfer | — | |
| | *Earliest documented cover: (July 11, 1889)* | | |

## 1882. JAMES GARFIELD ISSUE

154 *James Garfield. This design was issued to honor the late President, assassinated while in office.*

| 154 | | UnFVF | UseFVF |
|---|---|---|---|
| 5¢ | **olive brown** | 80.00 | 3.00 |
| | brown | 80.00 | 3.00 |
| | gray brown | 80.00 | 3.00 |
| | On cover | | 20.00 |
| | Plate block of 12, w/imprint | 3500. | |
| | Plate strip of 5, w/imprint | 900. | |
| | Plate strip of 6, w/imprint | 1100. | |
| | FDC *(April 10, 1882)* | | |

**1882-1883. ZACHARY TAYLOR SPECIAL PRINTING ISSUE** Regular Issue Series

Special printing of the 5¢ Garfield stamp of 1882 is very difficult to distinguish from the regular printing of the same year. The special printing was produced by the American Bank Note Co. *Intaglio on soft porous paper without gum, perforated 12.*

| SP58 | | UnFVF | UseFVF |
|---|---|---|---|
| 5¢ | **light brownish gray** *(2,463 sold)* | | |

## 1888. ZACHARY TAYLOR ISSUE

| 155 | | UnFVF | UseFVF |
|---|---|---|---|
| 5¢ | **indigo** | 75.00 | 4.00 |
| | dark blue | 75.00 | 4.00 |
| | blue | 75.00 | 4.00 |
| | On cover | | 20.00 |
| | Plate block of 10, w/imprint | 3000. | |
| | Plate block of 12, w/imprint | 3750. | |
| | Plate strip of 5, w/imprint | 900. | |
| | Plate strip of 6, w/imprint | 1100. | |
| | v. Imperforate pair | 1200. | |
| | *Earliest documented cover: (March 23, 1888)* | | |

# 1890 American Bank Note Co. Small Size Portrait Series

## 1890. BENJAMIN FRANKLIN ISSUE

156 *Benjamin Franklin*

**156**

| 1¢ | | UnFVF | UseFVF |
|---|---|---|---|
| | dull blue | 17.50 | .20 |
| | blue | 17.50 | .20 |
| | dark blue | 17.50 | .20 |
| | ultramarine | 17.50 | .20 |
| | On cover | | .50 |
| | Plate block of 10, w/imprint | 450. | |
| | Plate block of 12, w/imprint | 600. | |
| | Plate block of 14, w/imprint | 750. | |
| | Plate strip of 5, w/imprint | 125. | |
| | Plate strip of 6, w/imprint | 150. | |
| | Plate strip of 7, w/imprint | 175. | |
| | Double transfer | — | — |
| | v. Imperforate pair | 150. | |
| | FDC*(Feb. 22, 1890)* | | |

## 1890. George Washington Issue

157, 158 *George Washington*

158v *Cap on left "2".*

158v2 *Cap on right "2".*

**157**

| 2¢ | | UnFVF | UseFVF |
|---|---|---|---|
| | lake | 125. | .60 |
| | bright lilac carmine | 125. | .60 |
| | lilac carmine | 125. | .60 |
| | On cover | | 1.25 |
| | Plate block of 10, w/imprint | 2750. | |
| | Plate strip of 5, w/imprint | 800. | |
| | Double transfer | — | — |
| | v. Imperforate pair | 100. | |
| | FDC*(Feb. 22, 1890)* | | 17500. |

**158**

| 2¢ | | UnFVF | UseFVF |
|---|---|---|---|
| | carmine | 14.00 | .20 |
| | carmine rose | 14.00 | .20 |
| | dark carmine | 14.00 | .20 |
| | On cover | | .50 |
| | Plate block of 10, w/imprint | 400. | |
| | Plate block of 12, w/imprint | 500. | |
| | Plate block of 14, w/imprint | 650. | |
| | Plate strip of 5, w/imprint | 100. | |
| | Plate strip of 6, w/imprint | 130. | |
| | Plate strip of 7, w/imprint | 150. | |
| | Double transfer | — | 2.50 |
| | v. Cap on left "2" | 60.00 | 1.50 |
| | Plate block of 12, w/imprint | 1250. | |
| | v1. Pair, 1 w/cap, 1 without | | — |
| | v2. Cap on both "2's" | 150. | 12.50 |
| | v3. Pair, 1 w/cap on 1 "2", 1 w/cap on both "2's" | — | — |
| | v. Imperforate pair | 125. | |
| | Earliest documented cover: *(May 31, 1890)* | | |

## 1890. Andrew Jackson Issue

159 *Andrew Jackson*

**159**

| 3¢ | | UnFVF | UseFVF |
|---|---|---|---|
| | dark lilac | 47.50 | 5.00 |
| | bright lilac | 47.50 | 5.00 |
| | lilac | 47.50 | 5.00 |
| | On cover | | 12.50 |
| | Plate block of 10, w/imprint | 1750. | |
| | Plate strip of 5, w/imprint | 350. | |
| | v. Imperforate pair | 165. | |
| | FDC*(Feb. 22, 1890)* | | |

## 1890. Abraham Lincoln Issue

160 *Abraham Lincoln*

**160**

| 4¢ | | UnFVF | UseFVF |
|---|---|---|---|
| | dark brown | 47.50 | 2.00 |
| | black brown | 47.50 | 2.00 |
| | On cover | | 11.00 |
| | Plate block of 10, w/imprint | 1800. | |
| | Plate strip of 5, w/imprint | 350. | |
| | Double transfer | 70.00 | |
| | v. Imperforate pair | 165. | |
| | Earliest documented cover: *(Oct. 22, 1890)* | | |

## 1890. Ulysses Grant Issue

161 *Ulysses Grant*

**161**

| 5¢ | | UnFVF | UseFVF |
|---|---|---|---|
| | chocolate | 47.50 | 2.00 |
| | yellow brown | 47.50 | 2.00 |
| | On cover | | 9.00 |
| | Plate block of 10, w/imprint | 1750. | |
| | Plate strip of 5, w/imprint | 300. | |
| | Double transfer | 70.00 | 2.00 |
| | v. Imperforate pair | 165. | |
| | Earliest documented cover: *(June 14, 1890)* | | |

## 1890. James Garfield Issue

162 *James Garfield*

**162**

| 6¢ | | UnFVF | UseFVF |
|---|---|---|---|
| | brown red | 50.00 | 15.00 |
| | dark brown red | 50.00 | 15.00 |
| | On cover | | 30.00 |
| | Plate block of 10, w/imprint | 1800. | |
| | Plate strip of 5, w/imprint | 350. | |
| | v. Imperforate pair | 175. | |
| | FDC *(Feb. 22, 1890)* | | |

## 1890. W. T. Sherman Issue

163 *W.T. Sherman*

**163**

| 8¢ | | UnFVF | UseFVF |
|---|---|---|---|
| | **purple brown** | 37.50 | 9.00 |
| | gray lilac | 37.50 | 9.00 |
| | magenta | 37.50 | 9.00 |
| | On cover | | 25.00 |
| | Plate block of 10, w/imprint | 1250. | |
| | Plate strip of 5, w/imprint | 300. | |
| | v. Imperforate pair | 1250. | |

*Earliest documented cover: (May 21, 1893)*

## 1890. DANIEL WEBSTER ISSUE

164 *Daniel Webster*

**164**

| 10¢ | | UnFVF | UseFVF |
|---|---|---|---|
| | **deep bluish green** | 95.00 | 2.25 |
| | dark green | 95.00 | 2.25 |
| | green | 95.00 | 2.25 |
| | On cover | | 7.00 |
| | Plate block of 10, w/imprint | 3000. | |
| | Plate strip of 5, w/imprint | 800. | |
| | Double transfer | — | — |
| | v. Imperforate pair | 175. | |
| | FDC*(Feb. 22, 1890)* | | |

## 1890. HENRY CLAY ISSUE

165 *Henry Clay*

**165**

| 15¢ | | UnFVF | UseFVF |
|---|---|---|---|
| | **indigo** | 145. | 16.00 |
| | dark indigo | 145. | 16.00 |
| | On cover | | 55.00 |
| | Plate block of 10, w/imprint | 5500. | |
| | Plate strip of 5, w/imprint | 750. | |
| | Double transfer | — | — |
| | Triple transfer | — | — |
| | v. Imperforate pair | 500. | |
| | FDC*(Feb. 22, 1890)* | | |

## 1890. THOMAS JEFFERSON ISSUE

166 *Thomas Jefferson*

**166**

| 30¢ | | UnFVF | UseFVF |
|---|---|---|---|
| | **black** | 225. | 19.00 |
| | gray black | 225. | 19.00 |
| | full black | 225. | 19.00 |
| | On cover | | 500. |
| | Plate block of 10, w/imprint | 1450. | |
| | Plate strip of 5, w/imprint | 1000. | |
| | Double transfer | — | — |
| | v. Imperforate pair | 750. | |
| | FDC*(Feb. 22, 1890)* | | |

## 1890. OLIVER HAZARD PERRY ISSUE

167 *Oliver Hazard Perry*

**167**

| 90¢ | | UnFVF | UseFVF |
|---|---|---|---|
| | **orange** | 325. | 90.00 |
| | red orange | 325. | 90.00 |
| | yellow orange | 325. | 90.00 |
| | On cover | | — |
| | Plate block of 10, w/imprint | 19500. | |
| | Plate strip of 5, w/imprint | 2250. | |
| | Short transfer at bottom | | |
| | v. Imperforate pair | 1000. | |
| | FDC*(Feb. 22, 1890)* | | |

*Stamps of all values of the 1890 issue exist imperforate, which are considered finished proofs.*

## 1894. Bureau of Engraving and Printing Portrait Series

Issues from this point through the 1980's, stamps have been printed by the Bureau of Engraving and Printing, except where otherwise noted. The first issue of stamps by the Bureau was very similar in design to the issue of 1890 but triangles were added to the upper corners of the stamps and there were some differences in the denominations isssued. The stamps were *printed by intaglio on unwatermarked paper, and perforated 12.*

*All of the perforation varieties listed here are believed to have been issued legitimately. Other perforation and imperforate varieties exist on some values, but they were not released through regular postal methods.*

### 1894. BENJAMIN FRANKLIN ISSUE

168, 169, 187, 188 *Benjamin Franklin*

**168**

| 1¢ | | UnFVF | UseFVF |
|---|---|---|---|
| | **ultramarine** | 20.00 | 3.50 |
| | bright ultramarine | 20.00 | 3.50 |
| | dark ultramarine | 20.00 | 3.50 |
| | On cover | | 10.00 |
| | Plate block of 6, w/imprint | 250. | |
| | Plate strip of 3, w/imprint | 90.00 | |
| | Double transfer | 30.00 | 4.00 |

*Earliest documented cover: (Oct. 24, 1894)*

**169**

| 1¢ | | UnFVF | UseFVF |
|---|---|---|---|
| | **blue** | 47.50 | 2.00 |
| | bright blue | 47.50 | 2.00 |
| | dark blue | 47.50 | 2.00 |
| | On cover | | 14.00 |
| | Plate block of 6, w/imprint | 475. | |
| | Plate strip of 3, w/imprint | 225. | |
| | Double transfer | — | 3.00 |

*Earliest documented cover: (Nov. 11, 1894)*

### 1894. GEORGE WASHINGTON ISSUE

170-174, 189-192 *George Washington*

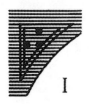 I

 II

 III

170-172, 189 *Type I. The horizontal lines of background are of same thickness.*

173, 190 *Type II. The horizontal lines are thin within the triangle.*

174, 191, 192 *Type III. The horizontal lines are interrupted by the frame of the triangle and thin within the triangle.*

| 170 | | UnFVF | UseFVF |
|---|---|---|---|
| 2¢ | **pink,** triangle I | 15.00 | 3.00 |
| | dull pink | 15.00 | 3.00 |
| | On cover | | 10.00 |
| | Plate block of 6, w/imprint | 175. | |
| | Plate strip of 3, w/imprint | 75.00 | |
| | Double transfer | — | — |
| | v. Vertical pair, imperforate horizontally | 2250. | |
| | *Earliest documented cover: (Oct. 20, 1894)* | | |

| 171 | | UnFVF | UseFVF |
|---|---|---|---|
| 2¢ | **carmine lake,** triangle I | 95.00 | 2.00 |
| | dark carmine lake | 95.00 | 2.00 |
| | On cover | | 7.50 |
| | Plate block of 6, w/imprint | 1000. | |
| | Plate strip of 3, w/imprint | 400. | |
| | Double transfer | — | 2.50 |
| | *Earliest documented cover: (Oct. 11, 1894)* | | |

| 172 | | UnFVF | UseFVF |
|---|---|---|---|
| 2¢ | **carmine,** triangle I | 17.50 | .35 |
| | dark carmine | 17.50 | .35 |
| | dull scarlet | 17.50 | .35 |
| | scarlet | 17.50 | .35 |
| | On cover | | 1.50 |
| | Plate block of 6, w/imprint | 250. | |
| | Plate strip of 3, w/imprint | 100. | |
| | Double transfer | — | 1.25 |
| | v. Vertical pair, imperforate horizontally | 1750. | |
| | v1. Horizontal pair, imperforate between | — | |
| | *Earliest documented cover: (Oct. 19, 1894)* | | |

| 173 | | UnFVF | UseFVF |
|---|---|---|---|
| 2¢ | **carmine,** triangle II | 150. | 3.25 |
| | dark carmine | 150. | 3.25 |
| | On cover | | 10.00 |
| | Plate block of 6, w/imprint | 1900. | |
| | Plate strip of 3, w/imprint | 700. | |
| | *Earliest documented cover: (Feb. 18, 1895)* | | |

| 174 | | UnFVF | UseFVF |
|---|---|---|---|
| 2¢ | **carmine,** triangle III | 85.00 | 3.50 |
| | dull carmine | 85.00 | 3.50 |
| | On cover | | 10.00 |
| | Plate block of 6, w/imprint | 1100. | |
| | Plate strip of 3, w/imprint | 400. | |
| | v. Horizontal pair, imperforate between | — | |
| | v1. Horizontal pair, imperforate vertically | — | |
| | *Earliest documented cover: (Oct. 11, 1894)* | | |

## 1894. ANDREW JACKSON ISSUE

175, 193 *Andrew Jackson*

| 175 | | UnFVF | UseFVF |
|---|---|---|---|
| 3¢ | **dark lilac** | 60.00 | 6.50 |
| | lilac | 60.00 | 6.50 |
| | On cover | | 20.00 |
| | Plate block of 6, w/imprint | 800. | |
| | Plate strip of 3, w/imprint | 350. | |
| | Margin block of 4, w/arrow | 375. | |
| | v. Imperforate pair | 200. | |
| | *Earliest documented cover: (Jan. 5, 1895)* | | |

## 1894. ABRAHAM LINCOLN ISSUE

176, 194, 195 *Abraham Lincoln*

| 176 | | UnFVF | UseFVF |
|---|---|---|---|
| 4¢ | **dark brown** | 75.00 | 3.50 |
| | brown | 75.00 | 3.50 |
| | On cover | | 15.00 |
| | Plate block of 6, w/imprint | 900. | |
| | Plate strip of 3, w/imprint | 425. | |
| | Margin block of 4, w/arrow | 500. | |
| | v. Imperforate pair | 200. | |
| | *Earliest documented cover: (Jan. 5, 1895)* | | |

## 1894. ULYSSES S. GRANT ISSUE

177, 196, 197 *Ulysses S. Grant*

| 177 | | UnFVF | UseFVF |
|---|---|---|---|
| 5¢ | **chocolate** | 65.00 | 4.00 |
| | dark chocolate | 65.00 | 4.00 |
| | yellow brown | 65.00 | 4.00 |
| | On cover | | 15.00 |
| | Plate block of 6, w/imprint | 700. | |
| | Plate strip of 3, w/imprint | 300. | |
| | Margin block of 4, w/arrow | 325. | |
| | Diagonal lines omitted in oval background (worn plate) | 80.00 | 5.00 |
| | Double transfer | 85.00 | 5.00 |
| | v. Imperforate pair | 250. | |
| | v1. Vertical pair, imperforate horizontally | 1500. | |
| | *Earliest documented cover: (Nov. 22, 1894)* | | |

## 1894. JAMES GARFIELD ISSUE

178, 198, 199 *James Garfield*

| 178 | | UnFVF | UseFVF |
|---|---|---|---|
| 6¢ | **red brown** | 115. | 17.50 |
| | On cover | | 37.50 |
| | Plate block of 6, w/imprint | 1800. | |
| | Plate strip of 3, w/imprint | 525. | |
| | Margin block of 4, w/arrow | 500. | |
| | v. Vertical pair, imperforate horizontally | 800. | |
| | *Earliest documented cover: (Aug. 11, 1894)* | | |

## 1894. WILLIAM T. SHERMAN ISSUE

179, 200 *W.T. Sherman*

| **179** | | **UnFVF** | **UseFVF** |
|---|---|---|---|
| **8¢** | **purple brown** | 95.00 | 12.50 |
| | dark purple brown | 95.00 | 12.50 |
| | On cover | | 37.50 |
| | Plate block of 6, w/imprint | 900. | |
| | Plate strip of 3, w/imprint | 475. | |
| | Margin block of 4, w/arrow | 525. | |

*Earliest documented cover: (Sept. 15, 1895)*

## 1894. DANIEL WEBSTER ISSUE

180, 201-203 *Daniel Webster*

| **180** | | **UnFVF** | **UseFVF** |
|---|---|---|---|
| **10¢** | **blue green** | 150. | 8.50 |
| | dark green | 150. | 8.50 |
| | dull green | 150. | 8.50 |
| | On cover | | 30.00 |
| | Plate block of 6, w/imprint | 1800. | |
| | Plate strip of 3, w/imprint | 700. | |
| | Double transfer | 200. | 9.00 |
| | v. Imperforate pair | 500. | |

*Earliest documented cover: (Nov. 19, 1894)*

## 1894. HENRY CLAY ISSUE

181, 204, 205 *Henry Clay*

| **181** | | **UnFVF** | **UseFVF** |
|---|---|---|---|
| **15¢** | **indigo** | 185. | 40.00 |
| | dark blue | 185. | 40.00 |
| | On cover | | 80.00 |
| | Plate block of 6, w/imprint | 3000. | |
| | Plate strip of 3, w/imprint | 875. | |
| | Margin block of 4, w/arrow | 900. | |

*Earliest documented cover: (Feb. 20, 1895)*

## 1894. THOMAS JEFFERSON ISSUE

182, 206 *Thomas Jefferson*

| **182** | | **UnFVF** | **UseFVF** |
|---|---|---|---|
| **50¢** | **orange** | 275. | 75.00 |
| | dark orange | 275. | 75.00 |
| | On cover | | 850. |
| | Plate block of 6, w/imprint | 4250. | |
| | Plate strip of 3, w/imprint | 1300. | |
| | Margin block of 4, w/arrow | 1500. | |

*Earliest documented cover: (Jan. 15, 1895)*

## 1894. OLIVER HAZARD PERRY ISSUE

183, 184, 207, 208 *Oliver Hazard Perry*

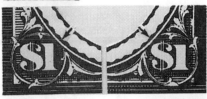

183, 207 *Type I. Circles enclosing "$1" are broken.*

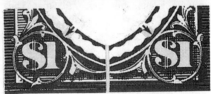

184, 208 *Type II. Circles are complete.*

| **183** | | **UnFVF** | **UseFVF** |
|---|---|---|---|
| **$1** | **black,** Type I | 575. | 225. |
| | gray black | 575. | 225. |
| | On cover | | 1950. |
| | Plate block of 6, w/imprint | 12500. | |
| | Plate strip of 3, w/imprint | 2850. | |
| | Margin block of 4, w/arrow | 3250. | |

*Earliest documented cover: (Aug. 1895)*

| **184** | | **UnFVF** | **UseFVF** |
|---|---|---|---|
| **$1** | **black,** Type II | | |
| | gray black | 1500. | 450. |
| | On cover | | 3400. |
| | Plate block of 6, w/imprint (including 2 of No. 183) | 22000. | |
| | Plate strip of 3, w/imprint (including 1 of No. 183) | 4800. | |
| | Block of 4, 2 each No. 183, 184 | 6000. | |
| | Pair, 1 each Type I and II | 2850. | |
| | Margin block of 4, w/arrow | 7250. | |

*Earliest documented cover: (March 22, 1895)*

## 1894. JAMES MADISON ISSUE

185, 209 *James Madison*

| **185** | | **UnFVF** | **UseFVF** |
|---|---|---|---|
| **$2** | **dark blue** | 1900. | 650. |
| | bright blue | 1900. | 650. |
| | On oover | | 3400. |
| | Plate block of 6, w/imprint | 28000. | |
| | Plate strip of 3, w/imprint | 9750. | |
| | Margin block of 4, w/arrow | 10500. | |

*Earliest documented cover: (July 18, 1895)*

## 1894. JOHN MARSHALL ISSUE

186, 210 *John Marshall, after painting by Henry Inman, the first great Chief Justice of the United States, was appointed to the office by John Adams in 1801. In 34 brilliant and forceful years' service, he firmly established the Constitution as the supreme law of the land, and the Court as its final arbiter. In the case of Marbury vs. Madison in 1803, he created a precedent in setting aside an act of Congress as unconstitutional.*

| 186 | | UnFVF | UseFVF |
|---|---|---|---|
| $5 | dark green | 2900. | 1250. |
| | On cover | | |
| | Plate strip of 3, w/imprint | | |
| | Margin block of 4, w/arrow | | |

## 1895-1898. BUREAU OF ENGRAVING AND PRINTING PORTRAIT DESIGNS ON WATERMARKED PAPER ISSUE

Although in the planning stages for some time, the issuance of U.S. postage stamps on watermarked paper coincided with the discovery of a counterfeit of the 2¢ denomination. It was believed that the new paper would add a measure of protection. The paper is watermarked with the letters "USPS" in double-lined capital letters, each letter 16mm high and so arranged that on each pane of 100 stamps they appear 90 times. The watermarks appear both horizontally and vertically on the stamps.

Denomination Portraits remained the same as on the previous series, the color changes of 1898 are integrated with this sequence of stamps. *Intaglio and perforated 12.*

187 *Double-line USPS Watermark (187)*

| 187 | | UnFVF | UseFVF |
|---|---|---|---|
| 1¢ | **deep blue** | 5.00 | .20 |
| | dark blue | 5.00 | .20 |
| | indigo | 5.00 | .20 |
| | pale blue | 5.00 | .20 |
| | On cover | | 1.00 |
| | Plate block of 6, w/imprint | 150. | |
| | Plate strip of 3, w/imprint | 20.00 | |
| | Double transfer | — | .75 |
| | *Earliest documented cover: (July 7, 1895)* | | |

| 188 | | UnFVF | UseFVF |
|---|---|---|---|
| 1¢ | **deep green** | 7.50 | .20 |
| | dark green | 7.50 | .20 |
| | dark yellow green | 7.50 | .20 |
| | yellow green | 7.50 | .20 |
| | On cover | | .50 |
| | Plate block of 6, w/imprint | 150. | |
| | Plate strip of 3, w/imprint | 32.00 | |
| | Double transfer | 10.00 | |
| | v. Imperforate pair | 150. | |
| | v1. Horizontal pair, imperforate vertically | — | |
| | FDC*(Jan. 25, 1898)* | | 700. |

| 189 | | UnFVF | UseFVF |
|---|---|---|---|
| 2¢ | **carmine**, Type I | 22.50 | .90 |
| | dark carmine | 22.50 | .90 |
| | dull carmine | 22.50 | .90 |
| | On cover | | 2.00 |
| | Plate block of 6, w/imprint | 300. | |
| | Plate strip of 3, w/imprint | 90.00 | |
| | Double transfer | 35.00 | 3.00 |
| | FDC *(July 7, 1895)* | · | 9500. |

| 190 | | UnFVF | UseFVF |
|---|---|---|---|
| 2¢ | **carmine**, Type II | 20.00 | 3.00 |
| | dark carmine | 20.00 | 3.00 |

| 190 | | UnFVF | UseFVF |
|---|---|---|---|
| | dull carmine | 20.00 | 3.00 |
| | On cover | | 6.00 |
| | Plate block of 6, w/imprint | 300. | |
| | Plate strip of 3, w/imprint | 90.00 | |
| | Horizontal pair, No. 189, 190 | 60.00 | |
| | *Earliest documented cover: (Oct. 25, 1895)* | | |

| 191 | | UnFVF | UseFVF |
|---|---|---|---|
| 2¢ | **carmine**, Type III | 4.00 | .20 |
| | dark carmine | 4.00 | .20 |
| | dull carmine | 4.00 | .20 |
| | On cover | | .50 |
| | Plate block of 6, w/imprint | 100. | |
| | Plate strip of 3, w/imprint | 15.00 | |
| | Double transfer | 12.50 | 1.00 |
| | Triple transfer | — | |
| | Shading omitted in right upper triangle (worn plate) | — | |
| | v. Imperforate pair | 175. | |
| | *Earliest documented cover: (July 7, 1895)* | | |

| 192 | | UnFVF | UseFVF |
|---|---|---|---|
| 2¢ | **red**, Type III | 7.50 | .20 |
| | deep red | 7.50 | .20 |
| | orange red | 8.00 | .30 |
| | rose carmine | 150. | 100. |
| | On cover | | .50 |
| | Plate block of 6, w/imprint | 150. | |
| | Plate strip of 3, w/imprint | 32.00 | |
| | Double transfer | 15.00 | |
| | n. Booklet pane of 6 | 325. | |
| | *Earliest documented cover: (Dec. 19, 1897)* | | |

| 193 | | UnFVF | UseFVF |
|---|---|---|---|
| 3¢ | **dark red violet** | 27.50 | 1.00 |
| | dark purple | 27.50 | 1.00 |
| | dull purple | 27.50 | 1.00 |
| | On cover | | 5.00 |
| | Plate block of 6, w/imprint | 425. | |
| | Plate strip of 3, 2/imprint | 120. | |
| | Margin block of 4, w/arrow | 140. | |
| | Double transfer | 35.00 | 2.25 |
| | v. Imperforate pair | 200. | |
| | *Earliest documented cover: (Feb. 18, 1896)* | | |

| 194 | | UnFVF | UseFVF |
|---|---|---|---|
| 4¢ | **dark brown** | 27.50 | 1.50 |
| | black brown | 27.50 | 1.50 |
| | dark yellow brown | 27.50 | 1.50 |
| | On cover | | 7.50 |
| | Plate block of 6, w/imprint | 450. | |
| | Plate strip of 3, w/imprint | 125. | |
| | Margin block of 4, w/arrow | 150. | |
| | Double transfer | 35.00 | 2.50 |
| | v. Imperforate pair | 200. | |
| | *Earliest documented cover: (Oct. 12, 1895)* | | |

| 195 | | UnFVF | UseFVF |
|---|---|---|---|
| 4¢ | **chocolate** | 22.50 | .90 |
| | brownish claret | 22.50 | .90 |
| | dark orange brown | 22.50 | .90 |
| | lilac brown | 22.50 | .90 |
| | orange brown | 22.50 | .90 |
| | rose brown | 22.50 | .90 |
| | On cover | | 8.00 |
| | Plate block of 6, w/imprint | 450. | |
| | Plate strip of 3, w/imprint | 100. | |
| | Margin block of 4, w/arrow | 120. | |
| | Double transfer | .30 | 1.25 |
| | Extra frame line at top | 45.00 | 3.50 |
| | FDC*(Oct. 7, 1898)* | | |

| 196 | | UnFVF | UseFVF |
|---|---|---|---|
| 5¢ | **dark orange brown** | 27.50 | 1.65 |
| | brown | 27.50 | 1.65 |
| | dark red brown | 27.50 | 1.65 |
| | reddish brown | 27.50 | 1.65 |
| | On cover | | 6.00 |

| 196 | | UnFVF | UseFVF |
|---|---|---|---|
| | Plate block of 6, w/imprint | 400. | |
| | Plate strip of 3, w/imprint | 120. | |
| | Diagonal lines omitted in oval background (worn plate) | 32.50 | 2.25 |
| | Double transfer | 35.00 | 3.00 |
| | Margin block of 4, w/arrow | 130. | |
| | v. Imperforate pair | 200. | |
| | *Earliest documented cover: (Sept. 14, 1895)* | | |

| 197 | | UnFVF | UseFVF |
|---|---|---|---|
| 5¢ | **dark blue** | 25.00 | .75 |
| | blue | .25 | .75 |
| | bright blue | 25.00 | .75 |
| | dull blue | 25.00 | .75 |
| | On cover | | 8.00 |
| | Plate block of 6, w/imprint | 450. | |
| | Plate strip of 3, w/imprint | 120. | |
| | Diagonal lines omitted in oval background (worn plate) | 35.00 | .75 |
| | Double transfer | 40.00 | 1.50 |
| | Margin block of 4, w/arrow | 140. | |
| | FDC*(March 8, 1898)* | | |

| 198 | | UnFVF | UseFVF |
|---|---|---|---|
| 6¢ | **red brown** | 55.00 | 4.00 |
| | dull brown | 55.00 | 4.00 |
| | On cover | | 22.50 |
| | Plate block of 6, w/imprint | 1100. | |
| | Plate strip of 3, w/imprint | 250. | |
| | Margin block of 4, w/arrow | 395. | |
| | p. Thin paper | 80.00 | 4.00 |
| | w. Watermarked "USIR" | 2000. | 325. |
| | v. Imperforate pair | 200. | |
| | *Earliest documented cover: (Sept. 14, 1895)* | | |

| 199 | | UnFVF | UseFVF |
|---|---|---|---|
| 6¢ | **lake** | 35.00 | 2.25 |
| | claret | 35.00 | 2.25 |
| | lilac carmine | 35.00 | 2.25 |
| | purple lake | 42.50 | 3.00 |
| | On cover | | 14.00 |
| | Plate block of 6, w/imprint | 700. | |
| | Plate strip of 3, w/imprint | 150. | |
| | Double transfer | 52.50 | 3.00 |
| | Margin block of 4, w/arrow | 150. | |
| | v. Imperforate pair | 200. | |
| | FDC*(Dec. 31, 1898)* | | |

| 200 | | UnFVF | UseFVF |
|---|---|---|---|
| 8¢ | **purple brown** | 40.00 | 1.25 |
| | dark lilac brown | 40.00 | 1.25 |
| | lilac brown | 40.00 | 1.25 |
| | On cover | | 11.00 |
| | Plate block of 6, w/imprint | 450. | |
| | Plate strip of 3, w/imprint | 200. | |
| | Double transfer | 62.50 | 2.25 |
| | Margin block of 4, w/arrow | 220. | |
| | w. Watermarked "USIR" | 1450. | 85.00 |
| | v. Imperforate pair | 300. | |
| | *Earliest documented cover: (Dec. 24, 1895)* | | |

**1895-1898. BUREAU OF ENGRAVING AND PRINTING PORTRAIT DESIGNS ON WATERMARKED PAPER ISSUE** Although in the planning stages for some time, the issuance of U.S. postage stamps on watermarked paper coincided with the discovery of a counterfeit of the 2¢ denomination. It was believed that the new paper would add a measure of protection. The paper is watermarked with the letters "USPS" in double-lined capital letters, each letter 16mm high and so arranged that on each pane of 100 stamps they appear 90 times. The watermarks appear both horizontally and vertically on the stamps.

The color changes of 1898 are integrated with this sequence of stamps. *Intaglio and perforated 12.*

*201, 202 Type I. Oval below "TEN CENTS" is intact.*

*203 Type II. Oval below "TEN CENTS" is broken by lines.*

| 201 | | UnFVF | UseFVF |
|---|---|---|---|
| 10¢ | **dark green,** Type I | 50.00 | 1.25 |
| | green | .50 | 1.25 |
| | On cover | | 12.50 |
| | Plate block of 6, w/imprint | 750. | |
| | Plate strip of 3, w/imprint | 275. | |
| | Double transfer | 80.00 | 3.25 |
| | v. Imperforate pair | 225. | |
| | *Earliest documented cover: (Feb. 16, 1896)* | | |

| 202 | | UnFVF | UseFVF |
|---|---|---|---|
| 10¢ | **brown,** Type I | 135. | 2.50 |
| | dark brown | 135. | 2.50 |
| | On cover | | 12.50 |
| | Plate block of 6, w/imprint | 700. | |
| | Plate strip of 3, w/imprint | 650. | |
| | Double transfer | 150. | 4.00 |
| | Pair, 1 each *(202,203)* | 13000. | |
| | FDC*(Nov. 11, 1898)* | | |

| 203 | | UnFVF | UseFVF |
|---|---|---|---|
| 10¢ | **orange brown,** Type II | 75.00 | 2.00 |
| | brown | 75.00 | 2.00 |
| | yellow brown | 75.00 | 2.00 |
| | On cover | | 14.00 |
| | Plate block of 6, w/imprint | 950. | |
| | Plate strip of 3, w/imprint | 400. | |
| | Margin block of 4, w/arrow | 425. | |
| | FDC*(Nov. 11, 1898)* | | |

| 204 | | UnFVF | UseFVF |
|---|---|---|---|
| 15¢ | **indigo** | 150. | 9.00 |
| | blackish blue | 150. | 9.00 |
| | On cover | | 50.00 |
| | Plate block of 6, w/imprint | 2100. | |
| | Plate strip of 3, w/imprint | 700. | |
| | Margin block of 4, w/arrow | 725. | |
| | v. Imperforate pair | 625. | |
| | *Earliest documented cover: (Feb. 27, 1897)* | | |

| 205 | | UnFVF | UseFVF |
|---|---|---|---|
| 15¢ | **olive green** | 115. | 7.50 |
| | dark olive green | 115. | 7.50 |
| | On cover | | 27.50 |
| | Plate block of 6, w/imprint | 1500. | |
| | Plate strip of 3, w/imprint | 500. | |
| | Margin block of 4, w/arrow | 625. | |
| | FDC*(Nov. 30, 1898)* | | |

| 206 | | UnFVF | UseFVF |
|---|---|---|---|
| 50¢ | **orange** | 200. | 20.00 |
| | dark red orange | 200. | 20.00 |
| | dull red orange | 200. | 20.00 |
| | red orange | 200. | 200. |
| | On cover | | 325. |
| | Plate block of 6, w/imprint | 3750. | |
| | Plate strip of 3, w/imprint | 850. | |
| | Margin block of 4, w/arrow | 900. | |
| | v. Imperforate pair | 675. | |
| | *Earliest documented cover: (Feb. 27, 1897)* | | |

| 207 | | UnFVF | UseFVF |
|---|---|---|---|
| $1 | **black,** Type I | 450. | 55.00 |
| | greenish black | 450. | 55.00 |
| | On cover | | 2000. |
| | Plate block of 6, w/imprint | 3000. | |
| | Plate strip of 3, w/imprint | 2100. | |
| | Margin block of 4, w/arrow | 2200. | |
| | *Earliest documented cover: (Sept. 5, 1898)* | | |

| 208 | | UnFVF | UseFVF |
|---|---|---|---|
| $1 | **black,** Type II | 900. | 125. |
| | greenish black | 900. | 125. |
| | On cover | | 3350. |
| | Plate block of 6, w/imprint (4 Type II, 2 Type I) | 19500. | |
| | Plate strip of 3, w/imprint (2 Type II, 1 Type I) | 3750. | |
| | Margin block of 4, w/arrow | 4750. | |
| | Pair, 1 each Nos. 207, 208 | 1950. | |
| | v. Imperforate pair | 1250. | |

*Earliest documented cover: (April 6, 1896)*

| 209 | | UnFVF | UseFVF |
|---|---|---|---|
| $2 | **dark blue** | 775. | 250. |
| | bright blue | 775. | 250. |
| | On cover | | 3200. |
| | Plate block of 6, w/imprint | 14000. | |
| | Plate strip of 3, w/imprint | 3500. | |
| | Margin block of 4, w/arrow | 4000. | |
| | v. Imperforate pair | 2250. | |

| 210 | | UnFVF | UseFVF |
|---|---|---|---|
| $5 | **dark green** | 1600. | 375. |
| | On cover | | 10000. |
| | Plate block of 6, w/imprint | 60000. | |
| | Plate strip of 3, w/imprint | 7250. | |
| | Margin block of 4, w/arrow | 8500. | |
| | v. Imperforate pair | 2250. | |

*Earliest documented cover: (Nov. 3, 1896)*

**1902-03. Regular Issue** had only two of its 14 values actually released in 1902, the balance being issued during 1903. All of these stamps were *perforated, with the 1¢, 4¢, and 5¢ being issued imperforate as well,* although the 4¢ imperforate now exists only with the large slots of the Schermack coil cut into the sides. The 1¢ and 5¢ also were issued in coil form. Finally the 1¢ and 2¢ stamps were issued as booklet panes, 6 stamps to a pane. *Intaglio, watermarked double line USPS (187) and perforated 12.*

211, 225, 228, 230 *Benjamin Franklin*

| 211 | | UnFVF | UseFVF |
|---|---|---|---|
| 1¢ | **deep bluish green** | 9.00 | .20 |
| | dark green | 9.00 | .20 |
| | gray green | 9.00 | .20 |
| | green | 9.00 | .20 |
| | yellow green | 9.00 | .20 |
| | On cover | | .50 |
| | Plate block of 6, w/imprint | 145. | |
| | Plate strip of 3, w/imprint | 27.50 | |
| | Cracked plate | 8.00 | .60 |
| | Double transfer | 11.00 | .75 |
| | Worn plate | 8.00 | .60 |
| | n. Booklet pane of 6 *(March 6, 1907)* | 425. | |
| | n1. Pane w/plate number on the left | — | |
| | v. Arrow block with "color ball" | — | |
| | FDC *Feb. 4, 1903)* | | |

212 *George Washington*

| 212 | | UnFVF | UseFVF |
|---|---|---|---|
| 2¢ | **carmine** | 12.00 | .20 |
| | bright carmine | 12.00 | .20 |
| | dark carmine | 12.00 | .20 |
| | carmine rose | 12.00 | .20 |
| | On cover | | .50 |
| | Plate block of 6, w/imprint | 150. | |
| | Plate strip of 3, w/imprint | 40.00 | |
| | Cracked plate | — | .75 |
| | Double transfer | 17.50 | .75 |
| | v. Vertical pair, imperforate horizontally | 2500. | |
| | v1. Vertical pair, imperforate between | 1000. | |
| | n. Booklet pane of 6 *(Jan. 24, 1903)* | 400. | 2750. |
| | FDC *(Jan. 19, 1903)* | | |

213 *Andrew Jackson after engraving by A. Sealey*

| 213 | | UnFVF | UseFVF |
|---|---|---|---|
| 3¢ | **dark red violet** | 52.50 | 2.25 |
| | bright violet | 52.50 | 2.25 |
| | violet | 52.50 | 2.25 |
| | Plate block of 6, w/imprint | 600. | |
| | Plate strip of 3, w/imprint | 175. | |
| | Cracked plate | — | |
| | Double transfer | 65.00 | 3.50 |
| | On cover | | 8.00 |
| | v. Arrow block w/"color ball" | — | |
| | *(Feb. 12, 1903)* | | |

214, 226 *U.S. Grant*

| 214 | | UnFVF | UseFVF |
|---|---|---|---|
| 4¢ | **brown** | 57.50 | 1.00 |
| | dark brown | 57.50 | 1.00 |
| | dark yellow brown | 57.50 | 1.00 |
| | orange brown | 57.50 | 1.00 |
| | reddish brown | 57.50 | 1.00 |
| | yellow brown | 57.50 | 1.00 |
| | On cover | | 10.00 |
| | Plate block of 6, w/imprint | 600. | |
| | Plate strip of 3, w/imprint | 175. | |
| | Double transfer | 60.00 | 2.25 |
| | FDC *(Feb. 11, 1903)* | | |

215, 227, 229 *Abraham Lincoln*

| 215 | | UnFVF | UseFVF |
|---|---|---|---|
| 5¢ | **deep blue** | 57.50 | 1.15 |
| | blue | 57.50 | 1.15 |
| | dark blue | 57.50 | 1.15 |
| | dull blue | 57.50 | 1.15 |
| | On cover | | 7.00 |
| | Plate block of 6, w/imprint | 600. | |
| | Plate strip of 3, w/imprint | 175. | |
| | Cracked plate | 55.00 | 4.00 |
| | Double transfer | 65.00 | 3.00 |
| | FDC *(Jan. 21, 1903)* | | |

216 *James Garfield*

**216**

| 6¢ | | UnFVF | UseFVF |
|---|---|---|---|
| | **brown red** | 70.00 | 2.00 |
| | claret | 70.00 | 2.00 |
| | deep claret | 70.00 | 2.00 |
| | dull brown red | 70.00 | 2.00 |
| | On cover | | 10.00 |
| | Plate block of 6, w/imprint | 700. | |
| | Plate strip of 3, w/imprint | 200. | |
| | Double transfer | 62.50 | 3.00 |
| | FDC*(Feb. 21, 1903)* | | |

217 *Martha Washington*

**217**

| 8¢ | | UnFVF | UseFVF |
|---|---|---|---|
| | **violet black** | 42.50 | 1.60 |
| | black | 42.50 | 1.60 |
| | blue black | 42.50 | 1.60 |
| | blue lilac | 42.50 | 1.60 |
| | blue violet | 42.50 | 1.60 |
| | On cover | | 7.50 |
| | Plate block of 6, w/imprint | 550. | |
| | Plate strip of 3, w/imprint | 120. | |
| | Double transfer | 37.50 | 2.00 |
| | FDC*(Dec. 8, 1902)* | | |

218 *Daniel Webster*

**218**

| 10¢ | | UnFVF | UseFVF |
|---|---|---|---|
| | **pale red brown** | 60.00 | 1.15 |
| | dark red brown | 60.00 | 1.15 |
| | red brown | 60.00 | 1.15 |
| | On cover | | 7.00 |
| | Plate block of 6, w/imprint | 750. | |
| | Plate strip of 3, w/imprint | 150. | |
| | Double transfer | 60.00 | 8.00 |
| | FDC*(Feb. 6, 1903)* | | |

219 *Benjamin Harrison*

**219**

| 13¢ | | UnFVF | UseFVF |
|---|---|---|---|
| | **black brown** | 42.50 | 6.50 |
| | purple black | 42.50 | 6.50 |
| | On cover | | 32.50 |
| | Plate block of 6, w/imprint | 500. | |
| | Plate strip of 3, w/imprint | 125. | |
| | FDC*(Nov. 19, 1902)* | | |

220 *Henry Clay*

**220**

| 15¢ | | UnFVF | UseFVF |
|---|---|---|---|
| | **olive green** | 150. | 4.50 |
| | dark olive green | 150. | 4.50 |
| | On cover | | 70.00 |
| | Plate block of 6, w/imprint | 1950. | |
| | Plate strip of 3, w/imprint | 500. | |
| | Double transfer | 160. | 8.00 |
| | Margin block of 4, w/arrow | 550. | |
| | FDC*(May 28, 1903)* | | |

221 *Thomas Jefferson*

**221**

| 50¢ | | UnFVF | UseFVF |
|---|---|---|---|
| | **orange** | 425. | 20.00 |
| | deep orange | 425. | 20.00 |
| | On cover | | 600. |
| | Plate block of 6, w/imprint | 5250. | |
| | Plate strip of 3, w/imprint | 1250. | |
| | Margin block of 4, w/arrow | 1500. | |
| | FDC*(March 24, 1903)* | | |

222 *David Farragut*

**222**

| $1 | | UnFVF | UseFVF |
|---|---|---|---|
| | **black** | 750. | 45.00 |
| | gray black | 750. | 45.00 |
| | On cover | | 1250. |
| | Plate block of 6, w/imprint | 10500. | |
| | Plate strip of 3, w/imprint | 1950. | |
| | Margin block of 4, w/arrow | 2250. | |
| | FDC*(June 2, 1903)* | | |

223, 365 *James Madison*

**223**

| $2 | | UnFVF | UseFVF |
|---|---|---|---|
| | **dark blue** | 1075. | 140. |
| | blue | 1075. | 140. |
| | On cover | | 2100. |
| | Plate block of 6, w/imprint | 22000. | |
| | Plate strip of 3, w/imprint | 3200. | |
| | Margin block of 4, w/arrow | 4000. | |
| | FDC *(June 2, 1903)* | | |

224, 366 *John Marshall*

**224**

| $5 | | UnFVF | UseFVF |
|---|---|---|---|
| | **dark green** | 2800. | 525. |
| | On cover | | 4250. |
| | Plate block of 6, w/imprint | 42000. | |
| | Plate strip of 3, w/imprint | 8000. | |
| | Margin block of 4, w/arrow | 10000. | |
| | FDC *(June 2, 1903)* | | |

## 1906-08. REGULAR ISSUES OF 1902-03 Imperforate

**225**

| 1¢ | | UnFVF | UseFVF |
|---|---|---|---|
| | **deep bluish green** | 20.00 | 17.50 |
| | dark green | 20.00 | 17.50 |
| | green | 20.00 | 17.50 |
| | On cover | | 17.50 |
| | Plate block of 6, w/imprint | 165. | |
| | Margin block of 4, w/arrow | 80.00 | 60.00 |
| | Center line block | 120. | 80.00 |
| | Double transfer | 30.00 | 15.00 |
| | FDC *(Oct. 2, 1906)* | | |

*226 Four Cent, imperforate, with slots at sides. These slots, aided in the vending of coil stamps by the machines of the Schermack Company.*

**226**

| 4¢ | | UnFVF | UseFVF |
|---|---|---|---|
| | **brown** | 22500. | 15000. |
| | On cover | | 57500. |
| | Pair | 52500. | |
| | Line pair | 135000. | |
| | FDC *(May 15, 1908)* | | |

**227**

| 5¢ | | UnFVF | UseFVF |
|---|---|---|---|
| | **blue** | 375. | 475. |
| | On cover | | — |
| | Plate block of 6, w/imprint | 2800. | |
| | Center line block | 2800. | |
| | Margin block of 4, w/arrow | 1800. | |
| | FDC *(March 30, 1908)* | | |

*Please exercise caution in buying singles of this stamp, particularly used copies. Certification by respected authorities recommended.*

**1908. COIL STAMP 1902-03 SERIES ISSUE** were the first coils issued. They have been faked extensively by fraudulently perforating the imperforates in the case of the 1¢ stamps and also by trimming off perforations on both the 1¢ and 5¢ stamps. It is recommended that these stamps be collected in pairs. *Perforated 12 horizontally.*

**228**

| 1¢ | | UnFVF | UseFVF |
|---|---|---|---|
| | **blue green,** pair | 68500. | |
| | Line pair | 110000. | |
| | FDC *(Feb. 18, 1908)* | | |

**229**

| 5¢ | | UnFVF | UseFVF |
|---|---|---|---|
| | **blue,** pair | 9000. | |
| | Line pair | 19500. | |
| | FDC *(Feb. 24, 1908)* | | |

*Perforated 12 vertically.*

**230**

| 1¢ | | UnFVF | UseFVF |
|---|---|---|---|
| | **blue green,** pair | 6000. | |
| | Line pair | 11000. | |
| | Double transfer | — | |
| | FDC *(July 31, 1908)* | | |

**1903. TWO-CENT SHIELD STAMP ISSUE** was issued because of public dislike for the 2¢ "Flag" design of the 1902-03 series. The "Shield" stamp comes in a wide range of shades. It was issued perforated, imperforate, in booklet panes, and also in coil form, so that a considerable display can be made of this single denomination. *The stamps were flat-plate printed and watermarked doubleline USPS (wmk 187).*

*Perforated 12.*
*Type I*

*231-236 George Washington*

Type I: The leaf next to the "2" at left penetrates the border.

Type II: Border to the left of the leaf is formed by a strong line.

**231**

| 2¢ | | UnFVF | UseFVF |
|---|---|---|---|
| | **carmine** | 4.00 | .20 |
| | bright carmine | 4.00 | .20 |
| | red | 4.00 | .20 |
| | carmine rose | 4.50 | .20 |
| | scarlet | 4.00 | .20 |
| | On cover | | .50 |
| | Plate block of 6, w/imprint | 75.00 | |
| | Plate strip of 3 w/imprint | 16.00 | |
| | Double transfer | 8.00 | 1.50 |
| | n. Booklet pane of 6 | 100. | |
| | v. Vertical pair, rouletted between | 800. | |
| | v1. Vertical pair, imperforate horizontally | 2500. | |
| | v2. Vertical pair, imperforate between | 1000. | |
| | *Earliest documented cover: Oct. 29, 1908* | | |
| | FDC *(Nov. 12, 1903)* | | |

**232**

| 2¢ | | UnFVF | UseFVF |
|---|---|---|---|
| | **lake,** Type II | 7.50 | .50 |
| | carmine | 7.50 | .50 |
| | carmine lake | 7.50 | .50 |
| | scarlet | 7.50 | .50 |
| | Plate block of 6 | 150. | |
| | n. Booklet pane of 6 | 150. | |
| | *Earliest documented cover: (June 11, 1908)* | | |

## 1903. TWO-CENT SHIELD COIL ISSUE Imperforate

**233**

| 2¢ | | UnFVF | UseFVF |
|---|---|---|---|
| | **carmine,** Type II | 20.00 | 15.00 |
| | scarlet | 20.00 | 15.00 |
| | carmine rose | 20.00 | 15.00 |
| | scarlet | 20.00 | 15.00 |
| | On cover | | 15.00 |
| | Plate block of 6, w/imprint | 200. | |
| | Center line block | 140. | 175. |
| | Double transfer | 22.50 | 12.50 |
| | Margin block of 4, w/arrow | 80.00 | 85.00 |
| | FDC *(Oct. 2, 1906)* | | |

**234**

| 2¢ | | UnFVF | UseFVF |
|---|---|---|---|
| | **lake,** Type II | 50.00 | 40.00 |
| | scarlet | 50.00 | 40.00 |
| | On cover | | 70.00 |
| | Plate block of 6, w/imprint | 700. | |
| | Center line block | 400. | |
| | Margin block of 4, w/arrow | 180. | |

## 1903. TWO-CENT SHIELD COIL ISSUE Coil stamp, perforated 12 horizontally.

**235**

| 2¢ | | UnFVF | UseFVF |
|---|---|---|---|
| | **carmine,** Type I, pair | 95000. | 100000. |
| | Line pair | — | |
| | FDC *(Feb. 18, 1908)* | | |

**236**

| 2¢ | | UnFVF | UseFVF |
|---|---|---|---|
| | **scarlet,** Type II, pair | 7000. | 4250. |
| | Double transfer | 7750. | |
| | Line pair | — | |
| | FDC *(July 31, 1908)* | | |

**1908-09 WASHINGTON & FRANKLIN ISSUE** consists of 12 stamps, ranging from 1¢ to $1. The 1¢ stamp has a portrait of Franklin in the central medallion with the words "ONE CENT" at the base of the stamp. The 2¢ stamp, with Washington in the medallion, is inscribed "TWO CENTS." The 3¢ stamp to $1 stamps have Washington in the medallion with numerals of value in each of the lower corners.

As an experiment to counteract the shrinking caused by printing on wet paper, some rows of stamps were separated by 3mm spacing instead of the usual 2mm. Intermediate-size spacings exist and command the lower of the two prices listed for different spacings. *Flat plate printing, watermarked double-line USPS (187), and perforated 12.*

A very few of this series, up through the 15¢ value, were printed on a grayish, hard, thick paper known as *China Clay*. The paper had up to 10 times the mineral content of normal stamp paper of the time.

*237 Benjamin Franklin*

| 237 | | UnFVF | UseFVF |
|---|---|---|---|
| 1¢ | **green** | 6.00 | 20.00 |
| | bright green | 6.00 | .20 |
| | dark green | 6.00 | .20 |
| | yellow green | 6.00 | .20 |
| | On cover | | .50 |
| | Plate block of 6, w/imprint | 45.00 | |
| | Plate block of 6, w/imprint & open star | 50.00 | |
| | Plate block of 6, w/small solid star | 75.00 | |
| | Block of 4, 2mm spacing | 25.00 | 1.25 |
| | Block of 4, 3mm spacing | 27.50 | 1.50 |
| | Cracked plate | — | |
| | Double transfer | 8.00 | .60 |
| | v. Horizontal pair, imperforate between | 1000. | |
| | n. Booklet pane of 6 *(Dec. 2, 1908)* | 140. | 120. |
| | FDC *(Dec. 14, 1908)* | | 20000. |
| | p. China Clay paper | 800. | |

| 238 | | UnFVF | UseFVF |
|---|---|---|---|
| 2¢ | **carmine** | 6.00 | .20 |
| | dark carmine | 6.00 | .20 |
| | pale carmine | 6.00 | .20 |
| | On cover | | .50 |
| | Plate block of 6, w/imprint | 45.00 | |
| | Plate block of 6, w/imprint & open star | 50.00 | |
| | Plate block of 6, w/small solid star | 70.00 | |
| | Block of 4, 2mm spacing | 22.50 | .60 |
| | Block of 4, 3mm spacing | 25.00 | .75 |
| | Cracked plate | — | |
| | Double transfer | 10.00 | |
| | Double transfer (1¢ design of No. 237) | 1250. | |
| | n. Booklet pane of 6 (Nov. 16, 1908) | 125. | 110. |
| | FDC *(Dec. 1, 1908)* | | 35000. |
| | p. China Clay paper | 1000. | |

**1908. GEORGE WASHINGTON TYPE I ISSUE Details of Type I:**

1. The top line of the toga from the front of the neck to the top of the button is very weak, as are the upper parts fo the fine lines of shading that join this top line. the top part of the fifth of these shading lines is missing.

2. Two shading lines under the point of the chin are heavy.

3. The line between the lips is thin. This usually is an easy checking point for this type. 4. The lock of hair behind the ear is formed at the bottom by two lines of shading, the lower line being considerably shorter than the upper/

5. The hair lines above and a little to the right of the ear form an "arrowhead."

6. The outline of the inner oval forms a solid line at the bottom.

*239 George Washington. Type I: All stamps of this design and perforated 12 are Type I. While the description of the type is given here in detail, the areas noted by the small figures "1" and "3" in the drawing will almost always prove sufficient as checking areas.*

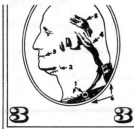

| 239 | | UnFVF | UseFVF |
|---|---|---|---|
| 3¢ | **violet,** Type I | 27.50 | 2.50 |
| | dark violet | 27.50 | 2.50 |
| | pale violet | 27.50 | 2.50 |
| | On cover | | 7.50 |
| | Plate block of 6, w/imprint | 200. | |
| | Plate block of 6, w/imprint & star | 300. | |
| | Block of 4, 2mm spacing | 110. | 15.00 |
| | Block of 4, 3mm spacing | 120. | 17.50 |
| | Double transfer | 37.50 | 4.00 |
| | p. China Clay paper | 800. | |
| | FDC *(Dec. 26, 1908)* | | |

| 240 | | UnFVF | UseFVF |
|---|---|---|---|
| 4¢ | **orange brown** | 30.00 | 1.00 |
| | brown | 30.00 | 1.00 |
| | dark orange brown | 30.00 | 1.00 |
| | dull orange brown | 30.00 | 1.00 |
| | On cover | | 5.00 |
| | Plate block of 6, w/imprint | 300. | |
| | Plate block of 6, w/imprint & star | 475. | |
| | Block of 4, 2mm spacing | 140. | 7.50 |
| | Block of 4, 3mm spacing | 150. | 9.00 |
| | Double transfer | 45.00 | |
| | p. China clay paper | 1000. | |
| | FDC *(Dec. 26, 1908)* | | |

| 241 | | UnFVF | UseFVF |
|---|---|---|---|
| 5¢ | **blue** | 40.00 | 2.00 |
| | bright blue | 40.00 | 2.00 |
| | dark blue | 40.00 | 2.00 |
| | On cover | | 8.00 |
| | Plate block of 6, w/imprint | 400. | |
| | Plate block of 6, w/imprint & star | 600. | |
| | Block of 4, 2mm spacing | 175. | 12.50 |
| | Block of 4, 3mm spacing | 185. | 10.00 |
| | Double transfer | 45.00 | |
| | p. China clay paper | 800. | |
| | FDC *(Dec. 21, 1908)* | | |

| 242 | | UnFVF | UseFVF |
|---|---|---|---|
| 6¢ | **red orange** | 47.50 | 5.00 |
| | dull orange | 47.50 | 5.00 |
| | orange | 47.50 | 5.00 |
| | On cover | | 17.50 |
| | Plate block of 6, w/imprint | 600. | |
| | p. China Clay paper | 625. | |
| | FDC *(Dec. 31, 1908)* | | |

| 243 | | UnFVF | UseFVF |
|---|---|---|---|
| 8¢ | **olive green** | 37.50 | 2.50 |
| | dark olive green | 37.50 | 2.50 |
| | On cover | | 16.00 |
| | Plate block of 6, w/imprint | 400. | |
| | Double transfer | 47.50 | |
| | p. China clay paper | 800. | |
| | FDC *(Dec. 18, 1908)* | | |

| 244 | | UnFVF | UseFVF |
|---|---|---|---|
| 10¢ | **yellow** | 55.00 | 1.50 |
| | On cover | | 8.00 |
| | Plate block of 6, w/imprint | 650. | |
| | Double transfer | — | |
| | p. China clay paper | 800. | |
| | p1. Very thin paper | — | |
| | FDC *(Jan. 7, 1909)* | | |

| 245 | | UnFVF | UseFVF |
|---|---|---|---|
| 13¢ | **blue green** | 37.50 | 20.00 |
| | dark blue green | 37.50 | 20.00 |
| | On cover | | 90.00 |
| | Plate block of 6, w/imprint | 400. | |
| | p. China Clay paper | 800. | |
| | FDC *(Jan. 11, 1909)* | | |

| 246 | | UnFVF | UseFVF |
|---|---|---|---|
| 15¢ | **gray blue** | 50.00 | 6.00 |
| | dull gray blue | 50.00 | 6.00 |
| | On cover | | 110. |
| | Plate block of 6, w/imprint | 525. | |
| | p. China Clay paper | 800. | |
| | FDC *(Jan. 18, 1909)* | | |

# Washington-Franklin Identifier

| PERF. | WMK. | 1c Text | 2c Text | 1c Numeral | 2c Numeral | Wash. Numeral | Frank. Numeral |
|---|---|---|---|---|---|---|---|
| 12 | Double | 237, 263 | 238, 264 | | | 239-248, 265-272 | 313-314 |
| | Single | 273 | 274 | 297 | 298 | 275-282 | 305-312 |
| Coil 12 | Double | 254-258 | 255,259 | | | 256, 257, 260-262 | |
| | Single | 285, 287 | 286, 288 | | | 289 | |
| Imperforate | Double | 249 | 250 | | | 251-253 | |
| | Single | 283 | 284 | 299 | 300, *342* | | |
| | Unwmk | | | 367, 406 | 368, **407-407D** | 369-370, **408** | |
| Coil 8 1/2 | Single | 290, 292 | 291, 293 | 301, 303 | 302, 304 | 294-296 | |
| 10 | Double | | | | | | 331 |
| | Single | | | 315 | 316 | 317-321 | 322-330 |
| | Unwmk | | | 348, **414** | 349 | 350-355 | 356-364 |
| Coil 10 | Double | | | 333, 335 | 334, 336 | 337-339 | |
| | Single | | | *340, 343* | *341, 344* | *345-347* | |
| | Unwmk | | | 371, 374 | 372, 375 | 373, 376-378 | 379 |
| 11 | Double | | 399 | | | | |
| | Single | | | | 332 | | |
| | Unwmk | | | 380, **403**, *415, 416* | 381, **404-404D**, *417* | 382-387, **405-405A** | 388-398 |
| 12x10, 10x12 | Single | | | 315 | 316 | 319 | |
| 12 1/2 | Unwmk | | | **409** | | | |
| 11x10, 10x11 | Unwmk | | | *410, 413* | *411-411A* | *412* | |

237 -- Numbers in normal type designate stamps printed by intaglio on a flat-bed press.
*340* -- Numbers in italic designate stamps printed by intaglio on a rotary press.

**407** -- Numbers in bold designate stamps printed by offset. These stamps are characterized by the smoothness of printed surface and by the blurred appearance of the image.

| 247 | | UnFVF | UseFVF |
|---|---|---|---|
| 50¢ | **gray lilac** | 250. | 17.50 |
| | dull gray lilac | 250. | 17.50 |
| | On cover | | 4500. |
| | Plate block of 6, w/imprint | 6000. | |
| | Margin block of 4, w/arrow | 1100. | |
| | FDC *(Jan. 13, 1909)* | | |

| 248 | | UnFVF | UseFVF |
|---|---|---|---|
| $1 | **violet brown** | 375. | 75.00 |
| | dull violet brown | 375. | 75.00 |
| | On cover | | 5250. |
| | Plate block of 6, w/imprint | 11500. | |
| | Margin block of 4, w/arrow | 1900. | |
| | Double transfer | — | |
| | FDC *(Jan. 29, 1909)* | | |

**1908. GEORGE WASHINGTON TYPE I ISSUE** Imperforate

| 249 | | UnFVF | UseFVF |
|---|---|---|---|
| 1¢ | **green** | 6.00 | 4.00 |
| | bright green | 6.00 | 4.00 |
| | dark green | 6.00 | 4.00 |
| | yellow green | 6.00 | 4.00 |
| | On cover | | 8.00 |
| | Plate block of 6, w/imprint | 55.00 | |
| | Plate block of 6, w/imprint & open star | 60.00 | |
| | Plate block of 6, w/small solid star | 600. | |
| | Block of 4, 2mm spacing | 25.00 | |
| | Block of 4, 3mm spacing | 25.00 | |
| | Center line block | 35.00 | |
| | Margin block of 4, 2 or 3mm spacing, w/arrow | 30.00 | |
| | Double transfer | — | |
| | FDC *(Dec. 23, 1908)* | | |

| 250 | | UnFVF | UseFVF |
|---|---|---|---|
| 2¢ | **carmine** | 7.50 | 3.00 |
| | dark carmine | 7.50 | 3.00 |
| | pale carmine | 7.50 | 3.00 |
| | On cover | | 4.50 |
| | Plate block of 6, w/imprint | 75.00 | |
| | Plate block of 6, w/imprint & star | 80.00 | |
| | Block of 4, 2 or 3mm spacing | 30.00 | |
| | Center line block | 40.00 | |
| | Double transfer | 12.50 | 3.50 |
| | Double transfer (1¢ design of No. 237) | 1000. | |
| | Margin block of 4, 2 or 3mm spacing, w/arrow | 35.00 | |
| | FDC *(Dec. 14, 1908)* | | |

| 251 | | UnFVF | UseFVF |
|---|---|---|---|
| 3¢ | **violet,** Type I | 17.50 | 20.00 |
| | On cover | | 40.00 |
| | Plate block of 6, w/imprint | 175. | |
| | Center line block | 75.00 | 80.00 |
| | Double transfer | 20.00 | |
| | Margin block of 4, w/arrow | 60.00 | 80.00 |
| | FDC *(March 3, 1909)* | | |

| 252 | | UnFVF | UseFVF |
|---|---|---|---|
| 4¢ | **brown** | 27.50 | 22.50 |
| | orange brown | 27.50 | 22.50 |
| | dark orange brown | 27.50 | 22.50 |
| | dull orange brown | 27.50 | 22.50 |
| | On cover | | 70.00 |
| | Plate block of 6 w/imprint | 200. | |
| | Plate block of 6, w/imprint & star | 225. | |
| | Block of 4, 2 or 3mm spacing | 95.00 | |
| | Center line block | 125. | |
| | Double transfer | 40.00 | |
| | Margin block of 4, 2 or 3mm spacing, w/arrow | 100. | |
| | FDC *(Feb. 25, 1909)* | | |

| 253 | | UnFVF | UseFVF |
|---|---|---|---|
| 5¢ | **blue** | 42.50 | 30.00 |
| | On cover | | 90.00 |
| | Plate block of 6, w/imprint | 350. | |
| | Center line block | 220. | 200. |
| | Cracked plate | — | |
| | Margin block of 4, w/arrow | 200. | 160. |
| | FDC *(Feb. 27, 1909)* | | |

**1908-10. WASHINGTON & FRANKLIN COIL ISSUE** Flat plate printing, double-line USPS watermark (wmk 187), and perforated 12 either on the sides or at the top and bottom of the stamp.
*Perforated 12 horizontally.*

| 254 | | UnFVF | UseFVF |
|---|---|---|---|
| 1¢ | **green** | 22.50 | 12.50 |
| | dark green | 22.50 | 12.50 |
| | On cover | | 35.00 |
| | Pair | 60.00 | 65.00 |
| | Line pair | 150. | 275. |
| | FDC *(Dec.29, 1908)* | | |

| 255 | | UnFVF | UseFVF |
|---|---|---|---|
| 2¢ | **carmine** | 37.50 | 8.00 |
| | dark carmine | 37.50 | 8.00 |
| | On cover | | 25.00 |
| | Pair | 65.00 | 30.00 |
| | Line pair | 275. | 135. |
| | Double transfer (1¢ design of No. 237) | — | 1350. |
| | FDC *(Jan. 2, 1909)* | | |

| 256 | | UnFVF | UseFVF |
|---|---|---|---|
| 4¢ | **brown** | 85.00 | 70.00 |
| | On cover | | 150. |
| | Pair | 225. | 300. |
| | Line pair | 650. | 550. |
| | FDC *(Aug. 15, 1910)* | | |

| 257 | | UnFVF | UseFVF |
|---|---|---|---|
| 5¢ | **blue** | 100. | 85.00 |
| | dark blue | 100. | 85.00 |
| | On cover | | 165. |
| | Pair | 275. | 300. |
| | Line pair | 750. | 550. |
| | FDC *(Jan. 2, 1909)* | | |

**1908-10. WASHINGTON & FRANKLIN COIL ISSUE**
Perforated 12 vertically.

| 258 | | UnFVF | UseFVF |
|---|---|---|---|
| 1¢ | **green** | 50.00 | 30.00 |
| | On cover | | 60.00 |
| | Pair, 2mm spacing | 135. | 105. |
| | Pair, 3mm spacing | 120. | 95.00 |
| | Line pair | 350. | 200. |
| | Double transfer | — | |
| | FDC *(Jan. 2, 1909)* | | |

| 259 | | UnFVF | UseFVF |
|---|---|---|---|
| 2¢ | **carmine** | 47.50 | 7.50 |
| | On cover | | 20.00 |
| | Pair, 2mm spacing | 125. | 30.00 |
| | Pair, 3mm spacing | 115. | 25.00 |
| | Line pair | 350. | 125. |
| | FDC *(Jan. 12, 1909)* | | |

| 260 | | UnFVF | UseFVF |
|---|---|---|---|
| 4¢ | **brown** | 115. | 55.00 |
| | On cover | | 90.00 |
| | Pair, 2mm spacing | 325. | 250. |
| | Pair, 3mm spacing | 340. | 270. |
| | Line pair | 850. | 400. |
| | FDC *(Feb. 23, 1909)* | | |

| 261 | | UnFVF | UseFVF |
|---|---|---|---|
| 5¢ | **blue** | 125. | 75.00 |
| | dark blue | 125. | 75.00 |
| | On cover | | 150. |
| | Pair | 350. | 325. |
| | Line pair | 900. | 550. |
| | FDC *(Feb. 23, 1909)* | | |

| 262 | | UnFVF | UseFVF |
|---|---|---|---|
| 10¢ | **yellow** | 1750. | 850. |
| | On cover | | 8500. |
| | Pair | 4200. | 3800. |
| | Line pair | 7500. | 6850. |
| | FDC *(Feb. 23, 1909)* | | |

**1909. WASHINGTON & FRANKLIN ISSUE Stamps of 1908-09 on Bluish Gray paper.** The paper used in this experimental printing was made with a 30% rag stock instead of all wood pulp. Here is a quote from the Report of the Third Assistant Postmaster General for the fiscal year ending June 30, 1909: "The intaglio process by which our postage stamps are printed necessitates a preliminary wetting down of the paper, which is bleached chemical wood stock. This wetting down causes a varying shrinkage, which has resulted in heavy waste from the cutting of the perforations into the stamp design. The Bureau of Engraving and Printing experimented with a paper made of about 30% rag stock, in the hope that it would show less shrinkage, but this paper did not overcome the difficulty as it was found to shrink very unevenly. Some of the stamps printed on this paper, which was of a slightly bluish tinge, were issued to the Postmaster of Washington D.C., and to others." Actually, the paper is of a distinctly different color than the normal paper, but this shows up better by comparison than it does by the examination of just a single copy of either the normal or the bluish gray paper. We have noted the presence of tiny black specks on much of the blue paper, sometimes only a few to a stamp and best seen with the aid of a glass. These stamps were *Flat Plate printing, watermarked double-line USPS (187), and perforated 12.*

| 263 | | UnFVF | UseFVF |
|---|---|---|---|
| 1¢ | **green** | 85.00 | 85.00 |
| | On cover | | 185. |
| | Plate block of 6, w/imprint | 900. | |
| | Plate block of 6, w/imprint and star | 2500. | |
| | Block of 4, 2mm spacing | 350. | 375. |
| | Block of 4, 3mm spacing | 675. | |
| | FDC *(Feb. 16, 1909)* | | |

| 264 | | UnFVF | UseFVF |
|---|---|---|---|
| 2¢ | **carmine** | 75.00 | 70.00 |
| | On cover | | 150. |
| | Plate block of 6, w/imprint | 900. | |
| | Plate block of 6, w/imprint & star | 1150. | |
| | Block of 4, 2mm spacing | 340. | 400. |
| | Block of 4, 3mm spacing | 380. | |
| | Double transfer | — | |
| | FDC *(Feb. 16, 1909)* | | |

| 265 | | UnFVF | UseFVF |
|---|---|---|---|
| 3¢ | **deep violet,** Type I | 1600. | 1600. |
| | On cover | | — |
| | Plate block of 6, w/imprint | 15000. | |

| 266 | | UnFVF | UseFVF |
|---|---|---|---|
| 4¢ | **orange brown** | 15000. | — |
| | Plate block of 6, w/imprint | 115000. | |
| | Plate strip of 3, w/imprint | — | |

| 267 | | UnFVF | UseFVF |
|---|---|---|---|
| 5¢ | **blue** | 3500. | 3750. |
| | On cover | | 5250. |
| | Plate block of 6, w/imprint | 30000. | |

| 268 | | UnFVF | UseFVF |
|---|---|---|---|
| 6¢ | **red orange** | 1150. | 1000. |
| | On cover | | 11000. |
| | Plate block of 6, w/imprint | 12500. | |
| | *Earliest documented cover:* Sept. 14, 1911 | | |

| 269 | | UnFVF | UseFVF |
|---|---|---|---|
| 8¢ | **olive green** | 16000. | — |
| | Plate block of 6, w/imprint | 120000. | |
| | Plate strip of 3 w/imprint | — | |

| 270 | | UnFVF | UseFVF |
|---|---|---|---|
| 10¢ | **yellow** | 1400. | 1150. |
| | On cover | | — |
| | Plate block of 6, w/imprint | 15000. | |
| | *Earliest documented cover:* Feb. 3, 1910 | | |

| 271 | | UnFVF | UseFVF |
|---|---|---|---|
| 13¢ | **blue green** | 2350. | 1450. |
| | On cover | | — |
| | Plate block of 6, w/imprint | 17500. | |

| 272 | | UnFVF | UseFVF |
|---|---|---|---|
| 15¢ | **pale ultramarine** | 1150. | 1000. |
| | On cover | | — |
| | Plate block of 6, w/imprint | 7500. | |

**1910-14. FRANKLIN & WASHINGTON ISSUE** This issue was identical with the 1908-09 series in design, but a 7¢ stamp was added while the 50¢ and $1 stamps were discontinued. The stamps were *printed on paper with a new watermark, single-line USPS. Flat plate printing. Perforated 12.*

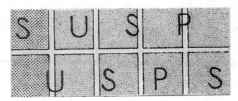

*273 Single-line USPS watermark.*

| 273 | | UnFVF | UseFVF |
|---|---|---|---|
| 1¢ | **green** | 6.00 | .20 |
| | dark green | 6.00 | .20 |
| | pale green | 6.00 | .20 |
| | yellowish green | 6.00 | .20 |
| | On cover | | .50 |
| | Plate block of 6, w/imprint & "A" | 60.00 | |
| | Plate block of 6, w/imprint & star | 70.00 | |
| | Block of 4, 2mm spacing | 22.50 | 2.75 |
| | Block of 4, 3mm spacing | 22.50 | 2.75 |
| | Cracked plate | — | |
| | Double transfer | 10.00 | |
| | n. Booklet pane of 6 | 125. | 100. |
| | *Earliest documented cover:* July 31, 1911 | | |
| | FDC *(Nov. 23, 1910)* | | |

| 274 | | UnFVF | UseFVF |
|---|---|---|---|
| 2¢ | **carmine** | 5.75 | .20 |
| | dull carmine | 5.75 | .20 |
| | lake | 200. | — |
| | On cover | | .50 |
| | Plate block of 6, w/imprint & "A" | 60.00 | |
| | Plate block of 6, w/imprint & star | 65.00 | |
| | Block of 4, 2mm spacing | 22.50 | 1.00 |
| | Block of 4, 3mm spacing | 21.00 | .80 |
| | Cracked plate | — | |
| | Double transfer | 9.00 | — |
| | Double transfer (1¢ design of No. 273) | — | 850. |
| | n. Booklet pane of 6 | 100. | |
| | *Earliest documented cover:* (June 1, 1911) | | |
| | FDC *(Nov. 23, 1910)* | | |

**1911. GEORGE WASHINGTON ISSUE**

*275-282 George Washington*

| 275 | | UnFVF | UseFVF |
|---|---|---|---|
| 3¢ | **violet,** Type I | 15.00 | 1.50 |
| | deep violet | 15.00 | 1.50 |
| | lilac | 17.50 | 1.50 |
| | On cover | | 7.00 |
| | Plate block of 6 | 125. | |
| | Plate block of 6, w/imprint & star | 165. | |
| | Block of 4, 2mm spacing | 65.00 | 8.00 |
| | Block of 4, 3mm spacing | 67.50 | 8.00 |
| | FDC *(Jan. 16, 1911)* | | |

| 276 | | UnFVF | UseFVF |
|---|---|---|---|
| 4¢ | **brown** | 22.50 | .75 |
| | dark brown | 22.50 | .75 |
| | orange brown | 22.50 | .75 |
| | On cover | | 7.00 |
| | Plate block of 6 | 240. | |
| | Plate block of 6, w/imprint & star | 200. | |
| | Block of 4, 2mm spacing | 100. | |
| | Block of 4, 3mm spacing | 95.00 | |
| | FDC *(Jan. 20, 1911)* | | |

| 277 | | UnFVF | UseFVF |
|---|---|---|---|
| 5¢ | **blue** | 22.50 | .75 |
| | dark blue | 22.50 | .75 |
| | pale blue | 22.50 | .75 |
| | On cover | | 4.50 |
| | Plate block of 6 | 200. | |
| | Plate block of 6 w/imprint | 180. | |
| | Plate block of 6, w/imprint & "A" | 200. | |
| | Plate block of 6, w/imprint & star | 175. | |
| | Block of 4, 2mm spacing | 100. | 5.00 |
| | Block of 4, 3mm spacing | 95.00 | 4.50 |
| | Double transfer | — | |
| | *Earliest documented cover: (March 28, 1911)* | | |

| 278 | | UnFVF | UseFVF |
|---|---|---|---|
| 6¢ | **red orange** | 30.00 | .85 |
| | dull red orange | 30.00 | .85 |
| | On cover | | .40 |
| | Plate block of 6, w/imprint | 300. | |
| | Plate block of 6, w/imprint & star | 275. | |
| | Block of 4, 2mm spacing | 125. | 8.00 |
| | Block of 4, 3mm spacing | 120. | 7.50 |
| | *FDC (Jan. 25, 1911)* | | |

| 279 | | UnFVF | UseFVF |
|---|---|---|---|
| 7¢ | **black** | 70.00 | 8.50 |
| | deep black | 70.00 | 8.50 |
| | gray black | 70.00 | 8.50 |
| | On cover | | 50.00 |
| | Plate block of 6 | 850. | |
| | *Earliest documented cover: (May 1, 1914)* | | |

| 280 | | UnFVF | UseFVF |
|---|---|---|---|
| 8¢ | **light olive green** | 95.00 | 12.50 |
| | dark olive green | 95.00 | 12.50 |
| | On cover | | 50.00 |
| | Plate block of 6, w/imprint | 900. | |
| | Plate block of 6, w/imprint & star | 1100. | |
| | Block of 4, 2 or 3mm spacing | 400. | 65.00 |
| | *FDC (Feb. 8, 1911)* | | |

| 281 | | UnFVF | UseFVF |
|---|---|---|---|
| 10¢ | **yellow** | 85.00 | 4.00 |
| | On cover | | 15.00 |
| | Plate block of 6, w/imprint | 900. | |
| | Plate block of 6, w/imprint & star | 850. | |
| | Block of 4, 2 or 3mm spacing | 375. | 25.00 |
| | *Earliest documented cover: (Feb. 17, 1911)* | | |
| | *FDC (Jan. 24, 1911)* | | |

| 282 | | UnFVF | UseFVF |
|---|---|---|---|
| 15¢ | **pale ultramarine** | 225. | 15.00 |
| | On cover | | 85.00 |
| | Plate block of 6 | 2000. | |
| | *FDC (March 1, 1911)* | | |

**1910. GEORGE WASHINGTON ISSUE** Imperforate

| 283 | | UnFVF | UseFVF |
|---|---|---|---|
| 1¢ | **green** | 3.00 | 275. |
| | dark green | 3.00 | 2.75 |
| | pale green | 3.00 | 2.75 |
| | yellowish green | 3.00 | 2.75 |
| | On cover | | 4.00 |
| | Plate block of 6 w/imprint & "A" | 40.00 | |
| | Plate block of 6, w/imprint & star | 65.00 | |
| | Block of 4, 2 or 3mm spacing | 9.50 | 11.00 |
| | Center line block | 20.00 | 15.00 |
| | Double transfer | 6.00 | |
| | Margin block of 4, w/arrow | 10.00 | 11.00 |
| | *Earliest documented cover: (March 1, 1911)* | | |
| | *FDC (Dec. 1910)* | | |

| 284 | | UnFVF | UseFVF |
|---|---|---|---|
| 2¢ | **carmine** | 5.50 | 3.00 |
| | On cover | | 3.00 |
| | Plate block of 6, w/imprint & "A" | 115. | |
| | Plate block of 6, w/imprint & star | 150. | |

| 284 | | UnFVF | UseFVF |
|---|---|---|---|
| | Block of 4, 2 or 3mm spacing | 20.00 | 12.50 |
| | Margin block of 4, w/arrow | 25.00 | 17.50 |
| | Center line block | 42.50 | 40.00 |
| | Cracked plate | — | |
| | Double transfer | 7.50 | |
| | Double transfer (1¢ design of No. 283) | 1200. | |
| | *Earliest documented cover: (April 23, 1911)* | | |
| | *FDC (Dec. 1910)* | | |

**1910. GEORGE WASHINGTON COIL ISSUE** This stamp is relatively common in singles and vertical pairs and blocks. Perforated 12 horizontally.

| 285 | | UnFVF | UseFVF |
|---|---|---|---|
| 1¢ | **green** | 22.50 | 12.50 |
| | dark green | 22.50 | 12.50 |
| | On cover | | 35.00 |
| | Pair | 50.00 | 35.00 |
| | Line pair | 250. | 225. |
| | *FDC (Nov. 1, 1910)* | | |

| 286 | | UnFVF | UseFVF |
|---|---|---|---|
| 2¢ | **carmine** | 37.50 | 17.50 |
| | dark carmine | 37.50 | 17.50 |
| | pale carmine | 37.50 | 17.50 |
| | On cover | | 40.00 |
| | Pair | 135. | 75.00 |
| | Line pair | 425. | |
| | *FDC (Nov. 1, 1910)* | | |

**1910. GEORGE WASHINGTON COIL ISSUE** Perforated 12 vertically.

| 287 | | UnFVF | UseFVF |
|---|---|---|---|
| 1¢ | **green** | 85.00 | 37.50 |
| | dark green | 85.00 | 37.50 |
| | On cover | | 60.00 |
| | Pair, 2mm spacing | 200. | 90.00 |
| | Pair, 3mm spacing | 220. | 100. |
| | Line pair | 325. | 260. |
| | *FDC (Nov. 1, 1910)* | | |

| 288 | | UnFVF | UseFVF |
|---|---|---|---|
| 2¢ | **carmine** | 575. | 250. |
| | dark carmine | 575. | 250. |
| | pale carmine | 575. | 250. |
| | On cover | | 600 |
| | Pair, 2 or 3mm spacing | 1950. | |
| | Line pair | 4000. | 3150. |
| | *FDC (Nov. 1, 1910)* | | |

| 289 | | UnFVF | UseFVF |
|---|---|---|---|
| 3¢ | **deep violet,** Type I | 28500. | 7000. |
| | red violet | 28500. | 7000. |
| | violet | 28500. | 7000. |
| | On cover | | 15500. |
| | Pair | 78500. | |
| | *FDC (Jan. 24, 1911)* | | |

**1910. GEORGE WASHINGTON ORANGEBURG COIL ISSUE** Known as the "Orangeburg Coil" (because it is only known used from Orangeburg, New York) No. 289 is the rarest of all U.S. coil stamps. One coil of 500 stamps was made and only about a dozen unused copies are known. The stamps were used by the Bell Chemical Company of Orangeburg to mail samples of products. Perforated 8 1/2 horizontally.

| 290 | | UnFVF | UseFVF |
|---|---|---|---|
| 1¢ | **green** | 450. | 5.00 |
| | dark green | 450. | 5.00 |
| | On cover | | 7.50 |
| | Pair | 8.00 | 16.50 |
| | Line pair | 25.00 | 40.00 |
| | *FDC (Dec. 12, 1910)* | | |

| 291 | | UnFVF | UseFVF |
|---|---|---|---|
| 2¢ | **carmine** | 30.00 | 12.50 |
| | dark carmine | 30.00 | 12.50 |
| | pale carmine | 30.00 | 12.50 |
| | On cover | | 20.00 |
| | Pair | 75.00 | 32.50 |
| | Line pair | 150. | 125. |
| | FDC *(Dec. 23, 1910)* | | |

**1910. GEORGE WASHINGTON COIL ISSUE** Perforated 8 1/2 vertically.

| 292 | | UnFVF | UseFVF |
|---|---|---|---|
| 1¢ | **green** | 20.00 | 20.00 |
| | dark green | 20.00 | 20.00 |
| | On cover | | 50.00 |
| | Double transfer | 20.00 | 20.00 |
| | Pair | 55.00 | 65.00 |
| | Line pair | 115. | 135. |
| | FDC *(Dec. 12, 1910)* | | |

| 293 | | UnFVF | UseFVF |
|---|---|---|---|
| 2¢ | **carmine** | 40.00 | 10.00 |
| | dark carmine | 40.00 | 10.00 |
| | pale carmine | 40.00 | 10.00 |
| | On cover | | 20.00 |
| | Pair | 85.00 | 22.50 |
| | Line pair | 165. | 80.00 |
| | FDC *(Dec. 16, 1910)* | | |

| 294 | | UnFVF | UseFVF |
|---|---|---|---|
| 3¢ | **violet,** Type I | 50.00 | 50.00 |
| | deep violet | 50.00 | 50.00 |
| | red violet | 50.00 | 50.00 |
| | On cover | | 100. |
| | Pair, 2 or 3mm spacing | 110. | 125. |
| | Line pair | 250. | 275. |
| | FDC *(Sept. 18, 1911)* | | |

| 295 | | UnFVF | UseFVF |
|---|---|---|---|
| 4¢ | **brown** | 50.00 | 50.00 |
| | dark brown | 50.00 | 50.00 |
| | On cover | | 100. |
| | Pair, 2 or 3mm spacing | 110. | 125. |
| | Line pair | 250. | 250. |
| | FDC *(April 15, 1912)* | | |

| 296 | | UnFVF | UseFVF |
|---|---|---|---|
| 5¢ | **blue** | 50.00 | 50.00 |
| | dark blue | 50.00 | 50.00 |
| | On cover | | 100. |
| | Pair | 110. | 105. |
| | Line pair | 250. | 300. |
| | FDC *(March 1913)* | | |

**1912. MODIFIED GEORGE WASHINGTON ISSUE** 1¢ and 2¢ stamps with numerals instead of words for denomination. *Flat Press printing, single-line USPS watermark (wmk 273), perforated 12.*

297, 298 *George Washington*

| 297 | | UnFVF | UseFVF |
|---|---|---|---|
| 1¢ | **green** | 5.00 | .20 |
| | dark green | 5.00 | .20 |
| | pale green | 5.00 | .20 |
| | yellow green | 5.00 | .20 |
| | On cover | | .25 |
| | Plate block of 6 | 55.00 | |
| | Plate block of 6, w/"A" | 60.00 | |
| | Plate block of 6, w/"A" & imprint | 65.00 | |
| | Cracked plate | 11.00 | |
| | Double transfer | 5.00 | |
| | n. Booklet pane of 6 *(Feb. 10, 1912)* | 65.00 | |
| | v. Vertical pair, imperforate horizontally | 700. | |
| | FDC *(Feb. 14, 1912)* | | |

298 *George Washington, Type I. The following detailed description is provided, although any 2¢ that fits Point 1 is a Type I.*

1. The line from the front of the neck to and over the top of the button is very weak. The shading lines that run into this line (top of toga) are thin in the area above the cross hatching lines.

2. One shading line in the first (upper) curve of the ribbon above the left numeral and one line in the second (middle) curve above the right numeral.

3. There is a white dash below the ear.

4. The shading lines of the face terminate in front of the ear and are not joined with each other.

5. The lock of hair behind the ear is formed at the bottom by two lines of shading, the lower one being considerably shorter than the other.

6. The hair lines above the ear and slightly to the right form an arrowhead.

7. The shading lines just to the left of the ear form a fairly solid color.

| 298 | | UnFVF | UseFVF |
|---|---|---|---|
| 2¢ | **carmine,** Type I | 4.50 | .20 |
| | dark carmine | 4.50 | .20 |
| | lilac carmine | 4.50 | .20 |
| | On cover | | .25 |
| | Plate block of 6 | 70.00 | |
| | Plate block of 6, w/"A" | 85.00 | |
| | Double transfer | 6.25 | |
| | n. Booklet pane of 6 | 65.00 | |
| | v. Double impression | — | |
| | *Earliest documented cover: (June 6, 1912)* | | |
| | FDC *(Feb. 14, 1912)* | | |

**1912. MODIFIED GEORGE WASHINGTON ISSUE** Imperforate

| 299 | | UnFVF | UseFVF |
|---|---|---|---|
| 1¢ | **green** | 1.25 | .60 |
| | dark green | 1.25 | .60 |
| | pale green | 1.25 | .60 |
| | yellow green | 1.25 | .60 |
| | On cover | | 1.00 |
| | Plate block of 6 | 17.50 | |
| | Plate block of 6, w/"A" | 25.00 | |
| | Plate block of 6, w/"A" & imprint | 42.50 | |
| | Center line block | 8.00 | 8.00 |
| | Cracked plate | — | |
| | Double transfer | 2.25 | .75 |
| | Margin block of 4, w/arrow | 4.50 | 2.75 |
| | FDC *(March 9, 1912)* | | |

| 300 | | UnFVF | UseFVF |
|---|---|---|---|
| 2¢ | **carmine,** Type I | 1.30 | .60 |
| | dark carmine | 1.30 | .60 |
| | scarlet red | 1.30 | .60 |
| | On cover | | 1.00 |
| | Plate block of 6 | 30.00 | |
| | Plate block of 6, w/"A" | 40.00 | |
| | Plate block of 6, w/"A" & imprint | 45.00 | |
| | Center line block | 9.00 | 8.00 |
| | Cracked plate | — | |
| | Margin block of 4, w/arrow | 5.50 | |
| | FDC *(Feb. 23, 1912)* | | |

**1912. GEORGE WASHINGTON MODIFIED DESIGN COIL ISSUE**
Perforated 8 1/2 horizontally.

**301**

| 1¢ | | UnFVF | UseFVF |
|---|---|---|---|
| | **green** | 5.50 | 4.50 |
| | dark green | 5.50 | 4.50 |
| | On cover | | 7.25 |
| | Pair | 12.50 | 8.00 |
| | Line pair | 27.50 | 20.00 |
| | Double transfer | — | |
| | FDC *(March 18, 1912)* | | |

**302**

| 2¢ | | UnFVF | UseFVF |
|---|---|---|---|
| | **carmine,** Type I | 7.50 | 4.50 |
| | dark carmine | 7.50 | 4.50 |
| | On cover | | 10.00 |
| | Pair | 20.00 | 9.00 |
| | Line pair | 35.00 | 25.00 |
| | Double transfer | 10.00 | |
| | FDC *(March 18, 1912)* | | |

**1912. GEORGE WASHINGTON MODIFIED DESIGN COIL ISSUE**
Perforated 8 1/2 vertically.

**303**

| 1¢ | | UnFVF | UseFVF |
|---|---|---|---|
| | **green** | 22.50 | 6.25 |
| | On cover | | 12.50 |
| | Pair | 45.00 | 12.50 |
| | Line pair | 75.00 | 40.00 |
| | FDC *(May 18, 1912)* | | |

**304**

| 2¢ | | UnFVF | UseFVF |
|---|---|---|---|
| | **carmine,** Type I | 35.00 | 1.25 |
| | dark carmine | 35.00 | 1.25 |
| | On cover | | 7.00 |
| | Pair | 75.00 | 7.00 |
| | Line pair | 150. | 20.00 |
| | Double transfer | 35.00 | |
| | FDC *(March 21, 1912)* | | |

**1912-14 BENJAMIN FRANKLIN REDESIGNED ISSUE** values from 8¢
through 50¢. *Flat plate printing, single-line USPS watermark (273),
perforated 12.*

305-314 *Benjamin Franklin*

**305**

| 8¢ | | UnFVF | UseFVF |
|---|---|---|---|
| | **pale olive green** | 30.00 | 1.25 |
| | olive green | 30.00 | 1.25 |
| | On cover | | 12.50 |
| | Plate block of 6, w/imprint & "A" | 400. | |
| | FDC *(Feb. 14, 1912)* | | |

**306**

| 9¢ | | UnFVF | UseFVF |
|---|---|---|---|
| | **salmon pink** | 45.00 | 12.50 |
| | rose red | 45.00 | 12.50 |
| | On cover | | 40.00 |
| | Plate block of 6 | 550. | |
| | *Earliest documented cover:* May 1, 1914 | | |
| | FDC *(April 1914)* | | |

**307**

| 10¢ | | UnFVF | UseFVF |
|---|---|---|---|
| | **orange yellow** | 32.50 | .50 |
| | brown yellow | 300. | 5.00 |
| | yellow | 32.50 | .50 |
| | On cover | | 2.25 |
| | Plate block of 6, w/"A" | 370. | |
| | Plate block of 6, w/"A" & imprint | 420. | |
| | Double transfer | — | |
| | FDC *(Jan. 20, 1912)* | | |

**308**

| 12¢ | | UnFVF | UseFVF |
|---|---|---|---|
| | **chocolate** | 40.00 | 4.25 |
| | deep chocolate | 40.00 | 4.25 |
| | On cover | | 22.50 |
| | Plate block of 6 | 450. | |
| | Double transfer | 47.50 | |
| | Triple transfer | 65.00 | |
| | *Earliest documented cover: (June 2, 1914)* | | |
| | FDC *(April 1914)* | | |

**309**

| 15¢ | | UnFVF | UseFVF |
|---|---|---|---|
| | **gray black** | 65.00 | 4.00 |
| | gray | 65.00 | 4.00 |
| | On cover | | 15.00 |
| | Plate block of 6 | 650. | |
| | Plate block of 6, w/"A" | 625. | |
| | Plate block of 6, w/"A" & imprint | 600. | |
| | Double transfer | — | |
| | FDC *(Feb. 14, 1912)* | | |

**310**

| 20¢ | | UnFVF | UseFVF |
|---|---|---|---|
| | **gray blue** | 150. | 17.50 |
| | ultramarine | 150. | 17.50 |
| | On cover | | 125. |
| | Plate block of 6 | 1650. | |
| | *Earliest documented cover: (May 1, 1914)* | | |
| | FDC *(April 1914)* | | |

**311**

| 30¢ | | UnFVF | UseFVF |
|---|---|---|---|
| | **orange red** | 115. | 17.50 |
| | dark orange red | 115. | 17.50 |
| | On cover | | 225. |
| | Plate block of 6 | 1250. | |
| | *Earliest documented cover: (May 1, 1914)* | | |
| | FDC *(April 1914)* | | |

**312**

| 50¢ | | UnFVF | UseFVF |
|---|---|---|---|
| | **violet** | 350. | 20.00 |
| | pale violet | 350. | 20.00 |
| | On cover | | 1750. |
| | Plate block of 6 | 8250. | |
| | *Earliest documented cover: (May 1, 1914)* | | |
| | FDC *(April 1914)* | | |

**1912-14 BENJAMIN FRANKLIN REDESIGNED ISSUE** Double-line
USPS watermark (wmk 187).

**313**

| 50¢ | | UnFVF | UseFVF |
|---|---|---|---|
| | **violet** | 225. | 20.00 |
| | On cover | | 1750. |
| | Plate block of 6, w/"A" & imprint | 4000. | |
| | Margin block of 4, w/arrow | 950. | |
| | FDC *(Feb. 14, 1912)* | | |

**314**

| $1 | | UnFVF | UseFVF |
|---|---|---|---|
| | **violet brown** | 425. | 65.00 |
| | On cover | | 6250. |
| | Plate block of 6, w/"A" & imprint | 9100. | |
| | Double transfer | 475. | |
| | Margin block of 4, w/arrow | 1950. | |
| | FDC *(Feb. 14, 1912)* | | |

**1914-15 GEORGE WASHINGTON ISSUE** with *perforation 10. Flat
plate printing, single-line USPS watermark (wmk 273).*

315-321 *George Washington*

**315**

| 1¢ | | UnFVF | UseFVF |
|---|---|---|---|
| | **green** | 2.75 | .20 |
| | bright green | 2.75 | .20 |

| 315 | | UnFVF | UseFVF |
|---|---|---|---|
| | dark green | 2.75 | .20 |
| | yellow green | 2.75 | .20 |
| | On cover | | .25 |
| | Plate block of 6 | 35.00 | |
| | Plate block of 10, w/"COIL STAMPS" | 120. | |
| | Cracked plate | — | |
| | Double transfer | 4.00 | |
| | n. Booklet pane of 6 | 3.75 | 1.25 |
| | n1v.Booklet pane of 6, ungummed, imperforate | 1000. | |
| | v. Perforated 12 x 10 | 750. | 650. |
| | v1. Perforated 10 x 12 | — | 300. |
| | v2. Vertical pair, imperforate horizontally | 425. | — |
| | v3. Vertical pair, imperforate between | 8000. | |
| | *Earliest documented cover: (Dec. 20, 1913)* | | |
| | FDC (Sept. 5, 1914) | | |

| 316 | | UnFVF | UseFVF |
|---|---|---|---|
| 2¢ | **rose red,** Type I | 225. | .20 |
| | dark carmine | 225. | .20 |
| | dark rose | 225. | .20 |
| | scarlet | 225. | .20 |
| | red | 225. | .20 |
| | rose | 225. | .20 |
| | On cover | | .25 |
| | Plate block of 6 | 25.00 | |
| | Plate block of 10, w/"COIL STAMPS" | 125. | |
| | Cracked plate | 8.00 | |
| | Double transfer | — | |
| | n. Booklet pane of 6 | 22.50 | 4.50 |
| | v. Perforated 12 x 10 | — | 750. |
| | *Earliest documented cover: (Jan. 6, 1914)* | | |
| | FDC (Sept. 5, 1914) | | |

| 317 | | UnFVF | UseFVF |
|---|---|---|---|
| 3¢ | **violet,** Type I | 12.50 | 2.00 |
| | bright violet | 12.50 | 2.00 |
| | dark violet | 12.50 | 2.00 |
| | reddish violet | 12.50 | 2.00 |
| | On cover | | 3.00 |
| | Plate block of 6 | 160. | |
| | FDC (Sept. 18, 1914) | | |

| 318 | | UnFVF | UseFVF |
|---|---|---|---|
| 4¢ | **brown** | 30.00 | .75 |
| | dark brown | 30.00 | .75 |
| | orange brown | 30.00 | .75 |
| | yellow brown | 30.00 | .75 |
| | On cover | | 475. |
| | Plate block of 6 | 450. | |
| | FDC (Sept. 7, 1914) | | |

| 319 | | UnFVF | UseFVF |
|---|---|---|---|
| 5¢ | **blue** | 27.50 | .70 |
| | bright blue | 27.50 | .70 |
| | dark blue | 27.50 | .70 |
| | indigo blue | 27.50 | .70 |
| | On cover | | 2.50 |
| | Plate block of 6 | 375. | |
| | Perforated 12 x 10 | — | 2000. |
| | *Earliest documented cover: April 14, 1915* | | |
| | FDC (Sept. 14, 1914) | | |

| 320 | | UnFVF | UseFVF |
|---|---|---|---|
| 6¢ | **red orange** | 45.00 | 2.00 |
| | dark red orange | 45.00 | 2.00 |
| | pale red orange | 45.00 | 2.00 |
| | On cover | | 7.50 |
| | Plate block of 6 | 475. | |
| | Plate block of 6, w/imprint & star | 375. | |
| | Block of 4, 2 or 3mm spacing | 170. | 12.50 |
| | FDC (Sept. 28, 1914) | | |

| 321 | | UnFVF | UseFVF |
|---|---|---|---|
| 7¢ | **black** | 75.00 | 5.00 |
| | deep black | 75.00 | 5.00 |
| | gray black | 75.00 | 5.00 |
| | On cover | | 32.50 |
| | Plate block of 6 | 800. | |
| | FDC (Sept. 10, 1914) | | |

*322-331 Benjamin Franklin*

| 322 | | UnFVF | UseFVF |
|---|---|---|---|
| 8¢ | **yellow olive** | 30.00 | 1.25 |
| | dull yellow olive | 30.00 | 1.25 |
| | On cover | | 7.00 |
| | Plate block of 6, w/"A" | 475. | |
| | Plate block of 6, w/"A" & imprint | 425. | |
| | Double transfer | — | |
| | v. Double impression | — | |
| | FDC (Sept. 26, 1914) | | |

| 323 | | UnFVF | UseFVF |
|---|---|---|---|
| 9¢ | **salmon** | 35.00 | 2.00 |
| | dark salmon | 35.00 | 2.00 |
| | On cover | | 22.50 |
| | Plate block of 6 | 550. | |
| | FDC (Oct. 6, 1914) | | |

| 324 | | UnFVF | UseFVF |
|---|---|---|---|
| 10¢ | **orange yellow** | 40.00 | .40 |
| | golden yellow | 40.00 | .40 |
| | yellow | 40.00 | .40 |
| | On cover | | 6.50 |
| | Plate block of 6 | 775. | |
| | Plate block of 6, w/"A" | 850. | |
| | Plate block of 6, w/"A" & imprint | 600. | |
| | FDC (Sept. 9, 1914) | | |

| 325 | | UnFVF | UseFVF |
|---|---|---|---|
| 11¢ | **deep bluish green** | 20.00 | 9.00 |
| | dark green | 20.00 | 9.00 |
| | green | 20.00 | 9.00 |
| | On cover | | 22.50 |
| | Plate block of 6 | 225. | |
| | FDC (Aug. 12, 1915) | | |

| 326 | | UnFVF | UseFVF |
|---|---|---|---|
| 12¢ | **maroon** | 23.00 | 4.25 |
| | dark maroon | 23.00 | 4.25 |
| | copper red | 25.00 | 4.50 |
| | On cover | | 17.50 |
| | Plate block of 6 | 275. | |
| | Double transfer | 25.00 | |
| | Triple transfer | 30.00 | |
| | FDC (Sept. 10, 1914) | | |

*So-called vertical pair, imperforate between, really have at least one perforation hole between the stamps.*

| 327 | | UnFVF | UseFVF |
|---|---|---|---|
| 15¢ | **gray black** | 110. | 8.50 |
| | gray | 110. | 8.50 |
| | On cover | | 47.50 |
| | Plate block of 6 | 900. | |
| | Plate block of 6, w/"A" | 925. | |
| | Plate block of 6, w/"A" & imprint | 900. | |
| | FDC (Sept. 16, 1914) | | |

| 328 | | UnFVF | UseFVF |
|---|---|---|---|
| 20¢ | **pale ultrmarine** | 175. | 4.50 |
| | ultramarine | 175. | 4.50 |
| | On cover | | 130. |
| | Plate block of 6 | 2850. | |
| | FDC (Sept. 19, 1914) | | |

| 329 | | UnFVF | UseFVF |
|---|---|---|---|
| 30¢ | **orange red** | 225. | 20.00 |
| | dark orange red | 225. | 20.00 |
| | On cover | | 225. |
| | Plate block of 6 | 3250. | |
| | FDC (Sept. 19, 1914) | | |

| 330 | | UnFVF | UseFVF |
|---|---|---|---|
| 50¢ | **violet** | 525. | 22.50 |
| | On cover | | 1500. |
| | Plate block of 6 | 11500. | |
| | FDC (Dec. 13, 1915) | | |

**1914-15. BENJAMIN FRANKLIN ISSUE** *Double-line watermark USPS (wmk 187).*

| 331 | | UnFVF | UseFVF |
|---|---|---|---|
| **$1** | **violet black** | 725. | 85.00 |
| | On cover | | 9500. |
| | Plate block of 6, w/"A" & imprint | 10500. | |
| | Margin block of 4, w/arrow | 3000. | |
| | Double transfer | 750. | |
| | FDC *(Feb. 8, 1915)* | | |

**1915. GEORGE WASHINGTON ISSUE** Single-line watermark USPS (wmk 273). Perforated 11.

| 332 | | UnFVF | UseFVF |
|---|---|---|---|
| **2¢** | **rose red,** Type I | 100. | 225. |
| | On cover | | 900. |
| | Plate block of 6 | 950. | |
| | *Earliest documented cover:* July 19, 1915 | | |

**1914. GEORGE WASHINGTON COIL ISSUE** As an experiment toward finding a more satisfactory perforation, 190,000 type I 2¢ stamps were perforated 11 and sold through the Washington post offices, mostly to large users who were asked to report concerning the perforations. *Coil stamps, perforated 10 horizontally.*

| 333 | | UnFVF | UseFVF |
|---|---|---|---|
| **1¢** | **green** | 1.25 | 1.25 |
| | dark green | 1.25 | 1.25 |
| | On cover | | 2.00 |
| | Pair | 2.75 | 3.50 |
| | Line pair | 6.50 | 6.00 |
| | FDC *(Nov. 14, 1914)* | | |

| 334 | | UnFVF | UseFVF |
|---|---|---|---|
| **2¢** | **carmine,** Type I | 8.50 | 8.00 |
| | dark carmine | 8.50 | 8.00 |
| | On cover | | 12.50 |
| | Pair | 17.50 | 17.50 |
| | Line pair | 45.00 | 60.00 |
| | FDC *(July 22, 1914)* | | |

**1914. GEORGE WASHINGTON COIL ISSUE**

| 335 | | UnFVF | UseFVF |
|---|---|---|---|
| **1¢** | **green** | 22.50 | 7.50 |
| | dark green | 22.50 | 7.50 |
| | On cover | | 12.50 |
| | Pair | 60.00 | 15.00 |
| | Line pair | 125. | 55.00 |
| | FDC *(May 29, 1914)* | | |

| 336 | | UnFVF | UseFVF |
|---|---|---|---|
| **2¢** | **carmine,** Type I | 32.50 | 1.75 |
| | dark carmine | 32.50 | 1.75 |
| | red | 32.50 | 1.75 |
| | On cover | | 10.00 |
| | Pair | 80.00 | 5.00 |
| | Line pair | 175. | 17.50 |
| | FDC *(April 25, 1914)* | | |

| 337 | | UnFVF | UseFVF |
|---|---|---|---|
| **3¢** | **violet,** Type I | 225. | 125. |
| | dark violet | 225. | 125. |
| | On cover | | 200. |
| | Pair | 475. | 280. |
| | Line pair | 900. | 775. |
| | FDC *(Dec. 18, 1914)* | | |

| 338 | | UnFVF | UseFVF |
|---|---|---|---|
| **4¢** | **brown** | 120. | 47.50 |
| | On cover | | 100. |
| | Pair | 275. | 220. |
| | Line pair | 600. | 550. |
| | FDC *(Oct. 2, 1914)* | | |

| 339 | | UnFVF | UseFVF |
|---|---|---|---|
| **5¢** | **blue** | 47.50 | 32.50 |
| | On cover | | 52.50 |
| | Pair | 90.00 | 175. |
| | Line pair | 200. | 425. |
| | FDC *(July 30, 1914)* | | |

**1914-16. WASHINGTON & FRANKLIN ROTARY PRESS COIL ISSUE The Rotary Press,** was first used in production of the following coil stamps. The Press plates are curved into a half circle. Two plates are fitted around a cylinder and when the cylinder is rotated it prints on the paper being passed beneath it. An increase in printing speed and efficiency is attained as the paper is a continuous roll.

When plates are curved to fit the cylinder, there is a slight increase in the size of each stamp design in the direction the plate is curved. Designs on the flat plate presses run about 18 1/2 to 19mm wide by 22mm high. They stretch to 19 1/2 to 22mm wide on the rotary plates that are curved sidewise to the design, and to 22 1/2 to 23mm high when the plates are curved lengthwise to the design. A line of ink is deposited on the paper between stamp designs, where the two plates are joined.

Designs 18 1/2 to 19mm wide by 22 1/2mm high, *single- line USPS watermark (wmk 273), perforated 10 horizontally.*

The designs of rotary press stamps are larger in one dimension than those of flat press stamps. The illustration below shows to the left the rotary press coil No. 340 being taller than the flat press No. 333.

| 340 | | UnFVF | UseFVF |
|---|---|---|---|
| **1¢** | **green** | 6.50 | 4.25 |
| | pale green | 6.50 | 4.25 |
| | On cover | | 8.00 |
| | Pair | 15.00 | 9.00 |
| | Line pair | 40.00 | 27.50 |
| | FDC *(Dec. 12, 1915)* | | |

341 *Type III. Same as Type II except two lines of shading in the curves of the ribbons.*

| 341 | | UnFVF | UseFVF |
|---|---|---|---|
| **2¢** | **carmine,** Type III | 10.00 | 4.25 |
| | carmine rose | 10.00 | 4.25 |
| | red | 10.00 | 4.25 |
| | On cover | | 9.00 |
| | Pair | 25.00 | 10.00 |
| | Line pair | 55.00 | 22.50 |
| | v. **carmine,** Type I | 2000. | 325. |
| | *Earliest documented cover: (Dec. 21, 1915)* | | |

**1914. WASHINGTON & FRANKLIN ROTARY PRESS SIDEWISE COIL ISSUE** Imperforate, sidewise coil. Design 19 1/2 to 20mm wide by 22mm high.

| 342 | | UnFVF | UseFVF |
|---|---|---|---|
| **2¢** | **carmine,** Type I | 375. | 750. |
| | On cover | | — |
| | Pair | 675. | 2250. |
| | Line pair | 1250. | 8500. |
| | FDC *(June 30, 1914)* | | |

**1914-16. WASHINGTON & LINCOLN ISSUE** Perforated 10 vertically. Designs 19 1/2 to 20mm wide by 22mm high.

| 343 | | UnFVF | UseFVF |
|---|---|---|---|
| 1¢ | **green** | 10.00 | 2.50 |
| | On cover | | 4.00 |
| | Pair | 25.00 | 2250. |
| | Line pair | 65.00 | 12.50 |

*Earliest documented cover: (March 22, 1915)*
FDC *(Nov. 11, 1914)*

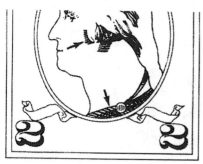

344 *Type II. Shading lines in ribbons same as Type I. The top line of toga rope is heavy and the rope is heavily shaded. The shading lines on the face, in front of the ear, are joined by a heavy vertical curved line.*

| 344 | | UnFVF | UseFVF |
|---|---|---|---|
| 2¢ | **carmine,** Type III | 10.00 | 1.15 |
| | carmine rose | 10.00 | 1.15 |
| | On cover | | 2.25 |
| | Pair | 22.50 | 2.75 |
| | Line pair | 55.00 | 7.25 |
| | v.  carmine, Type II *(June 1915)* | 85.00 | 10.50 |
| | v1. carmine, Type I *(June 30, 1914)* | 110. | 4.25 |

FDC *(Dec. 1915)*

| 345 | | UnFVF | UseFVF |
|---|---|---|---|
| 3¢ | **violet,**Type I | 225. | 115. |
| | dark violet | 225. | 115. |
| | red violet | 225. | 115. |
| | On cover | | 180. |
| | Pair | 550. | 300. |
| | Line pair | 1100. | 700. |

FDC *(Feb. 2, 1916)*

| 346 | | UnFVF | UseFVF |
|---|---|---|---|
| 4¢ | **yellow brown** | 27.50 | 20.00 |
| | brown | 27.50 | 20.00 |
| | On cover | | 45.00 |
| | Cracked plate | 35.00 | |
| | Pair | 60.00 | 50.00 |
| | Line pair | 150. | 100. |

FDC *(Nov. 5, 1915)*

| 347 | | UnFVF | UseFVF |
|---|---|---|---|
| 5¢ | **blue** | 32.50 | 17.50 |
| | On cover | | 42.50 |
| | Pair | 75.00 | 50.00 |
| | Line pair | 180. | 100. |
| | Double transfer | — | |

FDC *(March 9, 1916)*

**1916-17. WASHINGTON & LINCOLN ISSUE** Flat plate printing, unwatermarked, perforated 10.

| 348 | | UnFVF | UseFVF |
|---|---|---|---|
| 1¢ | **green** | 6.00 | .50 |
| | blue green | 6.00 | .50 |
| | dark green | 6.00 | .50 |
| | dull green | 6.00 | .50 |
| | On cover | | .50 |
| | Plate block of 6 | 150. | |
| | Booklet pane of 6 *(Oct. 15, 1916)* | 10.00 | |

FDC *(Sept. 27, 1916)*

| 349 | | UnFVF | UseFVF |
|---|---|---|---|
| 2¢ | **carmine,** Type I | 4.00 | 35.00 |
| | dark carmine | 4.00 | 35.00 |
| | rose red | 4.00 | 35.00 |
| | On cover | | .50 |
| | Double transfer | 6.00 | |
| | Plate block of 6 | 130. | |
| | Booklet pane of 6 *(Oct. 8, 1916)* | 85.00 | |

FDC *(Sept. 25, 1916)*

| 350 | | UnFVF | UseFVF |
|---|---|---|---|
| 3¢ | **violet,** Type I | 65.00 | 15.00 |
| | dark violet | 65.00 | 15.00 |
| | On cover | | 40.00 |
| | Plate block of 6 | 1400. | |
| | Double transfer in "CENTS" | 90.00 | |

FDC *(Nov. 11, 1916)*

| 351 | | UnFVF | UseFVF |
|---|---|---|---|
| 4¢ | **yellow brown** | 42.50 | 2.25 |
| | dark brown | 42.50 | 2.25 |
| | On cover | | 12.50 |
| | Double transfer | — | |
| | Plate block of 6 | 675. | |

FDC *(Oct. 7, 1916)*

| 352 | | UnFVF | UseFVF |
|---|---|---|---|
| 5¢ | **blue** | 65.00 | 2.25 |
| | dark blue | 65.00 | 2.25 |
| | dull blue | 65.00 | 2.25 |
| | On cover | | 12.50 |
| | Plate block of 6 | 900. | |

FDC *(Oct. 17, 1916)*

| 353 | | UnFVF | UseFVF |
|---|---|---|---|
| 5¢ | **carmine** | 550. | 700. |
| | On cover | | 1950. |
| | Block of 9, one 5¢ error in middle of block of 2¢ stamps | 750. | |
| | Block of 12, two 5¢ errors (2 middle stamps) w/ten 2¢ stamps | 1500. | |

*Earliest documented cover: (May 25, 1917)*

353 *The "Five Cent Red Error' was caused by mistakenly using a 5¢ transfer roll in reentering three positions on plate 7942, a plate of the 2¢ stamps. Of the 400 positions on the plate, 397 copies were 2¢ and three copies were 5¢. The error was not discovered until a considerable number of sheets were in the post offices and many of them were picked up by collectors. The errors exist perforated 10, perforated 11, and imperforate. The shade actually is carmine, but the stamp commonly is called the "Red Error."*

| 354 | | UnFVF | UseFVF |
|---|---|---|---|
| 6¢ | **red orange** | 80.00 | 7.50 |
| | orange | 80.00 | 7.50 |
| | On cover | | 40.00 |
| | Double transfer | — | |
| | Plate block of 6 | 1400. | |

FDC *(Oct. 10, 1916)*

| 355 | | UnFVF | UseFVF |
|---|---|---|---|
| 7¢ | **black** | 100. | 12.50 |
| | deep black | 100. | 12.50 |
| | gray black | 100. | 12.50 |
| | On cover | | 45.00 |
| | Plate block of 6 | 1400. | |

FDC *(Nov. 10, 1916)*

| 356 | | UnFVF | UseFVF |
|---|---|---|---|
| 8¢ | **yellow olive** | 55.00 | 6.50 |
| | dark yellow olive | 55.00 | 6.50 |
| | On cover | | 30.00 |
| | Plate block of 6, w/"A" | 625. | |
| | Plate block of , w/"A" & imprint | 575. | |

FDC *(Nov. 13, 1916)*

| 357 | | UnFVF | UseFVF |
|---|---|---|---|
| 9¢ | **salmon** | 50.00 | 15.00 |
| | On cover | | 40.00 |
| | Plate block of 6 | 775. | |

FDC *(Nov. 16,1916)*

| 358 | | UnFVF | UseFVF |
|---|---|---|---|
| 10¢ | **orange yellow** | 95.00 | 1.25 |
| | On cover | | 8.00 |
| | Plate block of 6 | 1400. | |
| | FDC *(Oct. 17, 1916)* | | |

| 359 | | UnFVF | UseFVF |
|---|---|---|---|
| 11¢ | **deep bluish green** | 35.00 | 22.50 |
| | On cover | | 45.00 |
| | Plate block of 6 | 375. | |
| | FDC *(Nov. 16, 1916)* | | |

| 360 | | UnFVF | UseFVF |
|---|---|---|---|
| 12¢ | **chocolate** | 45.00 | 5.50 |
| | On cover | | 22.50 |
| | Plate block of 6 | 650. | |
| | Double transfer | 60.00 | 6.00 |
| | Triple transfer | 70.00 | 9.00 |
| | FDC *(Oct. 10, 1916)* | | |

| 361 | | UnFVF | UseFVF |
|---|---|---|---|
| 15¢ | **gray black** | 165. | 12.50 |
| | gray | 165. | 12.50 |
| | On cover | | 85.00 |
| | Plate block of 6 | 2900. | |
| | Plate block of 6, w/"A" & imprint | — | |
| | FDC *(Nov. 16, 1916)* | | |

| 362 | | UnFVF | UseFVF |
|---|---|---|---|
| 20¢ | **pale blue** | 225. | 12.50 |
| | blue | 225. | 12.50 |
| | On cover | | 725. |
| | Plate block of 6 | 3750. | |
| | FDC *(Dec. 5, 1916)* | | |

| 362A | | UnFVF | UseFVF |
|---|---|---|---|
| 30¢ | **orange red** | 4500. | — |
| | Plate block of 6 | | |

362A Two sheets of 100 stamps of the 30¢ denomination were discovered without any trace of watermark. This fact was authenticated by The Philatelic Foundations's expert committee.

| 363 | | UnFVF | UseFVF |
|---|---|---|---|
| 50¢ | **light violet** | 950. | 65.00 |
| | On cover | | 2250. |
| | Plate block of 6 | 42500. | |
| | FDC *(March 2, 1917)* | | |

| 364 | | UnFVF | UseFVF |
|---|---|---|---|
| $1 | **violet black** | 625. | 20.00 |
| | On cover | | 3000. |
| | Block of 6, w/"A" & imprint | 14000. | |
| | Margin block of 4, w/arrow | 3250. | |
| | Double transfer | 850. | 22.50 |
| | FDC *(Dec. 22, 1916)* | | |

## 1917. JAMES MADISON ISSUE

*365 James Madison*

| 365 | | UnFVF | UseFVF |
|---|---|---|---|
| $2 | **dark blue** | 325. | 45.00 |
| | On cover | | 1750. |
| | Plate block of 6 | 5000. | |
| | Margin block 4, w/arrow | 1450. | |
| | Double transfer | — | |
| | FDC *(March 22, 1917)* | | |

## 1917. JOHN MARSHALL ISSUE

*366 John Marshall*

| 366 | | UnFVF | UseFVF |
|---|---|---|---|
| $5 | **light green** | 250. | 50.00 |
| | On cover | 1750. | |
| | Plate block of 6 | 4000. | |
| | Margin block 4, w/arrow | 1150. | |
| | FDC *(March 22, 1917)* | | |

## 1916-1917. GEORGE WASHINGTON ISSUE Imperforate

| 367 | | UnFVF | UseFVF |
|---|---|---|---|
| 1¢ | **green** | 1.15 | 1.00 |
| | bluish green | 1.15 | 1.00 |
| | dark green | 1.15 | 1.00 |
| | On cover | | 1.50 |
| | Plate block of 6 | 12.50 | |
| | Center line block | 8.50 | 6.25 |
| | Margin block of 4, w/arrow | 4.50 | 3.25 |
| | Double transfer | 2.50 | 1.25 |
| | FDC *(Dec. 8, 1916)* | | |

| 368 | | UnFVF | UseFVF |
|---|---|---|---|
| 2¢ | **carmine,** Type I | 1.40 | 1.30 |
| | carmine rose | 1.40 | 1.30 |
| | dark carmine | 1.40 | 1.30 |
| | dark rose | 1.40 | 1.30 |
| | On cover | | 2.50 |
| | Plate block of 6 | 22.50 | |
| | Plate block of 6, from plate No. 7942 | 175. | |
| | Center line block | 8.50 | 7.00 |
| | Cracked plate | — | |
| | Margin block of 4, w/arrow | 6.50 | 5.75 |
| | FDC *(Dec. 8, 1916)* | | |

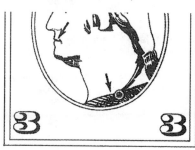

369 3¢. On Type II the top line of the toga rope is heavy and the rope shading lines are also heavy and complete. The line between the lips is heavy.

| 369 | | UnFVF | UseFVF |
|---|---|---|---|
| 5¢ | **violet,** Type I | 15.00 | 8.50 |
| | dull violet | 15.00 | 8.50 |
| | On cover | | 17.50 |
| | Plate block of 6 | 125. | |
| | Center line block | 70.00 | 70.00 |
| | Double transfer | 17.50 | |
| | Margin block of 4, w/arrow | 60.00 | 35.00 |
| | Triple transfer | — | |
| | v. violet, Type II *(484)* | 12.50 | 5.50 |
| | dark violet | 12.50 | 5.50 |
| | On cover | | 11.50 |
| | Plate block of 6 | 100. | |
| | Center line block | 60.00 | 60.00 |
| | Margin block of 4, w/arrow | 47.50 | 30.00 |
| | Double transfer | 12.50 | |
| | Earliest documented cover: *(April 30, 1918)* | | |
| | FDC *(Oct. 13, 1917)* | | |

| 370 | | UnFVF | UseFVF |
|---|---|---|---|
| 5¢ | **carmine** | 12500. | |
| | On cover | | — |
| | Block of 9, one 5¢ error in middle of block of 2¢ stamps | 15000. | |
| | Block of 12, two 5¢ errors (two middle stamps) w/ten 2¢ stamps | 27500. | |
| | FDC *(March 1917)* | | |

*This stamp commonly is called the "Red Error," but really is carmine.*

## 1916-22. WASHINGTON & LINCOLN ROTARY PRESS COIL ISSUE

unwatermarked, perforated 10 horizontally. Stamp designs 18 1/2 to 19mm wide by 22 1/2 high.

**371**

| | | UnFVF | UseFVF |
|---|---|---|---|
| **1¢** | **green** | .75 | .20 |
| | yellowish green | .75 | .20 |
| | On cover | | .50 |
| | Pair | 2.00 | .65 |
| | Line pair | 4.00 | .75 |
| | Cracked plate | — | |
| | Double transfer | 2.25 | |
| | FDC *(Jan. 10, 1918)* | | |

**372**

| | | UnFVF | UseFVF |
|---|---|---|---|
| **2¢** | **carmine,** Type III | 3.00 | 1.75 |
| | On cover | | 3.50 |
| | Pair | 5.75 | 4.00 |
| | Line pair | 20.00 | |
| | Cracked plate | 12.00 | 7.50 |
| | v. carmine, Type II *(487) (Nov. 15, 1916)* | 14.50 | 4.75 |
| | On cover | | 10.00 |
| | Pair | 32.50 | 7.50 |
| | Line pair | 125. | |
| | Cracked plate | — | |
| | FDC *(1919)* | | |

**373**

| | | UnFVF | UseFVF |
|---|---|---|---|
| **3¢** | **violet,** Type I | 4.50 | 1.50 |
| | bluish violet | 4.50 | 1.50 |
| | dull violet | 4.50 | 1.50 |
| | On cover | | 2.50 |
| | Pair | 11.00 | 4.00 |
| | Line pair | 27.50 | 10.00 |
| | FDC *(Oct. 10, 1917)* | | |

## 1916-22. WASHINGTON & LINCOLN ISSUE Perforated 10 vertically.

Stamp designs 19 1/2 to 20mm wide by 22mm high.

**374**

| | | UnFVF | UseFVF |
|---|---|---|---|
| **1¢** | **green** | .60 | .20 |
| | yellowish green | .60 | .20 |
| | On cover | | .50 |
| | Pair | 1.25 | .65 |
| | Line pair | 4.00 | 1.25 |
| | Cracked plate | 7.50 | |
| | Double transfer | — | |
| | Rosette crack on head | 50.00 | |
| | FDC *(Nov. 17, 1916)* | | |

**375**

| | | UnFVF | UseFVF |
|---|---|---|---|
| **2¢** | **carmine,** Type III | 8.50 | .20 |
| | carmine rose | 8.50 | .20 |
| | On cover | | .50 |
| | Pair | 21.00 | .65 |
| | Line pair | 50.00 | 3.50 |
| | Cracked plate | — | |
| | Double transfer | — | |
| | v. carmine, Type II *(491) (Nov. 17, 1916)* | 1650. | 800. |
| | On cover | | 850. |
| | Pair | 4000. | 17.50 |
| | Line pair | 9000. | 5000. |
| | FDC *(Nov. 17, 1916)* | | |

**376**

| | | UnFVF | UseFVF |
|---|---|---|---|
| **3¢** | **violet,** Type II | 11.50 | 1.25 |
| | dull violet | 11.50 | 1.25 |
| | gray violet | 11.50 | 1.25 |
| | On cover | | 1.00 |
| | Pair | 24.00 | 2.25 |
| | Line pair | 60.00 | 2.75 |
| | v1. violet, Type I *(493) (July 23, 1917)* | 17.50 | 3.25 |
| | reddish violet | 17.50 | 3.25 |
| | On cover | | 7.00 |
| | Pair | 35.00 | 8.00 |
| | Line pair | 125. | 45.00 |
| | FDC *(Feb. 4, 1918)* | | |

**377**

| | | UnFVF | UseFVF |
|---|---|---|---|
| **4¢** | **yellow brown** | | |
| | On cover | | 8.50 |
| | Pair | 24.00 | 10.00 |
| | Line pair | 65.00 | 17.50 |
| | Cracked plate | — | |
| | FDC *(Oct. 19, 1917)* | | |

**378**

| | | UnFVF | UseFVF |
|---|---|---|---|
| **5¢** | **blue** | 3.50 | 1.25 |
| | On cover | | 1.75 |
| | Pair | 8.00 | 2.25 |
| | Line pair | 25.00 | 7.00 |
| | FDC *(Jan. 15, 1919)* | | |

**379**

| | | UnFVF | UseFVF |
|---|---|---|---|
| **10¢** | **orange yellow** | 19.00 | 12.50 |
| | On cover | | 17.50 |
| | Pair | 47.50 | 27.50 |
| | Line pair | 125. | 50.00 |
| | FDC *(Jan. 31, 1922)* | | 5300. |

## 1917-19 WASHINGTON & LINCOLN ISSUE Flat Press printing, unwatermarked paper, and perforated 11.

**380**

| | | UnFVF | UseFVF |
|---|---|---|---|
| **1¢** | **green** | .55 | .20 |
| | dark green | .55 | .20 |
| | pale green | .55 | .20 |
| | yellowish green | .55 | .20 |
| | On cover | | .35 |
| | Plate block of 6 | 17.50 | |
| | Cracked plate | 7.50 | |
| | Double transfer | 5.50 | 2.00 |
| | n. Booklet pane of 6 | 2.75 | .35 |
| | n1. Booklet pane of 30 | 1100. | |
| | v. Double impression | 175. | |
| | v1. Horizontal pair, imperforate between | 200. | |
| | v2. Perforated 10 at top | 675. | |
| | v3. Perforated 10 at bottom | 675. | |
| | v4. Vertical pair, imperforate between | 500. | |
| | v5. Vertical pair, imperforate horizontally | 150. | |
| | *Earliest documented cover:* Sept. 10, 1917 | | |
| | FDC *(March 23, 1917)* | | |

**381**

| | | UnFVF | UseFVF |
|---|---|---|---|
| **2¢** | **rose red,** Type I | .50 | .20 |
| | dark rose | .50 | .20 |
| | rose carmine | .50 | .20 |
| | On cover | | .35 |
| | Plate block of 6 | 18.00 | |
| | Cracked plate | — | |
| | Double transfer | 6.00 | |
| | Retouch in hair | — | |
| | Double impression | 160. | |
| | n. Booklet pane of 6 *(March 31, 1917)* | 4.50 | |
| | n1. Booklet pane of 30 | 27500. | |
| | v. Horizontal pair, imperforate vertically | 200. | 125. |
| | v1. Vertical pair, imperforate between | 500. | 250. |
| | v2. Vertical pair, imperforate horizontally | 150. | |
| | a. deep rose, Type Ia *(500)* | 225. | 175. |
| | dark rose | 225. | 175. |
| | On cover | | 325. |
| | Plate block of 6 | 1800. | |
| | Plate block of 6, two stamps Type I | 7500. | |
| | Pair, 1 each Type I & Ia | 1000. | |
| | *Earliest documented cover:* Aug. 12, 1917 | | |
| | FDC *(March 23, 1917)* | | |

*Type Ia is similar to Type I, but lines of the design are stronger. this is particularly noticeable on the toga button, toga rope and rope shading lines, which are heavy. Lines in the ribbons are similar to Type I.*

| 382 | | UnFVF | UseFVF |
|---|---|---|---|
| 3¢ | **violet**, Type I | 12.50 | .20 |
| | dark violet | 12.50 | .20 |
| | dull violet | 12.50 | .20 |
| | reddish violet | 12.50 | .20 |
| | On cover | | .35 |
| | Plate block of 6 | 100. | |
| | n. Booklet pane of 6 *(Oct. 17, 1917)* | 60.00 | 17.50 |
| | v. Double impression | 200. | |
| | v1. Vertical pair, imperforate horizontally | 400. | |
| | FDC *(March 23, 1917)* | | |

| 382A | | UnFVF | UseFVF |
|---|---|---|---|
| 3¢ | **violet**, Type II | 15.00 | .40 |
| | dark violet | 15.00 | .40 |
| | On cover | | .65 |
| | Plate block of 6 | 150. | |
| | n. Booklet pane of 6 | 50.00 | |
| | v. Double impression | 200. | |
| | v1. Perforated 10 at top | 625. | |
| | v2. Perforated 10 at bottom | 625. | |
| | v3. Vertical pair, imperforate horizontally | 250. | 150. |
| | *Earliest documented cover:* June 18, 1918 | | |
| | FDC *(Feb. 25, 1918)* | | |

| 383 | | UnFVF | UseFVF |
|---|---|---|---|
| 4¢ | **yellow brown** | 11.50 | .30 |
| | brown | 11.50 | .30 |
| | dark brown | 11.50 | .30 |
| | orange brown | 11.50 | .30 |
| | On cover | | 2.00 |
| | Plate block of 6 | 140. | |
| | Double transfer | 15.00 | |
| | v. Double impression | — | |
| | FDC *(March 23, 1917)* | | |

| 384 | | UnFVF | UseFVF |
|---|---|---|---|
| 5¢ | **blue** | 8.50 | .25 |
| | dark blue | 8.50 | .25 |
| | dull blue | 8.50 | .25 |
| | On cover | | .35 |
| | Plate block of 6 | 125. | |
| | Double transfer | 10.50 | |
| | v. Horizontal pair, imperforate between | 2250. | |
| | FDC *(March 23, 1917)* | | |

| 385 | | UnFVF | UseFVF |
|---|---|---|---|
| 5¢ | **rose** | 400. | 500. |
| | On cover | | 1500. |
| | Strip of 3 (Nos. 381-385-381) | 500. | |
| | Block of 9, one 5¢ error in middle of 2¢ block | 600. | |
| | Block of 12, two 5¢ errors (2 middle stamps) within ten 2¢ stamps | 1000. | |
| | *Earliest documented cover:* (March 27, 1917) | | |

| 386 | | UnFVF | UseFVF |
|---|---|---|---|
| 6¢ | **red orange** | 12.50 | .40 |
| | orange | 12.50 | .40 |
| | On cover | | 2.50 |
| | Plate block of 6 | 145. | |
| | Double transfer | — | |
| | v. Perforated 10 at bottom | 650. | |
| | v1. Perforated 10 at top | 650. | |
| | FDC *(March 23, 1917)* | | |

| 387 | | UnFVF | UseFVF |
|---|---|---|---|
| 7¢ | **black** | 25.00 | 1.25 |
| | deep black | 25.00 | 1.25 |
| | gray black | 25.00 | 1.25 |
| | On cover | | 8.00 |
| | Plate block of 6 | 220. | |
| | Double transfer | — | |
| | FDC *(March 24, 1917)* | | |

| 388 | | UnFVF | UseFVF |
|---|---|---|---|
| 8¢ | **yellow olive** | 12.50 | 1.00 |
| | dark olive green | 12.50 | 1.00 |
| | olive green | 12.50 | 1.00 |
| | On cover | | 300. |
| | Plate block of 6 | 125. | |
| | Plate block of 6, w/"A" | 150. | |
| | Plate block of 6, w/"A" & imprint | 200. | |
| | v. Perforated 10 at bottom | 12.50 | |

| 388 | | UnFVF | UseFVF |
|---|---|---|---|
| | v1. Perforated 10 at top | 12.50 | |
| | v2. Vertical pair, imperforate between | — | |
| | FDC *(March 24, 1917)* | | |

| 389 | | UnFVF | UseFVF |
|---|---|---|---|
| 9¢ | **salmon** | 14.00 | 2.50 |
| | On cover | | 15.00 |
| | Plate block of 6 | 125. | |
| | Double transfer | 20.00 | 5.00 |
| | v. Perforated 10 at bottom | 1000. | |
| | v1. Perforated 10 at top | 1000. | |
| | FDC *(March 12, 1917)* | | |

| 390 | | UnFVF | UseFVF |
|---|---|---|---|
| 10¢ | **orange yellow** | 17.50 | .25 |
| | On cover | | 2.00 |
| | Plate block of 6 | 165. | |
| | Plate block of 6, w/"A" | 300. | |
| | FDC *(March 24, 1917)* | | |

| 391 | | UnFVF | UseFVF |
|---|---|---|---|
| 11¢ | **deep bluish green** | 9.00 | 3.00 |
| | dull green | 9.00 | 3.00 |
| | green | 9.00 | 3.00 |
| | On cover | | 8.50 |
| | Plate block of 6 | 115. | |
| | Double transfer | 12.50 | 3.25 |
| | v. Perforated 10 at bottom | 1000. | 375. |
| | v1. Perforated 10 at top | 1000. | 375. |
| | FDC *(May 19, 1917)* | | |

| 392 | | UnFVF | UseFVF |
|---|---|---|---|
| 12¢ | **brown purple** | 9.00 | .65 |
| | brown carmine | 9.00 | .65 |
| | On cover | | 4.00 |
| | Plate block of 6 | 115. | |
| | Double transfer | 12.50 | |
| | Triple transfer | 20.00 | |
| | v. Perforated 10 at bottom | 14.00 | 6.00 |
| | v1. Perforated 10 at top | 14.00 | 6.00 |
| | FDC *(May 12, 1917)* | | |

| 393 | | UnFVF | UseFVF |
|---|---|---|---|
| 13¢ | **apple green** | 10.50 | 6.50 |
| | dark apple green | 10.50 | 6.50 |
| | pale apple green | 10.50 | 6.50 |
| | On cover | | 20.00 |
| | Plate block of 6 | 125. | |
| | FDC *(Jan. 11, 1919)* | | |

| 394 | | UnFVF | UseFVF |
|---|---|---|---|
| 15¢ | **gray black** | 37.50 | 1.25 |
| | gray | 37.50 | 1.25 |
| | On cover | | 22.50 |
| | Plate block of 6 | 450. | |
| | Double transfer | — | |
| | FDC *(May 21, 1917)* | | |

| 395 | | UnFVF | UseFVF |
|---|---|---|---|
| 20¢ | **pale blue** | 47.50 | .50 |
| | dark blue | 47.50 | .50 |
| | gray blue | 47.50 | .50 |
| | On cover | | .75 |
| | Plate block of 6 | 500. | |
| | Double transfer | — | |
| | v. Double impression | 1250. | |
| | v1. Perforated 10 at bottom | 1600. | |
| | v2. Perforated 10 at top | 1600. | |
| | v3. Vertical pair, imperforate between | 425. | |
| | FDC *(May 12, 1917)* | | |

| 396 | | UnFVF | UseFVF |
|---|---|---|---|
| 30¢ | **orange red** | 37.50 | 1.25 |
| | dark orange red | 37.50 | 1.25 |
| | On cover | | 150. |
| | Plate block of 6 | 500. | |
| | Double transfer | — | |
| | v. Double impression | — | |
| | v1. Perforated 10 at bottom | 1100. | |
| | v2. Perforated 10 at top | 1100. | |
| | FDC *(May 12, 1917)* | | |

**397**

| 50¢ | **reddish violet** | UnFVF 65.00 | UseFVF .90 |
|---|---|---|---|
| | pale violet | 65.00 | .90 |
| | red violet | 65.00 | .90 |
| | On cover | | 400. |
| | Plate block of 6 | 1650. | |
| | Double transfer | 100. | 1.50 |
| | v. Perforated 10 at bottom | — | 950. |
| | v1. Perforated 10 at top | — | 950. |
| | v2. Vertical pair, imperforate between | 1800. | 1000. |
| | FDC *(May 19, 1917)* | | |

**398**

| $1 | **black purple** | UnFVF 55.00 | UseFVF 1.75 |
|---|---|---|---|
| | brown purple | 55.00 | 1.75 |
| | blackish brown | 1100. | 750. |
| | On cover | | 550. |
| | Plate block of 6, w/"A" & imprint | 1350. | |
| | Double transfer | 75.00 | 2.00 |
| | Margin block of 4, w/arrow | 250. | |
| | FDC *(May 19, 1917)* | | |

**1917. GEORGE WASHINGTON ISSUE** The 2¢ carmine stamp of 1908-09 issues existed in 1917 in the imperforate form at the New York Post Office. The old stock was returned to the Bureau of Engraving and Printing and was perforated with the then-current perforation. *Flat plate printing, double-line USPS watermark (187), perforated 11.*

**399**

| 2¢ | **carmine** | UnFVF 275. | UseFVF 450. |
|---|---|---|---|
| | On cover | | 2000. |
| | Plate block of 6, w/imprint | 2250. | |
| | *Earliest documented cover:* Oct. 10, 1917 | | |

**1918-20. BENJAMIN FRANKLIN ISSUE** Flat plate printing, unwatermarked, perforated 11.

400 *Benjamin Franklin*

**400**

| $2 | **orange & black** | UnFVF 650. | UseFVF 225. |
|---|---|---|---|
| | On cover | | 1850. |
| | Center line block | 3000. | |
| | Margin block of 4, w/arrow | 2800. | |
| | Plate block of 8, w/arrow | 13500. | |
| | FDC *(Aug. 23, 1918)* | | |

**1918-20. BENJAMIN FRANKLIN ISSUE** Flat plate printing, unwatermarked, perforated 11.

**401**

| $2 | **carmine & black** | UnFVF 190. | UseFVF 40.00 |
|---|---|---|---|
| | lilac carmine & black | 190. | 40.00 |
| | Plate block of 8, w/arrow | — | |
| | Center line block | — | |
| | Margin block of 4, w/arrow | — | |
| | On cover | | — |
| | FDC *(Nov. 1, 1920)* | | |

402 *Benjamin Franklin*

**402**

| $5 | **deep green & black** | UnFVF 225. | UseFVF 35.00 |
|---|---|---|---|
| | On cover | | 1500. |
| | Center line block | 1050. | |
| | Margin block of 4, w/arrow | 1000. | |
| | Plate block of 8, w/arrow | 3850. | |
| | FDC *(Aug. 23, 1918)* | | |

**1918-20. GEORGE WASHINGTON ISSUE Offset Printing.** This is the first time the Post Office Department did not use engraved plates. It was a direct result of World War I. During this period the Bureau of Engraving and Printing was hard pressed by the demands for stamps and government printing of all types. Printing inks for postage stamps used barites as a base, and as the war went on this basic material grew inferior in quality and contained a gritty substance which wore out the engraved plates quicker; high quality steel was difficult to obtain, so all conditions combined resulted in the unsatisfactory experiment of offset printing. These stamps can easily be identified by the smoothness of the printed surface when contrasted with any of the earlier stamps, all of which were engraved. This can be told apart by acutal touch, as the engraved stamps have a "rough" feeling, and the offsets a "soapy" feeling. If you hold an engraved stamp at a flat angle against a light and observe it through a magnifying glass, the actual ridges of the ink may be observed, while on the offsets there is no fine detail, and the stamps have a blurred appearance. The offsets are smaller than the engraved, usually about 1/2mm narrower in width (with the exception of the Type IV 3¢) and from 1/2mm to 1mm less in length. The offsets run from 21 to 21 1/2mm high. Three denominations were made in this style of printing, 1¢, 2¢, and 3¢, each value being *perforated 11* and *imperforate,* and the 1¢ also came *perforated 12 1/2.*

Unwatermarked, perforated 11.

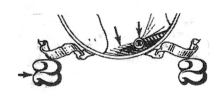

403 *George Washington*

Type IV: *Top line of toga rope is broken. Lines inside toga buttom read "D (reversed) ID." The line of color in the left "2" is very thin and is usually broken.*

Type VII: *The line of color in the left "2" is clear and unbroken, heavier than on Type V or Va but not as heavy as on Type VI. An extra vertical row of dots has been added on the lip, making four rows of three dots instead of two dots. Additional dots have been added to the hair on top of the head.*

Type V: *Top line of the toga is complete. Five vertical shading lines in toga button. Line of color in left "2" is very thin and usually broken. Shading dots on nose form a triangle with six dots in third row from bottom.*

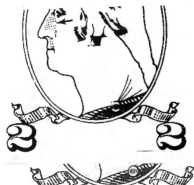

*Type Va: Same as Type V except on the shading dots on the nose, in which the the third row from the bottom has only four dots instead of six.*

*Type VI: Same as Type V but there is a heavy line of color in the left "2".*

| **403** | | UnFVF | UseFVF |
|---|---|---|---|
| **1¢** | **dull green** | 2.00 | .75 |
| | dark green | 2.25 | .75 |
| | emerald | 2.00 | .75 |
| | On cover | | 1.50 |
| | Plate block of 6 | 16.50 | |
| | "Flat nose" (nose appears so) | — | |
| | v. Double impression | 25.00 | |
| | v2. Horizontal pair, imperforate between | 95.00 | |
| | FDC (Dec. 24, 1918) | | |

There are five types of the 2¢ offset stamps, with each of these types appearing only on the offset stamps.

 404-404D

| **404** | | UnFVF | UseFVF |
|---|---|---|---|
| **2¢** | **rose red,** Type VII | 17.50 | .35 |
| | On cover | | .40 |
| | Plate block of 6 | 135. | |
| | Retouch on cheek | 375. | |
| | v. Double impression | 65.00 | |
| | *Earliest documented cover: (Nov. 10, 1920)* | | |

| **404A** | | UnFVF | UseFVF |
|---|---|---|---|
| **2¢** | **rose red,** Type V | 15.00 | 1.00 |
| | bright carmine | 15.00 | 1.00 |
| | rose carmine | 15.00 | 1.00 |
| | On cover | | 2.50 |
| | Plate block of 6 | 125. | |
| | Line through "2" & "EN" | 30.00 | |
| | v. Double impression | 55.00 | 8.50 |
| | v1. Horizontal pair, imperforate vertically | — | |
| | v2. Vertical pair, imperforate horizontally | 850. | |
| | *Earliest documented cover: (April 20, 1920)* | | |

| **404B** | | UnFVF | UseFVF |
|---|---|---|---|
| **2¢** | **rose red,** Type Va | 8.00 | .35 |
| | On cover | | 65.00 |
| | Plate block of 6 | 75.00 | |
| | Plate block of 6, w/monogram over number | 90.00 | |
| | "CRNTS" rather than "CENTS" | | |
| | Retouch of "P" in "POSTAGE" | 50.00 | |
| | Retouch on toga | — | |
| | v. Double impression | 25.00 | |
| | v1. Vertical pair, imperforate between | 1250. | |
| | *Earliest documented cover: (July 16, 1920)* | | |

| **404C** | | UnFVF | UseFVF |
|---|---|---|---|
| **2¢** | **rose red,** Type VI | 45.00 | 1.50 |
| | bright carmine | 45.00 | 1.50 |
| | On cover | | 3.75 |

| **404C** | | UnFVF | UseFVF |
|---|---|---|---|
| | Plate block of 6 | 350. | |
| | Plate block of 6, w/monogram over number | 450. | |
| | v. Double impression | 150. | |
| | v1. Vertical pair, imperforate between | — | |
| | v2. Vertical pair, imperforate horizontally | — | |
| | *Earliest documented cover: July 30, 1920* | | |

| **404D** | | UnFVF | UseFVF |
|---|---|---|---|
| **2¢** | **rose red,** Type IV | 25.00 | 4.25 |
| | carmine | 25.00 | 4.25 |
| | On cover | | 10.00 |
| | Plate block of 6 | 185. | |
| | Misformed "2" at left | 35.00 | |
| | Scar on forehead | 45.00 | |
| | FDC (March 15, 1920) | | 825. |

## 1918. GEORGE WASHINGTON ISSUE

405 *George Washington. There are two types of the 3¢ offset stamps, each of which appears only on the offset printing.*

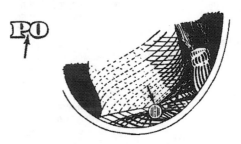

*Type III: Top line of toga is strong but the fifth shading line is missing. The center shading line of the toga button consists of two vertical dashes with a dot between them. The "P" and "O" of "POSTAGE" have a line of color between them.*

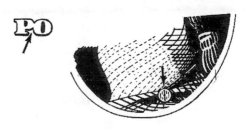

*Type IV: The "P" and "O" of "POSTAGE" are joined with no line of color between them. The center shading line runs right through the dot in the toga button.*

| **405** | | UnFVF | UseFVF |
|---|---|---|---|
| **3¢** | **purple,** Type III | 3.00 | .40 |
| | dark purple | 3.00 | .40 |
| | dull purple | 3.00 | .40 |
| | On cover | | .50 |
| | Plate block of 6 | 40.00 | |
| | v. Double impression | 35.00 | |
| | v1. Printed on both sides | 425. | |
| | FDC (March 23, 1918) | | |

| **405A** | | UnFVF | UseFVF |
|---|---|---|---|
| **3¢** | **purple,** Type IV | 1.25 | .20 |
| | dull purple | 1.25 | .20 |
| | violet | 1.25 | .20 |
| | On cover | | .25 |
| | Plate block of 6 | 15.00 | |
| | "Blister" under "U.S." | 4.25 | |
| | Retouch under "U.S." | 4.25 | |
| | v. Double impression | 17.50 | 6.00 |
| | v1. Printed on both sides | 225. | |

*Earliest documented cover: (June 30, 1918)*

**1919-20. GEORGE WASHINGTON ISSUE** Imperforate Offset Stamps.

| 406 | | UnFVF | UseFVF |
|---|---|---|---|
| 1¢ | **dull green** | 10.00 | 8.50 |
| | green | 10.00 | 8.50 |
| | On cover | | 15.00 |
| | Plate block of 6 | 75.00 | |
| | Center line block | 55.00 | 45.00 |
| | Margin block of 4, w/arrow | 40.00 | 36.00 |
| | FDC *(Jan. 21, 1919)* | | |

| 407 | | UnFVF | UseFVF |
|---|---|---|---|
| 2¢ | **rose red,** Type IV | 35.00 | 30.00 |
| | On cover | | 65.00 |
| | Plate block of 6 | 285. | |
| | Center line block | 200. | |
| | Margin block of 4, w/arrow | 175. | |
| | *Earliest documented cover: (April 30, 1920)* | | |

| 407A | | UnFVF | UseFVF |
|---|---|---|---|
| 2¢ | **rose red,** Type V | 190. | 85.00 |
| | On cover | | 200. |
| | Plate block of 6 | 1750. | |
| | Center line block | 900. | 450. |
| | Margin block of 4, w/arrow | 800. | |
| | *Earliest documented cover: (June 30, 1920)* | | |

| 407B | | UnFVF | UseFVF |
|---|---|---|---|
| 2¢ | **rose red,** Type Va | 12.50 | 8.50 |
| | carmine | 12.50 | 8.50 |
| | On cover | | 14.00 |
| | Plate block of 6 | 85.00 | |
| | Plate block of 6, w/monograph over number | 200. | |
| | Center line block | 50.00 | 60.00 |
| | Margin block of 4, w/arrow | 50.00 | 40.00 |
| | *Earliest documented cover: (July 3, 1920)* | | |

| 407C | | UnFVF | UseFVF |
|---|---|---|---|
| 2¢ | **rose red,** Type VI | 35.00 | 22.50 |
| | On cover | | 35.00 |
| | Plate block of 6 | 300. | |
| | Center line block | 190. | 175. |
| | Margin block of 4, w/arrow | 165. | |
| | *Earliest documented cover: (Sept. 7, 1920)* | | |

| 407D | | UnFVF | UseFVF |
|---|---|---|---|
| 2¢ | **rose red,** Type VII | 1500. | 575. |
| | On cover | | 1050. |
| | Plate block of 6 | 12500. | |
| | Center line block | 7700. | |
| | Margin block of 4, w/arrow | 5500. | |
| | *Earliest documented cover: (Nov. 3, 1920)* | | |

| 408 | | UnFVF | UseFVF |
|---|---|---|---|
| 3¢ | **violet,** Type IV | 8.75 | 6.00 |
| | On cover | | 11.00 |
| | Plate block of 6 | 50.00 | |
| | Center line block | 45.00 | 45.00 |
| | Margin block of 4, w/arrow | 40.00 | 30.00 |
| | v. Double impression | 100. | |
| | *Earliest documented cover: Oct. 5, 1918* | | |

**1919. GEORGE WASHINGTON ISSUE** Perforated 12 1/2 The 1¢ offset was issued with a trial perforation 12 1/2 made by the Rossbach perforating machine, a two-way rotary perforator that perforated a single sheet one direction, and then the other. The machine was proved unsatisfactory as nearly half of the sheets that were perforated had to be destroyed. Of the 6,641 sheets of 400 impages that were perforated by this machine, only 3,466 were good enough to send to the post offices. These were cut into panes of 100 before they were issued. Even the sheets that were released consisted, for the most part, of very badly centered stamps.

| 409 | | UnFVF | UseFVF |
|---|---|---|---|
| 1¢ | **dull green** | 14.00 | 16.50 |
| | On cover | | 50.00 |
| | Plate block of 6 | 140. | |
| | v. Horizontal pair, imperforate vertically | 450. | |
| | FDC *(Aug. 15, 1919)* | | |

**1914-15. THE ROTARY PRESS ISSUES** that follow form the final group of issues that bear the Washington design of 1914-15. Here is how Rotary Press intaglio stamps can be distinguished from stamps of similar designs printed by flat press intaglio or offset.

1. Rotary press stamps are always wider or taller than flat press or offset stamps. This measurement concerns the printed design only.

2. The back of a rotary press stamp is almost always free of color, while flat press stamps very often have small bits of color on the back.

3. With the exception of stamps printed from coil waste, the perforated rotary press stamps will show one or more ridges extending across the back of the stamp. These ridges were forced into the paper in an effort to keep the stamps from curling. This easily is apparent on unused stamps, but much more difficult to detect on used stamps. Most flat press stamps do not have these ridges.

**1919. GEORGE WASHINGTON ISSUE** Designs 19 1/2 to 20mm wide by 22mm high. Printed from coil waste sheets, no "breaker bar" ridges on back of stamps, *unwatermarked, perforated 11 x 10.*

     410, 411

| 410 | | UnFVF | UseFVF |
|---|---|---|---|
| 1¢ | **green** | 8.00 | 8.00 |
| | bluish green | 8.00 | 8.00 |
| | yellowish green | 8.00 | 8.00 |
| | On cover | | 20.00 |
| | Plate block of 4 | 75.00 | |
| | Plate block of 4, w/star | 90.00 | |
| | Plate block of , w/"S 30" | 100. | |
| | Double transfer | 15.00 | |
| | v. Vertical pair, imperforate horizontally | | 50.00 |
| | v1. Block of 4, imperforate horizontally | 100. | |
| | v2. Plate block of 6, imperforate horizontally | 750. | |
| | FDC *(June 14, 1919)* | | |

| 411 | | UnFVF | UseFVF |
|---|---|---|---|
| 2¢ | **carmine red,** Type II | 2500. | 3200. |
| | Plate block of 4 | 10500. | |
| | Plate block of 4, w/"S 20" | 17500. | |

| 411A | | UnFVF | UseFVF |
|---|---|---|---|
| 2¢ | **carmine red,** Type III | 10.00 | 9.00 |
| | On cover | | 22.50 |
| | Plate block of 4 | .75 | |
| | Plate block of 4, w/star | 125. | |
| | Plate block of 4, w/"S 30" | 75.00 | |
| | Plate block of 4, w/inverted "S 30" | 400. | |
| | Double transfer | 17.50 | |
| | v. Horizontal pair, imperforate vertically | 750. | |
| | v1. Vertical pair, imperforate horizontally | 50.00 | 50.00 |
| | v2. Block of 4, imperforate horizontally | 100. | |
| | FDC *(June 14, 1919)* | | |

| 412 | | UnFVF | UseFVF |
|---|---|---|---|
| 3¢ | **gray lilac,** Type II | 32.50 | 35.00 |
| | On cover | | 85.00 |
| | Plate block of 4 | 250. | |
| | FDC *(June 14, 1919)* | | |

**1920. GEORGE WASHINGTON ISSUE** Rotary press, stamp designs 18 1/2 to 19mm wide by 22 1/2mm high, *unwatermarked, perforated 10 x 11.* Breaker bar ridges on stamps.

| 413 | | UnFVF | UseFVF |
|---|---|---|---|
| 1¢ | **green** | 10.00 | 1.00 |
| | bluish green | 10.00 | 1.00 |
| | On cover | | 5.50 |
| | Plate block of 6 (vertical), w/plate number opposite center horizontal row | 135. | |
| | FDC *(May 26, 1920)* | | 2000. |

**1921. GEORGE WASHINGTON ISSUE** Rotary press, stamp designs 18 1/2 to 19mm wide by 22 1/2mm high, *unwatermarked, perforated 10,* breaker bar ridges on stamps.

| 414 | | UnFVF | UseFVF |
|---|---|---|---|
| 1¢ | green | .55 | .20 |
| | dark green | .55 | .20 |
| | On cover | | .35 |
| | Plate block of 6 (vertical), number opposite center horizontal row | 27.50 | |
| | Plate block of 4 | 12.50 | |
| | Double transfer | — | |
| | Triple transfer | — | |
| | v. Horizontal pair, imperforate between | 975. | |
| | FDC *(May 26, 1921)* | | |

**1922. GEORGE WASHINGTON ISSUE** Rotary press, stamp design 19mm wide by 22 1/2mm high, *unwatermarked, perforated 11,* breaker bar ridges on stamps.

| 415 | | UnFVF | UseFVF |
|---|---|---|---|
| 1¢ | green | 12000. | 2400. |
| | On cover | | 3500. |
| | Earliest documented cover: Dec. 21, 1922 | | |

**1921. GEORGE WASHINGTON ISSUE** Rotary press, stamp design 19 1/2 to 20mm wide by 22mm high, *unwatermarked, perforated 11,* no breaker bar ridges.

416, 417

| 416 | | UnFVF | UseFVF |
|---|---|---|---|
| 1¢ | green | 120. | 130. |
| | On cover | | 1800. |
| | Plate block of 4 | 900. | |
| | Plate block of 4, w/star | 950. | |
| | Plate block of 4, w/"S 30" | 850. | |
| | Earliest documented cover: (June 25, 1921) | | |

| 417 | | UnFVF | UseFVF |
|---|---|---|---|
| 2¢ | carmine, Type III | 85.00 | 115. |
| | On cover | | 700. |
| | Plate block of 4 | 700. | |
| | Plate block of 4, w/star | 725. | |
| | Plate block of 4, w/"S 30" | 675. | |
| | Recut in hair | 120. | |
| | v. Perforated 10 on left side | — | |
| | Earliest documented cover: (May 5, 1921) | | |

**1922-26. NATHAN HALE ISSUE** Some of the denominations were produced, in part, with what are known as "Star Plates". On these particular plates the vertical rows are spaced 3mm apart instead of 2 3/4mm in an effort to improve the perforating. The plates are identified with a large 5-point or 6-point star placed with the plate number. *Flat plate printing, unwatermarked, perforated 11.*

418 *Nathan Hale from a statue by Bela Lyon Pratt, Yale Campus. Hale, a 21-year -old captain in the Continental Army, in 1776 volunteered for spy duty behind the British lines on Long Island. Captured by the British on Sept. 21, he was hanged the next morning. His last words were: "I only regret that I have but one life to lose for my country."*

| 418 | | UnFVF | UseFVF |
|---|---|---|---|
| 1/2¢ | olive brown | .25 | .20 |
| | dark olive brown | .25 | .20 |
| | dull olive brown | .25 | .20 |
| | Plate block of 6 | 4.50 | |
| | Plate flaw on fraction bar | .75 | .20 |
| | FDC *(April 4, 1925)* (Washington D.C.) | | 18.00 |
| | FDC (New Haven) | | 25.00 |

**1923. BENJAMIN FRANKLIN ISSUE**

419 *Benjamin Franklin*

| 419 | | UnFVF | UseFVF |
|---|---|---|---|
| 1¢ | green | 1.45 | .20 |
| | dark green | 1.45 | .20 |
| | dull green | 1.45 | .20 |
| | Plate block of 6 | 17.50 | |
| | Double transfer | 3.50 | |
| | n. Booklet pane of 6 | 7.00 | |
| | Earliest documented cover: (Jan. 10, 1924) | | |
| | FDC *(Jan. 17, 1923)* FDC (Washington D.C.) | | 30.00 |
| | FDC (Philadelphia) | | 47.50 |

**1925. WARREN HARDING ISSUE**

420 *Warren Harding*

| 420 | | UnFVF | UseFVF |
|---|---|---|---|
| 1-1/2¢ | yellow brown | 2.75 | .25 |
| | brown | 2.75 | .25 |
| | dull yellow brown | 2.75 | .25 |
| | Plate block of 6 | 25.00 | |
| | Double transfer | — | |
| | FDC *(March 19, 1925)* | | 30.00 |

**1923. GEORGE WASHINGTON TYPE I ISSUE**

421 *George Washington. Type I has thin hair lines at top center of head.*

| 421 | | UnFVF | UseFVF |
|---|---|---|---|
| 2¢ | carmine, Type I | 1.75 | .20 |
| | Plate block of 6 | 17.50 | |
| | Plate block of 6, w/small 5- point star (top only) | 450. | |
| | Plate block of 6, w/large 5- point star (top only) | 550. | |
| | Plate block of 6, w/large 5- point star (side only) | 60.00 | |
| | Plate block of 6, w/large 6- point star (top only) | 700. | |
| | Plate block of 6, w/large 6- point star (side only) | 850. | |
| | Double transfer | 2.50 | .75 |
| | n. Booklet pane of 6 | 8.50 | 1.00 |
| | v. Horizontal pair, imperforate vertically | 200. | |
| | v1. Vertical pair, imperforate horizontally | 500. | |
| | v2. Perforated 10 at bottom | — | |
| | v3. Perforated 10 at top | — | |
| | Earliest documented cover: (Feb. 10, 1923) | | |
| | FDC *(Jan. 15, 1923)* | | 42.50 |

## 1923. ABRAHAM LINCOLN ISSUE

422 Abraham Lincoln

| 422 | | UnFVF | UseFVF |
|---|---|---|---|
| 3¢ | **reddish violet** | 17.50 | 1.25 |
| | bright violet | 17.50 | 1.25 |
| | dark violet | 17.50 | 1.25 |
| | violet | 17.50 | 1.25 |
| | Plate block of 6 | 125. | |
| | FDC (Feb. 12, 1923) (Washington D.C.) | | 35.00 |
| | FDC (Hodgeville, Ky.) | | 300. |

## 1923. MARTHA WASHINGTON ISSUE

423 Martha Washington

| 423 | | UnFVF | UseFVF |
|---|---|---|---|
| 4¢ | **yellow brown** | 17.50 | .20 |
| | brown | 17.50 | .20 |
| | Plate block of 6 | 130. | |
| | Double transfer | — | |
| | v.   Perforated 10 at bottom | 420. | |
| | v1. Perforated 10 at top | 420. | |
| | v2. Horizontal pair, imperforate between | — | |
| | v3. Vertical pair, imperforate horizontally | — | |
| | FDC (Jan. 15, 1923) | | 70.00 |

## 1922. THEODORE ROOSEVELT ISSUE

424 Theodore Roosevelt

| 424 | | UnFVF | UseFVF |
|---|---|---|---|
| 5¢ | **Prussian blue** | 17.50 | .20 |
| | Plate block of 6 | 145. | |
| | Double transfer | — | |
| | v.   Horizontal pair, imperforate vertically | 1500. | |
| | v1. Pair, imperforate | 1600. | |
| | v2. Perforated 10 at bottom | — | 450. |
| | v3. Perforated 10 at top | — | 450. |
| | FDC (Oct. 27, 1922) (Washington D.C.) | | 150. |
| | FDC (N.Y.) | | 200. |
| | FDC (Oyster Bay) | | 1350. |

## 1922. JAMES GARFIELD ISSUE

425 James Garfield

| 425 | | UnFVF | UseFVF |
|---|---|---|---|
| 6¢ | **red orange** | 32.50 | .85 |
| | dull red orange | 32.50 | .85 |
| | Plate block of 6 | 300. | |
| | Double transfer | 50.00 | 1.75 |
| | Double transfer, recut | 50.00 | 1.75 |
| | FDC (Nov. 20, 1922) | | 250. |

## 1923. WILLIAM McKINLEY ISSUE

426 William McKinley

| 426 | | UnFVF | UseFVF |
|---|---|---|---|
| 7¢ | **black** | 8.00 | .75 |
| | gray black | 8.00 | .75 |
| | Plate block of 6 | 55.00 | |
| | Double transfer | — | |
| | FDC (May 21, 1923) (Washington D.C.) | | 175. |
| | FDC (Niles, Oh.) | | 250. |

## 1923. ULYSSES S. GRANT ISSUE

427 Ulysses S. Grant

| 427 | | UnFVF | UseFVF |
|---|---|---|---|
| 8¢ | **yellow olive** | 42.50 | .85 |
| | dull yellow olive | 42.50 | .85 |
| | Plate block of 6 | 550. | |
| | Double transfer | — | |
| | FDC (May 1, 1923) | | 210. |

## 1923. THOMAS JEFFERSON ISSUE

428 Thomas Jefferson

| 428 | | UnFVF | UseFVF |
|---|---|---|---|
| 9¢ | **carmine rose** | 16.50 | 1.25 |
| | dull carmine rose | 16.50 | 1.25 |
| | Plate block of 6 | 150. | |
| | Double transfer | — | |
| | FDC (Jan. 15, 1923) | | 210. |

## 1923. JAMES MONROE ISSUE

429 James Monroe

| 429 | | UnFVF | UseFVF |
|---|---|---|---|
| 10¢ | **orange yellow** | 22.50 | .25 |
| | dull orange yellow | 22.50 | .25 |
| | Plate block of 6 | 150. | |
| | v.   Pair, imperforate | 1350. | |
| | v1. Vertical pair, imperforate horizontally | 750. | |
| | v2. Perforated 10 at bottom | — | 750. |
| | v3. Perforated 10 at top | — | 750. |
| | FDC (Jan. 15, 1923) | | 190. |

## 1922. RUTHERFORD B. HAYES ISSUE

*Rutherford B. Hayes*

| 430 | | UnFVF | UseFVF |
|---|---|---|---|
| 11¢ | **turquoise blue** | 1.50 | .50 |
| | dull bluish green | 1.50 | .50 |
| | dull yellowish green | 1.50 | .50 |
| | greenish blue | 1.50 | .50 |
| | Plate block of 6 | 24.00 | |
| | v. Pair, imperforate | — | |
| | FDC *(Oct. 4, 1922)* (Washington D.C.) | | 650. |
| | FDC (Freemont, Oh.) | | 2000. |

*No. 430 is known ina wide range of color shades, between yellow, green, and light blue.*

## 1923. GROVER CLEVELAND ISSUE

*431 Grover Cleveland*

| 431 | | UnFVF | UseFVF |
|---|---|---|---|
| 12¢ | **maroon** | 7.50 | .25 |
| | deep maroon | 7.50 | .25 |
| | Plate block of 6 | 80.00 | |
| | Plate block of 6, w/large 5- point star (side only) | 125. | |
| | Plate block of 6, w/large 6-po int star (side only) | 250. | |
| | Double transfer | 12.50 | 1.00 |
| | v. Horizontal pair, imperforate vertically | 1000. | |
| | v1. Pair, imperforate | — | |
| | FDC *(March 20, 1923)* (Washington D.C.) | | 210. |
| | FDC (Boston, Mass.) | | 210. |
| | FDC (Caldwell, N.J.) | | 240. |

## 1926. BENJAMIN HARRISON ISSUE

*432 Benjamin Harrison*

| 432 | | UnFVF | UseFVF |
|---|---|---|---|
| 13¢ | **green** | 14.00 | .65 |
| | dull green | 14.00 | .65 |
| | Plate block of 6 | 130. | |
| | Plate block of 6, w/large 5- point star | 1950. | |
| | FDC *(Jan. 11, 1926)* (Washington D.C.) | | 25.00 |
| | FDC (Indianapolis, Ind.) | | 35.00 |
| | FDC (North Bend Ind.) | | 175. |

## 1923. AMERICAN INDIAN ISSUE

*433 American Indian from a photograph of Chief Hollowhorn Bear of the Brule Sioux tribe, taken on his visit to Washington for the inauguration of Theodore Roosevelt.*

| 433 | | UnFVF | UseFVF |
|---|---|---|---|
| 14¢ | **blue** | 4.75 | .80 |
| | Plate block of 6 | 130. | |
| | Double transfer | — | |
| | FDC *(May 1, 1923)* (Washington D.C.) | | 450. |
| | FDC (Muskogee, Okla.) | | 1800. |

## 1922. STATUE OF LIBERTY ISSUE

*434 Statue of Liberty*

| 434 | | UnFVF | UseFVF |
|---|---|---|---|
| 15¢ | **gray black** | 22.50 | .20 |
| | light gray black | 22.50 | .20 |
| | Plate block of 6 | 225. | |
| | Plate block of 6, w/large 5- point star (side only) | 450. | |
| | FDC *(Nov. 11, 1922)* | | 600. |

## 1925. WOODROW WILSON ISSUE

*435 Woodrow Wilson*

| 435 | | UnFVF | UseFVF |
|---|---|---|---|
| 17¢ | **black** | 17.50 | .35 |
| | gray black | 17.50 | .35 |
| | Plate block of 6 | 170. | |
| | FDC *(Dec. 28, 1925)* (w/o cachet) | | 30.00 |
| | FDC (w/cachet) | | 275. |

## 1923. GOLDEN GATE ISSUE

*436 Golden Gate*

| 436 | | UnFVF | UseFVF |
|---|---|---|---|
| 20¢ | **carmine red** | 22.50 | .20 |
| | dark carmine red | 22.50 | .20 |
| | Plate block of 6 | 220. | |
| | Plate block of 6, w/large 5- point star (side only) | 425. | |
| | v. Horizontal pair, imperforate vertically | 2250. | |
| | FDC *(May 1, 1923)* (Washington D.C.) | | 550. |
| | FDC (San Francisco, Calif.) | | 3500. |
| | FDC (Oakland, Calif.) | | 7250. |

## 1922. NIAGARA FALLS ISSUE

*437 Niagra Falls*

| 437 | | UnFVF | UseFVF |
|---|---|---|---|
| 25¢ | **green** | 17.50 | .75 |
| | yellow green | 17.50 | .75 |
| | Plate block of 6 | 175. | |
| | Double transfer | — | |
| | v. Perforated 10 at bottom | — | |
| | v1. Perforated 10 at top | — | |
| | v2. Vertical pair, imperforate horizontally | 1000. | |
| | FDC *(Nov. 11, 1922)* | | 700. |

# Identifier of the 1922-32 Regular Issues

| Frame | Perf. 11 | Perf. 11 x 10 | Perf . 10 | Coil 10 | Perf. 11 x 10 1/2 or 10 1/2 x 11 | Imperf. |
|---|---|---|---|---|---|---|
|  | 418-434, 448-449 | 446, 447 | 450-460 | 461-471, 520, 522 | 473-489, 517, 519 | 443-445 472 |
|  | 435-442 | | | | 490-494 | |

## 1923. Bison Issue

438 Bison

| 438 | | UnFVF | UseFVF |
|---|---|---|---|
| 30¢ | **olive brown** | 32.50 | .50 |
| | Plate block of 6 | 220. | |
| | Double transfer | 50.00 | 2.00 |
| | FDC *(March 20, 1923)* | | 900. |

## 1922. Arlington Issue

439 Arlington

| 439 | | UnFVF | UseFVF |
|---|---|---|---|
| 50¢ | **gray lilac** | 55.00 | .20 |
| | dull gray lilac | 55.00 | .20 |
| | Plate block of 6 | 625. | |
| | FDC *(Nov. 11, 1922)* | | 1500. |

## 1923. Lincoln Memorial Issue

440 Lincoln Memorial

| 440 | | UnFVF | UseFVF |
|---|---|---|---|
| $1 | **purple brown** | 45.00 | .50 |
| | purple black | 45.00 | .50 |
| | Plate block of 6 | 350. | |

| 440 | | UnFVF | UseFVF |
|---|---|---|---|
| | Double transfer | 85.00 | 1.00 |
| | Margin block of 4, w/arrow | 175. | |
| | FDC *(Feb. 12, 1923)* (Washington D.C.) | | 6000. |
| | FDC (Springfield, Ill.) | | 6500. |

## 1923. U. S. Capitol Issue

441 U.S. Capitol

| 441 | | UnFVF | UseFVF |
|---|---|---|---|
| $2 | **blue** | 100. | 10.00 |
| | Plate block of 6 | 800. | |
| | Margin block of 4, w/arrow | 400. | |
| | FDC *(March 20, 1923)* | | 17500. |

## 1923. Head of Freedom Issue

442 Head of Freedom

| 442 | | UnFVF | UseFVF |
|---|---|---|---|
| $5 | **carmine & blue** | 200. | 13.50 |
| | lilac carmine & dark blue | 200. | 13.50 |
| | Plate block of 8, w/arrow & two plate numbers | 2150. | |
| | Center line block | 850. | |
| | Margin block of 4, w/arrow | 825. | |
| | FDC *(March 20, 1923)* | | 32500. |

**1923. ISSUE.** Imperforate

| 443 | | UnFVF | UseFVF |
|---|---|---|---|
| 1¢ | **green** | 7.50 | 4.50 |
| | dark green | | 4.50 |
| | dull green | 7.50 | 4.50 |
| | Plate block of 6 | 70.00 | |
| | Center line block | 40.00 | |
| | Margin block of 4, w/arrow | 35.00 | |
| | FDC (March 16, 1923) | | |

| 444 | | UnFVF | UseFVF |
|---|---|---|---|
| 1-1/2¢ | **yellow brown** | 1.50 | 1.45 |
| | brown | 1.50 | 1.45 |
| | Plate block of 6 | 17.50 | |
| | CEnter line block | 10.50 | |
| | Margin block of 4, w/arrow | 7.00 | |
| | Double transfer | — | |
| | FDC (April 4, 1925) | | 50.00 |

*No. 444 exists in a rotary press printing, No. 472.*

| 445 | | UnFVF | UseFVF |
|---|---|---|---|
| 2¢ | **carmine** | 1.50 | 1.45 |
| | dark carmine | 1.50 | 1.45 |
| | dull carmine | 1.50 | 1.45 |
| | Plate block of 6 | 25.00 | |
| | Plate block of 6, w/large 5- point star | 70.00 | |
| | Center line block | 12.50 | |
| | Margin block of 4, w/arrow | 7.50 | |
| | FDC (March 20, 1923) | | |

**1923-24. ROTARY PRESS PRINTINGS** from coil waste, no breaker bar ridges on back of stamps, designs 19 1/2 to 20mm wide by 22mm high, *unwatermarked, perforated 11 x 10.*

| 446 | | UnFVF | UseFVF |
|---|---|---|---|
| 1¢ | **green** | 70.00 | 110. |
| | Plate block of 4, w/star | 700. | |
| | *Earliest documented cover: March 26, 1924* | | |

| 447 | | UnFVF | UseFVF |
|---|---|---|---|
| 2¢ | **carmine** | 55.00 | 100. |
| | dark carmine | 55.00 | 100. |
| | Plate block of 4, w/star | 375. | |
| | Recut in eye | 90.00 | 125. |
| | *Earliest documented cover: Feb. 20, 1923* | | |

**1923-24. AMERICANA SERIES ROTARY PRESS PRINTINGS** Perforated 11

| 448 | | UnFVF | UseFVF |
|---|---|---|---|
| 1¢ | **green** | 15000. | 4000. |
| | dark green | 15000. | 4000. |
| | dull green | 15000. | 4000. |
| | *Earliest documented cover: March 25, 1924* | | |

| 449 | | UnFVF | UseFVF |
|---|---|---|---|
| 2¢ | **carmine** | 185. | 235. |
| | Plate block of 4, w/star | 1750. | |
| | Recut in eye | — | |
| | *Earliest documented cover: Nov. 17, 1923* | | |

*Nos. 448 and 449 were made from coil waste. Design 18 1/2 to 19mm wide by 22 1/2 high.*

| 449A | | UnFVF | UseFVF |
|---|---|---|---|
| 1¢ | **green** | — | 42500. |

**1923-26. AMERICANA SERIES ROTARY PRESS PRINTING ISSUE** breaker bar ridges on backs of stamps, designs 18 1/2mm to 19mm wide by 22 1/2mm high, *unwatermarked, perforated 10.*

| 450 | | UnFVF | UseFVF |
|---|---|---|---|
| 1¢ | **green** | 7.50 | 1.00 |
| | light green | 7.50 | 1.00 |
| | yellow green | 7.50 | 1.00 |
| | Plate block of 4 | 75.00 | |
| | FDC (Oct. 17, 1923) | | 70.00 |

| 451 | | UnFVF | UseFVF |
|---|---|---|---|
| 1-1/2¢ | **yellow brown** | 3.75 | 1.00 |
| | dark brown | 3.75 | 1.00 |
| | Plate block of 4 | 30.00 | |
| | Gutter pair, Horizontal or vertical | 150. | |
| | FDC (March 19, 1925) | | 45.00 |

| 452 | | UnFVF | UseFVF |
|---|---|---|---|
| 2¢ | **carmine** | 2.00 | .35 |
| | Plate block of 4 | 17.50 | |
| | n. Booklet pane of 6 (Aug. 27, 1926) | 75.00 | |
| | FDC (April 1924) | | 1400. |

| 453 | | UnFVF | UseFVF |
|---|---|---|---|
| 3¢ | **reddish violet** | 20.00 | 2.50 |
| | Plate block of 4 | 170. | |
| | FDC (Aug. 1, 1925) | | 60.00 |

| 454 | | UnFVF | UseFVF |
|---|---|---|---|
| 4¢ | **yellow brown** | 14.00 | .80 |
| | dark yellow brown | 14.00 | .80 |
| | Plate block of 4 | 125. | |
| | FDC (April 4, 1925) | | 60.00 |

| 455 | | UnFVF | UseFVF |
|---|---|---|---|
| 5¢ | **blue** | 14.00 | .80 |
| | deep blue | 14.00 | .80 |
| | Plate block of 4 | 120. | |
| | Double transfer | — | |
| | v. Horizontal pair, imperforate vertically | — | |
| | FDC (April 4, 1925) | | 65.00 |

| 456 | | UnFVF | UseFVF |
|---|---|---|---|
| 6¢ | **orange** | 6.25 | .75 |
| | dull orange | 6.25 | .75 |
| | Plate block of 4 | 60.00 | |
| | FDC (April 4, 1925) | | 65.00 |

| 457 | | UnFVF | UseFVF |
|---|---|---|---|
| 7¢ | **black** | 9.00 | 6.50 |
| | Plate block of 4 | 65.00 | |
| | FDC (May 29, 1926) | | 70.00 |

| 458 | | UnFVF | UseFVF |
|---|---|---|---|
| 8¢ | **yellow olive** | 20.00 | 4.00 |
| | pale yellow olive | 20.00 | 4.00 |
| | Plate block of 4 | 150. | |
| | FDC (May 29, 1926) | | 80.00 |

| 459 | | UnFVF | UseFVF |
|---|---|---|---|
| 9¢ | **red** | 4.25 | 2.50 |
| | Plate block of 4 | 32.50 | |
| | FDC (May 29, 1926) | | 80.00 |

| 460 | | UnFVF | UseFVF |
|---|---|---|---|
| 10¢ | **orange yellow** | 50.00 | .45 |
| | Plate block of 4 | 325. | |
| | FDC (June 8, 1925) | | 100. |

**1923-26. AMERICANA SERIES ROTARY PRESS COIL ISSUE**
Designs 19 1/2 to 20mm wide by 22 1/4mm high, *perforated 10 vertically.*

| 461 | | UnFVF | UseFVF |
|---|---|---|---|
| 1¢ | **yellow green** | .35 | .20 |
| | green | .35 | .20 |
| | Pair | .75 | .20 |
| | Line pair | 2.00 | .25 |
| | Double transfer | 2.50 | .75 |
| | Gripper cracks | 2.50 | .75 |
| | FDC (July 18, 1923) | | 550. |

| 462 | | UnFVF | UseFVF |
|---|---|---|---|
| 1-1/2¢ | **yellow brown** | .75 | .20 |
| | dark brown | .75 | .20 |
| | Pair | 2.00 | .25 |
| | Line pair | 6.00 | .50 |
| | FDC (March 19, 1925) | | 55.00 |

*463 George Washington*

*463 Type II. There are three heavy hair lines at the top center of the head.*

| 463 | | UnFVF | UseFVF |
|---|---|---|---|
| 2¢ | **carmine,** Type I | .45 | .20 |
| | dark carmine | .45 | .20 |
| | Pair | .75 | .20 |
| | Line pair | 2.00 | .25 |
| | Line pair, 1 each Type I & Type II | 625. | |
| | Double transfer | 1.75 | .50 |
| | Gripper cracks | 2.00 | 1.75 |
| | v. carmine, Type II (599A) | 115. | 12.50 |
| | dark carmine | 115. | 12.50 |
| | Pair | — | |
| | Line pair | 525. | |
| | FDC *(Jan. 10, 1923)* | | 2000. |

| 464 | | UnFVF | UseFVF |
|---|---|---|---|
| 3¢ | **reddish violet** | 5.50 | .30 |
| | dark violet | 5.50 | .30 |
| | Pair | 12.50 | .50 |
| | Line pair | 30.00 | 1.00 |
| | Cracked plate | — | |
| | FDC *(May 10, 1924)* | | 125. |

| 465 | | UnFVF | UseFVF |
|---|---|---|---|
| 4¢ | **yellow brown** | 3.75 | .50 |
| | brown | 3.75 | .50 |
| | Pair | 9.00 | 1.00 |
| | Line pair | 35.00 | 2.75 |

| 466 | | UnFVF | UseFVF |
|---|---|---|---|
| 5¢ | **blue** | 1.75 | .20 |
| | Pair | 3.50 | .40 |
| | Line pair | 12.50 | .60 |
| | FDC *(March 5, 1924)* | | 100. |

| 467 | | UnFVF | UseFVF |
|---|---|---|---|
| 6¢ | **orange** | 9.50 | .35 |
| | Pair | 22.50 | .50 |
| | Line pair | 50.00 | 2.50 |
| | FDC *(Aug. 18, 1932)* | | |

| 468 | | UnFVF | UseFVF |
|---|---|---|---|
| 10¢ | **orange yellow** | 3.50 | .20 |
| | Pair | 7.50 | .25 |
| | Line pair | 22.50 | 1.00 |
| | FDC *(Dec. 1, 1924)* | | 110. |

**1924. AMERICANA SERIES ROTARY COIL ISSUE**
*Designs 18 1/2 to 19mm wide by 22 1/2mm high, perforated 10 horizontally.*

| 469 | | UnFVF | UseFVF |
|---|---|---|---|
| 1¢ | **yellow green** | .35 | .20 |
| | green | .35 | .20 |
| | Pair | .75 | .25 |
| | Line pair | 3.00 | .50 |
| | FDC *(July 19, 1924)* | | 90.00 |

| 470 | | UnFVF | UseFVF |
|---|---|---|---|
| 1-1/2¢ | **yellow brown** | .35 | .20 |
| | brown | .35 | .20 |
| | Pair | .75 | .25 |
| | Line pair | 3.00 | .50 |
| | FDC *(May 9, 1925)* | | 75.00 |

| 471 | | UnFVF | UseFVF |
|---|---|---|---|
| 2¢ | **carmine** | .35 | .20 |
| | Pair | .75 | .25 |
| | Line pair | 2.00 | |
| | Cracked plate | 5.00 | 2.00 |
| | FDC *(Dec. 31, 1923)* | | 125. |

**1926. AMERICANA SERIES ROTARY COIL ISSUE** Imperforate
Design 18 1/2 to 19mm wide by 22 1/2mm high. Most of these stamps show the breaker bars on the back, but there was a printing of this stamp that did not have them. The stamp was issued in sheets of 400, with both vertical and horizontal gutters.

| 472 | | UnFVF | UseFVF |
|---|---|---|---|
| 1-1/2¢ | **yellow brown** | 2.25 | 2.00 |
| | brown | 2.25 | 2.00 |
| | Plate block of 4 | 55.00 | |
| | Center block w/crossed gutters & dashes | 20.00 | 22.50 |
| | Gutter block of 4 | 8.50 | 9.50 |
| | Margin block, w/dash | 9.50 | 13.50 |
| | Without gum breaker ridges | 2.50 | |
| | Gutter pair, vertical or horizontal | — | |
| | FDC *(Aug. 27, 1926)* | | 50.00 |

**1926-34. AMERICANA SERIES ROTARY PRESS ISSUE** Designs 18 1/2 to 19mm wide by 22 1/2mm high, breaker bar ridges on back of stamps, *unwatermarked, perforated 11 x 10 1/2.*

| 473 | | UnFVF | UseFVF |
|---|---|---|---|
| 1/2¢ | **olive brown** | .25 | .20 |
| | Plate block of 4 | 1.50 | |
| | Damaged plate | 1.35 | |
| | Gutter pair | 125. | |
| | Retouched plate | 1.35 | |
| | FDC *(May 25, 1929)* | | 30.00 |

| 474 | | UnFVF | UseFVF |
|---|---|---|---|
| 1¢ | **green** | .25 | .20 |
| | yellow green | .25 | .20 |
| | Plate block of 4 | 2.00 | |
| | FDC *(June 10, 1927)* | | 3500. |
| | Cracked plate | — | |
| | Gutter pair | 135. | |
| | n. Booklet pane of 6 (Nov. 2, 1927) | 5.50 | |
| | FDC *(Nov. 2, 1927)* Booklet pane | | 3500. |
| | v. Horizontal pair, imperforate between | — | |
| | v1. Vertical pair, imperforate between | 2650. | — |
| | *Earliest documented cover:* May 24, 1927 | | |

| 475 | | UnFVF | UseFVF |
|---|---|---|---|
| 1-1/2¢ | **yellow brown** | 2.00 | .20 |
| | dark brown | 2.00 | .20 |
| | Plate block of 4 | 70.00 | |
| | FDC *(May 17, 1927)* | | 45.00 |

| 476 | | UnFVF | UseFVF |
|---|---|---|---|
| 2¢ | **carmine red,** Type I | .25 | .20 |
| | lilac carmine | .25 | .20 |
| | Plate (corner) block of 4 | 2.00 | |
| | Plate block (vertical) of 10, w/number opposite 3rd horizontal row, (experimental electric eye plates) | 4.50 | |
| | Margin block of 4, w/electric eye marking | .35 | .25 |
| | Gutter pair | 180. | |
| | n. Booklet pane of 6 | 2.00 | |
| | FDC | | 45.00 |
| | p. Thin (experimental) paper | — | |
| | v. Horizontal pair, imperforate between | 2250. | |
| | v1. Vertical pair, imperforate between | — | |
| | FDC *(Dec. 10, 1926)* w/electric eye marking | | 1300. |

| 476A | | UnFVF | UseFVF |
|---|---|---|---|
| 2¢ | **carmine red,** Type II | 220. | 15.00 |
| | Plate block of 4 | 1800. | |
| | Gutter pair, vertical or horizontal | 1000. | |
| | *Earliest documented cover: (Dec. 19, 1928)* | | |

| 477 | | UnFVF | UseFVF |
|---|---|---|---|
| 3¢ | **reddish violet** | .55 | .20 |
| | Plate block of 4 | 8.00 | |
| | v. red violet (re-issue) (Feb. 7, 1934) (635a) | .25 | .20 |

| 477 | | UnFVF | UseFVF |
|---|---|---|---|
| | Plate block of 4 | 4.75 | |
| | Gripper cracks | 3.00 | |
| | FDC *(Feb. 3, 1927)* | | 47.50 |

| 478 | | UnFVF | UseFVF |
|---|---|---|---|
| 4¢ | **yellow brown** | 2.75 | .20 |
| | dark brown | 2.75 | .20 |
| | Plate block of 4 | 70.00 | |
| | Gutter pair | 200. | |
| | FDC *(May 17, 1927)* | | 55.00 |

| 479 | | UnFVF | UseFVF |
|---|---|---|---|
| 5¢ | **blue** | 2.25 | .20 |
| | Plate block of 4 | 15.00 | |
| | Gutter pair | 275. | |
| | Double transfer | — | |
| | FDC *(March 24, 1927)* | | 55.00 |

| 480 | | UnFVF | UseFVF |
|---|---|---|---|
| 6¢ | **orange** | 2.25 | .20 |
| | dull orange | 2.25 | .20 |
| | Plate block of 4 | 15.00 | |
| | Gutter pair, horizontal or vertical | 200. | |
| | FDC *(July 27, 1927)* | | 65.00 |

| 481 | | UnFVF | UseFVF |
|---|---|---|---|
| 7¢ | **black** | 2.25 | .20 |
| | Plate block of 4 | 15.00 | |
| | v. Vertical pair, imperforate between | 125. | 75.00 |
| | v1. Block of 4, imperforate between | 250. | |
| | FDC *(March 24, 1927)* | | 60.00 |

| 482 | | UnFVF | UseFVF |
|---|---|---|---|
| 8¢ | **yellow olive** | 2.25 | .20 |
| | pale yellow olive | 2.25 | .20 |
| | Plate block of 4 | 15.00 | |
| | FDC *(June 10, 1927)* | | 65.00 |

| 483 | | UnFVF | UseFVF |
|---|---|---|---|
| 9¢ | **red** | 2.00 | .20 |
| | orange red | 2.00 | .20 |
| | salmon | 2.00 | .20 |
| | Plate block of 4 | 15.00 | |
| | Gutter pair | — | |
| | v. rose *(May 17, 1927)* | 2.00 | .20 |
| | FDC (1931) | | 65.00 |

| 484 | | UnFVF | UseFVF |
|---|---|---|---|
| 10¢ | **orange yellow** | 4.00 | .20 |
| | Plate block of 4 | 25.00 | |
| | Double transfer | — | |
| | FDC *(Feb. 3, 1927)* | | 90.00 |

| 485 | | UnFVF | UseFVF |
|---|---|---|---|
| 11¢ | **turquoise green** | 2.75 | .20 |
| | Plate block of 4 | 12.50 | |
| | Retouch on forehead | 6.50 | .75 |
| | FDC *(Sept. 4, 1931)* | | 125. |

| 486 | | UnFVF | UseFVF |
|---|---|---|---|
| 12¢ | **brown purple** | 6.00 | .20 |
| | purple brown | 6.00 | .20 |
| | Plate block of 4 | 27.50 | |
| | FDC *(Aug. 25, 1931)* | 125. | |

| 487 | | UnFVF | UseFVF |
|---|---|---|---|
| 13¢ | **yellow green** | 2.25 | .20 |
| | blue green | 2.25 | .20 |
| | pale yellow green | 2.25 | .20 |
| | Plate block of 4 | 14.00 | |
| | Gutter pair | 1.50 | |
| | FDC *(Sept. 4, 1931)* | | 125. |

| 488 | | UnFVF | UseFVF |
|---|---|---|---|
| 14¢ | **blue** | 4.00 | .50 |
| | Plate block of 4 | 20.00 | |
| | FDC *(Sept. 8, 1931)* | | 125. |

| 489 | | UnFVF | UseFVF |
|---|---|---|---|
| 15¢ | **gray black** | 8.00 | .20 |
| | gray | 8.00 | .20 |
| | Plate block of 4 | .35 | |
| | FDC *(Aug. 27, 1931)* | | 140. |

**1931. ROTARY PRESS ISSUE** The designs of the following stamps are horizontal rather than vertical, so perforation measurements are 10 1/2 x 11.

| 490 | | UnFVF | UseFVF |
|---|---|---|---|
| 17¢ | **black** | 5.50 | .20 |
| | Plate block of 4 | 25.00 | |
| | FDC *(July 25, 1931)* (Washington D.C.) | | 450. |
| | FDC (Brooklyn, N.Y.) | | 3000. |

| 491 | | UnFVF | UseFVF |
|---|---|---|---|
| 20¢ | **carmine rose** | 9.50 | .20 |
| | Plate block of 4 | 50.00 | |
| | Double transfer | 20.00 | |
| | FDC *(Sept. 8, 1931)* | | 325. |

| 492 | | UnFVF | UseFVF |
|---|---|---|---|
| 25¢ | **green** | 11.00 | .20 |
| | Plate block of 4 | 50.00 | |
| | FDC *(July 25, 1931)* (Washington D.C.) | | 450. |
| | FDC (Brooklyn, N.Y.) | | 2500. |

| 493 | | UnFVF | UseFVF |
|---|---|---|---|
| 30¢ | **olive brown** | 17.50 | .20 |
| | Plate block of 4 | 85.00 | |
| | Cracked plate | 27.50 | .75 |
| | Retouch in head | 27.50 | .75 |
| | FDC *(Sept. 8, 1931)* | | 325. |

| 494 | | UnFVF | UseFVF |
|---|---|---|---|
| 50¢ | **lilac** | 42.50 | .20 |
| | red lilac | 42.50 | .20 |
| | Plate block of 4 | 200. | |
| | FDC *(Sept. 4, 1931)* | | 450. |

**1929. THE KANSAS AND NEBRASKA OVERPRINTS ISSUE** were issued to help prevent loss by post office burglaries. It was thought that stolen stamps could be traced more easily if they were overprinted. Approximately one year's supply was printed and delivered to the post offices in Kansas and Nebraska, but no further printings were made. The overprinting was done on the regular 1¢ to 10¢ stamps of the 1926-27 designs, *Rotary Press printing, unwatermarked, perforated 11 x 10 1/2.* All denominations were issued.

"Wide spacing pairs" noted below designate vertical pairs where the overprints are 32mm apart rather than 22mm.

Kans.

*495-505 Kansas overprint*

| 495 | | UnFVF | UseFVF |
|---|---|---|---|
| 1¢ | **green** | 2.00 | 1.50 |
| | Plate block of 4 | 30.00 | |
| | Wide spacing pair | 30.00 | |
| | v. Vertical pair, 1 w/out overprint | 300. | |
| | FDC (Washington D.C.) | | 50.00 |
| | FDC (Newton, Kans.) | | 450. |

| 496 | | UnFVF | UseFVF |
|---|---|---|---|
| 1-1/2¢ | **yellow brown** | 3.00 | 2.25 |
| | Plate block of 4 | 40.00 | |
| | Wide spacing pair | 60.00 | |
| | v. Vertical pair, 1 w/out overprint | 325. | |
| | FDC | | 60.00 |

| 497 | | UnFVF | UseFVF |
|---|---|---|---|
| 2¢ | **carmine red** | 3.00 | 1.00 |
| | Plate block of 4 | 35.00 | |
| | Wide spacing pair | 45.00 | |
| | FDC | | 60.00 |

| 498 | | UnFVF | UseFVF |
|---|---|---|---|
| 3¢ | **reddish violet** | 15.00 | 11.00 |
| | Plate block of 4 | 145. | |
| | v. Vertical pair, 1 w/out overprint | 400. | |
| | FDC | | 75.00 |

| 499 | | UnFVF | UseFVF |
|---|---|---|---|
| 4¢ | **yellow brown** | 15.00 | 8.50 |
| | Plate block of 4 | 145. | |
| | v. Vertical pair, 1 w/out overprint | 400. | |
| | FDC | | 100. |

| 500 | | UnFVF | UseFVF |
|---|---|---|---|
| 5¢ | **blue** | 12.50 | 9.00 |
| | Plate block of 4 | 120. | |
| | FDC | | 100. |

| 501 | | UnFVF | UseFVF |
|---|---|---|---|
| 6¢ | **orange** | 25.00 | 15.00 |
| | Plate block of 4 | 325. | |
| | FDC (Washington D.C.) | | 125. |
| | FDC (Newton, Ky.) | | 650. |

| 502 | | UnFVF | UseFVF |
|---|---|---|---|
| 7¢ | **black** | 25.00 | 20.00 |
| | Plate block of 4 | 375. | |
| | v. Vertical pair, 1 w/out overprint | 400. | |
| | FDC | | 150. |

| 503 | | UnFVF | UseFVF |
|---|---|---|---|
| 8¢ | **yellow olive** | 70.00 | 60.00 |
| | Plate block of 4 | 675. | |
| | FDC (Washington D.C.) | | |
| | FDC (Newton, Kans.) | | 650. |

| 504 | | UnFVF | UseFVF |
|---|---|---|---|
| 9¢ | **salmon** | 12.50 | 10.00 |
| | Plate block of 4 | 150. | |
| | FDC | | 150. |

| 505 | | UnFVF | UseFVF |
|---|---|---|---|
| 10¢ | **orange yellow** | 20.00 | 12.50 |
| | Plate block of 4 | 275. | |
| | Gutter pair | — | |
| | FDC | | 200. |

Nebr.

506-516 *Nebraska overprint*

| 506 | | UnFVF | UseFVF |
|---|---|---|---|
| 1¢ | **green** | 2.25 | 2.00 |
| | Plate block of 4 | 30.00 | |
| | Period omitted after "Nebr" | 40.00 | |
| | Wide spacing pair | 35.00 | |
| | v. Vertical pair, 1 w/out overprint | 275. | |
| | FDC (Washington D.C.) | | 50.00 |
| | FDC (Beatrice Nebr.) | | 400. |

| 507 | | UnFVF | UseFVF |
|---|---|---|---|
| 1-1/2¢ | **yellow brown** | 2.25 | 2.00 |
| | Plate block of 4 | 40.00 | |
| | Wide spacing pair | 35.00 | |
| | FDC (Washington D.C.) | | 60.00 |
| | FDC (Hartington, Nebr.) | | 350. |

| 508 | | UnFVF | UseFVF |
|---|---|---|---|
| 2¢ | **carmine red** | 2.25 | 1.00 |
| | Plate block of 4 | 25.00 | |
| | Wide spacing pair | 50.00 | |
| | FDC (Washington D.C.) | | 60.00 |
| | FDC (Auburn, Beatrice or Hartington Nebr.) | | 350. |

| 509 | | UnFVF | UseFVF |
|---|---|---|---|
| 3¢ | **reddish violet** | 11.00 | 8.00 |
| | Plate block of 4 | 120. | |
| | Wide spacing pair | 70.00 | |
| | v. Vertical pair, 1 w/out overprint | 400. | |
| | FDC (Washington D.C.) | | 75.00 |
| | FDC (Beatrice or Hartington Nebr.) | | 350. |

| 510 | | UnFVF | UseFVF |
|---|---|---|---|
| 4¢ | **yellow brown** | 15.00 | 10.00 |
| | Plate block of 4 | 175. | |
| | Wide spacing pair | 110. | |
| | FDC (Washington D.C.) | | 100. |
| | FDC (Beatrice or Hartington Nebr.) | | 350. |

| 511 | | UnFVF | UseFVF |
|---|---|---|---|
| 5¢ | **blue** | 12.50 | 11.50 |
| | Plate block of 4 | 175. | |
| | FDC (Washington D.C.) | | 100. |
| | FDC (Beatrice or Hartington Nebr.) | | 375. |

| 512 | | UnFVF | UseFVF |
|---|---|---|---|
| 6¢ | **orange** | 35.00 | 17.50 |
| | Plate block of 4 | 350. | |
| | FDC | | 125. |

| 513 | | UnFVF | UseFVF |
|---|---|---|---|
| 7¢ | **black** | 18.50 | 12.50 |
| | Plate block of 4 | 225. | |
| | FDC | | 150. |

| 514 | | UnFVF | UseFVF |
|---|---|---|---|
| 8¢ | **yellow olive** | 25.00 | 17.50 |
| | Plate block of 4 | 325. | |
| | Wide spacing pair | 160. | |
| | FDC | | 150. |

| 515 | | UnFVF | UseFVF |
|---|---|---|---|
| 9¢ | **salmon** | 30.00 | 22.50 |
| | Plate block of 4 | 350. | |
| | Wide spacing pair | 140. | |
| | v. Vertical pair, 1 w/out overprint | 600. | |
| | FDC | | 150. |

| 516 | | UnFVF | UseFVF |
|---|---|---|---|
| 10¢ | **orange yellow** | 85.00 | 17.50 |
| | Plate block of 4 | 775. | |
| | FDC | | 200. |

**1930-32. WARREN G. HARDING NEW DESIGN ISSUE** Rotary press printing, *unwatermarked, perforated 11 x 10 1/2.*

517, 520 *Warren G. Harding*

| 517 | | UnFVF | UseFVF |
|---|---|---|---|
| 1-1/2¢ | **yellow brown** | .25 | .20 |
| | dull brown | .25 | .20 |
| | Plate block of 4 | 2.25 | |
| | Gutter pair, horizontal or vertical | 175. | |
| | FDC *(Dec. 1, 1930)* w/o cachet | | 4.50 |
| | FDC w/cachet | | 45.00 |

**1930-32. GEORGE WASHINGTON ISSUE**

518, 521, 523 *George Washington*

**518**

| | | UnFVF | UseFVF |
|---|---|---|---|
| 3¢ | **reddish violet** | .25 | .20 |
| | pale reddish violet | .25 | .20 |
| | Plate block of 4 | 1.25 | |
| | Double transfer | 1.00 | .25 |
| | Gripper cracks | 1.10 | .30 |
| | Recut on nose | 1.75 | .60 |
| | Gutter pair | 2.00 | |
| | n. Booklet pane of 6 (July 25, 1932) | 37.50 | |
| | v. Vertical pair, imperforate between | 300. | |
| | FDC *(June 16, 1932)* | | 7.50 |
| | FDC w/o cachet | | |
| | FDC w/cachet | | 40.00 |
| | FDC Booklet Pane | | 200. |

## 1930-32 WILLIAM H. TAFT ISSUE

519, 522 *William H. Taft*

**519**

| | | UnFVF | UseFVF |
|---|---|---|---|
| 4¢ | **yellow brown** | .90 | .20 |
| | dark brown | .90 | .20 |
| | Plate block of 4 | 11.50 | |
| | Gouge on right "4" | 2.00 | .60 |
| | Recut on right "4" | 2.00 | .60 |
| | Gutter pair | — | |
| | FDC *(June 4, 1930)* w/o cachet | | 6.00 |
| | FDC w/cachet | | 60.00 |

## 1930-32. COIL STAMP ISSUE Coil Stamps. Perforated 10 vertically.

520 *Line pair*

**520**

| | | UnFVF | UseFVF |
|---|---|---|---|
| 1-1/2¢ | **yellow brown** | 1.50 | .20 |
| | Pair | 3.50 | .20 |
| | Line pair | 7.50 | .50 |
| | FDC *(Dec. 1, 1930)* w/o cachet | | 5.00 |
| | FDC w/cachet | | 60.00 |

**521**

| | | UnFVF | UseFVF |
|---|---|---|---|
| 3¢ | **reddish violet** | | .20 |
| | pale violet | 1.75 | .20 |
| | Pair | 4.25 | .50 |
| | Line pair | 5.50 | .60 |
| | Gripper cracks | — | |
| | Recut on nose | — | |
| | Recut around eyes | — | |
| | FDC *(June 24, 1932)* w/o cachet | | 25.00 |
| | FDC w/cachet | | 95.00 |

**522**

| | | UnFVF | UseFVF |
|---|---|---|---|
| 4¢ | **yellow brown** | 2.75 | .75 |
| | Pair | 6.00 | .85 |
| | Line pair | 17.50 | 1.50 |
| | FDC *(Sept. 18, 1930)* w/o cachet | | 15.00 |
| | FDC w/cachet | | 50.00 |

## 1930-32. COIL STAMPS Coil stamps. Perforated 10 horizontally.

**523**

| | | UnFVF | UseFVF |
|---|---|---|---|
| 3¢ | **reddish violet** | 1.00 | .75 |
| | pale violet | 1.00 | .75 |
| | Pair | 3.00 | .80 |
| | Line pair | 4.00 | 1.50 |
| | FDC *(Oct. 12, 1932)* w/o cachet | | 15.00 |
| | FDC w/cachet | | 50.00 |

## 1938-43 Presidential Series

These issues are known as the Presidential Series because all but three of its 32 values feature the portraits of former Presidents of the United States. *The values from 1/2c through 50c are printed by rotary press intaglio and are perforated 11 x 10 1/2. The $1, $2 and $5 values are printed by flat press intaglio, perforated 11.*

### 1938. BENJAMIN FRANKLIN ISSUE

524. *Benjamin Franklin (1706-1790), first Postmaster General appointed by the Continental Congress, began his career as a printer and editor in Philadelphia, where he founded the first circulating library in America, the American Philosophical Society, and the nucleus for the University of Pennsylvania; he invented the Franklin stove, and* made important experiments identifying lightning with electricity. He was deputy postmaster at Philadelphia 1737-53 and then (with William Hunter) postmaster general for the colonies until 1774, greatly expanding and improving postal service. An active patriot, both here and in England, for 20 years before the Revolution, he served in the 2nd Continental Congress, was appointed postmaster general, and aided in drafting the Declaration of Independence, of which he was a signer. Sent to France as a diplomat in 1776, he was enormously popular and successful there. With John Jay and John Adams, he negotiated the peace treaty with Great Britian in 1783. An important member of the Constitutional Convention in 1787, he signed the Constitution without entirely approving it. His last public act was in signing a petition to Congress for the abolition of slavery.

**524**

| | | UnFVF | UseFVF |
|---|---|---|---|
| 1/2¢ | **red orange** | .25 | .20 |
| | Plate block of 4 | .50 | |
| | FDC *(May 19, 1938)* | — | |

### 1938. GEORGE WASHINGTON ISSUE

525. *George Washington, unanimously elected first President, mainly supported the federalist and industrialist policies of Alexander Hamilton (see No. 106) against the states' rights and agrarian theories of Thomas Jefferson (see No. 47). He was criticized for "aristocratic tendencies," for the 1794 Jay's Treaty with Great Britain, and for the excise tax that led to* the Whiskey Rebellion of 1794; he brought the nation power and prestige, put down severe Indian troubles, and effected treaties opening the Mississippi to navigation.

**525**

| | | UnFVF | UseFVF |
|---|---|---|---|
| 1¢ | **green** | .25 | .20 |
| | pale green | .25 | .20 |
| | Plate block of 4 | .50 | |
| | FDC *(April 25, 1938)* | 3.00 | |
| | Gutter pair | — | |
| | n. Booklet pane of 6 | 2.00 | |
| | FDC Booklet Pane | | 15.00 |

### 1938. MARTHA WASHINGTON ISSUE

526. *Martha Washington, wife of the first President, was known as "the prettiest and richest widow in Virginia" when Washington met her in 1758. Married to him in January 1759, she managed his plantations during the Revolution, visited him at Valley Forge and Newburgh, and was a gracious and popular First Lady.*

| 526 | | UnFVF | UseFVF |
|---|---|---|---|
| 1-1/2¢ | **yellow brown** | .25 | .20 |
| | ocher | .25 | .20 |
| | Plate block of 4 | .50 | |
| | Gutter pair, horizontal or vertical | 175. | |
| | v. Horizontal pair, imperforate between | 175. | |
| | z. Tagged | — | |
| | FDC *(May 5, 1938)* | — | |

*No. 526z was produced circa 1955 as a result of experiments conducted by Pitney-Bowes for the Post Office Department. A single copy is known in collector's hands.*

## 1938. JOHN ADAMS ISSUE

527 *John Adams second President (1797-1801), attacked the Stamp Act in 1765, served in the 1st and 2nd Continental Congress, nominated George Washington to command the American forces, helped to draft the Declaration of Independence, and (according to Jefferson) was "the pillar of its support on the floor of Congress." He served as commissioner to France 1777-79, went with John Jay and Benjamin Franklin to England to negotiate the peace treaty, and was first American envoy to the Court of St. James. Serving as Vice President in both of Washington's terms, he was elected President in 1796. He was opposed by the Jefferson faction for the Alien and Sedition Acts, for which he was directly responsible, and by the Hamilton faction for his conciliatory policy toward France, which averted war. Defeated by Jefferson in the election of 1800, he retired to private life in Massachusetts.*

| 527 | | UnFVF | UseFVF |
|---|---|---|---|
| 2¢ | **rose** | .25 | .20 |
| | rose pink | .25 | .20 |
| | Plate block of 4 | .50 | |
| | Plate block of 10 (vertical), with number opposite 3rd horizontal row | 7.50 | |
| | Gutter pair, horizontal or vertical | — | |
| | Recut at top of head | 2.50 | 1.25 |
| | n. Booklet pane of 6 | 6.00 | |
| | p. Thin, translucent paper | — | |
| | FDC *(June 3, 1938)* | | 3.00 |
| | FDC Booklet Pane | | 15.00 |

## 1938. THOMAS JEFFERSON ISSUE

528 *Thomas Jefferson, third President (1801-09), was the chief author of the Declaration of Independence and one of its signers. As a wartime legislator and governor in Virginia, he worked to abolish a landed aristocracy, separate church from state, and establish public schools. Returning to Congress in 1783, he headed the committee debating the peace treaty, devised the American monetary system and laid the basis for later organization of western territories. He was minister to France 1785-89, became first Secretary of State, and was elected Vice President under John Adams. Strongly opposed to Alexander Hamilton, whose policies he felt led toward monarchy, he championed individual liberties, states' rights and an agrarian economy. Tied with Burr for electoral votes in 1800, he was supported by Hamilton and chosen President by the House of Representatives. In his 2 terms he authorized the Louisiana Purchase (CM32-CM36), warred against the Tripolitan pirates (CM178), dispatched the Lewis and Clark and Pike expeditions, and obtained a Congressional act abolishing the importation of slaves. A distinguished scholar, philosopher and patron of the arts, he founded the University of Virginia and greatly influenced the revival of classical architecture in America.*

| 528 | | UnFVF | UseFVF |
|---|---|---|---|
| 3¢ | **violet** | .25 | .20 |
| | Plate block of 4 | .50 | |
| | Plate block of 10 (vertical), with number opposite 3rd horizontal row | .25 | |
| | Gutter pair, horizontal or vertical | 175. | |
| | n. Booklet pane of 6 | 8.50 | |
| | v. Horizontal pair, imperforate between | 1100. | |
| | v1. Pair, imperforate | 2750. | |
| | FDC *(June 16, 1938)* | | 3.00 |
| | FDC Booklet Pane | | 15.00 |

## 1938. JAMES MADISON ISSUE

529 *James Madison, fourth President (1809-17), is known as "the father of the Constitution." A Virginian identified with Jefferson's liberal reforms there, he joined with Hamilton in proposing the Constitutional Convention, acted as recorder of the procedings, took a large part in framing the Constitution, greatly aided its ratification and proposed the first 10 amendments: The Bill of Rights. Criticized as inept in his leadership in the War of 1812, he successfully advocated a protective tariff, a strong military organization and a national system of roads and canals.*

| 529 | | UnFVF | UseFVF |
|---|---|---|---|
| 4¢ | **bright purple** | 1.15 | .20 |
| | rose lilac | 1.15 | .20 |
| | Plate block of 4 | 4.50 | |
| | FDC *(July 1, 1938)* | | 3.00 |

## 1938. WHITE HOUSE ISSUE  1938-43 Presidential Series

530 *The White House*

| 530 | | UnFVF | UseFVF |
|---|---|---|---|
| 4-1/2¢ | **gray** | .25 | .20 |
| | dark gray | .25 | .20 |
| | Plate block of 4 | 1.25 | |
| | FDC *(July 11, 1938)* | | 3.00 |

## 1938. JAMES MONROE ISSUE

531 *James Monroe, fifth President (1817-25), fought in the 3rd Virginia Regiment at Harlem Heights, White Plains, Trenton (where he was wounded), Brandywine, Germantown and Monmouth. He studied law under Jefferson, served in the Continental Congress, 1783-86, and fought the Constitution because he believed it made the federal government too powerful. As a senator, he bitterly opposed Washington and Hamilton. As minister to France, he was recalled for over-sympathizing with the French Revolution and failing to follow Washington's instrucitons. Four times governor of Virginia, he was sent back to France in 1803 to aid in negotiating the Louisiana Purchase (CM34). Secretary of State and of War under Madison, he was elected President in 1816, ushering in the "Era of Good Feeling," and re-elected in 1820 with all but one vote, which was given to John Quincy Adams so that only Washington might have the honor of unanimous election. Monroe acquired Florida from Spain, supported the Missouri Compromise, settled the Canadian border and eliminated its forts and proclaimed the Monore Doctrine prohibiting further European colonization or interference in the Americas.*

| 531 | | UnFVF | UseFVF |
|---|---|---|---|
| 5¢ | **light blue** | .25 | .20 |
| | pale blue | .25 | .20 |
| | Plate block of 4 | 1.25 | |
| | Gutter pair | — | |
| | FDC *(July 21, 1938)* | | 3.00 |

## 1938. JOHN QUINCY ADAMS ISSUE

 532 *John Quincy Adams, sixth President (1825-29), was the son of John Adams (No. 527). When appointed Secretary of State by Monroe, he already had seen diplomatic service in France, the Netherlands, Prussia, Russia and England; spent 5 years in the Senate; taught rhetoric at Harvard; and headed the peace commission that negotiated the Treaty of Ghent in 1814. He obtained the cession of Florida from Spain and shared credit with Monroe in formulating the Monroe Doctrine. Running second to Andrew Jackson in the popular vote in 1824, he was elected President by the House of Representatives through the support of Henry Clay (No. 103). As President, he expanded the executive powers, favored internal improvements and refused to build a personal politcal machine. Defeated by Jackson in 1828, he was elected to the House of Representatives in 1831 and served there until his death 17 years later.*

| 532 | | UnFVF | UseFVF |
|---|---|---|---|
| 6¢ | **orange** | .35 | .20 |
| | Plate block of 4 | 1.50 | |
| | FDC *(July 28, 1938)* | | 3.00 |

## 1938. ANDREW JACKSON ISSUE

 533 *Andrew Jackson, seventh President (1829-37), symbolized the common people's rise in power. A frontiersman, military hero (CM173) and senator from Tennessee, he received the largest popular vote in 1824, but was defeated in the House of Representatives when Henry Clay threw his own electoral votes to John Quincy Adams. Elected by a landslide in 1828, Jackson instituted national political conventions and the "spoils system," expanded the President's power, checked federal spending on internal improvements, paid off the national debt and destroyed the priviledged Bank of the United States. Opposed to the states'-rights theories of John Calhoun, he countered South Carolina's refusal to collect protective-tariff duties by sending troops and naval forces to Charleston.*

| 533 | | UnFVF | UseFVF |
|---|---|---|---|
| 7¢ | **sepia** | .45 | .20 |
| | lilac brown | .45 | .20 |
| | Plate block of 4 | 2.00 | |
| | FDC *(Aug. 4, 1938)* | | 3.00 |

## 1938. MARTIN VAN BUREN ISSUE

 534 *Martin Van Buren, eighth President (1837-41), was a senator, governor of New York and Secretary of State and Vice President under Jackson, whose policies he attemped to follow as President. He inaugurated the independent treasury, opposed federal spending for internal improvements and advocated tariffs for revenue only. Alienating the North by his appeasement of the British in a Canadian border incident, and the South by his opposition to the annexation of Texas,*

*he was defeated by William Henry Harrison in the 1840 election, failed to win the Democratic nomination in 1844 and was defeated by Zachary Taylor in 1848.*

| 534 | | UnFVF | UseFVF |
|---|---|---|---|
| 8¢ | **olive green** | .45 | .20 |
| | light olive green | .45 | .20 |
| | olive | .45 | .20 |
| | Plate block of 4 | 2.20 | |
| | FDC *(Aug. 11, 1938)* | | 3.00 |

## 1938. WILLIAM HENRY HARRISON ISSUE

 535 *William Henry Harrison, ninth President (1841), fought in the Battle of Fallen Timbers, served as secretary of the Northwest Territory and as its delegate to Congress, was first governor of the Indiana Territory (CM338), defeated the Indians under Tecumseh at Tippecanoe, defeated the British and Indians in the Battle of the Thames, was a member of both houses of Congress and served briefly as minister to Colombia. After his overwhelming victory in the 1840 election, he died of pneumonia a month after taking office.*

| 535 | | UnFVF | UseFVF |
|---|---|---|---|
| 9¢ | **rose pink** | .50 | .20 |
| | pink | .50 | .20 |
| | Plate block of 4 | 2.25 | |
| | Gutter pair | — | |
| | FDC *(Aug. 18, 1938)* | | 3.00 |

## 1938. JOHN TYLER ISSUE

 536 *John Tyler, 10th President (1841-45), had served as governor of Virginia and as a member of both houses of Congress before his election as Vice President in 1840. As President after Harrison's death, he differed with the Whig Party on constitutional principles and lost his party's support. He signed the Preemption Act enabling settlers to get government land, reorganized the Navy, annexed Texas and settled the boundary between Maine and Canada. Later, in 1861, he was chairman of the unsuccessful peace conference at Washington and remained loyal to Virginia when it seceded.*

| 536 | | UnFVF | UseFVF |
|---|---|---|---|
| 10¢ | **venetian red** | .45 | .20 |
| | dull Venetian red | .45 | .20 |
| | Plate block of 4 | 2.00 | |
| | FDC *(Sept. 2, 1938)* | | 3.00 |

## 1938. JAMES KNOX POLK ISSUE

 537 *James Knox Polk, 11th President (1845-49), served as Speaker of the House and as governor of Tennessee before his highly successful term as President. He fought the spoils system, settled the Oregon boundary dispute by accepting the 49th parallel and giving Vancouver to the British, reduced the tariff, restored the independent treasury system abolished under Tyler and won a war with Mexico. An expansionist but not an imperialist, he approved the acquistion of Texas. New Mexico and California, but opposed retaining Mexico by force.*

| 537 | | UnFVF | UseFVF |
|---|---|---|---|
| 11¢ | **cobalt** | .75 | .15 |
| | Plate block of 4 | 4.25 | |
| | FDC *(Sept. 8, 1938)* | | 5.00 |

## 1938. ZACHARY TAYLOR ISSUE

538 *Zachary Taylor, 12th President (1849-50), came to the White House after a distinguished 40-year Army career in which he gained the nickname "Old Rough and Ready." He fought in the War of 1812, the Black Hawk and Seminole Wars and the Mexican War, which he ended by defeating Santa Anna at Buena Vista in 1847. In his 16 months as President, he resumed the spoils system. A former slave-holder, he worked for California's admission as a free state. He died of typhus in 1850.*

| 538 | | UnFVF | UseFVF |
|---|---|---|---|
| 12¢ | light reddish violet | 1.40 | .20 |
| | Plate block of 4 | 6.00 | |
| | FDC *(Sept. 14, 1938)* | | 5.00 |

## 1938. MILLARD FILLMORE ISSUE

539 *Millard Fillmore, 13th President (1850-53), spent 4 terms in the House of Representatives before his election as Vice President under Taylor. As President he favored the compromise policy in the slavery issue, signed the Fugitive Slave Act, approved the negotiations leading to the opening of Japan (CM363), and maintained neutrality in foreign wars.*

| 539 | | UnFVF | UseFVF |
|---|---|---|---|
| 13¢ | blue green | 2.25 | .20 |
| | dark blue green | 2.25 | .20 |
| | Plate block of 4 | 9.50 | |
| | FDC *(Sept. 22, 1938)* | | 5.00 |

## 1938. FRANKLIN PIERCE ISSUE

540 *Franklin Pierce, 14th President (1853-57), Congressman, Senator and brigadier general in the Mexican War, won the Democratic nomination in 1852 on the 49th ballot. As President, he effected the Gadsden Purchase, sent Matthew Perry to open trade with Japan (CM363), attempted to secure a base in Santo Domingo and annex Cuba, Hawaii and Alaska, and signed the Kansas-Nebraska Bill leaving slavery in those territories to popular vote. Attempting impartiality in domestic policy and imperialism in foreign policy, he generally failed at both and retired to obscurity.*

| 540 | | UnFVF | UseFVF |
|---|---|---|---|
| 14¢ | blue | 1.15 | .20 |
| | Plate block of 4 | 6.00 | |
| | FDC *(Oct. 6, 1938)* | | 5.00 |

## 1938. JAMES BUCHANAN ISSUE

541 *James Buchanan, 15th President (1857-61), had served successively as Congressman, minister to Russia, senator, Secretary of State under Polk and minister to Great Britain. A conservative and ineffective President, he expressed moral opposition to slavery and secession, but furthered one and condoned the other. His administration saw the growth of the new Republican Party, the Lincoln-Douglas debates and the abolitionist John Brown's raid on the federal armory at Harper's*

Ferry, Virginia, for which Brown was hanged. Failing to meet the challenge of South Carolina's secession and her firing on Fort Sumter, Buchanan left the office on the brink of the Civil War.

| 541 | | UnFVF | UseFVF |
|---|---|---|---|
| 15¢ | slate | .65 | .20 |
| | Plate block of 4 | 3.00 | |
| | FDC *(Oct. 13, 1938)* | | 5.00 |

## 1938. ABRAHAM LINCOLN ISSUE

542 *Abraham Lincoln, 16th President (1861-65), worked as a rail-splitter, surveyor and postmaster of Salem, Ill.; served a term in Congress; and became an outstanding jury lawyer before attaining national prominence through a series of debates with Stephen A. Douglas, against whom he was running for the Senate in 1858. Nominated as the Republican Presidential candidate in 1860 because of his conservative views on slavery, his election signaled the secession of 7 Southern states. Given almost dictatorial powers in the Civil War, he followed a middle course between the radicals and defeatists, ably commanding the Union war effort and diplomatically handling his cabinet and his generals. Although he had hoped for a gradual, compensated abolition of slavery, in 1863 he issued the Emancipation Proclamation freeing all slaves in rebel territory. The same year marked his Gettysburg Address (CM320). Re-elected in the dark days of 1864, he made his great Second Inaugural Address; "With malice toward none, with charity for all...let us strive on to finish the work we are in; to bind up the nation's wounds...to do all which may achieve a just and lasting peace." His compassionate program for conciliation and reconstruciton was never achieved. Ten days later, 5 days after Lee's surrender at Appomattox, he was assassinated by a Southern fanatic while attending the theater.*

| 542 | | UnFVF | UseFVF |
|---|---|---|---|
| 16¢ | black | 1.25 | .60 |
| | Plate block of 4 | 6.00 | |
| | FDC *(Oct. 20, 1938)* | | 6.00 |

## 1938. ANDREW JOHNSON ISSUE

543 *Andrew Johnson, 17th President (1865-69), a self-educated tailor, was a Congressman, governor of Tennessee and the only Southern senator to support the Union in the Civil War. His success as military governor of Tennessee led to his election as Vice President. As President after Lincoln's death, he attempted to carry out Lincoln's conciliatory policies of Reconstruction, but was thwarted by the Radical Republicans in Congress. His removal of War Secretary Edwin M. Stanton (No. 101) for conspiracy led to his impeachment, which fell one vote short of the two-thirds majority needed to remove him from the White House. Elected to the Senate again in 1875, he died the same year.*

| 543 | | UnFVF | UseFVF |
|---|---|---|---|
| 17¢ | rose red | 1.25 | .20 |
| | Plate block of 4 | 6.00 | |
| | FDC *(Oct. 27, 1938)* | | 6.00 |

## 1938. ULYSSES S. GRANT

544 *Ulysses S. Grant, 18th President (1869-77), led the Union forces to victory in the Civil War (CM174). As President, he authorized harsh Reconstruction policies that kept sectional hatreds alive, and, although he was personally honest, his administration was involved in grave scandals. His achievements included civil*

service reform and the funding of the national debt. Left penniless by the collapse of a banking house in 1884, he was persuaded by Mark Twain (CM205) to write his "Personal Memoirs," which he finished 4 days before his death in 1885. They realized almost $450,000.

| 544 | | | UnFVF | UseFVF |
|---|---|---|---|---|
| 18¢ | **brown carmine** | | 2.25 | .25 |
| | rose brown | | 2.25 | .25 |
| | Plate block of 4 | | 10.00 | |
| | FDC (Nov. 3, 1938) | | | 6.00 |

### 1938. RUTHERFORD B. HAYES ISSUE

545 Rutherford B. Hayes, 19th President (1877-81), former Congressman and governor of Ohio, ran second to Samuel J. Tilden in the 1876 election, but was chosen President by a partisan electoral commission by a vote of 185-184. His administration returned local government to the South, ending the Reconstruction, and made ineffective attempts at civil service reform.

| 545 | | UnFVF | UseFVF |
|---|---|---|---|
| 19¢ | **light reddish violet** | 2.00 | .60 |
| | Plate block of 4 | 9.50 | |
| | FDC (Nov. 10, 1938) | | 6.00 |

### 1938. JAMES A. GARFIELD ISSUE

546 James A. Garfield, 20th President (1881), Republican leader of the House, was a Senator-elect when chosen President in 1880. Four months after his inauguration, he was fatally shot by a disappointed office-seeker.

| 546 | | UnFVF | UseFVF |
|---|---|---|---|
| 20¢ | **blue green** | 1.25 | .20 |
| | bright blue green | 1.25 | .20 |
| | Plate block of 4 | 5.00 | |
| | FDC (Nov. 10, 1938) | | 6.00 |

### 1938. CHESTER A. ARTHUR ISSUE

547 Chester A. Arthur, 21st President (1881-85), who succeeded to the office after Garfield's assassination, was an able and honest administrator. He supported civil service reform, arranged a canal treaty (unratified) with Nicaragua, vetoed a Chinese-exclusion bill and began the rebuilding of the Navy.

| 547 | | UnFVF | UseFVF |
|---|---|---|---|
| 21¢ | **slate blue** | 2.25 | .20 |
| | Plate block of 4 | 10.00 | |
| | FDC (Nov. 22, 1938) | | 7.00 |

### 1938. GROVER CLEVELAND ISSUE

548 Grover Cleveland, 22nd and 24th President (1885-89 and 1893-97), reform governor of New York, was an honest and independent President. In his first term he enlarged the civil service, followed a conciliatory policy toward the South, avoided the spoils system, opposed pork-barrel pension bills, and vetoed more than two-thirds of the Congressional acts presented to him. Defeated by Benjamin Harrison in 1888, he ran again and was re-elected in 1892. His 2nd term was marked by a severe depression, a fight against inflation, an income tax law (declared unconstitutional), the use of troops to end the mail stoppage in the Pullman strike, and a firm stand against the British use of force in a boundary dispute with Venezuela.

| 548 | | UnFVF | UseFVF |
|---|---|---|---|
| 22¢ | **vermilion** | 1.50 | .75 |
| | Plate block of 4 | 12.50 | |
| | FDC (Nov. 22, 1938) | | 7.00 |

### 1938. BENJAMIN HARRISON ISSUE

549 Benjamin Harrison, 23rd President (1889-93), was a grandson of William Henry Harrison, ninth President. A Union regimental commander in the Civil War and senator for one term, as President he greatly expanded the pension list, signed the McKinley high-tariff bill and the Sherman silver purchase act, followed imperialistic policies in the Pacific, convened the first Pan-American Conference in 1889 and aided the admission to the Union of the Dakotas, Montana and Washington in 1889 and Idaho and Wyoming in 1900.

| 549 | | UnFVF | UseFVF |
|---|---|---|---|
| 24¢ | **gray green** | 4.25 | .35 |
| | Plate block of 4 | 20.00 | |
| | FDC (Dec. 2, 1938) | | 8.00 |

### 1938. WILLIAM MCKINLEY ISSUE

550 William McKinley, 25th President (1897-1901), former Congressman and governor of Ohio, was elected on a platform of high tariff and maintenance of the gold standard; raised the tariff to the highest level in American history and signed the Gold Standard Act of 1900. After the sinking of the Maine at Havana, public opinion forced his intervention in the Cuban rebellion; the resulting Spanish-American War ended in a temporary American protectorate over Cuba, the purchase of the Philippine Islands, the annexation of Puerto Rico and Guam and the establishment of the United States as a world power. His administration also marked the annexation of Hawaii, intervention in China and agitation for a Panama Canal. Re-elected on the "full dinner pail" platform, he was fatally shot by an anarchist the following September while visiting the Pan-American Exposition (CM26-31).

| 550 | | UnFVF | UseFVF |
|---|---|---|---|
| 25¢ | **claret** | 1.20 | .20 |
| | rose lilac | 1.20 | .20 |
| | Plate block of 4 | 5.00 | |
| | FDC (Dec. 2, 1938) | | 8.00 |

### 1938. THEODORE ROOSEVELT ISSUE

551 Theodore Roosevelt, 26th President (1901-09), achieved early fame as Assistant Secretary of the Navy under McKinley, as organizer of the Rough Riders (CM315) in the Spanish-American War and as a crusading governor of New York. Given the Republican vice presidential nomination, "to get him out of the way," upon McKinley's death he became at 43, America's youngest President. He fought government corruption by big business, recognized Panama when it revolted from Colombia, began the construction of the Panama Canal (CM48 and CM198), won the Nobel Peace Prize for his successful mediation of the Russo-Japanese War, organized conservation of national

resources and instituted the Pure Food and Drugs Act. Virtually bequeathing the Presidency to William Howard Taft, he became dissatisfied with Taft's conservative policies and ran against him in 1912, splitting the Republican ticket so that both lost to Woodrow Wilson. He also was noted as a naturalist, explorer and writer.

| 551 | | UnFVF | UseFVF |
|---|---|---|---|
| 30¢ | **deep ultramarine** | 5.00 | .20 |
| | ultramarine | 5.00 | .20 |
| | blue | 15.00 | |
| | deep blue | 110. | |
| | Plate block of 4 | 22.50 | |
| | FDC (Dec. 8, 1938) | | 10.00 |

## 1938. WILLIAM HOWARD TAFT ISSUE

552 William Howard Taft, 27th President (1909-13), had distinguished careers before and after his Presidency. He was a federal judge, Solicitor General under Benjamin Harrison, dean of the University of Cincinnati Law School, president of the Philippines Commission, 1st civil governor of the Philippines, Secretary of War and provisional governor of Cuba. His administraion dissolved the Standard Oil and American Tobacco Company trusts, set up the Department of Labor and drafted the 16th and 17th Amendments (authorizing the income tax and the direct election of Senators). Defeated in 1912, he became a lecturer and Yale law professor. Appointed Chief Justice of the United States in 1919, he served until his death in 1930.

| 552 | | UnFVF | UseFVF |
|---|---|---|---|
| 50¢ | **light red violet** | 8.50 | .20 |
| | Plate block of 4 | 40.00 | |
| | FDC (Dec. 8, 1938) | | 15.00 |

Flat plate printing, perforated 11.

## 1938. WOODROW WILSON ISSUE

553 Woodrow Wilson, 28th President (1913-21), was president of Princeton University and a reform governor of New Jersey before his election in 1912. His first administration instituted the Federal Reserve Act, Farm Loan Act, Federal Trade Commission, Clayton Anti-Trust Act and Adamson Eight-House Law. (His entite tenure saw three Constitutional Amendments: direct election of Senators, prohibition and women's suffrage). In foreign affairs, in his first term he had difficulties with some Latin American countries, sent the Pershing Expedition into Mexico, established partial protectorates in Santo Domingo, Haiti and Nicaragua; and maintained neutrality in World War I despite foreign pressures and the infringement of American rights. Re-elected with the slogan, "He kept us out of war," within a month of his inauguration he was forced by German sinking of American ships to ask for a declaration of war. An apostle of international cooperation, he went to Paris to negotiate the peace treaty, in which he said the League of Nations was the "most essential part." When the Senate rejected both the treaty and the League, he toured the country for public support, suffered a stroke and became an invalid. He won the Nobel Peace Prize in 1919 and died in 1924.

| 553 | | UnFVF | UseFVF |
|---|---|---|---|
| $1 | **dark purple and black** | 10.00 | .20 |
| | Plate block of 4 | 45.00 | |
| | Center line block | 30.00 | |
| | Margin block of 4, w/arrow | 27.50 | |
| | FDC (Aug. 19, 1938) | | 60.00 |

| 553 | | UnFVF | UseFVF |
|---|---|---|---|
| | w. Watermarked "USIR" | 300. | 70.00 |
| | w. Plate block of 4 | 1800. | |
| | FDC (dry print 1954) | | 30.00 |
| | v. Vertical pair, imperforate between | 2750. | |
| | v1. Vertical pair, imperforate horizontally | 1500. | |
| | a. red violet and black Aug. 31, 1954) (dry print) (dry print) | 9.00 | .20 |
| | Plate block of 4 | 40.00 | |
| | av. Vertical pair, imperforate between | 7500. | |
| | av1.Vertical pair, imperforate horizontally | 1000. | |

553a is printed on pre-gummed, whiter and thicker paper. It was printed on "dry" paper; No. 553 was printed on pre-dampened paper.

## 1938. WARREN G. HARDING ISSUE

554 Warren G. Harding, 29th President (1921-23), was an Ohio newspaperman and senator who supported prohibition, anti-strike legislation, women's suffrage and high tariffs; opposed the League of Nations as a threat to national sovereignty. Overwhelmingly elected in 1920 on a "return to normalcy" platform, he worked to repeal excess profits and high income taxes and to revise the tariff. In 1921 he called the Washington Conference to limit naval armaments. Returning from a visit to Alaska in 1923, he died unexpectedly at San Francisco.

| 554 | | UnFVF | UseFVF |
|---|---|---|---|
| $2 | **green and black** | 27.50 | 4.75 |
| | yellow green and black | 27.50 | 4.75 |
| | Plate block of 4 | 135. | |
| | Center line block | — | |
| | Margin block of 4, w/arrow | — | |
| | FDC (Sept. 29, 1938) | | 125. |

## 1938. CALVIN COOLIDGE ISSUE

555 Calvin Coolidge, 30th President (1923-29), attained prominence in 1919, when, as governor of Mass., he suppressed the Boston police strike on the grounds that "there is no right to strike against the public safety." Elected Vice President, he succeeded to the Presidency upon Harding's death. In a period of prosperity, his administration was cautious and passive in domestic affairs and isolationist toward Europe. He opposed the League of Nations, approved the World Court, vetoed the Soldiers' Bonus Act, twice vetoed the Farm Relief Bill, refused to intervene in the coal strike of 1927 and reduced the national debt by $2 billion in 3 years. He declined to run for a 3rd term.

| 555 | | UnFVF | UseFVF |
|---|---|---|---|
| $5 | **carmine and black** | 115. | 4.50 |
| | red brown and black | 200. | — |
| | Plate block of 4 | 500. | |
| | Center line block | — | 12.50 |
| | Margin block of 4, w/arrow | — | |
| | FDC (Nov. 17, 1938) | | 210. |

## 1939 Presidential Series

### 1939. GEORGE WASHINGTON COIL ISSUE

| 556 | | UnFVF | UseFVF |
|---|---|---|---|
| 1¢ | **green** | .25 | .20 |
| | light green | .25 | .20 |
| | Pair | .50 | |
| | Line pair | 1.50 | |
| | FDC (Jan. 10, 1939) | | 5.00 |

## 1939. MARTHA WASHINGTON COIL ISSUE

| 557 | | UnFVF | UseFVF |
|---|---|---|---|
| 1-1/2¢ | **yellow brown** | .25 | .20 |
| | ocher | .25 | .20 |
| | Pair | .50 | |
| | Line pair | 1.50 | |
| | FDC *(Jan. 20, 1939)* | | 5.00 |

## 1939. JOHN ADAMS COIL ISSUE

| 558 | | UnFVF | UseFVF |
|---|---|---|---|
| 2¢ | **rose** | .25 | .20 |
| | Pair | .50 | |
| | Line pair | 1.50 | |
| | FDC *(Jan. 20, 1939)* | | 5.00 |

## 1939. THOMAS JEFFERSON COIL ISSUE

| 559 | | UnFVF | UseFVF |
|---|---|---|---|
| 3¢ | **violet** | .25 | .20 |
| | Pair | .50 | |
| | Line pair | 1.50 | |
| | Gripper cracks | — | |
| | p. Thin, translucent paper | — | |
| | FDC *(Jan. 20, 1939)* | | 5.00 |

## 1939. JAMES MADISON COIL ISSUE

| 560 | | UnFVF | UseFVF |
|---|---|---|---|
| 4¢ | **bright purple** | 7.50 | .75 |
| | Pair | 17.50 | |
| | Line pair | 32.50 | |
| | FDC *(Jan. 20, 1939)* | | 5.00 |

## 1939. THE WHITE HOUSE COIL ISSUE

| 561 | | UnFVF | UseFVF |
|---|---|---|---|
| 4-1/2¢ | **gray** | .75 | .50 |
| | Pair | 1.50 | |
| | Line pair | 5.50 | |
| | FDC *(Jan. 20, 1939)* | | 5.00 |

## 1939. JAMES MONROE COIL ISSUE

| 562 | | UnFVF | UseFVF |
|---|---|---|---|
| 5¢ | **bright blue** | 6.00 | .50 |
| | Pair | 12.50 | |
| | Line pair | 27.50 | |
| | FDC *(Jan. 20, 1939)* | | 5.00 |

## 1939. JOHN QUINCY ADAMS ISSUE

| 563 | | UnFVF | UseFVF |
|---|---|---|---|
| 6¢ | **orange** | 1.25 | .50 |
| | Pair | 2.00 | |
| | Line pair | 7.50 | |
| | FDC *(Jan. 20, 1939)* | | 7.00 |

## 1939. JOHN TYLER ISSUE

| 564 | | UnFVF | UseFVF |
|---|---|---|---|
| 10¢ | **Venetian red** | 12.50 | 1.25 |
| | Pair | 22.50 | |
| | Line pair | 50.00 | |
| | FDC *(Jan. 20, 1939)* | | 10.00 |

## 1939. GEORGE WASHINGTON COIL ISSUE  Perforated 10 horizontally.

| 565 | | UnFVF | UseFVF |
|---|---|---|---|
| 1¢ | **green** | .75 | .25 |
| | Pair | 1.25 | |
| | Line pair | 2.25 | |
| | FDC *(Jan. 27, 1939)* | | 6.00 |

## 1939. MARTHA WASHINGTON COIL ISSUE  Rotary Press, perforated 10 vertically.

| 566 | | UnFVF | UseFVF |
|---|---|---|---|
| 1-1/2¢ | **yellow brown** | 1.50 | .75 |
| | Pair | 4.50 | |
| | Line pair | 2.75 | |
| | FDC *(Jan. 27, 1939)* | | 6.00 |

## 1939. JOHN ADAMS COIL ISSUE

| 567 | | UnFVF | UseFVF |
|---|---|---|---|
| 2¢ | **rose** | 2.50 | .75 |
| | Pair | 6.00 | |
| | Line pair | 4.00 | |
| | FDC *(Jan. 27, 1939)* | | 6.00 |

## 1939. THOMAS JEFFERSON COIL ISSUE

| 568 | | UnFVF | UseFVF |
|---|---|---|---|
| 3¢ | **violet** | 2.25 | .75 |
| | Pair | 6.00 | |
| | Line pair | 4.00 | |
| | FDC *(Jan. 28, 1939)* | | 6.00 |

## 1955. BENJAMIN FRANKLIN ISSUE

569 *Benjamin Franklin*

| 569 | | MNHVF | UseVF |
|---|---|---|---|
| 1/2¢ | **vermillon,** wet paper | .25 | .20 |
| | Plate block of 4 | .50 | |
| | FDC *(Oct. 20, 1955)* | | 1.75 |
| | p. Dry paper *(May 1958)* | .25 | |
| | Plate block of 4 | .50 | |

## 1954. GEORGE WASHINGTON ISSUE

570, 587 *George Washington*

| 570 | | MNHVF | UseVF |
|---|---|---|---|
| 1¢ | **dull green,** wet paper | .25 | .20 |
| | Plate block of 4 | .50 | |
| | Gutter pair | — | |
| | FDC *(Aug. 26, 1954)* | | 1.75 |
| | p. Dry paper *(March 1956)* | .25 | |
| | Plate block of 4 | .50 | |
| | p1.Hi-Brite paper | — | |

## 1956. MOUNT VERNON ISSUE

571 *Mount Vernon, home of George Washington, on the south bank of the Potomac, 16 miles below Washington, D.C. Land was part of the Royal Grant to Lord Culpepper, who in 1674 granted 5,000 acres to Nicolas Spencer and John Washington, great-grandfather of George. Since 1858 preserved and restored by Mount Vernon Ladies Association.*

| 571 | | MNHVF | UseVF |
|---|---|---|---|
| 1-1/2¢ | **brown carmine,** dry paper | .25 | .20 |
| | Plate block of 4 | .50 | |
| | FDC *(Feb. 22, 1956)* | | 1.75 |

## 1954. THOMAS JEFFERSON ISSUE

572, 588 Thomas Jefferson

**572**

| | | MNHVF | UseVF |
|---|---|---|---|
| 2¢ | **rose,** dry paper | .25 | .20 |
| | Plate block of 4 | .50 | |
| | Gutter pair | — | |
| | FDC *(Sept. 15, 1954)* | | 1.75 |
| | p. Silkote paper *(Dec. 1954)* | 1250. | |
| | Plate block of 4 | — | |

*NOTE: These varieties need certificates.*

## 1954. STATUE OF LIBERTY ISSUE

573, 578, 589 *Statue of Liberty*

**573**

| | | MNHVF | UseVF |
|---|---|---|---|
| 3¢ | **violet,** wet paper | .25 | .20 |
| | Plate block of 4 | .50 | |
| | Gutter pair | — | |
| | n. Booklet pane of 6 *(June 30, 1954)* | 4.50 | |
| | nv. Booklet pane of 6, imperforate between vertically | — | |
| | pl. Dry paper *(Sept. 1956)* | .25 | .20 |
| | Plate block of 4 | .50 | |
| | pln. Booklet pane of 6 | 4.50 | |
| | plz. Tagged, Type II *(July 6, 1966)* | .25 | .20 |
| | Plate block of 4 | 5.00 | |
| | plz1. Tagged, Type III | — | |
| | Plate block of 4 | — | |
| | p2. Hi-Brite paper | — | |
| | Plate block of 4 | — | |
| | v. Horizontal pair, imperforate between | 1500. | |
| | v1. Imperforate pair (18 3/4 x 22 1/2mm) | 2000. | |
| | FDC *(June 24, 1954)* | | 1.75 |
| | FDC Booklet Pane | | 5.00 |
| | FDC Tagged | | 30.00 |

*Type II tagging: roll tagging. When continuously surfaced rolls replaced the previously used tagging mats. Only the plate number selvage margin is partially tagged and the plate number blocks have one untagged margin.*

*Type III tagging: curved metal plate tagging. Sheet margins are almost fully tagged but a "hot line" of intense phosphor-tagging or untagged narrow gap, 1mm or less in width, appears on stamps from any position in the pane.*

## 1954. ABRAHAM LINCOLN ISSUE

574, 590 *Abraham Lincoln*

**574**

| | | MNHVF | UseVF |
|---|---|---|---|
| 4¢ | **bright purple,** wet paper | .25 | .20 |
| | Plate block of 4 | .50 | |
| | Gutter pair | — | |
| | n. Booklet pane of 6 (July 31, 1958) | 2.75 | |
| | nv. Booklet pane of 6, imperforate between horizontally | — | |
| | p. Dry paper *(July 1956)* | .25 | .20 |
| | Plate block of 4 | .50 | |
| | Gutter pair | — | |
| | n. Booklet pane of 6 | 2.75 | |

**574**

| | | MNHVF | UseVF |
|---|---|---|---|
| | pz. Tagged, Type I *(Nov. 2, 1963)* | .50 | .45 |
| | Plate block of 4 | .50 | |
| | pz1. Tagged, Type II | .50 | |
| | Plate block of 4 | .50 | |
| | p1. Hi-Brite paper | — | |
| | Plate block of 4 | — | |
| | v. Horizontal pair, imperforate between | 3600. | |
| | FDC *(Nov. 19, 1954)* | | 1.75 |
| | FDC Booklet Pane | | 4.00 |
| | FDC tagged | | 100. |

*Type I tagging; mat tagging. The four separate mats used did not cover the entire sheet of 400 stamps and certain untagged areas help to identify this variety. See expanded definition in the Catalog Introduction.*

## 1954. JAMES MONROE ISSUE

575 *James Monroe*

**575**

| | | MNHVF | UseVF |
|---|---|---|---|
| 5¢ | **blue** | .25 | .20 |
| | Plate block of 4 | .65 | |
| | Gutter pair | — | |
| | FDC *(Dec. 2, 1954)* | | 1.75 |

## 1955. THEODORE ROOSEVELT ISSUE

576 *Theodore Roosevelt*

**576**

| | | MNHVF | UseVF |
|---|---|---|---|
| 6¢ | **rose red,** wet paper | .25 | .20 |
| | Plate block of 4 | 1.75 | |
| | FDC *(Nov. 18, 1955)* | | 1.75 |
| | p. Dry paper *(March 1957)* | .40 | |
| | Plate block of 4 | 1.70 | |

## 1956. WOODROW WILSON ISSUE

577 *Woodrow Wilson Issue*

**577**

| | | MNHVF | UseVF |
|---|---|---|---|
| 7¢ | **carmine red,** dry paper | .25 | .20 |
| | Plate block of 4 | 1.25 | |
| | FDC *(Jan. 10, 1956)* | | 1.75 |
| | p. Hi-Brite paper | — | |
| | Plate block of 4 | — | |

## 1954. STATUE OF LIBERTY ISSUE

**578**

| | | MNHVF | UseVF |
|---|---|---|---|
| 8¢ | **deep blue and carmine** | .25 | .20 |
| | Plate block of 4, both red & blue numbers | 2.00 | |
| | Plate block (corner) of 4, blue number only | — | |
| | Plate block (corner) of 4, red number only | — | |
| | FDC *(April 9, 1954)* | | 1.75 |
| | v. Double impression, carmine | — | |

*This stamp was produced on both flat-bed and rotary presses.*

## Liberty Sheet Stamp Series Booklets

### 1956. THE ALAMO ISSUE

579 The Alamo, called the "Cradle of Texas Liberty," founded in 1718 as Mission de San Antonio de Valero, beseiged in 1836 by Gen. Santa Anna and 1,000 Mexicans; the 184 Texan defenders under Col. William Barrett Travis, including Davy Crockett and James Bowie, fought to the last man. Site is now a historic shrine and museum.

| 579 | | MNHVF | UseVF |
|---|---|---|---|
| 9¢ | **rose lilac** | .25 | .20 |
| | Plate block of 4 | 1.25 | |
| | a.  deep rose lilac | — | |
| | Plate block of 4 | — | |
| | FDC (June 14, 1956) | | 2.00 |

### 1956. INDEPENDENCE HALL ISSUE

580 Independence Hall, where the Declaration of Independence was adopted and which for many years housed the Liberty Bell.

| 580 | | MNHVF | UseVF |
|---|---|---|---|
| 10¢ | **brown purple,** dry paper | .25 | .20 |
| | Plate block of 4 | 1.00 | |
| | FDC Tagged | | 30.00 |
| | a.  deep brown purple | — | |
| | Plate block of 4 | — | |
| | p.  Hi-Brite paper | — | |
| | Plate block of 4 | — | |
| | z.  Tagged, Type II (July 6, 1966) | 2.50 | 1.50 |
| | Plate block of 4 | 60.00 | |
| | z1. Tagged, Type III | — | |
| | Plate block of 4 | — | |
| | FDC (July 4, 1956) | | 2.00 |

### 1956. MONTICELLO ISSUE

581 Monticello, Thomas Jefferson's estate in Virginia.

| 581 | | MNHVF | UseVF |
|---|---|---|---|
| 20¢ | **bright blue** | .50 | .20 |
| | Plate block of 4 | 1.75 | |
| | FDC (April 13, 1956) | | 2.50 |
| | a.  deep blue | — | |
| | Plate block of 4 | — | |
| | p.  Hi-Brite paper | — | |
| | Plate block of 4 | — | |

### 1955. ROBERT E. LEE ISSUE

582 Robert E. Lee

| 582 | | MNHVF | UseVF |
|---|---|---|---|
| 30¢ | **black,** wet paper | 1.50 | .25 |
| | Plate block of 4 | 6.00 | |
| | p.  dry paper (June 1957) | 1.00 | .20 |
| | Plate block of 4 | 5.50 | |
| | FDC (Sept. 21, 1955) | | 2.50 |

### 1955. JOHN MARHSALL ISSUE

583 John Marshall

| 583 | | MNHVF | UseVF |
|---|---|---|---|
| 40¢ | **brown carmine,** wet paper | 2.75 | .25 |
| | Plate block of 4 | 13.00 | |
| | p.  Dry paper (April 1958) | 2.00 | |
| | Plate block of 4 | 8.00 | |
| | FDC (Sept. 24, 1955) | | 4.00 |

### 1955. SUSAN B. ANTHONY ISSUE

584 Susan B. Anthony

| 584 | | MNHVF | UseVF |
|---|---|---|---|
| 50¢ | **red violet,** wet paper | 2.00 | .20 |
| | Plate block of 4 | 13.00 | |
| | Cracked plate (No. 25231, top left) | — | |
| | p.  Dry paper (April 1958) | 1.50 | .20 |
| | Plate block of 4 | 7.00 | |
| | FDC (Aug. 25, 1955) | | 6.00 |

### 1955. PATRICK HENRY ISSUE

585 Patrick Henry

| 585 | | MNHVF | UseVF |
|---|---|---|---|
| $1 | **dark lilac,** wet paper | 7.00 | .20 |
| | Plate block of 4 | 25.00 | |
| | p.  Dry paper Oct. 1958) | 5.00 | |
| | Plate block of 4 | 22.50 | |
| | FDC (Oct. 7, 1955) | | 10.00 |

### 1956. ALEXANDER HAMILTON ISSUE

586 Alexander Hamilton

| 586 | | MNHVF | UseVF |
|---|---|---|---|
| $5 | **black** | 70.00 | 6.50 |
| | Plate block of 4 | 300. | |
| | FDC (March 19, 1956) | | 65.00 |

## Liberty Coil Series Stamps Series

### 1954. GEORGE WASHINGTON ISSUE Liberty Coil Series Stamps Series
Intaglio and perforated 10 vertically.

| 587 | | MNHVF | UseVF |
|---|---|---|---|
| 1¢ | **dull green,** wet paper | .45 | .25 |
| | Pair | .75 | |
| | Line pair | 1.50 | |
| | FDC (Oct. 8, 1954) | | 1.75 |
| | p.  Dry paper, large holes (Aug. 1957) | .50 | .20 |

**587**

| | | MNHVF | UseVF |
|---|---|---|---|
| | Pair | .35 | |
| | Line pair | .75 | |
| | pv. Dry paper, small holes, *(Feb. 1960)* | .50 | .20 |
| | Pair | .75 | |
| | Line pair | 1.00 | |
| | v.  Pair, imperforate | 2250. | |

## 1954. THOMAS JEFFERSON ISSUE

**588**

| | | MNHVF | UseVF |
|---|---|---|---|
| 2¢ | **rose,** wet paper | .25 | .20 |
| | Pair | .35 | |
| | Line pair | .75 | |
| | p1. Dry paper, large holes *(May 1957)* | .25 | .20 |
| | Pair | .35 | |
| | Line pair | .75 | |
| | p1ss. Dry paper, small holes, shiny gum *(Aug. 1961)* | .25 | .20 |
| | Pair | .35 | |
| | Line pair | .75 | |
| | p1ssz Tagged, Type II *(May 6, 1968)* | — | |
| | Pair | — | |
| | Line pair | — | |
| | p1sszv. Pair imperforate | 600. | |
| | Imperforate line pair | 900. | |
| | p1smz Dry paper, small holes, matt gum, tagged | .25 | .20 |
| | Pair | .70 | |
| | Line pair | 2.00 | |
| | p1smv Pair imperforate, dry paper, matt gum, untqgged | 575. | |
| | Line pair | | |
| | FDC | 1.75 | |
| | FDC tagged | 20.00 | |

*The imperforate pair, untagged, listed above (588p1smv) is known with a Bureau precancel of Riverdale, Md.*

## 1954. STATUE OF LIBERTY ISSUE

**589**

| | | MNHVF | UseVF |
|---|---|---|---|
| 3¢ | **purple,** wet paper | .25 | .20 |
| | Pair | .50 | |
| | Line pair | 1.00 | |
| | p.  Dry paper, large holes *(May 1957)* | .75 | .20 |
| | Pair | 1.00 | |
| | Line pair | 1.50 | |
| | Gripper cracks | — | |
| | p1m. Matt gum (dull finish) | — | |
| | p1s. Dry paper, small holes *(July 31, 1958)* | .30 | |
| | Pair | | |
| | Line pair | .50 | |
| | p1v. Imperforate pair, (19 1/2 x 22mm) | 1650. | 850. |
| | Imperforate Line pair | — | |
| | z.  Tagged *(Look)* Magazine printing, Oct. 1966) | 6.00 | 3.00 |
| | Pair | 12.00 | |
| | Line pair | 150. | |
| | ps1z1 Tagged, Type II philatelic printing, *(June 26, 1967)* | 2.50 | .75 |
| | Pair | 5.00 | |
| | Line pair | 25.00 | |
| | FDC *(July 20, 1954)* | | 1.75 |
| | FDC tagged | | 50.00 |

*No. 589p1sz., the "Look Coil," is so-called because the stamps were prepared for Look magazine in coil rolls of 3,000 subjects. All but 99,000 of this issue were affixed to outgoing mail and return addressed envelopes on an automatic labeling machine at Des Moines, Iowa. The common usage was in combination with a 2¢ Jefferson coil (No. 588). The paper on which the stamps were printed is plain, without fluorescent content and tagging is uniform and brilliant. A special printing was issued, in coils of 500 subjects, to satisfy collector demands (No. 589p1sz1). The stamps can be distinguished from the original printing by a sharper, more well-defined design, a more intense shade of purple ink and the slightly fluorescent paper on which they were printed. The tagging is less intense and, on some coils across-the-web tagging marks known as "hot lines" repeat every 24th stamp.*

## 1958. ABRAHAM LINCOLN ISSUE

**590**

| | | MNHVF | UseVF |
|---|---|---|---|
| 4¢ | **bright purple,** wet paper (Bureau precancel) | 25.00 | 1.00 |
| | Pair | 50.00 | |
| | Line pair | 350. | |
| | FDC *(July 31, 1958)* | .75 | .20 |
| | pl. Dry paper, large holes *(June 1958)* | .75 | .20 |
| | Pair | 1.00 | |
| | Line pair | 2.00 | |
| | pls. Dry paper, small holes *(July 31, 1958)* | .75 | .20 |
| | Pair | 1.00 | |
| | Line pair | 2.00 | |
| | plsv. Imperforate pair | 125. | 75.00 |
| | Imperforate line pair | 250. | |
| | p2. Hi-Brite paper | — | |
| | Pair | — | |
| | Line pair | — | |

## 1958. STATUE OF LIBERTY ISSUE

*Giori press printing differs from No. 578 in that the torch and flame do not break throug the working "U.S. POSTAGE," the Statue of Liberty is enlarged, the word "LIBERTY" is smaller and lower.*

*578, 591 Giori press printing differs from No. 578 in that the torch and flame do break through the wording "U.S. POSTAGE," the Statue of Liberty is englarged, the word "LIBERTY" is smaller and lower.*

**591**

| | | MNHVF | UseVF |
|---|---|---|---|
| 8¢ | **deep blue and carmine** | .25 | .20 |
| | Plate block of 4 | 1.00 | |
| | FDC *(March 22, 1958)* | | 1.75 |

## 1958. JOHN JAY ISSUE

*Intaglio, perforated 11 x 10 1/2.*

*592 John Jay (1745-1829), statesman, first Chief Justice of the Supreme Court (1789-94) and governor of New York (1795-1801). He was a delegate and, in 1778, president of the Continental Congress. Aided Franklin in negotiating peace with Great Britain.*

**592**

| | | MNHVF | UseVF |
|---|---|---|---|
| 15¢ | **brown purple** | .75 | .20 |
| | Plate block of 4 | 2.75 | |
| | FDC tagged | | 35.00 |
| | FDC *(Dec. 12, 1958)* | | 2.50 |
| | p1. Hi-Brite paper | — | |
| | Plate block of 4 | — | |
| | p1z. Tagged, Type II *(July 6, 1966)* | 1.25 | .50 |
| | Plate block of 4 | 9.00 | |
| | p1z1. Tagged, Type III | — | |
| | Plate block of 4 | — | |

## 1958. PAUL REVERE ISSUE

*593, 614 Paul Revere (1735-1818), silversmith, copper engraver, and one of three patriots made famous by Longfellow for his ride from Charleston to Lexington, April 18, 1775, to warn of British march. He designed and printed first issue of continental currency; and designed and engraved first official seal for colonies.*

**593**

| | | MNHVF | UseVF |
|---|---|---|---|
| 25¢ | **deep blue green** | 1.50 | .20 |
| | Plate block of 4 | 5.00 | |
| | FDC *(April 18, 1958)* | | 2.50 |
| | p1. Hi-Brite paper | — | |
| | Plate block of 4 | — | |

**1959. BUNKER HILL MONUMENT ISSUE** *Intaglio, 1 1/2¢, 12¢ (perforated 11 x 10 1/2), 4 1/2¢ (perforated 10 1/2 x 11).*

594 *Bunker Hill Monument (220 feet high) erected in 1843 on the site (then called Breed's Hill) of the first major battle of the Revolutionary War (June 17, 1775). Gen. Joseph Warren, commander of U.S. forces at this battle issued the now-famous order, "Don't shoot until you see the whites of their eyes." Outnumbered four-to-one, the colonists lost the battle but inflicted very heavy casualties on the British troops. This moral victory gave the colonists new inspiration. Background of the stamp shows the Pine Tree flag adopted by the Commonwealth of Massachusetts at the beginning of the Revolutionary War.*

| 594 | | MNHVF | UseVF |
|---|---|---|---|
| 2-1/2¢ | **slate blue** | .25 | .20 |
| | Plate block of 4 | .65 | |
| | FDC *(June 17, 1959)* | | 1.75 |

**1959. HERMITAGE ISSUE**

595, 597 *Hermitage, home of Andrew Jackson.*

| 595 | | MNHVF | UseVF |
|---|---|---|---|
| 4-1/2¢ | **blue green** | .25 | .20 |
| | Plate block of 4 | .75 | |
| | FDC *(March 16, 1959)* | | 1.75 |

**1959. BENJAMIN HARRISON ISSUE**

596 *Benjamin Harrison (see No. 549).*

| 596 | | MNHVF | UseVF |
|---|---|---|---|
| 12¢ | **carmine red** | .30 | .20 |
| | Plate block of 4 | 1.50 | |
| | FDC *(June 6, 1959)* | | 2.00 |
| | Plate block of 4 | 4.00 | |
| | FDC *(May 6, 1968)*, tagged | | 12.00 |
| | z. Tagged, Type IIa *(May 6, 1968)* | .35 | .20 |
| | FDC tagged | | 30.00 |

*Type IIa tagging: wide roll tagging. All margins are fully tagged.*

**1959. 4 1/2¢ COIL ISSUE** Liberty Coil Series Stamps Series *Coil, intaglio, perf. 10 horizontally*

| 597 | | MNHVF | UseVF |
|---|---|---|---|
| 4-1/2¢ | **blue green,** large holes | 2.00 | .50 |
| | Pair | 3.00 | |
| | Line pair | 15.00 | |
| | FDC *(May 1, 1959)* | | 1.75 |
| | s. Small holes *(April 1961)* | 20.00 | 2.00 |
| | Pair | 30.00 | |
| | Line pair | 425. | |

**1959. 2 1/2¢ COIL ISSUE** *Coil, intaglio, perf. 10 vertically*

| 598 | | MNHVF | UseVF |
|---|---|---|---|
| 2-1/2¢ | **slate blue,** large holes | .25 | .20 |
| | Pair | .50 | |
| | Line pair | | |
| | FDC *(Sept. 9, 1959)* | | 2.00 |
| | a. Small holes (Bureau precancel) *(Jan. 1961)* | — | .35 |
| | Pair | — | |
| | Line pair | — | |

**1960. PALACE OF THE GOVERNORS** *Intaglio and perforated 10 1/2 x 11*

599 *Palace of the Govenors, Santa Fe, New Mexico, was built in 1610. It is now an historical shrine and memorial to early Spanish life and culture in this country, and reflects the contributions made to the progress and developmment of the Southwestern United States.*

| 599 | | MNHVF | UseVF |
|---|---|---|---|
| 1-1/4¢ | **turquoise blue** | .25 | .20 |
| | Plate block of 4 | .50 | |
| | FDC *(June 17, 1960)* | | 2.00 |

**1960. 1 1/4¢ COIL ISSUE** *Coil, intaglio, perf. 10 horizontally*

| 600 | | MNHVF | UseVF |
|---|---|---|---|
| 1-1/4¢ | **turquoise blue,** large holes | .25 | .20 |
| | Pair | 2.00 | |
| | Line pair | .30 | |
| | FDC *(June 17, 1960)* | | 1.75 |
| | p. Small holes *(May 1960)* | 1.00 | .50 |
| | Pair | 250. | |
| | Line pair | 25.00 | |

**1961. STATUE OF LIBERTY ISSUE** *Giori Press Printing, perforated 11*

601 *Statue of Liberty*

| 601 | | MNHVF | UseVF |
|---|---|---|---|
| 11¢ | **carmine red and blue** | .30 | .20 |
| | Plate block of 4 | 1.25 | |
| | FDC *(June 15, 1961)* | | 2.50 |
| | z. Tagged, type OP *(Jan. 11, 1967)* | 2.00 | 1.00 |
| | Plate block of 4 | 33.00 | |
| | FDC tagged | | 30.00 |

*Type OP tagging: Used on mulicolor stamps previously designated to be printed on Giori presses.*

**1961. JOHN J. PERSHING ISSUE** *Rotary press printing, perforated 11 x 10 1/2*

602 *John J. Pershing (1860-1948) commanded the American Expeditionary Forces in Europe during World War I. A leader of vision and courage, Pershing was honored by Congress in 1917 with the title "General of the Armies."*

| 602 | | MNHVF | UseVF |
|---|---|---|---|
| 8¢ | **brown** | .25 | .20 |
| | Plate block of 4 | 1.00 | |
| | FDC *(Nov. 17, 1961)* | | 2.25 |

*There is disagreement concerning whether No. 602 is actually part of the Liberty series. Although printed within the same period, it does not match the design characteristics of other stamps in the series.*

## Christmas Series

**1962. EVERGREEN WREATH AND BURNING CANDLES ISSUE** This 1st Christmas stamp issued by the United States was intended for use on season's greeting cards and also to remind the public to shop and mail early. *Giori press printing, perforated 11.*

603 *Evergreen wreath and burning candles.*

| 603 | | MNHVF | UseVF |
|---|---|---|---|
| 4¢ | **green and red** | .25 | .20 |
| | Plate block of 4 | .75 | |
| | FDC (Nov. 1, 1962) | | 2.00 |

## Prominent Americans Series

### 1962. GEORGE WASHINGTON ISSUE *Intaglio, perforated 11 x 10 1/2.* Issued to meet the increased postal rates effective Jan. 7, 1963.

*604 George Washington from bust by Houdon.*

| 604 | | MNHVF | UseVF |
|---|---|---|---|
| 5¢ | **gray blue** | .25 | .20 |
| | Plate block of 4 | .45 | |
| | Gutter pair | — | |
| | FDC (Nov. 23, 1962) | | 1.75 |
| | v. Horizonal pair, imperforate between | 12.50 | |
| | p1. Hi-Brite paper | — | |
| | Plate block of 4 | — | |
| | z. Tagged, Type I (Oct. 28, 1963) | — | |
| | Plate block of 4 | — | |
| | zn. Tagged booklet pane of 5, with label (2 different) | 6.50 | 2.25 |
| | z1. Tagged, Type II (April 1964) | — | |
| | Plate block of 4 | — | |
| | z1n. Booklet pane of 5, with label | 15.00 | 9.50 |
| | FDC Booklet Pane | | 4.00 |
| | z2. Tagged, Type IIa | — | |
| | Plate block of 4 | — | |
| | z3. Tagged, Type III | — | |
| | z3n. Booklet pane of 5, with label | 2.75 | 2.25 |
| | FDC tagged single | | 25.00 |
| | FDC tagged Booklet Pane | | 125. |
| | FDC tagged Booklet Pane (Washington D.C.) | | 140. |

### 1962. GEORGE WASHINGTON COIL ISSUE *Coil, intaglio, perforated 10 vertically.*

| 605 | | MNHVF | UseVF |
|---|---|---|---|
| 5¢ | **gray blue** | .25 | .20 |
| | Pair | 2.00 | |
| | Line pair | 4.00 | |
| | FDC (Nov. 23, 1962) | | 1.75 |
| | p1. Hi-Brite paper | — | |
| | Pair | — | |
| | Line pair | — | |
| | p1v. Pair, imperforate | 350. | |
| | Line pair, imperforate | 750. | |
| | z. Tagged, Type I (Oct. 28, 1963) | .25 | .20 |
| | Pair | 2.50 | |
| | Line pair | 5.00 | |
| | z1. Tagged, Type II | — | |
| | Pair | — | |
| | Line pair | — | |
| | FDC tagged | | 30.00 |

### 1963. U.S. FLAG AND WHITE HOUSE ISSUE

*606 U.S. flag and White House.*

| 606 | | MNHVF | UseVF |
|---|---|---|---|
| 5¢ | **blue and red** | .25 | .20 |
| | Plate block of 4 | .75 | |
| | Gutter pair | — | |
| | FDC (Jan. 9, 1963) | | 1.75 |
| | z. Tagged, Type OP (Aug. 25, 1966) | .25 | .20 |
| | Plate block of 4 | 5.00 | |
| | FDC tagged | | 25.00 |
| | zv. Imperforate horizontal pair | 1250. | |

### 1963. ANDREW JACKSON ISSUE *Intaglio, perforated 11 x 10 1/2.*

*607 Andrew Jackson.*

| 607 | | MNHVF | UseVF |
|---|---|---|---|
| 1¢ | **green** | .25 | .20 |
| | Plate block of 4 | .75 | |
| | Gutter pair | — | |
| | FDC (March 22, 1963) | | 1.75 |
| | p1. Hi-Brite paper | — | |
| | Plate block of 4 | — | |
| | z. Tagged, Type II or III (July 6, 1966) (1209a) | .25 | .20 |
| | Plate block of 4 | .25 | |
| | FDC tagged | | 25.00 |

### 1963. ANDREW JACKSON COIL ISSUE *Coil, intaglio, perforated 10 vertically.*

| 608 | | MNHVF | UseVF |
|---|---|---|---|
| 1¢ | **green** | .25 | .20 |
| | Pair | .25 | |
| | Line pair | 2.00 | |
| | FDC (May 31, 1963) | | 1.75 |
| | z. Tagged, Type II (July 6, 1966) | .25 | .20 |
| | Pair | .25 | |
| | Line pair | .75 | |
| | FDC tagged | | 25.00 |

### 1963. CHRISTMAS TREE AND WHITE HOUSE This second Christmas stamp was based on an on-the-spot painting made by artist Lily Spandorf of President Kennedy lighting the National Christmas tree. *Giori press printing, perforated 11.*

*609 Christmas Tree and White House.*

| 609 | | MNHVF | UseVF |
|---|---|---|---|
| 5¢ | **dark blue, indigo and red** | .25 | .20 |
| | Plate block of 4 | .50 | |
| | Gutter pair | — | |
| | FDC (Nov. 1, 1963) | | 2.00 |
| | z. Tagged, Type OP (Nov 2, 1963) | .65 | .50 |
| | Plate block of 4 | 4.50 | |
| | FDC tagged | | 60.00 |

### 1964. HOLIDAY EVERGREENS ISSUE The third Christmas issue also was a U.S. postal first, featuring four different stamp designs in a regular size pane of 100 stamps. *Giori Press Printing, perforated 11.*

*610 Holly 611 Mistletoe 612 Poinsettia 613 Pine cone*

| 610 | | MNHVF | UseVF |
|---|---|---|---|
| 5¢ | **carmine, green and black** | .25 | .20 |

| 611 | | MNHVF | UseVF |
|---|---|---|---|
| 5¢ | **carmine, green and black** | .25 | .20 |

| 612 | | MNHVF | UseVF |
|---|---|---|---|
| 5¢ | **carmine, green and black** | .25 | .20 |

| 613 | | MNHVF | UseVF |
|---|---|---|---|
| 5¢ | **carmine, green and black** | .25 | .20 |
| | Se-tenant block of 4 | 1.00 | 1.00 |
| | Plate block of 4 | 1.25 | |
| | FDC *(Nov. 9, 1964)* any single | | 2.50 |
| | FDC, Block | | 4.00 |
| | z. Tagged, Type OP (any single) *Nov. 10, 1964)* | 1.75 | .50 |
| | Se-tenant block of 4 | 3.50 | |
| | Plate block of 4 | 5.00 | |
| | FDC tagged block | | 60.00 |
| | FDC tagged any single | | 20.00 |

**1965. Pine Cone Coil Issue** *Coil, intaglio and perforated 10 vertically.*

| 614 | | MNHVF | UseVF |
|---|---|---|---|
| 25¢ | **deep blue green,** large holes | .45 | .25 |
| | Pair | 1.00 | |
| | Line pair | 2.25 | |
| | FDC *(Feb. 25, 1965)* | | 2.50 |
| | v. Imperforate pair | .45 | |
| | Imperforate line pair | .90 | |
| | zss.Tagged, small holes, shiny gum *(April 3, 1973)* | .45 | .25 |
| | Pair | 1.25 | |
| | Line pair | 3.00 | |
| | zsm.Tagged, small holes, matt gum *(1980)* | .45 | .25 |
| | Pair | 1.50 | |
| | Line pair | 3.50 | |
| | FDC tagged | | 25.00 |

**1965. Angel Gabriel Issue** The design is based on a watercolor by Lucille Gloria Chabot. *Giori press printing, perforated 11.*

615 *Angel Gabriel blowing his horn.*

| 615 | | MNHVF | UseVF |
|---|---|---|---|
| 5¢ | **red, green and yellow** | .25 | .20 |
| | Plate block of 4 | .55 | |
| | Gutter pair | — | |
| | FDC *(Nov. 2, 1965)* any single | | 1.75 |
| | z. Tagged, Type OP *(Nov. 15, 1965)* | .75 | .20 |
| | Plate block of 4 | 5.50 | |
| | FDC tagged | | 50.00 |

**1968. Thomas Jefferson Issue** Prominent Americans Series.

616 *Thomas Jefferson*

| 616 | | MNHVF | UseVF |
|---|---|---|---|
| 1¢ | **green,** tagged type II or III | .25 | .20 |
| | FDC | | 1.75 |
| | Plate block of 4 | .25 | |
| | n. Booklet pane of 8 | | |
| | FDC *(Jan. 12, 1968)* | | 2.50 |

| 616 | | MNHVF | UseVF |
|---|---|---|---|
| | nm.Booklet pane of 8, matt gum | 90.00 | 1.25 |
| | FDC | | 2.50 |
| | n1.Booklet pane of 4 | 1.00 | |
| | FDC | | |
| | zo. Tagging omitted (error) | | |
| | Plate block of 4 | — | |
| | Plate block of 4, half untagged | — | |
| | Booklet pane of 8 | — | |
| | Untagged (Bureau precancel) | | .20 |

**1967. Albert Gallatin Issue** Prominent Americans Series.

617 *Albert Gallatin, statesman.*

| 617 | | MNHVF | UseVF |
|---|---|---|---|
| 1-1/4¢ | **light green** | .25 | .20 |
| | Plate block of 4 | 7.50 | |
| | FDC *(Jan. 30, 1967)* | | 1.75 |

**1966. Frank Lloyd Wright Issue** Prominent American Series.

618 *Frank Lloyd Wright, architect.*

| 618 | | MNHVF | UseVF |
|---|---|---|---|
| 2¢ | **blue,** tagged type II or III | .25 | .20 |
| | Plate block of 4 | .25 | |
| | Gutter pair | — | |
| | FDC *(June 8, 1966)* | | 1.75 |
| | n. Booklet pane of 5, plus label *(Jan. 8, 1968)* | 1.25 | |
| | FDC | | 4.00 |
| | n1.Booklet pane of 6, *(May 7, 1971)* | 1.00 | |
| | FDC | 1.00 | 15.00 |
| | zo. Tagging omitted (error) | — | |
| | Plate block of 4 | — | |
| | zn. Booklet pane of 5, plus label | — | |
| | zn1.Booklet pane of 6 | | |
| | FDC | | 100. |
| | zx. Untagged (Bureau precancel) | — | |
| | zxo.Tagged with Bureau precancel (error) | — | |

**1967. Francis Parkman Issue** Prominent Americans Series.

619 *Francis Parkman, historian.*

| 619 | | MNHVF | UseVF |
|---|---|---|---|
| 3¢ | tagged type II **purple,** | .25 | .20 |
| | Plate block of 4 | .30 | |
| | zo. Tagging omitted (error) | — | |
| | Plate block of 4 | — | |
| | zx. Untagged (Bureau precancel) | | |
| | FDC *(Sept. 16, 1967)* | | 1.75 |

**1965. Abraham Lincoln Issue** Prominent Americans Series.

620 *Abraham Lincoln*

| 620 | | MNHVF | UseVF |
|---|---|---|---|
| 4¢ | **black** | .25 | .20 |
| | Plate block of 4 | .40 | |
| | Gutter pair | — | |
| | FDC *(Nov. 19, 1965)* | | 1.75 |
| | z. Tagged, Type II or III *(Dec. 1, 1965)* | .25 | .20 |
| | Plate block of 4 | .55 | |
| | FDC tagged | | 40.00 |
| | FDC tagged (Washington D.C.) | | 45.00 |

**1965. GEORGE WASHINGTON ISSUE** Prominent Americans Series.

621 *George Washington*

| 621 | | MNHVF | UseVF |
|---|---|---|---|
| 5¢ | **deep blue** | .25 | .20 |
| | Plate block of 4 | .60 | |
| | Gutter pair | — | |
| | FDC *(Feb. 22, 1966)* | | 1.75 |
| | z. Tagged, Type II or III *(Feb. 23, 1966)* | .25 | .20 |
| | Plate block of 4 | .60 | |
| | FDC tagged | | 100. |
| | FDC tagged (Washington D.C.) | | 27.50 |

**1966. FRANKLIN D. ROOSEVELT ISSUE** Prominent Americans Series.

622 *Franklin D. Roosevelt*

| 622 | | MNHVF | UseVF |
|---|---|---|---|
| 6¢ | **black brown** | .25 | .20 |
| | Plate block of 4 | .65 | |
| | Gutter pair | | |
| | FDC *(Jan. 29, 1966)* | | 2.50 |
| | z. Tagged, Type II or III *(Dec. 29, 1966)* | .25 | .20 |
| | Plate block of 4 | .75 | |
| | FDC | | 20.00 |
| | zn. Booklet pane of 5 plus label *(Jan. 9, 1968)* | 1.50 | |
| | FDC | | 150. |
| | zn1. Booklet pane of 8 *(Dec. 28, 1967)* | 1.50 | |
| | FDC | | 3.00 |
| | zo. Tagging omitted (error) | — | |

**1966. ALBERT EINSTEIN ISSUE** Prominent Americans Series.

623 *Albert Einstein, physicist.*

| 623 | | MNHVF | UseVF |
|---|---|---|---|
| 8¢ | **violet** | .25 | .20 |
| | Plate block of 4 | 1.00 | |
| | FDC | | 2.50 |
| | z. Tagged, type II or III *(July 6, 1966)* | | |
| | Plate block of 4 | 1.00 | |
| | FDC tagged *(March 14, 1966)* | | 20.00 |

**1967. ANDREW JACKSON ISSUE** Prominent Americans Series.

624 *Andrew Jackson*

| 624 | | MNHVF | UseVF |
|---|---|---|---|
| 10¢ | **lavender,** tagged type II or III | .25 | .20 |
| | Plate block of 4 | 1.00 | |
| | FDC *(March 15, 1967)* | | 1.75 |
| | zo. Tagging omitted (error) | — | |
| | Plate block of 4 | — | |
| | zx. Untagged (Bureau precancel) | — | .20 |

**1968. HENRY FORD ISSUE** Prominent Americans Series.

624A *Henry Ford auto manufacturer.*

| 624A | | MNHVF | UseVF |
|---|---|---|---|
| 12¢ | **black,** tagged type II | .25 | .20 |
| | Plate block of 4 | 1.20 | |
| | FDC *(July 30, 1968)* | | 2.50 |
| | zo. Tagging omitted (error) | — | |
| | Plate block of 4 | — | |
| | zx. Untagged (Bureau precancel) | — | .25 |

**1967. JOHN F. KENNEDY ISSUE** Prominent Americans Series.

625 *John F. Kennedy*

| 625 | | MNHVF | UseVF |
|---|---|---|---|
| 13¢ | **brown,** tagged type II or III | .25 | .20 |
| | Plate block of 4 | 1.35 | |
| | FDC *(May 29, 1967)* | | 2.50 |
| | zo. Tagging omitted (error) | — | |
| | zx. Untagged (Bureau precancel) | — | |

**1968. OLIVER WENDELL HOLMES ISSUE** Prominent Americans Series.

| 626 | | MNHVF | UseVF |
|---|---|---|---|
| 15¢ | **maroon,** design type I, tagged Type II | | |
| | Plate block of 4 | 1.50 | |
| | Gutter pair | — | |
| | FDC *(March 8, 1968)* | | 1.75 |
| | zx. Untagged (Bureau precancel) | — | |
| | i. Type II (design) | .50 | .20 |
| | Plate block of 4 | 8.50 | |
| | iizo. Tagging omitted (error) | — | |
| | Plate block of 4 | — | |
| | iin. Booklet pane of 8, type III *(July 14, 1978)* | | |
| | FDC, single from booklet pane | | 1.75 |
| | FDC, Booklet pane | | 3.50 |
| | iinv. Imperforate between | — | |

*Type I: crosshatching on tie complete and strong; bottom of necktie just touches coat. Type II: crosshatching on tie (lines running upper left to lower right) very faint; necktie does not touch coat. Type III (only known on booklet pane) overall design smaller and "15¢" closer to head.*

**1967. GEORGE C. MARSHALL ISSUE** Prominent Americans Series.

627 *George C. Marshall, diplomat and general.*

| 627 | | MNHVF | UseVF |
|---|---|---|---|
| 20¢ | **olive brown** | .35 | .20 |
| | Plate block of 4 | 1.75 | |
| | FDC | | 2.00 |
| | z. Tagged, *(April 3, 1974)* | .40 | .20 |
| | Plate block of 4 | 2.00 | |
| | FDC *(Oct. 24, 1967)* | | 20.00 |

**1967. FREDERICK DOUGLASS ISSUE** Prominent Americans Series.

628 *Frederick Douglass, abolitionist and statesman.*

| 628 | | MNHVF | UseVF |
|---|---|---|---|
| 25¢ | **maroon** | .50 | .20 |
| | Plate block | 1.75 | |
| | FDC *(Feb. 14, 1967)* | | 3.50 |
| | a. lilac carmine | — | |
| | Plate block of 4 | — | |
| | z. Tagged *(April 3, 1973)* | .40 | .20 |
| | Plate block of 4 | 2.00 | |
| | FDC | | 25.00 |

**1968. JOHN DEWEY ISSUE** Prominent Americans Series.

629 *John Dewey, philosopher and educator.*

| 629 | | MNHVF | UseVF |
|---|---|---|---|
| 30¢ | **purple** | .55 | .25 |
| | Plate block of 4 | 2.75 | |
| | FDC *(Oct. 21, 1968)* | | 3.50 |
| | z. Tagged *April 3, 1973* | .45 | .25 |
| | Plate block of 4 | 2.25 | |
| | FDC | | 25.00 |

**1968. THOMAS PAINE ISSUE** Prominent Americans Series.

630 *Thomas Paine, essayist*

| 630 | | MNHVF | UseVF |
|---|---|---|---|
| 40¢ | **dark blue** | .75 | .25 |
| | Plate block of 4 | 3.30 | |
| | FDC *(Jan. 29, 1968)* | | 3.00 |
| | z. Tagged, *(April 3, 1973)* | .75 | .25 |
| | Plate block of 4 | 2.25 | |
| | zm.Matt gum | .75 | |
| | Plate block of 4 | 3.00 | .25 |
| | FDC | | 25.00 |

**1968. LUCY STONE ISSUE** Prominent Americans Series.

631 *Lucy Stone, suffrogist and reformer.*

| 631 | | MNHVF | UseVF |
|---|---|---|---|
| 50¢ | **maroon** | 1.00 | .25 |
| | Plate block of 4 | 4.50 | |
| | FDC *(Aug. 13, 1968)* | | 4.00 |
| | Gutter pair | — | |
| | z. Tagged *(April 3, 1973)* | 1.00 | .25 |
| | Plate block of 4 | 3.00 | |
| | FDC | | 30.00 |

**1967. EUGENE O'NEIL ISSUE** Prominent Americans Series.

632 *Eugene O'Neil, playwright.*

| 632 | | MNHVF | UseVF |
|---|---|---|---|
| $1 | **dark purple** | 2.25 | .50 |
| | Plate block of 4 | 10.00 | |
| | FDC *(Oct. 16, 1967)* | | 7.50 |
| | z. Tagged *(April 3, 1973)* | 1.75 | .50 |
| | Plate block of 4 | 7.00 | |
| | FDC | | 40.00 |

**1966. JOHN BASSETT MOORE ISSUE** Prominent Americans Series. High values of this series were tagged for use with automated equipment for postmarking large envelopes.

633 *John Bassett Moore, jurist.*

| 633 | | MNHVF | UseVF |
|---|---|---|---|
| $5 | **dark gray** | 10.00 | 3.00 |
| | Plate block of 4 | 40.00 | |
| | FDC *(Dec. 3, 1966)* | | 40.00 |
| | z. Tagged, *(April 3, 1973)* | 8.00 | 3.00 |
| | Plate block of 4 | 30.00 | |
| | FDC | | 100. |

**1968. THOMAS JEFFERSON COIL ISSUE** Prominent Americans Series. *Coil, intaglio, perforated 10 vertically.*

| 634 | | MNHVF | UseVF |
|---|---|---|---|
| 1¢ | **green,** tagged | .25 | .20 |
| | Pair | .25 | |
| | Line pair | .25 | |
| | FDC *(June 12, 1968)* | | 1.75 |
| | v. Pair, imperforate | 30.00 | |
| | Line pair, imperforate | 600. | |
| | zo. Tagging omitted (error) | — | |
| | Pair | — | |
| | Line pair | — | |
| | zx. Untagged (Bureau Precancel) | .20 | |
| | Pair | .25 | |
| | Line pair | .60 | |

**1966. ABRAHAM LINCOLN COIL ISSUE** Prominent Americans Series.

| 635 | | MNHVF | UseVF |
|---|---|---|---|
| 4¢ | **black,** tagged type II | .25 | .20 |
| | Pair | .25 | |
| | Line pair | .75 | |
| | FDC *(May 28, 1966)* | | 1.75 |
| | v. pair, imperforate | 800. | |
| | line pair, imperforate | 1500. | |
| | v1. Imperforate-between pair | — | |
| | zo. Tagging omitted (error) | — | |
| | Pair | — | |
| | Line pair | — | |
| | zx. Untagged (Bureau Precancel) | 1.00 | |
| | Pair | 10.00 | |
| | Line pair | 125. | |

**1966. GEORGE WASHINGTON COIL ISSUE** Prominent Americans Series.

| 636 | | MNHVF | UseVF |
|---|---|---|---|
| 5¢ | **deep blue,** tagged type II | .25 | .20 |
| | Pair | .25 | |
| | Line pair | .40 | |
| | FDC *(Sept. 8, 1966)* | | 1.75 |
| | v. Pair, imperforate | 200. | |
| | Line pair, imperforate | 350. | |
| | zo. Tagging omitted (error) | — | |
| | Pair | — | |
| | Line pair | — | |
| | zx. Untagged (Bureau Precancel) | 1.00 | |
| | Pair | 10.00 | |
| | Line pair | 100. | |
| | zxv.Imperforate untagged (precanceled) pair | 400. | |
| | Imperforate untagged (precanceled) line pair | 1000. | |
| | m. Matt gum | .25 | .20 |
| | Pair | 1.25 | |
| | Line pair | 6.00 | |

**1968. FRANKLIN D. ROOSEVELT COIL ISSUE** Prominent Americans Series.
*Coil, intaglio, perforated 10 vertically.*

637, 638 *Franklin D. Roosevelt*

| 637 | | MNHVF | UseVF |
|---|---|---|---|
| 6¢ | **black brown,** tagged | .25 | .20 |
| | Pair | .20 | |
| | Line pair | .55 | |
| | FDC *(Feb. 28, 1968)* | | |
| | v. Imperforate pair | 2250. | |
| | Imperforate line pair | — | |
| | zo. Tagging omitted | — | |
| | Pair | — | |
| | Line pair | — | |
| | zx. Untagged (Bureau Precancel) | | |
| | Pair | 17.50 | |
| | Line pair | 250. | |

**1967. FRANKLIN D. ROOSEVELT COIL ISSUE** Prominent Americans Series.
*Coil, intaglio, perforated 10 horizontally.*

| 638 | | MNHVF | UseVF |
|---|---|---|---|
| 6¢ | **black brown,** tagged | .25 | .20 |
| | Pair | .25 | |
| | Line pair | 1.25 | |
| | FDC *(Dec. 28, 1967)* | | 1.75 |
| | v. Pair, imperforate | 70.00 | |
| | Line pair, imperforate | 125. | |
| | zo. Tagging omitted (error) | — | |
| | Pair | — | |
| | Line pair | — | |

**1966. TRADITIONAL CHRISTMAS ISSUE** The fifth in the series, features a design showing a portion Hans Memling's 15th century painting *Madonna and Child with Angels. Giori press printing and offset, perforated 11.*

644 Madonna and Child

| 644 | | MNHVF | UseVF |
|---|---|---|---|
| 5¢ | **multicolored** | .25 | .20 |
| | Plate block of 4 | .75 | |
| | FDC | | 1.75 |
| | Tagged, type OP *(Nov. 2, 1966)* | .30 | .20 |
| | Plate block of 4 | 1.75 | |
| | FDC tagged | | 30.00 |

**1967. TRADITIONAL CHRISTMAS ISSUE** design was the same as the 1966 issue, but printed in much larger size. *Giori press printing and offset, perforated 11.*

645

| 645 | | MNHVF | UseVF |
|---|---|---|---|
| 5¢ | **multicolored** | .25 | .20 |
| | Plate block of 4 | .65 | |
| | FDC *(Nov. 6, 1967)* | | 2.00 |
| | Tagging omitted (error) | — | |
| | Plate block of 4 | — | |

**1967. GEORGE WASHINGTON ISSUE** Prominent Americans Series. The 5¢ George Washington stamp (No. 621) issued Feb. 22, 1966, was criticized severely by the American public. The Post Office Department prepared a redesigned version of the stamp (No. 646) with a socalled 'clean shaven' portrait. *Giori press printing and offset, perforated 11.*

621 *Original* 646 *Redesigned*

| 646 | | MNHVF | UseVF |
|---|---|---|---|
| 5¢ | **deep blue,** tagged, shiny gum | .25 | .20 |
| | Plate block of 4 | .75 | |
| | FDC *(Nov. 17, 1967)* | | 1.75 |
| | zo. Tagging omitted Shiny gumm (error) | — | |
| | Plate block of 4 | — | |
| | m. matt gum | .25 | .20 |
| | Plate block of 4 | 1.50 | |
| | mzo.Tagging omitted, matt gum (error) | — | |
| | Plate block of 4 | — | |
| | zx. Untagged (Bureau precancel) | — | |

## Flag Over White House Series

**1968. FLAG OVER WHITE HOUSE ISSUE** *Giori press printing, perforated 11.*

647, 650, 654 *Flag towering over the White House.*

| 647 | | MNHVF | UseVF |
|---|---|---|---|
| 6¢ | **dark blue, green and red,** tagging type OP | .25 | .20 |
| | Plate block of 4 | .50 | |
| | FDC | — | 1.75 |
| | v. Imperforate-between vertical pair | 500. | |
| | v1. Vertical pair, imperforate horizontally | 500. | |
| | zo. Tagging omitted (error) | — | |
| | Plate block of 4 | — | |
| | FDC *(January 24, 1968)* | | 200. |

**1968. FLYING EAGLE ISSUE SERVICEMAN'S AIRLIFT** *Giori press printing and offset, perforated 11.*

648 *Flying Eagle*

| 648 | | MNHVF | UseVF |
|---|---|---|---|
| $1 | **multicolored** | 3.00 | 2.00 |
| | Plate block of 4 | 12.75 | |
| | Gutter pair | — | |
| | FDC *(April 4, 1968)* | | 7.50 |

**1968. TRADITIONAL CHRISTMAS ISSUE** features a design showing a portion of *The Annunciation* by the 15th century Flemish artist Jan van Eyck. this was the first stamp printed on the multicolor Huck press. *Intaglio, perforated 11.*

649 *Angel Gabriel*

| 649 | | MNHVF | UseVF |
|---|---|---|---|
| 6¢ | **multicolored,** tagged type B | .25 | .20 |
| | Plate block of 10 | 2.00 | |
| | v. Light yellow omitted | 65.00 | |
| | FDC *(Nov. 1, 1968)* | | 2.00 |
| | v1. Imperforate pair | 250. | |
| | zx. Untagged *(Nov. 2, 1968)* | .30 | .20 |
| | Plate block of 10 | .30 | .20 |
| | zxv.Imperforate pair | 300. | |

*Type B tagging: Billet or bar-like shapes designed to register within the limits of a single stamp. Untagged areas surround the design and were intended to register with the perforations.*

*coil, intaglio and perforated 10 vertically. This was the first multicolored postage stamp to be produced in coil form. Same design as No. 647.*

**1969. FLAG OVER WHITE HOUSE COIL STAMP ISSUE** Flag Over White House Series

| 650 | | MNHVF | UseVF |
|---|---|---|---|
| 6¢ | **dark blue, green and red,** tagged | .25 | .20 |
| | Tagged | | |
| | Pair-Line pair | 2.00 | |
| | FDC *(May 30, 1969)* | | 1.75 |
| | v. Pair, imperforate | 500. | |
| | zo. Tagging omitted (error) | — | |

**1969. CONTEMPORARY CHRISTMAS ISSUE** features the 19th century painting by an unknown artist. From the collection of the New York State Historical Association, Cooperstown, NY. *Intaglio, perforated 11 x 10 1/2.*

651

| 651 | | MNHVF | UseVF |
|---|---|---|---|
| 6¢ | **multicolored,** tagged | .25 | .20 |
| | Plate block of 10 | 1.95 | |
| | FDC *(Nov. 3, 1969)* | | 2.00 |
| | Experimental precancel | | .25 |
| | FDC all 4 cities singles | | 2.75 |
| | Plate block of 10 | | 85.00 |
| | v. Light green omitted | 25.00 | 1.75 |
| | v1. Light green, red, and yellow omitted | 950. | |
| | v2. Yellow omitted | 2500. | |
| | v3. Yellow and red omitted | 2850. | |
| | v4. Imperforate pair | | 1100. |
| | zo. Tagging omitted (error) | 4.00 | |
| | Plate strip of 10 | — | |

**1970. DWIGHT D. EISENHOWER ISSUE** Prominent Americans Series.

652, 653 *Dwight D. Eisenhower*

| 652 | | MNHVF | UseVF |
|---|---|---|---|
| 6¢ | **blue,** tagged Type II | .25 | .20 |
| | Plate block of 4 | .50 | |
| | FDC *(Aug. 6, 1970)* | | 1.75 |
| | m. Matt gum | .25 | |
| | Plate block of 4 | 1.00 | |
| | n. Booklet pane of 8 | 1.50 | |
| | FDC | | 3.00 |
| | nm.Booklet pane of 8, matt gum | 2.00 | |
| | n1. Booklet pane of 5 plus label | 1.50 | |
| | FDC | | 75.00 |
| | zo. Tagging omitted (error) | — | |
| | zx. Untagged (Bureau precancel) | — | |

**1970. DWIGHT D. EISENHOWER COIL ISSUE** Prominent Americans Series.

| 653 | | MNHVF | UseVF |
|---|---|---|---|
| 6¢ | **blue,** tagged | .25 | .20 |
| | Pair | .25 | |
| | Line pair | .50 | |
| | FDC *(Aug. 6, 1970)* | | |
| | m. Matt gum | .25 | .20 |
| | Pair | .60 | |
| | Line pair | 1.50 | |
| | v. Imperforate pair | 1500. | |
| | Imperforate line pair | — | |
| | zo. Tagging omitted (error) | 8.50 | |
| | zx. Untagged (Bureau Precancel) | 1.00 | |

**1970. FLAG TOWERING OVER THE WHITE HOUSE ISSUE** Flag Over White House Series
Same design as No. 647 (Giori Press) and No. 650 (Huck Press). Huck Press printings are 0.05 inches smaller than Giori Printings. *Intaglio, perforated 11 x 101/2.*

| 654 | | MNHVF | UseVF |
|---|---|---|---|
| 6¢ | **dark blue, green and red,** tagged type B | | |
| | Margin block of 20 | 3.25 | |
| | FDC *(Aug. 7, 1970)* | | 1.75 |
| | v. Imperforate-between horizontal pair | — | |
| | zo. Tagging omitted (error) | — | |
| | Margin block of 20 | — | |

**1970. CONTEMPORARY CHRISTMAS ISSUE** consist of 4 different designs printed se-tenant, *Gravure at Guilford Gravure, Inc., Guilford, Conn. perforated 11 x 10 1/2;*

655 *Antique toy locomotive* 656 *Toy wheeled horse* 657 *Mechanical tricycle toy* 658 *Doll carriage toy*

| 655 | | MNHVF | UseVF |
|---|---|---|---|
| 6¢ | locomotive, **multicolored,** tagged | .25 | .20 |
| **656** | | **MNHVF** | **UseVF** |
| 6¢ | horse, **multicolored,** tagged | .25 | .20 |
| | v.  Black omitted | — | |
| | v1. Imperforate pair (No. 656, 658) | — | |
| **657** | | **MNHVF** | **UseVF** |
| 6¢ | tricycle, **multicolored,** tagged | .25 | .20 |
| **658** | | **MNHVF** | **UseVF** |
| 6¢ | doll carriage, **multicolored,** tagged | .25 | .20 |
| | FDC *(Nov. 5, 1970) (any single)* | | 2.50 |
| | w.  Se-tenant block of 4 | 1.50 | 2.50 |
| | Plate block of 8 | 3.50 | |
| | v.  Black omitted, any single | 2500. | |
| | Black omitted, block of 4 | — | |
| | x.  Precanceled, any single | .25 | .20 |
| | FDC Precanceled block | | 20.00 |
| | Precanceled Se-tenant block of 4 | 1.25 | |
| | xw. Se-tenant block of 4, precanceled | 1.50 | |
| | zo. Tagging omitted (error), any single | — | |
| | zow. Se-tenant block of 4, tagging omitted (error) | — | |

**1970. TRADITIONAL CHRISTMAS ISSUE** Gravure at Guilford Gravure, Inc., perforated 10 1/2 x 11.

659 The Nativity *by Lorenzo Lotto.*

| 659 | | MNHVF | UseVF |
|---|---|---|---|
| 6¢ | **multicolored,** tagged | .25 | .20 |
| | Plate block of 8 | 3.50 | |
| | FDC *(Nov. 5, 1970)* | | 1.75 |
| | v.  Black omitted | 575. | .20 |
| | x.  Precanceled | .25 | .20 |
| | Plate block of 8 | 3.50 | |
| | xv. Precanceled, blue omitted | | |
| | ii.  Type II | .25 | .20 |
| | Plate block of 8 | 3.50 | |
| | iix. Type II, precanceled | .25 | .20 |
| | Plate block of 8 | 3.50 | |
| | FDC | | 1.75 |

*Type I has a slightly blurry impression and no gum breaker ridges. Type II has a shiny surfaced paper, sharper impression, and both horizontal and vertical gum breaker ridges. Type I precancel is gray black; Type II precancel is intense black.*

**1971. ERNIE PYLE ISSUE** Prominent Americans Series.
 Honors the World War II correspondent and newsman who died by enemy gunfire on April 18, 1945. He won the Pulitzer Prize in 1943. *Cottrell press printing, perforated 11 x 10 1/2.*

660 *Ernie Pyle*

| 660 | | MNHVF | UseVF |
|---|---|---|---|
| 16¢ | **brown,** tagged | .30 | .20 |
| | Plate block of 4 | 1.30 | |
| | FDC *(May 7, 1971)* | | 2.50 |
| | zo. Tagging omitted (error) | — | |
| | Plate block of 4 | — | |
| | zx. Untagged (Bureau precancel) | — | |

**1971. FLAG OVER WHITE HOUSE ISSUE** Flag Over White House Series

661, 662 *Flag towering over White House. Printed by intaglio, perforated 11 x 10 1/2.*

| 661 | | MNHVF | UseVF |
|---|---|---|---|
| 8¢ | **dark blue, red and slate green,** tagged Type B | .25 | .20 |
| | Plate block of 20 | 3.75 | |
| | FDC *(May 10, 1971)* | | 1.75 |
| | v.  Green omitted | 500. | |
| | v1. Imperforate-between horizontal pair | 55.00 | |
| | v2. Imperforate vertical pair | 55.00 | |

**1971. FLAG OVER WHITE HOUSE COIL ISSUE** Flag Over White House Series

| 662 | | MNHVF | UseVF |
|---|---|---|---|
| 8¢ | **dark blue, red and slate green,** tagged Type B | .20 | .20 |
| | Pair | 1.75 | |
| | FDC *(May 10, 1971)* | | 1.75 |
| | v.  Imperforate pair | 50.00 | |
| | zo. Tagging omitted (error) | — | |
| | Pair | — | |

**1971. DWIGHT D. EISENHOWER ISSUE** Prominent Americans Series.
 *Giori press printing, perforated 11*

663, 664 *Dwight D. Eisenhower*

| 663 | | MNHVF | UseVF |
|---|---|---|---|
| 8¢ | **black, blue gray and red,** tagged Type OP | .25 | .20 |
| | Plate block of 4 | .75 | |
| | Gutter pair | 350. | |
| | p.  Hi-Brite paper | — | |
| | Plate block of 4 | — | |
| | zo. Tagging omitted (error) | — | |
| | Plate block of 4 | — | |
| | FDC *(May 10, 1971)* | | 1.75 |

## 1971. Dwight D. Eisenhower Booklet Issue Prominent Americans Series.

*Intaglio and perforated 11 x 10 1/2*

| 663A | | MNHVF | UseVF |
|---|---|---|---|
| 8¢ | **reddish brown,** tagged type II in booklet form only, or III, in booklet form only | | |
| | FDC | | 2.00 |
| | n. Booklet pane of 6 | 1.00 | |
| | nzo.Booklet pane of 6, tagging omitted (error) | — | |
| | n1.Booklet pane of 8 | 2.00 | |
| | FDC | | 3.00 |
| | n1zo.Booklet pane of 8, tagging omitted (error) | — | |
| | n2.Booklet pane of 7 plus label, tagged type II *(Jan. 28, 1972)* | 2.00 | |
| | n2zo.Booklet pane of 7 plus label, tagging omitted (error) | — | |
| | n2zl.Booklet pane of 7 plus label, tagged type III | 2.00 | |
| | n2v.Booklet pane of 7 plus label, imperforate between horizontally | 2.00 | |
| | n3.Booklet pane of 4 plus 2 labels, tagged type II *(Jan. 28, 1972)* | 1.50 | |
| | n3z1.Booklet pane of 4, plus 2 labels, tagged type III | 2.00 | |
| | n3zo.Tagging ommited, (error), single stamp | — | |
| | FDC *(May 10, 1971)* | | |

*All these booklet stamps have 1 or 2 straight edges.*

## 1971. Dwight D. Eisenhower Coil Issue Prominent Americans Series.

*Coil, intaglio and perforated 10 vertically.*

| 664 | | MNHVF | UseVF |
|---|---|---|---|
| 8¢ | **reddish brown,** tagged | .25 | .20 |
| | Pair | .60 | |
| | Line pair | — | |
| | FDC | | 1.75 |
| | v. Imperforate pair | 45.00 | |
| | Imperforate line pair | 75.00 | |
| | v1.Imperforate-between pair | 6250. | |
| | zx. Untagged (Bureau precancel) | 6.50 | 1.00 |
| | FDC *(May 10, 1971)* | | |

## 1971. U.S. Postal Service Issue

marks the transition from the U.S. Post Office Department to the U.S. Postal System under the direction of Postmaster General Winton M. Blount. *Gravure, perforated 11 x 10 1/2.*

665 *Postal service emblem.*

| 665 | | MNHVF | UseVF |
|---|---|---|---|
| 8¢ | **multicolored,** tagged | .25 | .20 |
| | Plate block of 12 | 2.00 | |
| | FDC *(July 1, 1971)* | | 1.75 |

## 1971. Contemporary Christmas Issue Christmas Series.

*Gravure, perforated 10 1/2 x 11.*

666 *A Partridge in a pear tree.*

| 666 | | MNHVF | UseVF |
|---|---|---|---|
| 8¢ | **multicolored,** tagged | .25 | .20 |
| | Plate block of 12 | 3.00 | |
| | FDC *(Nov. 10, 1971)* | | 2.00 |
| | zo. Tagging omitted (error) | — | |

## 1971. Traditional Christmas Issue

*Gravure, perforated 10 1/2 x 11.*

667 *Nativity by Giorgione.*

| 667 | | MNHVF | UseVF |
|---|---|---|---|
| 8¢ | **multicolored,** tagged | .25 | .20 |
| | Plate block of 12 | 3.00 | |
| | FDC *(Nov. 10, 1971)* | | 2.00 |
| | v. gold omitted | — | |

## 1972. Fiorello H. LaGuardia Issue Prominent Americans Series.

Pays tribute to a prominent American who served his country as a congressman and as mayor of New York City. *Intaglio, perforated 11 x 10 1/2.*

668 *Fiorello H. LaGuardia*

| 668 | | MNHVF | UseVF |
|---|---|---|---|
| 14¢ | **dark brown,** tagged | .25 | .20 |
| | Plate block of 4 | 1.25 | |
| | FDC *(Apr. 24, 1972)* | | 1.75 |
| | Gutter pair | 2.75 | |
| | zx. Untagged (Bureau precancel) | — | |

## 1972. Benjamin Franklin Issue Prominent Americans Series.

Honors the printer, writer, postmaster general and statesman with a stamp intended primarily to pay postage for educational materials. *Intaglio, perforated 10 1/2 x 11.*

669 *Benjamin Franklin*

| 669 | | MNHVF | UseVF |
|---|---|---|---|
| 7¢ | **light blue,** shiny gum tagged | .25 | .20 |
| | Plate block of 4 | .75 | |
| | m. matt gum | .25 | .20 |
| | Plate block of 4 | 1.35 | |
| | FDC *(Oct. 20, 1972)* | | 1.75 |
| | zo. Tagging omitted (error) | — | |
| | Plate block of 4 | — | |
| | zx. Untagged (Bureau precancel) | — | |

## 1972. CONTEMPORARY CHRISTMAS ISSUE Photogravure, perforated 11 x 10 1/2.

670 *Santa Claus*

| 670 | | | MNHVF | UseVF |
|---|---|---|---|---|
| 8¢ | **multicolored,** tagged | | .25 | .20 |
| | Plate block of 12 | | 3.00 | |
| | FDC *(Nov. 9, 1972)* | | | 1.75 |

## 1972. TRADITIONAL CHRISTMAS ISSUE

671 *Angels from painting* Mary, Queen of Heaven, *in the National Gallery of Art.*

| 671 | | | MNHVF | UseVF |
|---|---|---|---|---|
| 8¢ | **multicolored,** tagged | | .25 | .20 |
| | Plate block of 12 | | 3.00 | |
| | FDC *(Nov. 9, 1972)* | | | 1.75 |
| | v.  black omitted | | 4500. | |
| | v1. pink omitted | | 175. | |

## 1973. EUGENE O'NEILL COIL ISSUE see design for No. 632. *Intaglio and perforated 10 vertically. This was the first high-value stamp issued in tagged form.*

| 672 | | MNHVF | UseVF |
|---|---|---|---|
| $1 | **dark purple,** tagged | 2.00 | .75 |
| | Pair | 3.50 | |
| | Line pair | 5.00 | |
| | FDC *(Jan. 12, 1973)* | | 5.00 |
| | M. Matt gum | 2.00 | .75 |
| | Pair | 4.00 | |
| | Line pair | 10.00 | |
| | v.  Imperforate pair | 2250. | |
| | Imperforate line pair | 4250. | |

## 1973. AMADEO P. GIANNINI ISSUE Prominent Americans Series.
Honors the great American banker who rose from humble origins to develop the world's largest private bank. *Intaglio and perforated 11 x 10 1/2.*

673 *Amadeo P. Giannini*

| 673 | | MNHVF | UseVF |
|---|---|---|---|
| 21¢ | **banknote green,** tagged | .40 | .25 |
| | Plate block of 4 | 1.60 | |
| | FDC *(June 27, 1973)* | | 2.25 |

## 1973. TRADITIONAL CHRISTMAS ISSUE *Gravure, Andreotti press.*

664 Madonna and Child *by Raphael.*

| 674 | | MNHVF | UseVF |
|---|---|---|---|
| 8¢ | **multicolored,** tagged | .25 | .20 |
| | Plate block of 12 | 3.00 | |
| | Gutter pair | — | |
| | FDC *(Nov. 7, 1973)* | | 1.75 |

## 1973. CONTEMPORARY CHRISTMAS ISSUE

675 *Chirstmas Tree needlepoint by Dolli Tingle.*

| 675 | | MNHVF | UseVF |
|---|---|---|---|
| 8¢ | **multicolored,** tagged | .25 | .20 |
| | Plate block of 12 | 3.00 | |
| | Vertical gutter pair | — | |
| | FDC *(Nov. 7, 1973)* | | 1.75 |
| | v.  Imperforate-between vertical pair | 325. | |

## 1973. CROSSED FLAGS ISSUE was made available in anticipation of higher postal rates. Use of the 13-star flag in the design was in tribute to the American Revolution Bicentennial. *Intaglio, perforated 11 x 10 1/2.*

676, 677 *50-star and 13-star flags.*

| 676 | | MNHVF | UseVF |
|---|---|---|---|
| 10¢ | **red and blue,** tagged | .25 | .20 |
| | Plate block of 20 | 4.00 | |
| | FDC *(Dec. 8, 1973)* | | 1.75 |
| | v.  Blue omitted | 175. | |
| | v1. Imperforate-between horizontal pair | 50.00 | |
| | v2. Horizontal pair, imperforate vertically | — | |
| | v3. Imperforate-between horizontally vertical pair | 1150. | |
| | v4. Vertical pair, imperforate | 950. | |
| | zo. Tagging omitted (error) | 6.00 | |
| | Plate strip of 20 | — | |

## 1973. CROSSED FLAGS COIL ISSUE *Coil, intaglio, perforated 10 vertically.*

| 677 | | MNHVF | UseVF |
|---|---|---|---|
| 10¢ | **red and blue,** tagged | .40 | .25 |
| | Pair | 2.00 | |
| | Line pair | 4.75 | |
| | FDC *(Dec. 8, 1973)* | | 1.75 |
| | v.  Imperforate pair | 37.50 | |
| | Imperforate line pair | 10.00 | |
| | zo. Tagging omitted (error) | — | |
| | Pair | 20.00 | |

**1973. Jefferson Memorial Issue** met the new postal rates. *Intaglio, perforated 11 x 10 1/2.*

678, 679 *Jefferson Memorial*

| 678 | | MNHVF | UseVF |
|---|---|---|---|
| 10¢ | **blue,** tagged, type II or III | .25 | .20 |
| | Plate block of 4 | .85 | |
| | FDC *(Dec. 14, 1973)* | | 1.75 |
| | n. Booklet pane of 5 plus label | 1.50 | |
| | FDC | | 2.25 |
| | n1.Booklet pane of 6 *(Aug. 5, 1974)* | 5.75 | |
| | FDC | | 5.25 |
| | n2.Booklet pane of 8 | 1.75 | |
| | FDC | | 2.50 |
| | n2zo.Booklet pane of 8, tagging omitted (error) | — | |
| | v. Imperforate-between vertical pair | 800. | |
| | v1. Vertical pair, imperforate horizontally | 500. | |
| | zo. Tagging omitted (error) | — | |
| | zx. Untagged (Bureau precancel) | — | |
| | FDC | — | |

**1973. Jefferson Memorial Coil Issue**

| 679 | | MNHVF | UseVF |
|---|---|---|---|
| 10¢ | **blue,** tagged | .25 | .20 |
| | Pair | .40 | |
| | Line pair | .75 | |
| | FDC *(Dec. 14, 1973)* | | 1.75 |
| | v. Imperforate pair | — | |
| | Imperforate line pair | 40.00 | |
| | Imperforate, joint line pair | 75.00 | |
| | zx. Untagged (Bureau precancel) | 65.00 | |

**1974. Zip Code Issue** another in the series of new 10¢ stamps, underlined the importance of moving mail rapidly. *Gravure, perforated 11 x 10 1/2.*

680 *Zip moves mail rapidly*

| 680 | | MNHVF | UseVF |
|---|---|---|---|
| 10¢ | **multicolored,** tagged with small rectangle in center of stamp | .25 | .20 |
| | Plate block of 8 | 1.75 | |
| | Gutter pair | — | |
| | FDC *(Jan. 4, 1974)* | | 1.75 |
| | v. Yellow omitted | 50.00 | |
| | zv. Overall tagging (error) | — | |

## Prominent Americans Series

**1974. Elizabeth Blackwell Issue** honors the first woman medical doctor of modern time. *Intaglio and perforated 11 x 10 1/2.*

681 *Dr. Elizabeth Blackwell*

| 681 | | MNHVF | UseVF |
|---|---|---|---|
| 18¢ | **purple,** tagged | .30 | .25 |
| | Plate block of 4 | 1.25 | |
| | FDC *(Jan. 23, 1974)* | | 2.00 |

**1974. Swinging Bell Issue** Bulk rate coil. *Intaglio and perforated 10 vertically.*

682 *Swinging Bell*

| 682 | | MNHVF | UseVF |
|---|---|---|---|
| 6.3¢ | **brick red,** tagged | .25 | .20 |
| | Pair | .40 | |
| | Line pair | .75 | |
| | FDC *(Oct. 1, 1974)* | | 1.75 |
| | v. Imperforate pair | 200. | |
| | Imperforate line pair | 600. | |
| | zx. Untagged (Bureau precancel) | .25 | .20 |
| | Pair | .90 | |
| | Line pair | 1.50 | |
| | zxv.Imperforate pair | 100. | |
| | Imperforate line pair | 250. | |

**1974. Contemporary Christmas Issue** Gravure, perforated 11 x 10 1/2.

683 The Road - Winter, *by Currier and Ives.*

| 683 | | MNHVF | UseVF |
|---|---|---|---|
| 10¢ | **multicolored,** tagged | .25 | .20 |
| | Plate block of 12 | 2.25 | |
| | FDC *(Oct. 23, 1974)* | | 1.75 |
| | v. buff omitted, pane of 50 | 600. | |

**1974. Dove of Peace Issue** Christmas Series. The glue was very unstable, and has caused most stamps to discolor. *Imperforate, die cut, self-adhesive with backing.*

684 *Dove of Peace weather vane atop Mount Vernon.*

| 684 | | MNHVF | UseVF |
|---|---|---|---|
| 10¢ | **multicolored,** self-adhesive | .25 | .20 |
| | Plate block of 20 | 2.25 | |
| | FDC *(Nov. 15, 1974)* | | 3.00 |

## Christmas Series

**1974. Traditional Christmas Issue** *Perforated 10 1/2 x 11.*

685 The Perussis Altarpiece, *artist unknown, Metropolitan Museum of Art, New York City.*

| 685 | | MNHVF | UseVF |
|---|---|---|---|
| 10¢ | **multicolored,** tagged | .25 | .20 |
| | Plate block of 10 | 2.25 | |
| | FDC *(Oct. 23, 1974)* | | 1.75 |

**1975. CONTEMPORARY CHRISTMAS ISSUE** features stamps that for the first time in U.S. postal history were issued without a printed denomination. The stamps were valid for the first-class rate at the time of issue. *Gravure, perforated 11 1/4.*

686 *Louis Prang Christmas Card.*

| 686 | | MNHVF | UseVF |
|---|---|---|---|
| 10¢ | **multicolored,** tagged | .30 | .20 |
| | Plate block of 12 | 3.75 | |
| | FDC *(Oct. 14, 1975)* | | 1.75 |
| | v. Imperforate pair | 120. | |

**1974. CONTEMPORARY CHRISTMAS ISSUE** Gravure, perforated 11.

| 686A | | MNHVF | UseVF |
|---|---|---|---|
| 10¢ | **multicolored,** tagged | .30 | .20 |
| | Plate block of 12 | 3.75 | |
| | FDC *(Oct. 14, 1975)* | | |

**1975. CONTEMPORARY CHRISTMAS ISSUE** Gravure, perforated 10 1/2 x 11.

| 686B | | MNHVF | UseVF |
|---|---|---|---|
| 10¢ | **multicolored,** tagged | .30 | .20 |
| | Plate block of 12 | 3.75 | |
| | FDC *(Oct. 14, 1975)* | | |

**1975. TRADITIONAL CHRISTMAS ISSUE**

687 *Ghirlandaio* Madonna and Child

| 687 | | MNHVF | UseVF |
|---|---|---|---|
| 10¢ | **multicolored,** tagged | | |
| | Plate block of 12 | | |
| | Damaged "d" (plate flaw) | | |
| | FDC *(Oct. 14, 1975)* | | |
| | v. Imperforate pair | | |

## Americana Series

**1975. CAPITOL DOME ISSUE** *Intaglio, perforated 11*

688 *Capitol Dome*

| 688 | | MNHVF | UseVF |
|---|---|---|---|
| 9¢ | **green on gray paper,** tagged | .25 | .20 |
| | Plate block of 4 | .75 | |
| | FDC *(Nov. 24, 1975)* | | 1.75 |
| | m. Matt gum | 1.00 | .20 |
| | Plate block of 4 | 5.25 | |
| | zo. Tagging omitted (error) | — | |
| | zx. Untagged (Bureau precancel) | — | |

**1975. COLONIAL PRINTING PRESS ISSUE** Americana Series

689 *Early printing press*

| 689 | | MNHVF | UseVF |
|---|---|---|---|
| 11¢ | **orange on gray paper,** tagged | .25 | .20 |
| | Plate block of 4 | 1.00 | |
| | Gutter pair | — | |
| | FDC *(Nov. 13, 1975)* | | 1.75 |
| | zo. Tagging omitted (error) | 3.00 | |

**1975. FLAG OVER INDEPENDENCE HALL ISSUE** Americana Series Perforated 11 x 10 1/2. Huck Press.

690, 690A, 694 *Flag over Independence Hall.*

| 690 | | MNHVF | UseVF |
|---|---|---|---|
| 13¢ | **Dark blue and red,** perforated 11 x 10 1/2, tagged | .25 | .20 |
| | Plate block of 20 | 5.50 | |
| | FDC *(Nov. 15, 1975)* | | 1.75 |
| | v. Imperforate-between horizontal pair | 50.00 | |
| | v1. Imperforate vertical pair | 1000. | |

**1981. FLAG OVER INDEPENDENCE HALL COIL ISSUE** Americana Series
*Intaglio, Combination Press, perforated 11.*

| 690A | | MNHVF | UseVF |
|---|---|---|---|
| 13¢ | **dark blue and red,** perforated 11, tagged | .75 | 1.00 |
| | Plate block of 20 | 70.00 | |
| | v. Horizontal pair, imperforate vertically | — | |
| | v1. Imperforate vertical pair | 150. | |
| | zo. Tagging omitted (error) | 3.00 | |

**1975. EAGLE AND SHIELD ISSUE** Americana Series

691 *Eagle and shield.*

| 691 | | MNHVF | UseVF |
|---|---|---|---|
| 13¢ | **multicolored,** perforated 11 1/4, tagged with eagle-shape untagged area | .25 | .20 |
| | Plate block of 12 | 3.50 | |
| | Gutter pair | — | |
| | FDC *(Dec. 1, 1975)* | | |
| | v. Yellow omitted | 175. | |
| | v1. Imperforate pair | 50.00 | |

| 691A | | MNHVF | UseVF |
|---|---|---|---|
| 13¢ | **multicolored,** perforated 10 (line perforation) | 40.00 | 15.00 |
| | Plate block of 12 | 400. | |
| | FDC *(Dec. 1, 1975)* | | |

## 1975. OLD NORTH CHURCH ISSUE Americana Series

692 Old North Church, Boston

| 692 | | MNHVF | UseVF |
|---|---|---|---|
| 24¢ | **red on blue paper,** tagged | .50 | .25 |
| | Plate block of 4 | 2.00 | |
| | FDC *(Nov. 14, 1975)* | | 1.75 |
| | zo. Tagging omitted (error) | 5.00 | |
| | Plate block of 4 | 20.00 | |

## 1975. FRANCIS PARKMAN ISSUE Prominent Americans Series
*Coil, intaglio, perforated 10 horizontally.*

693 Francis Parkman

| 693 | | MNHVF | UseVF |
|---|---|---|---|
| 3¢ | **purple,** tagged | .25 | .20 |
| | Pair | .30 | |
| | Line pair | .35 | |
| | FDC *(Nov. 4, 1975)* | | 1.75 |
| | m. Matt gum | .25 | |
| | Pair | .30 | |
| | Line pair | .35 | |
| | v. Imperforate pair | 27.50 | |
| | Imperforate line pair | 45.00 | |
| | zx. Untagged (Bureau precancel) | .25 | |
| | Pair | .30 | |
| | Line pair | .35 | |
| | zxv. Imperforate pair | 6.50 | |
| | Imperforate line pair | 20.00 | |

## 1981. FLAG OVER INDEPENDENCE HALL COIL ISSUE Americana Series
*Intaglio, Combination Press, perforated 11.*

694 Flag over Independence Hall.

| 694 | | MNHVF | UseVF |
|---|---|---|---|
| 13¢ | **dark blue and red,** tagged | .25 | .20 |
| | Pair | .30 | |
| | Line pair | .45 | |
| | FDC *(Nov. 15, 1975)* | | |
| | v. Imperforate pair | 25.00 | |
| | zo. Tagging omitted (error) | — | |

## 1975. LIBERTY BELL ISSUE Americana Series
*Booklet panes, intaglio, perforated 11 x 10 1/2, matt gum.*

695, 696 Liberty Bell

| 695 | | MNHVF | UseVF |
|---|---|---|---|
| 13¢ | **brown,** from booklet panes only, tagged | .25 | .20 |
| | v. Imperforate-between vertical pair | 525. | |
| | FDC *(Oct. 31, 1975)* | | 1.75 |
| | Booklet pane of 5 plus label *April 2, 1976)* | 1.50 | 2.00 |
| | FDC | | 2.25 |
| | n. Booklet pane of 6 | 2.00 | 2.00 |
| | FDC | | 2.25 |
| | n1. Booklet pane of 7 plus label | 1.75 | 2.50 |
| | FDC | | 2.75 |
| | n2zo. Booklet pane of 7 plus label, tagging omitted (error) | — | |
| | n3. Booklet pane of 8 | 2.00 | 2.75 |
| | n3zo. Booklet pane of 8, tagging omitted (error) | — | |
| | FDC | | |

## 1975. LIBERTY BELL COIL ISSUE Americana Series
*Coil, intaglio, perforated 10 vertically*

| 696 | | MNHVF | UseVF |
|---|---|---|---|
| 13¢ | **brown,** shiny gum, tagged | .25 | .20 |
| | Pair | .50 | |
| | Line pair | .80 | |
| | FDC *(Nov. 25, 1975)* | | 1.75 |
| | m. Matt gum | .30 | |
| | Pair | .60 | |
| | Line pair | 2.00 | |
| | v. Imperforate pair | 25.00 | |
| | Imperforate line pair | 60.00 | |
| | v1. Imperforate-between pair | 1400. | |
| | zx. Untagged (Bureau precancel) | .50 | .50 |
| | Pair | 1.00 | |
| | Line pair | 6.50 | |
| | zx. Untagged (Bureau precancel) matt gum | — | |
| | zo. Tagging omitted (error) | — | |

## 1976. CAPITOL DOME ISSUE Americana Series

697 Capitol Dome

| 697 | | MNHVF | UseVF |
|---|---|---|---|
| 9¢ | **green on gray paper,** shiny gum, tagged | .25 | .20 |
| | Pair | .40 | |
| | Line pair | 1.00 | |
| | FDC *(March 5, 1976)* | | 1.75 |
| | m. Matt gum | — | |
| | Pair | — | |
| | Line pair | — | |
| | v. Imperforate pair | 160. | |
| | v1. Imperforate line pair | 375. | |
| | zx. Untagged (Bureau precancel) | — | .35 |
| | zxv. Imperforate pair | 800. | |
| | Imperforate line pair | 2000. | |

## 1976. AMERICAN EAGLE AND DRUM ISSUE Americana Series

698 American eagle and drum.

| 698 | | MNHVF | UseVF |
|---|---|---|---|
| 7.9¢ | **red on canary paper,** shiny gum, tagged | .25 | .20 |
| | Pair | .50 | |
| | Line pair | 3.75 | |
| | FDC *(April 23, 1976)* | | 1.75 |
| | m. Matt gum | — | |
| | Pair | — | |
| | Line pair | — | |
| | zx. Untagged (Bureau precancel) | 2.00 | |
| | v. Imperforate pair | 575. | |
| | v1. Imperforate line pair | — | |

**1976. CONTEMPORARY CHRISTMAS ISSUE** Currier's Winter Pastime. Two presses were used in its production - a gravure press and a new multicolor press. The gravure press has all-over tagging and the lettering at the base is black; The multicolor press printing (70 percent of the issue) has block tagging and gray-black lettering at the base.

699, 699A *Winter Pastime*

| 699 | | MNHVF | UseVF |
|---|---|---|---|
| 13¢ | **multicolored,** overall tagging | .40 | .25 |
| | Plate block of 10 | 4.00 | |
| | FDC *(Oct. 27, 1976)* | | 1.75 |
| | v. Imperforate pair | 95.00 | |

| 699A | | MNHVF | UseVF |
|---|---|---|---|
| 13¢ | **multicolored,** block tagging | .40 | .25 |
| | Plate block of 20 | 7.75 | |
| | FDC *(Oct. 27, 1976)* | | 2.00 |
| | v. Imperforate pair | 1.00 | |
| | v1. Imperforate-between vertical pair | — | |
| | v2. red omitted | — | |
| | v3. yellow omitted | — | |
| | zo. Tagging omitted (error) | 12.50 | |

**1976. TRADITIONAL CHRISTMAS ISSUE** The religious theme features John Singleton Copley's *Nativity*, Gravure.

700 *Nativity*

| 700 | | MNHVF | UseVF |
|---|---|---|---|
| 13¢ | **multicolored,** tagged | .40 | .25 |
| | Plate block of 12 | 4.75 | |
| | FDC *(Oct. 27, 1976)* | | |
| | v. Imperforate pair | 120. | |

**1976. SAXHORNS ISSUE** Americana Series
*Coil, intaglio, perforated 10 vertically.*

701 *Saxhorns*

| 701 | | MNHVF | UseVF |
|---|---|---|---|
| 7.7¢ | **brown on canary paper,** tagged | .25 | .20 |
| | Pair | .50 | |
| | Line pair | 1.00 | |
| | FDC *(Nov. 20, 1976)* | | 1.75 |
| | zx. Untagged (Bureau precancel) | 4.00 | |
| | zxv. Imperforate pair | 1750. | |
| | Imperforate line pair | 4500. | |

**1977. CAPITOL DOME ISSUE** Americana Series
**Americana Series Vending Machine Booklet** consists of seven 13¢ stamps and one 9¢ stamp in a single pane. *Intaglio, produced with two different perforations.*

702, 703 *Capitol dome and flag over Capitol.*

| 702 | | MNHVF | UseVF |
|---|---|---|---|
| 9¢ | **green,** tagged | 50.00 | .75 |
| | FDC *(March 11, 1977)* | | 10.00 |

**1977. CAPITOL DOME ISSUE** Americana Series
*Perforated 10*

| 702A | | MNHVF | UseVF |
|---|---|---|---|
| 9¢ | **green** | 20.00 | 22.50 |
| | FDC *(March 11, 1977)* | | 15.00 |

**1977. FLAG OVER CAPITOL ISSUE** Americana Series
Perforated 11 x 10 1/2.

| 703 | | MNHVF | UseVF |
|---|---|---|---|
| 13¢ | **red and blue,** tagged | .25 | .20 |
| | FDC *(March 11, 1977)* | | 2.50 |
| | n. Booklet pane of 8 (7 No. 703 and 1 No. 702) | 2.75 | |
| | FDC Bureau precancel | | 25.00 |
| | y. Se-tenant pair, No. 703, 702 | 1.00 | 1.00 |

**1977. FLAG OVER CAPITOL ISSUE** Americana Series
Perforated 10.

| 703A | | MNHVF | UseVF |
|---|---|---|---|
| 13¢ | **red and blue** | .75 | .50 |
| | FDC *(March 11, 1977)* | | 2.00 |
| | n. Booklet pane of 8 (7 No. 703A and 1 No. 702A) | 30.00 | 18.50 |
| | FDC Bureau precancel | | 15.00 |
| | y. Se-tenant pair, No. 703A, 702A | 25.00 | |

**1977. RURAL MAIL BOX ISSUE** Christmas Series
*Gravure*

704 *Rural mail box*

| 704 | | MNHVF | UseVF |
|---|---|---|---|
| 13¢ | **multicolored** | .40 | .20 |
| | Plate block of 10 | 4.00 | |
| | FDC *(Oct. 21, 1977)* | | 1.75 |
| | v. Imperforate pair | 300. | |
| | zv. Overall tagging (error) | — | |

## 1977. WASHINGTON KNEELING AT PRAYER Christmas Series

705 *Gen. Washington kneeling at prayer.*

| 705 | | MNHVF | UseVF |
|---|---|---|---|
| 13¢ | **multicolored,** tagged | .40 | .20 |
| | Plate strip of 20 | 8.00 | |
| | FDC *(Oct. 21, 1977)* | | 1.75 |
| | v. Imperforate pair | 70.00 | |
| | zv. Overall tagging (error) | — | |

*The multicolor combination press issue (No. 705) has "floating" plate numbers, a set of five numbers sandwiched between two or three blanks, so that on a plate strip of 20 there are five numbers and five blanks, six numbers and four blanks, seven numbers and three blanks or eight numbers and two blanks. There are no Zip or Mail Early slogans.*

## 1977. CONTEMPLATION OF JUSTICE ISSUE Americana Series
*Intaglio and perforated 11 x 10 1/2.*

708, 709 *Contemplation of Justice*

| 708 | | MNHVF | UseVF |
|---|---|---|---|
| 10¢ | **purple on gray paper,** shiny gum, tagged | .25 | .20 |
| | Plate block of 4 | .70 | |
| | FDC *(Nov. 17, 1977)* | | 1.75 |
| | m. Matt gum | .25 | .20 |
| | Plate block of 4 | 1.00 | |
| | zo. Tagging omitted (error) | — | |
| | zx. Untagged (Bureau precancel) | — | |

## 1977. CONTEMPLATION OF JUSTICE COIL ISSUE Americana Series
*Coil, intaglio and perforated 10 vertically.*

| 709 | | MNHVF | UseVF |
|---|---|---|---|
| 10¢ | **purple on gray paper,** tagged | .25 | .20 |
| | Pair | .40 | |
| | Line pair | 1.00 | |
| | FDC *(Nov. 4, 1977)* | | 1.75 |
| | v. Imperforate pair | 70.00 | |
| | Imperforate line pair | 125. | |
| | m. Matt gum | .50 | .20 |
| | Pair | .75 | |
| | Line pair | 2.50 | |
| | mv. Imperforate pair | 70.00 | |
| | Imperforate line pair | — | |
| | zx. Untagged (Bureau precancel) | 2.00 | |

## 1977. QUILL PEN AND INKWELL ISSUE Americana Series
*Intaglio.*

710 *Quill pen and inkwell*

| 710 | | MNHVF | UseVF |
|---|---|---|---|
| 1¢ | **blue on green paper,** tagged | .25 | .20 |
| | Plate block of 4 | .25 | |
| | Gutter pair | — | |
| | FDC *(Dec. 8, 1977)* | | 1.75 |
| | m. Matt gum | .25 | .20 |
| | Plate block of 4 | .25 | |
| | z. Untagged (Bureau precancel) | — | |
| | zo. Tagging omitted (error) | — | |
| | p. White paper | — | |

## 1977. SYMBOLS OF SPEECH ISSUE Americana Series

711 *Symbols of speech*

| 711 | | MNHVF | UseVF |
|---|---|---|---|
| 2¢ | **brown on green paper** | .50 | .20 |
| | Plate block of 4 | 2.00 | |
| | FDC *(Dec. 8, 1977)* | | |
| | m. Matt gum | .25 | .20 |
| | Plate block of 4 | .25 | |
| | xo. Tagging omitted (error) | — | |
| | zx. Untagged (Bureau precancel) | — | |

## 1981. SYMBOLS OF SPEECH ISSUE Americana Series

| 711A | | MNHVF | UseVF |
|---|---|---|---|
| 2¢ | **brown on white paper,** matt gum, tagged | .25 | .20 |
| | Plate block of 4 | .30 | |
| | FDC *(Nov. 7, 1981)* | | 1.00 |

## 1977. BALLOT BOX ISSUE Americana Series

712 *Ballot box*

| 712 | | MNHVF | UseVF |
|---|---|---|---|
| 3¢ | **olive on green paper,** shiny gum, tagged | .25 | .20 |
| | Plate block of 4 | .30 | |
| | Gutter pair | — | |
| | FDC *(Dec. 8, 1977)* | | 1.75 |
| | m. Matt gum | .25 | .20 |
| | Plate block of 4 | .50 | |
| | zo. Tagging omitted (error) | — | |
| | zx. Untagged (Bureau precancel) | — | |

## 1977. READING AND LEARNING ISSUE Americana Series

713 *Reading and learning*

| 713 | | MNHVF | UseVF |
|---|---|---|---|
| 4¢ | **maroon on green paper,** tagged | .25 | .20 |
| | Plate block of 4 | .50 | |
| | FDC *(Dec. 8, 1977)* | | 1.75 |
| | m. Matt gum | .25 | .20 |
| | Plate block of 4 | 1.25 | |
| | zo. Tagging omitted (error) | — | |
| | zx. Untagged (Bureau precancel) | — | |

## 1978. INDIAN HEAD PENNY ISSUE Experimental Stamp Issue.
For the first time, a U.S. difinitive was specially designed in a smaller size so that 150 stamps could be produced in place of the usual 100 stamp pane. *Intaglio, perforated 11.*

714 *Indian Head smaller penny*

**714**

| | | MNHVF | UseVF |
|---|---|---|---|
| 13¢ | **brown and blue on tan paper,** tagged | .25 | .20 |
| | Plate block of 4 | 1.75 | |
| | Gutter pair | — | |
| | FDC *(Jan. 11, 1978)* | | 1.75 |
| | v. Horizontal pair, imperforate vertically | 275. | |
| | zo. Tagging omitted (error) | — | |

**1978. STATUE OF LIBERTY ISSUE** Americana Series
*Intaglio and perforated 11 x 10 1/2.*

715, 716 *Statue of Liberty*

**715**

| | | MNHVF | UseVF |
|---|---|---|---|
| 16¢ | **blue,** tagged | .30 | .20 |
| | Plate block of 4 | 1.50 | |
| | FDC *(March 31, 1978)* | | |

**1978. STATUE OF LIBERTY COIL ISSUE** Americana Series
*Coil, intaglio, perforated 10 vertically.*

**716**

| | | MNHVF | UseVF |
|---|---|---|---|
| 16¢ | **blue,** overall tagging | .35 | .20 |
| | Pair | .70 | |
| | Line pair | 1.50 | |
| | FDC *(March 31, 1978)* | | 1.75 |
| | z. Block tagging | — | |
| | Pair | — | |

**1978. SANDY HOOK LIGHTHOUSE ISSUE** Americana Series
*Intaglio and perforated 11 x 10 1/2.*

717 *Sandy Hook Lighthouse*

**717**

| | | MNHVF | UseVF |
|---|---|---|---|
| 29¢ | **blue on blue paper,** shiny gum, tagged | .50 | .65 |
| | Plate block of 4 | 2.75 | |
| | FDC *(April 14, 1978)* | | 1.75 |
| | m. Matt gum | 2.00 | .25 |
| | Plate block of 4 | 15.25 | |

**1978. "A" STAMP ISSUE** Non-Denominated "A" Stamp Issue marks the new first class postage rate (15 cents) which went into effect May 29. The stamps were printed in 1975 and 1976 and had been stored for use in this contingency. Gravure.

718-720 *"A" design to left of stylized eagle.*

**718**

| | | MNHVF | UseVF |
|---|---|---|---|
| 15¢ | **orange,** perforated 11, tagged | .30 | .25 |
| | Plate block of 4 | 1.50 | |
| | FDC *(May 22, 1978)* | | 1.75 |
| | v. Imperforate pair | 95.00 | |
| | v1. Vertical pair, imperforate horizontally | 750. | |

**1978. "A" STAMP ISSUE**

**718A**

| | | MNHVF | UseVF |
|---|---|---|---|
| 15¢ | **orange,** perforated 11 1/4, tagged | .30 | .25 |
| | Plate block of 4 | 1.50 | |
| | FDC *(May 22, 1978)* | | |

**1978. "A" BOOKLET STAMP ISSUE** *Booklet stamps, intaglio, perforated 11 x 10 1/2.*

**719**

| | | MNHVF | UseVF |
|---|---|---|---|
| 15¢ | **orange,** tagged | .25 | .20 |
| | FDC *(May 22, 1978)* | | 1.75 |
| | n. Booklet pane of 8 | 2.25 | 2.75 |
| | FDC | | 3.00 |
| | v. Vertical pair, imperforate between | 1750. | |

**1978. "A" STAMP COIL ISSUE** *Coil, intaglio, perforated 10 vertically.*

**720**

| | | MNHVF | UseVF |
|---|---|---|---|
| 15¢ | **orange,** tagged | .25 | .15 |
| | Pair | .50 | |
| | Line pair | .75 | |
| | FDC *(May 22, 1978)* | | 1.75 |
| | v. Imperforate pair | 95.00 | |
| | Imperforate line pair | 195. | |

## Great American Series

**1978. OLIVER W. HOLMES ISSUE** same design as No. 626 issued to meet the new postal rates. *Intaglio, coil, perforated 10 vertically.*

**721**

| | | MNHVF | UseVF |
|---|---|---|---|
| 15¢ | **maroon,** Type I, tagged | .25 | .20 |
| | Pair | .50 | |
| | Line pair | 1.25 | |
| | FDC *(June 14, 1978)* | | |
| | m. Matt gum , type I | .25 | .20 |
| | Pair | 1.25 | |
| | Line pair | 2.00 | |
| | zx. Untagged (Bureau precancel) | 42.50 | 4.00 |
| | v. Imperforate pair | 30.00 | |
| | Imperforate line pair, shiny gum | 75.00 | |
| | mv. Imperforate pair, matt gum | 50.00 | |
| | v1. Imperforate-between pair | — | |
| | Imperforate-between line pair | 225. | |

**721A**

| | | MNHVF | UseVF |
|---|---|---|---|
| 15¢ | **maroon,** type II shiny gum, tagged | .25 | .20 |
| | Pair | .50 | |
| | Line pair | 2.50 | |
| | m. Matt gum | .35 | |
| | Pair | .70 | |
| | Line pair | 2.00 | |
| | mv. Imperforate pair, matt gum | .90 | |
| | Imperforate line pair, matt gum | 300. | |

*For booklet pane issued the same date see No. 626.*

**1978. AMERICAN FLAG ISSUE** Americana Series
Fort McHenry flag which, in 1814, inspired Francis Scott Key to compose the *The Star Spangled Banner. Intaglio.*

722, 722A, 723 *American flag*

**722**

| | | MNHVF | UseVF |
|---|---|---|---|
| 15¢ | **red, blue and gray,** perforated 10, tagged | .30 | .20 |
| | Plate block of 20 | 7.00 | |
| | FDC *(June 30, 1978)* | | 1.75 |
| | v. Gray omitted | 600. | |
| | v1. Imperforate vertical pair | 25.00 | |
| | zo. Tagging omitted (error) | — | |

**1978. AMERICAN FLAG BOOKLET ISSUE** Americana Series

**722A**

| | | MNHVF | UseVF |
|---|---|---|---|
| 15¢ | **red, blue and gray,** booklet stamp, perforated 11 x 10 1/2, tagged | .35 | .20 |
| | FDC *(June 30, 1978)* | | 1.75 |
| | n. Booklet pane of 8 | 3.50 | 2.50 |
| | FDC Bureau precancel | | 2.75 |

## 1978. AMERICAN FLAG COIL ISSUE Americana Series
*Coil, intaglio, perforated 10 vertically.*

| 723 | | MNHVF | UseVF |
|---|---|---|---|
| 15¢ | **red, blue and gray** | .25 | .20 |
| | Pair | 1.00 | |
| | FDC *(June 30, 1978)* | | 1.75 |
| | v. Imperforate pair | 25.00 | |
| | v1. Imperforate-between pair | 165. | |
| | v2. Gray omitted | 35.00 | |
| | zo. Tagging omitted (error) | — | |

## 1978. AMERICAN ROSES ISSUE *Perforated 10, booklet, intaglio.*

724 Two roses: Red Masterpiece (1974 Rose of the Year) and Medallion (winner of two high honors).

| 724 | | MNHVF | UseVF |
|---|---|---|---|
| 15¢ | **orange, red and green,** booklet stamp, tagged | .25 | .20 |
| | FDC *(July 11, 1978)* | | 1.75 |
| | n. Booklet pane of 8 | 2.25 | 3.00 |
| | nv. Imperforate pane of 8 | — | |
| | nv1. Imperforate pair | 400. | |
| | nzo. Pane of 8, tagging omitted (error) | — | |

## 1978. STEINWAY GRAND PIANO ISSUE Americana Series
bulk rate coil. *Intaglio, perforated 10 vertically.*

725 Steinway grand piano

| 725 | | MNHVF | UseVF |
|---|---|---|---|
| 8.4¢ | **blue on canary paper,** shiny gum, tagged | .25 | .20 |
| | Pair | .40 | |
| | Line pair | 3.75 | |
| | FDC *(July 13, 1978)* | | 1.75 |
| | zx. Untagged (Bureau precancel) | 40.00 | 25.00 |
| | zxv. Imperforate pair | 15.00 | |
| | Imperforate line pair | 25.00 | |
| | zxv1. Imperforate-between pair | 50.00 | |
| | Imperforate-between line pair | 135. | |
| | m. Matt gum | — | |
| | Pair | — | |
| | Line pair | — | |

## 1978. BLOCKHOUSE ISSUE Americana Series
*Intaglio, perforated 11 x 10 1/2.*

726 Reconstructed blockhouse at Fort Nisqually, Washington.

| 726 | | MNHVF | UseVF |
|---|---|---|---|
| 28¢ | **brown on blue paper,** tagged, shiny gum | .50 | .20 |
| | Plate block of 4 | 2.40 | |
| | FDC *(Aug. 11, 1978)* | | 1.75 |
| | m. Matt gum | 1.25 | .25 |
| | Plate block of 4 | 10.00 | |

## 1978. CONTEMPORARY CHRISTMAS ISSUE Christmas Series
*Gravure, perforated 11.*

727 Child astride a hobby horse, by Dolli Tingle.

| 727 | | MNHVF | UseVF |
|---|---|---|---|
| 15¢ | **multicolored,** tagged | .40 | .20 |
| | Plate block of 12 | 5.50 | |
| | Gutter pair | — | |
| | FDC *(Oct, 18, 1978)* | | 1.75 |
| | v. Imperforate pair | 95.00 | |
| | v1. Vertical pair, imperforate horizontally | 2250. | |

## 1978. MADONNA AND CHILD WITH CHERUBIM ISSUE

728 Madonna and Child with Cherubim, sculpture by Andrea della Robbia.

| 728 | | MNHVF | UseVF |
|---|---|---|---|
| 15¢ | **multicolored,** tagged | .40 | .20 |
| | Plate block of 12 | 5.50 | |
| | FDC *(Oct. 18, 1978)* | | 1.75 |
| | v. Imperforate pair | 90.00 | |
| | v1. Verticle pair, imperforate between | 22.50 | |
| | v2. Vertical pair, imperforate horizontal | | 725. |

## 1978. KEROSENE TABLE LAMP ISSUE Americana Series
*Intaglio and offset.*

729 Kerosene table lamp

| 729 | | MNHVF | UseVF |
|---|---|---|---|
| $2 | **multicolored,** tagged | 3.50 | 1.00 |
| | Plate block of 4 | 14.50 | |
| | FDC *(Nov. 16, 1978)* | | 7.00 |

## 1979. RUSH LAMP AND CANDLE HOLDER ISSUE Americana Series
*Intaglio and offset, perforated 11.*

730 Rush lamp and candle holder

| 730 | | MNHVF | UseVF |
|---|---|---|---|
| $1 | **multicolored,** tagged | 2.00 | 1.25 |
| | Plate block of 4 | 9.50 | |
| | FDC *(July 2, 1979)* | | 3.50 |
| | v. Brown inverted | — | |
| | v1. Brown omitted | 275. | |
| | v2. Orange, tan and yellow omitted | 350. | |
| | zo. Tagging omitted (error) | — | |

## 1979. RAILROAD CONDUCTOR'S LANTERN ISSUE Americana Series

731 *Railroad conductor's lantern*

| 731 | | MNHVF | UseVF |
|---|---|---|---|
| $5 | **multicolored,** tagged | 8.50 | 2.25 |
| | Plate block of 4 | 33.00 | |
| | FDC *(Aug. 23, 1979)* | | |

## 1979. COUNTRY SCHOOLHOUSE ISSUE Americana Series
*Intaglio, perforated 11 x 10 1/2.*

732 *Country schoolhouse, Morris Township School No. 2*

| 732 | | MNHVF | UseVF |
|---|---|---|---|
| 30¢ | **green on blue paper,** tagged | 1.00 | .30 |
| | Plate block of 4 | 2.50 | |
| | FDC *(Aug. 27, 1979)* | | 1.75 |
| | zo. Tagging omitted (error) | — | |

## 1979. IRON "BETTY" LAMP ISSUE Americana Series

733 *Iron "Betty" lamp*

| 733 | | MNHVF | UseVF |
|---|---|---|---|
| 50¢ | **black, orange and tan,** tagged | 1.00 | .30 |
| | Plate block of 4 | 3.50 | |
| | FDC *(Sept. 11, 1979)* | | 2.00 |
| | v. Black omitted | 300. | |
| | v1. Vertical pair, imperforate horizontally | 1750. | |
| | zo. Tagging omitted (error) | — | |

## 1979. SANTA CLAUS CHRISTMAS TREE ORNAMENT ISSUE *Gravure press, perforated 11.*

734 *Santa Claus Christmas tree ornament.*

| 734 | | MNHVF | UseVF |
|---|---|---|---|
| 15¢ | **multicolored,** tagged | .45 | .20 |
| | Plate block of 12 | 5.50 | |
| | FDC *(Oct. 18, 1979)* | | 1.75 |
| | v. Green & yellow omitted | 575. | |
| | v1. Green, yellow & tan omitted | 650. | |

## 1979. TRADITIONAL CHRISTMAS ISSUE Gravure, perforated 11.

735 *Madonna and Child from the Gerard David painting* The Rest on the Flight into Egypt. National gallery of Art, Washington D.C.

| 735 | | MNHVF | UseVF |
|---|---|---|---|
| 15¢ | **multicolored,** tagged | .45 | .20 |
| | Plate block of 12 | 5.50 | |
| | FDC *(Oct. 18, 1979)* | | 1.75 |
| | v. Imperforate pair | 90.00 | |
| | v1. Imperforate-between vertical pair | 2250. | |
| | v2. Vertical pair, imperforate horizontally | 750. | |

## 1979. STANDARD SIX-STRING GUITAR ISSUE Americana Series
Non-profit coil, *Intaglio, perforated 10 vertically.*

736 *Standard six-string guitar.*

| 736 | | MNHVF | UseVF |
|---|---|---|---|
| 3.1¢ | **brown on canary paper,** tagged | .25 | .20 |
| | Pair | .35 | |
| | Line pair | 1.50 | |
| | FDC *(Oct. 25, 1979)* | | 1.75 |
| | v. Imperforate pair | 1500. | |
| | Imperforate line pair | 3750. | |
| | zx. Untagged (Bureau precancel) | 4.00 | .25 |

## 1980. HISTORIC WINDMILLS ISSUE  *Intaglio, perforated 10 1/2 .*

737 *Robertso Windmill, Williamsburg, Va.;* 738 *Replica of The Old Windmill, Portsmouth, Rhode Island;* 739 *Cape Cod Windmill, Eastham, Massachusetts;* 740 *Dutch Mill at Fabyan Park Forest Preserve, near Batavia, Illinois;* 741 *A Southwestern Windmill*

| 737 | | MNHVF | UseVF |
|---|---|---|---|
| 15¢ | Virginia, **brown on yellow paper,** tagged | .30 | .20 |

| 738 | | MNHVF | UseVF |
|---|---|---|---|
| 15¢ | Rhode Island, **brown on yellow paper,** tagged | .30 | .20 |

| 739 | | MNHVF | UseVF |
|---|---|---|---|
| 15¢ | Massachusetts, **brown on yellow paper,** tagged | .30 | .20 |

| 740 | | MNHVF | UseVF |
|---|---|---|---|
| 15¢ | Illinois, **brown on yellow paper,** tagged | .30 | .20 |

| 741 | | MNHVF | UseVF |
|---|---|---|---|
| 15¢ | South Western, **brown on yellow paper,** tagged | .30 | .20 |
| | FDC *(Feb. 7, 1980)* any singles, Date | | 2.00 |
| | a. Se-tenant strip of 5 | 1.50 | .75 |
| | n. Booklet pane of 10 (2 of each design) | 3.50 | 4.50 |
| | FDC Bureau precancel | | 10.00 |

## 1980. QUILL PEN AND INKWELL ISSUE Americana Series
"The Ability to Write - A Root of Democracy - same design as No. 710. *Intaglio, perforated 10 vertically.*

| 742 | | MNHVF | UseVF |
|---|---|---|---|
| 1¢ | **blue on green paper,** shiny gum, tagged | .25 | .20 |
| | Pair | .25 | |
| | Line pair | .50 | |
| | FDC *(March 6, 1980)* | | 1.75 |
| | m. Matt gum | .25 | .20 |
| | Pair | .25 | |
| | Line pair | .50 | |
| | mv. Imperforate pair | 175. | |
| | Imperforate line pair | 275. | |
| | zo. Tagging omitted (error) | — | |

**1980. DOLLEY MADISON ISSUE** honors the wife of James Madison on the anniversary of her death. The stamp was produced on the mini-stamp format identical in size to the 1978 Indian Head Cent stamp (No. 714). *Intaglio, perforated 11.*

743 *Dolley Madison, pencil sketch from Gilbert Stuart painting.*

| 743 | | MNHVF | UseVF |
|---|---|---|---|
| 15¢ | **red brown and sepia,** tagged | .40 | .20 |
| | Plate block of 4 | 2.00 | |
| | FDC *(May 20, 1980)* | | 1.75 |

**1980. WEAVER MANUFACTURED VIOLINS ISSUE** Americana Series Coil stamp to meet non-profit organization rate. *Intaglio, perforated 10 vertically.*

744 *Weaver manufactured violins.*

| 744 | | MNHVF | UseVF |
|---|---|---|---|
| 3.5¢ | **purple on yellow paper,** tagged | .25 | .20 |
| | Pair | .25 | |
| | Line pair | 1.00 | |
| | FDC *(June 12, 1980)* | | 1.75 |
| | v.  Imperforate pair | 225. | |
| | Imperforate line pair | 325. | |
| | zx. Untagged (Bureau precancel) | .25 | .20 |
| | Pair | .50 | |
| | Line pair | 2.00 | |

**1980. CONTEMPORARY CHRISTMAS ISSUE** *Gravure, perforated 11.*

745 *Season's Greetings, toys on a window sill.*

| 745 | | MNHVF | UseVF |
|---|---|---|---|
| 15¢ | **multicolored,** tagged | .50 | .20 |
| | Plate block of 20 | 10.00 | |
| | v.  Light brown omitted | 25.00 | |
| | v1. Imperforate pair | 85.00 | |
| | v2. Vertical pair, imperforate horizontally | — | |
| | v3. Plate block of 20, imperforate | 850. | |
| | v4. Horizontal pair, imperforate vertically | 3400. | |
| | zo. Tagging omitted (error) | — | |
| | FDC *(Oct. 31, 1980)* | | 1.75 |

**1980. TRADITIONAL CHRISTMAS ISSUE** Gravure, perforated 11.

746 *Vignette of Madonna and Child from the Epiphany Window. Bethlehem Chapel at Washington Cathedral.*

| 746 | | MNHVF | UseVF |
|---|---|---|---|
| 15¢ | **multicolored,** tagged | .50 | .20 |
| | Plate block of 12 | 5.50 | |
| | Gutter Pair | — | |
| | FDC *(Oct. 31, 1980)* | | 1.75 |
| | v.  Imperforate pair | 85.00 | |
| | v1. Plate block of 12, imperforate | 650. | |

**1980. SEQUOYAH ISSUE** Great American Series honored the Cherokee Indian scholar who devised a written alphabet for his tribe. This was the first issue of a new series. *Intaglio, perforated 11 x 10 1/2.*

747 *Sketch from portrait of Sequoyah by Charles Banks Wilson.*

| 747 | | MNHVF | UseVF |
|---|---|---|---|
| 19¢ | **brown,** tagged | .30 | .20 |
| | Plate block of 4 | | |
| | FDC *(Dec. 27, 1980)* | 1.25 | 1.75 |

**1980. WASHINGTON COIL ISSUE** Great American Series

747A *"Shaved" Washington coil*

| 747A | | MNHVF | UseVF |
|---|---|---|---|
| 5¢ | **deep blue,** tagged | | |
| | Pair | | |
| | Line pair | | |
| | FDC *(April 1981)* | | |
| | v.  Imperforate pair | | |

**1981. NON-DENOMINATED "B" STAMP ISSUE** marks the change of the 1st class domestic postage rate to 18¢ which went into effect March 22, 1981. The design was identical to the "A" stamp except for the background color and the letter. *Gravure, perforated 11.*

748-750 *"B" to left of stylized eagle.*

| 748 | | MNHVF | UseVF |
|---|---|---|---|
| 18¢ | **purple,** tagged | .30 | .20 |
| | Plate block of 4 | 1.40 | |
| | Gutter Pair | — | |
| | FDC *(March 15, 1981)* | | 200. |

**1981. NON-DENOMINATED "B" BOOKLET PANE ISSUE** Booklet pane, intaglio, perforated 10.

| 749 | | MNHVF | UseVF |
|---|---|---|---|
| 18¢ | **purple,** tagged | | |
| | FDC *(March 15, 1981),* single | | 1.75 |
| | n.  Booklet pane of 8 | 3.50 | 3.50 |
| | FDC Bureau precancel | | 4.00 |

**1981. NON-DENOMINATION "B" COIL ISSUE** Coil, intaglio, perforated 10 vertically.

| 750 | | MNHVF | UseVF |
|---|---|---|---|
| 18¢ | **purple,** tagged | .60 | .25 |
| | Pair | .80 | |
| | Line pair | 1.65 | |
| | FDC *(March 15, 1981)* | | 1.75 |
| | v. Imperforate pair | 120. | |
| | Imperforate line pair | 200. | |

**U.S. Postal Service Plate-Numbering Change**

*In response to collector complaints that its plate-numbering system resulted in many inconvenient and costly blocks of 10, 12 and 20 stamps, the USPS in Jan. 1981 instituted a new plate number arrangement. Under the new system, most sheets were to contain a single plate number consisting of 1 (for monocolor stamps) to 6 digits, each digit representing a given printing plate and color, thus, under this system most plate blocks returned to blocks of 4.*

*Booklet panes hereafter also contain a plate number in the selvage.*

*In coils, a plate number was incorporated into some stamps in the roll, at various intervals between stamps.*

**1981. FREEDOM OF CONSCIENCE ISSUE** Americana Series
Freedom of Conscience - an American right. *Intaglio, perforated 11 x 10 1/2.*

751, 752 *Torch in the upraised right hand of the Statue of Liberty.*

| 751 | | MNHVF | UseVF |
|---|---|---|---|
| 12¢ | **brown on gray paper,** tagged | .25 | .20 |
| | Plate block of 4 | 1.15 | |
| | FDC *(April 8, 1981)* | | 1.75 |
| | zo. Tagging omitted (error) | — | |

**1981. FREEDOM OF CONSCIENCE ISSUE** Americana Series
Coil, intaglio, perforated 10 vertically.

| 752 | | MNHVF | UseVF |
|---|---|---|---|
| 12¢ | **brown on gray paper,** tagged | | |
| | Pair | | |
| | Line pair | | |
| | FDC *(April 8, 1981)* | | |
| | v. Imperforate pair | | |
| | Imperforate line pair | | |
| | zx. Untagged (Bureau precancel) | | |

**1981. AMERICA THE BEAUTIFUL ISSUE** features an American flag across the top and a scene beneath and a phrase from the song *America the Beautiful,* written by Katherine Lee Bates in 1893. *Intaglio, perforated 11.*

753 *"...for amber waves of grain"*

| 753 | | MNHVF | UseVF |
|---|---|---|---|
| 18¢ | **multicolored,** tagged | .30 | .20 |
| | Plate block of 20 | 8.50 | |
| | FDC *(April 24, 1981)* | | 1.75 |
| | v. Imperforate pair | 100. | |
| | v1. Vertical pair, imperforate horizontally | 1000. | |

**1981. AMERICA THE BEAUTIFUL ISSUE** Coil, perforated 10 vertically.

754 *"...from sea to shining sea"*

| 754 | | MNHVF | UseVF |
|---|---|---|---|
| 18¢ | **multicolored,** tagged | .30 | .20 |
| | Pair | .50 | |
| | v. Imperforate pair | 25.00 | |
| | v1. Imperforate-between pair | — | |
| | zo. Tagging omitted (error) | — | |
| | FDC *(April 24, 1981)* | | 1.75 |

*Listings and prices for plate number coil strips and singles appear at the end of this definitives section of the Krause- Minkus catalog.*

**1981. AMERICA THE BEAUTIFUL COMBINATION BOOKLET** consisting of two 6¢ and six 18¢ stamps. *Intaglio, perforated 11 x 10 1/2.*

755 *Circle of Stars*

756 *"...for purple mountain majesties"*

| 755 | | MNHVF | UseVF |
|---|---|---|---|
| 6¢ | **blue,** tagged | .55 | .20 |
| | FDC *(April 24, 1981)* | | 2.00 |

| 756 | | MNHVF | UseVF |
|---|---|---|---|
| 18¢ | **multicolored,** tagged | .30 | .20 |
| | FDC *(April 24, 1981)* | | 1.75 |
| | x. Se-tenant pair, No. 756,755 | .90 | |
| | n. Booklet pane of 8 (2 No. 755, (two No. 755, six No. 756) | 3.00 | |
| | nv. Booklet pane, vertically imperforate between | 75.00 | |
| | FDC Bureau precancel | | 5.00 |

**1981. GEORGE MASON ISSUE** Great American Series
honored an early leader of pre-Revolutionary Virginia patriots. *Intaglio, perforated 11 x 10 1/2.*

757 *George Mason*

| 757 | | MNHVF | UseVF |
|---|---|---|---|
| 18¢ | **blue,** tagged | .30 | .20 |
| | Plate block of 4 | 2.50 | |
| | FDC *(May 7, 1981)* | | 1.75 |
| | zo. Tagging omitted (error) | — | |

# Great Americans Series Identifier

Entries are in denomination order. All stamps listed provide basic data: denomination, person honored, and catalog number. There is information in the columns for perforation, gum and tagging **only** when such information better identifies the different varieties of the stamp. This series is still being issued, and as such, this listing will be updated and modified in future editions.

| Denomination/Name | Cat. | Perf. | Gum | Tagging | Without Tagging |
|---|---|---|---|---|---|
| 1¢ Dorothea Dix | 807 | 11/1/4 H | | | |
| 1¢ Dorothea Dix | 807A | 11 L | | | |
| 1¢ Margaret Mitchell | 857 | | | | Error (857zo) |
| 2¢ Igor Stravinsky | 798 | | | | Error (798zo) |
| 2¢ Mary Lyon | 872 | | | | Error (872zo) |
| 2¢ Mary Lyon | 872zx | | | | Intentional |
| 3¢ Henry Clay | 804 | | | | Error (804zo) |
| 3¢ Paul Dudley White, MD | 861 | | | | Error (861zo) |
| 3¢ Paul Dudley White, MD | 861zx | | | | Intentional |
| 4¢ Carl Schurz | 801 | | | | Error (801zo) |
| 4¢ Father Flanagan | 858 | | | | |
| 4¢ Father Flanagan | 858zx | | | | Intentional (light gray violet) |
| 4¢ Father Flanagan | 858zl | | | | Intentional (slate violet) |
| 5¢ Pearl Buck | 803 | | | | |
| 5¢ Hugo L. Black | 854 | | | | Error (854zo) |
| 5¢ Luis Muñoz Martin | 927 | | | | Error (927zo) |
| 5¢ Luis Muñoz Martin | 927z | | | | Intentional |
| 6¢ Walter Lippmann | 848 | | | | |
| 7¢ Abraham Baldwin | 819 | | | | |
| 8¢ Henry Knox | 847 | | | | |
| 9¢ Sylvanus Thayer | 842 | | | | |
| 10¢ Richard Russell | 815 | | | | |
| 10¢ Red Cloud | 877 | | | Block | Error (877zo) |
| 10¢ Red Cloud | 877pz | | | Pre-Phosphored | |
| 10¢ Red Cloud | 877zl | | | Overall | |
| 10¢ Red Cloud | 877zx | | | | Intentional |
| 11¢ Alden Partridge | 823 | | | | Error (823zo) |
| 13¢ Crazy Horse | 785 | | | | Error (785zo) |
| 14¢ Sinclair Lewis | 826 | | | | |
| 14¢ Julia Ward Howe | 871 | | | | |
| 15¢ Buffalo Bill Cody | 894 | | | Block | |
| 15¢ Buffalo Bill Cody | 894z | | | Overall | |
| 15¢ Buffalo Bill Cody | 894z2 | | | Pre-phosphored | Error (894zo) |
| 17¢ Rachel Carson | 769 | | | | Error (769zo) |
| 17¢ Belva Ann Lockwood | 856 | | | | Error (856zo) |
| 18¢ George Mason | 757 | | | | Error (757zo) |
| 19¢ Sequoyah | 747 | | | | |
| 20¢ Ralph Bunch | 784 | | | | Error (784zo) |
| 20¢ Thomas H. Gallaudet | 802 | | | | Error (802zo) |
| 20¢ Harry S. Truman | 811 | 11 L | | Block | |
| 20¢ Harry S. Truman | 904 | 11 1/2 H | | Block | Error (904zo)* |
| 20¢ Harry S. Truman | 904zl | 11 1/2 H | | Overall | Error (904zo)* |
| 20¢ Harry S. Truman | 904pz | | | Pre-phosphored | |
| 20¢ Virginia Apgar | 1052 | | | | |
| 21¢ Chester Carlson | 911 | | | | |
| 22¢ John J. Audubon | 839 | 11 L | | | Error (839zo) |
| 22¢ John J. Audubon | 839A | 11 1/2 H | | | |
| 23¢ Mary Cassatt | 915 | | | Block | |
| 23¢ Mary Cassatt | 915zl | | | Pre-phosphored | |
| 23¢ Mary Cassatt | 915z | | | Overall | Error (915zo) |
| 25¢ Jack London (sheet) | 853 | 11 L | | | |
| 25¢ Jack London (booklet) | 888 | 11 L | | | Error (888zo) |
| 25¢ Jack London (booklet) | 889 | 10 | | | Error (889zo) |

| Denomination/Name | Cat. | Perf. | Gum | Tagging | Without Tagging |
|---|---|---|---|---|---|
| 28¢ Sitting Bull | 919 | | | | |
| 29¢ Earl Warren | 983 | | | | |
| 29¢ Thomas Jefferson | 1009 | | | | |
| 30¢ Frank C. Laubach | 816 | 11 L | | Block (small) | |
| 30¢ Frank C. Laubach | 816A | 11 1/2 H | | Block (large) | |
| 30¢ Frank C. Laubach | 816Azl | 11 1/2 H | | Overall | |
| 32¢ Cal Farley | 1124 | | | | |
| 32¢ Milton S. Hershey | 1096 | | | | |
| 32¢ Henry R. Luce | 1168 | | | | |
| 32¢ Lila & DeWitt Wallace | 1171 | | | | |
| 35¢ Charles Drew | 770 | | | | Error (770zo) |
| 35¢ Dennis Chavez | 946 | | | | |
| 37¢ Robert Millikan | 786 | | | | Error (786zo) |
| 39¢ Grenville Clark | 825 | 11 L | | | |
| 39¢ Grenville Clark | 825A | 11 1/2 H | | | |
| 40¢ Lillian M. Gilbreth | 813 | 11 L | | | |
| 40¢ Lillian M. Gilbreth | 813A | 11 1/2 H | | | |
| 40¢ Claire Channault | 932 | | | Overall | |
| 40¢ Claire Channault | 932zl | | Shiny | Pre-phosphored | |
| 45¢ Harvey Cushing MD | 895 | | | Block | Error (895zo) |
| 45¢ Harvey Cushing MD | 895z | | | Overall | |
| 46¢ Ruth Benedict | 1114 | | | | |
| 50¢ Chester W. Nimitz | 824 | 11 L | Shiny | Overall | Error (824zo) |
| 50¢ Chester W. Nimitz | 824A | 11 1/2 H | Matt | Block | Error (824Azo) |
| 50¢ Chester W. Nimitz | 824Apz | 11 1/2 H | Shiny | Pre-phosphored | |
| 50¢ Chester W. Nimitz | 824zo | 11 1/2 H | Matt | Overall | |
| 50¢ Chester W. Nimitz | 824pzm | 11 1/2H | Matt | Pre-phosphored | |
| 52¢ Hubert H. Humphrey | 957 | | Matt | | |
| 52¢ Hubert H. Humphrey | 957zl | | Shiny | Pre-phosphored | |
| 55¢ Alice Hamilton MD | 1093 | | | | |
| 56¢ John Harvard | 860 | | | | |
| 65¢ H.H. "Hap" Arnold | 916 | | | | Error (916zo) |
| 75¢ Wendell Wilkie | 981 | | Matt | Pre-phosphored | |
| 75¢ Wendell Wilkie | 981zl | | Shiny | Pre-phosphored | |
| 77¢ Mary Breckinridge | 1200 | | | | |
| 78¢ Alice Paul | 1095 | | | | |
| $1 Bernard Revel | 862 | | | | |
| $1 Johns Hopkins | 918 | | Matt | Block | |
| $1 Johns Hopkins | 918zl | | Matt | Pre-phosphored | |
| $1 Johns Hopkins | 918z2 | | Shiny | Pre-phosphored | |
| $1 John Hopkins | 918z | | Matt | Overall | Error (918zo) |
| $2 William Jennings Bryan | 855 | | | | Error (855zo) |
| $5 Bret Harte | 878 | | | Block | Error (878zo) |
| $5 Bret Harte | 878pz | | | Pre-phosphored | |

Symbols: (in *Perf.* column) H = Harrow (perfect corners); L = L perforator

*Footnotes*

* Impossible to tell if "tagging omitted" version is from block- or overall-tagged version.

**1981. WILDLIFE BOOKLET ISSUE** featured 10 wild animals native to the United States. *Intaglio, perforated 11 x 10 1/2.*

758 *Bighorned sheep*
759 *Puma*
760 *Harbor seal*
761 *Bison*
762 *Brown bear*
763 *Polar bear*
764 *Elk*
765 *Moose*
766 *White-tailed deer*
767 *Pronghorned antelope*

| 758 | | MNHVF | UseVF |
|---|---|---|---|
| 18¢ | Bighorned Sheep, **brown,** tagged | .50 | .20 |

| 759 | | MNHVF | UseVF |
|---|---|---|---|
| 18¢ | Puma, **brown,** tagged | .50 | .20 |

| 760 | | MNHVF | UseVF |
|---|---|---|---|
| 18¢ | Harbor Seal, **brown,** tagged | .50 | .20 |

| 761 | | MNHVF | UseVF |
|---|---|---|---|
| 18¢ | Bison, **brown,** tagged | .50 | .20 |

| 762 | | MNHVF | UseVF |
|---|---|---|---|
| 18¢ | Brown Bear, **brown,** tagged | .50 | .20 |

| 763 | | MNHVF | UseVF |
|---|---|---|---|
| 18¢ | Polar Bear, **brown,** tagged | .50 | .20 |

| 764 | | MNHVF | UseVF |
|---|---|---|---|
| 18¢ | Elk (wapiti) **brown,** tagged | .50 | .20 |

| 765 | | MNHVF | UseVF |
|---|---|---|---|
| 18¢ | Moose, **brown,** tagged | .50 | .20 |

| 766 | | MNHVF | UseVF |
|---|---|---|---|
| 18¢ | White tailed dear, **brown,** tagged | .50 | .20 |

| 767 | | MNHVF | UseVF |
|---|---|---|---|
| 18¢ | Pronghorned antelope, **brown,** tagged | .50 | .20 |
| | FDC (May 14, 1981) | | 1.75 |
| | n. Booklet pane of 10 | 8.50 | 4.00 |
| | nv. Booklet pane of 10, | | |
| | untagged pane (3 known) | 750. | |
| | imperforate-between vertically | 1500. | |
| | FDC Bureau precancel | | 6.00 |

## Transportation Series

**1981. SURREY WITH THE FRINGE ON TOP ISSUE** *Coil, intaglio, perforated 10 vertically.*

"Surrey with the Fringe on Top"

| 768 | | MNHVF | UseVF |
|---|---|---|---|
| 18¢ | **brown,** tagged | .35 | .35 |
| | Pair | .50 | |
| | v. Imperforate pair | 125. | |
| | FDC (May 18, 1981) | | 2.00 |

*Listings and prices for plate number coil strips and singles appear at the end of this definitives section of the Krause- Minkus catalog.*

**1981. RACHEL CARSON ISSUE** Great American Series honors the scientist and author of *Silent Spring.* When published, the book touched off an international controversy over pesticides. *Intaglio, perforated 11 x 10 1/2.*

769 *Rachel Carson*

| 769 | | MNHVF | UseVF |
|---|---|---|---|
| 17¢ | **green,** tagged | .30 | .20 |
| | Plate block of 4 | 1.50 | |
| | FDC (May 28, 1981) | | 1.75 |
| | zo. Tagging omitted (error) | — | |

**1981. CHARLES R. DREW ISSUE** Great American Series honors the scientist and surgeon who discovered and developed methods to preserve blood plasma in large quantities. He was the first black surgeon selected for membership on the American Board of Surgery. *Intaglio, perforated 11 x 10 1/2.*

770 *Charles R. Drew, MD*

| 770 | | MNHVF | UseVF |
|---|---|---|---|
| 35¢ | **gray,** tagged | .50 | .25 |
| | Plate block of 4 | 3.50 | |
| | FDC (June 3, 1981) | | 2.50 |
| | zo. Tagging omitted (error) | — | |

*Note: Plate blocks from plate 3 & 4 carry a premium.*

## Transportation Series

**1981. ELECTRIC AUTO ISSUE** *Coil, intaglio, perforated 10 vertically.*

771 *1917 Electric Auto*

| 771 | | MNHVF | UseVF |
|---|---|---|---|
| 17¢ | **blue,** tagged | .35 | .35 |
| | Pair | .50 | |
| | FDC (June 25, 1981) | | 2.00 |
| | v. Imperforate pair | — | |
| | zx1.Untagged Bureau precancel, Type 1: "PRESORTED/FIRST CLASS" 11 1/2mm | .35 | .35 |
| | zx2.Untagged Bureau precancel Type II: "PRESORTED / FIRST CLASS" 11 1/2mm (1906ab) | .75 | .60 |
| | zx3.Untagged Bureau precancel Type II: "PRESORTED/FIRST CLASS" 13 1/2mm (1906ae) | 1.00 | .50 |
| | zv. Imperforate pair | 650. | |
| | z1. Tagging omitted (error) | — | |

*Listings and prices for plate number coil strips and singles appear at the end of this definitives section of the Krause- Minkus catalog.*

**1981. NON-DENOMINATED "C" ISSUE** marked the new first-class postage rate of 20¢, which went into effect Nov. 1, 1981. The stamp was intended for domestic use only. Design same as the "A" and "B" issues, except for letter and background color. *Gravure, perforated 11 x 10 1/2, design size 19 x 22mm.*

772-774 *"C" to left of stylized eagle.*

| 772 | | MNHVF | UseVF |
|---|---|---|---|
| 20¢ | **brown,** from booklet pane, tagged | .35 | .20 |
| | Plate block of 4 | 1.00 | |
| | FDC *(Oct. 11, 1981)* | | 1.75 |
| | zo. Tagging omitted (error) | — | |

**1981. NON-DENOMINATED "C" BOOKLET PANE ISSUE** Booklet panes, intaglio, perforated 11 x 10 1/2 design size 15 x 18mm.

| 773 | | MNHVF | UseVF |
|---|---|---|---|
| 20¢ | **brown,** tagged | .50 | .20 |
| | FDC *(Oct. 11, 1981)* any single | | 1.75 |
| | n. Booklet pane of 10 | 5.00 | 5.00 |
| | FDC Bureau precancel | | 5.50 |

**1981. NON-DENOMINATED "C" COIL ISSUE** Intaglio, perforated 10 vertically, design size 19 x 22mm.

| 774 | | MNHVF | UseVF |
|---|---|---|---|
| 20¢ | **brown,** tagged | .60 | .20 |
| | Pair | 1.00 | |
| | Line pair | 1.50 | |
| | FDC *(Oct. 11, 1981)* | 1.75 | |
| | v. Imperforate pair | 2000. | |
| | Imperforate line pair | — | |

**1981. CHRISTMAS ISSUE** Consisted of two stamps. A contemporary design depicting a Teddy Bear on a Sleigh and a Traditional design of Madonna and child by Botticeli. *Gravure, perforated 11.*

775 *Teddy Bear on a Sleigh.*

| 775 | | MNHVF | UseVF |
|---|---|---|---|
| 20¢ | **multicolored,** tagged | .50 | .20 |
| | Plate block of 4 | 2.50 | |
| | FDC *(Oct. 28, 1981)* | | 1.75 |
| | v. Imperforate pair | 250. | |
| | v1. Vertical pair, imperforate horizontally | — | |

776 Madonna and Child, Detail, by *Sandro Botticeli, in the collection of The Art Institure of Chicago.*

| 776 | | MNHVF | UseVF |
|---|---|---|---|
| 20¢ | **multicolored,** tagged | .50 | .20 |
| | Plate block of 4 | 2.50 | |
| | FDC *(Oct. 28, 1981)* | | 1.75 |
| | v. Imperforate pair | 110. | |
| | v1. Vertical pair, imperforate horizontally | 1550. | |

**1981. FIRE PUMPER ISSUE** Transportation Series *Coil, intaglio, perforated 10 vertically.*

777 *Fire pumper, 1860s*

| 777 | | MNHVF | UseVF |
|---|---|---|---|
| 20¢ | **fire engine red,** tagged | .40 | .40 |
| | Pair | .60 | |
| | FDC *(Dec. 10, 1981)* | | 2.00 |
| | v. Imperforate pair | 1000. | |

*Listings and prices for plate number coil strips and singles appear at the end of this definitives section of the Krause- Minkus catalog.*

**1981. MAIL WAGON ISSUE** Transportation Series bulk rate. *Coil, printed by intaglio, perforated 10 vertically.*

778 *Mail Wagon, 1880s*

| 778 | | MNHVF | UseVF |
|---|---|---|---|
| 9.3¢ | **dark red,** tagged | .25 | .20 |
| | Pair | .25 | |
| | FDC *(Dec. 15, 1981)* | | 2.00 |
| | zv. Imperforate pair | 115. | |
| | zx. Untagged (Bureau precancel) | — | |
| | FDC Bureau precancel | | 300. |

*Listings and prices for plate number coil strips and singles appear at the end of this definitives section of the Krause- Minkus catalog.*

**1981. FLAG OVER SUPREME COURT ISSUE** Booklet pane, perforated 11 x 10 1/2.

779-782 *Flag over Supreme Court Building; in the foreground is statue Contemplation of Justice by noted American James Earle Fraser.*

| 779 | | MNHVF | UseVF |
|---|---|---|---|
| 20¢ | **black, dark blue and red,** perforated 11, tagged | .35 | .20 |
| | Plate block of 20 | 15.00 | |
| | FDC *(Dec. 17, 1981)* | | 1.75 |
| | v. Vertical pair, imperforate | 35.00 | |
| | v1. Vertical pair, imperforate horizontally | 500. | |
| | v2. Block of 4, imperforate | .75 | |
| | v3. Black omitted | 300. | |
| | v4. Blue omitted | 85.00 | |
| | v5. Dark blue omitted | — | |
| **779A** | | **MNHVF** | **UseVF** |
| 20¢ | **black, dark blue and red,** perforated 11 1/4, tagged | .35 | .20 |
| | Plate block of 20 | 9.00 | |

**1981. FLAG OVER SUPREME COURT COIL ISSUE** *Coil, intaglio, perforated 10 vertically.*

| 780 | | MNHVF | UseVF |
|---|---|---|---|
| 20¢ | **black, dark blue and red,** tagged | | |
| | Pair | .60 | |
| | FDC *(Dec. 17, 1981)* | | 1.75 |
| | a. slate blue, dark blue and red | — | |
| | b. black, dark blue and brick red | — | |
| | v. Black omitted | 50.00 | |
| | v1. Dark blue omitted | 1500. | |
| | v2. Imperforate pair | 8.00 | |
| | v3. Imperforate pair between | 1000. | |
| | zx. Untagged (Bureau precancel) | .50 | .20 |
| | z1. Tagging omitted (error) | — | |

*Listings and prices for plate number coil strips and singles appear at the end of this definitives section of the Krause- Minkus catalog.*

**1981. FLAG OVER SUPREME COURT ISSUE** Booklet pane, perforated 11 x 10 1/2.

| 781 | | MNHVF | UseVF |
|---|---|---|---|
| **20¢** | **black, dark red and blue,** tagged | .35 | .20 |
| | FDC *(Dec. 17, 1981)* | | 1.75 |
| | n. Booklet pane of 6 | 2.50 | 3.00 |
| | FDC Bureau precancel | | 6.00 |
| | n1.Booklet pane of 10 | | |
| | *(July 1, 1982)* | 4.50 | 4.75 |
| | FDC Bureau precancel | | 10.00 |

**1981. FLAG OVER INDEPENDENCE HALL ISSUE** *Intaglio, perforated 11.*

782 *Flag over Independence Hall.*

| 782 | | MNHVF | UseVF |
|---|---|---|---|
| **13¢** | **dark blue and red,** tagged | .60 | .25 |
| | Plate block of 20 | 70.00 | |
| | v. Imperforate vertical pair | — | |
| | zo. Tagging omitted (error) | — | |

**1982. BIGHORN SHEEP ISSUE** features the bighorned sheep used in the 1981 Wildlife booklet. *Booklet pane, intaglio, perforated 11.*
Type I: is 18 3/4mm wide, Type II: is 18 1/2mm wide.

783 *Bighorn Sheep*

| 783 | | MNHVF | UseVF |
|---|---|---|---|
| **20¢** | **blue,** type I, overall tagged | .45 | .20 |
| | FDC *(Jan. 8, 1982)* any singe | | 1.75 |
| | n. Booklet pane of 10 | 5.00 | 5.00 |
| | nv. Booklet pane, imperforate- between | — | |
| | vertically | | |
| | zo. Tagging omitted (error) | — | |
| | Booklet pane of 10 | — | |

| 783A | | MNHVF | UseVF |
|---|---|---|---|
| **20¢** | **blue,** type II, block tagged | .45 | .20 |
| | n. Booklet pane of 10 | 5.00 | .50 |
| | zo. Tagging omitted (error) | — | |
| | Booklet pane of 10 | — | |

## Great American Series

**1982. RALPH BUNCHE ISSUE** Honors the 1st black Nobel Peace Prize winner. Dr. Bunche was awarded the Prize in 1950 for his successful efforts in negotiating an armistice between the Palastinian Arabs and the Israelis in 1949. *Intaglio.*

784 *Ralph Bunche*

| 784 | | MNHVF | UseVF |
|---|---|---|---|
| **20¢** | **maroon,** tagged | .35 | .20 |
| | Plate block of 4 | 2.75 | |
| | FDC *(Jan. 12, 1982)* | | 2.00 |
| | zo. Tagging omitted (error) | — | |

**1982. CRAZY HORSE ISSUE** Great American Series honors the Oglala Sioux Indian leader who, joining Sitting Bull and other Sioux on the Little Big Horn River, was prominent in the defeat of Gen. George A. Custer and the Seventh Cavalry there on June 25, 1876. *Intaglio, perforated 11 x 10 1/2.*

785 *Crazy Horse*

| 785 | | MNHVF | UseVF |
|---|---|---|---|
| **13¢** | **light maroon,** tagged | .35 | .20 |
| | Plate block of 4 | 1.50 | |
| | FDC *(Jan. 15, 1982)* | | 1.75 |
| | zo. Tagging omitted (error) | — | |

**1982. ROBERT MILLIKAN ISSUE** Great American Series honors the Novel prizewinning physicist, educator, humanitarian, and key figure in the development of the California Institute of Technology. *Intaglio*

786 *Robert Millikan*

| 786 | | MNHVF | UseVF |
|---|---|---|---|
| **37¢** | **blue,** tagged | .60 | .20 |
| | Plate block of 4 | 3.50 | |
| | FDC *(Jan. 26, 1982)* | | 1.75 |
| | zo. Tagging omitted (error) | — | |

**1982. HIGH WHEELER BICYCLE ISSUE** Transportation Series for bulk mailings by non-profit organizations. *Coil, intaglio, perforated 10 vertically.*

787 *High Wheeler Bicycle, 1870's*

| 787 | | MNHVF | UseVF |
|---|---|---|---|
| **5.9¢** | **blue,** tagged | .25 | .20 |
| | Pair | .30 | |
| | FDC *(Feb. 17, 1982)* | | 2.00 |
| | z. Untagged (Bureau precancel) | — | |
| | FDC Bureau precancel | | 200. |
| | zv. Imperforate pair | 200. | |
| | Imperforate line pair | — | |

*Listings and prices for plate number coil strips and singles appear at the end of this definitives section of the Krause- Minkus catalog.*

**1982. HANSOM CAB ISSUE** Transportation Series bulk rate. *Coil, intaglio, perforated 10 vertically.*

788 *Hansom Cab, 1890's*

# Transportation Series Identifier

As with the Great Americans Identifier, entries here are by denomination, in order of issue of that denomination. All stamps listed provide basic data: denomination, form of transportation depicted, and catalog number. There is information in the gum, tagging and without tagging columns **only** when such information will assist in properly identifying a stamp.

| Denomination/Name | Cat. | Gum | Tagging | Without Tagging |
|---|---|---|---|---|
| 1c Omnibus (USA 1) | 806 | | | |
| 1c Omnibus (1 USA) | 867pz | | Prephosphored | |
| 1c Omnibus | 867zxm | Matt | | |
| 1c Omnibus | 867zxs | Shiny | | |
| 2c Locomotive (USA 2c) | 790 | | | |
| 2c Locomotive (2c USA) | 873 | | | |
| 3c Handcar | 800 | | | |
| 3c Conestoga Wagon | 883 | | | |
| 3c Conestoga Wagon | 883zxm | Matt | | Intentional |
| 3c Conestoga Wagon | 883zxs | Shiny | | Intentional |
| 3.4c School Bus | 843 | | | |
| 3.4c School Bus | 843z | | | Bureau precancel |
| 4c Stagecoach (19 1/2mm long) | 791 | | | Error (791zo) |
| 4c Stagecoach | 791z | | | Bureau precancel |
| 4c Stagecoach (17mm long) | 868 | | Block | |
| 4c Stagecoach | 868z1 | | Overall | |
| 4c Steam Carriage | 943 | | | |
| 4c Steam Carriage | 943z | | | Intentional |
| 4.9c Buckboard | 846 | | | |
| 4.9c Buckboard | 846z | | | Bureau precancel |
| 5c Motorcycle | 808 | | | |
| 5c Milk Wagon | 879 | | | |
| 5c Circus Wagon (05 USA,intaglio) | 931 | | | |
| 5c Circus Wagon | 931z | | | Intentional |
| 5c Circus Wagon (05 USA, gravure) | 1007 | | No | Intentional |
| 5c Circus Wagon (USA 5c) | 1077 | | No | Intentional |
| 5c Canoe (brown) | 955 | | No | Bureau service indicator |
| 5c Canoe (red) | 979 | | No | Bureau service indicator |
| 5.2c Sleigh | 799 | | | Error (799zo) |
| 5.2c Sleigh | 799zx | | | Bureau precancel |
| 5.3c Elevator | 906 | | | Bureau service indicator |
| 5.5c Star Route Truck | 865 | | | |
| 5.5c Star Route Truck | 865zx | | | Bureau service indicator |
| 5.9c Bicycle | 787 | | | |
| 5.9c Bicycle | 787z | | | Bureau precancel |
| 6c Tricycle | 841 | | | |
| 6c Tricycle | 841z | | | Bureau precancel |
| 7.1c Tractor | 870 | | | |
| 7.1c Tractor | 871z | | | Bureau service indicator ("Nonprofit Org.") |
| 7.1c Tractor | 871zt | | | Bureau service indicator ("Nonprofit 5-Digit Zip+4") |
| 7.4c Baby buggy | 814 | | | |
| 7.4c Baby buggy | 814z | | | Bureau precancel |
| 7.6c Carreta | 903 | | No | Bureau service indicator |
| 8.3c Ambulance (18 1/2 mm long) | 845 | | | |
| 8.3c Ambulance | 845z | | | Bureau precancel |
| 8.3c Ambulance (18mm long) | 846A | | No | Bureau precancel |
| 8.4c Wheel Chair | 901 | | No | Bureau service indicator |
| 8.5c Tow Truck | 869 | | | |
| 8.5c Tow Truck | 869z | | | Bureau service indicator |

| Denomination/Name | Cat. | Gum | Tagging | Without Tagging |
|---|---|---|---|---|
| 9.3c Mail Wagon | 778 | | | |
| 9.3c Mail Wagon | 778zx | | | Bureau precancel |
| 10c Canal Boat | 874 | Matt | Block | |
| 10c Canal Boat | 874pz | Shiny | Pre-phosphored | |
| 10c Canal Boat | 874zx1 | Matt | Overall | |
| 10c Tractor Trailer | 954 | | No | Bureau service indicator, gray |
| 10c Tractor Trailer | 1042 | | | Bureau service indicator, black |
| 10.1c Oil Wagon | 837 | | | |
| 10.1c Oil Wagon | 837zx | | | Bureau precancel, red |
| 10.1c Oil Wagon | 837zx1 | | | Bureau precancel, black |
| 10.9c Hansom Cab | 788 | | | |
| 10.9c Hansom Cab | 788z | | | Bureau precancel |
| 11c Caboose | 812 | | | |
| 11c Caboose | 812zx | | | Bureau precancel |
| 11c Caboose | 812zx1 | | | Intentional |
| 11c Stutz Bearcat | 844 | | | |
| 12c Stanley Steamer (18mm long) | 831 | | Block | Error (831zo) |
| 12c Stanley Steamer | 831p | | Hi-Brite Paper | |
| 12c Stanley Steamer | 831zx | | No | Bureau precancel |
| 12c Stanley Steamer (17.5mm long) | 831A | | No | Bureau precancel |
| 12.5c Pushcart | 838 | | | |
| 12.5c Pushcart | 838zx | | No | Bureau precancel |
| 13c Police Patrol Wagon | 914 | | No | Bureau service indicator |
| 13.2c Coal Car | 900 | | No | Bureau service indicator |
| 14c Iceboat (17 1/2mm long) | 827 | | Overall | Error (827zo) |
| 14c Iceboat (17 1/4mm long) | 827A | | Block | |
| 15c Tugboat | 899 | | Block | |
| 15c Tugboat | 899z1 | | Overall | |
| 16.7c Popcorn Wagon | 898 | | No | Bureau service indicator |
| 17c Electric Auto | 771 | | | Error (771zo) |
| 17c Electric Auto | 771zx1 | | | Bureau precancel 11 1/2mm |
| 17c Electric Auto | 771zx2 | | | Bureau precancel 12 1/2mm |
| 17c Electric Auto | 771zx3 | | | Bureau precancel 13 1/2mm |
| 17c Dog Sled | 859 | | | |
| 17.5c Racing Car | 880 | | | |
| 17.5c Racing Car | 880zx | | | Bureau service indicator |
| 18c Surrey | 768 | | | |
| 20c Fire Pumper | 777 | | | |
| 20c Cable Car | 913 | | Block | |
| 20c Cable Car | 913zx | | Overall | |
| 20c Cog Railway | 1086 | | | |
| 20.5c Fire Engine | 907 | | No | Bureau service indicator |
| 21c Railroad Mail Car | 902 | | No | Bureau service indicator |
| 23c Lunch Wagon | 949 | Matt | Overall* | |
| 23c Lunch Wagon | 949zs | Shiny | Prephosphored* | |
| 23c Lunch Wagon | 949zm | Dull | Prephosphored** | |
| 24.1c Tandem Bicycle | 912 | | No | Bureau service indicator |
| 25c Bread Wagon | 866 | | | Error (866zo) |
| 32c Ferryboat | 1085 | | | |
| $1 Seaplane | 928 | | | |

*Footnotes*

\* Tagging is solid, smooth-appearing
\*\* Tagging is mottled

| 788 | | MNHVF | UseVF |
|---|---|---|---|
| 10.9¢ | **purple,** tagged | .25 | .20 |
| | Pair | .30 | |
| | FDC | | 2.00 |
| | z. Untagged (Bureau precancel) | — | |
| | FDC *(March 26, 1982)* Bureau precancel | | 300. |
| | zv. Imperforate pair | 160. | |
| | Imperforate line pair | — | |

*Listings and prices for plate number coil strips and singles appear at the end of this definitives section of the Krause- Minkus catalog.*

## 1982. CONSUMER EDUCATION ISSUE

served to bring attention to consumer education issues by educators, government agencies, consumer organizations, business, labor organizations, and media. *Coil, intaglio, perforated 10 vertically.*

789 *Consumer education, wise shoppers stretch dollars.*

| 789 | | MNHVF | UseVF |
|---|---|---|---|
| 20¢ | **blue,** tagged | .50 | .20 |
| | Pair | .75 | |
| | FDC *(April 27, 1982)* | | 1.75 |
| | v. Imperforate pair | 95.00 | |
| | Imperforate line pair | — | |
| | zo. Tagging omitted (error) | 4.00 | |

*Listings and prices for plate number coil strips and singles appear at the end of this definitives section of the Krause- Minkus catalog.*

## 1982. LOCOMOTIVE ISSUE Transportation Series
*Coil, intaglio, perforated 10 vertically.*

790 *Locomotive, 1870s*

| 790 | | MNHVF | UseVF |
|---|---|---|---|
| 2¢ | **black,** tagged | .25 | .20 |
| | Pair | .30 | |
| | FDC *(May 20, 1982)* | | 2.00 |
| | v. Imperforate pair | 50.00 | |
| | Imperforate line pair | — | |

*(For similar design with "2 USA" see No. 873.)*

*Listings and prices for plate number coil strips and singles appear at the end of this definitives section of the Krause- Minkus catalog.*

## 1982. STAGECOACH ISSUE Transportation Series
"STAGECOACH 1890s" measures 19 1/2mm long. *Coil, intaglio, perforated 10 vertically.*

791 *Stagecoach, 1890s*

| 791 | | MNHVF | UseVF |
|---|---|---|---|
| 4¢ | **brown,** tagged | .25 | .20 |
| | Pair | .30 | |

| 791 | | MNHVF | UseVF |
|---|---|---|---|
| | FDC *(Aug. 19, 1982)* | | 2.00 |
| | v. imperforated pair | 850. | |
| | z. Untagged (Bureau precanel: "Nonprofit Org") | | |
| | zxv.Imperforate pair, untagged (precanceled) | — | |
| | zo. Tagging omitted (error) | — | |

*For similar design with "Stagecoach 1890s" measuring 17mm long. see No. 868.*

*Listings and prices for plate number coil strips and singles appear at the end of this definitives section of the Krause- Minkus catalog.*

## 1982. CONTEMPORARY CHRISTMAS ISSUE

consists of a single traditional design and a block of 4 contemporary designs. The single stamp depicts a Madonna and Child by Giovanni Battista Tiepolo, 18th-century painter. The contemporary design features a block of 4 of children and snow scenes designed by Dolli Tingle. *Gravure, perforated 11.*

792-795

| 792 | | MNHVF | UseVF |
|---|---|---|---|
| 20¢ | Sleding, **multicolored,** tagged | .35 | .20 |

| 793 | | MNHVF | UseVF |
|---|---|---|---|
| 20¢ | Building snowman **multicolored,** tagged | .35 | .20 |

| 794 | | MNHVF | UseVF |
|---|---|---|---|
| 20¢ | Skating, **multicolored,** tagged | .35 | .20 |

| 795 | | MNHVF | UseVF |
|---|---|---|---|
| 20¢ | Decorating tree, **multicolored,** tagged | .35 | .20 |
| | FDC *(Oct. 28, 1982)* any single | | 2.00 |
| | a. Se-tenant block of 4 | 1.50 | |
| | Plate block of 4 | 3.50 | |
| | FDC block of 4 | | 4.00 |
| | v. Imperforate block of 4 | 3250. | |
| | v1. Block of 4, imperforate horizontally | | |

## 1982. TRADITIONAL CHRISTMAS ISSUE Gravure, perforated 11.

796 *Madonna and Child, by Giovanni Battista Tiepolo, National Gallery of Art.*

| 796 | | MNHVF | UseVF |
|---|---|---|---|
| 20¢ | **multicolored,** tagged | .35 | .20 |
| | Plate block of 20 | 13.75 | |
| | FDC *(Oct. 28, 1982)* | | 1.75 |
| | v. Horizontal pair, imperforate vertically | — | |
| | v1. Vertical pair, imperforate horizontally | — | |
| | v2. Imperforate pair | — | |

**1982. KITTEN AND PUPPY ISSUE** was a postcard-rate stamp issued to satisify demand for those who sent a holiday postcard. *Gravure, perforated 11 .*

797 *Kitten and puppy playing in snow*

| 797 | | MNHVF | UseVF |
|---|---|---|---|
| 13¢ | **multicolored,** tagged | .35 | .20 |
| | Plate block of 4 | 2.00 | |
| | FDC *(Nov. 3, 1982)* | | 2.00 |
| | v. Imperforate pair | 650. | |

**1982. IGOR STRAVINSKY ISSUE** Great American Series
marks the 100th anniversary of the birth of the Russian born Stravinsky. He became a U.S. citizen in 1945. *Intaglio.*

798 *Igor Stravinsky*

| 798 | | MNHVF | UseVF |
|---|---|---|---|
| 2¢ | **brown,** tagged | .25 | .20 |
| | Plate block of 4 | .30 | |
| | Gutter pair | 7.50 | |
| | FDC *(Nov. 18, 1982)* | | 1.75 |
| | zo. Tagging omitted (error) | — | |

**1983. SLEIGH ISSUE** Transportation Series
for use by authorized non-profit organizations. *Coil, intaglio, perforated 10 vertically.*

799 *Sleigh, 1880's*

| 799 | | MNHVF | UseVF |
|---|---|---|---|
| 5.2¢ | **red,** tagged | .25 | .20 |
| | Pair | .30 | |
| | FDC *(March 21, 1983)* | | 2.00 |
| | zx. Untagged (Bureau precancel) | .25 | |
| | FDC Bureau precancell | | 150. |

*Listings and prices for plate number coil strips and singles appear at the end of this definitives section of the Krause- Minkus catalog.*

**1983. HANDCAR ISSUE** Transportation Series
*Coil, intaglio, perforated 10 vertically.*

800 *Handcar, 1880*

| 800 | | MNHVF | UseVF |
|---|---|---|---|
| 3¢ | **green,** tagged | .25 | .20 |
| | Pair | .30 | |
| | FDC *(March 25, 1983)* | | 2.00 |

*Listings and prices for plate number coil strips and singles appear at the end of this definitive section of the Krause- Minkus catalog.*

**1983. CARL SCHURZ ISSUE** Great American Series
Honors the German-born American reformer, public official, and journalist. *Intaglio, perforated 11 x 10 1/2.*

801 *Carl Schurz*

| 801 | | MNHVF | UseVF |
|---|---|---|---|
| 4¢ | **purple,** tagged | .25 | .20 |
| | Plate block of 4 | .30 | |
| | FDC *(June 3, 1983)* | | 1.75 |
| | zo. Tagging omitted (error) | 4.00 | |

**1983. THOMAS H. GALLAUDET ISSUE** Great American Series
Honors the pioneer educator who devoted his life to the education of the speaking - and hearing-impaired. *Intaglio, perforated 11 x 10 1/2.*

802 *Thomas H. Gallaudet*

| 802 | | MNHVF | UseVF |
|---|---|---|---|
| 20¢ | **green,** tagged | .35 | .20 |
| | Plate block of 4 | | 1.00 |
| | Plate Nos. 5 & 6 carry a premium | — | |
| | Plate Nos. 7 & 9 carry a large premium | — | |
| | FDC *(June 10, 1983)* | | 2.00 |
| | zo. Tagging omitted (error) | 4.00 | |

**1983. PEARL BUCK ISSUE** Great American Series
Honors the author, humanitarian, and winner of both the Pulitzer and Nobel Prizes. *Intaglio, perforated 11 x 10 1/2.*

803 *Pearl Buck*

| 803 | | MNHVF | UseVF |
|---|---|---|---|
| 5¢ | **red brown,** tagged | .25 | .20 |
| | Plate block of 4 | .30 | |
| | FDC *(June 25, 1983)* | | 1.75 |

**1983. HENRY CLAY ISSUE** Great American Series
Honors the American statesman. *Intaglio, perforated 11 x 10 1/2.*

804 *Henry Clay*

| 804 | | MNHVF | UseVF |
|---|---|---|---|
| 3¢ | **olive,** tagged | .25 | .20 |
| | Plate block of 4 | | |
| | zo. Tagging omitted (error) | 4.00 | |
| | FDC *(July 13, 1983)* | | 1.75 |

**1983. Express Mail Issue** although not labeled as such nor restricted to that class of mail, was released principally for Express Mail Next Day Service use. *Booklet pane, gravure, perforated 10 vertically.*

805 *Eagle and Moon*

| 805 | | MNHVF | UseVF |
|---|---|---|---|
| $9.35 | **multicolored,** tagged | 25.00 | 20.00 |
| | n.  Booklet pane of 3 | 60.00 | |
| | FDC single | | 70.00 |
| | FDC *(Aug. 12, 1983)* Bureau precancel | | |

**1983. Omnibus Issue** Transportation Series
*Coil, intaglio, perforated 10 vertically.*

806 *Omnibus, 1880s*

| 806 | | MNHVF | UseVF |
|---|---|---|---|
| 1¢ | **purple,** tagged | .25 | .20 |
| | Pair | .30 | |
| | FDC *(Aug. 19, 1983)* | | 2.00 |
| | v.  Imperforate pair | 675. | |

*For similar design with "1 USA" see(No. 867.) Listings and prices for plate number coil strips and singles appear at the end of this definitives section of the Krause-Minkus catalog.*

**1983. Dorothea Dix Issue** Great American Series
Honors the 19th century crusader for the poor and mentally impaired. *Intaglio, perforated 11 x 10 1/2 or 11 x 10 3/4.*

807 *Dorothea Dix*

| 807 | | MNHVF | UseVF |
|---|---|---|---|
| 1¢ | **black,** tagged, perforated 11 x 10 1/2 | .25 | .20 |
| | Plate block of 20 | .30 | |
| | FDC *(Dec. 1983)* | | 1.75 |
| | v.  Imperforate pair | 450. | |
| | v1. Imperforate-between vertical pair | — | |

| 807A | | MNHVF | UseVF |
|---|---|---|---|
| 1¢ | **black,** tagged, perforated 11 x 10 3/4 | .25 | .20 |
| | Plate block of 20 | .30 | |
| | FDC *(Sept. 23, 1983)* | | 1.75 |
| | v.  Vertical pair, imperforate horizontally | — | |

**1983. Pope Motorcycle Issue** Transportation Series
*Coil, intaglio, perforated 10 vertically .*

808 *Motorcycle, 1913*

| 808 | | MNHVF | UseVF |
|---|---|---|---|
| 5¢ | **dark green,** tagged | .25 | .20 |
| | Pair | .30 | |
| | FDC *(Oct. 10, 1983)* | | 2.00 |
| | v.  Imperforate pair | 2750. | |

*Listings and prices for plate number coil strips and singles appear at the end of this definitives section of the Krause-Minkus catalog.*

**1983. Christmas Issue** Consisted of a Santa Claus design and a Modonna and child by Raphael. Gravure, perforated 11.

809 *Santa Claus*

| 809 | | MNHVF | UseVF |
|---|---|---|---|
| 20¢ | **multicolored,** tagged | .35 | .20 |
| | Plate block of 20 | 12.50 | |
| | FDC *(Oct. 28, 1983)* | | 2.00 |
| | v.  Imperforate pair | — | |

810 Madonna and Child, *by Raphael, National Gallery Of Art*

| 810 | | MNHVF | UseVF |
|---|---|---|---|
| 20¢ | **multicolored,** tagged | .35 | .20 |
| | Plate block of 4 | 2.50 | |
| | FDC *(Oct. 28, 1983)* | | 1.75 |

**1984. Harry S. Truman Issue** Great American Series
honors the former president on the centennial of his birth. *Intaglio, perforated 11.*

811 *Harry S. Truman*

| 811 | | MNHVF | UseVF |
|---|---|---|---|
| 20¢ | **black,** tagged perforated 11, overall | .35 | .20 |
| | Plate block of 20 | 12.00 | |
| | FDC *(Jan. 26, 1984)* | | 2.00 |

*(See also No. 904.)*

**1984. Railroad Caboose Issue** Transportation Series
Issued to meet the bulk rate. *Coil, intaglio, perforated 10 vertically.*

812 *Railroad caboose, 1890s*

| 812 | | MNHVF | UseVF |
|---|---|---|---|
| 11¢ | **red,** tagged | .25 | .20 |
| | Pair | .35 | |
| | FDC*(Feb. 3, 1984)* | | |
| | zx. Untagged (Bureau precancel) | — | |
| | zx1.Untagged unprecaancelled *(Sept. 25, 1991)* | | |

*Listings and prices for plate number coil strips and singles appear at the end of this definitive section of the Krause-Minkus catalog.*

**1984. LILLIAN GILBRETH ISSUE** Great American Series
honors the pioneering American engineer who searched for efficient working methods in industry and the home. Together with her husband, she laid the foundation for the field of industrial engineering. *Intaglio, perforated 11 or 11 1/4.*

 813 813A *Lillian Gilbreth*

| 813 | | MNHVF | UseVF |
|---|---|---|---|
| 40¢ | **green,** tagged, perforated 11 | .60 | .20 |
| | Plate block of 20 | 10.00 | |
| | FDC *(Feb. 24, 1984)* | | 2.00 |

*Perforated 11*

| 813A | | MNHVF | UseVF |
|---|---|---|---|
| 40¢ | **green,** tagged, perforated 11 1/4 | .60 | .20 |
| | Plate block of 4 | 2.00 | |
| | FDC *(April 7, 1984)* | | |

*Perforated 11 1/4*

**1984. BABY BUGGY ISSUE** Transportation Series
Issued to meet rate for carrier-route presorted bulk mailings. *Coil, intaglio, perforated 10 vertically.*

 814 *Baby Buggy, 1880's*

| 814 | | MNHVF | UseVF |
|---|---|---|---|
| 7.4¢ | **brown,** tagged | .25 | .20 |
| | Pair | .35 | |
| | FDC *(April 7, 1984)* | | 2.00 |
| | ZX. Untagged (Bureau precancel: ("Blk. Rt. CAR-RT SORT") | .25 | .20 |
| | FDC | | 300. |

*Listings and prices for plate number coil strips and singles appear at the end of this definitive section of the Krause- Minkus catalog.*

**1984. RICHARD RUSSELL ISSUE** Great American Series
honors the former U. S. Senator and his 50 years of public service. Two years after becoming, at age 33, the youngest governor in Georgia's history, Russell was elected to fill the unexpired term of 1 of the state's U.S. Senators. He was subsequently re-elected 6 times to the U.S. Senate. *Intaglio.*

 815 *Richard Russell*

| 815 | | MNHVF | UseVF |
|---|---|---|---|
| 10¢ | **blue,** tagged | .25 | .20 |
| | Plate block of 20 | 7.00 | |
| | FDC *(May 31, 1984)* | | 1.75 |
| | v. Horizontal pair, imperforate between | 2000. | |
| | v1. Imperforate-between vertical pair | | |
| | v2. Vertical pair, imperforate horizontally | — | |
| | v3. Imperforate pair | 1250. | |

*Imperforate printer's waste is known to exist, and in 1 case was used as postage.*

**1984. FRANK C. LAUBACH ISSUE** Great American Series
honors the literacy advocate and educator. Who developed methods to educate the illiterate and created alphabets and written languages where none previously existed. *Intaglio.*

 816,816A *Frank C. Laubach*

| 816 | | MNHVF | UseVF |
|---|---|---|---|
| 30¢ | **green,** tagged, perforated 11 | .75 | .20 |
| | Plate block of 20 | 18.00 | |
| | FDC *(Sept. 2, 1984)* | | 1.75 |

| 816A | | MNHVF | UseVF |
|---|---|---|---|
| 30¢ | **green,** block tagging, perforated 11 1/4 | .75 | .20 |
| | Plate block of 4 | 2.25 | |
| | FDC *(June 25, 1988)* | | |
| | z1. Overall tagging (1990) | .75 | |
| | Plate block of 4 | 2.25 | |

**1984. CHRISTMAS ISSUE** Consisted of a Saturday design and a Madonna and Child by Lippi. *Gravure, perforated 11.*

 817 *Santa Claus, by Danny La Boccetta. Winner of a stamp design project.*

| 817 | | MNHVF | UseVF |
|---|---|---|---|
| 20¢ | **multicolored,** tagged | .25 | .20 |
| | Plate block of 4 | 1.50 | |
| | FDC *(Oct. 30, 1984)* | | 1.75 |
| | v. Horizontal pair, imperforate vertically | 975. | |

 818 *Madonna and Child, by Fra Filippo Lippi, National Gallery of Art.*

| 818 | | MNHVF | UseVF |
|---|---|---|---|
| 20¢ | **multicolored,** tagged | .25 | .20 |
| | Plate block of 4 | 1.50 | |
| | FDC *(Oct. 30, 1984)* | | 1.75 |

**1985. ABRAHAM BALDWIN ISSUE** Great American Series
honors the man who wrote the charter for Franklin College, the 1st to establish a state university in the United States. *Intaglio, perforated 11.*

 819 *Abraham Baldwin*

| 819 | | MNHVF | UseVF |
|---|---|---|---|
| 7¢ | **red,** tagged | .25 | .20 |
| | Plate block of 20 | 4.00 | |
| | FDC *(Jan. 25, 1985)* | | 1.75 |

**1985. NON-DENOMINATED "D" ISSUE** marks the new 1st class post rate of 22¢, which went into effect Feb. 17, 1985. The issue was for domestic use only. Issued in sheet, coil, and booklet form. *Gravure, perforated 11.*

820-822 *"D" and stylized eagle.*

| 820 | | MNHVF | UseVF |
|---|---|---|---|
| 22¢ | **green,** tagged | .45 | .20 |
| | Plate block of 20 | 25.00 | |
| | FDC *(Feb. 1, 1985)* | | 1.75 |
| | v. Imperforate vertical pair | 50.00 | |
| | v1. Vertical pair, imperforate horizontally | 1300. | |

*Coil, perforated 10 vertically*

**1985. NON-DENOMINATED "D" COIL ISSUE**

| 821 | | MNHVF | UseVF |
|---|---|---|---|
| 22¢ | **green,** tagged | .80 | .20 |
| | Pair | 1.00 | |
| | FDC *(Feb. 1,1985)* | | 1.75 |
| | v. Imperforate pair | 45.00 | |
| | vzo.Imperforate pair, tagging omitted (error) | 85.00 | |

*Listing and prices for plate number coil strips and singles appear at the end of this definitive section of the Krause- Minkus catalog.*

**1985. NON-DENOMINATED "D" RATE BOOKLET ISSUE**

| 822 | | MNHVF | UseVF |
|---|---|---|---|
| 22¢ | **green,** tagged | .40 | .20 |
| | FDC *(Feb. 1, 1985)* single | | 1.75 |
| | n. Booklet pane of 10 | 8.50 | |
| | nv. Booklet pane of 10, imperforate between horizontally | — | |
| | FDC Bureau precancel | | 7.50 |

**1985. ALDEN PARTRIDGE ISSUE** Great American Series honors the military educator on his 200th birthday. *Intaglio, perforated 11.*

823 *Alden Partridge*

| 823 | | MNHVF | UseVF |
|---|---|---|---|
| 11¢ | **blue,** tagged | .25 | .20 |
| | Plate block of 4 | 1.20 | |
| | FDC *(Feb. 12, 1985)* | | 2.00 |
| | zo. Tagging omitted (error) | .85 | |

**1985. CHESTER W. NIMITZ ISSUE** Great American Series honors the fleet admiral, whose leadership during World War II brought about key naval victories. He was acknowledged as one of the Navy's foremost administrators and strategists. *Gravure.*

824-824A *Chester W. Nimitz*

| 824 | | MNHVF | UseVF |
|---|---|---|---|
| 50¢ | **brown,** overall tagging, perforated 11, shiny gum | .90 | .20 |
| | Plate block of 4 | 8.00 | |
| | FDC *(Feb. 22, 1985)* | | 3.00 |
| | zo. Tagging omitted (error) | 7.00 | |

| 824A | | MNHVF | UseVF |
|---|---|---|---|
| 50¢ | **brown,** block tagging, perforated 11 1/4, matt gum | .90 | .20 |
| | Plate block of 4 | 6.50 | |
| | FDC *(Aug. 28, 1986)* | | |
| | zo. Tagging omitted (error) | 7.00 | |
| | z1. Overall tagging | .90 | |
| | Plate block of 4 | 6.50 | |
| | pz. Pre-phosphored paper, shiny gum | .90 | |
| | pxm.Matt gum | .90 | |

**1985. GRENVILLE CLARK ISSUE** Great American Series honors a leading advocate of civil liberties and peace through world federalism. *Intaglio perforated 11.*

825-825A *Grenville Clark*

| 825 | | MNHVF | UseVF |
|---|---|---|---|
| 39¢ | **purple,** tagged (small block) | .75 | .20 |
| | Plate block of 20 | 24.00 | |
| | FDC *(March 20, 1985)* | | 2.00 |
| | v. Imperforate-between vertical pair | 2000. | |
| | v1. Vertical pair, imperforate horizontally | 575. | |

*Perforated 11 1/4*

| 825A | | MNHVF | UseVF |
|---|---|---|---|
| 39¢ | **purple,** tagged (large block) | .75 | .20 |
| | Plate block of 4 | 4.00 | |
| | FDC *(Aug. 25, 1986)* | | |

**1985. SINCLAIR LEWIS ISSUE** Great American Series honors the novelist and short story writer on the centennial of his birth. In 1930, Lewis became the 1st American to win a Nobel Prize for Literature. *Intaglio, perforated 11.*

826 *Sinclair Lewis*

| 826 | | MNHVF | UseVF |
|---|---|---|---|
| 14¢ | **gray,** tagged | .25 | .20 |
| | Plate block of 20 | 9.00 | |
| | FDC *(March 21, 1985)* | | 1.75 |
| | v. Horizontal pair, imperforate between | 8.00 | |
| | v1. Vertical pair, imperforate between | 2000. | |
| | v2. Vertical Imperforate pair horizontally | 125. | |

**1985. ICEBOAT ISSUE** Transportation Series
Issued to meet the new first-class rate for postcards. *Coil, intaglio, perforated 10 vertically.*

827, 827A, *Iceboat 1880s*

| 827 | | MNHVF | UseVF |
|---|---|---|---|
| 14¢ | **blue,** type I, overall tagged | .25 | .20 |
| | Pair | .35 | |
| | FDC (March 23, 1985) | | 1.75 |
| | v. Imperforate pair | 100. | |
| | zo. Tagging omitted (error) | — | |

| 827A | | MNHVF | UseVF |
|---|---|---|---|
| 14¢ | **blue,** type II, block tagged | .25 | .20 |
| | Pair | .35 | |

*Type I is 17 1/2 mm wide with overall tagging. Type II is 17 1/4 mm wide with block tagging.*

*Listings and prices for plate number coil strips and singles appear at the end of this definitives seciton of this krause -Minkus catalog.*

**1985. FLAG OVER THE CAPITOL ISSUE** consists of sheet and coil versions, and a booklet stamp the width of two normal definitive stamps. *Coil, intaglio, perforated 11.*

828, 829, 876 *Flag over the U.S. Capitol.*

| 828 | | MNHVF | UseVF |
|---|---|---|---|
| 22¢ | **black, blue, and red,** tagged | .35 | .20 |
| | Plate block of 4 | 3.00 | |
| | Gutter pair | — | |
| | FDC (March 29, 1985) | | 1.75 |

**1985. FLAG OVER THE U.S. CAPITOL COIL ISSUE** Coil, intaglio.

| 829 | | MNHVF | UseVF |
|---|---|---|---|
| 22¢ | **black, blue, and red,** tagged | .40 | .20 |
| | Pair | 1.00 | |
| | FDC (March 29, 1985) | | 1.75 |
| | a. Black stars in flag (rather than blue) | 1.00 | |
| | b. slate blue, blue, and red | — | |
| | v. Imperforate pair | 12.50 | |
| | zo. Tagging omitted (error) | 3.00 | |

*For similar design with "T" at bottom, see No. 876. Listings and prices for plate number coil strips and singles appear at the end of this definitive section of the Krause-Minkus catalog.*

**1985. FLAG OVER THE CAPITOL BOOKLET ISSUE** This was the first U.S. booklet pane in the format of a single row of 5 stamps. *Booklet pane, intaglio, perforated 10 horizontally.*

830 *Flag over the U.S. Capitol.*

| 830 | | MNHVF | UseVF |
|---|---|---|---|
| 22¢ | **black, blue, and red,** tagged | .40 | .20 |
| | FDC (March 29, 1985) | | 1.75 |
| | n. Booklet pane of 5 | 3.00 | 2.50 |
| | FDC booklet pane | | 3.50 |

*Issued for use in vending machines, and was available with 1 or 2 panes.*

**1985. STANLEY STEAMER ISSUE** Transportation Series

The Stanley Steamer, was the first successfully operated steam automobile in New England. *Coil, intaglio, perforated 10 vertically.*

831, 831A *Stanley Steamer, 1909.*

| 831 | | MNHVF | UseVF |
|---|---|---|---|
| 12¢ | **blue,** type I, tagged | .25 | .20 |
| | Pair | .30 | |
| | FDC (April 2, 1985) | | 1.75 |
| | p. Hi-Brite paper | — | |
| | zx. Untagged, Bureau precancel: PRESORTED FIRST-CLASS | .25 | .20 |
| | Pair | — | |
| | zo. Tagging omitted (error) | — | |

| 831A | | MNHVF | UseVF |
|---|---|---|---|
| 12¢ | **blue,** type II, untagged, Bureau precancel: PRESORTED FIRST-CLASS | .25 | .20 |
| | Pair | .30 | |
| | FDC (Sept. 3, 1987) | | 60.00 |

*Type I: "Stanley Steamer 1909" is 18mm long;*

*Type II: "Stanley Steamer 1909" is 17 1/2 mm long.*

*Listings and prices for plate number coil strips and singles appear at the end of this definitive section of the Krause- Minkus catalog.*

**1985. SEASHELL BOOKLET ISSUE**

832 *Frilled dogwinkle*

833 *Reticulated helmet*

834 *New England nepturn*

835 *Calico scallop*

836 *Lightning whelk*

| 832 | | MNHVF | UseVF |
|---|---|---|---|
| 22¢ | Frilled dogwinkle, **black and brown,** tagged | .35 | .20 |

| 833 | | MNHVF | UseVF |
|---|---|---|---|
| 22¢ | Reticulated helmet, **black and multicolored,** tagged | .35 | .20 |

| 834 | | MNHVF | UseVF |
|---|---|---|---|
| 22¢ | New England neptune, **black and brown,** tagged | .35 | .20 |

| 835 | | MNHVF | UseVF |
|---|---|---|---|
| 22¢ | Calico scallop, **black and purple, tagged** | .35 | .20 |

| 836 | | MNHVF | UseVF |
|---|---|---|---|
| 22¢ | Lightning whelk, **multicolored,** tagged | .35 | .20 |
| | FDC *(April 4, 1985)* any single | | 2.00 |
| | a. Se-tenant strip of 5 | 3.00 | |
| | n. Booklet pane of 10 (2 of each design) | 4.00 | |
| | FDC booklet pane | | 7.50 |
| | nv. Purple omitted, horizontal pair of 835, pane | 700. | |
| | nv. Booklet pane, imperforate between vertically | 1500. | |
| | nv1.Imperforate booklet pane | — | |
| | zo. Tagging omitted (error) | — | |

*Mis-registered tagging is common on this issue.*

### 1985. OIL WAGON ISSUE Transportation Series
The 10.1¢ denomination first was issued to meet the rate for bulk 3rd class mail presorted to the 5-digit zip code. *Coil, intaglio, perforated 10 vertically.*

 837 *Oil Wagon 1890's*

| 837 | | MNHVF | UseVF |
|---|---|---|---|
| 10.1¢ | **blue,** tagged | .25 | .20 |
| | Pair | .35 | |
| | FDC *(April 18, 1985)* | | 1.75 |
| | zx. Untagged, Bureau precancel: in black: "Bulk Rate" | .25 | .20 |
| | FDC | | 2.50 |
| | zxv.Imperforate pair | 85.00 | |
| | zx1.Untagged, Bureau precancel: in red: "Bulk Rate/Carrier Route Sort" | .25 | .20 |
| | FDC | | 1.75 |
| | zx1v.Imperforate pair | 1.00 | |

### 1985. PUSHCART ISSUE Transportation Series
The 12.5 denomination was issued as the basic rate for bulk 3rd class mail.

 838 *Pushcart 1880's*

| 838 | | MNHVF | UseVF |
|---|---|---|---|
| 12.5¢ | **olive,** tagged | .25 | .20 |
| | Pair | .35 | |
| | FDC *(April 18, 1985)* | | 1.75 |
| | zx. Untagged, Bureau precancel: "Bulk Rate" | 50.00 | |
| | zxv.Imperforate pair | 50.00 | |

*Listings and prices for plate number coil strips and singles appear at the end of this definitive sections of the Krause-Minkus catalog.*

### 1985. JOHN J. AUDUBON ISSUE Great American Series
honors the 200th birthday of the artist-naturalist. *Intaglio, perforated 11.*

 839, 839A *John J. Audubon*

| 839 | | MNHVF | UseVF |
|---|---|---|---|
| 22¢ | **blue,** tagged | .40 | .20 |
| | Plate block of 20 | 16.00 | |
| | v. Horizontal pair, imperforate between | 2750. | |
| | v1. Vertical pair, imperforate between | — | |
| | v2. Vertical pair, imperforate horizontally | 2500. | |
| | FDC *(April 23, 1985)* | | 2.00 |

| 839A | | MNHVF | UseVF |
|---|---|---|---|
| 22¢ | perforated 11 1/4, **blue,** tagged | .40 | .20 |
| | Plate block of 4 | 1.50 | |
| | FDC *(June 1, 1987)* | | |

### 1985. EXPRESS MAIL ISSUE
Although valid for use on other classes of mail, was intended for use in 4 types of Express Mail Service: 1) Same Day Airport Service, 2) Custom Designed Service, 3) Next Day Service, and 4) International Service. *Booklet pane, gravure, perforated 10 vertically.*

 840 *Eagle and Moon*

| 840 | | MNHVF | UseVF |
|---|---|---|---|
| $10.75 | **multicolored,** type I, tagged | 15.00 | 9.00 |
| | FDC *(April 29, 1985)* | | 50.00 |
| | n. Booklet pane of 3 | 52.00 | |
| | FDC | | 150. |
| | a. Type II *(June 19, 1989)* | 17.00 | 12.00 |
| | FDC | | |
| | an.Booklet pane of 3 | 52.00 | |
| | FDC | | 700. |

*Type I: overall dull appearance, "$10.75" appears grainy. Type II: more intense colors, "$10.75" smoother, much less grainy.*

### 1985. TRICYCLE ISSUE Transportation Series
for basic rate for 3rd class bulk mailings by non-profit organizations. *Coil, intaglio, perforated 10 vertically.*

 841 *Tricycle, 1880s*

| 841 | | MNHVF | UseVF |
|---|---|---|---|
| 6¢ | **brown,** tagged | .25 | .20 |
| | Pair | .30 | |
| | FDC *(May 6, 1985)* | | 1.75 |
| | z. Untagged, Bureau precancel: "Nonprofit Org." | .25 | .20 |
| | Pair | .30 | |
| | zxv.Imperforate pair | 225. | |

*Listings and prices for plate number coil strips and singles appear at the end of this definitives sections of the Krause-Minkus catalog.*

### 1985. SYLVANUS THAYER ISSUE Great American Series
honors the former commandant of the U.S. Military Academy at West Point, NY. *Intaglio, perforated 11.*

 842 *Sylvanus Thayer*

| 842 | | MNHVF | UseVF |
|---|---|---|---|
| 9¢ | **green,** tagged | .25 | .20 |
| | Plate block of 20 | 4.25 | |
| | FDC *(June 7, 1985)* | | 2.00 |

## 1985. SCHOOL BUS ISSUE Transportation Series
Issued for basic rate for carrier-route presort 3rd class bulk mailings by non-profit organizations. *Coil, intaglio, perforated 10 vertically.*

 843 *School Bus, 1920s*

| 843 | | MNHVF | UseVF |
|---|---|---|---|
| 3.4¢ | **green,** tagged | .25 | .20 |
| | Pair | .30 | |
| | FDC | | 1.75 |
| | z. Untagged, Bureau precancel: "Nonprofit Org. CAR-RT SORT" | .25 | .20 |
| | FDC *(June 8, 1985)* | | 200. |

*Listings and prices for plate number coil strips and singles appear at the end of this definitive section of the Krause- Minkus catalog.*

## 1985. STUTZ BEARCAT ISSUE Transportation Series
*Coil, intaglio, perforated 10 vertically.*

 844 *Stutz Bearcat, 1933*

| 844 | | MNHVF | UseVF |
|---|---|---|---|
| 11¢ | **green,** tagged | .25 | .20 |
| | Pair | .30 | |
| | FDC *(June 11, 1985)* | | 1.75 |

*Listings and prices for plate number coil strips and singles appear at the end of this definitive section of the Krause- Minkus catalog.*

## 1985. AMBULANCE ISSUE Transportation Series
The 8.3¢ denomination was issued for 3rd class mail presorted by carrier route. *Coil, intaglio, perforated 10 vertically.*

 845, 845A *Ambulance, 1860s*

| 845 | | MNHVF | UseVF |
|---|---|---|---|
| 8.3¢ | **green,** type I, tagged | .25 | .20 |
| | Pair | .30 | |
| | FDC *(June 21, 1985)* | | 1.75 |
| | z. Untagged, Bureau precancel: "Blk. Rt. CAR-RT SORT" | .25 | .20 |
| | Pair | .30 | |
| | FDC | | 250. |

| 845A | | MNHVF | UseVF |
|---|---|---|---|
| 8.3¢ | **green,** type II, untagged, Bureau precancel: "Blk. Rt./CAR-RT/SORT" | .25 | .20 |
| | Pair | .30 | |
| | FDC *(Aug. 29, 1986)* | | 250. |

*Type I: "Ambulance 1860's is 18 1/2mm long. Type II: "Ambulance 1860's" is 18mm long.*

## 1985. BUCKBOARD ISSUE Transportation Series
The 4.9¢ denomination was issued for non-profit 3rd class mail presorted to the 5-digit Zip code.

 846 *Buckboard, 1880s*

| 846 | | MNHVF | UseVF |
|---|---|---|---|
| 4.9¢ | **brown,** tagged | .25 | .20 |
| | pair | .30 | |
| | FDC | | 1.75 |
| | z. Untagged, Bureau precancel: "Nonprofit Org." | .35 | .20 |
| | FDC *(June 21, 1985)* | | 2.50 |

*Listings and prices for plate number coil strips and singles appear at the end of this definitives section of the Krause- Minkus catalog.*

## 1985. HENRY KNOX ISSUE Great American Series
honors the first U.S. Secretary of War during the 200th anniversary year of his appointment. *Intaglio, perforated 11.*

 847 *Henry Knox*

| 847 | | MNHVF | UseVF |
|---|---|---|---|
| 8¢ | **olive,** tagged | .25 | .20 |
| | Plate block of 4 | .40 | |
| | FDC *(July 26, 1985)* | | 1.75 |

## 1985. WALTER LIPPMANN ISSUE Great American Series
honors the newsman, political analyst, and author. Among many other awards and prizes Lippmann earned, 2 Pulitzer Prizes and a Peabody award. *Intaglio, perforated 11.*

 848 *Walter Lippmann*

| 848 | | MNHVF | UseVF |
|---|---|---|---|
| 6¢ | **orange,** tagged | .25 | .20 |
| | Plate block of 20 | 2.90 | |
| | FDC *(Sept. 9, 1985)* | | 1.75 |
| | v. Vertical pair, imperforate- between | 2450. | |

## 1985. ENVELOPE STAMP ISSUE prepaid first-class rate for mailers using ZIP + 4. *Coil, gravure, perforated 10 vertically.*

 849 *Letters*

| 849 | | MNHVF | UseVF |
|---|---|---|---|
| 21.1¢ | **multicolored,** tagged | .35 | .20 |
| | Pair | .50 | |
| | FDC *(Oct. 22, 1985)* | | 1.75 |
| | z. Untagged, Bureau-printed service indicator: "ZIP+4" | .35 | .20 |
| | Pair | .50 | |

*Some precanceled stamps are known with light tagging.*

**1985. CONTEMPORARY CHRISTMAS ISSUE** consists of 2 stamps. The contemporary stamp is a painting of poinsettias by James Dean of Annandale, Va. The traditional stamp depicts 1 of the 4 versions of *The Genoa Madonna*, an enameled terra-cotta Madonna and Child by Luca della Robbia. *Gravure, perforated 11.*

850 *Poinsettia plants*

| 850 | | MNHVF | UseVF |
|---|---|---|---|
| 22¢ | **multicolored,** tagged | .35 | .20 |
| | Plate block of 4 | 1.00 | |
| | FDC *(Oct. 30, 1985)* | | 1.75 |
| | v. Imperforate pair | 125. | |

**1985. TRADITIONAL CHRISTMAS ISSUE** Gravure, perforated 11.

851 *Sculpture by Luca della Robbia, Detroit Institute of Arts.*

| 851 | | MNHVF | UseVF |
|---|---|---|---|
| 22¢ | **multicolored,** tagged | .35 | .20 |
| | Plate block of 4 | 1.00 | |
| | FDC *(Oct. 30, 1985)* | | 1.75 |
| | v. Imperforate pair | 100. | |

**1985. GEORGE WASHINGTON & MONUMENT ISSUE** met the basic presort rate for first-class letter mail. *Coil, intaglio, perforated 10 vertically.*

852 *George Washington and the Washington Monument*

| 852 | | MNHVF | UseVF |
|---|---|---|---|
| 18¢ | **multicolored,** tagged | .35 | .20 |
| | Pair | .50 | |
| | FDC *(Nov. 6, 1985)* | | 1.75 |
| | v. Imperforate pair | 975. | |
| | z. Untaggeed (Bureau-printed service indicator: "PRESORTED FIRST-CLASS" | .35 | .20 |
| | zo. Taggimg omitted (error) | — | |
| | zm.Matt gum | .35 | |
| | Pair | .50 | |
| | zxv.Imperforate pair, precancelled | 800. | |

*Some precanceled stamps are known with light tagging. Listings and prices for plate number coil strips and singles appear at the end of this definitives section of the Krause- Minkus catalog.*

**1986. JACK LONDON ISSUE** Great American Series honors the author of 50 books including *The Call of the Wild, White Fang,* and *The Sea-Wolf. Intaglio, perforated 11.*

853, 888, 889 *Jack London*

| 853 | | MNHVF | UseVF |
|---|---|---|---|
| 25¢ | **blue,** perforated 11, block tagging | .45 | .20 |
| | Plate block of 4 | 1.50 | |
| | FDC *(Jan. 11, 1986)* | | 2.00 |
| | zo. Tagging omitted (error) | — | |

*For booklet panes of 10, see Nos. 888-889.*

**1986. HUGO L. BLACK ISSUE** Great American Series honors the Supreme Court justice on his 100th birthday. *Intaglio, perforated 11.*

854 *Hugo L. Black*

| 854 | | MNHVF | UseVF |
|---|---|---|---|
| 5¢ | **deep olive green, tagged** | .25 | .20 |
| | Plate block of 4 | .90 | |
| | FDC *(Feb. 27, 1986)* | | 1.75 |
| | zo. Tagging omitted (error) | — | |

**1986. WILLIAM JENNINGS BRYAN ISSUE** Great American Series honors the famed orator and legislator. *Intaglio, perforated 11.*

855 *William Jennings Bryan*

| 855 | | MNHVF | UseVF |
|---|---|---|---|
| $2 | **purple,** tagged | 3.25 | .75 |
| | Plate block of 4 | 20.00 | |
| | FDC *(March 19, 1986)* | | 7.00 |
| | zo. Tagging omitted (error) | 10.00 | |

**1986. BELVA ANN LOCKWOOD ISSUE** Great American Series honors the first woman candidate for president and the first woman admitted to practice before the U.S. Supreme Court. *Intaglio, perforated 11.*

856 *Belva Ann Lockwood*

| 856 | | MNHVF | UseVF |
|---|---|---|---|
| 17¢ | **blue green,** tagged | .35 | .20 |
| | Plate block of 4 | 1.75 | |
| | FDC *(June 18, 1986)* | | 1.75 |
| | zo. Tagging omitted (error) | 5.00 | |

**1986. MARGARET MITCHELL ISSUE** Great American Series honors the famed author of the novel *Gone With the Wind. Intaglio, perforated 11.*

857 *Margaret Mitchell*

| 857 | | MNHVF | UseVF |
|---|---|---|---|
| 1¢ | **brown,** tagged | .25 | .20 |
| | Plate block of 4 | .30 | |
| | FDC *(June 30, 1986)* | | 2.50 |
| | zo. Tagging omitted (error) | 3.00 | |

**1986. FATHER FLANAGAN ISSUE** Great American Series
released on the centennial of his birth, honors Rev. Edward Joseph
Flanagan, the founder of Boys Town. The center protects and educates abused and underpriviledged youth. *Intaglio, perforated 11.*

  *858 Father Flanagan*

| 858 | | MNHVF | UseVF |
|---|---|---|---|
| 4¢ | **purple,** tagged | .25 | .20 |
| | Plate block of 4 | .40 | |
| | FDC *(July 14, 1986)* | | 1.75 |
| | zx. Untagged, light gray violet (1991) | .25 | .20 |
| | Plate block of 4 | .40 | |
| | z1. Untagged, slate violet (1993) | .25 | .20 |
| | Plate block of 4 | 40.00 | |

**1986. DOG SLED ISSUE** Transportation Series
The 17¢ denomination represents the rate for the 2nd ounce of first
class mail. *Coil, intaglio, perforated 10 vertically.*

 *859 Dog Sled, 1920s*

| 859 | | MNHVF | UseVF |
|---|---|---|---|
| 17¢ | **blue,** tagged | .30 | .20 |
| | Pair | .50 | |
| | FDC *(Aug. 20, 1986)* | | 1.75 |
| | v. Imperforate pair | 475. | |

*Listings and prices for plate number coil strips and singles appear at the
end of this definitives section of the Krause- Minkus catalog.*

**1986. JOHN HARVARD ISSUE** Great American Series
honors the 17th century American colonist and philanthropist , coinciding with th 350th anniversary of Harvard University , the oldest institution of higher learning in the United States. *Intaglio, perforated 11.*

 *860 John Harvard*

| 860 | | MNHVF | UseVF |
|---|---|---|---|
| 56¢ | **crimsom,** tagged | 1.10 | .20 |
| | Plate block of 4 | 5.25 | |
| | FDC *(Sept. 3, 1986)* | | 2.00 |

**1986. PAUL DUDLEY WHITE ISSUE** Great American Series
honors the authority on cardiovascular disease and a pioneer in its diagnosis, treatment, and prevention. *Intaglio, perforated 11.*

*861 Dr. Paul Dudley White*

| 861 | | MNHVF | UseVF |
|---|---|---|---|
| 3¢ | **blue,** tagged | .25 | .20 |
| | Plate block of 4 | .35 | |
| | FDC *(Sept. 15, 1986)* | | 1.75 |
| | zo. Tagging omitted (error) | — | |
| | zx. Untagged (intentional) shining Gum | — | |
| | FDC dull gum | | |

**1986. BERNARD REVEL ISSUE** Great American Series
honors the scholar and educator in conjunction with the centennial of
Yeshiva University, the nation's oldest and largest Jewish institution
of higher learning. *Intaglio, perforated 11.*

 *862 Dr. Bernard Revel*

| 862 | | MNHVF | UseVF |
|---|---|---|---|
| $1 | **blue,** tagged | 2.00 | .25 |
| | Plate block of 4 | 13.00 | |
| | FDC *(Sept. 23, 1986)* | | 4.00 |

**1986. CHRISTMAS ISSUE** The contemporary stamp features a winter
village scene, which was designed by Dolli Tingle of Westport, Conn.
The traditional stamp depicts the oil-on-wood painting *Perugino Madonna,* by Il Perugino. *Gravure, perforated 11.*

 *863 Village Scene*

| 863 | | MNHVF | UseVF |
|---|---|---|---|
| 22¢ | **multicolored,** tagged | .50 | .20 |
| | Plate block of 4 | 2.75 | |
| | FDC *(Oct. 24, 1986)* | | 2.00 |

 *864 Perugino Madonna*

| 864 | | MNHVF | UseVF |
|---|---|---|---|
| 22¢ | **multicolored,** tagged | .50 | .20 |
| | Plate block of 4 | 2.75 | |
| | FDC *(Oct. 24, 1986)* | | 2.00 |

**1986. STAR ROUTE TRUCK ISSUE** Transportation Series
The 5.5¢ rate was for nonprofit 3rd class mail presorted to the carrier route. *Coil, intaglio, perforated 10 vertically.*

 *865 Star Route Truck, 1910s*

| 865 | | MNHVF | UseVF |
|---|---|---|---|
| 5.5¢ | **maroon, tagged** | .25 | .20 |
| | Pair | .35 | |
| | FDC *(Nov. 1, 1986)* | | 1.75 |
| | ZX. Untagged, Bureau-printed | | |
| | service indicator: "Nonprofit | | |
| | Org. CAR-RT SORT" | .25 | .20 |
| | FDC | | 5.00 |

*Listings and prices for plate number coil strips and singles appear at the
end of this definitives section of the Krause- Minkus catalog.*

## 1986. BREAD WAGON ISSUE Transportation Series
*Coil, intaglio, perforated 10 vertically.*

 866 *Bread Wagon, 1880s*

| 866 | | MNHVF | UseVF |
|---|---|---|---|
| 25¢ | *orange brown,* tagged | .40 | .20 |
| | Pair | 1.00 | |
| | FDC *(Nov. 22, 1986)* | | 1.75 |
| | v. Imperforate pair | 10.00 | |
| | v1. Imperforate-between pair | 500. | |
| | zo. Tagging omitted (error) | — | |

*Listings and prices for plate number coil strips and singles appear at the end of this definitives section of the Krause- Minkus catalog.*

## 1986. OMNIBUS ISSUE Transportation Series
Type of No. 806, redesigned, ("1 USA" instead of "USA 1"). *Coil, intaglio, perforated 10 vertically.*

 867 *Omnibus, 1880s*

| 867 | | MNHVF | UseVF |
|---|---|---|---|
| 1¢ | *violet,* tagged | .25 | .20 |
| | Pair | .30 | |
| | FDC *(Nov. 26, 1986)* | | 1.75 |
| | v. Imperforate pair | 2400. | |
| | pz. Prephosphored paper | .25 | .20 |
| | Pair | .30 | |
| | zxm. Untagged, matt gum | .25 | .20 |
| | Pair | .30 | |
| | zxs. Untagged, shiny gum | .25 | .20 |
| | Pair | .30 | |

*(For similar design with "USA 1¢" see No. 806) Listings and prices for plate number coil strips and singles appear at the end of this definitives section of the Krause - Minkus catalog.*

## 1986. STAGECOACH ISSUE Transportation Series
type of No. 791, re-engraved. "Stagecoach 1890s " is 17mm long. *Coil, intaglio, perforated 10 vertically.*

 868 *Stagecoach, 1890s*

| 868 | | MNHVF | UseVF |
|---|---|---|---|
| 4¢ | *red brown,* block tagging | .25 | .20 |
| | Pair | .30 | |
| | FDC *(Aug. 1986)* | | 1.75 |
| | v. Imperforate pair | 600. | |
| | z1. Overall tagging *(1990) (2228a)* | .50 | .20 |
| | Pair | .75 | |

*(See also No. 791.) Listings and prices for plate number coil strips and singles appear at the end of this definitives section of the Krause-Minkus catalog.*

## 1987. TOW TRUCK ISSUE Transportation Series
The 8.5¢ rate was for nonprofit, third class mail. *Coil, intaglio, perforated 11 vertically.*

 869 *Tow Truck, 1929's*

| 869 | | MNHVF | UseVF |
|---|---|---|---|
| 8.5¢ | *dark gray,* tagged | .50 | .20 |
| | Pair | .50 | .20 |
| | FDC *(Jan. 24, 1987)* | | 1.75 |
| | z. Untagged, Bureau-printed red service indicator: "Nonprofit Org." | .25 | .20 |
| | Pair | — | |
| | FDC | | 5.00 |

*Listings and prices for plate number coil strips and singles appear at the end of this definitives section of the Krause- Minkus catalog.*

## 1987. TRACTOR ISSUE Transportation Series
The 7.1¢ value was issued for third-class non-profit mail presorted by Zip code. *Coil, intaglio, perforated 11.*

 870 *Tractor, 1920s*

| 870 | | MNHVF | UseVF |
|---|---|---|---|
| 7.1¢ | *dark red,* tagged | .25 | .20 |
| | Pair | .50 | |
| | FDC *(Feb. 6, 1987)* | | 1.75 |
| | z. Untagged, Bureau-printed service indicator: "Nonprofit Org." *(Feb. 6, 1987)* | .25 | .20 |
| | FDC | | 5.00 |
| | z. Pair | .50 | |
| | zt. Untagged, Bureau-printed service indicator: "Nonprofit 5-Digit Zip+4" *(May 26, 1989)* | .25 | .20 |
| | Pair | .50 | |
| | FDC | | 1.75 |

## 1987. JULIA WARD HOWE ISSUE Great American Series
honors the social reformer and author of *The Battle Hymn of the Republic.* Well-known for her abolitionist sentiment, she also ws a champion of the rights of women and the less fortunate. *Intaglio, perforated 11.*

 871 *Julia Ward Howe*

| 871 | | MNHVF | UseVF |
|---|---|---|---|
| 14¢ | *red,* tagged | .25 | .20 |
| | Plate block of 4 | .75 | |
| | FDC *(Feb. 12, 1987)* | | 1.75 |

## 1987. MARY LYON ISSUE Great American Series
honors a pioneer of higher education for women. Lyon organiz ed Wheaton College in 1834 and founded Mount Holyoke College in 1837. *Intaglio, perforated 11.*

 872 *Mary Lyon*

| 872 | | MNHVF | UseVF |
|---|---|---|---|
| 2¢ | *blue,* tagged | .25 | .20 |
| | Plate block of 4 | .30 | |
| | FDC *(Feb. 28, 1987)* | | 1.75 |
| | zo. Tagging omitted (error) | — | |
| | zx. Untagged (intentional) | .25 | |

**1987. LOCOMOTIVE ISSUE** Transportation Series
type of No. 790, redesinged. *Coil, intaglio, perforated 11.*

873 *Locomotive, 1870s*

| 873 | | MNHVF | UseVF |
|---|---|---|---|
| 2¢ | **black,** tagged | .25 | .20 |
| | Pair | .30 | |
| | FDC *(March 6, 1987)* | | 2.00 |

*(For similar design with "USA 2¢" see No. 790.) Listings and prices for plate number coil strips and singles appear at the end of this definitives section of the Krause- Minkus catalog.*

**1987. CANAL BOAT ISSUE** Transportation Series
*Coil, intaglio, perforated 11.*

874 *Canal Boat, 1880s*

| 874 | | MNHVF | UseVF |
|---|---|---|---|
| 10¢ | **sky blue,** block tagging, matt gum | .25 | .20 |
| | Pair | .35 | |
| | FDC *(April 11, 1987)* | | 1.75 |
| | z1. Overall tagging, matt gum (1993) | .25 | .20 |
| | Prephosphored paper, shiny gum | .25 | .20 |
| | Overall tagging, matt gum | .25 | .20 |

*Listings and prices for plate number coil strips and singles appear at the end of this definitives section of the Krause- Minkus catalog.*

**1987. FLAG WITH FIREWORKS ISSUE** This stamp was released to re-place the Flag over Historic Buildings issues. *Gravure, perforated 11.*

875 *Flag with Fireworks*

| 875 | | MNHVF | UseVF |
|---|---|---|---|
| 22¢ | **multicolored,** tagged | .35 | .20 |
| | Plate block of 4 | 1.75 | |
| | FDC *(May 9, 1987)* single | | 1.75 |
| | n. Booklet pane of 20 | | |
| | *(Nov. 30, 1987)* | 8.50 | |
| | FDC, booklet pane | | 12.00 |

**1987. FLAG OVER CAPITOL TEST COIL ISSUE** This stamp was is-sued to test prephosphored paper, which is tagged before printing. Every stamp has an imprinted "T" in the lower margin. *Coil, intaglio, perforated 10 vertically.*

| 876 | | MNHVF | UseVF |
|---|---|---|---|
| 22¢ | **black, blue, and red,** with "T" at bottom | .40 | .20 |
| | Pair | .75 | |
| | FDC *(May 23, 1987)* | | 2.50 |

*Listings and prices for plate number coil strips and singles appear at the end of this definitives section of the Krause- Minkus catalog.*

**1987. RED CLOUD ISSUE** honors the Chief of the Oglala Sioux. Great American series. *Intaglio, perforated 11.*

877 *Red Cloud*

| 877 | | MNHVF | UseVF |
|---|---|---|---|
| 10¢ | **carmine red,** block tagging | .25 | .20 |
| | Plate block of 4 | .75 | |
| | FDC *(Aug. 15, 1987)* | | 2.00 |
| | z. Tagging omitted (error) | — | |
| | pz. Prephosphored paper | .25 | .20 |
| | Plate block of 4 | .75 | |
| | z1. Overall tagging (1991) | .25 | .20 |
| | Plate block of 4 | .75 | |
| | zx. Untagged (intentional) | .25 | .20 |
| | v. carmine (1995)- shinny gum | .25 | |

**1987. BRET HARTE ISSUE** Great American Series honors the author and poet. Famous for stories and poems of the American West. *Intaglio, perforated 11.*

878 *Bret Harte*

| 878 | | MNHVF | UseVF |
|---|---|---|---|
| $5 | **Venetian red,** block tagging | 8.00 | 2.00 |
| | Plate block of 4 | 40.00 | |
| | FDC *(Aug. 25, 1987)* | | 20.00 |
| | zo. Tagging omitted (error) | | |
| | pz. Prephosphored paper | | |
| | *(March 1992)* | 8.00 | 2.00 |
| | Plate block of 4 | 35.00 | |

**1987. MILK WAGON ISSUE** Transportation Series
*Coil, intaglio, perforated 10 vertically.*

879 *Milk Wagon, 1900s*

| 879 | | MNHVF | UseVF |
|---|---|---|---|
| 5¢ | **charcoal,** tagged | .25 | .20 |
| | Pair | .30 | |
| | FDC *(Sept. 25, 1987)* | | 1.75 |

*Listings and prices for plate number coil strips and singles appear at the end of this definitives section of the Krause- Minkus catalog.*

**1987. RACING CAR ISSUE** Transportation Series
The Marmon Wasp, a 1911 racing car. Denomination covers rate for ZIP+4 presorted mail. *Coil, intaglio, perforated 10 vertically.*

880 | | MNHVF | UseVF |
|---|---|---|---|
| 17.5¢ | **blue violet,** tagged | .30 | .20 |
| | Pair | .50 | |
| | FDC *(Sept. 25, 1987)* | | 1.75 |
| | v. Imperforate pair | 2250. | |
| | zx. Untagged, Bureau-printed red service indicator: "ZIP+4 Pre-sort" | .30 | .20 |
| | Pair | .50 | |

*Listings and prices for plate number coil strips and singles appear at the end of this definitives section of the Krause- Minkus catalog.*

**1987. Christmas Issue** The contemporary design consists of tree ornaments; the traditional desgin displays a portion of Giovanni Battista Moroni's painting *A Gentleman in Adoration before the Madonna.* Gravure, perforated 11.

881 *Madonna and Child*

| 881 | | | MNHVF | UseVF |
|---|---|---|---|---|
| 22¢ | multicolored, tagged | | .50 | .20 |
| | Plate block of 4 | | 2.75 | |
| | FDC *(Oct. 23, 1987)* | | | 2.00 |

882 *Tree Ornament*

| 882 | | | MNHVF | UseVF |
|---|---|---|---|---|
| 22¢ | multicolored, tagged | | .50 | .20 |
| | Gutter Pair | | — | |
| | FDC *(Oct. 23, 1987)* | | | 2.00 |
| | Plate block of 4 | | 2.75 | |

## Transportation Series

**1988. Conestoga Wagon Issue** *Intaglio, perforated 10 vertically.*

883 *Conestoga Wagon, 1800s*

| 883 | | | MNHVF | UseVF |
|---|---|---|---|---|
| 3¢ | dark lilac purple, tagged | | .25 | .20 |
| | Pair | | .30 | |
| | FDC *(Feb. 29, 1988)* | | | 1.75 |
| | zxm.Untagged, matt gum *(1992) (2252a)* | | .25 | .30 |
| | zxs.Untagged, shiny gum (2252b) | | .30 | |

*Listings and prices for plate number coil strips and singles appear at the end of this definitives section of the Krause- Minkus catalog.*

**1988. Non-Denominated "E" Issue** consists of 3 versions: sheet, coil, and booklet. The stamps were released to meet the new 25¢ first class rate. *Gravure, perforated 11.*

884-886 *"E" and Earth*

| 884 | | | MNHVF | UseVF |
|---|---|---|---|---|
| 28¢ | multicolored, tagged | | .50 | .20 |
| | Plate block of 4 | | 1.50 | |
| | FDC *(March 22, 1988)* | | | 1.75 |
| | zo. Tagging omitted (error) | | — | |

**1988. Non-Denominated "E" Coil Issue** Intaglio, perforated 10 vertically.

| 885 | | | MNHVF | UseVF |
|---|---|---|---|---|
| 25¢ | multicolored, tagged | | .50 | .20 |
| | Pair | | .75 | |
| | FDC *(March 22, 1988)* | | | 1.75 |
| | v. Imperforate pair | | 100. | |

*Listings and prices for plate number coil strips and singles appear at the end of this definitives section of the Krause- Minkus catalog.*

**1988. Non-Denominated "E" Booklet Issue** Booklet, perforated 10

| 886 | | | MNHVF | UseVF |
|---|---|---|---|---|
| 25¢ | multicolored, tagged | | .50 | .20 |
| | FDC *(March 22, 1988)* | | | 1.75 |
| | n. Booklet pane of 10 | | 6.50 | |
| | FDC, booklet pane | | | 7.50 |

**1988. Pheasant Booklet Issue** Designed for sale in vending machines as well as over the counter, this booklet is the 1st produced for the U.S. Postal Service by the American Bank Note Co. *Gravure*

887 *Pheasant*

| 887 | | | MNHVF | UseVF |
|---|---|---|---|---|
| 25¢ | multicolored, tagged | | .50 | .20 |
| | Booklet pane of 10 | | 6.00 | |
| | FDC *(April 29, 1988)* single | | | 1.75 |
| | a. Red removed from background sky | | 6.00 | .50 |
| | an.Booklet pane of 10 | | | 75.00 |
| | nv. Horizontally imperforate - between booklet pane of 10 | | 2250. | 65.00 |
| | FDC, booklet pane | | | 8.00 |

*Fully imperforate panes were cut from printer's waste.*

## Great American Series

**1988. Jack London Booklet Issue** are of the same design as No. 853. *Intaglio*

| 888 | | | MNHVF | UseVF |
|---|---|---|---|---|
| 25¢ | blue, perforated 11, tagged | | | |
| | Booklet pane of 10 | | 4.50 | 5.00 |
| | FDC *(May 3, 1988)* booklet pane | | | 8.00 |
| | FDC, single | | | 1.75 |

| 889 | | | MNHVF | UseVF |
|---|---|---|---|---|
| 25¢ | blue, perforated 10, booklet stamps only, tagged | | | |
| | FDC *(May 3, 1988)* single | | | 1.75 |
| | n. Booklet pane of 6 | | 2.75 | |
| | FDC, booklet pane | | | 4.00 |
| | zo. Tagging omitted (error) | | 3.00 | |
| | zon.Tagging omitted, booklet pane of 6 | | 25.00 | |

**1988. Flags with Clouds Issue** *Gravure, perforated 11.*

890, 890A *Flag with Clouds*

| 890 | | | MNHVF | UseVF |
|---|---|---|---|---|
| 25¢ | multicolored, tagged | | .35 | .20 |
| | Plate block of 4 | | 3.25 | |
| | Gutter Pair | | — | |
| | FDC *(May 6, 1988)* | | | 1.75 |

**1988. Flags with Clouds Booklet Issue** Gravure, perforated 11.

| 890A | | | MNHVF | UseVF |
|---|---|---|---|---|
| 25¢ | multicolored, tagged | | .50 | .20 |
| | FDC *(May 6, 1988)* single | | | 1.75 |
| | n. Booklet pane of 6 | | 2.75 | 3.00 |
| | FDC, booklet pane | | | 4.50 |

**1988. FLAG OVER YOSEMITE ISSUE** shows the U.S. flag billowing over Half Dome, Yosemite's most striking example of glacier-carved granite. *Coil, intaglio, perforated 10 vertically.*

891 *Flag over Yosemite*

| 891 | | MNHVF | UseVF |
|---|---|---|---|
| 25¢ | **multicolored,** tagged | .40 | .20 |
| | Pair | .75 | |
| | FDC *(May 20, 1988)* | | 1.75 |
| | v. Imperforate pair | 35.00 | |
| | pz. Pre-phosphored paper | | |
| | *(Feb. 14, 1989)* | .40 | .20 |
| | Pair | .75 | |
| | FDC | | 1.75 |
| | pzv. Imperforate pair, prephosphored-paper | 20.00 | |
| | v1. Imperforate-between pair | 450. | |
| | a. Black trees | 150. | |
| | zo. Tagging omitted (error) | 3.00 | |

*Listings and prices for plate number coil strips and singles appear at the end of this definitives section of the Krause- Minkus catalog.*

**1988. OWL AND GROSBEAK ISSUE** depicts 2 colorful birds in a booklet format. *Gravure, perforated 10.*

892 *Saw-whet owl*

| 892 | | MNHVF | UseVF |
|---|---|---|---|
| 25¢ | **multicolored,** tagged | .40 | .20 |
| | FDC *(May 28, 1988)* | | 1.75 |

893 *Rose-breasted Grosbeak*

| 893 | | MNHVF | UseVF |
|---|---|---|---|
| 25¢ | **multicolored,** tagged | .40 | .20 |
| | y. Se-tenant pair, No. 892-93 | 1.00 | .50 |
| | FDC (either single) | | 1.75 |
| | n. Booklet pane of 10 | 4.50 | 6.00 |
| | yzo. Tagging omitted (error), Se-tenant pair | 7.50 | |

**1988. BUFFALO BILL CODY ISSUE** Great American Series honors the military scout, showman, and raconteur of the Wild West. *Intaglio, perforated 11.*

894 *Buffalo Bill Cody*

| 894 | | MNHVF | UseVF |
|---|---|---|---|
| 15¢ | **maroon,** block tagging | .30 | .20 |
| | Plate block of 4 | 3.50 | |
| | FDC *(June 6, 1988)* | | 2.00 |
| | z1. Overall tagging (1990) | .30 | .20 |
| | Plate block of 4 | 2.00 | |
| | z2. Phosphored paper (surface tagged) | .30 | .20 |
| | Plate block of 4 | 2.00 | |
| | zo. Tagging omitted (error) | 10.00 | |

**1988. HARVEY CUSHING ISSUE** Great American Series honors the "father of neurosurgery." He is credited with laying the foundation for the field of brain surgery. *Intaglio, perforated 11.*

895 *Harvey Cushing*

| 895 | | MNHVF | UseVF |
|---|---|---|---|
| 45¢ | **blue,** block tagging | 1.00 | .20 |
| | Plate block of 4 | 4.00 | |
| | FDC *(June 17, 1988)* | | 2.00 |
| | z1. Overall tagging (1990) | 1.50 | .50 |
| | Plate block of 4 | 11.00 | |
| | zo. Tagging omitted (error) | 7.00 | |

| 896 | MNHVF | UseVF |
|---|---|---|
| *Not assigned* | | |

*Not assigned*

| 897 | MNHVF | UseVF |
|---|---|---|
| *Not assigned* | | |

*Not assigned.*

**1988. POPCORN WAGON ISSUE** Transportation Series This value represented the prepaid base bulk mail rate. *Coil, intaglio, perforated 10 vertically.*

898 *Popcorn Wagon, 1902*

| 898 | | MNHVF | UseVF |
|---|---|---|---|
| 16.7¢ | **dark rose,** Bureau-printed service indicatior "Bulk Rate." | .35 | .20 |
| | Pair | .50 | |
| | FDC *(July 7, 1988)* | | 1.75 |
| | v. Imperforate pair | 175. | |

*Listings and prices for plate number coil strips and singles appear at the end of this definitives section of the Krause- Minkus catalog.*

**1988. TUGBOAT ISSUE** Transportation Series *Coil, intaglio, perforated 10 vertically.*

899 *Tugboat, 1900s*

| 899 | | MNHVF | UseVF |
|---|---|---|---|
| 15¢ | **purple,** block tagging | .30 | .20 |
| | Pair | .50 | |
| | FDC *(July 12, 1988)* | | 1.75 |
| | z1. Overall tagging *(July 1990)* | .30 | .20 |
| | Pair | .50 | |

*Listings and prices for plate number coil strips and singles appear at the end of this definitives section of the Krause- Minkus catalog.*

**1988. Coal Car Issue** Transportation Series Issued to pay a single 3rd-class bulk mail item presorted to 5-digit zip codes. *Coil, intaglio, perforated 10 vertically.*

900 *Coal Car, 1870s*

| 900 | | MNHVF | UseVF |
|---|---|---|---|
| 13.2¢ | **dark green,** Bureau-printed red service indicator "Bulk Rate" | .30 | .20 |
| | Pair | .50 | |
| | FDC *(July 19, 1988)* | | 1.75 |
| | v. Imperforate pair | 100. | |

*Listings and prices for plate number coil strips and singles appear at the end of this definitives section of the Krause- Minkus catalog.*

**1988. Wheel Chair Issue** Transportation Series Issued to pay postage for non-profit bulk rate mail. *Coil, intaglio, perforated 10 vertically.*

901 *Wheel Chair, 1920s*

| 901 | | MNHVF | UseVF |
|---|---|---|---|
| 8.4¢ | **dark violet,** Bureau-printed red service indicator: "Non-profit" | .30 | .20 |
| | Pair | .50 | |
| | FDC *(Aug. 12, 1988)* | | 1.75 |
| | v. Imperforate pair | 650. | |

*Listings and prices for plate number coil strips and singles appear at the end of this definitives section of the Krause- Minkus catalog.*

**1988. Railroad Mail Car Issue** Transportation Series Issued to meet the single-piece rate for presorted 1st-class mail to either the 3- or 5 digit ZIP code. *Coil, intaglio, perforated 10 vertically.*

902 *Railroad Mail Car, 1920s*

| 902 | | MNHVF | UseVF |
|---|---|---|---|
| 21¢ | **green,** Bureau-printed red service indicator "Presorted 1st Class" | .35 | .20 |
| | Pair | .75 | |
| | FDC *(Aug. 16, 1988)* | | 1.75 |
| | v. Imperforate pair | 65.00 | |

**1988. Carreta Issue** Transportation Series The Caretta was a cart used by settlers in Spanish Calif. Issued to pay the rate for non-profit bulk mailers. *Coil, gravure, perforated 10 vertically.*

903 *Carreta, 1770s*

| 903 | | MNHVF | UseVF |
|---|---|---|---|
| 7.6¢ | **brown,** Bureau-printed red service indicator: "Nonprofit" | .25 | .20 |
| | Pair | .30 | |
| | FDC *(Aug. 30, 1988)* | | 1.75 |

*Listings and prices for plate number coil strips and singles appear at the end of this definitives section of the Krause- Minkus catalog.*

**1988. Harry S. Truman Issue** Great American Series A new version. *perforated 11 1/4.*

| 904 | | MNHVF | UseVF |
|---|---|---|---|
| 20¢ | **black,** perforated 11 1/4 block tagging | .35 | .20 |
| | Plate block of 4 | 3.50 | |
| | FDC *(Sept. 1, 1988)* | | — |
| | z1. Overall tagging *(1990)* | .35 | .20 |
| | Plate block of 4 | 4.00 | |
| | pz. Phosphored paper (embedded) | — | |
| | Plate block of 4, shinny gum | — | |
| | zo. Tagging omitted error | — | |

*(See also No. 811)*

**1988. Honeybee Issue** *Coil, intaglio, perforated 11.*

905 *Honeybee*

| 905 | | MNHVF | UseVF |
|---|---|---|---|
| 25¢ | **multicolored,** tagged | .40 | .20 |
| | Pair | .75 | |
| | FDC *(Sept. 2, 1988)* | | 1.75 |
| | v. Black (intaglio) omitted | 65.00 | |
| | v1. Black (offset) omitted | 550. | |
| | v2. Yellow (offset) omitted | — | |
| | v3. Imperforate pair | 55.00 | |
| | v4. Imperforate-between pair | 1000. | |
| | zo. Tagging omitted (error) | 7.00 | |

*Listings and prices for plate number coil strips and singles appear at the end of this definitives section of the Krause- Minkus catalog.*

**1988. Elevator Issue** Transportation Series Issued to pay the non-profit 3rd-class rate for mail presorted to the carrier route. *Coil, intaglio, perforated 10 vertically.*

906 *Elevator, 1900s*

| 906 | | MNHVF | UseVF |
|---|---|---|---|
| 5.3¢ | **black,** Bureau-printed red service indicator: "Nonprofit/Carrier Route Sort" | .25 | .20 |
| | Pair | .30 | |
| | FDC *(Sept. 16, 1988)* | | 1.75 |

*Listings and prices for plate number coil strips and singles appear at the end of this definitives section of the Krause- Minkus catalog.*

**1988. Fire Engine Issue** Transportation Series. Issued to prepay the 1st-class mail rate presorted by ZIP+4. *Coil, intaglio, perforated 10 vertically.*

907 *Fire Engine, 1900s*

**907**
**20.5¢** **red,** Bureau-printed black service indicator: MNHVF .35 / UseVF .20
"ZIP+4 Presort"
Pair .30
FDC *(Sept. 28, 1988)* 2.00

*Listings and prices for plate number coil strips and singles appear at the end of this definitives section of the Krause- Minkus catalog.*

**1988. Eagle and Moon Issue** was designed to meet the increased rate for Express Mail. Although inteneded for that use, it also was valid for postage classes where a high value was needed. *Offset and intaglio, perforated 11.*

*908 Eagle and Moon*

**908**
**$8.75** **multicolored,** tagged MNHVF 25.00 / UseVF 8.00
Plate block of 4 110.
FDC *(Oct. 4, 1988)* 30.00

## Christmas Series

**1988. Christmas Issue** The contemporary issue depicts a snowy scene and was released at Berlin, N.H., to honor Irving Berlin and his song *White Christmas. Gravure, perforated 11 1/2.*

*909 Snowy Village Scene*

**909**
**25¢** **multicolored,** tagged MNHVF .40 / UseVF .20
Plate block of 4 1.25
FDC *(Oct. 20, 1988)* 2.00
Gutter Pair —

**1988. Madonna And Child by Botticelli Issue** Christmas Series The traditional issue is based on the painting *Madonna and Child* by Italian master Sandro Botticelli. *Intaglio and offset, perforated 11 1/2.*

*910 Madonna and Child by Botticelli.*

**910**
**25¢** **multicolored,** tagged MNHVF .40 / UseVF .20
Plate block of 4 1.25
FDC *(Oct. 20, 1988)* 2.00
v. Gold omitted 30.00

**1988. Chester Carlson Issue** Great American Series honors the man who invented xerography and began an office copying revolution. *Intaglio, perforated 11.*

*911 Chester Carlson*

**911**
**21¢** **blue violet,** tagged MNHVF .35 / UseVF .20
Plate block of 4 1.25
FDC *(Oct. 21, 1988)* 1.75

**1988. Tandem Bicycle Issue** Transportation Series Issued to meet the rate for unpresorted ZIP +4 mail, of particular use to mid-size businesses. *Coil, intaglio, perforated 10 vertically.*

*912 Tandem Bicycle, 1890s*

**912**
**24.1¢** **deep blue violet,** Bureau-printed red MNHVF .40 / UseVF .20
service indicator: "ZIP+4"
Pair .75
FDC *(Oct. 26, 1988)* 1.75

*Listings and prices for plate number coil strips and singles appear at the end of this definitives section of the Krause-Minkus catalog.*

**1988. Cable Car Issue** Transportation Series Issued to prepay the rate for the 2nd ounce of 1st-class mail. *Coil, intaglio, perforated 10 vertically.*

*913 Cable Car, 1880s*

**913**
**20¢** **dark violet,** block tagged MNHVF .35 / UseVF .20
Pair .75
FDC *(Oct. 28, 1988)* 1.75
v. Imperforate pair 75.00
z1. Overall tagging (1990) .35 / .20
Pair .75

*Listings and prices for plate number coil strips and singles appear at the end of this definitives section of the Krause-Minkus catalog.*

**1988. Police Patrol Wagon Issue** Transportation Series Issued to meet the single-piece rate for presorted 1st class mailings of postcards. *Coil, intaglio, perforated 10 vertically.*

*914 Police Patrol Wagon, 1880s*

**914**
**13¢** **black,** Bureau-printed red service indicator: MNHVF .30 / UseVF .20
"Presorted First- Class"
Pair .50
FDC *(Oct. 29, 1988)* 1.75

*Listings and prices for plate number coil strips and singles appear at the end of this definitives section of the Krause-Minkus catalog.*

**1988. Mary Cassatt Issue** Great American Series Honors the famed painter. *Intaglio, perforated 11.*

*915 Mary Cassatt*

| 915 | | MNHVF | UseVF |
|---|---|---|---|
| 23¢ | **purple,** block tagging | .45 | .20 |
| | Plate block of 4 | 2.25 | |
| | FDC | | 1.75 |
| | z. Overall tagging (1990) | .60 | .20 |
| | Plate block of 4 | 3.00 | |
| | z1. Phosphored paper (surface shiny gum | .60 | .20 |
| | Plate block of 4 | 3.00 | |
| | zo. Tagging omitted (error) | — | |

**1988. H.H. "HAP" ARNOLD ISSUE** Great American Series honors the "father of the modern air force." The stamp met the rate for a 3-ounce 1st-class letter. *Intaglio, perforated 11.*

916 *H.H. "Hap" Arnold*

| 916 | | MNHVF | UseVF |
|---|---|---|---|
| 65¢ | **dark blue,** tagged | 1.25 | .20 |
| | Plate block of 4 | 5.00 | |
| | FDC *(Nov. 5, 1988)* | | 2.50 |
| | zo. Tagging omitted (error) | 7.50 | |

| 917 | | MNHVF | UseVF |
|---|---|---|---|
| | *Not assigned* | | |

**1989. JOHNS HOPKINS ISSUE** Great American Series honors the founder of the hospital and university that bears his name. Hopkins dedicated his fortune to the relief of suffering and advancement of knowledge. *Intaglio, perforated 11.*

918 *Johns Hopkins*

| 918 | | MNHVF | UseVF |
|---|---|---|---|
| $1 | **blackish blue,** block tagged, matt gum | 1.75 | .20 |
| | Plate block of 4 | 7.00 | |
| | FDC *(June 7, 1989)* | | 5.00 |
| | z. Overall tagged (1990) | 1.75 | .20 |
| | Plate block of 4 | 7.00 | |
| | z1. Phosphored paper (tagged on surface) | 1.75 | .20 |
| | Plate block of 4 | 7.50 | |
| | z2. Phosphored paper (tagged embedded) | 1.75 | .20 |
| | Plate block of 4 | 8.00 | |
| | zo. Tagging omitted | 5.50 | |

**1989. SITTING BULL ISSUE** Great American Series honors the chief, spiritual and political leader of the Hunkpapa Sioux. Issued to meet the rate for postcards sent via surface mail from the United States to all foreign destinations other than Canada and Mexico. Intaglio, perforated 11.

919 *Sitting Bull*

| 919 | | MNHVF | UseVF |
|---|---|---|---|
| 28¢ | | .50 | .20 |
| | Plate block of 4 | 3.00 | |
| | FDC *(Sept. 14, 1989)* | | 2.25 |

**1989. SLEIGH WITH GIFTS ISSUE** Christmas Series Both the traditional and contemporary stamps were available in both sheet and booklet versions. The 2 versions of the sleigh contemporary design are noticeably different. The booklet version is printed in 5 colors, the sheet stamp in four. Sleigh runners of the booklet version are decidedly thicker than on the sheet version. The package to the rear of the sleigh has a bow the same color as the package on the booklet stamp, where the bow is of a different color on the sheet version. Finally, the board running under the sleigh is pink on the booklet version and the same color as the sleigh on the sheet version. The 2 versions of the tradition al are identical, other than the booklet stamp having perforations on only 2 or 3 sides. *Gravure, perforated 11.*

920, 921 *Sleigh with gifts.*

| 920 | | MNHVF | UseVF |
|---|---|---|---|
| 25¢ | **multicolored,** tagged | .40 | .20 |
| | Plate block of 4 | 1.25 | |
| | FDC *(Oct. 19, 1989)* | | 1.75 |
| | v. Verticle pair, imperforate horizontally | 650. | |

**1989. SLEIGH WITH GIFTS BOOKLET ISSUE** Christmas Series

| 921 | | MNHVF | UseVF |
|---|---|---|---|
| 25¢ | **multicolored,** booklet stamp, tagged | .40 | .20 |
| | FDC *(Oct. 19, 1989)* single | | 1.75 |
| | n. Booklet pane of 10 | 3.00 | |
| | FDC booklet pane | — | 8.00 |
| | nv. Booklet pane of 10, Red omitted | 7150. | |
| | nv1.Booklet pane of 10, horizontally imperforate between | — | |

**1989. THE DREAM OF ST. ALEXANDRIA ISSUE** Christmas Series *Intaglio, perforated 11 1/2.*

922 The Dream of St. Alexandria *by Lucovico Carracci.*

| 922 | | MNHVF | UseVF |
|---|---|---|---|
| 25¢ | **multicolored,** tagged | .40 | .20 |
| | Plate block of 4 | 1.25 | |
| | FDC *(Oct. 19, 1989)* single | | 1.75 |
| | n. Booklet pane of 10 | 3.00 | |
| | FDC booklet pane | — | 8.00 |
| | nv. Booklet pane of 10, offset red omitted | 750. | |
| | nv1.Imperforate booklet pane of 10 | — | |

| 923 | | MNHVF | UseVF |
|---|---|---|---|
| | *Not assigned* | | |

**1989. EAGLE AND SHIELD SELF-ADHESIVE ISSUE** was available in a do-it-yourself booklet format that permitted the purchaser to fold the pane of 18 die-cut stamp s into a more convenient pocket-sized package. The stamps also were available in strips of 18 with the stamps spaced apart for use in affixing machines. *Gravure, imperforate and die-cut between.*

924 *Eagle and Shield*

| 924 | | MNHVF | UseVF |
|---|---|---|---|
| 25¢ | **multicolored,** tagged | .40 | .20 |
| | n. Booklet pane of 18 | 16.00 | |
| | FDC *(Nov. 10, 1989)* single | | 1.75 |
| | v. Vertical pair, no die cutting between | 850. | |
| | v1. Pair, no die cutting | — | |

| 925 | *Not assigned* | MNHVF | UseVF |
|---|---|---|---|

**1990. BEACH UMBRELLA ISSUE** equates the idea of vacations and a stamp meeting for the postcard rate. *Booklet stamp, gravure, perforated 11 1/2.*

926 *Beach umbrella*

| 926 | | MNHVF | UseVF |
|---|---|---|---|
| 15¢ | **multicolored,** booklet stamp, tagged | .30 | .20 |
| | n. Booklet pane of 10 | 4.25 | |
| | FDC *(Feb. 3, 1990)* | | 1.75 |
| | nv. Booklet pane of 10, blue omitted | 1650. | |
| | nv1. Single stamp, blue omitted | 225. | |

**1990. LUIS MUÑOZ MARIN ISSUE** Great American Series honors the 1st popularly elected governor of Puerto Rico. This is a major design change for the Great American series in which a zero precedes denominations of less than 10¢, and information about the subject ("Governor, Puerto Rico") appears in the selvage. *Intaglio.*

927 *Luis Muñoz Marin*

| 927 | | MNHVF | UseVF |
|---|---|---|---|
| 5¢ | **dark rose,** tagged | .25 | .20 |
| | Plate block of 4 | .30 | |
| | FDC *(Feb. 18, 1990)* | | 1.75 |
| | z. Untagged | .25 | .20 |
| | Plate block of 4 (plate No. 2) | .65 | |
| | zo. Tagging omitted, plate block of 4 (Plate No. 1) | .65 | |

**1990. SEAPLANE ISSUE** Transportation Series *Coil, intaglio.*

928 *Seaplane, 1914*

| 928 | | MNHVF | UseVF |
|---|---|---|---|
| $1 | **dark blue and red,** tagged | 2.00 | .50 |
| | Pair | | |
| | FDC *(April 20, 1990)* | | 3.00 |
| | v. Imperforate pair | 2500. | — |

*Listings and prices for plate number coil strips and singles appear at the end of this definitives section of the Krause- Minkus catalog.*

**1990. FLAG ISSUE FOR AUTOMATIC TELLER MACHINES** The USPS tested dispensing of stamps through bank ATM equipment. This stamp was *self-adhesive, die cut, imperforate.* Available in panes of 12 the same size as a dollar bill - and *printed on polyester film by gravure.* This issue was available as a test through 22 machines in the Seattle, Wash. area.

929 *U.S. Flag*

| 929 | | MNHVF | UseVF |
|---|---|---|---|
| 25¢ | **red and dark blue,** tagged | .50 | .50 |
| | n. Pane of 12 | 6.00 | |
| | FDC *(May 18, 1990)* | | 1.75 |

**1990. BOBCAT ISSUE** was the first high-value stamp in the Wildlife Series. Printed in panes of 20, with 4 plate numbers, copyright notice and descriptive information on the selvage. *Intaglio and offset, perforated 11.*

930 *Bobcat*

| 930 | | MNHVF | UseVF |
|---|---|---|---|
| $2 | **multicolored,** tagged | 4.00 | 1.25 |
| | Plate block of 4 | 18.00 | |
| | FDC *(June 1, 1990)* | | 7.00 |
| | v. Intaglio black omitted | 300. | |
| | zo. Tagging omitted (error) | 10.50 | 7.00 |

**1990. CIRCUS WAGON ISSUE** Transportation Series *Coil, intaglio, perforated 10 vertically.*

931 *Circus Wagon, 1900s*

| 931 | | MNHVF | UseVF |
|---|---|---|---|
| 5¢ | **carmine red,** tagged | .25 | .20 |
| | Pair | .30 | |
| | FDC *Aug. 31, 1990)* | | 1.75 |
| | z. Untagged | .25 | .20 |
| | Pair | .30 | |
| | v. Imperforate pair | 875. | |

*For stamps of this design inscribed "USA 5¢" see No. 1007 (gravure) or No. 1077 (intaglio).*

*Listings and prices for plate number coil strips and singles appear at the end of this definitives section of the Krause- Minkus catalog.*

**1990. CLAIRE LEE CHENNAULT ISSUE** Great American Series honors the pioneer air power tactician who led the Flying Tigers in China in World War II. *Intaglio, perforated 11.*

932 *Clair Chennault*

| 932 | | MNHVF | UseVF |
|---|---|---|---|
| 40¢ | **dark blue,** overall tagging | .75 | .20 |
| | Plate block of 4 | 3.75 | |
| | z1. Phosphored paper | | |
| | (taggant on surface), shiny gum | .75 | .20 |
| | Plate block of 4 | 4.00 | |
| | FDC *(Sept. 6, 1990)* | | 2.00 |

**1990. CONTEMPORARY CHRISTMAS ISSUE** features a cut-paper Christmas tree. There are noticeable design and color differences between the sheet and booklet versions of this stamp. *Gravure, perforated 11 1/2.*

933, 934 *Christmas tree*

| 933 | | MNHVF | UseVF |
|---|---|---|---|
| 25¢ | **multicolored,** tagged | .40 | .20 |
| | Plate block of 4 | 1.50 | |
| | FDC *(Oct. 18, 1990)* | | 2.00 |
| | v. Vertical pair, imperforate horizontally | 1100. | |

| 934 | | MNHVF | UseVF |
|---|---|---|---|
| 25¢ | **multicolored,** booklet stamp, tagged | .40 | .20 |
| | FDC *(Oct. 18, 1990)* single | | 2.00 |
| | n. Booklet pane of 10 | 8.00 | |
| | FDC, booklet pane | | 6.00 |

*There are noticeable design and color differences between the sheet and booklet versions of this stamp.*

**1990. MADONNA AND CHILD BOOKLET ISSUE** Christmas Series.

935, 936 Madonna and Child *by Antonello da Messina.*

| 935 | | MNHVF | UseVF |
|---|---|---|---|
| 25¢ | **multicolored,** tagged | .40 | .20 |
| | Plate block of 4 | 1.50 | |
| | FDC *(Oct. 18, 1990)* | | 2.00 |

| 936 | | MNHVF | UseVF |
|---|---|---|---|
| 25¢ | **multicolored,** booklet stamp, tagged | .40 | .20 |
| | FDC *(Oct. 18, 1990)* single | | 2.00 |
| | n. Booklet pane of 10 | 8.00 | |
| | FDC, booklet pane | | 6.50 |

*The booklet version has a much heavier shading in the Madonna's veil where it meets the right frame line.*

**1991. "F" (FLOWER) NON-DENOMINATED ISSUE** came in sheet, coil, and two different booklet types. Its face value was 29¢, the new first-class mail rate. *Gravure, perforated 13.*

937-940 *"F" and tulip*

| 937 | | MNHVF | UseVF |
|---|---|---|---|
| 29¢ | **multicolored,** tagged | .50 | .20 |
| | Plate block of 4 | 2.25 | |
| | FDC *(Jan. 22, 1991)* | | 1.75 |
| | v. Vertical pair, imperforate | 750. | |
| | v1. Horizontal pair, imperforate vertically | 1200. | |

**1991. "F" (FLOWER) NON-DENOMINATION BOOKLET ISSUE** Dark green leaf. BEP, perforated 11 1/4.

| 938 | | MNHVF | UseVF |
|---|---|---|---|
| 29¢ | **multicolored,** booklet stamp, tagged | .50 | .20 |
| | FDC *(Jan. 22, 1991)* | | 1.75 |
| | n. Booklet pane of 10 | 6.00 | |
| | FDC, booklet pane | | 7.50 |

**1991. "F" (FLOWER) NON-DENOMINATION BOOKLET ISSUE** Bright green leaf, pale yellow less pronounced, black dies in leaf. KCS, perforated 11.

| 939 | | MNHVF | UseVF |
|---|---|---|---|
| 29¢ | **multicolored,** booklet stamp, printed by | .50 | .20 |
| | KCS Industries, tagged | | |
| | FDC *(Jan. 22, 1991)* single | | 1.75 |
| | n. Booklet pane of 10 | 25.00 | |
| | z. Phosphored paper (1993) | .50 | .20 |
| | z1. Booklet pane of 10 | 25.00 | |
| | FDC, booklet pane | | 9.50 |

**1991. "F" (FLOWER) NON-DENOMINATION COIL ISSUE** Coil, perforated 10 vertically.

| 940 | | MNHVF | UseVF |
|---|---|---|---|
| 29¢ | **multicolored,** tagged | .60 | .20 |
| | Pair | .75 | |
| | FDC *(Jan. 22, 1991)* | | 1.75 |
| | v. Imperforate pair | 35.00 | |

**1991. NON-DENOMINATED 4¢ MAKE UP ISSUE** has a value of 4¢, to be used with a 25¢ stamp to meet the new 29¢ first-class rate. *Offset, perforated 11.*

941 *Text explaining how to use stamp.*

| 941 | | MNHVF | UseVF |
|---|---|---|---|
| 4¢ | **bister and carmine** | .25 | .20 |
| | Plate block of 4 | .30 | |
| | FDC *(Jan. 22, 1991)* | | 1.75 |
| | v. Vertical pair, imperforate horizontally | 100. | |

**1991. "F" NON-DENOMINATED ATM FLAG ISSUE** was identical in design and material to No. 929, with the denomination replaced by an "F" and the inclusion of "For U.S. Addresses Only." *Gravure, die cut, imperforate.*

942 *"F" and U.S. flag*

| 942 | | MNHVF | UseVF |
|---|---|---|---|
| 29¢ | **black, dark blue and red,** tagged | .50 | .20 |
| | n. Pane of 12 | 7.00 | |
| | FDC *(Jan. 22, 1991)* single | | 1.75 |
| | FDC (pane of 12) | | 10.00 |

**1991. STEAM CARRIAGE ISSUE** Transportation Series Depicts the "Richard Dudgeon," which is now in the Museum of American History of the Smithsonian Insitution. *Coil, intaglio, perforated 10 vertically.*

*943 Steam carriage, 1866*

| 943 | | MNHVF | UseVF |
|---|---|---|---|
| 4¢ | **maroon,** tagged | .25 | .20 |
| | Pair | .30 | |
| | FDC *(Jan. 25, 1991)* | | 1.75 |
| | v. Imperforate pair | 625. | |
| | zx. Untagged (intentional) | .25 | |
| | Pair | .30 | |

*Listings and prices for plate number coil strips and singles appear at the end of this definitives section of the Krause- Minkus catalog.*

**1991. FAWN ISSUE** Meet the rate for postcards. Wildlife Series. *Gravure, perforated 11.*

*944 Fawn*

| 944 | | MNHVF | UseVF |
|---|---|---|---|
| 19¢ | **multicolored,** tagged | .40 | .20 |
| | Plate block of 4 | 1.50 | |
| | FDC *(March 11, 1991)* | | 1.75 |
| | v. Red omitted | 850. | |
| | zo. Tagging omitted (error) | 8.50 | |

**1991. FLAG OVER MOUNT RUSHMORE** marks the 50th anniversary of the South Dakota monument. *Coil, intaglio, perforated 10 vertically.*

*945 Flag, Mt. Rushmore*

| 945 | | MNHVF | UseVF |
|---|---|---|---|
| 29¢ | **red, blue, and maroon,** tagged | .50 | .20 |
| | Pair | .75 | |
| | FDC *(March 29, 1991)* | | 1.75 |
| | v. Imperforate pair | 25.00 | |

| 945A | | MNHVF | UseVF |
|---|---|---|---|
| 29¢ | **red, blue and brown** color change (error), tagged | .50 | .20 |
| | Pair | 3.00 | |
| | FDC | | 1.75 |

*For gravure version of this design, see No. 963.*

*Listings and prices for plate number coil strips and singles appear at the end of this definitives section of the Krause- Minkus catalog.*

**1991. DENNIS CHAVEZ ISSUE** Great American Series honors the first U.S. born Hispanic elected to the U.S. Senate. *Intaglio, by Stamp Venturers, perforated 11.*

*946 Dennis Chavez*

| 946 | | MNHVF | UseVF |
|---|---|---|---|
| 35¢ | **black,** tagged | .75 | .20 |
| | Plate block of 4 | 3.50 | |
| | FDC *(April 3, 1991)* | | 2.00 |

**1991. FLOWER ISSUE** is a "denominated" version of the"F" stamp, initially released in sheet and booklet types. *Gravure, perforated 11.*

*947, 947A, 948 Tulip*

| 947 | | MNHVF | UseVF |
|---|---|---|---|
| 29¢ | **multicolored,** tagged, perforated 11 | .45 | .20 |
| | Plate block of 4 | 1.75 | |
| | FDC *(April 5, 1991)* | | 1.75 |

**1991. FLOWER ISSUE**

| 947A | | MNHVF | UseVF |
|---|---|---|---|
| 29¢ | **multicolored,** tagged, perforated 12 1/2 x 13 | .45 | .20 |
| | Plate block of 4 | 1.75 | |

**1991. FLOWER BOOKLET ISSUE**

| 948 | | MNHVF | UseVF |
|---|---|---|---|
| 29¢ | **multicolored,** booklet stamp, tagged, perforated 11 | .45 | .20 |
| | n. Booklet pane of 10 | 8.00 | |
| | FDC *(April 5, 1991)* single | | |
| | nv. Pane of 10, vertically imperforate between | 1900. | |
| | nv1.Pane of 10, imperforate horizontally | — | |
| | nv2.Horizontal pair, imperforate vertically | 375. | |
| | FDC booklet pane | | 7.50 |

*For coil version of the Flower Issue, see Nos. 966 and 982.*

**1991. LUNCH WAGON ISSUE** Transportation Series met the new second-ouce first-class mail rate. *Coil, intaglio, perforated 10 vertically.*

*949 Lunch Wagon, 1890s*

| 949 | | MNHVF | UseVF |
|---|---|---|---|
| 23¢ | **blue,** tagged, matt gum | .50 | .20 |
| | Pair | .75 | |
| | FDC *(April 12, 1991)* | | 1.75 |
| | zs. Prephosphored paper, (mottled tagging), shiny gum (1993) | .50 | .20 |
| | Pair | .75 | |
| | zm.Prephosphored paper (mottled tagging) matt gum (1993) | .50 | .20 |
| | Pair | .75 | |
| | v. Imperforate pair | 150. | |

*Listings and prices for plate number coil and singles appear at the end of this definitives section of the Krause-Minkus catalog.*

## Wildlife Series

**1991. WOOD DUCK ISSUE** produced by the Bureau of Engraving and Printing with lettering and numbers in black and by KCS Industries with the lettering and numbers in red. *Gravure, perforated 10.*

*950, 951 Wood duck*

**950**

| | | MNHVF | UseVF |
|---|---|---|---|
| 29¢ | **multicolored,** booklet stamp, black inscription (BEP), tagged | .75 | .20 |
| | FDC *(April 12, 1991)NI* | | 1.75 |
| | n. Booklet pane of 10 | 8.00 | |
| | FDC booklet pane | — | 9.00 |
| | nv. Pane of 10, horizontaly imperforate-between | 1200. | |
| | nv1.Vertical pair, imperforate horizontally | 275. | |

**1991. WOOD DUCK ISSUE** Wildlife Series *Perforated 11*

**951**

| | | MNHVF | UseVF |
|---|---|---|---|
| 29¢ | **multicolored,** booklet stamp, red inscription (KCS Industries), tagged | 1.00 | .20 |
| | FDC *(April 12, 1991)* | | 1.75 |
| | n. Booklet pane of 10 | 8.75 | |
| | FDC booklet pane | | 9.00 |

**1991. U.S. FLAG, WITH OLYMPIC RINGS ISSUE** was a booklet version with a flag motif. *Gravure, perforated 11.*

**U.S. Flag with Olympic Rings Issue** was a booklet version with a flag motif. *Gravure, perforated 11.*

**952**

| | | MNHVF | UseVF |
|---|---|---|---|
| 29¢ | **multicolored,** booklet stamp, tagged | | |
| | FDC *(Aprl 21, 1991)* | | |
| | n. Booklet pane of 10 | | |
| | FDC booklet pane | | |
| | nv. Pane of 10, horizontally imperforate-between | | |
| | nv1.Vertical pair, imperforate between | | |

**1991. HOT AIR BALLOON ISSUE** met the postcard rate for first-class mail and was available in booklet form. *Gravure, perforated 10.*

953 *Hot air balloon*

**953**

| | | MNHVF | UseVF |
|---|---|---|---|
| 19¢ | **multicolored,** booklet stamp, tagged | .30 | .20 |
| | FDC *(May 17, 1991)* | | 1.75 |
| | n. Booklet pane of 10 | 4.50 | |
| | FDC booklet pane | — | 7.50 |

**1991. TRACTOR TRAILER ISSUE** Transportation Series Was for use by bulk business mailers. *Coil, intaglio, perforated 10 vertically.*

954 *Tractor trailer, 1930s*

**954**

| | | MNHVF | UseVF |
|---|---|---|---|
| 10¢ | **green,** Bureau-printed gray service indicator: "Additional Presort Postage Paid" | .25 | .20 |
| | Pair | .30 | |
| | FDC *(May 25, 1991)* | | 1.75 |
| | v. Imperforate pair | 400. | |

*For version with service indicator in black, see No. 1042.*

**1991. CANOE ISSUE** Transportation Series Was for use by non-profit mailers.

955 *Canoe, 1800s*

**955**

| | | MNHVF | UseVF |
|---|---|---|---|
| 5¢ | **brown,** printed gray service indicator: "Additional Nonprofit Postage Paid" | .25 | .20 |
| | Pair | .30 | |
| | FDC *(May 25, 1991)* | | 1.75 |
| | v. Imperforate pair | 325. | |

*For gravure version of No. 955 in red, see No. 979. Listings and prices for plate number coil strips and singles appear at the end of this definitives section of the Krause-Minkus catalog.*

**1991. FLAGS ON PARADE ISSUE** celebrates the 125th anniversary of Memorial Day. *Gravure, perforated 11.*

956 *Flags on Parade*

**956**

| | | MNHVF | UseVF |
|---|---|---|---|
| 29¢ | **multicolored,** tagged | .50 | .20 |
| | Plate block of 4 | 2.00 | |
| | FDC *(May 30, 1991)* | | 1.75 |

**1991. HUBERT H. HUMPHREY ISSUE** Great American Series honors the former vice president, Minnesota senator and mayor of Minneapolis. A date error in the selvage incription, showing the wrong beginning date of his tenure as vice president, was corrected with a re-lease of the stamp in 1993. *Intaglio, perforated 11.*

957 *Hubert H. Humphrey*

**957**

| | | MNHVF | UseVF |
|---|---|---|---|
| 52¢ | **purple,** tagged | 1.50 | .20 |
| | Plate block of 4 | 6.00 | |
| | FDC *(June 3, 1991)* | | 2.00 |
| | z1. Phosphored paper (taggant on surface) | 1.50 | .20 |
| | Plate block of 4 | 5.00 | |

**1991. EAGLE AND OLYMPIC RINGS ISSUE** met eight-ounce Express Mail rate. The stamp was valid for other mail as well. *Intaglio and offset, perforated 11.*

958 *Eagle and Olympic rings.*

**958**

| | | MNHVF | UseVF |
|---|---|---|---|
| $9.95 | **multicolored,** tagged | .25 | .11 |
| | Plate block of 4 | 100. | |
| | FDC *(June 6, 1991)* | | 25.00 |

**1991. KESTREL ISSUE** Wildlife Series *Offset, perforated 11.*

959 *Kestrel*

**959**

| | | MNHVF | UseVF |
|---|---|---|---|
| 1¢ | **multicolored** | .25 | .20 |
| | Plate block of 4 | .30 | |
| | FDC *(June 22, 1991)* | | 1.75 |

*For versions inscribed "USA 1¢", see No. 1079 (sheet) and No. 1115 (Coil).*

**1991. BLUEBIRD ISSUE** Wildlife Series

960 *Bluebird*

**960**

| | | MNHVF | UseVF |
|---|---|---|---|
| 3¢ | **bluebird** | .25 | .20 |
| | Plate block of 4 | .30 | |
| | FDC *(June 22, 1991)* | | 1.75 |

**1991. CARDINAL ISSUE** Wildlife Series Met the postcard rate to Canada and Mexico. *Gravure, perforated 11 1/2 x 11.*

961 *Cardinal*

**961**

| | | MNHVF | UseVF |
|---|---|---|---|
| 30¢ | **multicolored,** on phosphored paper | .45 | .20 |
| | Plate block of 4 | 2.00 | |
| | FDC *(June 22, 1991)* | | 1.75 |

**1991. STATUE OF LIBERTY TORCH ISSUE** was designed for sale through ATM machines. This issue provided 18 stamps on a backing sheet the same size as a dollar bill. Unlike its predecessor, this issue was printed on paper. *Gravure, die cut, imperforate.*

962 *Liberty torch*

**962**

| | | MNHVF | UseVF |
|---|---|---|---|
| 29¢ | **black, gold and green,** tagged | .60 | .30 |
| | FDC *(June 25, 1991)* | | 1.75 |
| | n. Pane of 18, plain paper back | 14.50 | |
| | FDC (pane of 18) | | 14.00 |
| | nv. Pane of 18, printed backing paper | 15.00 | |
| | nv1.Pair, die cut omitted | 3750. | |

**1991. FLAG OVER MT. RUSHMORE ISSUE** type of No. 945 re-issued with essentially the same colors. *Coil, gravure, American Bank Note Co., perforated 10 vertically.*

963 *Flag over Mt. Rushmore.*

**963**

| | | MNHVF | UseVF |
|---|---|---|---|
| 29¢ | **blue, red and brown,** tagged | .50 | .25 |
| | Pair | 1.00 | |
| | FDC *(July 4, 1991)* | | 1.75 |
| | p. Phosphor-coated "Lenz" paper | 2.00 | .50 |

*For intaglio version of the same design, see No. 945. Listings and prices for plate number coil strips and singles appear at the end of this definitives section of the Krause-Minkus catalog.*

**1991. EAGLE AND OLYMPIC RINGS ISSUE** met the Priority Mail rate for second-day delivery of up to two pounds. *Intaglio and offset, perforated 11.*

964 *Eagle and Olympic rings*

**964**

| | | MNHVF | UseVF |
|---|---|---|---|
| $2.90 | **multicolored,** tagged | 5.00 | 2.75 |
| | Plate block of 4 | 25.00 | |
| | v. Intaglio Black omitted | 3500. | |
| | FDC *(July 7, 1991)* | | 9.00 |

**1991. FISHING BOAT ISSUE** met the first class rate for domestic postcards. *Coil, gravure, American Bank Note Co., perforated 11.*

965 *Fishing boat*

**965**

| | | MNHVF | UseVF |
|---|---|---|---|
| 19¢ | **multicolored, Type I,** tagged | .40 | .20 |
| | Pair | .75 | |
| | FDC *(Aug. 8, 1991)* | | 1.75 |
| | a. Type II (lighter colors, sharper printing) *(1992)* | .40 | .20 |
| | Pair | .75 | |
| | zo. Tagging omitted (error, wrong paper used) | 100. | |
| | Pair | 200. | |
| | z. Untagged *(1993)* | .75 | .20 |

*Imperforates in this design came from printer's waste. For version with one loop of rope tying boat to piling, see No. 1044.*

**1991. FLOWER COIL ISSUE** The separations are "roulettes" rather than "perforations". With rouletting, only a series of slits are made to facilitate separation, rather than drilling holes to create perforations. *Coil, gravure, Stamp Venturers, rouletted 10 vertically.*

966 *Tulip*

| 966 | | MNHVF | UseVF |
|---|---|---|---|
| 29¢ | **multicolored,** tagged | .75 | .20 |
| | Pair | 1.25 | |
| | FDC *(Aug. 16, 1991)* | | 1.75 |

**1991. EAGLE OVER COASTLINE, OLYMPIC RINGS ISSUE** met the rate for international Express Mail pieces weighing up to eight ounces to 109 counries. *Intaglio and offset, perforated 11.*

967 *Eagle over Coastline, Olympic rings.*

| 967 | | MNHVF | UseVF |
|---|---|---|---|
| $14 | **multicolored,** tagged | 30.00 | 17.50 |
| | Plate block of 4 | 130. | |
| | v.  Intaglio red, omitted (value and rings). | — | |
| | FDC *(Aug. 31, 1991)* | | 32.50 |

No. 968 is not assigned.

**1991. U.S. FLAG ISSUE** includes a service indicator and met the first class presort rate. *Coil, gravure, American Bank Note Co., perforated 10 vertically.*

969 *U.S. Flag*

| 969 | | MNHVF | UseVF |
|---|---|---|---|
| 23¢ | **red and blue,** printed service indicator: "Presorted First-Class," tagged | .65 | .20 |
| | Pair | 1.00 | |
| | FDC *(Sept. 27, 1991)* | | 1.75 |

**1991. USPS OLYMPIC SPONSOR ISSUE** was released to promote the USPS sponsorship of the olympic games in Barcelona, Spain. *Gravure, perforated 11.*

970 *Eagle and Olympic rings.*

| 970 | | MNHVF | UseVF |
|---|---|---|---|
| $1 | **multicolored,** tagged | 2.75 | .75 |
| | Plate block of 4 | 12.00 | |
| | FDC *(Sept. 20, 1991)* | | 3.00 |

**1991. SANTA DESCENDING A CHIMNEY ISSUE**

971, 972, 972A *Santa descending a chimney*

| 971 | | MNHVF | UseVF |
|---|---|---|---|
| 29¢ | **multicolored,** tagged | .45 | .20 |
| | Plate block of 4 | 1.50 | |
| | FDC *(Oct. 17, 1991)* | | 1.75 |
| | v.  Vertical pair, imperforate horizontally | 500. | |
| | v1. Horizontal pair, imperforate vertically | 325. | |

**1991. SANTA BOOKLET ISSUE** Of these 6 designs four are totally different and two are modifications of the sheet stamp design. *Perforated 11, Gravure.*

| 972 | | MNHVF | UseVF |
|---|---|---|---|
| 29¢ | **multicolored,** booklet stamp, Type I, tagged | .45 | .20 |
| | FDC *(Oct. 17, 1991)* single | | 2.00 |
| | n.  Booklet pane of 4 | — | 4.00 |
| | FDC booklet pane | 2.00 | |

| 972A | | MNHVF | UseVF |
|---|---|---|---|
| 29¢ | **multicolored,** booklet stamp, Type II, tagged | .45 | .20 |
| | FDC single | | 2.00 |
| | y.  Se-tenant pair, Nos. 972, 972A | .90 | |
| | n.  Booklet pane of 4 | 2.00 | |
| | FDC booklet pane | — | 4.00 |

*Type I has an extra vertical line of brick in the top row of bricks at left; type II is missing that vertical line of brick.*

973 *Santa checking his list.*

| 973 | | MNHVF | UseVF |
|---|---|---|---|
| 29¢ | **multicolored,** booklet stamp, tagged | .45 | .20 |
| | FDC *(Oct. 17, 1991)* single | | 2.00 |
| | n.  Booklet pane of 4 | 1.50 | |
| | FDC booklet pane | — | 4.00 |

974 *Santa leaving gifts.*

| 974 | | MNHVF | UseVF |
|---|---|---|---|
| 29¢ | **multicolored,** booklet stamp, tagged | .45 | .20 |
| | FDC, single | | 2.00 |
| | n.  Booklet pane of 4 | 1.50 | |
| | FDC booklet pane | — | 4.00 |

975 *Santa ascending chimney.*

| 975 | | MNHVF | UseVF |
|---|---|---|---|
| 29¢ | **multicolored,** booklet stamp, tagged | .45 | .20 |
| | FDC single | | 2.00 |
| | n.  Booklet pane of 4 | 1.50 | |
| | FDC booklet pane | | 4.00 |

976 *Santa departing in sleigh.*

| 976 | | MNHVF | UseVF |
|---|---|---|---|
| 29¢ | **multicolored,** booklet stamp, tagged | .45 | .20 |
| | FDC single | | 2.00 |
| | n. Booklet pane of 4 | 1.50 | |
| | FDC booklet pane | | 4.00 |

**1991. TRADITIONAL CHRISTMAS ISSUE** *Intaglio and offset, perforated 11.*

977 *From* Madonna and Child with Donor *by Antoniazzo Romano.*

| 977 | | MNHVF | UseVF |
|---|---|---|---|
| 29¢ | **multicolored,** tagged | .45 | .20 |
| | Plate block of 4 | 1.50 | |
| | FDC *(Oct. 17, 1991)* single | | 1.75 |
| | n. Booklet pane of 10 | 8.00 | |
| | v. Booklet single, red & black (intaglio) omitted | 3750. | |
| | FDC booklet pane | | 8.00 |

*No. 978 is not assigned.*

**1991. CANOE ISSUE** Transportation Series *Coil, gravure, Stamp Venturers, perforated 10 vertically.*

979 *Canoe, 1800's*

| 979 | | MNHVF | UseVF |
|---|---|---|---|
| 5¢ | **red,** printed service indicator: "Additional Nonprofit Postage Paid" | .25 | .20 |
| | Pair | .30 | |
| | FDC *(Oct. 22, 1991)* | | 1.75 |

*For intaglio version in brown, see No. 955. Listings and prices for plate number coil strips and singles appear at the end of this definitives section of the Krause-Minkus catalog.*

**1991. EAGLE AND SHIELD NON-DENOMINATED ISSUE** met the needs of permit mailers on presorted bulk mail pieces. The value of the stamp is 10¢, with additional postage paid by mailers at the time of mailing. *Coil, gravure, American Bank Note Co. (plate numbers beginning with "A"), perforated 10 vertically.*

980 *Eagle and Shield*

| 980 | | MNHVF | UseVF |
|---|---|---|---|
| 10¢ | **multicolored,** printed service indicator: "Bulk Rate" | .25 | .20 |
| | Pair | .30 | |
| | FDC *(Dec. 13, 1991)* | | 1.75 |
| | v. Imperforate pair | — | |

*See Nos. 1011 and 1012 for similar stamps printed by the Bureau of Engraving and Printing and Stamp Venturers.*

**1992. WENDELL L. WILKIE ISSUE** Great American Series honors the man who lost in the 1940 presidential election and then served the Roosevelt administrtion on a diplomatic mission. *Intaglio, perforated 11.*

981 *Wendell L. Wilkie*

| 981 | | MNHVF | UseVF |
|---|---|---|---|
| 75¢ | **maroon,** phosphored paper (taggant on surface), matt gum, tagged | 1.25 | .50 |
| | Plate block of 4 | 5.50 | |
| | FDC *(Feb. 16, 1992)* | | 3.00 |
| | z1. Pre-phosphored (taggant embedded) paper, shiny gum | 1.25 | .50 |
| | Plate block of 4 | 5.50 | |

*Listings and prices for plate number coil strips and singles appear at the end of this definitives section of the Krause-Minkus catalog.*

**1992. FLOWER PEFORATED COIL ISSUE** Gravure, perforated 10 vertically.

982 *Tulip*

| 982 | | MNHVF | UseVF |
|---|---|---|---|
| 29¢ | **multicolored,** tagged | .75 | .20 |
| | Pair | 1.25 | |
| | FDC *(March 3, 1992)* | | 1.75 |

*Listings and prices for plate number coil strips and singles appear at the end of this definitives section of the Krause-Minkus catalog.*

## Great American Series

**1992. EARL WARREN ISSUE** honors the former Chief Justice of the United States. *Intaglio, perforated 11.*

983 *Earl Warren*

| 983 | | MNHVF | UseVF |
|---|---|---|---|
| 29¢ | **blue,** tagged | .50 | .20 |
| | Plate block of 4 | 2.75 | |
| | FDC *(March 9, 1992)* | | 2.00 |

**1992. FLAG OVER WHITE HOUSE ISSUE** honors the 200th anniversary of the home and office of the President of the United States. *Intaglio, perforated 10 vertically.*

984 *U.S. flag, White House*

| 984 | | MNHVF | UseVF |
|---|---|---|---|
| 29¢ | **blue & red,** tagged | .50 | .20 |
| | Pair | 2.00 | |
| | FDC *(April 23, 1992)* | | |
| | a. indigo & red | — | |
| | Pair | — | |
| | v. Imperforate pair | 20.00 | |

**1992. USA Issue** was for presorted first class mailings. The background is a graduated blue. *Coil, gravure, American Bank Note Co., perforated 10 vertically.*

985 *"USA"*

| 985 | | MNHVF | UseVF |
|---|---|---|---|
| 23¢ | **multicolored,** printed service indicator: "Presorted First-Class" | .50 | .20 |
| | Pair | .75 | |
| | FDC *(July 21, 1992)* | | 1.75 |

*See Nos. 994 and 1010 for similar stamps printed by the Bureau of Engraving and Printing and by Stamp Venturers.*

*Listings and prices for plate number coil strips and singles appear at the end of this definitives section of the Krause-Minkus catalog.*

**1992. ECA GARD Variable Denomination Issue** was released as a test of new postage and mail center equipment that weighed items for mailing, determined the postage necessary for the desired level of service, and printed stamps with the appropriate amount of postage. *Coil, intaglio, perforated 11 horizontally.*

986 *Shield & bunting*

| 986 | | MNHVF | UseVF |
|---|---|---|---|
| | **red & blue,** tagged on surface, denomination (.01 to 9.99) printed in black, matt gum | 1.50 | .50 |
| | a. Embedded taggant, shiny gum | 1.50 | .50 |
| | FDC *(Aug. 20, 1992)* | | 7.50 |

*For narrow, tall format, see No. 1040.*

**1992. Pledge of Allegiance Issue** honors the centennial of the pledge, first recited by school children for the 400th anniversary of Columbus' voyage of discovery. *Gravure, perforated 10.*

987, 1008 *Flag, "I pledge allegiance..."*

| 987 | | MNHVF | UseVF |
|---|---|---|---|
| 29¢ | **multicolored,** black inscription, booklet stamp, tagged | .75 | .20 |
| | FDC *(Sept. 8, 1992)* single | | 1.75 |
| | n. Booklet pane of 10 | 7.50 | |
| | a. Perforated 10 x 11 on 2 or 3 sides | 1.25 | .50 |
| | an. Booklet pane of 10 | 12.00 | |
| | anv. Imperforate pair | 900. | — |
| | FDC booklet pane | | 7.00 |

*For version with red inscription see No. 1008.*

**1992. Eagle and Shield Self-Adhesive Issue** was produced by three different contractors, each is identifiable through the color of the inscription "(USA 29)": red for Stamp Venturers of Fairfax, Va.; green for Dittler Brothers, Inc., of Oakwood, Ga.; and brown for Banknote Corporation of America, Inc., of Suffern, N.Y. These stamps were issued in panes of 17 plus a label on flexible backing paper, suitable for folding into a booklet. The stamps also were available in strips of 17 with the stamps spaced apart for use in affixing machines. *Imperforate (die cut).*

  *Gravure*

988, 990, 992 *Eagle and shield*

| 988 | | MNHVF | UseVF |
|---|---|---|---|
| 29¢ | **multicolored,** red inscription, tagged | .45 | .30 |
| | FDC *(Sept. 25, 1992)* single | | 2.00 |
| | n. pane of 17, plus label | 12.00 | |
| | FDC booklet pane | | 12.00 |

| 989 | | MNHVF | UseVF |
|---|---|---|---|
| | *Not assigned* | | |

**1992. Eagle and Shield Self-Adhesive Issue** Dittler Brothers, printer.

| 990 | | MNHVF | UseVF |
|---|---|---|---|
| 29¢ | **multicolored,** green inscription, tagged | .45 | .30 |
| | FDC *(Sept. 25, 1992)* single | | 2.00 |
| | n. Pane of 17, plus label | 12.00 | |
| | FDC booklet pane | | 12.00 |

| 991 | | MNHVF | UseVF |
|---|---|---|---|
| | *Not assigned* | | |

**1992. Eagle and Shield Self-Adhesive Issue** Banknote Corporation of America, printer.

| 992 | | MNHVF | UseVF |
|---|---|---|---|
| 29¢ | **multicolored,** brown inscription, tagged | .45 | .30 |
| | FDC *(Sept 25, 1992)* | | 2.00 |
| | n. Pane of 17, plus label | 12.00 | |
| | FDC pane of 17 | | 12.00 |
| | v. Imperforate pair | 500. | |
| | v1. Brown omitted | 450. | |

| 993 | | MNHVF | UseVF |
|---|---|---|---|
| | *Not assigned* | | |

**1992. "USA" Issue** for presorted first class mailings was reformatted in larger coils. The background is solid blue,. *Coil, gravure, Bureau of Printing and Engraving (plate number beginning with a numeral rather than a letter), perforated 10 vertically.*

994 *"USA"*

| 994 | | MNHVF | UseVF |
|---|---|---|---|
| 23¢ | **multicolored,** printed service indicator: "Presorted First-Class," shiny gum | .50 | .20 |
| | Pair | .75 | |
| | FDC *(Oct. 9, 1992)* | | 1.75 |
| | m. Matt gum | .50 | .20 |
| | Pair | .75 | |
| | v. Imperforate pair | 125. | |

*In this version, "23" is 7mm long. See Nos. 985 and 1010 for versions printed by the American Bank Note Co. or by Stamp Venturers.*

*Listings and prices for plate number coil strips and singles appear at the end of this definitives section of the Krause-Minkus catalog.*

**1992. Contemporary Christmas Issue** consists of a se-tenant block of four stamps in both sheet and booklet formats (with design differences between the two formats) and a self-adhesive stamp with essentially the same basic design as one of the sheet and booklet designs. *Offset, perforated 11 1/2 x 11.*

995, 999, 1005, *Locomotive*

996, 1000, *Pony and rider.*

997, 1001, *Engine.*

998, 1002, *Steamship*

| 995 | | MNHVF | UseVF |
|---|---|---|---|
| 29¢ | Locomotive **multicolored,** tagged | .45 | .20 |

| 996 | | MNHVF | UseVF |
|---|---|---|---|
| 29¢ | Pony & Rider **multicolored,** tagged | .45 | .20 |

| 997 | | MNHVF | UseVF |
|---|---|---|---|
| 29¢ | Fire Engine **multicolored,** tagged | .45 | .20 |

| 998 | | MNHVF | UseVF |
|---|---|---|---|
| 29¢ | Steam Ship **multicolored,** tagged | .45 | .20 |
| | FDC *(Oct. 22, 1992)* any single | | 2.50 |
| | y. Se-tenant block of 4 | 3.50 | |
| | Plate block of 4 | 4.50 | |
| | FDC block of 4 | | 4.00 |

**1992. CONTEMPORARY BOOKLET ISSUE** *Gravure, Multi-Color Corporation, perforated 11.*

| 999 | | MNHVF | UseVF |
|---|---|---|---|
| 29¢ | Locomotive **multicolored,** booklet single | .45 | .20 |
| | FDC *(Oct. 22, 1992)* | | |

| 1000 | | MNHVF | UseVF |
|---|---|---|---|
| 29¢ | Pony & Rider **multicolored,** booklet single | .45 | .20 |

| 1001 | | MNHVF | UseVF |
|---|---|---|---|
| 29¢ | Fire Engine **multicolored,** booklet single | .45 | .20 |

| 1002 | | MNHVF | UseVF |
|---|---|---|---|
| 29¢ | Steam Ship **multicolored,** booklet single | .45 | .20 |
| | FDC any single | | 2.50 |
| | n. Booklet pane of 4 | 3.50 | |
| | FDC block of 4 | | 4.00 |
| | Imperforate pane of 4 | — | |
| | nv1.Pane of 4, imperforate horizontally | — | |

**1992. TRADITIONAL CHRISTMAS ISSUE** *Intaglio and offset, perforated 11 1/2 x 11.*

1003, 1005 Madonna and Child *by Bellini.*

| 1003 | | MNHVF | UseVF |
|---|---|---|---|
| 29¢ | **multicolored,** tagged | .45 | .20 |
| | Plate block of 4 | 3.00 | |
| | FDC *(Oct. 22, 1992)* single | | 1.75 |
| | a. Booklet pane of 10 | 8.00 | |
| | FDC booklet pane | | 8.00 |

| 1004 | | MNHVF | UseVF |
|---|---|---|---|
| | *Not assigned* | | |

**1992. TRADITIONAL CHRISTMAS SELF-ADHESIVE ISSUE** *Gravure, die cut, self-adhesive.*

| 1005 | | MNHVF | UseVF |
|---|---|---|---|
| 29¢ | **multicolored,** tagged | .75 | .20 |
| | FDC *(Oct. 22, 1992)* | | 1.75 |
| | n. Pane of 18 | 12.00 | |
| | FDC pane of 18 | | 14.00 |

**1992. PUMKINSEED SUNFISH ISSUE** This Wildlife series stamp meets the second half-ounce rate for international mail and the one-ounce rate to Mexico. *Intaglio and offset, perforated 11 1/2 x 11.*

1006 Pumpkinseed sunfish

| 1006 | | MNHVF | UseVF |
|---|---|---|---|
| 45¢ | **multicolored,** tagged | 1.00 | .20 |
| | Plate block of 4 | 5.50 | |
| | FDC *(Dec. 2, 1992)* | | 2.00 |
| | v. Intaglio black omitted | 600. | |

## Transportation Series

**1992. CIRCUS WAGON ISSUE** This is a redesigned version of the stamp of 1990 (No. 931). *Coil, gravure, perforated 10 vertically.*

| 1007 | | MNHVF | UseVF |
|---|---|---|---|
| 5¢ | red | .25 | .20 |
| | Pair | .30 | |
| | FDC *(Dec. 8, 1992)* | | 1.75 |

*For intaglio stamps of this design see No. 931 ("05 USA") and No. 1077 ("USA" 5¢).*

*Listings and prices for plate number coil strips and singles appear at the end of this definitives section of the Krause-Minkus catalog.*

**1993. PLEDGE OF ALLEGIANCE ISSUE** new version with red, "USA" and denomination, printed by Stamp Venturers. The booklets in which the stamps are found were assembled by KCS, a division of Banta Corp.

| 1008 | | MNHVF | UseVF |
|---|---|---|---|
| 29¢ | **multicolored,** red inscription, tagged | .75 | .20 |
| | FDC *(March 1993)* single | | 1.75 |
| | n. Booklet pane of 10 | 7.50 | |
| | FDC booklet pane | | 7.00 |
| | v. Imperforate pair | 900. | |

*For similar stamp with black inscription see No. 987.*

**1993. THOMAS JEFFERSON ISSUE** Great American Series honors the third president of the United States on the 250th anniversary of his birth. *Intaglio, Stamp Venturers, perforated 11 1/2 x 11.*

1009 *Thomas Jefferson*

| 1009 | | MNHVF | UseVF |
|---|---|---|---|
| 29¢ | indigo | .50 | .30 |
| | Plate block of 4 | 2.50 | |
| | Plate block of 8, w/position diagram | 5.50 | |
| | FDC *(April 13, 1993)* | | 2.00 |

**1993. USA ISSUE** for presorted first-class mailings. The background is violet blue. *Coil, gravure, Stamp Venturers (plate number beginning with an "S"), perforated 10 vertically.*

| 1010 | | MNHVF | UseVF |
|---|---|---|---|
| 23¢ | **multicolored,** printed service indicator: "Presorted First-Class" | .75 | .20 |
| | Pair | 1.00 | |
| | FDC *(Oct. 9, 1992)* | | 1.75 |
| | v. Imperforate pair | — | |

*In this version, "23" is 8 1/2mm long. See No. 985 and No. 994 for versions printed by the American Bank Note Co. and by the Bureau of Engraving and Printing.*

**1993. EAGLE AND SHIELD NON-DENOMINATED ISSUE** met the needs of permit mailers on presorted bulk mail pieces. Similar to earlier version, No. 980. Design differences include reversal of "USA" and "BULK RATE" and colors reversed to "USA" in blue and "BULK RATE" in red. The stamp's face value is 10¢, with additional postage paid by mailers at the time of mailing. *Coil, printed by gravure by the Bureau of Engraving and Printing (plate number beginning with numeral rather than letter) and Stamp Venturers (plate numbers beginning with "S"), perforated 10 vertically. The Stamp Venturers version has the eagle in metallic gold, the BEP version in orange yellow.*

1011, 1012 "USA" before "Bulk Rate".

| 1011 | | MNHVF | UseVF |
|---|---|---|---|
| 10¢ | **multicolored,** (BEP) | .30 | .20 |
| | Pair | .40 | |
| | FDC *(May 29, 1993)* | | 1.75 |
| | v. Imperforate pair | 27.50 | |

| 1012 | | MNHVF | UseVF |
|---|---|---|---|
| 10¢ | **multicolored,** (Stamp Venturers) | .30 | .20 |
| | Pair | .40 | |
| | FDC *(May 29, 1993)* | | 1.75 |

*See No. 980 for similar design printed by the American Bank Note Co.*

**1993. FUTURISTIC SPACE SHUTTLE ISSUE** prepaid the Priority Mail rate. *Offset and intaglio, perforated 11.*

1013

| 1013 | | MNHVF | UseVF |
|---|---|---|---|
| $2.90 | **multicolored,** | 6.50 | 2.50 |
| | Plate block of 4 | 27.50 | |
| | FDC *(June 23, 1993)* | | 7.50 |

**1993. RED SQUIRREL ISSUE** Wildlife Series. Self-adhesive first-class letter-rate stamp. *Gravure, Dittler Brothers, Inc., imperforate (die cut).*

1014 *Red Squirrel*

| 1014 | | MNHVF | UseVF |
|---|---|---|---|
| 29¢ | **multicolored,** from booklet, tagged | .50 | .20 |
| | FDC *(June 25, 1993)* single | | 1.75 |
| | n. Pane of 18 | 15.00 | |
| | FDC pane of 18 | | 14.00 |

| 1015 | | MNHVF | UseVF |
|---|---|---|---|
| | *Not assigned* | | |

**1993. ROSE ISSUE** self-adhesive stamp with design characteristics of the Wildlife Series. *Gravure by Stamp Venturers, imperforate and die cut.*

1016 *Rose*

| 1016 | | MNHVF | UseVF |
|---|---|---|---|
| 29¢ | **multicolored,** from booklet, tagged | .50 | .20 |
| | FDC *(Aug. 1994)* single | | 1.75 |
| | n. Pane of 18 | 15.00 | |
| | FDC pane of 18 | | 14.00 |

| 1017 | | MNHVF | UseVF |
|---|---|---|---|
| | *Not assigned* | | |

**1993. AFRICAN VIOLET BOOKLET ISSUE** *Gravure by KCS Industries, perforated 10 x 11.*

1017 *African Violet*

| 1018 | | MNHVF | UseVF |
|---|---|---|---|
| 29¢ | **multicolored,** from booklet, tagged | .75 | .20 |
| | FDC *(Oct. 8, 1993)* single | | 1.75 |
| | n. Pane of 10 | 8.50 | |
| | FDC pane of 10 | | 8.00 |

**1993. CONTEMPORARY CHRISTMAS ISSUE** consisted of four contemporary designs available in sheets, booklets and self-adhesive panes. The Snowman design of the Contemporary issues is available self-adhesive both with the other three designs and by itself in panes available through ATM machines. Printed by gravure by the Bureau of Engraving and Printing (sheets and booklets), and Avery Dennison (self-adhesive); perforated 11 .

1019 *Jack-in-the-box*

1020 *Reindeer*

1021 *Snowman*

1022 *Toy soldier*

| 1019 | | MNHVF | UseVF |
|---|---|---|---|
| 29¢ | **Jack-in-the-box,** tagged | .50 | .20 |

| 1020 | | MNHVF | UseVF |
|---|---|---|---|
| 29¢ | **Reindeer,** tagged | .50 | .20 |

| 1021 | | MNHVF | UseVF |
|---|---|---|---|
| 29¢ | **Snowman,** tagged | .50 | .20 |

| 1022 | | MNHVF | UseVF |
|---|---|---|---|
| 29¢ | **Toy Soldier,** tagged | .50 | .20 |

| 1023 | | MNHVF | UseVF |
|---|---|---|---|
| 29¢ | **Jack-in-the-box,** single, tagged | .50 | .20 |

| 1024 | | MNHVF | UseVF |
|---|---|---|---|
| 29¢ | **Reindeer,** single, tagged | .50 | .20 |

| 1025 | | MNHVF | UseVF |
|---|---|---|---|
| 29¢ | **Snowman,** single, tagged | .50 | .20 |

| 1026 | | MNHVF | UseVF |
|---|---|---|---|
| 29¢ | **Toy Soldier,** tagged | .50 | .20 |
| | FDC booklet pane | | 4.00 |
| | FDC *(Oct. 21, 1993)* any single | | 2.50 |
| | n. Booklet pane of 10 (three each Nos. 1023, 1024; two each Nos. 1025, 1026) | 9.50 | |
| | n1. Booklet pane of 10 (two each Nos. 1023, 1024; three each Nos. 1025, 1026) | 9.50 | |

**1993. TRADITIONAL CHRISTMAS ISSUE** was available in sheet and booklet form. The booklet version is larger than the sheet version (booklet overall stamp 28.95 x 22.09mm; sheet overall stamp 23.1 x 30.2mm). There are design differences between the two items, also. *Perforated 11 1/2 x 11.*

1027

| 1027 | | MNHVF | UseVF |
|---|---|---|---|
| 29¢ | **multicolored,** tagged | .50 | .20 |
| | Plate block of 4 | 3.50 | |
| | FDC *(Oct. 21, 1993)* | | 1.75 |

| 1028 | | MNHVF | UseVF |
|---|---|---|---|
| 29¢ | **multicolored,** booklet single, tagged | .50 | .20 |
| | FDC *(Oct. 21, 1993)* single | | 1.75 |
| | n. Booklet pane of 4 | | |
| | FDC booklet pane | | 4.00 |

**1993. CONTEMPORARY CHIRSTMAS SELF-ADHESIVE ISSUE** *Printed by Avery Dennison, imperforate and die cut.*

| 1029 | | MNHVF | UseVF |
|---|---|---|---|
| 29¢ | **Jack-in-the-box,** single, tagged | .50 | .20 |

| 1030 | | MNHVF | UseVF |
|---|---|---|---|
| 29¢ | **Reindeer,** single, tagged | .50 | .20 |

| 1031 | | MNHVF | UseVF |
|---|---|---|---|
| 29¢ | **Snowman,** single, tagged | .50 | .20 |

| 1032 | | MNHVF | UseVF |
|---|---|---|---|
| 29¢ | **Toy Soldier,** single, tagged | .50 | .20 |
| | FDC *(Oct. 28, 1993)* any single | | 2.25 |
| | n. Pane of 12 (3 of each design) | 9.50 | |
| | FDC pane of 12 | | 10.00 |

*Nos. 1033-1036 are not assigned.*

**1993. SNOWMAN ATM PANE ISSUE** *Imperforate and die-cut (self-adhesive).*

1037 *Snowman*

| 1037 | | MNHVF | UseVF |
|---|---|---|---|
| 29¢ | **Snowman,** single, tagged | .75 | .25 |
| | n. Pane of 18 | 15.00 | |
| | FDC *(Oct. 28, 1993)* any single | | 1.75 |
| | FDC pane of 18 | | 14.00 |

*Although the placement is different, the Snowmen depicted on Nos. 1021 and 1031 have three buttons and seven snowflakes beneath the nose. No. 1025 has two buttons and five snowflakes beneath the nose.*

## Wildlife Series

**1993. PINE CONE ISSUE** Self-adhesive stamp with design characteristics of the Wildlife Series. *Gravure by the Banknote Corporation of America, imperforate and die cut.*

1038 *Pine cone*

| 1038 | | MNHVF | UseVF |
|---|---|---|---|
| 29¢ | **multicolored,** from booklet, tagged | .50 | .20 |
| | FDC *(Nov. 5, 1993)* single | | 1.75 |
| | n. Pane of 18 | 15.00 | |
| | FDC booklet pane | | 14.00 |

**1994. EAGLE ISSUE** Wildlife Series

1039 *Eagle*

| 1039 | | MNHVF | UseVF |
|---|---|---|---|
| 29¢ | **red, cream & blue,** single, tagged | .50 | .20 |
| | FDC *(Feb. 4, 1994)* single | | 1.75 |
| | n. Pane of 18 | 15.00 | |
| | FDC pane of 18 | | 12.50 |

**1994. POSTAGE AND MAIL CENTER (PMC) ISSUE** Similar to No. 986, issued in 1992, this issue is perforated horizontally. *Gravure by Guilford Gravure for American Bank Note Co., perforated 10 vertically.*

1040 *Shield & bunting*

| 1040 | | MNHVF | UseVF |
|---|---|---|---|
| | **(variable rate) red and blue,** denomination | 1.50 | .50 |
| | - 20¢-$99.99 printed in black | | |
| | FDC *(Feb. 19, 1994)* | | 7.50 |

**1994. SURRENDER OF BURGOYNE AT SARATOGA ISSUE** Design of this stamp was taken from an engraving originally prepared to be part of the 1869 definitive series, the first U.S. pictorial postage stamps. John Trumbull's painting *The Surrender of Gen. Burgoyne at Saratoga* is the basis for the stamp design. *Intaglio by Stamp Venturers in panes of 20, perforated 11 1/2.*

1041 *Surrender of Burgoyne at Saratoga.*

| 1041 | | MNHVF | UseVF |
|---|---|---|---|
| $1 | **dark blue,** tagged | 2.00 | .75 |
| | Plate block of 4 | 9.00 | |
| | FDC *(May 5, 1994)* | | |

**1994. TRACTOR TRAILER ISSUE** Transportation Series
Reprint of No. 954, showing a 1930's tractor trailer, issued for use by permit mailers. *Gravure, perforated 10 vertically.*

1042 *Tractor Trailer*

| 1042 | | MNHVF | UseVF |
|---|---|---|---|
| 10¢ | **green.** Bureau-printed gray service indicator (in gray): "Additional Presort Postage Paid" | .25 | .20 |
| | Pair | .30 | |
| | FDC *(May 25, 1994)* | | 1.75 |
| | v. Pair, imperforate | — | |

**1994. STATUE OF LIBERTY ISSUE** Self-adhesive pane. Imperforate and die cut.

1043 *Statue of Liberty*

| 1043 | | MNHVF | UseVF |
|---|---|---|---|
| 29¢ | **multicolored,** single, tagged | .50 | .20 |
| | FDC *(June 24, 1994)* single | | 1.75 |
| | a. Pane of 18 | 9.50 | |
| | FDC pane of 18 | | 12.50 |

**1994. FISHING BOAT ISSUE** Originally issued in 1991, (No. 965), this design was reprinted in 1992 in lighter colors (No. 965z1). This reprinting easily is identifiable by counting the "loops" of rope on the mooring. The original and initial two reprintings had two loops, this reprinting has a single loop. *Gravure by Stamp and Venturers, perforated 10 vertically.*

 1044 *Boat, single loop on mooring*

| 1044 | | MNHVF | UseVF |
|---|---|---|---|
| 19¢ | **multicolored,** untagged | .50 | .20 |
| | Pair | .60 | |
| | FDC *(June 25, 1994)* | | 1.75 |

**1994. MOON LANDING ISSUE** Celebrated the 25th Anniversary of the Moon Landing with an Express Mail denomination.

 1045 *Moon Landing, 25th Anniversary.*

| 1045 | | MNHVF | UseVF |
|---|---|---|---|
| $9.95 | **multicolored,** tagged | 25.00 | 10.00 |
| | Plate block of 4 | 100. | |
| | FDC *(July 20, 1994)* | | 25.00 |

**1994. WASHINGTON AND JACKSON ISSUE** A design submitted by a firm seeking to win the contract for the 1869 issue. *Intaglio by Stamp Venturers in panes of 20, perforated 11 1/2.*

 1046 *Washington and Jackson*

| 1046 | | MNHVF | UseVF |
|---|---|---|---|
| $5 | **dark green,** tagged | 10.00 | 3.75 |
| | Plate block of 4 | 50.00 | |
| | FDC *(Aug. 19, 1994)* | | 13.50 |

**1994. CONTEMPORARY CHRISTMAS ISSUE** consists of two designs. The Santa Clause stamp was issued only as a self-adhesive. The Holiday Stocking design was issued both in sheet form and in booklets of 20 stamps. Printed by gravure by Avery Dennison (Santa self-adhesive), by Ashton-Potter USA Ltd. (Holiday Stocking). *Perforated 11 (No. 1047).*

 1047 *Christmas Stocking*

| 1047 | | MNHVF | UseVF |
|---|---|---|---|
| 29¢ | **multicolored,** tagged | .50 | .20 |
| | Plate block of 4 | 3.50 | |
| | FDC *(Oct. 20, 1994)* | | 1.75 |

**1994. TRADITIONAL CHRISTMAS ISSUE** was issued both in sheet and booklet form, with the total size of the booklet version 0.05mm more horizontally and 0.03mm less vertically than the sheet version. *Printed by offset and intaglio by the Bureau of Printing and Engraving, perforated 11 (No. 1048), 10 x 11 (No. 1049).*

 1048 *Madonna and Child*

| 1048 | | MNHVF | UseVF |
|---|---|---|---|
| 29¢ | **multicolored,** tagged | .50 | .20 |
| | Plate block of 4 | 3.50 | |
| | FDC | | 1.75 |
| **1049** | | **MNHVF** | **UseVF** |
| 29¢ | **multicolored,** single, tagged, self-adhesive | .50 | .20 |
| | FDC single | | 1.75 |
| | n. Pane of 20 | 17.50 | |
| | FDC booklet pane of 20 | | 14.50 |

**1994. CONTEMPORARY SANTA CLAUS ISSUE**

 1050 *Santa Claus*

| 1050 | | MNHVF | UseVF |
|---|---|---|---|
| 29¢ | **multicolored,** tagged | .50 | .20 |
| | FDC single | | 1.75 |
| | n. Pane of 12 | 10.50 | |
| | FDC pane of 12 | | 10.00 |

**1994. CARDINAL IN SNOW ISSUE** This is a self-adhesive stamp in panes of 18 for automated teller machines (ATM). The stamp released at the same time as the Christmas issues, with the design having a decidedly winter motif. *Gravure by Avery. Imperforate and die cut.*

 1051 *Cardinal in snow*

| 1051 | | MNHVF | UseVF |
|---|---|---|---|
| 29¢ | **multicolored,** tagged | .50 | .20 |
| | FDC *(Oct. 20, 1994)* single | | 1.75 |
| | n. Pane of 18 | 14.50 | |
| | FDC pane of 18 | | |

**1994. VIRGINIA APGAR ISSUE** Great American Series honored medical researcher whose simple assessment method allows doctors and nurses in the delivery room to make an immediate evaulation of newborn baby's general condition. This process aids in the identification of those infants who need immediate medical attention. *Intaglio by the Banknote Corporation of America, perforated 11.*

 1052 *Virginia Apgar*

| 1052 | | MNHVF | UseVF |
|---|---|---|---|
| 29¢ | **brown,** tagged | .50 | .20 |
| | Plate block of 4 | 2.50 | |
| | FDC *(Oct. 24, 1994)* | | 1.75 |

**1994. POSTAGE AND MAIL CENTER (PMC) ISSUE** with variable denomination, similar to No. 1040, with different type font. Initial release was in Detroit, Mich.

 1053 *Shield and bunting*

| 1053 | | MNHVF | UseVF |
|---|---|---|---|
| 32¢ | **(variable rate) red and blue,** | .75 | .50 |
| | denomination printed in black | | |
| | FDC *(Nov. 9, 1994)* | | 7.50 |

## Non-denominated Service-Inscribed Coils Series

**1994. BLACK "G" SHEET ISSUE** is the most prolific of the rate-change issues. A total of 16 items were released, including specific items for first class letter rate, first class presort, postal card rate, coils and booklets, and two types of self-adhesives.

Sheet stamps, overall dimensions 0.84 x 0.99 inches. *gravure.* Printed by Bureau of Engraving and Printing, black "G".

 1054 *Old Glory*

| 1054 | | MNHVF | UseVF |
|---|---|---|---|
| 32¢ | **red, blue, gray & black,** tagged | .50 | .20 |
| | Plate block of 4 | 3.50 | |
| | FDC | | 1.90 |

**1994. RED "G" SHEET BOOKLET ISSUE** Printed by Stamp Venturers, red "G".

| 1055 | | MNHVF | UseVF |
|---|---|---|---|
| 32¢ | **red, blue, gray & black** tagged | .50 | .20 |
| | Plate block of 4 | 3.50 | |
| | FDC | | 1.90 |

**1994. BLACK "G" BOOKLET ISSUE** Printed by Bureau of Engraving and printing, black "G".

| 1056 | | MNHVF | UseVF |
|---|---|---|---|
| 32¢ | **red, blue, gray & black** tagged | .50 | .20 |
| | FDC single | | 1.90 |
| | v. Booklet pane of 10 | 9.00 | |
| | FDC booklet pane | | 8.50 |

**1994. BLUE "G" BOOKLET ISSUE** Printed by American Bank Note Co., blue "G".

| 1057 | | MNHVF | UseVF |
|---|---|---|---|
| 32¢ | **red, blue, gray & black,** tagged | .50 | .20 |
| | FDC single | | 1.90 |
| | n. Booklet pane of 10 | 9.00 | |
| | v. Imperforate between pair | 375. | |
| | FDC booklet pane | | 8.50 |

**1994. RED "G" BOOKLET ISSUE** Printed by KCS, red "G".

| 1058 | | MNHVF | UseVF |
|---|---|---|---|
| 32¢ | **red, blue, gray & black,** tagged | .50 | .20 |
| | FDC single | | 1.90 |
| | n. Booklet pane of 10 | 9.00 | |
| | FDC booklet pane | | 8.50 |

**1994. BLACK "G" COIL ISSUE** Printed by Bureau of Engraving and Printing, black "G", by *gravure.*

| 1059 | | MNHVF | UseVF |
|---|---|---|---|
| 32¢ | **red, blue, gray & black,** tagged | .50 | .20 |
| | v. Imperforate pair | 600. | |
| | Pair | 1.25 | |

**1994. BLUE "G" COIL ISSUE** Printed by American Bank Note Co., Blue "G".

| 1060 | | MNHVF | UseVF |
|---|---|---|---|
| 32¢ | **red, blue, gray & black,** tagged | .50 | .20 |
| | Pair | 1.25 | |
| | FDC | | 1.90 |

**1994. RED "G" COIL ISSUE** Printed by Stamp Venturers, red "G", perforated 10 vertically.

| 1061 | | MNHVF | UseVF |
|---|---|---|---|
| 32¢ | **red, blue, gray & black,** tagged | .50 | .20 |
| | Pair | 1.00 | |
| | FDC | | 1.90 |

**1994. RED "G" COIL ISSUE** Rouletted verticaly.

| 1061A | | MNHVF | UseVF |
|---|---|---|---|
| 32¢ | **red, blue gray & black,** tagged | .50 | .20 |
| | Pair | 1.00 | |
| | FDC | | 1.90 |

**1994. "G" SELF ADHESIVE ISSUE** Printed by gravure by Avery Dennison, imperforate and die cut.

 1062

| 1062 | | MNHVF | UseVF |
|---|---|---|---|
| 32¢ | **red, dark blue, light blue, gray & black,** | 1.00 | .35 |
| | tagged | | |
| | FDC single | | 1.90 |
| | n. Pane of 18 | 17.50 | |
| | FDC pane of 18 | | 15.00 |

**1994. "G" SELF ADHESIVE ATM ISSUE** dispensed sheetlet, self-adhesive, *printed by gravure by Avery Dennison, imperforate and die cut.*

| 1063 | | MNHVF | UseVF |
|---|---|---|---|
| 32¢ | **red, blue and black,** tagged | 1.00 | .35 |
| | FDC single | | 1.90 |
| | n. Pane of 18 | 17.50 | |
| | FDC pane of 18 | | 15.00 |

**1994. "G" FIRST CLASS PRESORT RATE ISSUE** *Gravure by Stamp Venturers. Coil Stamp, perforated 10 vertically.*

 1064

| 1064 | | MNHVF | UseVF |
|---|---|---|---|
| 25¢ | **Red, dark blue, gray, black & light blue** | .75 | .20 |
| | Pair | 1.50 | |
| | FDC | | 1.90 |

**1994. BLACK "G" POSTCARD RATE ISSUE** Printed by Bureau of Engraving and Printing, black "G". *Gravure, perforated 11.*

 1065

**1065**

| | | MNHVF | UseVF |
|---|---|---|---|
| **20¢** | **red, blue, gray, yellow & black,** tagged | .50 | .20 |
| | Plate block of 4 | 3.00 | |
| | FDC | | |

**1994. RED "G" POSTCARD RATE ISSUE** Printed by Stamp Venturers, red "G".

**1066**

| | | MNHVF | UseVF |
|---|---|---|---|
| **20¢** | **red, blue, gray, yellow & black,** tagged | .50 | .20 |
| | Plate block of 4 | 3.00 | |
| | FDC | | 1.95 |

**1994. NON-DENOMINATED "MAKE-UP " RATE ISSUE** had a value of three cents, to be used with a 29-cent stamp to meet the new first calss rate. *Offset, perforated 11.* Printed by American Bank Note Co. *bright blue with thin lettering.*

1067 *Dove*

**1067**

| | | MNHVF | UseVF |
|---|---|---|---|
| **3¢** | **red, bright blue & tan** | .25 | .20 |
| | Plate block of 4 | .50 | |
| | FDC | | 1.90 |

**1994. NON-DENOMINATED "MAKE-UP" RATE** Printed by Stamp Venturers, *darker blue with thick lettering.*

**1068**

| | | MNHVF | UseVF |
|---|---|---|---|
| **3¢** | **red, dark blue & tan** | .25 | .20 |
| | Plate block of 4 | .50 | |
| | FDC | | 1.90 |

**1995. "G" NONPROFIT PRESORT COIL ISSUE** *Coil, gravure by American Bank Note Co., perforated 10 vertically.*

1069 *Old Glory and 'Nonprofit Presort'.*

*Waiting for
Scan*

**1069**

| | | MNHVF | UseVF |
|---|---|---|---|
| **5¢** | **green & multicolored,** untagged | .25 | .20 |
| | Pair | .30 | .25 |
| | FDC *(Jan. 12, 1995)* | | 1.90 |

*First-day covers received a Dec. 13, 1994 cancellation although these stamps were not yet available on that date.*

**1995. BUTTE AND "NON-PROFIT ORGANIZATION" ISSUE** Non-denominated Service-Inscribed Coils Series

Beginning early in 1995, the USPS introduced several series of coils for use by various mass mailers that showed the service but no denomination. The additional cost of the mail service was prepaid directly by the mailer at the time and post office where the mailing took place. *Gravure.*

*Printed by J.W. Fergusson & Sons for Stamp Venturers, perforated 10 vertically.*

1070 *Butte and "Non-profit Organization"*

**1070**

| | | MNHVF | UseVF |
|---|---|---|---|
| **5¢** | **yellow, blue red,** untagged | .25 | .20 |
| | Pair | .30 | .25 |
| | v. Imperforate pair | 675. | |
| | FDC *(March 10, 1995)* | | 1.90 |

**1995. CAR HOOD AND "BULK RATE" ISSUE** Non-denominated Service-Inscribed Coils Series

J.W. Fergusson & Sons for Stamp Venturers, serpentine die cut 11 1/4 vertically.

1071 *Car Hood and "Bulk Rate"*

**1071**

| | | MNHVF | UseVF |
|---|---|---|---|
| **10¢** | **black, brown & red brown,** untagged | .30 | .20 |
| | Pair | .35 | .25 |
| | FDC *(March 17, 1995)* | | 1.90 |

**1995. TAIL FIN PRESORTED FIRST CLASS COIL ISSUE** Non-denominated Service-Inscribed Coils Series

*Printed by BEP, serpentine die cut 11 1/2 vertically.*

1072 *Tail Fin and 'Presorted First-Class Card'*

**1072**

| | | MNHVF | UseVF |
|---|---|---|---|
| **15¢** | **yellow orange & multicolored,** untagged | .40 | .30 |
| | Pair | .50 | .35 |
| | FDC *(March 17, 1995)* (1072 & 1073) | | 2.25 |

**1995. TAIL FIN 'PRESORTED FIRST CLASS COIL ISSUE** Non-denominated Service-Inscribed Coils Series

J.W. Fergusson & Sons for Stamp Venturers, serpentine die cut 11 1/2 vertically.

1073 *Tail Fin and "Presorted First-Class Card"*

**1073**

| | | MNHVF | UseVF |
|---|---|---|---|
| **15¢** | **buff & multicolored,** untagged | .40 | .30 |
| | Pair | .50 | .35 |
| | FDC *(March 17, 1995)* (1072 & 1073) | | 2.25 |

**1995. JUKE BOX PRESORTED FIRST-CLASS COIL ISSUE** Non-denominated Service-Inscribed Coils Series

1074-75, 1134, 1153 *Juke Box and 'Presorted First- Class'*
*Printed by BEP, serpentine die cut 11 1/2 vertically.*

1074 *Juke Box and "Presorted First-Class"*

**1074**

| | | MNHVF | UseVF |
|---|---|---|---|
| **25¢** | **dark red, yellow green and multicolored,** untagged | .65 | .40 |
| | Pair | .75 | .50 |
| | FDC *(March 17, 1995)* | | 1.90 |

**1995. JUKE BOX 'PRESORTED FIRST CLASS 'COIL ISSUE** Non-denominated Service-Inscribed Coils Series

J.W. Fergusson & Sons for Stamp Venturers.

**1075**

| | | MNHVF | UseVF |
|---|---|---|---|
| **25¢** | **orange red, bright yellow green and multicolored,** untagged | .65 | .40 |
| | Pair | .75 | .50 |
| | FDC *(March 17, 1995)* | | 1.90 |

**1995. FLAG OVER FIELD ISSUE** *Avery Denison, self-adhesive, imperforate (die cut).*

1076 *Flag over Field*

| 1076 | | MNHVF | UseVF |
|---|---|---|---|
| 32¢ | **multicolored,** tagged | 1.00 | .30 |
| | FDC *(March 17, 1995)* | | 1.90 |
| | n. Pane of 18 | 14.50 | |
| | FDC pane of 18 | | 14.50 |

**1995. CIRCUS WAGON ISSUE** Transportation Series
This was a redesigned gravure version of the earlier coil issued in intaglio (No. 931) and gravure (No. 1007). Coil, intaglio by Stamp Venturers, perforated 9 3/4 vertically.

1077 *Circus Wagon, 1900's*

| 1077 | | MNHVF | UseVF |
|---|---|---|---|
| 5¢ | **red,** untagged | .25 | .20 |
| | Pair | .30 | |
| | FDC *(March 20, 1995)* | | 1.90 |

*For intalgio & gravure versions of this design inscribed "05 USA" see Nos. 931 & 1007.*

**1995. FLAG OVER PORCH SELF ADHESIVE BOOKLET ISSUE** *Gravure by Avery Dennison, serpentine die cut 8 3/4.*

1078 *Flag over Porch*

| 1078 | | MNHVF | UseVF |
|---|---|---|---|
| 32¢ | **multicolored,** phosphored paper, large "1995" | 1.00 | .30 |
| | FDC single | | 4.00 |
| | n. Pane of 20 plus label | 17.50 | |
| | a. Small '1995' (2920b) | 2.00 | .60 |
| | FDC pane of 20 | | 14.50 |
| | n1. Pane of 15 plus label (various layouts) | | |
| | an. Pane of 20 plus label | 38.00 | |
| | FDC | | 1.90 |

**1995. AMERICAN KESTRIL ISSUE** Wildlife Series
Redesigned denomination. *Offset by BEP, perforated 11 1/4 X 11.*

1079 *American Kestrel*

| 1079 | | MNHVF | UseVF |
|---|---|---|---|
| 1¢ | **multicolored,** tagged | .25 | .20 |
| | Plate block of 4 | .30 | |
| | FDC *(May 10, 1995)* | | 1.75 |

*For version inscribed "USA 01" see No. 959. For coil see No. 1115.*

**1995. FLAG OVER PORCH ISSUE** *Gravure by J.W. Ferguson & Sons for Stamp Venturers, perforated 10 1/4 x 10 1/2.*

1080-83 *Flag over Porch*

| 1080 | | MNHVF | UseVF |
|---|---|---|---|
| 32¢ | **multicolored,** tagged | .70 | .20 |
| | Plate block of 4 | 1.75 | |
| | FDC *(May 19, 1995)* | | 1.90 |
| | v. Imperforate pair | 300. | |

**1995. FLAG OVER PORCH BOOKLET ISSUE**

| 1081 | | MNHVF | UseVF |
|---|---|---|---|
| 32¢ | **multicolored,** tagged | .80 | .20 |
| | FDC *(May 19, 1995)* single | | 1.90 |
| | n. Booklet pane of 10 | 8.00 | |
| | FDC booklet pane | | 8.50 |
| | nv. Imperforate booklet pane of 10 | — | |

**1995. FLAG OVER PORCH COIL ISSUE** *Coil, gravure by BEP, perforated 9 3/4 vertically.*

| 1082 | | MNHVF | UseVF |
|---|---|---|---|
| 32¢ | **multicolored,** tagged, red "1995" | .50 | .20 |
| | Pair | 1.00 | |
| | FDC *(May 19, 1995)* | | 1.90 |
| | v. Imperforate pair | 75.00 | |

**1995. FLAG OVER PORCH COIL ISSUE** *Coil, gravure by J.W. Fergusson & Sons for Stamp Venturers, perforated 9 3/4 vertically.*

| 1083 | | MNHVF | UseVF |
|---|---|---|---|
| 32¢ | **multicolored,** tagged, blue "1995" | .75 | .20 |
| | Pair | 1.00 | |
| | FDC *(May 19,1995)* | | 1.90 |

*Listings and prices for plate number coil strips and singles appear at the end of this definitive section of the Krause-Minkus catalog.*

**1995. PINK ROSE ISSUE** A new color, denomination and die-cut format to simulate perforations undated this self-adhesive booklet for use in the 32¢ rate period. *Gravure by J.W. Fergusson & Sons for Stamp Venturers, serpentine die cut.*

1084 *Pink Rose*

| 1084 | | MNHVF | UseVF |
|---|---|---|---|
| 32¢ | **pink, green and black,** phosphored | .80 | .30 |
| | FDC *(June 2, 1995)* single | | 1.90 |
| | n. Booklet pane of 20 plus label | 16.00 | |
| | FDC booklet pane | | 15.50 |
| | n1. Booklet pane of 15 plus label | 11.00 | |
| | n2. Booklet pane of 14 | 40.00 | |
| | n3. Booklet pane of 16 | 40.00 | |
| | v. Imperforate between horizontal pair (no die cut) | — | |
| | v1. Black omitted | 1000. | |

## Transportation Series

**1995. FERRYBOAT ISSUE** New York City steam ferry boat. *Coil, intaglio, perforated 9 3/4 vertically.*

1085 *Ferryboat 1900s*

| 1085 | | MNHVF | UseVF |
|---|---|---|---|
| 32¢ | **deep blue,** phosphored paper | .75 | .20 |
| | Pair | 1.25 | |
| | FDC *(June 2, 1995)* | | .20 |
| | v. Imperforate pair | — | |
| | x. dull gum | — | 1.90 |

**1995. Cog Railway Issue** Transportation Series The Cog railway is used for steep inclines, and prevents slippage. *Coil, intaglio, perforated 9 3/4 vertically.*

 1086 *Cog Railway 1870s*

| 1086 | | MNHVF | UseVF |
|---|---|---|---|
| 20¢ | **green,** phosphored paper | .40 | .20 |
| | Pair | .75 | |
| | FDC *(June 9, 1995)* | | 1.90 |
| | v. Imperforate pair | .75 | |

## Wildlife Series

**1995. Blue Jay Issue** Produced in booklet form to pay the first-class domestic postcard rate. *Gravure by Stamp Venturers, perforated 11 x 10 on two or three margins.*

 1087, 1135-36 *Blue Jay*

| 1087 | | MNHVF | UseVF |
|---|---|---|---|
| 20¢ | **multicolored,** phosphored paper | .45 | .20 |
| | FDC *(June 15, 1995)* single | | 1.90 |
| | n. Booklet pane of 10 | 6.00 | |
| | FDC booklet pane | | 8.50 |

**1995. Space Shuttle Challenger Issue** Prepaid the Priority Mail rate. *Offset and intaglio (panes of 20) by Ashton-Potter (USA) Ltd., perforated 11.*

 1088 *Space Shuttle Challenger*

| 1088 | | MNHVF | UseVF |
|---|---|---|---|
| $3 | **multicolored,** phosphored paper | 6.00 | 3.00 |
| | Plate block of 4 | 25.00 | |
| | FDC *(June 22, 1995)* | | 7.75 |

**1995. Peaches and Pear Issue** *Gravure, perforated 11 x 9 3/4.*

 1089-90 *Peaches and Pear*

| 1089 | | MNHVF | UseVF |
|---|---|---|---|
| 32¢ | **multicolored,** phosphored paper | .75 | .20 |
| | FDC *(July 8, 1995)* | | 1.90 |

| 1090 | | MNHVF | UseVF |
|---|---|---|---|
| 32¢ | **multicolored,** phosphored paper | .75 | .20 |
| | FDC *(July 8, 1995)* single | | 1.90 |
| | y. Se-tenant pair, No. 1089-90 | 1.50 | 1.20 |
| | n. Booklet pane of 10 (5 each Nos. 1089-90) | 8.50 | |
| | FDC booklet pane | | 8.50 |

**1995. Peaches and Pear Self-adhesive Issue** *Gravure by Avery Dennison, self-adhesive, serpentine die cut.*

| 1091 | | MNHVF | UseVF |
|---|---|---|---|
| 32¢ | **multicolored,** phosphored paper | .85 | .30 |
| | FDC *(July 8, 1995)* | | 1.90 |

| 1092 | | MNHVF | UseVF |
|---|---|---|---|
| 32¢ | **multicolored,** phosphored paper | .85 | .30 |
| | FDC *(July 8, 1995)* single | | 1.90 |
| | n. Booklet pane of 20 (10 each each Nos. 1091-92 plus label) | 16.00 | |
| | FDC booklet pane of 20 | | 15.50 |

## Great American Series

**1995. Alice Hamilton Issue** paid tribute to a pioneer in industrial medicine, the first woman on the faculty of Harvard University and a socially committed physician who played a key role in documenting and taking steps to prevent lead poisoning in the workplace. Issued to pay two-ounce first-class letter rate. *Intaglio by Banknote Corp. of America, perforated 11 1/4 x 11.*

 1093 *Alice Hamilton*

| 1093 | | MNHVF | UseVF |
|---|---|---|---|
| 55¢ | **green,** phosphored paper | | |
| | Plate block of 4 | | |
| | FDC *(July 11, 1995)* | | |

**1995. Space Shuttle Endeavor Issue** Prepaid the basic Express Mail rate. *Offset and intaglio (panes of 20) by Ashton-Potter (USA) Ltd., perforated 11.*

 1094 *Space Shuttle Endeavor*

| 1094 | | MNHVF | UseVF |
|---|---|---|---|
| 10.75¢ | **multicolored,** phosphored paper | 21.00 | 8.00 |
| | Plate block of 4 | 92.50 | |
| | FDC *(Aug. 4, 1995)* | | 25.00 |

**1995. Alice Paul Issue** Great American Series recognizes a leader in the U.S. movement to extend the right to vote to women (honored at about the same time on a commemorative, CM1745) and one of the earliest proponents of the Equal Rights Amendment. Issue to pay three-ounce first-class letter rate. *Intaglio by Banknote Corporation of America, perforated 11 1/4 x 11.*

 1095 *Alice Paul*

| 1095 | | MNHVF | UseVF |
|---|---|---|---|
| 78¢ | **purple,** phosphored paper | 1.75 | .25 |
| | Plate block of 4 | 8.00 | |
| | FDC *)Aug. 18, 1995)* | | 2.25 |
| | a. Dark violet, shiny gum *(April 1996)* | 1.75 | — |
| | Plate block of 4 | 8.00 | |

**1995. Milton S. Hershey Issue** Great American Series celebrates the chocolate manufacturer and p1ilanthropist whose orphans' home, established in 1909, has provided a home and education for generations of disadvantaged boys and girls. Issued to pay basic first-class letter rate. *Intaglio by Banknote Corporation of America, perforated 11 1/4 x 11.*

1096 *Milton S. Hershey*

| 1096 | | MNHVF | UseVF |
|---|---|---|---|
| 32¢ | **chocolate brown,** phosphored paper | .65 | .20 |
| | Plate block of 4 | 3.75 | |
| | FDC *(Sept. 13, 1995)* | | 1.50 |

## Pioneers of Aviation Series

**1995. EDDIE RICKENBACKER ISSUE** honors the racing car driver and automotive and aviation manufacturer who earned his greatest recognition as a flying ace during World War I, in which he shot down 22 enemy aircraft and 4 observation balloons. Issued to pay the half-ounce rate for letters to foreign nations other than Canada and Mexico - mail typically carried by air, in keeping with the subject of the stamp, but without the "airmail" designation - no longer needed on such mail, all of which is now typically carried by air. *Gravure by BEP, perforated 11 1/4.*

1097 *Eddie Rickenbacker*

| 1097 | | MNHVF | UseVF |
|---|---|---|---|
| 60¢ | **multicolored,** phosphored paper | .75 | .20 |
| | Plate block of 4 | 6.00 | |
| | FDC *(Sept. 25, 1995)* | | 1.75 |

**1995. CONTEMPORARY CHRISTMAS ISSUE** Contemporary stamps included four Victorian-era designs - two depicting Santa Claus and two portraying children with toys - produced in sheet, booklet and self-adhesive booklet and coil form *Offset by Sterling Sommer for Ashton-Potter (USA) Ltd., perforated 11 1/2.*

1098-1101 and 1102-1105

| 1098 | | MNHVF | UseVF |
|---|---|---|---|
| 32¢ | Santa on roof top, phosphored paper | .60 | .20 |
| | FDC *(Sept. 30, 1995)* | | |

| 1099 | | MNHVF | UseVF |
|---|---|---|---|
| 32¢ | Child and Jumpimg jack, phosphored paper | .60 | .20 |

| 1100 | | MNHVF | UseVF |
|---|---|---|---|
| 32¢ | Child and tree, phosphored paper | .60 | .20 |

| 1101 | | MNHVF | UseVF |
|---|---|---|---|
| 32¢ | Santa in workshop, phosphored paper | .60 | .20 |
| | FDC *(Sept. 30, 1995)* single | | 2.25 |
| | y. Se-tenant block or strip of 4 | 3.00 | |
| | Plate block of 4 | 3.50 | |
| | v. Imperforate block or strip of 4 | — | |
| | n. Booklet pane of 10 (3 of Nos. 1098-99 & 2 of Nos. 1100-01) | 7.50 | |
| | n1.Booklet pane of 10 (2 of Nos. 1098-99 & 3 of Nos. 1100-01 | 7.50 | |
| | FDC block of 4 1098-1101 | | 5.00 |

**1995. CONTEMPORARY CHRISTMAS COIL ISSUE** *Gravure for Avery Dennison, vertical serpentine die cut.*

| 1102 | | MNHVF | UseVF |
|---|---|---|---|
| 32¢ | Santa on Rooftop, phosphored paper | .60 | .20 |
| | FDC | | 2.25 |

| 1103 | | MNHVF | UseVF |
|---|---|---|---|
| 32¢ | Child and Jumping jack, phosphored paper | .60 | .20 |
| | FDC | | 2.25 |

| 1104 | | MNHVF | UseVF |
|---|---|---|---|
| 32¢ | Child and tree, phosphored paper | .60 | .20 |
| | FDC | | 2.25 |

| 1105 | | MNHVF | UseVF |
|---|---|---|---|
| 32¢ | Santa in workshop, phosphored paper | .60 | .20 |
| | FDC | | 2.25 |
| | y. Coil strip of 4 (1 each of Nos. 1102-1105) | 3.00 | |
| | FDC set of 4 on cover | | 5.00 |

**1995. CONTEMPORARY CHRISTMAS BOOKLET ISSUE** *Gravure for Avery Dennison, serpentine die cut.*

| 1106 | | MNHVF | UseVF |
|---|---|---|---|
| 32¢ | **multicolored,** phosphored paper | .60 | .20 |
| | FDC *(Sept. 30, 1995)* | | |

| 1107 | | MNHVF | UseVF |
|---|---|---|---|
| 32¢ | **multicolored,** phosphored paper | .60 | .20 |
| | FDC | | 2.25 |

| 1108 | | MNHVF | UseVF |
|---|---|---|---|
| 32¢ | **multicolored,** phosphored paper | .60 | .20 |
| | FDC | | 2.25 |

| 1109 | | MNHVF | UseVF |
|---|---|---|---|
| 32¢ | **multicolored,** phosphored paper | .60 | .20 |
| | n. Booklet pane of 20 (5 each of 1106-09 plus label | | |
| | FDC | | 2.25 |

**1995. MIDNIGHT ANGEL CHRISTMAS BOOKLET ISSUE**

1110, 1110A *Midnight Angel*

| 1110 | | MNHVF | UseVF |
|---|---|---|---|
| 32¢ | **multicolored,** phosphored paper | 1.75 | .45 |
| | FDC *(Oct. 19, 1995)* | | 1.50 |
| | v. Imperforate vertical pair (no die cutting between) | — | |
| | n. Booklet pane of 20 plus label | 15.00 | |

**1995. MIDNIGHT ANGEL CHRISTMAS COIL ISSUE** *Offset by Banknote Corporation of America, vertical serpentine die cut.*

| 1110A | | MNHVF | UseVF |
|---|---|---|---|
| 32¢ | **multicolored,** phosphored paper | .75 | .45 |
| | FDC *(Oct. 19, 1995)* | | 1.50 |

*Listing and prices for plate number coil strips and singles appear at the end of this definitive section of the Krause-Minkus catalog.*

**1995. CONTEMPORARY CHRISTMAS BOOKLET ISSUE** *Gravure for Avery Dennison, serpentine die cut.*

1111 *Children Sledding.*

| 1111 | | MNHVF | UseVF |
|---|---|---|---|
| 32¢ | **multicolored,** phosphored lacquer on surface of stamps | .75 | .45 |
| | FDC *(Oct. 19, 1995)* | | 1.25 |
| | n. Booklet pane of 18 | 14.00 | |
| | FDC booklet | | 10.00 |

**1995. Traditional Christmas Issue** the traditional stamp, adapted from an altar panel titled Enthroned Madonna and Child by 14th century Florentine artist Giotto di Bodone, was offered in conventional sheet form and booklet form. *Offset and intaglio by BEP.*

1112 *Enthroned Madonna and Child by Giotto.*

| 1112 | | MNHVF | UseVF |
|---|---|---|---|
| 32¢ | **multicolored,** phosphored paper, perforated 11 1/4 | .75 | .20 |
| | FDC *(Oct. 19, 1995)* | | 1.50 |
| | Plate block of 4 | 3.50 | |

| 1113 | | MNHVF | UseVF |
|---|---|---|---|
| 32¢ | **multicolored,** phosphored paper, perforated 9 3/4 by 11 | .75 | .20 |
| | Booklet pane of 10 | 7.50 | |
| | FDC *(Oct. 19, 1995)* | | 1.50 |

**1995. Ruth Benedict Issue** Great American Series celebrates a social anthropologist whose 1934 text, Patterns of Culture, was influential throughout the world and who fought racism and intolerance through numerous other publications. Issued to pay the half-ounce letter rate to Canada and the ounce letter rate to Mexico. *Intaglio by BEP, perforated 11 1/4 x 11.*

1114 *Ruth Benedict*

| 1114 | | MNHVF | UseVF |
|---|---|---|---|
| 45¢ | **carmine,** phosphored paper | 1.00 | .25 |
| | Plate block of 4 | 4.75 | |
| | FDC *(Oct. 20, 1995)* | | 1.60 |

**1996. American Kestrel Issue** Wildlife Series Coil, *offset by BEP, perforated 9 3/4 vertically.*

1115 *American Kestrel*

| 1115 | | MNHVF | UseVF |
|---|---|---|---|
| 1¢ | **multicolored,** untagged | .25 | .20 |
| | Pair | .30 | |
| | FDC *(Jan. 20, 1996)* | | 1.50 |

*For sheet version see No. 1079. For version inscribed "USA 01" see No. 959.*

**1996. Flag over Porch Issue** Self-adhesive booklet with stamps showing "1996" in blue. *Gravure by Avery Dennison, serpentine die cut 11 1/4.*

1116 *Flag over Porch.*

| 1116 | | MNHVF | UseVF |
|---|---|---|---|
| 32¢ | **multicolored,** phosphored paper | .75 | .30 |
| | n. Booklet pane of 10 | 7.50 | |
| | FDC *(Jan. 20, 1996)* | | 1.25 |

**1996. Unisys Variable Denomination Issue** Vended through postage and mail centers. Coil stamp showing "1996" in red at bottom-left corner of design. *Gravure by BEP, perforated 9 3/4.*

1117 *Shield and Bunting*

| 1117 | | MNHVF | UseVF |
|---|---|---|---|
| 32¢ | **red and blue,** denomination (.20 to $20.00) printed in black | .95 | .50 |
| | FDC *(Jan. 26, 1996)* | | 1.25 |

**1996. Red-headed Woodpecker Issue** Wildlife Series *Offset by BEP, perforated 11 1/4 x 11.*

1118 *Red-headed Woodpecker*

| 1118 | | MNHVF | UseVF |
|---|---|---|---|
| 2¢ | **multicolored,** untagged | .25 | .20 |
| | Plate block of 4 | .50 | |
| | FDC *(Feb. 2, 1996)* | | 1.50 |

**1996. Space Shuttle Challenger Issue** Stamps show "1996" in bottom-left corner. *Offset and intaglio (panes of 20) by Ashton-Potter (USA) Ltd., perforated 11. No first day cancel. (Issued March 1996.)*

1119 *Space Shuttle*

| 1119 | | MNHVF | UseVF |
|---|---|---|---|
| $3 | **multicolored,** phosphored paper | 6.00 | 3.00 |
| | Plate block of 4 | 25.00 | |

**1996. Jacqueline Cochran Issue** Pioneers of Aviation Series memoralizes the first woman ever to break the sound barrier, a highly skilled pilot who won the Bendix Transcontinental air race in 1938, and founded the Woman's Air Force Service Pilots program during World War II. Issued to pay the international postcard rate. *Offset and intaglio by BEP, perforated 11 1/4.*

1120 *Jacqueline Cohran*

| 1120 | | MNHVF | UseVF |
|---|---|---|---|
| 50¢ | **multicolored,** phosphored paper | 1.20 | .40 |
| | Plate block of 4 | 5.00 | |
| | FDC *(March 9, 1996)* | | 2.00 |
| | v. Intaglio black (inscriptions) omitted | 150. | |

## Non-denominated Service-Inscribed Coils Series

**1996. Mountain Coil Issue** coil stamp with small "1996" in purple in bottom-left corner. *Gravure by BEP, perforated 9 3/4.*

1121 *Mountains*

**1121**

| | | MNHVF | UseVF |
|---|---|---|---|
| 5¢ | **purple & multicolored,** untagged | .25 | .20 |
| | FDC *(March 16, 1996)* | | 1.25 |

**1996. MOUNTAIN COIL ISSUE** Non-denominated Service-Inscribed Large "1996" in blue in bottom-left corner. *Gravure by J. W. Fergusson & Sons for Stamp Venturers, perforated 9 3/4.*

**1122**

| | | MNHVF | UseVF |
|---|---|---|---|
| 5¢ | **blue & multicolored,** untagged | .25 | .20 |
| | FDC *(March 16, 1996)* | | 1.25 |

**1996. EASTERN BLUEBIRD ISSUE** Wildlife Series Redesigned denomination. *Offset by BEP, perforated 11 1/4 x 11.*

 1123 *Eastern Bluebird*

**1123**

| | | MNHVF | UseVF |
|---|---|---|---|
| 3¢ | **multicolored,** untagged | .25 | .20 |
| | Plate block of 4 | .65 | |
| | FDC *(April 3, 1996)* | | 1.50 |

**1996. CAL FARLEY ISSUE** Great American Series recalls the founder of the Cal Farley's Boys Ranch foster home near Amarillo, Tex. Issued to pay standard first-class letter rate. *Intaglio by Banknote Corporation of America, perforated 11 1/4 x 11.*

 1124 *Cal Farley*

**1124**

| | | MNHVF | UseVF |
|---|---|---|---|
| 32¢ | **green,** phosphored paper | .65 | .20 |
| | Plate block of 4 | 3.75 | |
| | FDC *(April 26, 1996)* | | 1.75 |

**1996. FLAG OVER PORCH BOOKLET STAMP ISSUE** Self-adhesive booklet stamps with small red "1996". *Gravure by BEP, serpentine die cut 9 3/4 on two or three sides.*

 1125

**1125**

| | | MNHVF | UseVF |
|---|---|---|---|
| 32¢ | **multicolored,** phosphored paper | .75 | .30 |
| | n. Booklet pane of 10 | 7.50 | |
| | FDC *(May 21, 1996)* | | 1.50 |

**1996. FLAG OVER PORCH COIL STAMP ISSUE** Self-adhesive coil stamps with small red "1996". *Gravure by BEP, serpentine die cut 9 3/4 vertically.*

**1126**

| | | MNHVF | UseVF |
|---|---|---|---|
| 32¢ | **multicolored,** phosphored paper | 1.00 | .30 |
| | FDC *(May 21, 1996)* | | 1.50 |

**1996. FLAG OVER PORCH COIL STAMP ISSUE** Self-adhesive coil stamps with small red "1996". *Gravure by BEP, serpentine die cut 11 vertically.*

**1127**

| | | MNHVF | UseVF |
|---|---|---|---|
| 32¢ | **multicolored,** phosphored paper | 1.50 | .50 |
| | FDC *(May 21, 1996)* | | 1.50 |

**1996. EAGLE AND SHIELD NON-DENOMINATED ISSUE** Self-adhesive coil stamps with large blue "1996". *Gravure by J. W. Fergusson & Sons for Stamp Venturers, serpentine die cut.*

 1128 *Eagle and Shield*

**1128**

| | | MNHVF | UseVF |
|---|---|---|---|
| 32¢ | **multicolored,** phosphored paper | .75 | .30 |
| | Pair | | |
| | FDC *(June 15, 1996)* | | 1.50 |

*On this issue, stamps are spaced apart on the 10,000 stamp coil roll.*

**1996. EAGLE AND SHIELD NON-DENOMINATED ISSUE** Self-adhesive coil with blue "1996". On this issue, stamps are spaced apart on the 10,000 stamp coil roll. *Gravure by J. W. Fergusson & Sons for Stamp Venturers, serpentine die cut perforations.*

**1129**

| | | MNHVF | UseVF |
|---|---|---|---|
| 10¢ | **multicolored,** untagged | .25 | .25 |
| | FDC *(May 21, 1996)* | | 1.50 |

**1996. BUTTE COIL ISSUE** Non-denominated Service-Inscribed Coils Series Self-adhesive coils with "1996". *Gravure by J. W. Fergusson & Sons for Stamp Venturers, serpentine die cut vertically.*

 1130 *Butte*

**1130**

| | | MNHVF | UseVF |
|---|---|---|---|
| 5¢ | **yellow, blue and red,** untagged | .25 | .20 |
| | FDC *(June 15, 1996)* | | 1.50 |

**1996. MOUNTAINS COIL ISSUE** Non-denominated Service-Inscribed Coils Series Self-adhesive coils with "1996". *Gravure by J. W. Fergusson & Sons for Stamp Venturers, serpentine die cut vertically.*

 1131 *Mountains*

**1131**

| | | MNHVF | UseVF |
|---|---|---|---|
| 5¢ | **purple and multicolored,** untagged | .25 | .20 |
| | FDC | | 1.50 |

**1996. AUTOMOBILE COIL ISSUE** Non-denominated Service-Inscribed Coils Series Self-adhesive coils with "1996". *Gravure by J. W. Fergusson & Sons for Stamp Venturers, serpentine die cut vertically.*

 1132 *Auto*

**1132**

| | | MNHVF | UseVF |
|---|---|---|---|
| 10¢ | **black, brown and red brown,** untagged | .25 | .20 |
| | FDC | | 1.50 |

**1996. AUTO TAIL FIN COIL ISSUE** Non-denominated Service-Inscribed Coils Series Self-adhesive coils with "1996". *Gravure by J. W. Fergusson & Sons for Stamp Venturers, serpentine die cut vertically.*

 1133 *Auto Tail Fin*

**1133**
**15¢**    **buff and multicolored,** untagged    .35    .30
            FDC                                          1.75

**1996. JUKE BOX COIL ISSUE** Non-denominated Service-Inscribed Coils Series Self-adhesive coils with "1996". *Gravure by J. W. Fergusson & Sons for Stamp Venturers, serpentine die cut vertically.*

1134 *Juke Box*

**1134**
**25¢**    **orange red, bright yellow green and**    .60    .30
            **multicolored,** untagged

*Listings and prices for plate number coil strips and singles appear at the end of this definitive section of the Krause-Minkus catalog.*

**1996. BLUE JAY BOOKLET ISSUE** Wildlife Series Self-adhesive Blue Jay booklets and coils with "1996". *Gravure by J. W. Fergusson & Sons for Stamp Venturers, sperpentine die cut perforations.*

1135 *Blue Jay*

**1135**                                     **MNHVF**    **UseVF**
**20¢**    **multicolored,** phosphored paper    .45    .25
            n.  Booklet pane of 10              4.50
            FDC *(Aug. 2, 1996)*                       1.50

**1996. BLUE JAY COIL ISSUE** Wildlife Series

1136 *Blue Jay*

**1136**                                     **MNHVF**    **UseVF**
**20¢**    **multicolored,** phosphored paper    .40    .20
            v.  Imperforated coil pair         1000.
            FDC *(Aug. 2, 1996)*                       1.50

**1996. CONTEMPORARY CHRISTMAS ISSUE** Contemporary Christmas stamps included se-tenant sheets and self-adhesive booklets of four Christmas Family scenes and a generic Holiday Skater design for sale in ATMs offered in self-adhesive booklets only. *Offset by Ashton-Potter (USA) Ltd., perforated 11 1/4.*

1137-1140, 1141-1144

**1137**                                     **MNHVF**    **UseVF**
**32¢**    Family at Yule Hearth, phosphored paper    .60    .20
            FDC *(Oct. 8, 1996)*

**1138**                                     **MNHVF**    **UseVF**
**32¢**    Family Trimming Tree, phosphored paper    .60    .20

**1139**                                     **MNHVF**    **UseVF**
**32¢**    Dreaming of Santa, phosphored paper    .60    .20

**1140**                                     **MNHVF**    **UseVF**
**32¢**    Holiday Shopping, phosphored paper    .60    .20
            y.  Se-tenant block strip of 4     3.00
            Plate block of 4                           3.50
            FDC 1137-1140 on one cover                 7.00

**1996. CONTEMPORARY SELF ADHESIVE BOOKLET ISSUE** *Offset by Banknote Corporation of America, serpentine die cut.*

**1141**                                     **MNHVF**    **UseVF**
**32¢**    Family at Yule Hearth, phosphored paper    .60    .20

**1142**                                     **MNHVF**    **UseVF**
**32¢**    Family Trimming Tree, phosphored paper    .60    .20
            FDC                                        1.75

**1143**                                     **MNHVF**    **UseVF**
**32¢**    Dreaming of Santa, phosphored paper    .60    .20
            FDC                                        1.75

**1144**                                     **MNHVF**    **UseVF**
**32¢**    Holiday Shopping, phosphored paper    .60    .20
            n.  Booklet pane of 20 (five each of Nos.    15.00
            1141-44 plus label)
            FDC *(Oct. 8, 1996)*                       1.50
            FDC 1141-1144 on one cover                 7.00

**1996. HOLIDAY SKATERS BOOKLET ISSUE** Christmas Series *Gravure by Avery Dennison, imperforate (die cut).*

1145 *Holiday Skaters*

**1145**                                     **MNHVF**    **UseVF**
**32¢**    **multicolored,** phosphored lacquer on    .75    .30
            surface of stamps
            n.  Booklet pane of 18             14.00
            FDC *(Oct. 8, 1996)*                       1.75

**1996. TRADITIONAL CHRISTMAS ISSUE** Christmas Series The traditional stamp taken from a detail of *Adoration of the Shepherds* by the 18th century Italian artist Paolo de Matteis, was offered in convential sheets and self-adhesive booklets, supplemented by new stocks of the Midnight Angel stamps that had proven popular the previous year. *Offset and intaglio by BEP, perforated 11 1/4.*

1146

**1146**                                     **MNHVF**    **UseVF**
**32¢**    **multicolored,** phosphored paper    .70    .20
            Plate block of 4                   3.50
            FDC *(Nov. 1, 1996)*                       1.80

**1147**                                     **MNHVF**    **UseVF**
**32¢**    **multicolored,** tagged             .95    .30
            m.  Booklet pane of 10 plus label    15.00
            v.  No die cutting                 1250.
            FDC *(Nov. 1, 1996)*                       2.00

**1996. YELLOW ROSE ISSUE** This hardy perennial gained a renewed lease on life in a new color, issued in self-adhesive form in booklets of three sizes. *Gravure by J. W. Fergusson & Sons for Stamp Venturers, serpentine die cut.*

 1149, 1163 *Yellow rose*

**1149** MNHVF UseVF
**32¢** **yellow and multicolored,** phosphored .75 .25
   paper
  n. Booklet pane of 20 plus label 14.00
  FDC *(Oct. 24, 1996.* 1.50
  n1. Booklet pane of 15 plus label *(Dec.* 12.00
   *1996)*
  pn1. Plate number single (bottom left corner 1.00
   of pane)
  n2. Booklet pane of 30 *(December 1996)* 17.50
  pn2. Plate number single (bottom right 1.00
   corner of pane)

**1997. FLAG OVER PORCH BOOKLET ISSUE** Self-adhesive booklet stamps with red "1997". *Gravure by BEP, serpentine die cut on two or three sides.*

 1150 *Flag over Porch*

**1150** MNHVF UseVF
**32¢** **multicolored,** phosphored paper .75 .30
  FDC *(Jan. 24, 1997)* 1.25
  n. Booklet pane of 5 4.00
  n1. Booklet pane of 10 7.50

**1997. FLAG OVER PORCH COIL ISSUE** Self-adhesive coil stamps with red "1997". *Gravure by BEP, serpentine die cut vertically.*

**1151** MNHVF UseVF
**32¢** **multicolored,** phosphored paper .75 .30
  FDC *(Jan. 24, 1997)* 1.25

**1997. MOUNTAIN COIL ISSUE** Non-denominated Service-Inscribed Coils Series Self-adhesive, 3,000 stamp coil with "1997". *Gravure by BEP, serpentine die cut vertically.*

 1152 *Mountains*

**1152** MNHVF UseVF
**5¢** **purple and multicolored,** untagged .25 .20
  FDC *(Jan. 24, 1997)* 1.25

**1997. JUKE BOX COIL ISSUE** Non-denominated Service-Inscribed Coils Series Self-adhesive, 3,000 stamp coils with "1997". *Gravure by BEP, serpentine die cut vertically.*

 1153 *Juke Box*

**1153** MNHVF UseVF
**25¢** **multicolored,** untagged .60 .20
  FDC 1.25

**1997. STATUE OF LIBERTY ISSUE** Revised denomination version of the 1994 design for use at the 32¢ first-class domestic letter rate. Self-adhesive booklets. *Gravure by Avery Dennison, serpentine die cut on two or three sides.*

 1154 *Statue of Liberty*

**1154** MNHVF UseVF
**32¢** **multicolored,** phosphored paper .75 .20
  FDC *(Feb. 1, 1997)* 1.25
  pn. Plate number single (botton left corner —
   of booklet pane)
  n. Booklet pane of 4 275.
  n1. Booklet pane of 5 plus label 350.
  n2. Booklet pane of 6 4.00
  n3. Booklet pane of 20 13.00

**1997. CITRON AND INSECT ISSUE** Self-adhesive booklet stamps in two distinct sizes and die-cutting guages, based upon two botanical prints made by Anna Maria Sibylla Merian during her 1699-1701 travels in Surinam. *Gravure by Stamp Venturers.*
  Design 20 x 27 mm, serpentine die cut 10 3/4 x 10 1/4 on two, three or four sides.

 1155 *Citron and insects*

**1155** MNHVF UseVF
**32¢** **multicolored,** tagged .75 .20
  FDC *(March 3, 1997)* 2.00

**1997. FLOWERING PINEAPPLE ISSUE**

 1156 *Flowering Pineapple*

**1156** MNHVF UseVF
**32¢** **multicolored,** tagged .75 .20
  FDC 2.00
  n. Booklet pane of 20 (10 each Nos. 1155- 13.00
   56 plus label)

**1997. CITRON AND INSECT BOOKLET ISSUE** Design 18 1/2 x 24mm, serpentine die cut 11 1/4 x 10 3/4 on two or three sides (Nos. 1157-58) or 11 1/4 x 11 1/4 x 11 1/4 x 10 3/4 (Nos. 1159-60).

 1157, 1159 *Citron and Insects*

**1157** MNHVF UseVF
**32¢** **multicolored,** tagged .75 .20
  FDC *(March 3, 1997)* 2.00

**1997. FLOWERING PINEAPPLE BOOKLET ISSUE** design 18 1/2 x 24mm.

1158, 1160 Flowering Pineapple

| 1158 | | MNHVF | UseVF |
|---|---|---|---|
| 32¢ | multicolored, tagged | .75 | .20 |
| | FDC | | 2.00 |

**1997. CITRON AND INSECT BOOKLET ISSUE** Design 18 1/2 x 24mm, serpentine die cut 11 1/4 x 10 3/4 on two or three sides (Nos. 1157-58) or 11 1/4 x 11 1/4 x 11 1/4 x 10 3/4 (Nos. 1159-60).

| 1159 | | MNHVF | UseVF |
|---|---|---|---|
| 32¢ | multicolored, tagged | 1.25 | .50 |
| | FDC | | 2.00 |
| | n. Booklet pane of 5 (one No. 1159 sideways, two each of No. 1157-58) | 3.50 | |

**1997. FLOWERING PINEAPPLE BOOKLET ISSUE** design 18 1/2 x 24mm.

| 1160 | | MNHVF | UseVF |
|---|---|---|---|
| 32¢ | multicolored, tagged | 1.25 | .50 |
| | FDC | | 2.00 |
| | n. Booklet pane of 5 (one No. 1160 sideways, two each of No. 1157-58) | 3.75 | |

*Nos. 1159-60, which are die cut on all four sides, have a single irregular large serration near the middle of the right side created by die cutting.*

**1997. JUKE BOX ISSUE** Non-denominated Service-Inscribed Coils Series Self-adhesive 10,000- and 30,000-stamp experimental linerless (no backing paper) coils, *manufactured by 3M Corp. and finished by Stamp Venturers, gravure, imperforate with simulated perforations (black circles) and black bars at top and bottom.*

1161 *Juke Box with simulated perforations*

| 1161 | | MNHVF | UseVF |
|---|---|---|---|
| 25¢ | multicolored, untagged | .60 | .20 |
| | FDC *(March 14, 1997)* | | 1.50 |

**1997. FLAG OVER PORCH ISSUE** Self-adhesive 100-stamp experimental linerless (no backing paper) coils, *manufactured by 3M Corp. and finished by Stamp Venturers, gravure, serpentine die cut 10 vertically.*

1162 *Flag over porch.*

| 1162 | | MNHVF | UseVF |
|---|---|---|---|
| 32¢ | multicolored | .60 | .20 |
| | FDC | | 1.50 |

*Listings and prices for plate number coil strips and singles appear at the end of this definitive section of the Krause-Minkus catalog.*

**1997. ROSE ISSUE** Self-adhesive coil. *Gravure by BEP, serpentine die cut vertically.*

1163 *Rose*

| 1163 | | MNHVF | UseVF |
|---|---|---|---|
| 32¢ | yellow and multicolored, tagged | .65 | .20 |
| | Imperforate coil of 100 | — | |
| | FDC *(Aug. 1, 1997)* | | 1.50 |

**1997. CHRISTMAS ISSUE** For the first time in several years the Traditional and Contemporary Christmas stamps were issued in moderation. Only one design of each, and in a total of four formats. The Traditional design depicts Sano di Pietro's *Madonna and Child with Saints* from the collection of the National Gallery of Art. *Offset by the Bureau of Engraving and Printing,* in self-adhesive panes of 20. The Contemporary design depicts American Holly. *Offset by Banknote Corporation of America in self-adhesive* panes of 20, and self-adhesive booklets of 15 and 30. All with serpentine die-cut perforations.

1164 Sano di Pietro's *Madonna and child with saints.*

| 1164 | | MNHVF | UseVF |
|---|---|---|---|
| 32¢ | multicolored, tagged, single | .50 | .20 |
| | FDC *(Oct. 27, 1997)* | | 1.00 |
| | Booklet of 20 | 8.50 | |

1165 *American Holly*

| 1165 | | MNHVF | UseVF |
|---|---|---|---|
| 32¢ | multicolored, tagged, single | .50 | .20 |
| | FDC *(Oct. 30, 1997)* | | 1.00 |
| | Booklet of 15 | 6.00 | |
| | Booklet of 20 | 8.50 | |
| | Booklet of 30 | 12.50 | |

**1997. MARS PATHFINDER ISSUE** This Priority Mail stamp commemorated the Pathfinder's Mission to Mars and the successful landing of July 4, 1997, and the subsequent deployment of the Sojourner rover. The view on the sheetlet is based on one of the first views sent back showing the rover and the Ares Vallis region of Mars. The stamp design incorporates hidden images. *Gravure, Stamp Ventures.*

1166 *Soujourner rover on Mars surface*

| 1166 | | MNHVF | UseVF |
|---|---|---|---|
| $3 | multicolored, tagged *(15,000,000)* | 4.50 | 2.50 |
| | FDC *(Dec. 10, 1997)* | | 4.50 |

**1998. MARS PATHFINDER PRESS SHEET ISSUE** Uncut, but perforated press sheets of 18 subjects of the $3.00 Mars Pathfinder were made available in January 1998. There are vertical perforations between the three columns, thus the single subject measures 152mm wide, rather than the 146mm wide on the single imperforate examples of December 1997.

Varieties exist with perforations on left, right or on both sides make the single souvenir sheet 6mm larger than the imperforate souvenir sheet. Once the stamp is removed from the frame, it is undistinguishable from No. 1166.

| 1167 | | MNHVF | UseVF |
|---|---|---|---|
| $3 | multicolored | 15.00 | — |
| | uncut press sheet of 18 | | |

**1998. HENRY R. LUCE ISSUE** Great American Series Magazine editor and publisher, founder of Time, Fortune, Life, and Sports Issustrated. Mr. Luce (1898-1967) also had interests in radio. Design is based on an Alfred Eisentadt photo. Printed by intaglio, Banknote Corporation of America, perforated 11.

 1168

| 1168 | | MNHVF | UseVF |
|---|---|---|---|
| 32¢ | | .50 | .20 |
| | y. Pane of 20 | 10.00 | |
| | FDC (April 3, 1998) | | 1.00 |

**1998. SWAMP COIL ISSUE** Non-denominated Service-Inscribed Coils Series Non-profit organization rate. Printed by Sennett Security Products in 10,000 stamp coils.

 1169

| 1169 | | MNHVF | UseVF |
|---|---|---|---|
| 5¢ | multicolored | .25 | .20 |
| | FDC (June 5, 1998) | | 1.00 |

**1998. DINER NON-DENOMINATED COIL ISSUE** Non-denominated Service-Inscribed Coils Series Pre-sorted First-Class rate. Printed by Sennett Security Products in 10,000 stamp coils.

 1170

| 1170 | | MNHVF | UseVF |
|---|---|---|---|
| 25¢ | multicolored | .40 | .20 |
| | FDC (June 5, 1998) | | 1.00 |

**1998. LILA AND DE WITT WALLACE ISSUE** Founders of Readers Digest magazine, and in later life, Philanthropists. Printed by Ashton Potter USA Ltd. perforated 11.

 1171

| 1171 | | MNHVF | UseVF |
|---|---|---|---|
| 32¢ | | .50 | .20 |
| | y. Pane of 20 | 7.50 | |
| | FDC (July 16, 1998) | | 1.00 |

**1998. RING-NECKED PHEASANT COIL ISSUE** Wildlife Series Self-adhesive coil, rolls of 100 stamps. Printed by BEP, serpentine die cut.

 1172

| 1172 | | MNHVF | UseVF |
|---|---|---|---|
| 20¢ | multicolored | .40 | .20 |
| | FDC (July 30, 1998) | | 1.00 |

**1998. RING-NECKED PHEASANT BOOKLET ISSUE** Wildlife Series Self-adhesive booklet, serpentine die cut. Printed by Avery Dennison.

| 1173 | | MNHVF | UseVF |
|---|---|---|---|
| 20¢ | multicolored, single | .40 | .20 |
| | n. Booklet of 10 | 3.50 | |
| | FDC (July 30, 1998) | | 1.00 |

**1998. RED FOX ISSUE** Wildlife Series Printed by Banknote Corp. of America, serpentine die cut.

 1174

| 1174 | | MNHVF | UseVF |
|---|---|---|---|
| $1 | multicolored | 1.50 | .75 |
| | y. Pane of 20 | 25.00 | |
| | FDC (Aug. 14, 1998) | | 2.00 |

**1998. BICYCLE COIL ISSUE** Pre-sorted standard rate. Printed by Sennett Security Products in rolls of 500 and 10,000 stamps.

 1175

| 1175 | | MNHVF | UseVF |
|---|---|---|---|
| 10¢ | multicolored | .30 | .20 |
| | FDC (Aug. 14, 1998) | | 1.00 |

**1998. BICYCLE SELF ADHESIVE COIL ISSUE** Pre-sorted standard rate. Printed by Sennett Security Products in rolls of 500 and 10,000, and in rolls of 3,000 by BEP with no distinguishing markings.

| 1176 | | MNHVF | UseVF |
|---|---|---|---|
| 10¢ | multicolored | .30 | .20 |
| | FDC (Aug. 14, 1998) | | 1.00 |

**1998. DINER COIL ISSUE** Self-adhesive 3,000 stamp coil. Printed by BEP, serpentine die cut.

| 1177 | | MNHVF | UseVF |
|---|---|---|---|
| 25¢ | multicolored | .30 | .20 |
| | FDC (Sept. 30, 1998) | | 1.00 |

**1998. TRADITIONAL CHRISTMAS ISSUE** A Florentine Terracotta from Ca. 1425 by unknown artisan. It is in the collection of the National Gallery of Art. Self-adhesive booklet of 20, serpentine die cut 10 on 2, 3 or 4 sides.

 1177 Florentine Terracotta

| 1177 |  | MNHVF | UseVF |
|---|---|---|---|
| 32¢ | multicolored | .50 | .20 |
|  | Booklet of 20 | 7.50 |  |
|  | FDC *(Oct. 15, 1998)* |  | 1.00 |

**1998. CONTEMPORARY CHRISTMAS ISSUE** Festive holiday wreaths in a traditional, colonial, Chili and tropical design. Stamp measures 23 x 30mm. Serpentine die cut 11 1/2, on 2, 3, or 4 sides. Panes of 20, printed by Banknote Corporation of America.

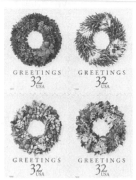

1178-1181

| 1179 |  | MNHVF | UseVF |
|---|---|---|---|
| 32¢ | Traditional wreath, tagged | .50 | .20 |
| 1180 |  | MNHVF | UseVF |
| 32¢ | Colonial wreath, tagged | .50 | .20 |
| 1181 |  | MNHVF | UseVF |
| 32¢ | Chili wreath, tagged | .50 | .20 |
| 1182 |  | MNHVF | UseVF |
| 32¢ | Tropical wreath, tagged | .50 | .20 |
|  | FDC *(Oct. 15, 1998),* any single |  | 1.00 |
|  | y.  Pane of 20 | 7.50 |  |

**1998. CONTEMPORARY CHRISTMAS BOOKLET ISSUE** measures 23 x 30mm. Serpentine die cut 11 1/2 on 2, 3, 4 sides. Printed by Banknote Corporation of American.

| 1183 |  | MNHVF | UseVF |
|---|---|---|---|
| 32¢ | Traditional wreath | .50 | .20 |
| 1184 |  | MNHVF | UseVF |
| 32¢ | Colonial wreath | .50 | .20 |
| 1185 |  | MNHVF | UseVF |
| 32¢ | Chili wreath | .50 | .20 |
| 1186 |  | MNHVF | UseVF |
| 32¢ | Tropical wreath | .50 | .20 |
|  | FDC *(Oct. 15, 1998),* any single |  | 1.00 |
|  | n.  Booklet of 20 | 7.50 |  |
| 1187 |  | MNHVF | UseVF |
| 32¢ | Traditional wreath | .50 | .20 |
| 1188 |  | MNHVF | UseVF |
| 32¢ | Colonial wreath | .50 | .20 |
| 1189 |  | MNHVF | UseVF |
| 32¢ | Chili wreath | .50 | .20 |
| 1190 |  | MNHVF | UseVF |
| 32¢ | Tropical wreath, | .50 | .20 |
|  | FDC *(Oct. 15, 1998),* any single |  | 1.00 |
|  | n.  Booklet of 15 | 6.00 |  |

**1998. "H" MAKE-UP RATE, USA WHITE ISSUE** Weather Vane Rooster, a 1¢ strip to be added to the 32¢ to take the new 33¢ first class rate of Jan. 10, 1999. Sheet of 50. Printed by Ashton Potter, perforated 11 1/2.

| 1191 |  | MNHVF | UseVF |
|---|---|---|---|
| 1¢ | multicolor | .25 | .20 |
|  | FDC *(Nov. 9, 1998)* |  | 1.00 |
|  | Plate block of 4 |  | .30 |

**1998. "H" MAKE-UP RATE, USA LIGHT BLUE ISSUE** Weather Vane Rooster in panes of 50, printed by Banknote Corporation of America, perforated 11 1/2.

| 1192 |  | MNHVF | UseVF |
|---|---|---|---|
| 1¢ | multicolor | .25 | .20 |
|  | FDC *(Nov. 9, 1998)* |  | 1.00 |
|  | Plate block of 4 | .30 |  |

**1998. HAT "H" FIRST CLASS ISSUE** Uncle Sam's hat. Gummed pane of 50. Printed by Stamp Ventures, perforated 11 1/2.

1193

| 1193 |  | MNHVF | UseVF |
|---|---|---|---|
| 33¢ | multicolored | .50 | .20 |
|  | Plate block of 4 | 1.50 |  |

**1998. HAT "H" FIRST CLASS COIL ISSUE** Gummed coil rolls of 100 and 3,000. Printed by BEP, perforated 10.

| 1194 |  | MNHVF | UseVF |
|---|---|---|---|
| 33¢ | multicolored | .50 | .20 |

**1998. HAT "H" FIRST CLASS BOOKLET ISSUE** Self adhesive. Printed by Avery Dennison, serpentine die cut on 2, 3 or 4 sides.

| 1195 |  | MNHVF | UseVF |
|---|---|---|---|
| 33¢ | multicolored | .50 | .20 |
|  | FDC *(Nov. 9, 1998)* |  |  |
|  | n.  Booklet of 10 | 4.00 | 1.00 |
|  | y.  Pane of 18 | 6.50 |  |
|  | n1. Booklet of 20 | 7.00 |  |

**1998. HAT "H" FIRST CLASS BOOKLET ISSUE** Self-adhesive. Printed by BEP, folded booklet, serpentine die cut on 2 or 3 sides.

| 1196 |  | MNHVF | UseVF |
|---|---|---|---|
| 33¢ | multicolored | .50 | .20 |
|  | FDC *(Nov. 9, 1998)* |  | 1.00 |
|  | n.  Booklet of 20 | 7.00 |  |

**1998. HAT "H" FIRST CLASS COIL ISSUE** Self-adhesive coil roll of 100 or 3,000 stamps. Printed by BEP, serpentine die cut 10.

| 1197 |  | MNHVF | UseVF |
|---|---|---|---|
| 33¢ | multicolored | .50 | .20 |
|  | FDC *(Nov. 9, 1998)* |  | 1.00 |

**1998. UNCLE SAM ISSUE** Panes of 20, serpentine die cut 10 1/2. Printed by Sennett Security Products.

1198

| 1198 |  | MNHVF | UseVF |
|---|---|---|---|
| 33¢ | multicolored | .50 | .20 |
|  | FDC *(Nov. 9, 1998)* |  | 1.00 |
|  | Plate block | 1.50 |  |
|  | y.  Pane of 20 | 7.00 |  |

**1998.** U**NCLE** S**AM** C**OIL** I**SSUE** Self-adhesive, coil rolls of 100. Printed by BEP, serpentine die cut 10.

| 1199 | | MNHVF | UseVF |
|---|---|---|---|
| 22¢ | **multicolored** | .50 | .20 |
| | FDC | | 1.00 |

**1998.** M**ARY** B**RECKENRIDGE** I**SSUE** Great American Series The first of this series to be issued in a self-adhesive format. Breckenridge was the founder of the frontier nursing service which brought health-care to remote Appalacian homesteads and communities.

Printed by Banknote Corp. of America, serpentine die cut 11 1/2.

 1200

| 1200 | | MNHVF | UseVF |
|---|---|---|---|
| 77¢ | | 1.00 | .20 |
| | FDC *(Nov. 9, 1998)* | | 1.25 |
| | Plate block of 4 | 3.50 | |
| | Pane of 20 | 16.00 | |

**1998.** S**HUTTLE** L**ANDING** I**SSUE** to meet the January 10, 1999 priority mail rate, this self-adhesive stamp was issued. Printed by Banknote Corporation of America, serpentine die cut 11 1/2.

 1201

| 1201 | | MNHVF | UseVF |
|---|---|---|---|
| $3.20 | **multicolore** | 4.00 | 2.75 |
| | FDC *Nov. 9, 1998)* | | 4.50 |
| | Plate block of 4 | 15.00 | |
| | y. Pane of 20 | 75.00 | |

**1998.** S**HUTTLE** P**IGGYBACK** T**RANSPORT** I**SSUE** January 10, 1999 Express mail rate. The Piggyback Shuttle on a converted jumbo jet is how the powerless shuttles are transported from the west coast landing field at Edwards Air Force Base in Cailfornia to the Kennedy Space Center in Florida to prepare for re-use. Printed by Banknote Corporation of American, serpentine die cut 11 1/2.

 1202

| 1202 | | MNHVF | UseVF |
|---|---|---|---|
| $11.75 | **multicolor** | 14.00 | 8.00 |
| | FDC *(Nov. 17, 1998)* | | 16.50 |
| | Plate block of 4 | 50.00 | |
| | y. Pane of 20 | 300. | |

# Plate Number Coil Strips

| | Strip of 5 | Strip of 3 | Single Used |
|---|---|---|---|
| **806** | | | |
| **1c Omnibus,** (USA 1c) | | | |
| Pl# 1, 2, 3, 4, 5, 6 | .60 | .50 | .25 |
| **867** | | | |
| **1c Omnibus,** (1c USA) | | | |
| Pl# 1, 2 | 1.00 | .75 | .25 |
| **867zxm** | | | |
| **1c Omnibus,** (1c USA) untagged | | | |
| Pl# 2, 3 | 1.00 | .75 | .30 |
| **867zxs** | | | |
| **1c Omnibus,** (1c USA) shiny gum, tagged, error | | | |
| Pl# 3 | 6.50 | 6.25 | 3.50 |
| **867zo** | | | |
| **1c Omnibus,** untagged | | | |
| Pl# 3 | .65 | .55 | .30 |
| **790** | | | |
| **2c Locomotive,** (USA 2c) | | | |
| Pl# 2, 3, 4, 6, 8, 10 | .60 | .55 | .30 |
| **873** | | | |
| **2c Locomotive,** (2c USA) | | | |
| Pl# 1 | 1.00 | .80 | .35 |
| **873zo** | | | |
| **2c Locomotive,** untagged | | | |
| Pl#2 | 1.00 | .80 | .35 |
| **800** | | | |
| **3c Handcar** | | | |
| Pl# 1, 2, 3, 4 | .75 | .70 | .35 |
| **883** | | | |
| **3c Conestoga Wagon** | | | |
| Pl#1 | 1.25 | 1.00 | .40 |
| **883zxm** | | | |
| **3c Conestoga Wagon,** untagged, matt gum | | | |
| Pl# 2, 3 | 1.50 | 1.25 | .50 |
| **883zxs** | | | |
| **3c Conestoga Wagon,** shiny gum | | | |
| Pl# 3, 5 | 1.50 | 1.25 | .65 |
| Pl# 6 | 2.75 | 2.50 | 1.00 |
| **843** | | | |
| **3.4c School Bus** | | | |
| Pl# 1, 2 | 1.20 | 1.00 | .45 |
| **843z** | | | |
| **3.4c School Bus,** Nonprofit Org. | | | |
| Pl# 1, 2 | 4.75 | 4.25 | 2.50 |
| **791** | | | |
| **4c Stagecoach,** title 19 1/5mm long | | | |
| Pl# 1, 2, 3, 4 | 1.25 | 1.00 | .50 |
| Pl# 5, 6 | 2.50 | 2.00 | .80 |
| **791z** | | | |
| **4c Stagecoach,** Nonprofit Org. | | | |
| Pl# 3, 4, 5, 6 | 5.50 | 5.00 | 2.25 |
| **868** | | | |
| **4c Stagecoach,** title 17mm long | | | |
| Pl# 1 | 1.75 | 1.50 | .75 |

| | Strip of 5 | Strip of 3 | Single Used |
|---|---|---|---|
| **868z1** | | | |
| **4c Stagecoach,** overall tagging | | | |
| Pl#1 | 11. | 10.50 | 5.00 |
| **943** | | | |
| **4c Steam Carriage** | | | |
| Pl# 1 | 1.75 | 1.50 | .55 |
| **943zx** | | | |
| **4c Steam Carriage,** untagged | | | |
| Pl# 1 | 1.75 | 1.50 | .50 |
| **846** | | | |
| **4.9c Buckboard** | | | |
| Pl# 3, 4 | 1.00 | .90 | .45 |
| **846z** | | | |
| **4.9c Buckboard,** Nonprofit Org. | | | |
| Pl# 1, 2, 3, 4, 5, 6 | 1.50 | 1.25 | .60 |
| **808** | | | |
| **5c Motorcycle** | | | |
| Pl# 1, 2, 3, 4 | 1.25 | 1.00 | .45 |
| **879** | | | |
| **5c Milk Wagon** | | | |
| Pl# 1 | 1.25 | 1.00 | .50 |
| **931** | | | |
| **5c Circus Wagon,** Intaglio, Tagged | | | |
| Pl# 1 | 1.75 | 1.50 | .65 |
| **931z** | | | |
| **5c Circus Wagon,** untagged | | | |
| Pl# 1 | 1.75 | 1.50 | .65 |
| **1007** | | | |
| **5c Circus Wagon,** Gravure | | | |
| Pl# A1, A2 | 1.50 | 1.45 | .75 |
| Pl# A3, Hi-Brite paper | 1.50 | 1.45 | .75 |
| **1077** | | | |
| **5c Circus Wagon (sign)** | | | |
| Pl# S1, S2 | 1.50 | 1.45 | .75 |
| **955** | | | |
| **5c Canoe,** Brown, Intaglio | | | |
| Pl# 1, 2, 3 | 1.50 | 1.45 | .75 |
| **979** | | | |
| **5c Canoe,** Red, Gravure | | | |
| Pl# S11 | 1.25 | 1.15 | .75 |
| Pl # S11, dull gum | 10.00 | 9.75 | — |
| **799** | | | |
| **5.2c Sleigh** | | | |
| Pl# 1, 2 | 10.00 | 5.00 | 4.00 |
| Pl# 3 | 175.00 | 150.00 | 100.00 |
| Pl# 5 | 250.00 | 175.00 | 100.00 |
| **799zx** | | | |
| **5.2c Sleigh,** precancel | | | |
| Pl# 1, 2, 3, 4 | 10.00 | 9.50 | 7.00 |
| Pl# 5, 6 | 14.00 | 12.00 | 7.00 |
| **906** | | | |
| **5.3c Elevator** | | | |
| Pl# 1 | 1.25 | 1.00 | 1.00 |
| **865** | | | |
| **5.5c Star Route Truck** | | | |
| Pl# 1 | 2.00 | 1.50 | 1.00 |

| | Strip of 5 | Strip of 3 | Single Used |
|---|---|---|---|
| **865zx** | | | |
| **5.5c Star Route Truck**, Nonprofit Orig. | | | |
| Pl# 1 | 1.50 | 1.40 | 1.00 |
| Pl# 2 | 2.50 | 2.25 | 1.00 |
| **787** | | | |
| **5.9c Bicycle** | | | |
| Pl# 3, 4 | 15.00 | 7.50 | 10.00 |
| **787z** | | | |
| **5.9c Bicycle**, precancel | | | |
| Pl# 3, 4 | 32.50 | 30.00 | 20.00 |
| Pl# 5, 6 | 95.00 | 85.00 | 45.00 |
| **841** | | | |
| **6c Tricycle** | | | |
| Pl# 1 | 2.00 | 1.50 | 1.00 |
| **841z** | | | |
| **6c Tricycle**, Nonprofit Org. | | | |
| Pl# 1 | 2.25 | 2.00 | 2.25 |
| Pl# 2 | 8.75 | 8.00 | 4.50 |
| **870** | | | |
| **7.1c Tractor** | | | |
| Pl# 1 | 2.50 | 2.25 | 1.50 |
| **870z** | | | |
| **7.1c Tractor**, Nonprofit Org. | | | |
| Pl# 1 | 4.00 | 3.50 | 2.00 |
| **870zt** | | | |
| **7.1c Tractor**, Zip + 4 | | | |
| Pl# 1 | 1.75 | 1.50 | 1.50 |
| **814** | | | |
| **7.4c Baby Buggy** | | | |
| Pl# 2 | 9.00 | 8.00 | 7.00 |
| **814zx** | | | |
| **7.4c Baby Buggy**, Blk. Rt. Car. Rt. Sort | | | |
| Pl# 2 | 6.50 | 5.75 | 3.25 |
| **903** | | | |
| **7.6c Carreta** | | | |
| Pl# 1, 2 | 2.50 | 2.00 | 3.00 |
| Pl# 3 | 6.00 | 5.50 | 3.00 |
| **845** | | | |
| **8.3c Ambulance**, title 18 1/2mm long | | | |
| Pl# 1, 2 | 2.00 | 1.25 | 1.00 |
| **845z** | | | |
| **8.3c Ambulance**, Blk. Rt. | | | |
| Pl# 1, 2 | 2.00 | 1.50 | 1.00 |
| Pl# 3, 4 | 5.00 | 4.50 | 5.00 |
| **845a** | | | |
| **8.3c Ambulance**, title 18mm long | | | |
| Pl# 1 | 5.00 | 4.50 | 5.00 |
| Pl# 2 | 8.00 | 5.50 | 4.00 |
| **901** | | | |
| **8.4c Wheel Chair** | | | |
| Pl# 1, 2 | 2.50 | 2.00 | 1.25 |
| Pl# 3 | 15.00 | 14.00 | 7.50 |
| **869** | | | |
| **8.5c Tow Truck** | | | |
| Pl# 1 | 3.50 | 3.00 | 2.00 |
| **869z** | | | |
| **8.5c Tow Truck**, Nonprofit Org. | | | |
| Pl# 1 | 3.00 | 2.50 | 1.50 |
| Pl# 2 | 12.50 | 12.00 | 7.00 |
| **778** | | | |
| **9.3c Mail Truck** | | | |
| Pl# 1, 2 | 14.00 | 6.00 | 8.00 |
| Pl# 3, 4 | 35.00 | 20.00 | 17.50 |
| Pl# 5, 6 | 275.00 | 250.00 | 120.00 |
| **778zx** | | | |
| **9.3c Mail Truck** | | | |
| Pl# 1 | 13.00 | 12.75 | 8.50 |
| Pl# 2 | 10.00 | 9.50 | 8.00 |
| Pl# 3 | 27.50 | 25.00 | 20.00 |
| Pl# 4 | 18.00 | 16.00 | 10.00 |
| Pl# 5, 6 | 3.00 | 2.75 | 2.50 |
| Pl# 8 | 190.00 | 185.00 | 100.00 |
| **874** | | | |
| **10c Canal Boat** | | | |
| Pl# 1 | 3.50 | 3.00 | 1.00 |
| **874z1** | | | |
| **10c Canal Boat**, overall tagging | | | |
| Pl# 1, 2 | 3.25 | 3.00 | 2.00 |
| Pl# 3 Sluggerin | 4.50 | 4.00 | 2.00 |
| **874pz** | | | |
| **10c Canal Boat**, overall tagging, matt gum | | | |
| Pl# 1 | 5.00 | 4.00 | 3.00 |
| **954** | | | |
| **10c Tractor Trailer**, Intaglio | | | |
| Pl# 1 | 3.00 | 2.50 | 1.50 |
| **1042** | | | |
| **10c Tractor Trailer**, Gravure | | | |
| Pl# 11, 22 | 2.50 | 2.00 | 1.50 |
| **1071** | | | |
| **(10c) Automobile Hood**, Bulk rate | | | |
| Pl# S111, S222, S333 | 3.00 | 2.50 | 1.50 |
| **837** | | | |
| **10.1c Oil Wagon** | | | |
| Pl# 1 | 3.00 | 2.50 | 1.50 |
| **837zx** | | | |
| **10.1c Oil Wagon**, Black precancel | | | |
| Pl# 1, 2 | 3.00 | 2.50 | 1.50 |
| **837zx1** | | | |
| **10.1c Oil Wagon**, Red precancel | | | |
| Pl# 2, 3 | 2.50 | 2.00 | 1.00 |
| **788** | | | |
| **10.9c Hansom Cab** | | | |
| Pl# 1, 2 | 32.50 | 11.00 | 20.00 |
| **788 10.9c Hansom Cab**, Precancel | | | |
| Pl# 1, 2 | 35.00 | 27.00 | 20.00 |
| Pl# 3, 4 | 350.00 | 300.00 | 150.00 |
| **812** | | | |
| **11c Caboose** | | | |
| Pl# 1 | 4.25 | 4.00 | 2.50 |
| **812x1** | | | |
| **11c Caboose**, untagged, precancel | | | |
| Pl# 1 | 4.00 | 3.50 | 2.00 |
| **812zx** | | | |
| **11c Caboose**, untagged, precancel | | | |
| Pl# 2 | 3.00 | 2.75 | 1.50 |
| **844** | | | |
| **11c Stutz Bearcat** | | | |
| Pl# 1, 2, 3, 4 | 1.75 | 1.50 | 1.00 |
| **831** | | | |
| **12c Stanley Steamer**, title 18mm long, tagged | | | |
| Pl# 1, 2 | 3.00 | 2.50 | 1.50 |
| **831zx** | | | |
| **12c Stanley Steamer**, untagged | | | |
| Pl# 1, 2 | 3.00 | 2.50 | 1.50 |
| **831A** | | | |
| **12c Stanley Steamer**, title 17 1/2mm long | | | |
| Pl# 1 | 25.00 | 20.00 | 15.00 |
| **838** | | | |
| **12.5c Pushcart** | | | |
| Pl# 1 | 3.00 | 2.75 | 1.50 |
| Pl# 2 | 5.00 | 4.50 | 2.50 |

| | Strip of 5 | Strip of 3 | Single Used |
|---|---|---|---|
| **838** | | | |
| **12.5c Pushcart,** precancel | | | |
| Pl# 1 | 4.00 | 3.50 | 1.50 |
| Pl# 2 | 4.00 | 3.50 | — |
| **914** | | | |
| **13c Patrol Wagon** | | | |
| Pl# 1 | 4.00 | 3.25 | 2.00 |
| **900** | | | |
| **13.2c Coal Car** | | | |
| Pl# 1, 2 | 3.00 | 2.75 | 1.50 |
| **827** | | | |
| **14c Iceboat,** overall tagged | | | |
| Pl# 1, 2, 3, 4 | 2.75 | 2.25 | 1.50 |
| **827A** | | | |
| **14c Iceboat,** block tagged | | | |
| Pl# 2 | 4.00 | 3.50 | 2.50 |
| **899** | | | |
| **15c Tugboat,** block tagged | | | |
| Pl# 1 | 2.25 | 2.00 | 1.50 |
| Pl# 2 | 3.00 | 2.75 | 1.50 |
| **899zl** | | | |
| **15c Tugboat,** overall tagged | | | |
| Pl# 2 | 3.50 | 3.00 | 2.50 |
| **898** | | | |
| **16.7c Popcorn Wagon** | | | |
| Pl# 1 | 3.00 | 2.75 | 1.50 |
| Pl# 2 | 4.50 | 4.00 | 2.00 |
| **771** | | | |
| **17c Electric Car** | | | |
| Pl# 1, 2, 3, 4, 5 | 2.75 | 2.50 | 1.25 |
| Pl# 6 | 15.00 | 15.00 | 6.50 |
| Pl# 7 | 6.00 | 5.75 | 3.50 |
| **771zx1** | | | |
| **17c Electric Car,** precancel 11 1/2mm long | | | |
| Pl# 3A, 4A, 5A | 4.25 | 4.00 | 2.25 |
| Pl# 6A, 7A | 12.50 | 10.50 | 10.00 |
| **771zx2** | | | |
| **17c Electric Car,** precancel 12 1/2mm long | | | |
| Pl# 3B | 30.00 | 27.50 | 16.00 |
| Pl# 4B | 25.00 | 22.50 | 15.00 |
| Pl# 5B, 6B | 30.00 | 27.50 | 18.00 |
| **771zx3** | | | |
| **17c Electric Car,** precancel 13 1/2mm long | | | |
| Pl# 1C, 2C, 3C, 4C | 10.00 | 9.50 | 7.50 |
| Pl# 5C | 30.00 | 29.00 | 15.00 |
| Pl# 7C | 25.00 | 22.00 | 13.00 |
| **859** | | | |
| **17c Dog Sled** | | | |
| Pl# 2 | 3.50 | 3.25 | 2.00 |
| **880** | | | |
| **17.5c Racing Car** | | | |
| Pl# 1 | 4.00 | 3.25 | 2.50 |
| **880zx** | | | |
| **17.5c Racing Car,** Zip+4 Presort | | | |
| Pl# 1 | 3.50 | 3.25 | 2.50 |
| **768** | | | |
| **18c Surrey** | | | |
| Pl# 1 | 95.00 | 75.00 | 40.00 |
| Pl# 2, 5, 6, 13, 14, 17, 18 | 3.50 | 3.00 | 1.75 |
| Pl# 3, 4 | 70.00 | 65.00 | 35.00 |
| Pl# 7 | 35.00 | 30.00 | 20.00 |
| Pl# 9, 10, 11, 12 | 14.00 | 12.50 | 7.50 |
| Pl# 15, 16 | 20.00 | 18.00 | 8.00 |
| **777** | | | |
| **20c Fire Pumper** | | | |
| Pl# 1 | 150.00 | 33.00 | 17.50 |
| Pl# 2 | 800.00 | 170.00 | 80.00 |
| Pl# 3, 4, 13, 15, 16 | 5.00 | 4.50 | 3.00 |

| | Strip of 5 | Strip of 3 | Single Used |
|---|---|---|---|
| **777** | | | |
| **20c Fire Pumper** | | | |
| Pl# 5, 9, 10 | 3.00 | 2.25 | 1.75 |
| Pl# 6 | 37.50 | 27.50 | 17.50 |
| Pl# 7 | 8165.00 | 100.00 | 85.00 |
| Pl# 11 | 90.00 | 35.00 | 25.00 |
| Pl# 12, 14 | 7.00 | 6.50 | 4.00 |
| **913** | | | |
| **20c Cable Car,** block tagged | | | |
| Pl# 1, 2 | 4.00 | 3.00 | 2.50 |
| **913zl** | | | |
| **20c Cable Car,** overall tagged | | | |
| Pl# 2 | 5.00 | 3.75 | 2.25 |
| **1086** | | | |
| **20c Cog Railway** | | | |
| Pl# 1, 2 | 5.50 | 4.75 | 3.00 |
| **907** | | | |
| **20.5c Fire Engine** | | | |
| Pl# 1 | 4.75 | 4.00 | 2.50 |
| **902** | | | |
| **21c Railroad Mail Car** | | | |
| Pl# 1, 2 | 4.00 | 3.00 | 2.50 |
| **949** | | | |
| **23c Lunch Wagon,** tagged, matt gum | | | |
| Pl# 2, 3 | 4.00 | 3.50 | 2.00 |
| **949zm** | | | |
| **23c Lunch Wagon,** prephosphored, matt gum | | | |
| Pl# 3 | 5.75 | 4.75 | 3.00 |
| **949zs** | | | |
| **23c Lunch Wagon,** prephosphored, shiny gum | | | |
| Pl# 4, 5 | 5.75 | 4.75 | 3.00 |
| **912** | | | |
| **24.1c Tandem Bicycle** | | | |
| Pl# 1 | 4.25 | 4.00 | 2.75 |
| **866** | | | |
| **25c Bread Wagon** | | | |
| Pl# 1, 5 | 4.00 | 3.50 | 2.50 |
| Pl# 2, 3, 4 | 3.50 | 3.00 | 2.00 |
| **1085** | | | |
| **32c Ferry Boat,** shiny gum | | | |
| Pl# 2, 3, 4 | 6.25 | 6.00 | 3.00 |
| Pl# 5 | 10.00 | 9.50 | 4.00 |
| **1085** | | | |
| **32c Ferry Boat,** low gloss gum | | | |
| Pl# 3, 5 | 6.00 | 5.75 | 3.00 |
| Pl# 4 | 17.50 | 16.00 | 9.00 |
| **928** | | | |
| **$1 Seaplane,** dull gum | | | |
| Pl# 1 | 14.00 | 10.00 | 7.50 |
| **1115** | | | |
| **1c Kestrel** | | | |
| Pl# 1111 | 1.00 | .75 | .25 |
| **1030** | | | |
| **(5c) "G" Butte,** Non-Profit | | | |
| Pl# A11111, A21111 | 1.75 | 1.50 | .75 |
| **1170** | | | |
| **(5c) Butte** (1995) | | | |
| Pl# S111, S222, S333 | 1.75 | 1.50 | .90 |
| **1121** | | | |
| **(5c) Mountain,** BEP | | | |
| Pl# 11111 | 1.75 | 1.50 | .75 |
| **1122** | | | |
| **(5c) Mountain,** SVS | | | |
| Pl# S111 | 1.75 | 1.50 | .75 |

| | Strip of 5 | Strip of 3 | Single Used |
|---|---|---|---|
| **980** | | | |
| **(10c) Eagle & Shield** | | | |
| A11111, A11112, A21112, A22112, A22113, A33333, A43334, A43335, A53334 | 2.75 | 2.25 | 1.50 |
| A12213 | 28.00 | 25.00 | 14.00 |
| A2113, A33335, A43324, A43325, A43326, A43426, A54444, A54445 | 3.25 | 2.75 | 1.50 |
| A34424, A34426 | 6.50 | 5.75 | 3.00 |
| A32333 | 240.00 | — | 125.00 |
| A3334 | 85.00 | — | 45.00 |
| A77777, A88888, A88889, A89999, A99998, A99999 | 3.00 | 2.50 | 1.50 |
| A1010101010, A1110101010, A1011101011, etc | 4.00 | 3.00 | 2.00 |
| A111010101011 | 14.00 | 13.00 | 7.00 |
| **1011** | | | |
| **(10c) Eagle & Shield,** BEP | | | |
| Pl# 11111, 22221, 22222 | 2.75 | 2.50 | 1.50 |
| **(10c) Eagle & Shield,** matt gum | | | |
| Pl# 22222, 33333 | 4.25 | 3.50 | 2.50 |
| **(10c) Eagle & Shield,** tagged | | | |
| Pl# 11111, 22221 | 17.00 | 16.00 | 8.50 |
| **1012** | | | |
| **(10c) Eagle & Shield,** SVS | | | |
| Pl# S11111, S22222 | 3.75 | 3.25 | 2.00 |
| **1072** | | | |
| **(15c) Auto Tail Fin,** BEP | | | |
| Pl# S11111 | 3.50 | 3.00 | 1.50 |
| **1073** | | | |
| **(15c) Auto Tail Fin,** SVS | | | |
| Pl# S11111 | 3.75 | 3.00 | 1.50 |
| **754** | | | |
| **18c Flag** | | | |
| Pl# 1 | 345.00 | 85.00 | 150.00 |
| Pl# 2 | 50.00 | 25.00 | 25.00 |
| Pl# 3 | 840.00 | 225.00 | 100.00 |
| Pl# 4 | 10.00 | 6.00 | 5.00 |
| Pl# 5 | 6.75 | 6.00 | 3.50 |
| Pl# 6 | 3,500.00 | — | — |
| Pl# 7 | 38.00 | 33.00 | 20.00 |
| **852** | | | |
| **18c George Washington & Monument** | | | |
| Pl# 1112, 3333 | 3.00 | 2.75 | 1.75 |
| Pl# 11121, 33333 | 5.00 | 4.50 | 2.25 |
| **852zm** | | | |
| **18c George Washington & Monument,** dry gum | | | |
| Pl# 33333 | 4.50 | 4.75 | 2.50 |
| Pl# 43444 | 7.50 | 6.50 | 5.00 |
| **965** | | | |
| **19c Fishing Boat,** Type I | | | |
| Pl# A1111, A1212, A2424 | 3.25 | 3.00 | 2.25 |
| Pl# A1112 | 7.00 | 6.00 | 5.00 |
| **965a** | | | |
| **19c Fishing Boat,** Type II, Gravure | | | |
| Pl# A5555, A5556, A6667, A7667, A7679, A7766, A7779 | 4.50 | 4.00 | 2.25 |
| **965z** | | | |
| **19c Fishing Boat,** Type II, untagged error | | | |
| Pl# A5555 | 9.50 | 8.50 | 7.50 |
| **1044** | | | |
| **19c Fishing Boat,** Type III | | | |
| Pl# S111 | 5.00 | 4.00 | 3.00 |
| **780** | | | |
| **20c Flag over Supreme Court** | | | |
| Pl# 1 | 100.00 | 8.50 | 4.00 |
| Pl# 2, 11, 12 | 10.00 | 7.50 | 3.50 |
| Pl# 3, 5, 9, 10, 13, 14 | 5.25 | 2.75 | 1.75 |

| | Strip of 5 | Strip of 3 | Single Used |
|---|---|---|---|
| **780** | | | |
| **20c Flag over Supreme Court** | | | |
| Pl# 4 | 600.00 | 35.00 | 10.00 |
| Pl# 6 | 185.00 | 90.00 | 45.00 |
| Pl# 8 | 15.00 | 7.50 | 7.50 |
| **780zx** | | | |
| **20c Flag over Supreme Court,** precancel | | | |
| Pl# 14 | 8.00 | 5.00 | 4.00 |
| **789** | | | |
| **20c Consumer Education** | | | |
| Pl# 1, 2 | 175.00 | 30.00 | 85.00 |
| Pl# 3, 4 | 135.00 | 25.00 | 65.00 |
| **849** | | | |
| **21.1c Envelopes** | | | |
| Pl# 111111 | 4.00 | 3.00 | 2.50 |
| Pl# 111121 | 5.00 | 4.50 | 2.75 |
| **849z** | | | |
| **21.1c Envelopes,** Zip+4 | | | |
| Pl# 111111 | 4.00 | 3.00 | 2.75 |
| Pl# 111121 | 5.25 | 4.75 | 3.00 |
| **821** | | | |
| **(22c) "D" Series,** Eagle | | | |
| Pl# 1, 2 | 8.00 | 5.50 | 4.00 |
| **829** | | | |
| **22c Flag over Capitol** | | | |
| Pl# 1, 7, 13 | 12.50 | 10.00 | 7.50 |
| Pl# 2, 8, 10, 12, 15, 19, 22 | 3.50 | 3.00 | 2.00 |
| Pl# 3 | 55.00 | 12.50 | 20.00 |
| Pl# 4, 5, 6, 11, 16, 17, 18, 20, 21 | 7.00 | 6.00 | 3.50 |
| Pl# 14 | 35.00 | 30.00 | 16.00 |
| **876** | | | |
| **22c Flag over Capitol Test Coil** | | | |
| Pl# T1 | 3.50 | 3.25 | 2.50 |
| **969** | | | |
| **23c Flag,** Pre-sorted First Class | | | |
| Pl# A111, A212, A222 (Thick) | 3.75 | 3.55 | 2.25 |
| Pl# A112, A122, A333, A222 (Thin) | 4.25 | 3.75 | 2.50 |
| **985** | | | |
| **23c USA, Pre-sorted first Class,** ABNCo. | | | |
| Pl# A1111, A2222, A2232, A2233, A3333, A4443, A4444, A4453, A4364 | 4.50 | 4.00 | 2.50 |
| **994** | | | |
| **23c USA, Pre-sorted First Class,** BEP | | | |
| Pl# 1111 | 5.00 | 4.00 | 3.00 |
| **994m** | | | |
| **23c USA, Pre-sorted First Class,** matt gum | | | |
| #1111 | 5.00 | 4.00 | 3.00 |
| **1010** | | | |
| **23c USA, Pre-sorted First Class,** SVS | | | |
| Pl# S111 | 5.50 | 4.50 | 3.00 |
| **885** | | | |
| **(25c) "E" Series,** Earth | | | |
| Pl# 1111, 1222 | 3.50 | 2.75 | 2.00 |
| Pl# 1211, 2222 | 5.00 | 4.50 | 3.00 |
| **891** | | | |
| **25c Flag over Yosemite,** block tagged | | | |
| Pl# 1, 7 | 7.50 | 6.25 | 4.00 |
| Pl# 2, 3, 4, 5, 8 | 4.00 | 3.50 | 2.00 |
| Pl# 9 | 11.00 | 9.50 | 7.00 |
| **891pzv** | | | |
| **25c Flag over Yosemite,** phosphored tagged | | | |
| Pl# 1 | 45.00 | 42.50 | 20.00 |
| Pl# 2, 3, 7, 8, 9, 10, 11, 13, 14 | 4.00 | 3.50 | 2.00 |
| Pl# 5, 15 | 7.00 | 6.50 | 4.00 |
| Pl# 6 | 14.00 | 13.00 | 8.00 |
| **905** | | | |
| **25c Honeybee** | | | |
| Pl# 1, 2 | 4.00 | 3.25 | 2.00 |

| | Strip of 5 | Strip of 3 | Single Used |
|---|---|---|---|
| **1064** | | | |
| **(25c) "G" Series, Old Glory** | | | |
| Pl# S11111 | 6.00 | 5.00 | 3.50 |
| **1075** | | | |
| **(25c) Juke Box,** BEP | | | |
| Pl# 111111, 212222, 222222, 332222 | 5.00 | 4.25 | 3.00 |
| **1075** | | | |
| **(25c) Juke Box,** SVS | | | |
| Pl# S11111, S22222 | 4.25 | 3.75 | 2.50 |
| **940** | | | |
| **(29c) "F" Series, Tulip flower** | | | |
| Pl# 1111, 1222, 2222 | 4.00 | 3.50 | 2.50 |
| Pl# 1211 | 25.00 | 23.00 | 11.00 |
| Pl# 2211 | 6.00 | 5.00 | 3.50 |
| **945** | | | |
| **29c Flag over Mt. Rushmore,** Intaglio | | | |
| Pl# 1, 2, 3, 4, 5, 6, 7 | 4.75 | 4.25 | 2.50 |
| Pl# 8 | 7.00 | 6.00 | 3.50 |
| Pl# 9 | 10.00 | 8.00 | 6.00 |
| 2523c Brown | | | |
| Pl# 7 | 160.00 | 150.00 | 80.00 |
| **963** | | | |
| **29c Flag over Mt. Rushmore,** Gravure | | | |
| Pl# A11111, A22211 | 5.00 | 4.25 | 3.00 |
| **966** | | | |
| **29c Tulip flower,** rouletted | | | |
| Pl# S1111, S2222 | 5.00 | 4.25 | 2.50 |
| **982** | | | |
| **29c Tulip flower,** perforated | | | |
| Pl# S2222 | 5.00 | 4.25 | 2.50 |
| **984** | | | |
| **29c Flag over White House** | | | |
| Pl# 1, 2, 3, 4, 5, 6, 7, 8 | 5.50 | 4.25 | 2.50 |
| Pl# 9, 10, 11, 12, 13, 14, 15, 16, 18 | 6.75 | 5.50 | 3.50 |
| **1059** | | | |
| **(32c) Black "G" Series, Old Glory** | | | |
| Pl# 1111, 2222 | 8.75 | 7.50 | 4.50 |
| **1060** | | | |
| **(32c) Blue "G" Series, Old Glory** | | | |
| Pl# A1111, A1112, A1113, A1211, | | | |
| A1212, A1211, A1313, A1314, A1324, | | | |
| A1417, A1344, A2211, A2212, A2213, | | | |
| A2214, A2223, A3113, A3314, A3315, | | | |
| A3323, A3324, A3423, A3433, A3435, | | | |
| A3436, A4426, A4427, A5327, A5417, | | | |
| A5427, A5437 | 6.50 | 5.25 | 3.25 |
| Pl# A1222, A3114, A3426 | 9.00 | 7.75 | 4.50 |
| Pl# A4435 | 170.00 | 165.00 | 85.00 |
| **1061** | | | |
| **(32c) Red "G" Series, Old Glory** | | | |
| Pl# S1111 | 6.50 | 5.25 | 3.00 |
| **1061A** | | | |
| **(32c) "G" Series, Old Glory,** rouletted | | | |
| Pl# S1111, S2222 | 8.00 | 6.50 | 4.00 |
| **1082** | | | |
| **32c Flag over Porch,** BEP | | | |
| Pl# 11111, 22222, 33333, 44444, | | | |
| 45444, 66646, 66666, | | | |
| 77767, 78767, 99999 | 6.25 | 5.25 | 3.00 |
| Pl# 22322 | 50.00 | 48.00 | 25.00 |
| **32c Flag over Porch,** matt gum | | | |
| Pl# 11111, 22221, 22222 | 6.25 | 5.25 | 3.00 |
| **1083** | | | |
| **32c Flag over Porch,** SVS | | | |
| Pl# S11111 | 5.75 | 4.75 | 2.50 |
| **OF130** | | | |
| **20c Official** | | | |
| Pl# 3 | 85.00 | 15.00 | 10.00 |
| **OF132** | | | |
| **(22c) "D" Official** | | | |
| Pl# 1 | 90.00 | 48.00 | 15.00 |

# Variable-Denomination Coils

| | Strip of 5 | Strip of 3 | Single Used |
|---|---|---|---|
| **986** | | | |
| **29c Shield, horizontal,** matt gum | | | |
| Pl# 1 | 11.00 | 10.00 | 5.00 |
| **986a** | | | |
| **29c Shield, horizontal,** shiny gum | | | |
| Pl# 1 | 11.00 | 10.00 | 5.00 |
| **1053** | | | |
| **32c Shield, horizontal,** matt gum | | | |
| Pl# 1 | 15.00 | 13.00 | 7.50 |
| **32c Shield, horizontal,** shiny gum | | | |
| Pl# 1 | 14.00 | 12.00 | 7.00 |
| **1040** | | | |
| **29c Shield,** vertical design | | | |
| Pl# A11 | 10.00 | 8.75 | 5.00 |
| **1117** | | | |
| **32c Shield,** vertical design | | | |
| Pl# 11 | 10.00 | 8.75 | 5.00 |

# Self-Adhesive Plate Number Strips

| | Strip of 5 | Strip of 3 | Single Used |
|---|---|---|---|
| **1130** | | | |
| **(5c) Butte** | | | |
| Pl# S111 | 2.00 | 1.75 | 1.00 |
| **1131** | | | |
| **(5c) Mountain,** perforated 11 1/2 | | | |
| Pl# V222222, V333323, V333333, | | | |
| V333342, V333343 | 2.00 | 1.75 | 1.00 |
| **1152** | | | |
| **(5c) Mountain,** perforated 10 | | | |
| Pl# 1111 | 2.00 | 1.75 | 1.00 |
| **1129** | | | |
| **(10c) Eagle & Shield** | | | |
| Pl# S111 | 3.00 | 2.75 | 1.50 |
| **1132** | | | |
| **(10c) Automobile** | | | |
| Pl# S11111 | 3.00 | 2.75 | 1.50 |
| **1133** | | | |
| **(15c) Auto Tail Fin** | | | |
| Pl# S11111 | 3.50 | 3.00 | 1.75 |
| **1134** | | | |
| **(25c) Juke Box,** perforated 11 1/2 | | | |
| Pl# S11111 | 5.00 | 4.50 | 2.50 |
| **(25c) Juke Box,** perforated 10 | | | |
| Pl# 111111 | 5.00 | 4.50 | 2.50 |
| **1128** | | | |
| **32c Flag over Porch,** perforated 9 | | | |
| Pl# V11111 | 8.00 | 6.75 | 4.00 |
| **1163** | | | |
| **32c Pink Rose** | | | |
| Pl# 5111 | 7.50 | 6.00 | 3.50 |

| | Strip of 5 | Strip of 3 | Single Used |
|---|---|---|---|
| **1043** | | | |
| **29c Statue of Liberty** | | | |
| Pl# D1111 | 8.00 | 6.75 | 4.00 |
| **1051** | | | |
| **29c Christmas** | | | |
| Pl# V1111111 | 11.00 | 10.00 | 5.00 |
| **1050** | | | |
| **29c Santa Claus** | | | |
| Pl# V1111 | 8.25 | 7.50 | 4.00 |
| **1061A** | | | |
| **(32c) "G" Series** | | | |
| Pl# V11111 | 8.25 | 7.50 | 4.00 |
| **1126** | | | |
| **32c Flag over Porch,** perforated 9 3/4 | | | |
| Pl# 66666, 78777, 87888, 87898, | | | |
| 88888, 89878, 89888, | | | |
| 97898, 99899, 99999 | 9.00 | 7.50 | 4.50 |
| **1128** | | | |
| **32c Flag over Porch,** perforated 11 1/2 | | | |
| Pl# S11111 | 8.00 | 6.75 | 4.00 |
| **32c Flag over Porch,** perforated 11 | | | |
| Pl# 55555, 66666 | 8.00 | 6.75 | 2.00 |
| **32c Flag over Porch,** perforated 10, stamps seperate | | | |
| Pl# 1111 | 8.00 | 6.75 | 2.00 |
| **1106A-1109A** | | | |
| **32c Stanta & Children** | | | |
| Pl# V1111 | 8.00 | 7.50 | 2.00 |
| **1110A** | | | |
| **32c Midnight Angel** | | | |
| Pl# B1111 | 7.50 | 5.75 | 2.00 |
| **1136** | | | |
| **20c Blue Jay** | | | |
| Pl# S1111 | 4.75 | 4.00 | 2.50 |
| **1161** | | | |
| **(25c) Juke Box,** Linerless | | | |
| Pl# M11111 | 5.00 | 4.00 | 2.50 |
| **1162** | | | |
| **32c Flags over Porch,** Linerless | | | |
| Pl# M11111 | 5.50 | 4.25 | 2.75 |

## Self-Adhesive Panes and Booklets

| | Full Pane |
|---|---|
| **924** | |
| **25c Eagle & Shield (18)** | |
| Pl# A1111 | 16.50 |
| **929** | |
| **25c Flag,** Plastic **(12)** | 10.50 |
| **1014** | |
| **29c Red Squirrel (18)** | |
| Pl# D11111, D22211, D23133, | 15.50 |
| D22222, D22221 | 20.00 |
| **1016** | |
| **29c Rose (18)** | |
| Pl# S111 | 16.50 |
| **1038** | |
| **29c Pine Cone (18)** | |
| Pl# B1 | 20.00 |
| Pl# B3, 4, 6, 7, 9, | |
| 10, 11, 13, 14, 16 | 16.50 |
| Pl# B2, 5, 8, 12, 15 | 17.50 |
| **1084** | |
| **32c Pink Rose (20)** | |
| Pl# S111, S112, S333 | 17.50 |
| **1084nl** | |
| **32c Pink Rose,** Die-Cut "Time to Reorder" | |
| Pl# S444 | 18.00 |

| | Full Pane |
|---|---|
| **1091-92** | |
| **32c Peach & Pear (20)** | |
| Pl# V11111, V11122, V11131, V11132, V12131, | |
| V12132, V12141, V12211, V12221, V12232, | |
| V22212, V22221, V22222, V33142, V33143, | |
| V33243, V33323, V33333, V33353, V33343, | |
| V33353, V33363, V44424, V44434, V44454, | 18.00 |
| V45434, V45464, V54365, V54565, V55365, V55565 | 20.00 |
| V11232 | 250.00 |
| **942** | |
| **(29c) "F" Flag (12)** | 11.00 |
| **962n** | |
| **29c Statue of Liberty Torch (18)** | 16.00 |
| **962nv** | |
| **29c Statue of Liberty Torch,** revised back | 16.50 |
| **992** | |
| **29c Eagle,** Brown text **(17)** | |
| Pl# B1111-1, B111102, B3434-1, | |
| B4344-1, B4444-1, B4444-3 | 14.50 |
| Pl# B2222-1, B2222-2, B3333-1, | |
| B3333-3, B3434-3 | 18.00 |
| Pl# 4344-4 | 225.00 |
| **990** | |
| **29c Eagle,** Green text **(17)** | |
| Pl# D11111, D21221, D22322, | |
| D32322, D54573, D65784 | 15.00 |
| Pl# D54561, D54563 | 16.00 |
| Pl# D43352, D43452, D43453, | |
| D54571, D32342, D61384 | 20.00 |
| **988** | |
| **29c Eagle,** Red text **(17)** | |
| Pl# S1111 | 15.00 |
| **1039** | |
| **29c Eagle (18)** | |
| Pl# M1111, M1112 | 15.00 |
| **1943** | |
| **29c Statue of Liberty (18)** | |
| Pl# D1111, D1212 | 15.00 |
| **1029-32** | |
| **29c Christmas (12)** | |
| Pl# V111-1111, V222-1222, | |
| V222-2112, V222-2122, | |
| V222-2221, V222-2222, V333-3333 | 14.00 |
| **1037** | |
| **29c Snowman (18)** | |
| Pl# V11111 | 16.50 |
| Pl# V22222 | 20.00 |
| **29c Love & Sunrise (18)** | |
| Pl# B111-1, B111-2, B111-3, B111-4, | |
| B222-4, B222-5, B222-6, B333-9, B333-10, | |
| B333-11, B333-12, B333-17, B344-12, B344-13, | |
| B444-7, B444-8, B444-9, B444-10,. B444-13, | |
| B444-14, B444-15, B444-17, B444-18, B444-19, | |
| B555-20, B555-21 | 15.00 |
| Pl# B111-5 | 115.00 |
| Pl# B121-5, B221-5 | 16.00 |
| Pl# B333-5, B333-7, B333-8 | 25.00 |
| Pl# B333-14 | 90.00 |
| Pl# B334-11 | 750.00 |
| Pl# B344-11 | 75.00 |
| Pl# B434-10 | 120.00 |
| Pl# B444-16 | 16.00 |

|  | Full Pane |
|---|---|
| **1050** | |
| 29c Santa Claus (12) | |
| Pl# V1111 | 11.50 |
| **1051** | |
| 29c Cardinal in Snow (18) | |
| Pl# V1111, V2222 | 16.00 |
| **1062** | |
| (32c) "G" Surface (18) | |
| Pl# V11111, V22222 | 18.50 |
| **1063** | |
| (32c) "G" Overall (18) | |
| No Plate Number | 18.50 |
| **1076** | |
| 32c Flag over Field (18) | |
| Pl# V1111 | 17.50 |
| **1078** | |
| 32c Flag over Porch, large 1995 (20) | |
| Pl# V12211, V12212, V12312,V12321, V12322, V12331, V13322, V13831, V13834, V13836, V22211, V23322, V23422, V23432, V34743, V34745, V36745, V42556, V45554, V56663, V56665, V56763, V65976, V78989 | 18.50 |
| **1078** | |
| 32c Flag over Porch, small 1995 (20) | |
| Pl# V11111 | 60.00 |
| **1078** | |
| 32c Flag over Porch, perforated 11 1/4 (10) | |
| Pl# V11111, V12111, V23222, V31121, V32111, V32121, V44444, V55555, V66666, V66886, V67886, V76989, V77666, V77668, V77776, V78698, V78898 | 8.00 |
| Pl# 44322 | 17.50 |
| **CM1695** | |
| (32c) Love & Cherub (20) | |
| Pl# B1111-1, B2222-1, B2222-2, B3333-2 | 17.50 |
| **CM1706** | |
| 55c Love Cherub (20) | |
| Pl# B1111-1, B2222-1 | 27.50 |
| **1101n** | |
| 32c Santa & Children (20) | |
| Pl# V1111, V1211, V3233, V3333, V4444 | 17.50 |
| Pl# V1212 | 20.00 |

|  | Full Pane |
|---|---|
| **1110n** | |
| 32c Midnight Angel (20) | |
| Pl# B1111, B2222 | 17.50 |
| **1111** | |
| 32c Children Sledding (20) | |
| Pl# V1111 | 16.50 |
| **CM1798n** | |
| 32c Love Cherub (20) | |
| Pl# B1111-1, B1111-2, B2222-1, B2222-2 | 17.50 |
| **1149n** | |
| 32c Yellow Rose (20) | |
| Pl# S1111, S2222 | 15.00 |
| **CM1830** | |
| 32c Tennessee (20) | |
| Pl# S11111 | 17.50 |
| 32c Iowa (20) | 17.50 |
| **1147** | |
| 32c Madonna (20) | |
| Pl# 1111-1, 1211-1, 2212-1, 2222-1, 2323-1, 3333-1, 3334-1, 4444-1, 5556-2, 5656-2, 6666-2, 6766-1, 7887-1, 7887-2, 7888-2, 7988-2 | 16.50 |
| Pl# 5544-1 | 75.00 |
| Pl# 5555-1, 5556-1, 6656-2 | 30.00 |
| Pl# 3323-1, 6666-1 | 25.00 |
| **1144n** | |
| 32c Family Scenes (20) | |
| Pl# B1111, B2222, B3333 | 16.50 |
| **1145** | |
| 32c Skaters (18) | |
| Pl# V1111 | 16.50 |
| **1154** | |
| 32c Liberty & Torch (20) | |
| Pl# V1111, V1211, V2122, V2222 | 15.00 |
| **CM1884** | |
| 32c Love & Swans (20) | |
| Pl# B1111, B2222, B3333, B4444, B5555 | 15.00 |
| **CM1885** | |
| 55c Love & Swans (20) | |
| Pl# B1111, B2222, B3333, B4444 | 25.00 |
| **1156n** | |
| 32c Botanical Prints (20) | |
| Pl# S11111, S22222 | 15.00 |
| Pl# S33333 | 12.00 |

# BROOKMAN STAMP COMPANY
# CAN SAVE YOU MONEY!!!

# THE BROOKMAN BARGAIN BONANZA
## WILL SAVE YOU UP TO 70% ON YOUR PURCHASES
## AND UPDATE THE 1999 BROOKMAN PRICE GUIDE!

THE BROOKMAN BARGAIN BONANZA IS PUBLISHED SIX TIMES PER YEAR AND CONTAINS **48** PAGES OF BARGAINS WITH SOMETHING FOR VIRTUALLY EVERY COLLECTOR. IT IS AUTOMATICALLY SENT TO OUR ACTIVE CUSTOMERS AND, IF YOU ARE NOT ALREADY RECEIVING THIS VALUABLE PUBLICATION, WE SUGGEST YOU SEND FOR A **FREE** SAMPLE TODAY.

JULY - AUGUST 1998 EDITION     PRICE $2.00     VOLUME 4, NO. 6

IT'S TIME TO PLACE YOUR ORDER FOR THE 1999 BROOKMAN PRICE GUIDE! see back page for details.

**NEW DISCOVERY!!**
**Self-adhesive Test Coils!**

### BIGGER AND BETTER THAN EVER!
THE BROOKMAN BARGAIN BONANZA HAS BEEN EXPANDED TO 48 PAGES IN ORDER TO PROVIDE YOU WITH A WIDER VARIETY OF STAMPS AND OTHER SPECIAL OFFERS FROM AROUND THE WORLD. IN ADDITION TO OUR REGULAR SALES FOR U.S., U.N. AND CANADA STAMPS, WE WILL ALSO INCLUDE WORLDWIDE SETS AND PACKETS PLUS UPDATES ON SUPPLIES.

We recently obtained a small supply of two new testing coil varieties - both of which bear the design and wording of previous test coils except they are self-adhesive. You can obtain them now, at modest prices, although we don't know how long we will be able to hold to these prices. Order today.

#TC46 black on white paper
Pair $1.25  Strip-4 $2.50  Strip-10 $6.25
Plate #V1 Strip of 5 $11.95
#TC47 black on blue paper
Pair $1.25  Strip-4 $2.50  Strip-8 $4.00
Plate #1H1 Strip of 5 $11.95

### MONEY- SAVING SPECIALS IN THE JULY-AUGUST BARGAIN BONANZA

**COMPUTER VENDED POSTAGE AT 1/3 OFF**

CVP11, CVP12 set of 2 First Day Dated 29¢ Computer Vended Postage stamps from Washington, DC and Kensington, MD
Scott Cat. $8.50     Sale Price $5.95

| | PAGE | | PAGE |
|---|---|---|---|
| DON'S BARGAIN BASEMENT | 2 | U.S. MINT SE-TENANT STAMPS & SETS | 32-33 |
| LAST-CHANCE DISNEY STAMP SALE | 8-9 | U.S. 1945-1978 MINT SHEET SALE | 34-35 |
| PRINCESS DIANA MEMORIAL ISSUES | 10-13 | MODERN U.S. BOOKLET PANES INCLUDING | |
| MUSIC ON STAMPS OF THE WORLD | 14-16 | UNFOLDED PANES | 36 |
| NEW WORLD WILDLIFE FUND SETS | 17 | U.S. COMMEMORATIVE SOUVENIR SHEETS | |
| COUNTRY PACKETS FROM EUROPE | 18-19 | AND MINIATURE PANES | 37 |
| CANADA BACK OF THE BOOK ISSUES | 20 | U.S. BUREAU OF ENGRAVING AND | |
| CANADA GEORGE V AND VI DEFINITIVES | 21 | PRINTING SOUVENIR CARDS | 38-39 |
| UNITED NATIONS OFFICES IN GENEVA | 22-23 | U.S. COMMEMORATIVE PANELS SALE | 40-41 |
| SELECTED U.S. REGULARS, AIRMAILS AND | | MICRONESIA MINT SETS | 42 |
| BACK OF THE BOOK SINGLES SALE | 24-25 | U.S. SPACE STAMPS AND ALBUM | 43 |
| BETTER U.S. PLATE BLOCK SALE | 26-27 | SPACE TOPICAL STAMP PACKETS | 43 |
| U.S. 1920-34 COMMEMORATIVES | 28 | SCOTT MOUNT SALE | 44 |
| U.S. MINT COMMEMORATIVE YEAR SETS | 29 | 1998 ALBUM SUPPLEMENTS | 45 |
| U.S. MINT 1938-1966 SETS SALE | 30-31 | WHAT'S NEW IN US, UN, TT, CANADA | 46 |
| | | 1999 BROOKMAN PRICE LIST | 48 |

**ORDER TOLL FREE**
**1-800-545-4871 or**
**1-888-BROOKMAN**

**BROOKMAN** Stamp Company
email: dave@brookmanstamps.com

PO BOX 90
VANCOUVER WA 98666
FAX 1-360-695-1616
LOCAL 1-360-695-1391

## Call or Send for your FREE copy Today
## TOLL FREE 1-888-BROOKMAN

### LOOK AT WHAT YOU ARE LIKELY TO FIND AT LOW SALE PRICES!

* BETTER U.S. SINGLES AND SETS
* U.S. COMMEMORATIVE YEAR SETS
* U.S. MINIATURE SHEET SPECIALS
* U.S. COILS INCLUDING PLATE NUMBERS
* U.S. BOOKLETS AND BOOKLET PANES
* U.S. PLATE BLOCK BONANZA
* U.S. SOUVENIR SHEET SALE
* U.S. MINT SHEETS
* U.S. SE-TENANT SPECIALS
* U.S. SOUVENIR CARDS AND SOUVENIR PAGES - SAVE 70%
* U.S. COMMEMORATIVE PANELS
* U.S. & U.N. POSTAL STATIONERY
* CANADA & PROVINCES SINGLES AND SETS
* CANADA YEAR AND POPULAR SETS
* U.N. YEAR SETS AND SPECIALS
* MARSHALL IS., MICRONESIA & PALAU
* WORLDWIDE DISNEY STAMPS
* BASEBALL AND ENTERTAINMENT STAMPS
* WORLD WILDLIFE FUND STAMPS
* PACKETS FROM AROUND THE WORLD
* CHANGING COUNTRY AND TOPICAL SPECIALS
* MOUNTS, ALBUMS AND OTHER SUPPLIES
* BROOKMAN'S BACK-OF-THE-BOOK

PO BOX 90, VANCOUVER WA 98666
PHONE (360) 695-1391  FAX (360) 695-1616
email to: dave@brookmanstamps.com

### FREE BONUS!
Our *"What's New"* listings, which appear in every issue, include new U.S., Canada, U.N. & Trust Territory issues - keeping the Brookman Price Guide up-to-date.

# Commemorative Issues

**1893. COLUMBIAN ISSUES** Released in connection with the World's Columbian Exposition held in Chicago, Il., commemorated the 400th anniversary of the first voyage to America by Christopher Columbus. They are considered to be the First True Commemoratives. All the stamps except the 8¢ were issued Jan. 2nd. The 8¢ value, not originally planned with the others, appeared on March 3rd, 1893.

Christoforo Colombo was born in Genoa, Italy, ca. 1451. He went to sea at an early age and settled in Portugal. His wife was Felipa Perestrello, daughter of a distinguished navigator who left many charts that Columbus studied with care. He conceived the idea of reaching Asia by sailing due west and vainly sought support in Portugal, Spain, Italy and England for such an expedition.

In 1491, Columbus was on his way to France when he paused to stay with old friends at the monastery of La Rabida (CM10) in Spain. Juan Perez, former confessor to Queen Isabella, obtained for him an audience with the queen, who listened to his theories (CM5) and brought him before King Ferdinand.

Columbus was turned down by the sovereigns, whose treasury had been depleted by war with the Moors. Setting out overland for France, he had gone only six miles when a royal courier overtook him (CM11) to summon him back to court. Isabella had decided to raise the needed money, tradition says, by pledging her jewels (CM12). An agreement was signed giving Columbus three caravels: The *Santa Maria* (CM3), a 100-ton ship with a crew of 52; the 50-ton *Pinta;* and the 40-ton *Niña*. The latter two each had a crew of 18. The little fleet sailed from Palos on August 2.

After rebellious outbursts among the crews, on the night of Oct. 11, 1492, Columbus thought he saw a light. The next morning Rodrigo de Triana sighted land (CM1): Guanahani, now believed to be Watling's Island in the Bahamas. Naming the place San Salvador (Holy Savior), Columbus kissed the soil and gave thanks to God (CM2).

Excited by the native tales of gold, the fleet sailed south, finding Cuba on Oct. 28 and Hispaniola on Dec. 6. Leaving a colony of 40 men to build a fort at Hispaniola, where the *Santa Maria* had run aground, Columbus returned to Spain. At court, in Barcelona, he was given a great welcome (CM6), reported his discoveries (CM9) and displayed the natives he brought back with him (CM8).

He sailed again Sept. 25 with 3 galleons, 14 caravels, and 1,500 men. He reached Dominica, Guadaloupe, and Puerto Rico, found his Haitian colony destroyed by natives, and returned to Spain in March with 225 men and 30 natives.

Charged by enemies in court with mistreating the natives, he successfully defended himself, but his third voyage was delayed until May 1498. Given six vessels, he sent three to Hispaniola and took the others south to explore.

Returning to Hispaniola, he was put in chains (CM13) by Francisco de Bobadilla, sent from Spain to investigate new rumors of mistreatment of natives. Stripped of his honors and returned to Spain, he was released by the queen (CM7). Telling of the discoveries of his third expedition (CM14), he obtained four vessels and set out again in May 1502, discovering Honduras and Panama. The queen's death after his return in 1504 marked the end of his fortunes. He died at Valladolid in 1504, convinced that he had discovered the coast of Asia.

*Intaglio, American Bank Note Company, unwatermarked paper, perforated 12.*

CM1 *Columbus in Sight of Land. From a painting by William H. Powell.*

| CM1 | | UnFVF | UseFVF |
|---|---|---|---|
| 1¢ | **deep blue** *(449,195,550)* | 17.50 | .35 |
| | pale blue | 17.50 | .35 |
| | Plate strip of 3, w/imprint | 95.00 | |
| | Plate strip of 4, w/imprint & letter | 100. | |
| | Plate block of 6, w/imprint | 325. | |
| | Plate block of 8, w/imprint & letter | 500. | |
| | Double transfer | 25.00 | 1.00 |
| | Cracked plate | 90.00 | 5.00 |
| | On cover | | .75 |
| | FDC *(Jan. 2, 1893)* | | 5000. |

CM2 *Columbus Landing on Guanahani. From a painting by Vanderlyn in the Rotunda of the Capitol in Washington, D.C.*

| CM2 | | UnFVF | UseFVF |
|---|---|---|---|
| 2¢ | **dull purple** *(1,464,588,750)* | 17.50 | .20 |
| | brown violet | 20.00 | .20 |
| | gray violet | 20.00 | .20 |
| | Plate strip of 3, w/imprint | 75.00 | |
| | Plate strip of 4, w/imprint & letter | 125. | |
| | Plate block of 6, w/imprint | 225. | |
| | Plate block of 8, w/imprint & letter | 450. | |
| | Double transfer | 25.00 | .30 |
| | Triple transfer | 75.00 | |
| | Quadruple transfer | 90.00 | |
| | Broken frame line | 25.00 | .20 |

| CM2 | | UnFVF | UseFVF |
|---|---|---|---|
| | Recut frame lines | 25.00 | .20 |
| | Cracked plate | 90.00 | |
| | On cover | | .50 |
| | FDC *(Jan. 2, 1893)* | | 3750. |

CM2v The Broken Hat variety is found in the hat of the knight to the left of Columbus.

| | | | |
|---|---|---|---|
| v. | Broken Hat variety | 65.00 | .50 |

*Imperforate 2¢ Columbians are from printer's waste.*

CM3 *Columbus' flagship, Santa Maria. From a Spanish engraving.*

| CM3 | | UnFVF | UseFVF |
|---|---|---|---|
| 3¢ | **deep bluish green** *(11,501,250)* | 40.00 | 11.00 |
| | dull green | 40.00 | 11.00 |
| | Plate strip of 3, w/imprint | 200. | |
| | Plate strip of 4, w/imprint & letter | 275. | |
| | Plate block of 6, w/imprint | 650. | |
| | Plate block of 8, w/imprint & letter | 1200. | |
| | Double transfer | 75.00 | |
| | On cover | | 35.00 |
| | FDC *(Jan. 2, 1893)* | | 10000. |

CM4 *Santa Maria, Pinta and Niña. From a Spanish engraving.*

**CM4**

| | | UnFVF | UseFVF |
|---|---|---|---|
| 4¢ | **gray blue** *(19,181,550)* | 60.00 | 5.50 |
| | dull ultramarine | 60.00 | |
| | Plate strip of 3, w/imprint | 275. | |
| | Plate strip of 4, w/imprint & letter | 3.50 | |
| | Plate block of 6, w/imprint | 1100. | |
| | Plate block of 8, w/imprint & letter | 2000. | |
| | Double transfer | 125. | 25.00 |
| | On cover | | |
| | FDC *(Jan. 2, 1893)* | | 10500. |
| | v. blue (error) | | |
| | Plate strip of 4, w/imprint & letter | | |

CM5 *Columbus soliciting aid from Isabella. From a painting by Brozik in the Metropolitan Museum of Art, New York.*

**CM5**

| | | UnFVF | UseFVF |
|---|---|---|---|
| 5¢ | **brown** *(35,248,250)* | 65.00 | 6.00 |
| | pale brown | 65.00 | 6.00 |
| | yellow brown | 65.00 | 6.00 |
| | Plate strip of 3, w/imprint | 300. | |
| | Plate strip of 4, w/imprint & letter | 450. | |
| | Plate block of 6, w/imprint | 1400. | |
| | Plate block of 8, w/imprint & letter | 2400. | |
| | Double transfer | 125. | 25.00 |
| | On cover | | 25.00 |
| | FDC *(Jan. 2, 1893)* | | 17500. |

CM6 *Columbus Welcomed at Barcelona. From a panel by Randolph Rogers in the bronze doors of the Capitol, Washington, D.C.*

**CM6**

| | | UnFVF | UseFVF |
|---|---|---|---|
| 6¢ | **dark lilac** *(4,707,550)* | 60.00 | 17.50 |
| | dull purple | 60.00 | 17.50 |
| | Plate strip of 3, w/imprint | 275. | |
| | Plate strip of 4, w/imprint & letter | 360. | |
| | Plate block of 6, w/imprint | 1250. | |
| | Plate block of 8, w/imprint & letter | 2250. | |
| | Double transfer | 125. | |
| | On cover | | 3500. |
| | FDC *(Jan. 2, 1893)* | | 22500. |
| | a. red violet | — | |

CM7 *Columbus Restored to Favor. From a painting by Francesco Jover.*

**CM7**

| | | UnFVF | UseFVF |
|---|---|---|---|
| 8¢ | **brown purple** *(10,656,550)* | 50.00 | 7.00 |
| | pale brown purple | 50.00 | 7.00 |
| | Plate strip of 3, w/imprint | 225. | |
| | Plate strip of 4, w/imprint & letter | 300. | |
| | Plate block of 6, w/imprint | 750. | |
| | Plate block of 8, w/imprint & letter | 1150. | |
| | Double transfer | 75.00 | |
| | On cover | | 25.00 |

*Earliest known use is March 3, 1893.*

CM8 *Columbus Presenting Natives. From a painting by Luigi Gregori at the University of Notre Dame, South Bend, Ind.*

**CM8**

| | | UnFVF | UseFVF |
|---|---|---|---|
| 10¢ | **black brown** *(16,516,950)* | 95.00 | 5.50 |
| | dark brown | 95.00 | 5.50 |
| | gray black | 95.00 | 5.50 |
| | Plate strip of 3, w/imprint | 475. | |
| | Plate strip of 4, w/imprint & letter | 650. | |
| | Plate block of 6, w/imprint | 2800. | |
| | Plate block of 8, w/imprint & letter | 4250. | |
| | Double transfer | 175. | 12.00 |
| | Triple transfer | — | |
| | On cover | | 35.00 |
| | FDC *(Jan. 2, 1893)* | | |

CM9 *Columbus Announcing his Discovery. From a painting by R. Baloca in Madrid, Spain.*

**CM9**

| | | UnFVF | UseFVF |
|---|---|---|---|
| 15¢ | **deep bluish green** *(1,576,950)* | 175. | 50.00 |
| | dull green | 175. | 50.00 |
| | Plate strip of 3, w/imprint | 900. | |
| | Plate strip of 4, w/imprint & letter | 1200. | |
| | Plate block of 6, w/imprint | 4800. | |
| | Plate block of 8, w/imprint & letter | 7500. | |
| | Double tranfer | — | |
| | On cover | | 250. |

*Earliest known use is Jan. 26, 1893.*

CM10 *Columbus at La Rabida. From a painting by R. Maso.*

**CM10**

| | | UnFVF | UseFVF |
|---|---|---|---|
| 30¢ | **orange brown** *(617,250)* | 225. | 65.00 |
| | bright orange brown | 225. | 65.00 |
| | Plate strip of 3, w/imprint | 1250. | |
| | Plate strip of 4, w/imprint & letter | 1600. | |
| | Plate block of 6, w/imprint | 7500. | |
| | Plate block of 8, w/imprint & letter | 11500. | |
| | On cover | | 400. |

*Earliest known use is Feb. 8, 1893.*

CM11 *Recall of Columbus. From a painting by Augustus G. Heaton in the Capitol, Washington, D.C.*

**CM11**

| | | UnFVF | UseFVF |
|---|---|---|---|
| 50¢ | **slate black** *(243,750)* | 350. | 125. |
| | dull slate black | 350. | 125. |
| | Plate strip of 3, w/imprint | 1750. | |
| | Plate strip of 4, w/imprint & letter | 2500. | |
| | Plate block of 6, w/imprint | 12000. | |
| | Plate block of 8, w/imprint & letter | 17500. | |

**CM11**

|  | UnFVF | UseFVF |
|---|---|---|
| Double transfer | — | |
| Triple transfer | — | |
| On cover | | 650. |

*Earliest known use is Feb. 8, 1893.*

CM12 *Isabella Pledging her Jewels. From a painting by Muãoz Degrain in the Hall of Legislature in Madrid, Spain.*

**CM12**

| $1 | | UnFVF | UseFVF |
|---|---|---|---|
| | **Venetian red** *(55,050)* | 1000. | 450. |
| | pale Venetian red | 1000. | 450. |
| | Plate strip of 3, w/imprint | 5250. | |
| | Plate strip of 4, w/imprint & letter | 7250. | |
| | Plate block of 6, w/imprint | 35000. | |
| | Plate block of 8, w/imprint & letter | 55000. | |
| | Double transfer | — | |
| | On cover | | 2850. |

*Earliest known use is Jan. 21, 1893.*

CM13 *Columbus in Chains. From a painting by K. Leutze, Germantown, Penn.*

**CM13**

| $2 | | UnFVF | UseFVF |
|---|---|---|---|
| | **brown red** *(45,550)* | 1100. | 400. |
| | dark brown red | | |
| | Plate strip of 3, w/imprint | 1650. | |
| | Plate strip of 4, w/imprint & letter | 8000. | |
| | Plate block of 6, w/imprint | 45000. | |
| | Plate block of 8, w/imprint & letter | 2500. | |
| | On cover | | |
| | FDC *(Jan. 2, 1893)* | | 65000. |

CM14 *Columbus Describing his Third Voyage. From a painting by Francesco Jover.*

**CM14**

| $3 | | UnFVF | UseFVF |
|---|---|---|---|
| | **bronze green** *(27,650)* | 1700. | 725. |
| | pale bronze green | 1700. | 725. |
| | Plate strip of 3, w/imprint | 8500. | |
| | Plate strip of 4, w/imprint & letter | 14000. | |
| | Plate block of 6, w/imprint | 65000. | |
| | Plate block of 8, w/imprint & letter | 85000. | |
| | On cover | | 4000. |
| | a. olive green | 2300. | 850. |

*Earliest known use is April 4, 1893.*

CM15 *Queen Isabella and Columbus. Isabella from a painting in Madrid, Columbus by Lotto.*

**CM15**

| $4 | | UnFVF | UseFVF |
|---|---|---|---|
| | **deep rose** *(26,350)* | 2250. | 1000. |
| | pale analine rose | 2250. | 1000. |
| | Plate strip of 3, w/imprint | 12500. | |
| | Plate strip of 4, w/imprint & letter | — | |
| | Plate block of 6, w/imprint | — | |
| | Plate block of 8, w/imprint & letter | — | |
| | On cover | | 4000. |
| | a. rose carmine | 3000. | 1250. |

*Earliest known use is Jan. 6, 1893.*

CM16 *Profile of Columbus. From the sculpture of the commemorative half dollar.*

**CM16**

| $5 | | UnFVF | UseFVF |
|---|---|---|---|
| | **black** *(27,350)* | 2750. | 1600. |
| | gray black | 2750. | 1600. |
| | Plate strip of 3, w/imprint | 14000. | |
| | Plate strip of 4, w/imprint & letter | 20000. | |
| | Plate block of 6, w/imprint | — | |
| | Plate block of 8, w/imprint & letter | — | |
| | On cover | | 5000. |

*Earliest known use is Jan. 6, 1893.*

*For stamps of these designs, but with "1992" instead of "1893" in the top-right corner see Nos. CM1456-61.*

**1898. TRANS-MISSISSIPPI ISSUE** was released for the Trans-Mississippi Exposition held at Omaha, Nebraska. Commemorating the settling of the Middle West. Jacques Marquette (CM17), a French Jesuit, founded a mission and in 1673 explored the Mississippi with Joliet John Charles Fremont (CM20) mapped the Oregon Trail in 1842 and later surveyed railway routes in the South west.

All denominations issued June 17. *Printed in Intaglio, Bureau of Engraving and Printing, Washington, D.C. ,on paper with double-line 'USPS' watermark.*

CM17 *Marquette Exploring the Mississippi. From a painting by Lamprecht.*

**CM17**

| | | UnFVF | UseFVF |
|---|---|---|---|
| 1¢ | **green** *(70,993,400)* | 22.50 | 4.75 |
| | dark yellow green | 22.50 | 4.75 |
| | yellow green | 22.50 | 4.75 |
| | Plate pair, w/imprint | 75.00 | |
| | Plate strip of 3, w/imprint | 95.00 | |
| | Plate block of 4, w/imprint | 200. | |
| | Plate block of 6, w/imprint | 300. | |
| | Margin block of 4, w/arrow | 95.00 | |
| | Double transfer | 40.00 | 7.50 |
| | On cover | | 10.00 |
| | FDC *(June 17, 1898)* | | 12500. |

CM18 *Farming in the West, from a photograph.*

**CM18**

| | | UnFVF | UseFVF |
|---|---|---|---|
| 2¢ | **brown red** *(159,720,800)* | 19.00 | 1.25 |
| | pale brown red | 19.00 | 1.25 |
| | Plate pair, w/imprint | 55.00 | |
| | Plate strip of 3, w/imprint | 85.00 | |
| | Plate block of 4, w/imprint | 175. | |
| | Plate block of 6, w/imprint | 240. | |
| | Margin block of 4, w/arrow | 85.00 | |
| | Double transfer | 35.00 | 2.50 |
| | Worn plate | 25.00 | 2.00 |
| | On cover | | 2.50 |
| | FDC *(June 17, 1898)* | | 11500. |

*Earliest known use is June 16, 1898.*

CM19 *Indian Hunting Buffalo. From an engraving in Schoolcraft's History of the Indian Tribes.*

**CM19**

| | | UnFVF | UseFVF |
|---|---|---|---|
| 4¢ | **orange red** *(94,924,500)* | 100. | 17.50 |
| | orange | 100. | 17.50 |
| | Plate pair, w/imprint | 250. | 20.00 |
| | Plate strip of 3, w/imprint | 450. | 20.00 |
| | Plate block of 4, w/imprint | 750. | |
| | Plate block of 6, w/imprint | 1250. | |
| | Margin block of 4, w/arrow | 500. | |
| | On cover | | 75.00 |
| | FDC *(June 17, 1898)* | | 20000. |

CM20 *Fremont on Rocky Mountains. From old wood engraving.*

**CM20**

| | | UnFVF | UseFVF |
|---|---|---|---|
| 5¢ | **deep blue** *(7,694,180)* | 100. | 17.50 |
| | bright blue | 100. | 17.50 |
| | dull blue | | |
| | Plate pair, w/imprint | 150. | 17.50 |
| | Plate strip of 3, w/imprint | 250. | |
| | Plate block of 4, w/imprint | 700. | |
| | Plate block of 6, w/imprint | 1250. | |
| | Margin block of 4, w/arrow | 450. | |
| | On cover | | 75.00 |
| | FDC *(June 17, 1898)* | | 20000. |

CM21 *Troops Guarding Train. From a drawing by Frederic Remington.*

**CM21**

| | | UnFVF | UseFVF |
|---|---|---|---|
| 8¢ | **chocolate** *(2,927,200)* | 135. | 32.50 |
| | violet brown | 135. | 32.50 |
| | Plate pair, w/imprint | 350. | |
| | Plate strip of 3, w/imprint | 500. | |
| | Plate block of 4, w/imprint | 1750. | |
| | Plate block of 6, w/imprint | 2500. | |
| | Margin block of 4, w/arrow | 650. | |
| | On cover | | 150. |
| | FDC *(June 17, 1898)* | | 25000. |
| | v. Horizontal pair, imperforate vertically between | 17500. | |
| | v1. Plate block of 4, w/imprint | 75000. | |

CM22 *Hardships of Emigration. From a painting by A. G. Heaton.*

**CM22**

| | | UnFVF | UseFVF |
|---|---|---|---|
| 10¢ | **violet black** *(4,629,760)* | 135. | 17.50 |
| | gray violet | 135. | 17.50 |
| | Plate pair, w/imprint | 250. | |
| | Plate strip of 3, w/imprint | 525. | |
| | Plate block of 4, w/imprint | 1750. | |
| | Plate block of 6, w/imprint | 2750. | |
| | Margin block of 4, w/arrow | 750. | |
| | On cover | | 100. |
| | FDC *(June 17, 1898)* | | 30000. |

CM23 *Western Mining Prospector. From a drawing by Frederic Remington.*

**CM23**

| | | UnFVF | UseFVF |
|---|---|---|---|
| 50¢ | **bronze green** *(530,400)* | 450. | 130. |
| | dark bronze green | 450. | 130. |
| | Plate pair, with imprint | 150. | |

**CM23**

| | UnFVF | UseFVF |
|---|---|---|
| Plate strip of 3, w/imprint | 2000. | |
| Plate block of 4, w/imprint | 10250. | |
| Plate block of 6, w/imprint | 16000. | |
| Margin block of 4, w/arrow | 2250. | |
| On cover | | 1500. |
| FDC *(June 17, 1898)* | | 35000. |

CM24 *Western Cattle in a Storm. From a painting by John MacWhirter.*

**CM24**

| | | UnFVF | UseFVF |
|---|---|---|---|
| $1 | **black** *(56,900)* | 950. | 400. |
| | Plate pair, w/imprint | 2750. | |
| | Plate strip of 3, w/imprint | 5500. | |
| | Plate block of 4, w/imprint | 30000. | |
| | Plate block of 6, w/imprint | 42500. | |
| | Margin block of 4, w/arrow | 5500. | |
| | On cover | | 4500. |
| | FDC *(June 17, 1898)* | | 20000. |

CM25 *Mississippi River Bridge at St. Louis, MO. From a photograph.*

**CM25**

| | | UnFVF | UseFVF |
|---|---|---|---|
| $2 | **red brown** *(56,200)* | | |
| | dark red brown | 1600. | 650. |
| | Plate pair, with imprint | 4750. | |
| | Plate strip of 3, w/imprint | 7500. | |
| | Plate block of 4, w/imprint | 65000. | |
| | Plate block of 6, w/imprint | 100000. | |
| | Margin block of 4, w/arrow | 10500. | |
| | On cover | | 60000. |
| | FDC *(June 17, 1898)* | | — |

**1901. PAN-AMERICAN ISSUE** commemorates the Pan-American Exposition at Buffalo, NY, promoting friendly relations among the countries of the New World. The stamps illustrating engineering achievements of the age were printed in two colors, and the first three denominations are known with inverted centers. The stamps were on sale only during the exposition, from May 1 to October 31. *Intaglio, perforated 12.*

CM26 *Navigation on the Great Lakes (S.S. City of Alpena).*

**CM26**

| | | UnFVF | UseFVF |
|---|---|---|---|
| 1¢ | **emerald and black** *(91,401,500)* | 15.00 | 2.75 |
| | dark blue green & black | 15.00 | 2.75 |
| | Plate strip of 3, w/imprint | 100. | |
| | Plate block of 4, w/imprint & arrow | — | |
| | Plate strip of 5 (2 numbers), w/imprint | 175. | |
| | Plate block of 6, w/imprint | 275. | |
| | Plate block of 10 (2 numbers), w/imprint | — | |
| | Margin block of 4, w/imprint and arrow | 125. | |
| | Double transfer | 22.50 | 2.75 |
| | On cover | | 8.00 |
| | FDC *(May 1, 1901)* | | 5000. |
| | v. Center inverted *(1,000 reported)* | 12500. | 6000. |
| | v1. Center inverted plate strip of 3, w/imprint | 45000. | |
| | v2. Center inverted single on cover | | 18500. |

CM27 *Fast Rail Transportation (Empire State Express).*

**CM27**

| | | UnFVF | UseFVF |
|---|---|---|---|
| 2¢ | **rose red and black** *(209,759,700)* | 15.00 | 1.00 |
| | carmine & gray black | 15.00 | 1.00 |
| | Plate strip of 3, w/imprint | 85.00 | |
| | Plate block of 4, w/imprint & arrow | — | |
| | Plate strip of 5 (2 numbers), w/imprint | 200. | |
| | Plate block of 6, w/imprint | 275. | |
| | Plate block of 10 (2 numbers), w/imprint | — | |
| | Margin block of 4, w/imprint & arrow | 100. | |
| | Double transfer | 30.00 | 4.00 |
| | On cover | | 2.00 |
| | FDC *May 1, 1901)* | 2750. | |
| | v. Center inverted *(158 known)* | — | |
| | v1. Center inverted block of 4 | — | |

CM28 *Electric Automobile.*

**CM28**

| | | UnFVF | UseFVF |
|---|---|---|---|
| 4¢ | **orange brown and black** *(5,737,100)* | 70.00 | 12.50 |
| | red brown & black | 70.00 | 12.50 |
| | Plate strip of 3, w/imprint | 350. | |
| | Plate block of 4, w/imprint & arrow | — | |
| | Plate strip of 5 (2 numbers), w/imprint | 600. | |
| | Plate block of 6, w/imprint | 2500. | |
| | Plate block of 10 (2 numbers), w/imprint | 4500. | |
| | Margin block of 4, w/imprint & arrow | 350. | |
| | On cover | | 50.00 |
| | FDC *(May 1, 1901)* | | 8500. |
| | v. Center inverted *(206 known)* | — | |
| | v1. Center inverted plate strip of 4, w/imprint | 13500. | |
| | v2. Center inverted, overprinted "Specimen" | — | |

CM29 *Bridge at Niagara Falls.*

**CM29**

| | | UnFVF | UseFVF |
|---|---|---|---|
| 5¢ | **gray blue and black** *(7,201,300)* | 75.00 | 12.50 |
| | dark gray blue & black | 75.00 | 12.50 |
| | Plate strip of 3, w/imprint | 400. | |
| | Plate block of 4, w/imprint & arrow | — | |
| | Plate strip of 5 (2 numbers), w/imprint | 725. | |
| | Plate block of 6, w/imprint | 3000. | |
| | Plate block of 10 (2 numbers), w/imprint & arrow | 5250. | |
| | Margin block of 4, w/imprint & arrow | 425. | |
| | On cover | | 55.00 |
| | FDC *(May 1, 1901)* | | 16000. |

CM30 *Canal Locks, Sault Ste. Marie.*

**CM30**

| | | UnFVF | UseFVF |
|---|---|---|---|
| 8¢ | **chocolate and black** *(4,921,700)* | 100. | 45.00 |
| | purple brown & black | 100. | 45.00 |

**CM30**

| | UnFVF | UseFVF |
|---|---|---|
| Plate strip of 3, w/imprint | 500. | |
| Plate block of 4, w/imprint & arrow | — | |
| Plate strip of 5 (2 numbers), w/imprint | 900. | |
| Plate block of 6, w/imprint | 4500. | |
| Plate block of 10 (2 numbers), w/imprint | 8000. | |
| Margin block of 4, w/imprint & arrow | 500. | |
| On cover | | 125. |
| FDC *(May 1, 1901)* | | — |

CM31 *Fast Ocean Navigation (S.S. St. Paul).*

**CM31**

| 10¢ | | UnFVF | UseFVF |
|---|---|---|---|
| | **yellow brown and black** *(5,043,700)* | 140. | 22.50 |
| | dark yellow brown & black | 140. | 22.50 |
| | Plate strip of 3, w/imprint | 750. | |
| | Plate block of 4, w/imprint & arrow | — | |
| | Plate strip of 5 (2 numbers), w/imprint | 1400. | |
| | Plate block of 6, w/imprint | 7000. | |
| | Plate block of 10 (2 numbers), w/imprint | 12500. | |
| | Margin block of 4, w/imprint & arrow | 800. | |
| | On cover | | 150. |
| | FDC *(May 1, 1901)* | | — |

**1904. LOUISIANA PURCHASE ISSUE** prepared for the World's Fair at St. Louis, MO. commemorating the 1803 acquisition of the Louisiana Territory from France. All values were placed on sale April 30, the opening day of the fair.

Robert Livingston (CM32) was appointed minister to France in 1801. In 1803 President Jefferson (CM33) instructed him to negotiate with Napoleon for the purchase of New Orleans and the mouth of the Mississippi. James Monroe (CM34), former minister to France, was sent to aid in the negotiations. Francois de Barbe-Marbois, Napoleon's finance minister, astounded them by offering to sell the entire Louisiana Territory, an offer which they accepted without delay or authority. The price was $11,250,000; claims and interest accruals raised it to $27,000,000 - about 4c an acre. The territory (CM36) eventually became ten entire states and parts of three others. President McKinley (CM35) signed the Act of Congress approving the 1904 World's Fair but never lived to see it. In September 1901 he was assassinated while attending the Pan-American Exposition. *Intaglio, perforated 12.*

CM32 *Robert Livingston. From a painting by Gilbert Sullivan.*

**CM32**

| 1¢ | | UnFVF | UseFVF |
|---|---|---|---|
| | **green** *(79,779,200)* | 20.00 | 3.50 |
| | dark green | 20.00 | 3.50 |
| | Plate pair, w/imprint | 65.00 | |
| | Plate strip of 3, w/imprint | 100. | |
| | Plate block of 4, w/imprint | 160. | |
| | Plate block of 6, w/imprint | 175. | |
| | Margin block of 4, w/arrow | 75.00 | |
| | Diagonal line through left "1" | 50.00 | 10.00 |
| | Double transfer | — | |
| | On cover | | 75.00 |
| | FDC *(April 30, 1904)* | | 6500. |

CM33 *Thomas Jefferson. From a painting attributed to Gilbert Stuart.*

**CM33**

| 2¢ | | UnFVF | UseFVF |
|---|---|---|---|
| | **carmine** *(192,732,400)* | 19.00 | 1.25 |
| | bright carmine | 19.00 | 1.25 |
| | Plate pair, w/imprint | 75.00 | |
| | Plate strip of 3, w/imprint | 125. | |
| | Plate block of 4, w/imprint | 160. | |
| | Plate block of 6, w/imprint | 175. | |
| | Margin block of 4, w/arrow | 100. | |
| | On cover | | 6.00 |
| | FDC *(April 30, 1904)* | | 5000. |
| | v. Vertical pair, imperforate horizontally | — | |

CM34 *James Monroe. From a painting by Vanderlyn in New York City Hall.*

**CM34**

| 3¢ | | UnFVF | UseFVF |
|---|---|---|---|
| | **dark red violet** *(4,542,600)* | 60.00 | 25.00 |
| | Plate pair, w/imprint | 150. | |
| | Plate strip of 3, w/imprint | 275. | |
| | Plate block of 4, w/imprint | 550. | |
| | Plate block of 6, w/imprint | 800. | |
| | Margin block of 4, w/arrow | 325. | |
| | Doulbe transfer | — | |
| | On cover | | 75.00 |
| | FDC *(April 30, 1904)* | | 18000. |

CM35 *William McKinley*

**CM35**

| 5¢ | | UnFVF | UseFVF |
|---|---|---|---|
| | **indigo** *(6,926,700)* | 75.00 | 17.50 |
| | Plate pair, w/imprint | 200. | |
| | Plate strip of 3, w/imprint | 325. | |
| | Plate block of 4, w/imprint | 625. | |
| | Plate block of 6, w/imprint | 900. | |
| | Margin block of 4, w/arrow | 350. | |
| | On cover | | 75.00 |
| | FDC *(April 30, 1904)* | | 26000. |

CM36 *Map of Louisiana Purchase.*

**CM36**

| 10¢ | | UnFVF | UseFVF |
|---|---|---|---|
| | **red brown** *(4,011,200)* | 125. | 25.00 |
| | dark red brown | 125. | 25.00 |
| | Plate pair, w/imprint | 325. | |
| | Plate strip of 3, w/imprint | 500. | |
| | Plate block of 4, w/imprint | 1250. | |
| | Plate block of 6, w/imprint | 1750. | |
| | Margin block of 4, w/arrow | 575. | |
| | On cover | | 125. |
| | FDC *(April 30, 1904)* | | 27500. |

**1907. JAMESTOWN ISSUE** was created for the Jamestown Exposition at Hampton Roads, VA, commemorating the 300th anniversry of the oldest permanent English settlement in America. In 1607, on their way to reattempt a settlement at Roanoke Island, three London Company ships with 105 men were blown off course and discovered the entrance to Chesapeake Bay. Sailing 50 miles up a river they named the James (for King James I), they began a settlement called Jamestown (CM38). Constant Indian trouble brought out the leadership qualities of Captain John Smith (CM37). Captured while foraging and condemned to death by the Indian chief Powhatan, Smith is said by legend to have been saved by the chief's beautiful daughter Pocahontas (CM39). Married to a settler named John Rolfe, she was received with royal honors in England, where she died in 1617. The 1¢ and 2¢ stamps were placed on sale April 25, 1907. The 5¢ value was first sold May 3, 1907. *Intaglio, perforated 12.*

CM37 *Captian John Smith. From a painting in the State Library, Virginia.*

| CM37 | | UnFVF | UseFVF |
|---|---|---|---|
| 1¢ | **deep bluish green** *(77,728,794)* | 17.50 | 3.00 |
| | dark green | 17.50 | 3.00 |
| | Plate strip of 3, w/imprint | 65.00 | |
| | Plate block of 6, w/imprint | 275. | |
| | Margin block of 4, w/arrow | 75.00 | |
| | Double transfer | 25.00 | 8.00 |
| | On cover | | 12.50 |
| | FDC *(April 6, 1907)* | | 12000. |

CM38 *Founding of Jamestown. From a lost painting.*

| CM38 | | UnFVF | UseFVF |
|---|---|---|---|
| 2¢ | **rose red** *(149,497,994)* | 22.50 | 2.75 |
| | bright rose red | 22.50 | 2.75 |
| | Plate strip of 3, w/imprint | 75.00 | |
| | Plate block of 6, w/imprint | 375. | |
| | Margin block of 4, w/arrow | 90.00 | |
| | Double transfer | | 6.00 |
| | On cover | | 7.50 |
| | FDC *(April 6, 1907)* | | 12000. |

CM39 *Pocahontas. From a painting in Norfolk, England.*

| CM39 | | UnFVF | UseFVF |
|---|---|---|---|
| 5¢ | **indigo** *(7,980,594)* | 85.00 | 22.50 |
| | blue | 85.00 | 22.50 |
| | Plate strip of 3, w/imprint | 300. | |
| | Plate block of 6, w/imprint | 2100. | |
| | Margin block of 4, w/arrow | 350. | |
| | Double transfer | 125. | 45.00 |
| | On cover | | 75.00 |

*Earliest known use is May 9, 1907.*

**1909. LINCOLN MEMORIAL CENTENNIAL ISSUE** commemorated the 100th anniversary of the birth of Abraham Lincoln. As an experiment to counteract the shrinking caused by printing on wet paper, some rows of stamps were separated by 3mm spacing instead of the usual 2mm. Some of the perforated stamps were printed on a 35- percent rag stock known as 'bluish paper,' which is actually grayish in appearance. *Intaglio, perforated 12 and imperforate.*

CM40-42 *Abraham Lincoln. From statue by St. Gaudens, Grant Park, Chicago.*

*Perforated 12*

| CM40 | | UnFVF | UseFVF |
|---|---|---|---|
| 2¢ | **carmine** *(148,387,191)* | 5.00 | 1.75 |
| | bright carmine | 5.00 | 1.75 |
| | Block of 4 (2mm spacing) | 25.00 | 17.50 |
| | Block of 4 (3mm spacing) | 25.00 | 17.50 |
| | Plate block of 6, w/imprint | 125. | |
| | Double transfer | 12.50 | 5.00 |
| | On cover | | 9.00 |
| | FDC *(Feb. 12, 1909)* | | 500. |

*Imperforate*

| CM41 | | UnFVF | UseFVF |
|---|---|---|---|
| 2¢ | **carmine** *(1,273,900)* | 22.50 | 1750. |
| | Block of 4 (2mm spacing) | 100. | |
| | Block of 4 (3mm spacing) | 100. | |
| | Plate block of 6, w/imprint | 225. | |
| | Center line block | 200. | |
| | Margin block of 4, w/arrow | 100. | |
| | Double transfer | 60.00 | 30.00 |
| | On cover | | 50.00 |
| | FDC *(Feb. 12, 1909)* | | 17000. |

*Bluish gray paper, perforated 12 (February 1909)*

| CM42 | | UnFVF | UseFVF |
|---|---|---|---|
| 2¢ | **carmine** *(637,000)* | 175. | 195. |
| | Block of 4 (2mm spacing) | 900. | 750. |
| | Block of 4 (3mm spacing) | 900. | 750. |
| | Plate block of 6, w/imprint | 3000. | |
| | On cover | | 450. |

*Earliest known use is March 27, 1909.*

**1909. ALASKA-YUKON ISSUE** released in connection with a Seattle, WA exposition, commemorating the development of the Alaska-Yukon-Pacific Territory. William H. Seward, Secretary of State under Lincoln and Johnson, negotiated the purchase of Alaska from Russia, begun in 1859 but postponed by the Civil War. The treaty of March 30, 1867, set the purchase price at $7,200,000. The formal transfer was made October 18 at Sitka. *Intaglio, perforated 12 and imperforate.*

CM43, 44 *William Seward. From a drawing by Marcus W. Baldwin.*

*Perforated 12*

| CM43 | | UnFVF | UseFVF |
|---|---|---|---|
| 2¢ | **carmine** *(152,887,311)* | 7.00 | 1.50 |
| | bright carmine | 7.00 | 1.50 |
| | Plate block of 6, w/imprint | 250. | |
| | Double transfer | 1750. | 6.00 |
| | On cover | | 7.50 |
| | FDC *(June 1, 1909)* | | 4500. |

*Imperforate*

| CM44 | | UnFVF | UseFVF |
|---|---|---|---|
| 2¢ | **carmine** *(525,400)* | 30.00 | 22.50 |
| | Plate block of 6, w/imprint | 275. | |
| | Center line block | 175. | 150. |
| | Margin block of 4, w/arrow | 150. | 120. |
| | Double transfer | 55.00 | 35.00 |
| | On cover | | 45.00 |

*Earliest known use is June 9, 1909.*

**1909. HUDSON-FULTON ISSUE** commemorated historic voyages 200 years apart up the Hudson River to Albany. Henry Hudson, an English navigator commanding the Dutch East India Company ship, *Half Moon,* explored the river when he sailed into New York Bay September 3, 1609. Robert Fulton, aided by Robert Livingston (CM32), constructed the first practical steamship, named *Clermont* after Livingston's home, and steamed to Albany and back August 17-22, 1807. *Intaglio, perforated 12 and imperforate.*

CM45 *Half Moon and S.S. Clermont.*

*Perforated 12*

**CM45**
| | | UnFVF | UseFVF |
|---|---|---|---|
| **2¢** | **carmine** *(72,634,631)* | 10.00 | 3.50 |
| | Plate block of 6, w/imprint | 350. | |
| | Double transfer | 25.00 | 7.50 |
| | On cover | | 800. |
| | FDC *(Sept. 25, 1909)* | | — |

*Imperforate*

**CM46**
| | | UnFVF | UseFVF |
|---|---|---|---|
| **2¢** | **carmine** *(216,480)* | 35.00 | 22.50 |
| | Plate block of 6, w/imprint | 350. | |
| | Center line block | 275. | 140. |
| | Margin block of 4, w/arrow | 175. | 120. |
| | Double transfer | 55.00 | 35.00 |
| | On cover | | 45.00 |
| | FDC *(Sept. 25, 1909)* | | 7500. |

**1912-13. PANAMA-PACIFIC ISSUE** commemorates Balboa's sighting of the Pacific Ocean in 1513; the opening of the Panama Canal in 1914; and the Panama-Pacific Exposition at San Francisco, Calif. in 1915.

Balboa (CM47), Spanish governor of Darien (Panama), marched across the isthmus and from the peak of Mount Darien sighted the waters of "the South Sea" on September 25, 1513. Magellan named it the Pacific Ocean in 1520. A canal connecting the Atlantic and Pacific oceans (CM48), was built by the United States during 1904-14 at a cost of $336,650,000. San Francisco Bay (CM99) is said to have been sighted by Drake in 1579, but the city's site was discovered (CM50),in 1770 by Don Gaspar de Portola, Spanish governor of the Californias, who, with the Franciscan missionary Juniper Serra (A116), led a 1,000-mile march establishing settlements from Lower California to Monterey. *Stamps issued on with single-line "USPS" watermark. Intaglio, perforated 12 (1913) and perforated 10 (1914-15). (Quantities shown include both perforation types).*

CM47, 52 *Vasco Nunãez de Balboa*

**CM47**
| | | UnFVF | UseFVF |
|---|---|---|---|
| **1¢** | **green** *(334,796,926)* | 13.50 | 1.25 |
| | yellow green | 13.50 | 1.25 |
| | Plate block of 6 | 150. | |
| | Double transfer | 25.00 | 5.00 |
| | On cover | | 7.50 |
| | FDC *(Jan. 1, 1913)* | | 5000. |

CM48, CM53 *Panama Canal. From a model of the Pedro Miguel Locks.*

**CM48**
| | | UnFVF | UseFVF |
|---|---|---|---|
| **2¢** | **rose red** *(503,713,086)* | 15.00 | .50 |
| | deep carmine | 15.00 | .50 |

**CM48**
| | | UnFVF | UseFVF |
|---|---|---|---|
| | carmine lake | 15.00 | .50 |
| | Plate block of 6 | 250. | |
| | Double transfer | 45.00 | 5.00 |
| | On cover | | 4.00 |
| | FDC *(Jan. 18, 1913)* | | 2000. |

*Earliest known use is January 17, 1913.*

CM49, CM54 *The Golden Gate. From a photograph.*

**CM49**
| | | UnFVF | UseFVF |
|---|---|---|---|
| **5¢** | **blue** *(29,088,726)* | 55.00 | 8.00 |
| | dark blue | 55.00 | 8.00 |
| | Plate block of 6 | 2000. | |
| | On cover | | 45.00 |
| | FDC *(Jan. 1, 1913)* | | 22000. |

CM50-51, CM55 *Dicovery of San Francisco Bay. From a painting by Charles F. Matthews, San Francisco Art Museum.*

**CM50**
| | | UnFVF | UseFVF |
|---|---|---|---|
| **10¢** | **orange yellow** *(16,968,365)* | 100. | 20.00 |
| | Plate block of 6 | 2500. | |
| | On cover | | 100. |
| | FDC *(Jan. 1, 1913)* | | 17500. |

**CM51**
| | | UnFVF | UseFVF |
|---|---|---|---|
| **10¢** | **orange** *(16,968,365)* *(Aug. 1913)* | 175. | 15.00 |
| | Plate block of 6 | 8250. | |
| | On cover | | 125. |

**1914-15. PANAMA-PACIFIC ISSUE** *Perforated 10.*

**CM52**
| | | UnFVF | UseFVF |
|---|---|---|---|
| **1¢** | **green** | 20.00 | 5.25 |
| | dark green | 20.00 | 5.25 |
| | Plate block of 6 | 300. | |
| | On cover | | 30.00 |

*Earliest known use is Dec. 21, 1914.*

**CM53**
| | | UnFVF | UseFVF |
|---|---|---|---|
| **2¢** | **rose red** *(Jan. 1915)* | 60.00 | 1.50 |
| | dark carmine | 60.00 | 1.50 |
| | red | 60.00 | 1.50 |
| | Plate block of 6 | 1300. | |
| | On cover | | 12.50 |

*Earliest known use is Jan. 13, 1915.*

**CM54**
| | | UnFVF | UseFVF |
|---|---|---|---|
| **5¢** | **blue** | 125. | 13.50 |
| | dark blue | 125. | 13.50 |
| | Plate block of 6 | 4250. | |
| | On cover | | 75.00 |

*Earlist known use is Feb. 6, 1915.*

**CM55**
| | | UnFVF | UseFVF |
|---|---|---|---|
| **10¢** | **orange** | 750. | 55.00 |
| | Plate block of 6 | 13000. | |
| | On cover | | 225. |

*Earliest known use is Aug. 27, 1915.*

**1919. VICTORY ISSUE** commemorated the winning of World War I by the Allies. The design shows a female allegory of "Victory" and the U.S. flag flanked by the flags of Great Britain, Belgium Italy and France. *Intaglio, perforated 11.*

CM56 *"Victory" and Flags.*

| CM56 | | UnFVF | UseFVF |
|---|---|---|---|
| 3¢ | **dark lilac** *(99,585,200)* | 7.50 | 3.00 |
| | Plate block of 6 | 75.00 | |
| | FDC *(March 3, 1919)* | | 200. |
| | a. dark red lilac | 350. | 125. |
| | a1. Plate block of 6 | — | |
| | b. pale red lilac | 13.50 | 3.50 |
| | b1. Plate block of 6 | — | |
| | c. bright red lilac | 40.00 | 15.00 |
| | c1. Plate block of 6 | — | |

**1920. PILGRIM TERCENTENARY ISSUE** marks the 300th anniversary of the landing of the Pilgrims at Plymouth, MA (CM58), in December 1620. Of the *Mayflower's* (CM57) 102 passengers, 41 Pilgrim "fathers" en route signed a compact (CM59) in which they pledged to adhere to the principles of self-government in the colony. *Intaglio, perforated 11.*

CM57 *The Mayflower. From a watercolor by Harrison Eastman, Smithsonian Institution, Washington, D.C.*

| CM57 | | UnFVF | UseFVF |
|---|---|---|---|
| 1¢ | **green** *(137,978,207)* | 3.50 | 2.50 |
| | dark green | 3.50 | 2.00 |
| | Plate block of 6 | 35.00 | |
| | Double transfer | — | |
| | On cover | | 8.00 |
| | FDC *(Dec. 21, 1920)* | | 1600. |

CM58 *Landing of the Pilgrims. From an 1846 engraving by Burt based on a sketch by White.*

| CM58 | | UnFVF | UseFVF |
|---|---|---|---|
| 2¢ | **rose red** *(196,037,327)* | 5.25 | 1.75 |
| | carmine | 5.25 | 1.75 |
| | rose | 5.25 | 1.75 |
| | Plate block of 6 | 50.00 | |
| | On cover | | 5.00 |
| | FDC *(Dec. 20, 1920)* | | 1500. |

CM59 *Signing of the Compact. From a painting by Edwin White.*

| CM59 | | UnFVF | UseFVF |
|---|---|---|---|
| 5¢ | **deep blue** *(11,321,607)* | 35.00 | 12.50 |
| | dark blue | 35.00 | 12.50 |
| | Plate block of 6 | 375. | |
| | On cover | | 30.00 |
| | FDC *(Dec. 21, 1920)* | | 3000. |

**1923. HARDING MEMORIAL ISSUE** Honored President Warren G. Harding, who died August 2 in San Francisco, CA. An Ohio newspaper editor elected to the U.S. Senate in 1914, he won the presidency in 1920 on a platform pledging a "return to normalcy." First President to visit Alaska, he died on the way home. The stamp was issued less than a month later. *Intaglio.*

The printed design of the flat plate printing measures 19 x 21 7/8mm. Small specks of black color usually are seen on the backs of these stamps, a characteristic of almost all flat-press-printed stamps.

The printed design of the rotary press printings measures 19 x 22 1/2mm. Color specks are almost always absent from the backs of these stamps.

CM60-63 *Warren G. Harding*

*Flat plate printing, perforated 11*

| CM60 | | UnFVF | UseFVF |
|---|---|---|---|
| 2¢ | **black** *(1,459,487,085)* | .60 | .20 |
| | grayish black | .60 | .20 |
| | Plate block of 6 | 17.50 | |
| | Double transfer | 3.00 | .75 |
| | On cover | | 1.00 |
| | FDC *(Sept. 1, 1923)* | | 40.00 |
| | v. Horizontal pair, imperforate vertically | 1500. | |

*Flat plate printing, imperforate*

| CM61 | | UnFVF | UseFVF |
|---|---|---|---|
| 2¢ | **black** *(770,000)* | 6.50 | 4.50 |
| | Plate block of 6 | 90.00 | |
| | Block of 4, w/arrow | 40.00 | |
| | Center line block of 4 | 75.00 | |
| | On cover | | 12.50 |
| | FDC *(Nov. 15, 1923)* | | 125. |

*Rotary press printing, perforated 10*

| CM62 | | UnFVF | UseFVF |
|---|---|---|---|
| 2¢ | **gray black** *(99,950,300)* | 15.00 | 1.75 |
| | black | 15.00 | 1.75 |
| | Plate block of 4 | 275. | |
| | Gutter pair | 450. | |
| | On cover | | 6.00 |
| | FDC *(Sept. 12, 1923)* | | 175. |

*Rotary press printing, perforated 11*

| CM63 | | UnFVF | UseFVF |
|---|---|---|---|
| 2¢ | **gray black** | 15000. | |

**1924. HUGUENOT-WALLOON ISSUE** commemorated the 300th anniversary of the Walloon settlement of New York, and the restoration of a monument to earlier Huguenot settlements in the South.

During the religious wars of the 16th century, thousands of French and Belgian Protestants, known as Huguenots, settled in Holland, where they were called Walloons (foreigners). Although Dutch traders had visited Manhattan since 1613, the first Dutch immigrants were 30 Walloon families sent by the Dutch West India Company in 1624. Under Peter Minuit they bought Manhattan from the Indians and tried founding settlements all the way from the Delaware River to Fort Orange, now Albany (CM65). In 1562, French Huguenots unsuccessfully had tried a settlement at Port Royal, SC. In 1564 a colony was established at Fort Caroline (now Mayport) on the St. Johns River in Florida, and had a stone column erected bearing the French coat of arms. The colony was massacred in 1565 by the Spanish under Pedro Menendez de Aviles. This column was replaced and dedicated May 2, 1924. *Intaglio, perforated 11.*

CM64 *The New Netherland.*

| CM64 | | UnFVF | UseFVF |
|---|---|---|---|
| 1¢ | **green** *(51,378,023)* | 2.75 | 2.75 |
| | dark green | 2.75 | 2.75 |

| CM64 | | UnFVF | UseFVF |
|---|---|---|---|
| | Plate block of 6 | 30.00 | |
| | Double transfer | 10.00 | 6.50 |
| | On cover | | 7.00 |
| | FDC *(May 1, 1924)* | | 40.00 |

CM65 *Landing of Walloons at Fort Orange. From History of New York by Martha Lamb.*

| CM65 | | UnFVF | UseFVF |
|---|---|---|---|
| 2¢ | **carmine red** *(77,753,423)* | 5.00 | 2.00 |
| | Plate block of 6 | 55.00 | |
| | Double transfer | 15.00 | 4.25 |
| | On cover | | 5.00 |
| | FDC *(May 1, 1924)* | | 60.00 |

CM66 *Monument of Huguenots at Mayport, Florida.*

| CM66 | | UnFVF | UseFVF |
|---|---|---|---|
| 5¢ | **Prussian blue** *(5,659,023)* | 27.50 | 14.00 |
| | dark blue | 27.50 | 14.00 |
| | Plate block of 6 | 250. | |
| | On cover (UPU rate) | | 30.00 |
| | FDC *(May 1, 1924)* | | 85.00 |
| | v. broken circle below right numeral "5" | 65.00 | 22.50 |

**1925. LEXINGTON-CONCORD ISSUE** commemorated the 150th anniversary of the first armed conflicts of the American Revolution, which took place on April 19, 1775.

When Gen. Thomas Gage, colonial governor of Massachusetts, sent 800 troops to Lexington and Concord to destroy military supplies stored there by the colonists, Paul Revere made his famous ride on horseback to warn the colonists. Calling themselves the Minute Men (ready to fight on a minute's notice) (CM69), the colonists gathered on the Green at Lexington with the watchword, "If they mean to have a war, let it begin here" (CM68). Eight of the 70 Minute Men were killed; the rest fell back, and the British went to Concord. In fighting on the North Bridge there, and continuing all the way back to the protection of naval guns at Charlestown Harbor, the British suffered 273 casualties; the colonists 93. Chosen to head a Continental Army, George Washington took command at Cambridge in July (CM67). *Intaglio, perforated 11.*

CM67 *Washington at Cambridge. From an engraving in the Cambridge Public Library.*

| CM67 | | UnFVF | UseFVF |
|---|---|---|---|
| 1¢ | **green** *(15,615,000)* | 2.75 | 2.50 |
| | dark green | 2.75 | 2.50 |
| | Plate block of 6 | 40.00 | |
| | On cover | | 5.00 |
| | FDC *(April 4, 1925)* | | 30.00 |

CM68 *Battle of Lexington. Painting by Henry Sandham, Town Hall, Lexington, Massachusetts.*

| CM68 | | UnFVF | UseFVF |
|---|---|---|---|
| 2¢ | **carmine red** *(26,596,600)* | 5.00 | 3.50 |
| | Plate block of 6 | 65.00 | |
| | On cover | | 7.50 |
| | FDC *(April 4, 1925)* | | 35.00 |

CM69 *The Minute Man. From a statue by Daniel Chester French in Concord, the poetry by Ralph Waldo Emerson.*

| CM69 | | UnFVF | UseFVF |
|---|---|---|---|
| 5¢ | **Prussian blue** *(5,348,800)* | 25.00 | 14.00 |
| | Plate block of 6 | 225. | |
| | On cover (UPU rate) | | 22.50 |
| | FDC *(April 4, 1925)* | | 85.00 |
| | v. Line over head | 65.00 | 25.00 |

**1925. NORSE-AMERICAN ISSUE** commemorated the 100th anniversary of the first Norwegian immigrants' arrival on the *Restaurationen* on October 9, 1825. Sagas tell of Norse exploration of the North American coast ca. 1000 A.D. *Intaglio, perforated 11.*

CM70 *Sloop Restaurationen. Adapted from a drawing of a sister ship.*

| CM70 | | UnFVF | UseFVF |
|---|---|---|---|
| 2¢ | **carmine and black** *(9,104,983)* | 4.00 | 3.00 |
| | dark carmine and black | 4.00 | 3.00 |
| | Plate block of 8 w/2 numbers & arrow | 200. | |
| | Plate block of 8, w/carmine number (only) & arrow | 3250. | |
| | Center line block of 4 | 27.50 | |
| | Margin block of 4, w/arrow | 35.00 | |
| | On cover | | 8.00 |
| | FDC *(May 18, 1925)* | | 20.00 |

CM71 *Viking ship. Built in Norway, by popular subscription, as a gift to the people of the United States.*

| CM71 | | UnFVF | UseFVF |
|---|---|---|---|
| 5¢ | **indigo and black** *(1,900,983)* | 15.00 | 12.50 |
| | Plate block of 8, w/2 numbers & arrow | 575. | |
| | Center line block of 4 | 90.00 | |
| | Margin block of 4, w/arrow | 85.00 | |
| | On cover (UPU rate) | | 22.50 |
| | FDC *(May 18, 1925)* | | 30.00 |
| | FDC CM70 & 71 on 1 cover | | 50.00 |

**1926. SESQUICENTENNIAL ISSUE** in connection with the Exposition at Philadelphia, Pa, commemorated the 150th anniversary of the Declaration of Independence. *Intaglio, perforated 11.*

CM72 *The Liberty Bell. Designed from the entrance to the exposition.*

| CM72 | | UnFVF | UseFVF |
|---|---|---|---|
| 2¢ | carmine red *(307,731,900)* | 2.50 | .50 |
| | Plate block of 6 | 35.00 | |
| | Double transfer | — | |
| | FDC *(May 10, 1926)* | | 10.00 |

**1926. ERICSSON MEMORIAL ISSUE** Honored John Ericsson, the Swedish-born engineer who built the ironclad *USS Monitor,* which engaged the Confederate ironclad *Virginia* (formerly *USS Merrimac*) off Hampton Roads, Va., in 1862. Ericsson's inventions include a screw propeller that revolutionized shipbuilding. The stamp shows a statue of him unveiled in Washington by the Crown Prince of Sweden. *Intaglio, perforated 11.*

CM73 *Statue of John Ericsson. Sculpted by James Earl Fraser, Washington D.C.*

| CM73 | | UnFVF | UseFVF |
|---|---|---|---|
| 5¢ | slate violet *(20,280,500)* | 6.00 | 2.50 |
| | Plate block of 6 | 75.00 | |
| | FDC *(May 29, 1929)* | | 25.00 |

**1926. WHITE PLAINS ISSUE** commemorated the 150th anniversary of the Battle of White Plains, NY, October 28, 1776. The British, attempting to outflank Washington's forces in upper Manhattan, caused him to withdraw his main force northward. In a sharp battle at White Plains, the British captured a key hill, but Washington escaped while they were awaiting reinforcements. *Intaglio, perforated 11.*

CM74 *Alexander Hamilton's battery. From a painting by E. L. Ward.*

| CM74 | | UnFVF | UseFVF |
|---|---|---|---|
| 2¢ | carmine red *(40,639,485)* | 2.00 | 1.50 |
| | Plate block of 6 | 40.00 | |
| | FDC *(Oct. 18, 1926)* | | 8.00 |
| | v. Vertical pair, inperforated between | 2500. | |

**1926. WHITE PLAINS PHILATELIC EXHIBITION ISSUE** Sheets of 25 stamps with marginal inscription reading "International Philatelic Exhibition, Oct. 16 to 23, 1926, N.Y., U.S.A." Sheet size 161 x 149mm.

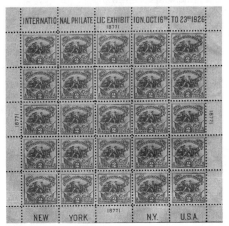

CM75 *White Plains souvenir sheet.*

sheet of 25

| CM75 | | UnFVF | UseFVF |
|---|---|---|---|
| 2¢ | carmine red, *(107,398)* | 400. | 425. |
| | v. Dot over first "S" of "States" on stamp in position 9 of lower left pane of plate 18774 or position 11 of the lower left pane of plate 18773. | 425. | 450. |
| | FDC Full sheet *(Oct. 18, 1926)* | | 1700. |

**1927. VERMONT SESQUICENTENNIAL ISSUE** commemorated the 150th anniversary of the Battle of Bennington and the independence of the State of Vermont. In 1777, badly needing supplies at Saratoga, NY, Burgoyne sent a force to capture American military stores at Bennington, VT. In a battle August 16th with 2,600 militiamen (the "Green Mountain Boys") under Gen. John Stark, almost the entire British force was killed or captured. *Intaglio, perforated 11.*

CM76 *Green Mountain Boy.*

| CM76 | | UnFVF | UseFVF |
|---|---|---|---|
| 2¢ | carmine red *(39,974,900)* | 1.25 | 1.00 |
| | Plate block of 6 | 40.00 | |
| | FDC *(Aug. 3, 1927)* | | 6.00 |

**1927. BURGOYNE CAMPAIGN ISSUE** commemorated the Battle of Bennington, Oriskany, Fort Stanwix and Saratoga. On October 17, 1777, surrounded by a force three times his own, Burgoyne surrendered to the Americans. His 5,700 men went back to England, pledged not to fight again in the war. *Intaglio, perforated 11.*

CM77 *Surrender of Gen. John Burgoyne. From a painting by Trumbull in the Capitol Rotunda, Washington, D.C.*

| CM77 | | UnFVF | UseFVF |
|---|---|---|---|
| 2¢ | carmine red *(25,628,450)* | 3.50 | 2.25 |
| | Plate block of 6 | 40.00 | |
| | FDC *(Aug. 3, 1927)* | | 11.00 |

**1928. VALLEY FORGE ISSUE** recalled the 150th anniversary of Washington's winter encampment at Valley Forge, about 20 miles northwest of Philadelphia, PA. Beaten at Brandywine and Germantown, desperately short of food, clothing and supplies, the American troops at Valley Forge showed courage in the darkest period of American history. *Intaglio, perforated 11.*

CM78 *General Washington at Prayer. From an engraving by John C. McRae.*

| CM78 | | UnFVF | UseFVF |
|---|---|---|---|
| 2¢ | carmine red *(101,330,328)* | 1.00 | .50 |
| | Plate block of 6 | 25.00 | |
| | FDC *(May 26, 1928)* | | 5.00 |

**1928. HAWAIIAN SESQUICENTENNIAL ISSUE** marked the 150th anniversary of the arrival in the Hawaiian Islands of English navigator Capt. James Cook. These makeshift commemoratives, made by overprinting ordinary definitive stamps (Nos. 476 and 479), disappointed collectors who expected something more elaborate. The overprints caused confusion; when some postal clerks would not honor them because they thought they were precancels. *Intaglio, perforated 11 x 10 1/2.*

CM79 2¢ overprint.

CM80 5¢ overprint.

**CM79**

| | | | UnFVF | UseFVF |
|---|---|---|---|---|
| 2¢ | carmine *(5,519,897)* | | 4.50 | 4.50 |
| | Plate block of 4 | | 100. | |
| | Vertical pair with wide spacing (28mm rather than 18mm) | | 100. | |
| | FDC *(Aug. 13, 1928)* | | | 15.00 |

**CM80**

| | | | UnFVF | UseFVF |
|---|---|---|---|---|
| 5¢ | blue *(1,459,897)* | | 12.50 | 12.50 |
| | Plate block of 4 | | 200. | |
| | FDC *(Aug. 13, 1928)* | | | 20.00 |
| | FDC CM79 & 80 on 1 cover | | | 40.00 |

**1928. MOLLY PITCHER ISSUE** another two-line overprint of No. 476, commemorated the 150th anniversary of the Battle of Monmouth, NJ, June 28, 1778, and honored Mary Ludwig Hays, whose husband was a cannoneer in the battle. Called "Molly Pitcher" because she carried water to the tired and wounded soldiers, she also took her husband's place when he was overcome by the heat, and manned his cannon throughout the rest of the battle. (See also the 1978 10c postal card, No. PC73). *Intaglio, perforated 11.*

CM81 *The 2¢ Molly Pitcher overprint.*

**CM81**

| | | | UnFVF | UseFVF |
|---|---|---|---|---|
| 2¢ | carmine *(9,779,896)* | | 1.00 | 1.25 |
| | Plate block of 4 | | 25.00 | |
| | Vertical pair with wide spacing (28mm rather than 18mm) | | 2750. | |
| | FDC *(Oct. 20, 1928)* | | | 12.50 |

**1928. AERONAUTICS CONFERENCE ISSUE** in connection with the International Civil Aeronautics Conference held December 12-14 in Washington, commemorated the 25th anniversary of the first airplane flight (December 17, 1903) by the Wright brothers at Kitty Hawk, NC. The plane (CM80), in England for 20 years, was returned to the United States in 1948 and is now on view at the Smithsonian Institution in Washington, DC. *Intaglio, perforated 11.*

CM82 *Wright Airplane*

**CM82**

| | | | UnFVF | UseFVF |
|---|---|---|---|---|
| 2¢ | carmine red *(51,342,273)* | | 1.25 | 1.00 |
| | Plate block of 6 | | 12.50 | |
| | FDC *(Dec. 12, 1928)* | | | 6.00 |

CM83 *Globe and Airplane.*

**CM83**

| | | | UnFVF | UseFVF |
|---|---|---|---|---|
| 5¢ | Prussian blue *(10,319,700)* | | 5.00 | 3.00 |
| | Plate block of 6 | | 55.00 | |

**CM83**

| | | | UnFVF | UseFVF |
|---|---|---|---|---|
| | "Prairie dog" plate flaw (position 50 of bottom-lower left pane of plate 19658) | | 30.00 | |
| | FDC *(Dec. 12, 1928)* | | | 10.00 |

**1929. GEORGE ROGERS CLARK ISSUE** commemorated the 150th anniversary of Clark's recapture of Fort Sackville (now Vincennes, Ind.), from a force of British, Loyalists and Indians commanded by Col. Henry Hamilton. From winter quarters at Kaskaskia, Clark sent 40 men by boat, led another 130 across the flooded plains, tricked Hamilton's Indians into deserting, took the fort on February 25, and secured the Northwest for the colonists. *Intaglio, perforated 11.*

CM84 *Surrender of Fort Sackville. From a painting by Frederick C. Yohn.*

**CM84**

| | | | UnFVF | UseFVF |
|---|---|---|---|---|
| 2¢ | carmine and black *(16,684,674)* | | .60 | .50 |
| | Plate block of 6, w/two numbers & "TOP" | | 12.50 | |
| | Plate block of 10, w/red number only | | — | |
| | Margin block of 4, w/arrow | | 3.50 | |
| | Double transfer | | 5.50 | 3.00 |
| | FDC *(Feb. 25, 1929)* | | | 5.00 |

**1929. EDISON COMMEMORATIVE ISSUE** celebrated the 50th anniversary of the invention of the incandescent electric lamp by Thomas Alva Edison (CM287). *Issued in both flat and rotary press intaglio printings and as a rotary press coil stamp.*

CM85-87 *Edison's First Electric Lamp.*

*Flat press, perforated 11*

**CM85**

| | | | UnFVF | UseFVF |
|---|---|---|---|---|
| 2¢ | carmine red *(31,679,200)* | | .75 | .75 |
| | Plate block of 6 | | 30.00 | |
| | FDC *(June 5, 1929)* | | | 40.00 |

*Rotary press, perforated 11 x 10 1/2*

**CM86**

| | | | UnFVF | UseFVF |
|---|---|---|---|---|
| 2¢ | carmine red *(210,119,474)* | | .75 | .25 |
| | Plate block of 4 | | 35.00 | |
| | FDC *(June 11, 1929)* | | | 375. |

*Rotary press coil, perforated 10 vertically*

**CM87**

| | | | UnFVF | UseFVF |
|---|---|---|---|---|
| 2¢ | carmine red *(133,530,000)* | | 12.50 | 1.50 |
| | Pair | | 22.50 | 7.00 |
| | Joint line pair | | 60.00 | 40.00 |
| | FDC *(June 11, 1929)* | | | 375. |

**1929. SULLIVAN EXPEDITION ISSUE** notes the 150th anniversary of the campaign by Gens. John Sullivan and James Clinton against the Loyalists and Iroquois Indians ravaging Pennsylvania and New York frontier settlements. They defeated the Iroquois at Newtown (now Elmira), NY, August 29, 1779. *Intaglio, perforated 11.*

CM88 *Mag. Gen. John Sullivan*

| CM88 | | UnFVF | UseFVF |
|---|---|---|---|
| 2¢ | carmine red *(51,451,880)* | .75 | .75 |
| | Plate block of 6 | 25.00 | |
| | FDC *(June 17, 1929)* w/o cachet | | 4.00 |
| | FDC w/cachet | | 27.50 |

**1929. BATTLE OF FALLEN TIMBERS ISSUE** commemorated Gen. Anthony Wayne's defeat of Chief Little Turtle, August 1794, near what is now Toledo. His victory led to the settlement of Ohio. *Intaglio, perforated 11.*

CM89 *Gen. Wayne Memorial. Monument by Bruce W. Laville at Fallen Timbers Park, Ohio.*

| CM89 | | UnFVF | UseFVF |
|---|---|---|---|
| 2¢ | carmine red *(29,338,274)* | .75 | .75 |
| | Plate block of 6 | 25.00 | |
| | FDC *(Sept. 14, 1929)* w/o cachet | | 3.50 |
| | FDC w/cachet | | 35.00 |

**1929. OHIO RIVER CANALIZATION ISSUE** saluted the Army Engineers' completion of America's most extensive canal system. Its 46 locks and dams provided a dependable 9-foot channel between Pittsburgh, Penn. and Cairo, Ill. a distance of 981 miles. *Intaglio, perforated 11.*

CM90 *Monongahela River Lock*

| CM90 | | UnFVF | UseFVF |
|---|---|---|---|
| 2¢ | carmine red *(32,680,900)* | .50 | .75 |
| | Plate block of 6 | 17.50 | 35.00 |
| | FDC *(Oct. 19, 1929)* w/o cachet | | 3.50 |
| | FDC w/cachet | | 30.00 |

**1930. MASSACHUSETTS BAY COLONY ISSUE** commemorated the 300th anniversary of the arrival of the Puritans under Gov. John Winthrop. When the charter given to the Massachusetts Bay Company neglected to specify where its annual meetings were to be held, the company took advantage of the oversight by moving itself to New England as a self-governing commonwealth, the first in the New World. *Intaglio, perforated 11.*

CM91 *Seal of the Massachusetts Bay Colony.*

| CM91 | | UnFVF | UseFVF |
|---|---|---|---|
| 2¢ | carmine red *(74,000,774)* | .75 | .45 |
| | Plate block of 6 | 25.00 | |
| | FDC *(April 8, 1930)* w/o cachet | | 3.50 |
| | FDC w/cachet | | 35.00 |

**1930. CAROLINA-CHARLESTON ISSUE** commemorated the 260th anniversary of the Province of Carolina and 250th anniversary of the City of Charleston. In 1670, Gov. William Sayle and 150 colonists landed at Albemarle Point on the Ashley River, founding a settlement called Charles Town. In 1680 they moved into a walled city they had built at Oyster Point, present site of Charleston. This was the first permanent settlement in the Carolinas. *Intaglio, perforated 11.*

CM92 *Colonial Governor and Indian.*

| CM92 | | UnFVF | UseFVF |
|---|---|---|---|
| 2¢ | carmine red *(25,215,574)* | 1.25 | 1.00 |
| | Plate block of 6 | 40.00 | |
| | FDC *(April 10, 1930)* w/cachet | | 35.00 |
| | FDC w/o cachet | | 3.50 |

**1930. BRADDOCK'S FIELD ISSUE** commemorated the 175th anniversary of the Battle of the Wilderness in the French and Indian War. Advancing on Fort Duquesne (now Pittsburgh), Gen. Braddock's forces were defeated, and Braddock was killed. Lt. Col. George Washington, 23, commanding Braddock's colonials, led the remnant troops in a safe retreat. *Intaglio, perforated 11.*

CM93 *Col. George Washington. Monument by Frank Vittor, at Braddock's Field, PA.*

| CM93 | | UnFVF | UseFVF |
|---|---|---|---|
| 2¢ | carmine red *(25,609,470)* | 1.00 | 1.00 |
| | Plate block of 6 | 30.00 | |
| | FDC *(July 9, 1930)* w/cachet | | 30.00 |
| | FDC w/o cachet | | 4.00 |

**1930. VON STEUBEN ISSUE** commemorated the 200th birthday of Baron Friedrich Wilhelm von Steuben, a Prussian officer who joined Washington at Valley Forge to serve as inspector general. Von Steuben reorganized and trained the army, lifted its morale, and fought at Monmouth and Yorktown. Naturalized in 1783, he was given 16,000 acres of land by New York State and an annual pension by Congress. *Intaglio, perforated 11.*

CM94 *Gen. von Steuben. From a memorial tablet by Karl Dautert, Magdeburg, Germany.*

| CM94 | | UnFVF | UseFVF |
|---|---|---|---|
| 2¢ | carmine red *(66,487,000)* | .50 | .50 |
| | Plate block of 6 | 20.00 | |
| | FDC *(Sept. 17, 1930)* w/cachet | | 30.00 |
| | FDC w/o cachet | | 4.00 |
| | v1. Imperforate pair | 3000. | |
| | v2. Imperforate plate block of 6 | 12000. | |

**1931. PULASKI ISSUE** tardily commemorated the 150th anniversary of the October 11, 1779 death of Count Casimir Pulaski, Polish patriot and hero of the American Revolution. Known as the Father of the U.S. Cavalry, he was mortally wounded leading a cavalry charge against the British at Savannah, GA. *Intaglio, perforated 11.*

CM95 *Gen. Casimir Pulaski. From an etching by H. B. Hall.*

| CM95 | | UnFVF | UseFVF |
|---|---|---|---|
| 2¢ | carmine red *(96,559,400)* | .25 | .20 |
| | dark carmine red | .25 | .20 |
| | Plate block of 6 | 12.50 | |
| | FDC *(Jan. 16, 1931)* w/cachet | | 30.00 |
| | FDC w/o cachet | | 4.00 |

**1931. RED CROSS ISSUE** commemorated the 50th anniversary of the founding of the American Red Cross Society at Dansville, NY. Clara Barton (see CM309, CM1723) was its first president. The design of the stamp is adapted from the popular poster, *The Greatest Mother*, by Laurence Wilbur. *Intaglio, perforated 11.*

CM96 *Red Cross Nurse and Globe.*

| CM96 | | UnFVF | UseFVF |
|---|---|---|---|
| 2¢ | **black and scarlet** *(99,074,600)* | .25 | .20 |
| | Plate block of 4 | 2.00 | |
| | Margin block of 4, w/arrow | 1.00 | |
| | Double transfer | 1.25 | |
| | FDC *(May 21, 1931)* w/cachet | | 30.00 |
| | FDC w/o cachet | | 3.00 |
| | v. Red (cross) omitted | 40000. | |

**1931. YORKTOWN ISSUE** commemorated the 150th anniversary of Lord Cornwallis' surrender at Yorktown, the last important battle of the Revolutionary War. When Lafayette's small force in Virginia was joined in June 1781 by Wayne and von Steuben, Cornwallis moved to Yorktown to maintain sea communication with Clinton's forces in New York. The sudden arrival of De Grasse's French fleet with 3,000 troops hemmed Cornwallis in completely. Washington, who had been preparing an attack on New York, suddenly marched his troops and the French forces of Rochambeau to Virginia, where, with almost 17,000 men, he began the siege of Yorktown. Cornwallis' attempt to escape across the York River by night was thwarted by a storm. On October 19 he surrendered almost 8,000 British and Hessian troops.

*Flat press, two plate layouts used. Most panes have a straight edge along one side, but about 10% of printing was from plates that permitted perforation all around, and thus these sheets have no straight edges. Perforated 11.*

CM97 *Rochambeau, Washington, De Grasse. From paintings by J. D. Court and J. Trumbull and an engraving.*

| CM97 | | UnFVF | UseFVF |
|---|---|---|---|
| 2¢ | **carmine red and black** *(25,006,400)* | .35 | .20 |
| | Plate block of 4, 2 numbers | 3.50 | |
| | Plate block of 4, 2 numbers & arrow | 3.50 | |
| | Plate block of 6, 2 numbers, "TOP" & arrow | 4.50 | |
| | Plate block of 8, 2 numbers & "TOP" | 6.00 | |
| | Center line block of 4 | 2.75 | |
| | Margin block of 4, w/arrow | 2.75 | |
| | Double transfer | 4.50 | |
| | a. dark lake & black | 375. | |
| | a1. Plate block of 4, 2 numbers | 2000. | |
| | b. lake & black | 4.50 | |
| | v. Horizontal pair, imperforated vertically | 4500. | |
| | FDC *(Oct. 19, 1931)* | | 45.00 |

**1932. WASHINGTON BICENTENNIAL ISSUE** commemorated the 200th birthday of George Washington, February 22, 1932, in Westmoreland County, VA. *Intaglio, perforated 11 x 10 1/2.*

CM98 *Washington. After miniature by Charles W. Peale, Metropolitan Museum of Art, New York, NY.*

| CM98 | | UnFVF | UseFVF |
|---|---|---|---|
| 1/2¢ | **olive brown** *(87,969,700)* | .25 | .20 |
| | Plate Block of 4 | 3.75 | |
| | Broken circle (position 8 of top-right pane of plate No. 20560) | .60 | |
| | FDC *(Jan. 1, 1932)* | | 17.50 |

CM99 *Washington. From bust by Jean A. Houdon, Mount Vernon, VA.*

| CM99 | | UnFVF | UseFVF |
|---|---|---|---|
| 1¢ | **yellow green** *(1,265,555,100)* | .25 | .20 |
| | Plate block of 4 | 3.75 | |
| | Gripper cracks (top left & top-right panes of plate No. 20742) | 2.50 | |
| | FDC *(Jan. 1, 1932)* | | 17.50 |

CM100 *Washington at 40. After painting by Peale, Washington & Lee University, Lexington, VA.*

| CM100 | | UnFVF | UseFVF |
|---|---|---|---|
| 1-1/2¢ | **yellow brown** *(304,926,800)* | .50 | .20 |
| | Plate block of 4 | 19.00 | |
| | FDC *(Jan. 1, 1932)* | | 17.50 |

CM101 *Washington at 64. After painting by Gilbert Stuart, Boston Museum, Boston, MA.*

| CM101 | | UnFVF | UseFVF |
|---|---|---|---|
| 2¢ | **carmine red** *(4,222,198,300)* | .25 | .20 |
| | Plate block of 4 | 2.00 | |
| | Gutter pair | — | |
| | Gripper cracks | 1.75 | |
| | FDC *(Jan. 1, 1932)* | | 17.50 |

CM102 *Washington at 46. Painted by Peale at Valley Forge. West Chester State University, PA.*

| CM102 | | UnFVF | UseFVF |
|---|---|---|---|
| 3¢ | **slate purple** *(456,198,500)* | .50 | .20 |
| | Plate block of 4 | 15.00 | |
| | Broken top frame line (position 8 of bottom-left pane of plate No. 20847) | 3.75 | |
| | Double transfer | 1.60 | |
| | FDC *(Jan. 1, 1932)* | | 17.50 |

CM103 *Washinton at 49. After painting by Polk, Rhinebeck, NY.*

**CM103**

| | | UnFVF | UseFVF |
|---|---|---|---|
| 4¢ | **yellow brown** *(151,201,300)* | .40 | .20 |
| | Plate block of 4 | 7.50 | |
| | Broken bottom fram line (position 100 of bottom-right pane of plate No. 20568) | 1.50 | |
| | Retouch in eyes (position 89 of bottom-right pane of plate No. 20568) | 2.00 | |
| | Double transfer | 1.50 | |
| | FDC *(Jan. 1, 1932)* | | 17.50 |

CM104 *Washington at 63. After painting by Peale, New York Historical Society, NY.*

**CM104**

| | | UnFVF | UseFVF |
|---|---|---|---|
| 5¢ | **Prussian blue** *(170,656,100)* | 1.75 | .20 |
| | Plate block of 4 | 19.00 | |
| | Cracked plate (position 80 of top-right pane of plate No. 20637) | 5.00 | |
| | FDC *(Jan. 1, 1932)* | | 17.50 |

CM105 *Washington at 60. After a painting by John Trumbull, Yale University, New Haven, CT.*

**CM105**

| | | UnFVF | UseFVF |
|---|---|---|---|
| 6¢ | **orange** *(111,739,400)* | 3.50 | .20 |
| | Plate block of 4 | 65.00 | |
| | FDC *(Jan. 1, 1932)* | | 17.50 |

CM106 *Washington at 48. After painting by Trumbull, Metropolitan Museum of Art, New York, NY.*

**CM106**

| | | UnFVF | UseFVF |
|---|---|---|---|
| 7¢ | **black** *(83,257,400)* | .40 | .20 |
| | Plate block of 4 | 7.00 | |
| | Double transfer | — | |
| | FDC *(Jan. 1, 1932)* | | 20.00 |

CM107 *Washington at 66. After drawing by Charles Saint Memin, Brooklyn, NY.*

**CM107**

| | | UnFVF | UseFVF |
|---|---|---|---|
| 8¢ | **bister** *(96,506,100)* | 3.00 | .75 |
| | Plate block of 4 | 65.00 | |
| | FDC *(Jan. 1, 1932)* | | 20.00 |

CM108 *Washington at 62. After drawing by W. Williams, Alexandria, VA.*

**CM108**

| | | UnFVF | UseFVF |
|---|---|---|---|
| 9¢ | **salmom** *(75,706,200)* | 2.50 | .20 |
| | orange red | 2.50 | .20 |
| | Plate block of 4 | 40.00 | |
| | FDC *(Jan. 1, 1932)* | | 20.00 |

CM109 *Washington at 63. After portrait by Gilbert Stuart, Metropolitan Museum, New York, NY.*

**CM109**

| | | UnFVF | UseFVF |
|---|---|---|---|
| 10¢ | **orange yellow** *(147,216,000)* | 12.50 | .20 |
| | Plate block of 4 | 125. | |
| | FDC *(Jan. 1, 1932)* | | 20.00 |

**1932. OLYMPIC WINTER GAMES ISSUE** honored the Third Winter games, February 4-13 at Lake Placid, N.Y. *Intaglio, perforated 11.*

CM110 *Ski Jumper*

**CM110**

| | | UnFVF | UseFVF |
|---|---|---|---|
| 2¢ | **carmine red** *(51,102,800)* | .40 | .25 |
| | dark carmine red | .40 | .25 |
| | Plate block of six | 12.50 | |
| | Cracked plate | 5.00 | |
| | Recut (position 61 of top-right pane of plate No. 20823) | 3.00 | |
| | "Snowball" (position 64 of top-right pane of plate No. 20815) | 25.00 | |
| | FDC *(Jan. 25, 1932)* | | 25.00 |

**1932. ARBOR DAY ISSUE** hailed the 60th anniversary of Arbor Day, observed in many individual states for the planting of trees. First celebrated in Nebraska, it was originated by Julius Sterling Morton, agriculturist, newspaper editor, Secretary of the Nebraska Territory, and national Secretary of Agriculture from 1893 to 1897. *Intaglio, perforated 11 x 10 1/2.*

CM111 *Children Planting Tree.*

**CM111**

| | | UnFVF | UseFVF |
|---|---|---|---|
| 2¢ | **carmine red** *(100,869,300)* | .25 | .20 |
| | Plate block of 4 | 7.00 | |
| | FDC *(April 22, 1932)* | | 15.00 |

**1932. OLYMPIC SUMMER GAMES ISSUE** honored the 10th Modern Olympic Games, held July 30-August 14 in Los Angeles, CA. The ancient games began in 776 B.C. and were banned in 394 A.D. Through the efforts of Pierre de Coubertin, French educator and sportsman, they were revived in 1896 in Greece. *Intaglio, perforated 11 x 10 1/2.*

CM112 *Modern Athlete Preparing to Run.*

**CM112**

| | | UnFVF | UseFVF |
|---|---|---|---|
| 3¢ | **reddish violet** *(168,885,300)* | 1.50 | .20 |
| | dark reddish violet | 1.50 | .20 |
| | Plate block of 4 | 15.00 | |
| | Gripper cracks | 4.00 | |
| | FDC *(June 15, 1932)* | | 25.00 |

 CM113 *Discus Thrower, by Myron, 5 B.C.*

**CM113**

| | | UnFVF | UseFVF |
|---|---|---|---|
| 5¢ | **blue** *(52,376,100)* | 2.25 | .30 |
| | dark blue | 2.25 | .30 |
| | Plate block of 4 | 27.50 | |
| | Gripper cracks | 4.00 | |
| | FDC *(June 15, 1932)* | | 25.00 |

**1932. WILLIAM PENN ISSUE** commemorated the 250th anniversary of the arrival of William Penn (1644-1718) to found a colony. A Quaker at 18, Penn was imprisoned three times for religious nonconformity before he was 26. Inheriting a £16,000 claim against King Charles II, he asked for a grant of land in America and was given Pennsylvania in 1681. Landing October 24, 1682, at New Castle, Del., he organized the colony on a liberal basis guaranteeing freedom of conscience, made fair treaties with the Indians, laid out the city of Philadelphia and established the first successful postal system in America. *Intaglio, perforated 11.*

 CM114 *Young William Penn. From a painting, Pennsylvania Historical Society, Philadelphia, PA.*

**CM114**

| | | UnFVF | UseFVF |
|---|---|---|---|
| 3¢ | **reddish violet** *(49,949,000)* | .35 | .25 |
| | Plate block of 6 | 12.50 | |
| | Vertical pair, imperforate horizontally | — | |
| | FDC *(Oct. 24, 1932)* | | 17.50 |

**1933. DANIEL WEBSTER ISSUE** Commemorated the 150th anniversary of the birth of Daniel Webster and the 80th anniversary of his death. Famed orator, constitutional lawyer and statesman, Webster was elected four times to the Senate and twice appointed secretary of state. In 1840 he submitted a Senate resolution advocating reduced postal rates and the use of postage stamps in America. *Intaglio, perforated 11.*

 CM115 *Daniel Webster. From a bust by Daniel Chester French, Franklin, NH.*

**CM115**

| | | UnFVF | UseFVF |
|---|---|---|---|
| 3¢ | **reddish violet** *(49,538,500)* | .35 | .40 |
| | light violet | .35 | .40 |
| | Plate block of 6 | 20.00 | |
| | FDC *(Oct. 24, 1932)* | | 17.50 |

**1933. OGLETHORPE ISSUE** commemorated the 200th anniversary of the founding of Georgia and the city of Savannah, and honored Gen. James Edward Oglethorpe. A philanthropist concerned with religious tolerance and the relief the debtors, Oglethorpe obtained a royal charter and led 120 immigrants in settling the colony. He successfully repulsed Spanish attacks and attempted a siege of St. Augustine, FL. *Intaglio, perforated 11.*

 CM116 *Gen. James Edward Oglethorpe. From a painting at Oglethorpe University, Atlanta, GA.*

**CM116**

| | | UnFVF | UseFVF |
|---|---|---|---|
| 3¢ | **reddish violet** *(61,719,200)* | .35 | .25 |
| | Plate block of 6 | 14.00 | |
| | FDC *(Feb. 12, 1933)* | | 17.50 |

**1933. NEWBURGH STAMP** commemorated the 150th anniversary of the Proclamation of Peace issued by Gen. George Washington from his headquarters at Newburgh, ending the Revolutionary War. *Perforated 10 1/2 x 11.*

 CM117, CM142 *Washington's Headquarters at Newburgh, NY. From an engraving by James Smille.*

**CM117**

| | | UnFVF | UseFVF |
|---|---|---|---|
| 3¢ | **reddish violet** *(73,382,400)* | .25 | .20 |
| | Plate block of 4 | 6.00 | |
| | Block of 4, horizontal gutter between | — | |
| | Block of 4, vertical gutter between | — | |
| | Center block, w/crossed gutters | — | |
| | FDC *(April 19, 1933)* | | 17.50 |

*For ungummed stamp (Farley Issue), see CM142.*

*Although not regularly issued that way, CM117 was also available in full sheets of 400 subjects.*

**1933. CENTURY OF PROGRESS ISSUE** commemorated the World's Fair held in Chicago Ill. to honor the 100th anniversary of its incorporation as a city. *Intaglio, perforated 10 1/2 x 11.*

 CM118 *Fort Dearborn Blockhouse. From a painting by Dwight Benton.*

**CM118**

| | | UnFVF | UseFVF |
|---|---|---|---|
| 1¢ | **yellow green** *(348,266,800)* | .25 | .20 |
| | Plate block of 4 | 3.00 | |
| | Block of 4, horizontal gutter between | — | |
| | Block of 4, vertical gutter between | — | |
| | Center block, w/crossed gutters | — | |
| | Gripper cracks | — | |
| | FDC *(May 25, 1933)* | | 17.50 |

 CM119 *Federal Building at Fair.*

**CM119**

| | | UnFVF | UseFVF |
|---|---|---|---|
| 3¢ | **reddish violet** *(480,239,300)* | .25 | .20 |
| | Plate block of 4 | 3.00 | |
| | Block of 4, horizontal gutter between | — | |
| | Block of 4, vertical gutter between | — | |
| | Center block, w/crossed gutters | — | |
| | FDC *(May 25, 1933)* | | 17.50 |

*Although not regularly issued that way, CM118 and CM119 were also available in full sheets of 400 subjects.*

**1933. CENTURY OF PROGRESS SOUVENIR SHEETS** were issued in honor of the American Philatelic Society convention held in Chicago in August. Each sheet measures 134 x 120mm, contains 25 ungummed, inperforate stamps and is inscribed in the margin: "PRINTED BY THE TREASURY DEPARTMENT. BUREAU OF ENGRAVING AND PRINTING-UNDER AUTHORITY OF JAMES A. FARLEY, ·POSTMASTER GENERAL, AT A CENTURY OF PROGRESS-IN COMPLIMENT TO THE AMERICAN PHILATELIC SOCIETY FOR ITS CONVENTION AND EXHIBITION-CHICAGO, ILLINOIS, AUGUST 1933." *Intaglio, imperforate.*

CM120, CM156

*Sheet of 25*

**CM120**

| | | | UnFVF | UseFVF |
|---|---|---|---|---|
| 1¢ | **yellow green,** *(456,704)* | | 35.00 | 32.50 |
| | FDC *(Aug. 25, 1933)* | | | 200. |
| | Single stamp | | .75 | .20 |
| | FDC (single stamp) | | | 15.00 |

CM121, CM157

*Sheet of 25*

**CM121**

| | | | UnFVF | UseFVF |
|---|---|---|---|---|
| 3¢ | **reddish violet,** *(441,172)* | | 30.00 | 27.50 |
| | FDC *(Aug. 25, 1933)* | | | 200. |
| | Single stamp | | .75 | .50 |
| | FDC (single stamp) | | | 15.00 |

*For ungummed stamps (Farley issue) see CM156 & CM157.*

**1933. NRA ISSUE** publicized the National Recovery Administration, one of the first acts of the New Deal aimed at recovery from the Depression of the 1930's. The NRA was declared unconstitutional in 1935. In the original drawing for this stamp, the second figure was said by some to resemble President Roosevelt. A mustache was added since postal custom is against depicting a living person on a stamp. *Intaglio, perforated 10 1/2 x 11.*

CM122 *Workers Marching Forward. From a poster drawn by Rudolph L. Bortel.*

**CM122**

| | | | UnFVF | UseFVF |
|---|---|---|---|---|
| 3¢ | **reddish violet** *(1,978,707,300)* | | .25 | .20 |
| | Plate block of 4 | | 2.00 | |
| | Gripper cracks | | — | |
| | Recut at right (position 47 of top-right pane of plate No. 21151) | | — | |
| | FDC *(Aug. 15, 1933)* | | | 17.50 |

**1933. BYRD ANTARCTIC STAMP** publicized the second expedition of Rear Adm. Richard E. Byrd to the South Pole. Flight routes used by Byrd, as well as proposed new routes, are indicated on the stamp. Letters mailed with this 3c stamp from the camp at Little America, Antarctica were subject to an additional service charge of 50c each. *Intaglio, perforated 11.*

CM123, CM143 *Globe with Antarctic Routes.*

**CM123**

| | | | UnFVF | UseFVF |
|---|---|---|---|---|
| 3¢ | **blue** *(5,735,944)* | | .75 | .60 |
| | Plate block of 6 | | 17.50 | |
| | Double transfer | | — | |
| | FDC *(Oct. 9, 1933)* | | | 25.00 |

*For ungummed stamp (Farley issue), see CM143.*

**1933. KOSCIUSZKO ISSUE** commemorated Polish patriot Tadeusz Kosciuszko and the 150th anniversary of his naturalization as an American citizen. Gen. Kosciuszko fought throughout the Revolutionary War, served as aide to Washington, and laid out the fortifications of West Point. Afterward he led a rebellion that briefly liberated his native Poland from Russia. *Intaglio, perforated 11.*

CM124 *Gen. Tadeusz Kosciuszko. From a statue by Anton Popiel, Lafayette Park, Washington, DC.*

**CM124**

| | | | UnFVF | UseFVF |
|---|---|---|---|---|
| 5¢ | **blue** *(45,137,700)* | | .75 | .35 |
| | Plate block of 6 | | .35 | |
| | Cracked plate | | — | |
| | FDC *(Oct. 13, 1933)* | | | 17.50 |
| | v. Horizontal pair, imperforate vertically | | 2250. | |

**1934. BYRD SOUVENIR SHEET** honored the National Stamp Exhibition held in New York. It measured 87 x 93mm, contained six imperforate stamps without gum. The margins of the sheets inscribed: "PRINTED BY THE TREASURY DEPARTMENT, BUREAU OF ENGRAVING AND PRINTING-UNDER AUTHORITY OF JAMES A. FARLEY, POSTMASTER GENERAL-IN COMPLIMENT TO THE NATIONAL STAMP EXHIBITION OF 1934-NEW YORK, N.Y. FEBRUARY 10-18, 1934." *Intaglio, imperforated.*

CM125, CM158 *Globe with Antarctic routes, Souvenir Sheet of 6.*

| CM125 | | UnFVF | UseFVF |
|---|---|---|---|
| 3¢ | blue, *(811,404)* | 17.50 | 16.50 |
| | FDC *(Feb. 10, 1934)* | | 75.00 |
| | Single stamp | 3.00 | 2.75 |
| | FDC (single stamp) | | 15.00 |

*For Farley issue, see CM158.*

**1934. MARYLAND TERCENTENARY ISSUE** marked the 300th anniversary of the settlement of Maryland by about 200 colonists under a charter held by Cecilius Calvert, second Lord Baltimore, a Catholic. He made the colony a haven of religious tolerance. The *Ark* and the *Dove* were sailing vessels used in the voyage to America. *Intaglio, perforated 11.*

CM126 *The Ark and the Dove. From a drawing by Edwin Tunis.*

| CM126 | | UnFVF | UseFVF |
|---|---|---|---|
| 3¢ | carmine red *(46,258,300)* | .25 | .20 |
| | Plate block of 6 | 10.00 | |
| | Double transfer (position 1 of top-left pane of plate No. 21190) | — | |
| | FDC *(March 23, 1934)* | | 15.00 |
| | Horizontal pair, imperforated horizontaly | 6500. | |

**1934. MOTHER'S DAY ISSUE** commemorated the 20th anniversary of Woodrow Wilson's proclamation of the second Sunday in May as Mother's Day. The design shows the painting popularly known as "Whistler's Mother," a world symbol of motherhood, although the painter, James Abbott McNeill Whistler, called the picture simply *An Arrangement in Grey and Black.* Stamp issued in both rotary and flat-press printings. *Intaglio.*

CM127-128, CM144 *Whistler's Mother. From a painting by James McNeill Whistler, Louvre Museum, Paris, France.*

*Rotary press, perforated 11 x 10 1/2*

| CM127 | | UnFVF | UseFVF |
|---|---|---|---|
| 3¢ | reddish violet *(193,239,100)* | .25 | .20 |
| | Plate block of 4 | 1.25 | |
| | FDC *(May 2, 1934)* | | 15.00 |

*Flat press, perforated 11*

| CM128 | | UnFVF | UseFVF |
|---|---|---|---|
| 3¢ | reddish violet *(15,432,200)* | .25 | .20 |
| | Plate block of 6 | 5.00 | |
| | FDC *(May 2, 1934)* | | 1.00 |

*For ungummed stamp (Farley issue), see CM144.*

**1934. WISCONSIN TERCENTENARY ISSUE** memorialized the 300th anniversary of the arrival of the French explorer, Jean Nicolet, onto the shores of Green Bay in Lake Michigan. The first white man to reach that region, he appears in oriental garb as he thought he was landing in China. *Intaglio.*

CM129, CM145 *Nicolet's Landing on Green Bay. From a painting by Edward W. Deming, Wisconsin Historical Society.*

| CM129 | | UnFVF | UseFVF |
|---|---|---|---|
| 3¢ | reddish violet *(64,525,400)* | .25 | .20 |
| | violet | .25 | .20 |
| | Plate block of 6 | 4.00 | |
| | FDC *(July 7, 1934)* | | 15.00 |
| | v. Horizontal pair, imperforate vertically | 325. | |
| | v1. Vertical pair, imperforate horizontally | 275. | |

*For ungummed stamp (Farley issue), see CM145.*

**1934. NATIONAL PARKS ISSUE** commemorated National Parks Year and publicized the great American park system. *Intaglio.*

CM130, CM146 *El Capitan, Yosemite (California).*

| CM130 | | UnFVF | UseFVF |
|---|---|---|---|
| 1¢ | green *(84,896,350)* | .25 | .20 |
| | light green | .25 | .20 |
| | Plate block of 6 | 1.50 | |
| | Recut | — | |
| | FDC *(July 16, 1934)* | | 10.00 |
| | v. Vertical pair, imperforate horizontally (with gum) | 550. | |

CM131, CM147 *Grand Canyon (Arizona).*

| CM131 | | UnFVF | UseFVF |
|---|---|---|---|
| 2¢ | red *(74,400,200)* | .25 | .20 |
| | Plate block of 6 | 1.75 | |
| | Double transfer | — | |
| | FDC *(July 24, 1934)* | | 10.00 |
| | v. Horizontal pair, imperforate vertically (with gum) | 300. | |
| | v1. Vertical pair, imperforate horizontally (with gum) | 400. | |

CM132, CM148 *Mt. Rainier and Mirror Lake (Washington).*

| CM132 | | UnFVF | UseFVF |
|---|---|---|---|
| 3¢ | **reddish violet** *(95,089,000)* | .25 | .20 |
| | Plate block of 6 | 2.00 | |
| | Recut | — | |
| | FDC *(Aug. 3, 1934)* | | 10.00 |
| | v. Vertical pair, imperforate horizontally (with gum) | 450. | |

CM133, CM149 *The Cliff Palace, Mesa Verde (Colorado).*

| CM133 | | UnFVF | UseFVF |
|---|---|---|---|
| 4¢ | **yellow brown** *(19,178,650)* | .50 | .35 |
| | light brown | 8.00 | |
| | Plate block of 6 | — | |
| | FDC *(Sept. 25, 1934)* | | 10.00 |
| | v. Vertical pair, imperforate horizontally (with gum) | 650. | |

CM134, CM150 *Old Faithful, Yellowstone (Wyoming).*

| CM134 | | UnFVF | UseFVF |
|---|---|---|---|
| 5¢ | **light blue** *(30,980,100)* | 1.00 | .75 |
| | blue | 1.00 | .75 |
| | Plate block of 6 | 10.00 | |
| | FDC *(July 30, 1934)* | | 10.00 |
| | v. Horizontal pair, imperforate vertically (with gum) | 475. | |

CM135, CM151 *Crater Lake (Oregon).*

| CM135 | | UnFVF | UseFVF |
|---|---|---|---|
| 6¢ | **blue** *(16,923,350)* | 1.25 | 1.00 |
| | Plate block of 6 | 20.00 | |
| | FDC *(Sept. 5, 1934)* | | 22.50 |

CM136, CM152 *Great Head, Bar Harbor (Maine).*

| CM136 | | UnFVF | UseFVF |
|---|---|---|---|
| 7¢ | **black** *(15,988,250)* | 1.00 | .75 |
| | Plate block of 6 | 12.50 | |
| | Double transfer | — | |
| | FDC *(Oct. 2, 1934)* | | 10.00 |
| | v. Horizontal pair, imperforate vertically (with gum) | 550. | |

CM137, CM153 *Great White Throne, Zion (Utah).*

| CM137 | | UnFVF | UseFVF |
|---|---|---|---|
| 8¢ | **gray green** *(15,288,700)* | 2.00 | 1.75 |
| | Plate block of 6 | 20.00 | |
| | FDC *(Sept. 18, 1934)* | | 10.00 |

CM138, CM154 *Mt. Rockwell and Two Medicine Lake, Glacier (Montana).*

| CM138 | | UnFVF | UseFVF |
|---|---|---|---|
| 9¢ | **orange red** *(17,472,600)* | 2.00 | .75 |
| | orange | 2.00 | .75 |
| | Plate block of 6 | 20.00 | |
| | FDC *(Aug. 17, 1934)* | | 10.00 |

CM139, CM155 *Great Smokey Mountains (North Carolina).*

| CM139 | | UnFVF | UseFVF |
|---|---|---|---|
| 10¢ | **gray black** *(18,874,300)* | 3.25 | 1.25 |
| | gray | 3.25 | 1.25 |
| | Plate block of 6 | 30.00 | |
| | FDC *(Oct. 8, 1934)* | | 10.00 |

*For ungummed stamp, (Farley issue), see CM146-CM155.*

**1934. TRANS-MISSISSIPPI PHILATELIC EXPOSITION ISSUE** was released in honor of the Philatelic Exposition and Convention held at Omaha, NE. The sheet measured 94 x 99mm, contained six imperforate, gummed 1¢ National Parks stamps, and was inscribed in the margin: "PRINTED BY THE TREASURY DEPARTMENT, BUREAU OF ENGRAVING AND PRINTING-UNDER AUTHORITY OF JAMES A. FARLEY, POSTMASTER GENERAL-IN COMPLIMENT TO THE TRANS-MISSISSIPPI PHILATELIC EXPOSITION AND CONVENTION-OMAHA, NEBRASKA, OCTOBER 1934."

CM140, CM159 *El Capitan, Yosemite (California).*

| CM140 | | UnFVF | UseFVF |
|---|---|---|---|
| 1¢ | **green,** sheet of 6 *(793,551)* | 14.00 | 12.50 |
| | FDC *(Oct. 10, 1934)* | | 75.00 |
| | a. Single stamp | 2.00 | 1.75 |
| | FDC, single stamp | | 20.00 |

*For ungummed stamp, (Farley issue), see CM159.*

**1934. AMERICAN PHILATELIC SOCIETY ISSUE** honored the American Philatelic Society convention and exhibition held at Atlantic City, NJ. The sheet measured 97 x99mm, contained six imperforate, gummed 3¢ National Parks stamps, and was inscribed in the margin: "PRINTED BY THE TREASURY DEPARTMENT, BUREAU OF ENGRAVING AND PRINTING-UNDER AUTHORITY OF JAMES A. FARLEY, POSTMASTER GENERAL-IN COMPLIMENT TO THE AMERICAN PHILATELIC SOCIETY FOR ITS CONVENTION AND EXHIBITION-ATLANTIC CITY, NEW JERSEY, AUGUST 1934."

CM141, CM160 *Mt. Rainier and Mirror Lake (Washington).*

| CM141 | | UnFVF | UseFVF |
|---|---|---|---|
| 3¢ | **reddish violet,** sheet of 6 *(511,391)* | 40.00 | 30.00 |
| | FDC *(Aug. 28, 1934)* | | 75.00 |
| | a. Single stamp | 4.50 | 4.00 |
| | a1.FDC, single stamp | | 20.00 |

*For ungummed stamp, (Farley issue), see CM160.*

## The Farley Series(CM142-CM161)

**The Farley Series** is a collective term commonly applied to 20 stamps which were issued to the public as a direct result of protests by collectors against the practice of presenting to a few favored collectors full sheets of stamps in forms not available to the general public. Original "Farley Sheets"-signed by various government officials, including Franklin D. Roosevelt, President; Harold L. Ickes, Secretary of the Interior; and James A. Farley, Postmaster General were given as philatelic favors to political friends.

The full sheets of the Farley Series contained four or more post office panes separated by spaces (called gutters) or by guide lines and arrows (to guide the cutting machine). Blocks showing two crossed gutters or crossed lines are called "cross gutter" and "center line" blocks, respectively.

All of the Farley stamps were issued ungummed. In 1940 the Post Office Department gummed full sheets of CM144-61 sent in by collectors for that purpose. With the exception of CM142-43, all Farley stamps were imperforate.

The Farley Series were first placed on sale March 15, 1935, at the Philatelic Agency in Washington, DC, and were sold through June 15, 1935.

**1935. NEWBURGH FARLEY ISSUE** was printed in sheets of 400 stamps: 4 panes of 100 stamps, separated by gutters. Newburgh Farley stamps differ slightly in color from the original Newburgh issue (CM117); there seems to be a tinge of blue in the violet. They usually are not well-centered and the perforations are ragged. *Intaglio, ungummed and perforated 10 1/2 x 11.*

| CM142 | | UnFVF | UseFVF |
|---|---|---|---|
| 3¢ | **reddish violet** *(3,274,556)* | .25 | 20.00 |
| | Plate block of 4 | 16.50 | |
| | Plate block of 4, w/arrow at top or bottom | 15.00 | |
| | Plate block of 4, w/arrow at side | 8.50 | |
| | Pair w/vertical line | 7.50 | |
| | Pair w/horizontal line | 4.00 | |
| | Center line block | 50.00 | |
| | FDC *(March 15, 1935)* | | 35.00 |

**1935. BYRD FARLEY ISSUE** was printed in sheets of 200, so that arrows and guide- lines along which the sheets normally were cut into panes of 50 before being sent to the post office, are complete. The stamps were issued *without gum and perforated 11.* Since it is virtually impossible to distinguish between a used copy of this and the original Byrd stamp (CM123), they must be considered interchangeable in used condition.

| CM143 | | UnFVF | UseFVF |
|---|---|---|---|
| 3¢ | **blue** *(2,040,760)* | .50 | .45 |
| | Plate block of 6 | 17.50 | |
| | Pair, w/vertical line | 2.00 | |
| | Pair, w/horizontal line | 40.00 | |
| | Block of 4, w/arrow at top or bottom | 85.00 | |
| | Block of 4, w/arrow at side | 4.00 | |
| | Center line block | 90.00 | |
| | FDC *(March 15, 1935)* | | 35.00 |

**1935. MOTHER'S DAY FARLEY ISSUE** was printed in sheets of 200 with arrows and guidelines, identical in design to CM127, but issued *without gum* and *imperforate.*

| CM144 | | UnFVF | UseFVF |
|---|---|---|---|
| 3¢ | **reddish violet** *(2,389,288)* | .60 | .60 |
| | Plate block of 6 | 18.50 | |
| | Block of 4, w/arrow at top or bottom | — | |
| | Block of 4, w/arrow at side | 4.50 | |
| | Pair, w/vertical line | 1.75 | |
| | Pair, w/horizontal line | 2.25 | |
| | Center line block | 10.00 | |
| | FDC *(March 15, 1935)* | | 35.00 |

**1935. WISCONSIN FARLEY ISSUE** was printed in sheets of 200 with arrows and guidelines, identical in design to CM129, but issued *without gum* and *imperforate.*

| CM145 | | UnFVF | UseFVF |
|---|---|---|---|
| 3¢ | **reddish violet** *(2,294,948)* | .60 | .60 |
| | Plate block of 6 | 18.50 | |
| | Block of 4, w/arrow at top or bottom | 3.50 | |
| | Block of 4, w/arrow at side | 4.50 | |
| | Pair, w/vertical line | 1.75 | |
| | Pair, w/horizontal line | 2.25 | |
| | Center line block | 10.00 | |
| | FDC *(March 15, 1935)* | | 35.00 |

**1935. NATIONAL PARKS FARLEY ISSUE** were printed in sheets of 200 with arrows and guidelines. The designs are identical to CM130-39, but the Farley versions were issued *without gum* and *imperforate.*

| CM146 | | UnFVF | UseFVF |
|---|---|---|---|
| 1¢ | **green** *(3,217,636)* | .25 | .20 |
| | Plate block of 6 | 6.50 | |
| | Block of 4, w/arrow at top or bottom | 1.25 | |
| | Block of 4, w/arrow at sides | 1.00 | |
| | Pair, w/vertical line | .60 | |
| | Pair, w/horizontal line | .45 | |
| | Center line block | 4.50 | |
| | FDC *(March 15, 1935)* | | 30.00 |

| CM147 | | UnFVF | UseFVF |
|---|---|---|---|
| 2¢ | **red** *(2,746,640)* | .25 | .20 |
| | Plate block of 6 | 7.50 | |
| | Block of 4, w/arrow at top or bottom | 1.50 | |
| | Block of 4, w/arrow at sides | 1.50 | |
| | Pair, w/vertical line | .60 | |
| | Pair, w/horizontal line | .65 | |
| | Center line block | 5.00 | |
| | Double transfer | — | |
| | FDC *March 15, 1935)* | | 30.00 |

| CM148 | | UnFVF | UseFVF |
|---|---|---|---|
| 3¢ | **reddish violet** *(2,168,088)* | .50 | .45 |
| | Plate block of 6 | 17.50 | |
| | Block of 4, w/arrow at top or bottom | 3.00 | |
| | Block of 4, w/arrow at sides | 3.75 | |
| | Pair, w/vertical line | 1.25 | |
| | Pair, w/horizontal line | 1.75 | |
| | Center line block | 12.50 | |
| | FDC *(March 15, 1935)* | | 30.00 |

| CM149 | | UnFVF | UseFVF |
|---|---|---|---|
| 4¢ | **yellow brown** *(1,822,684)* | 1.25 | 1.25 |
| | Plate block of 6 | 22.50 | |
| | Block of 4, w/arrow at top or bottom | 5.50 | |
| | Block of 4, w/arrow at sides | 6.50 | |
| | Pair, w/vertical line | 2.50 | |
| | Pair, w/horizontal line | 3.00 | |
| | Center line block | 12.50 | |
| | FDC *(March 15, 1935)* | | 30.00 |

| CM150 | | UnFVF | UseFVF |
|---|---|---|---|
| 5¢ | **light blue** *(1,724,576)* | 1.75 | 1.75 |
| | Plate block of 6 | 27.50 | |
| | Block of 4, w/arrow at top or bottom | 12.00 | |
| | Block of 4, w/arrow at sides | 10.00 | |
| | Pair, w/vertical line | 5.25 | |
| | Pair, w/horizontal line | 4.25 | |
| | Center line block | 20.00 | |
| | Double transfer | — | |
| | FDC *(March 15, 1935)* | | 30.00 |

| CM151 | | UnFVF | UseFVF |
|---|---|---|---|
| 6¢ | **blue** *(1,647,696)* | | |
| | Plate block of 6 | 2.25 | 2.25 |
| | Block of 4, w/arrow at top or bottom | 40.00 | |
| | Block of 4, w/arrow at sides | 15.00 | |
| | Pair, w/vertical line | 6.00 | |
| | Pair, w/horizontal line | 6.75 | |
| | Center line block | 22.50 | |
| | FDC *(March 15, 1935)* | | 30.00 |

| CM152 | | UnFVF | UseFVF |
|---|---|---|---|
| 7¢ | **black** *(1,682,948)* | 2.00 | 1.75 |
| | Plate block of 6 | 37.50 | |
| | Block of 4, w/arrow at top or bottom | 10.00 | |
| | Block of 4, w/arrow at sides | 12.00 | |
| | Pair, w/vertical line | 4.50 | |
| | Pair, w/horizontal line | 5.00 | |
| | Center line block | 2.00 | |
| | Double transfer | — | |
| | FDC *(March 15, 1935)* | | 30.00 |

| CM153 | | UnFVF | UseFVF |
|---|---|---|---|
| 8¢ | **gray green** *(1,638,644)* | 2.00 | 2.00 |
| | Plate block of 6 | 45.00 | |
| | Block of 4, w/arrow at top or bottom | 14.00 | |
| | Block of 4, w/arrow at sides | 12.50 | |
| | Pair, w/vertical line | 6.50 | |
| | Pair, w/horizontal line | 5.00 | |
| | Center line block | 22.50 | |
| | FDC *(March 15, 1935)* | | 30.00 |

| CM154 | | UnFVF | UseFVF |
|---|---|---|---|
| 9¢ | **orange red** *(1,625,224)* | 2.00 | 2.00 |
| | Plate block of 6 | 47.50 | |
| | Block of 4, w/arrow at top or bottom | 12.50 | |
| | Block of 4, w/arrow at sides | 14.00 | |
| | Pair, w/vertical line | 12.50 | |
| | Pair, w/horizontal line | 10.00 | |
| | Center line block | 35.00 | |
| | FDC *(March 15, 1935)* | | 30.00 |

| CM155 | | UnFVF | UseFVF |
|---|---|---|---|
| 10¢ | **gray black** *(1,644,900)* | 4.00 | 3.50 |
| | Plate block of 6 | 55.00 | |
| | Block of 4, w/arrow at top or bottom | 25.00 | |
| | Block of 4, w/arrow at sides | 22.50 | |
| | Pair, w/vertical line | 12.50 | |
| | Pair, w/horizontal line | 10.00 | |
| | Center line block | 35.00 | |
| | FDC *(March 15, 1935)* | | 30.00 |

**1935. CENTURY OF PROGRESS SOUVENIR SHEET, FARLEY ISSUE** contained nine souvenir sheets of 25 stamps each, separated by gutters, issued *without gum* and *imperforate.* Identification of single stamps is possible only with stamps that come from the outside rows of the miniature sheets, in which the margins are wider than those from the regular sheets. CM120-21.

*pane of 25*

| CM156 | | UnFVF | UseFVF |
|---|---|---|---|
| 1¢ | **yellow green,** *(2,467,800)* | 22.50 | 22.50 |
| | Horizontal gutter block | — | |
| | Vertical gutter block | — | |
| | Cross-gutter block | 12.50 | |
| | a. Single stamp | .75 | .30 |
| | FDC *(March 15, 1935)* | | 40.00 |

*pane of 25*

| CM157 | | UnFVF | UseFVF |
|---|---|---|---|
| 3¢ | **reddish violet,** *(2,147,856)* | 20.00 | 20.00 |
| | Horizontal gutter block | — | |
| | Vertical gutter block | — | |
| | Cross-gutter block | 12.50 | |
| | a. Single stamp | .75 | .30 |
| | FDC *(March 15, 1935)* | | 40.00 |

**1935. BYRD SOUVENIR SHEET, FARLEY ISSUE** contained 25 souvenir sheets of six stamps each, separated by gutters, issued *without gum* and *imperforate.*

Identification of single stamps is possible only if their margins are wider than those from the regular sheet, CM125.

*pane of six*

| CM158 | | UnFVF | UseFVF |
|---|---|---|---|
| 3¢ | **blue,** *(1,603,200)* | 17.50 | 12.50 |
| | Horizontal gutter block | — | |
| | Vertical gutter block | — | |
| | Cross-gutter block | 17.50 | |
| | a. Single stamp | 2.75 | 2.25 |
| | FDC *(March 15, 1935)* | | 40.00 |

**1935. NATIONAL PARKS SOUVENIR SHEETS, FARLEY ISSUE** contained 20 souvenir sheets of six stamps each, separated by gutters, issued *without gum* and *imperforate.* Identification of single stamps is possible only if their margins are wider than those from the regular sheets CM140-41.

*pane of six*

| CM159 | | UnFVF | UseFVF |
|---|---|---|---|
| 1¢ | **green,** *(1,679,760)* | 10.00 | 9.00 |
| | Horizontal gutter block | — | |
| | Vertical gutter block | — | |
| | Cross-gutter block | 12.50 | |
| | a. Single stamp | 1.75 | 1.75 |
| | FDC *(March 15, 1935)* | | 40.00 |

*pane of six*

| CM160 | | UnFVF | UseFVF |
|---|---|---|---|
| 3¢ | **reddish violet** *(1,295,520)* | 25.00 | 20.00 |
| | Horizontal gutter block | — | |
| | Vertical gutter block | — | |
| | Cross-gutter block | 25.00 | |
| | a. Single stamp | 3.00 | 2.75 |
| | FDC *(March 15, 1935)* | | 40.00 |

**1935. AIRMAIL SPECIAL DELIVERY FARLEY ISSUE** was printed in sheets of 200 stamps with arrows and guide- lines. It is listed in this section of the catalog because it always has been considered an integral part of the Farley Series. *Intaglio, without gum, imperforate.*

| CM161 | | UnFVF | UseFVF |
|---|---|---|---|
| 16¢ | **blue** *(1,370,560)* | 2.75 | 2.50 |
| | Plate block of 6 | 70.00 | |
| | Block of 4, w/arrow at top or bottom | 13.50 | |
| | Block of 4, w/arrow at sides | 17.00 | |
| | Horizontal gutter block | — | |
| | Vertical gutter block | — | |
| | Center-line block | 77.50 | |
| | FDC *(March 15, 1935)* | | 40.00 |

**1935. CONNECTICUT TERCENTENARY ISSUE** commemorated the 300th anniversary of the settlement of Connecticut by dissatisfied members of the Massachusetts Bay Colony. The tree depicted is the oak in which the Colonial charter was hidden when it was demanded by the British in 1687. *Intaglio, perforated 11 x 10 1/2.*

CM162 *The Charter Oak. From a painting by Charles D. Browenell, State Library, Hartford, CT.*

| CM162 | | UnFVF | UseFVF |
|---|---|---|---|
| 3¢ | **purple** *(70,726,800)* | .25 | .20 |
| | rose violet | .25 | .20 |
| | Plate block of 4 | 2.00 | |
| | Defect in ¢ sign (position 4 of top-right pane of plate No. 21395) | — | |
| | FDC *(April 26, 1935)* | | 10.00 |

*For imperforates, see No. CM168.*

**1935. CALIFORNIA-PACIFIC ISSUE** commemorated the California-Pacific Exposition at San Diego, CA. *Intaglio, perforated 11 x 10 1/2.*

CM163 *View of the San Diego Exposition. From a sketch by Larrinague.*

| CM163 | | UnFVF | UseFVF |
|---|---|---|---|
| 3¢ | **dark lilac** *(100,839,600)* | .25 | .20 |
| | Plate block of 4 | 1.50 | |
| | Gutter pair | — | |
| | FDC *(May 29, 1935)* | | 12.50 |

*For imperforates, see No. CM168.*

**1935. BOULDER DAM ISSUE** commemorates the dedication of the largest dam on the Colorado River. Built to supply power, water and flood control, its name was changed in 1933 to Boulder Dam, which appears on the stamp. Its original name, Hoover Dam, was restored in 1947. *Intaglio, perforated 11.*

CM164 *Boulder (Hoover) Dam.*

| CM164 | | UnFVF | UseFVF |
|---|---|---|---|
| 3¢ | **dark lilac** *(73,610,650)* | .25 | .20 |
| | purple | .25 | .20 |
| | Plate block of 6 | 2.25 | |
| | FDC *(Sept. 30, 1935)* | | 15.00 |

**1935. MICHIGAN CENTENNIAL ISSUE** commemorates the 100th anniversary of the admission of Michigan as the 26th state. *Intaglio, perforated 11 x 10 1/2.*

CM165 *Michigan State Seal.*

| CM165 | | UnFVF | UseFVF |
|---|---|---|---|
| 3¢ | **dark lilac** *(75,823,900)* | .25 | .20 |
| | Plate block of 4 | 1.50 | |
| | FDC *(Nov. 1, 1935)* | | 12.50 |

*For imperforates, see No. CM168.*

**1936. TEXAS CENTENNIAL ISSUE** commemorates the 100th anniversary of Texas independence, established after the Texans under Gen. Sam Houston defeated the Mexicans at the Battle of San Jacinto. The first Texas colony was founded by Stephen P. Austin under a Mexican charter in 1821. *Intaglio, perforated 11 x 10 1/2.*

CM166 *Sam Houston, Stephen F. Austin and The Alamo. From artwork by S. Salamo, T. A. Butler and F. Pauling.*

| CM166 | | UnFVF | UseFVF |
|---|---|---|---|
| 3¢ | **dark lilac** *(124,324,500)* | .25 | .20 |
| | Plate block of 4 | 1.50 | |
| | FDC *(March 2, 1936)* | | 15.00 |

*For imperforates, see No. CM168.*

**1936. RHODE ISLAND TERCENTENARY ISSUE** honors the 300th anniversary of the founding of Rhode Island as a haven of tolerance by Roger Williams. This was the only New England colony to tolerate a permanent Jewish community in the 17th century. *Intaglio, perforated 10 1/2 x 11.*

CM167 *Roger Williams, a statue by Franklin Simmons in Williams Park, Providence, R.I.*

| CM167 | | UnFVF | UseFVF |
|---|---|---|---|
| 3¢ | **dull purple** *(67,127,650)* | .25 | .20 |
| | rose violet | .25 | .20 |
| | Plate block of 4 | 1.50 | |
| | Gutter pair | — | |
| | FDC *(May 4, 1936)* | | 10.00 |

**1936. TIPEX SOUVENIR SHEET** was issued in compliment to the Third International Philatelic Exhibition held in New York City. The sheet measured 98 x 66mm and contains one each of the Connecticut, California-Pacific, Michigan and Texas stamps. *Intaglio, imperforate.* The sheet is inscribed in the margins: "PRINTED BY THE TREASURY DEPARTMENT, BUREAU OF ENGRAVING AND PRINTING-UNDER AUTHORITY OF JAMES A. FARLEY, POSTMASTER GENERAL-IN COMPLIMENT TO THE THIRD INTERNATIONAL PHILATELIC EXHIBITION OF 1936-NEW YORK, N.Y., MAY 9-17, 1936."

CM168 *TIPEX Souvenir Sheet of 4.*

**CM168**

| | | UnFVF | UseFVF |
|---|---|---|---|
| 4x3c | reddish purple *(2,809,039)* | 2.75 | 2.50 |
| | FDC *(May 9, 1936)* | | 17.50 |
| | a. Any single from souvenir sheet | .75 | .60 |

**1936. ARKANSAS CENTENNIAL ISSUE** commemorated the 100th anniversary of the admission of Arkansas into the Union as the 25th state. *Intaglio, perforated 11 x 10 1/2.*

CM169 *Old State House in Little Rock, Ark.*

**CM169**

| | | UnFVF | UseFVF |
|---|---|---|---|
| 3¢ | dark lilac *(72,992,650)* | .25 | .20 |
| | Plate block of 4 | 1.50 | |
| | FDC *(June 15, 1936)* | | 10.00 |

**1936. OREGON TERRITORY CENTENNIAL ISSUE** commemorated the 100th anniversary of the opening of the Oregon Territory, comprising the present states of Oregon, Washington, Idaho and parts of Montana and Wyoming. *Intaglio, perforated 11 x 10 1/2.*

CM170 *Map of Oregon Territory.*

**CM170**

| | | UnFVF | UseFVF |
|---|---|---|---|
| 3¢ | dark lilac *(74,407,450)* | .25 | .20 |
| | Plate block of 4 | 1.25 | |
| | Double transfer | — | |
| | FDC *(July 14, 1936)* | | 1.50 |

**1936. SUSAN B. ANTHONY ISSUE** honored the 16th anniversary of the ratification of the 19th Amendment, which granted suffrage to women. Anthony was a pioneer in temperance and social reform, and it was in part through her leadership and effort that women in the United States won the right to vote. *Intaglio, perforated 11 x 10 1/2.*

CM171 *Susan B. Anthony*

**CM171**

| | | UnFVF | UseFVF |
|---|---|---|---|
| 3¢ | reddish purple *(269,522,200)* | .25 | .20 |
| | Plate block of 4 | 1.25 | |
| | FDC *(Aug. 20, 1936)* | | 10.00 |

**1936-37. ARMY ISSUE** honored the U.S. Army and paid tribute to its early leaders and heroes.
CM172 *George Washington commanded the Continental Army throughout the Revolutionary War. (See CM98-CM109) Mount Vernon was his home in Virginia. Nathanial Greene led the patriot forces in the Southern theater. Both portraits are from Trumbull paintings.*

**CM172**

| | | UnFVF | UseFVF |
|---|---|---|---|
| 1¢ | green *(105,196,150)* | .25 | .20 |
| | Plate block of 4 | 1.00 | |
| | FDC *(Dec. 15, 1936)* | | 7.50 |

CM173 *Andrew Jackson (from a statue by Belle Scholtz in the U.S. Hall of Fame) defeated the Creek Indians at Horseshoe Bend in 1814, and the British at New Orleans in 1815. The Hermitage was his Tennessee home. Winfield Scott (from a statue by Launt Thomas in the U.S. Soldiers' Home at Washington) fought gallantly at Chippewa and Lundy's Lane in the War of 1812 and led the U.S. Army in the Mexican War.*

**CM173**

| | | UnFVF | UseFVF |
|---|---|---|---|
| 2¢ | rose red *(93,848,500)* | .25 | .20 |
| | Plate block of 4 | 1.00 | |
| | FDC *(Jan. 15, 1937)* | | 10.00 |

CM174 *William Tecumseh Sherman has been called "the first modern general." His march from Atlanta to the sea in the Civil War aimed at weakening his adversaries by the destruction of supplies rather than lives. Ulysses S. Grant split the Confederacy in two by capturing Vicksburg in 1863. After his successful Tennessee campaigns, he was given command under Lincoln of all Union forces and fought a war of attrition that brought the war to an end in 1865. Philip H. Sheridan, a cavalry commander, distinguished himself at Chickamauga and Chattanooga, and commanded the army that laid waste to the Shenandoah Valley.*

**CM174**

| | | UnFVF | UseFVF |
|---|---|---|---|
| 3¢ | dull purple *(87,741,150)* | .25 | .20 |
| | Plate block of 4 | 1.50 | |
| | FDC *(Feb. 18, 1937)* | | 7.50 |

CM175 *Robert E. Lee, whom Lincoln offered command of the Union field forces in 1861, resigned his commission instead to command the forces of Virginia. After his defeat at Gettysburg, July 1863, he fought bravely and brilliantly against hopeless odds, surrendering to Grant in 1865. Stratford Hall was his birthplace. Thomas J. Jackson, greatest of Lee's generals, won his nickname "Stonewall" by holding off strong Union assaults at the first Battle of Bull Run. After forcing back the Union troops at Chancellorsville, he was mistakenly shot by one of his own pickets.*

**CM175**

| | | UnFVF | UseFVF |
|---|---|---|---|
| 4¢ | slate *(35,794,150)* | .50 | .20 |
| | Plate block of 4 | 10.00 | |
| | FDC *(March 23, 1937)* | | 7.50 |

CM176 *The U.S. Military Academy at West Point, New York, was established in 1802. Upon completion of a four-year course, cadets are eligible for commission as second lieutenants in the Army. Its graduates include all five generals pictured on CM174 and CM175. Among its civilian alumni were James Abbott McNeill Whistler (CM227) and Edgar Allan Poe (CM328).*

**CM176**

| | | UnFVF | UseFVF |
|---|---|---|---|
| 5¢ | gray blue *(36,839,250)* | .75 | .20 |
| | Plate block of 4 | 12.50 | |
| | FDC *(May 26, 1937)* | | 7.50 |

**1936-37. NAVY ISSUE** honored the U.S. Navy and paid tribute to early naval leaders and heroes. *Intaglio, perforated 11 x 10 1/2.*

CM177 *John Paul Jones (from a painting by Peale) destroyed British ships, preyed upon the British coast and captured the man-of-war* Serapis *in a battle in which his own flagship* Bonhomme Richard *(shown) was sunk. John Barry (from a painting by Stuart) commanded the* Lexington *when he captured the first ship ever taken by a commanding officer of the U.S. Navy.*

| CM177 | | UnFVF | UseFVF |
|---|---|---|---|
| 1¢ | **green** *(104,773,450)* | .25 | .20 |
| | Plate block of 4 FDC *(Dec. 15, 1936)* | 1.00 | |
| | FDC *(Dec. 15, 1936)* | | 7.50 |

CM178 *Stephen Decatur (from a painting by Alonzo Chappel), fighting the Tripolitan pirates, effected the daring recapture of the frigate* Philadelphia. *He commanded the ship* United States *in the War of 1812. The stamp shows a contemporary warship under full sail. Thomas Macdonough (from a painting by Carl Becker), commanded the American fleet on Lake Champlain, where his brilliant victory over the British in 1814 saved New York and Vermont from invasion. The* Saratoga *was his flagship.*

| CM178 | | UnFVF | UseFVF |
|---|---|---|---|
| 2¢ | **rose red** *(92,054,550)* | .25 | .20 |
| | Plate block of 4 | 1.00 | |
| | FDC *(Jan. 15, 1937)* | | 7.50 |

CM179 *David Farragut (from a photograph by Brady), in 1862 destroyed the Confederate fleet at New Orleans. His foster brother David Dixon Porter aided him there and at Vicksburg; later, as superintendent of the U.S. Naval Academy, Porter greatly improved its organization and curriculum. The stamp mentions ships commanded and depicts a warship of the period.*

| CM179 | | UnFVF | UseFVF |
|---|---|---|---|
| 3¢ | **dull purple** *(93,291,650)* | .25 | .20 |
| | Plate block of 4 | 1.50 | |
| | FDC *(Feb. 18, 1937)* | | 7.50 |

CM180 *William T. Sampson commanded North Atlantic Squadron which destroyed the Spanish fleet at Santiago, Cuba, in 1898 sharing the victory with Winfield S. Schley, his second in command. Schley earlier had led the expedition that rescued the Artic explorer Adolphus Greely in 1884. George Dewey, commanding the Asiatic Squadron, destroyed the Spanish fleet in the Philippines in 1898.*

| CM180 | | UnFVF | UseFVF |
|---|---|---|---|
| 4¢ | **slate** *(34,521,950)* | .50 | .20 |
| | Plate block of 4 | 10.00 | |
| | FDC *(March 23, 1937)* | | 7.50 |

CM181 *The U.S. Naval Academy at Annapolis, Maryland, was established in 1805. Upon completion of a four-year course, midshipmen are eligible for commissions as ensigns in the Navy. Its graduates include all three admirals pictured on CM180. The stamp pictures the Academy's seal and cadets of early days and the 1930's.*

| CM181 | | UnFVF | UseFVF |
|---|---|---|---|
| 5¢ | **gray blue** *(36,819,050)* | .75 | .20 |
| | Plate block of 4 | 12.50 | |
| | Gutter pair | — | |
| | FDC *(May 26, 1937)* | | 7.50 |

**1937. NORTHWEST ORDINANCE ISSUE OF 1787** marked the 150th anniversary of the adoption of the Northwest Ordinance by the Congress of the Confederation. The confederation's greatest achievement, it provided for the governing of the Northwest Territory, dividing it into five parts that are now Ohio, Indiana, Illinois, Wisconsin and Michigan. The Rev. Manasseh Cutler, a distinguished botanist, aided in drafting the ordinance and organizing the colonization. Rufus Putnam led the first settlers (see CM192), who founded Marietta, Ohio. *Intaglio, perforated 11 x 10 1/2.*

CM182 *Manasseh Cutler (from an engraving by J. C. Buttre), Rufus Putnam (from a Trumbull miniature), map of the Northwest Territory.*

| CM182 | | UnFVF | UseFVF |
|---|---|---|---|
| 3¢ | **dull purple** *(84,825,250)* | .25 | .20 |
| | Plate block of 4 | 8.50 | |
| | FDC *(July 13, 1937)* | | 10.00 |

**1937. VIRGINIA DARE ISSUE** commemorated the 350th birthday of Virginia Dare, first child of English parentage born in America, at Roanoke Island off the North Carolina coast. Her grandfather, John White, leader of the expedition for Sir Walter Raleigh, returned to England for supplies a week after her birth in 1579. The Spanish War delayed his return until 1591, by which time the entire colony had mysteriously vanished. The stamps were printed 48 to the pane. *Flat plate printing, intaglio, perforated 11.*

CM183 *Virginia Dare and parents. From a drawing by William A. Roache.*

| CM183 | | UnFVF | UseFVF |
|---|---|---|---|
| 5¢ | **light slate blue** *(25,040,400)* | .25 | .20 |
| | Plate block of 6 | 8.50 | |
| | FDC *(Aug. 18, 1937)* | | 10.00 |

**1937. SOCIETY OF PHILATELIC AMERICANS SOUVENIR SHEET** was issued for the 43rd annual convention of the S.P.A. at Asheville, N.C. It consisted of a single stamp, the 10¢. Great Smokey Mountains National Park design (CM139), printed in blue green on a sheet measuring 67 x 78mm. *Intaglio, imperforate.* The margin is inscribed: "PRINTED BY THE TREASURY DEPARTMENT, BUREAU OF ENGRAVING AND PRINTING-UNDER THE AUTHORITY OF JAMES A. FARLEY, POSTMASTER GENERAL-IN COMPLIMENT TO THE 43RD ANNUAL CONVENTION OF THE SOCIETY OF PHILATELIC AMERICANS-ASHEVILLE, N.C., AUGUST 26-28, 1937."

CM184
| | | UnFVF | UseFVF |
|---|---|---|---|
| 10¢ | blue green *(5,277,445)* | .75 | .65 |
| | FDC *(Aug. 26, 1937)* | | 10.00 |

**1937. CONSTITUTION SESQUICENTENNIAL ISSUE** marked the 150th anniversary of the signing of the U.S. Constitution. The Articles of Confederation having proved ineffectual, a convention was called in Philadelphia to revise and strengthen them. The convention, presided over by Washington, sat for four months in closed sessions, scrapping the Articles altogether and vigorously debating a new constitution point by point. On September 17, 1787, a final draft was signed by 39 of the 42 delegates present and sent to Congress for submission to the states. *Intaglio, perforated 11 x 10 1/2.*

CM185 *Adoption of the Constitution. From a painting by J. B. Sterns.*

CM185
| | | UnFVF | UseFVF |
|---|---|---|---|
| 3¢ | bright purple *(99,882,300)* | .25 | .20 |
| | Plate block of 4 | 1.75 | |
| | FDC *(Sept. 17, 1937)* | | 7.50 |

**1937. HAWAII TERRITORY ISSUE** honors Hawaii, which voluntarily joined the United States in 1898. King Kamehameha the Great (1737-1819) united the Hawaiian Islands under one rule and allowed the first foreign traders to settle there. *Intaglio, perforated 10 1/2 x 11.*

CM186 *Kamehameha I. From statue by T. R. Gould, Iolani Castle, Honolulu.*

CM186
| | | UnFVF | UseFVF |
|---|---|---|---|
| 3¢ | violet *(78,454,450)* | .25 | .20 |
| | Plate block of 4 | 1.50 | |
| | FDC *(Oct. 18, 1937)* | | 20.00 |

**1937. ALASKA TERRITORY ISSUE** honors Alaska purchased from Russia in 1867 (see CM43). Mount Mckinley, pictured on the stamp, is the highest North American peak. *Intaglio, perforated 10 1/2 x 11.*

CM187 *Mount Mckinley*

CM187
| | | UnFVF | UseFVF |
|---|---|---|---|
| 3¢ | violet *(77,004,200)* | .25 | .20 |
| | Plate block of 4 | 1.50 | |
| | Gutter pair | — | |
| | FDC *(Nov. 12, 1937)* | | 15.00 |

**1937. PUERTO RICO TERRITORY ISSUE** honors Puerto Rico, ceded to the Unived States by Spain after the Spanish-American War of 1898. The stamp shows the old Governor's Palace in San Juan known as La Fortaleza. *Intaglio, perforated 10 1/2 x 11.*

CM188 *La Fortaleza Palace.*

CM188
| | | UnFVF | UseFVF |
|---|---|---|---|
| 3¢ | light reddish violet *(81,292,450)* | .25 | .20 |
| | Plate block of 4 | 1.50 | |
| | FDC *(Nov. 25, 1937)* | | 15.00 |

**1937. VIRGIN ISLANDS ISSUE** honored the Virgin Islands Territory, purchased from Denmark in 1917 to serve as a naval base for the defense of the Panama Canal. *Intaglio, perforated 10 1/2 x 11.*

CM189 *Harbor at Charlotte Amalie, St. Thomas, Virgin Islands.*

CM189
| | | UnFVF | UseFVF |
|---|---|---|---|
| 3¢ | lilac *(76, 474,550)* | .25 | .20 |
| | Plate block of 4 | .50 | |
| | Gutter pair | — | |
| | FDC *(Dec. 15, 1937)* | | 15.00 |

**1938. CONSTITUTION RATIFICATION ISSUE** commemorated the 150th anniversary of the ratification of the Constitution of the United States. The endorsement of nine states was needed to make the Constitution effective. Maryland was the first state to ratify it. New Hampshire became the ninth (June 21, 1788). *Intaglio, perforated 11 x 10 1/2.*

CM190 *Colonial Court House, Williamsburg, VA.*

CM190
| | | UnFVF | UseFVF |
|---|---|---|---|
| 3¢ | violet *(73,043,650)* | .50 | .20 |
| | Plate block of 4 | 4.50 | |
| | FDC *(June 21, 1938)* | | 10.00 |

**1938. SWEDES AND FINNS ISSUE** commemorated the 300th anniversary of the settlement by Swedish and Finnish colonists of Fort Christina (now Wilmington, Del.). They were led by Peter Minuit, who was a leader in the earlier settlement of New York (see CM64). The stamps were printed 48 to the sheet. *Intaglio, perforated 11.*

CM191 *Landing of the Swedes and Finns. From a painting by Stanley M. Arthurs, Wilmington, DE.*

| CM191 | | UnFVF | UseFVF |
|---|---|---|---|
| 3¢ | **carmine purple** *(58,564,368)* | .25 | .20 |
| | Plate block of 6 | 3.25 | |
| | FDC *(June 27, 1938)* | | 10.00 |

**1938. NORTHWEST TERRITORY ISSUE** commemorated the 150th anniversary of the settlement of the Northwest Territory after the Northwest Ordinance of 1787 (see CM182). *Intaglio, perforated 11 x 10 1/2.*

CM192 *Colonization of the West. From a statue by Gutzon Borglum, Marietta, OH.*

| CM192 | | UnFVF | UseFVF |
|---|---|---|---|
| 3¢ | **light reddish violet** *(65,939,500)* | .25 | .20 |
| | violet | .25 | .20 |
| | Plate block of 4 | 10.00 | |
| | FDC *(July 15, 1938)* | | 10.00 |

**1938. IOWA TERRITORY ISSUE** commemorated the 100th anniversary of the establishment of the Iowa Territory, July 3, 1838. The stamp was placed on sale in Des Moines at the opening of the Iowa State Fair. The building pictured was the old Iowa capitol in Iowa City. *Intaglio, perforated 11 x 10 1/2.*

CM193 *Old Capitol Building, Iowa City, IA.*

| CM193 | | UnFVF | UseFVF |
|---|---|---|---|
| 3¢ | **violet** *(47,064,300)* | .25 | .20 |
| | Plate block of 4 | 7.50 | |
| | Gutter pair | — | |
| | FDC *(Aug. 24, 1938)* | | 10.00 |

**1939. GOLDEN GATE EXPOSITION ISSUE** commemorated the international fair held in San Francisco, CA. The exposition's Tower of the Sun is shown. *Intaglio, perforated 10 1/2 x 11.*

CM194 *Tower of the Sun.*

| CM194 | | UnFVF | UseFVF |
|---|---|---|---|
| 3¢ | **light reddish violet** *(114,439,600)* | .25 | .20 |
| | Plate block of 4 | 1.75 | |
| | FDC *(Feb. 18, 1939)* | | 10.00 |

**1939. NEW YORK WORLD'S FAIR ISSUE** commemorated the enormous fair and exhibition, "The World of Tomorrow," held in New York City during 1939-40. The Trylon and Perisphere served as a focal point for the fair. *Intaglio, perforated 10 1/2 x 11.*

CM195 *Trylon and Perisphere.*

| CM195 | | UnFVF | UseFVF |
|---|---|---|---|
| 3¢ | **bluish violet** *(101,699,550)* | .25 | .20 |
| | Plate block of 4 | 2.25 | |
| | FDC *(April 1, 1939)* | | 12.00 |

**1939. WASHINGTON INAUGURATION ISSUE** commemorated the 150th anniversary of George Washington's inauguration as first President of the United States. The oath of office was administered on the balcony of Federal Hall, at the corner of Wall and Broad Streets in New York City, by Robert Livingston, chancellor of New York State. *Intaglio, perforated 11.*

CM196 *Washington Taking the Oath of Office. From an engraving by Alonzo Chappel.*

| CM196 | | UnFVF | UseFVF |
|---|---|---|---|
| 3¢ | **bright purple** *(73,764,550)* | .25 | .20 |
| | Plate block of 6 | 5.50 | |
| | FDC *(April 30, 1939)* | | 9.00 |

**1939. BASEBALL CENTENNIAL ISSUE** Commemorated the 100th aniversary of this popular American sport. According to a story now generally held to be spurious, while attending school at Cooperstown, NY, in 1839, Abner Doubleday laid out the base and player pattern still used today. The National Baseball Hall of Fame and Museum at Cooperstown, was selected as the First Day site. *Intaglio, perforated 11 x 10 1/2.*

CM197 *Sandlot Baseball Game.*

| CM197 | | UnFVF | UseFVF |
|---|---|---|---|
| 3¢ | **Violet** *(81,269,600)* | 2.25 | .20 |
| | Plate block of 4 | 11.00 | |
| | FDC *(June 12, 1939)* | | 40.00 |

**1939. PANAMA CANAL ISSUE** commemorated the 25th anniversary of the opening of the Panama Canal (see CM48). Authorized by President Theodore Roosevelt, who arranged the requisite treaty with Panama in 1904, it was built under the direction of Col. George W. Goethals. *Intaglio, perforated 11.*

CM198 *Theodore Roosevelt, George W. Goethals and a ship in the Gaillard Cut of the Panama Canal.*

**CM198**

| | | UnFVF | UseFVF |
|---|---|---|---|
| 3¢ | deep reddish purple *(67,813,350)* | .50 | .20 |
| | Plate block of 6 | 4.00 | |
| | FDC *(Aug. 15, 1939)* | | 10.00 |

**1939. PRINTING TERCENTENARY ISSUE** recalled the 300th anniversary of printing in Colonial America. The press shown was brought to the colonies by the Rev. Joseph Glover, who died en route. Stephen Daye set up the press at Cambridge, MA. Its first publication, in March 1639, was a single sheet. "Oath of a Free-man." In 1640 it printed *The Bay Psalm Book,* the first American book in English. The press is now in the Harvard University Museum. *Intaglio, perforated 10 1/2 x 11.*

CM199 *Stephen Daye press.*

**CM199**

| | | UnFVF | UseFVF |
|---|---|---|---|
| 3¢ | violet *(71,394,750)* | .25 | .20 |
| | Plate block of 4 | 1.50 | |
| | FDC *(Sept. 25, 1939)* | | 8.00 |

**1939. FOUR STATES ISSUE** commemorated the 50th anniversary of the states of North Dakota, South Dakota, Montana and Washington. The stamp had three different first-day dates (November 2nd for the Dakotas, November 8th for Montana and November 11th for Washington) before being placed on general sale November 13. *Intaglio, perforated 11 x 10 1/2.*

CM200 *Map of North Dakota, South Dakota, Montana and Washington.*

**CM200**

| | | UnFVF | UseFVF |
|---|---|---|---|
| 3¢ | reddish purple *(66,835,000)* | .25 | .20 |
| | Plate block of 4 | 1.50 | |
| | FDC *(Nov. 2, 1939)* | | 7.50 |

**1940. FAMOUS AMERICANS SERIES** Issued over a nine-month period, paid tribute to America's men and women who have distinguished themselves and their country in their creative dedication to the betterment of all mankind. They were grouped by the following topics: authors, poets, educators, scientists, musicians, artists, and inventors. Honorees were chosen mainly through a poll conducted by the National Federation of Stamp Clubs. *Intaglio, perforated 10 1/2 x 11.*

CM201 *Washington Irving (1783-1859), America's first internationally accepted man of letters, is best remembered for his stories such as* The Legend of Sleepy Hollow *(see CM754) and* Rip Van Winkle.

**CM201**

| | | MNHVF | UseVF |
|---|---|---|---|
| 1¢ | emerald *(56,348,320)* | .25 | .20 |
| | Plate block of 4 | 1.25 | |
| | FDC *(Jan. 29, 1940)* | | 4.00 |

CM202 *James Fenimore Cooper (1789-1851), lives on through his adventure stories, notably* The Leather-Stocking Tales, *five novels about a pioneer scout named Natty Bumppo.*

**CM202**

| | | MNHVF | UseVF |
|---|---|---|---|
| 2¢ | carmine *(53,177,110)* | .25 | .20 |
| | Plate block of 4 | 1.25 | |
| | FDC *(Jan. 29, 1940)* | | 4.00 |

CM203 *Ralph Waldo Emerson (1803-82), New England philosopher, is known for the practical idealism of his essays and for poems such as* The Concord Hynm.

**CM203**

| | | MNHVF | UseVF |
|---|---|---|---|
| 3¢ | bright purple *(53,260,270)* | .25 | .20 |
| | Plate block of 4 | 1.25 | |
| | FDC *(Feb. 5, 1940)* | | 4.00 |

CM204 *Louisa May Alcott (1832-88), teacher, social reformer and Civil War nurse, wrote the spectacularly popular novel* Little Women *and many others.*

**CM204**

| | | MNHVF | UseVF |
|---|---|---|---|
| 5¢ | gray blue *(22,104,950)* | .40 | .25 |
| | Plate block of 4 | 12.00 | |
| | FDC *(Feb. 5, 1940)* | | 5.00 |

CM205 *Samuel Langhorne Clemens (1835-1910), is known to the world as Mark Twain. His best-known character is Tom Sawyer, his greatest work* Adventures of Huckleberry Finn, *published in 1884.*

**CM205**

| | | MNHVF | UseVF |
|---|---|---|---|
| 10¢ | sepia *(13,201,270)* | 2.25 | 1.75 |
| | Plate block of 4 | 45.00 | |
| | FDC *(Feb. 13, 1940)* | | 10.00 |

CM206 *Henry Wadsworth Longfellow*

**CM206**

| | | MNHVF | UseVF |
|---|---|---|---|
| 1¢ | emerald *(51,603,580)* | .25 | .20 |
| | Plate block of 4 | 2.00 | |
| | FDC *(Feb. 16, 1940)* | | 4.00 |

CM207 *John Greenleaf Whittier (1807-92), poet and abolitionist, is best remembered for his* Snow-Bound, The Barefoot Boy, Maude Muller *and* Barbara Frietchie.

| CM207 | | MNHVF | UseVF |
|---|---|---|---|
| 2¢ | **carmine** *(52,100,510)* | .25 | .20 |
| | Plate block of 4 | 2.00 | |
| | FDC *(Feb. 16, 1940)* | | 4.00 |

CM208 *James Russell Lowell (1819-91), also was a diplomat, teacher and satirist. His best-known works are* The Biglow Papers *and* The Vision of Sir Launfal.

| CM208 | | MNHVF | UseVF |
|---|---|---|---|
| 3¢ | **bright purple** *(51,666,580)* | .25 | .20 |
| | Plate block of 4 | 2.75 | |
| | FDC *(Feb. 20, 1940)* | | 4.00 |

CM209 *Walt Whitman (1819-92), poet of democracy and the individual, pioneered the free-verse form with a collection of poems called* Leaves of Grass, *first published in 1855.*

| CM209 | | MNHVF | UseVF |
|---|---|---|---|
| 5¢ | **gray blue** *(22,207,780)* | .45 | .25 |
| | Plate block of 4 | 12.00 | |
| | FDC *(Feb. 20, 1940)* | | 5.00 |

CM210 *James Whitcomb Riley (1853-1916), wrote kindly, cheerful poems in Indiana dialect. His best-known works are* Little Orphan Annie *and* The Raggedy Man.

| CM210 | | MNHVF | UseVF |
|---|---|---|---|
| 10¢ | **sepia** *(11,835,530)* | 2.25 | 1.75 |
| | Plate block of 4 | 50.00 | |
| | FDC *(Feb. 24, 1940)* | | 10.00 |

CM211 *Horace Mann (1796-1859), founded the nation's first normal school and revolutionized the organization and teaching of the American public school system.*

| CM211 | | MNHVF | UseVF |
|---|---|---|---|
| 1¢ | **emerald** *(52,471,160)* | .25 | .20 |
| | Plate block of 4 | 2.75 | |
| | FDC *(March 14, 1940)* | | 4.00 |

CM212 *Mark Hopkins (1802-87), for 36 years president of Williams College in Massachusetts, did much to raise American educational standards.*

| CM212 | | MNHVF | UseVF |
|---|---|---|---|
| 2¢ | **carmine** *(52,366,440)* | .25 | .20 |
| | Plate block of 4 | 1.25 | |
| | FDC *(March 14, 1940)* | | 4.00 |

CM213 *Charles W. Eliot (1834-1926), president of Harvard, 1869-1909, made the school America's leading university and edited the* Harvard Classics, *commonly known as "Dr. Eliot's Five-Foot Shelf of Books.'*

| CM213 | | MNHVF | UseVF |
|---|---|---|---|
| 3¢ | **bright purple** *(51,636,270)* | .25 | .20 |
| | Plate block of 4 | 2.75 | |
| | FDC *(March 28, 1940)* | | 4.00 |

CM214 *Frances E. Williard (1839-98), dean of women at Northwestern University, was a pioneer worker for the improvement of education for women.*

| CM214 | | MNHVF | UseVF |
|---|---|---|---|
| 5¢ | **gray blue** *(20,729,030)* | .40 | .30 |
| | Plate block of 4 | 12.00 | |
| | FDC *(March 28, 1940)* | | 5.00 |

CM215 *Booker T. Washington (1856-1910), born a slave, was America's leading Black educator. In 1881 he founded Tuskegee Normal and Industrial Institute.*

| CM215 | | MNHVF | UseVF |
|---|---|---|---|
| 10¢ | **sepia** *(14,125,580)* | 2.50 | 1.75 |
| | Plate block of 4 | 42.50 | |
| | FDC *(April 7, 1940)* | | 10.00 |

CM216 *John James Audubon (1785-1851), ornithologist, painted birds from life. His* Birds of America, *published 1827-38, has been called "the most magnificent monument yet raised by art to science."*

| CM216 | | MNHVF | UseVF |
|---|---|---|---|
| 1¢ | **emerald** *(59,409,000)* | .25 | .20 |
| | Plate block of 4 | 1.25 | |
| | FDC *(April 8, 1940)* | | 4.00 |

CM217 *Dr. Crawford W. Long (1815-78), a Georgia physician, is believed to have been the first surgeon to use ether as an anaesthetic in 1842.*

| CM217 | | MNHVF | UseVF |
|---|---|---|---|
| 2¢ | **carmine** *(57,888,600)* | .25 | .20 |
| | Plate block of 4 | 1.25 | |
| | FDC *(April 8, 1940)* | | 4.00 |

CM218 *Luther Burbank (1849-1926), horticulturist, developed the Burbank potato and many new and better varieties of fruits, flowers and vegetables.*

| CM218 | | MNHVF | UseVF |
|---|---|---|---|
| 3¢ | **bright purple** *(58,273,180)* | .25 | .20 |
| | Plate block of 4 | 1.25 | |
| | FDC *(April 17, 1940)* | | 4.00 |

CM219 *Dr. Walter Reed (1851-1902), led the experiments in Cuba establishing that yellow-fever is transmitted by a variety of mosquito, a discovery that made possible the virtual elimination of disease.*

| CM219 | | MNHVF | UseVF |
|---|---|---|---|
| 5¢ | **gray blue** *(23,779,000)* | .50 | .20 |
| | Plate block of 4 | 7.75 | |
| | FDC *(April 17, 1940)* | | 5.00 |

CM220 *Jane Addams (1860-1935), noted humanitarian, in 1889 founded Hull House, a social settlement to improve community life in the slums of Chicago. It was the first institution if its kind in the United States.*

| CM220 | | MNHVF | UseVF |
|---|---|---|---|
| 10¢ | **sepia** *(15,112,580)* | 1.50 | 1.50 |
| | Plate block of 4 | 32.50 | |
| | FDC *(April 26, 1940)* | | 6.00 |

CM221 *Stephen Collins Foster (1826-64), most popular of all American composers, wrote such songs as* O Susanna, Swanee River, Camptown Races, *and* Jeannie with the Light Brown Hair.

| CM221 | | MNHVF | UseVF |
|---|---|---|---|
| 1¢ | **emerald** *(57,322,790)* | .25 | .20 |
| | Plate block of 4 | 1.25 | |
| | FDC *(May 3, 1940)* | | 4.00 |

CM222 *John Philip Sousa (1854-1932), a bandmaster and composer, was known as The March King. His most popular march is* The Stars and Stripes Forever.

| CM222 | | MNHVF | UseVF |
|---|---|---|---|
| 2¢ | **carmine** *(58,281,580)* | .25 | .20 |
| | Plate block of 4 | 1.25 | |
| | FDC *(May 3, 1940)* | | 4.00 |

CM223 *Victor Herbert (1859-1924), Irish-born cellist and conductor, wrote many operettas, including* Babes in Toyland, The Red Mill *and* Naughty Marietta. *His best-known song is* Ah, Sweet Mystery of Life.

| CM223 | | MNHVF | UseVF |
|---|---|---|---|
| 3¢ | **bright purple** *(56,398,790)* | .25 | .20 |
| | Plate block of 4 | 1.25 | |
| | FDC *(May 13, 1940)* | | 4.00 |

CM224 *Edward A. MacDowell (1861-1908), composed piano and orchestral works and songs. He is best known for his* Woodland Sketches *and* To a Wild Rose.

| CM224 | | MNHVF | UseVF |
|---|---|---|---|
| 5¢ | **gray blue** *(21,147,000)* | .75 | .30 |
| | Plate block of 4 | 12.50 | |
| | FDC *(May 13, 1940)* | | 5.00 |

CM225 *Ethelbert Nevin (1862-1901), composed 70 songs, including* Narcissus, The Rosary *and* Mighty Like a Rose.

| CM225 | | MNHVF | UseVF |
|---|---|---|---|
| 10¢ | **sepia** *(13,328,000)* | 5.00 | 2.00 |
| | Plate block of 4 | 50.00 | |
| | FDC *(June 10, 1940)* | | 6.00 |

CM226 *Gilbert Charles Stuart (1755-1828), was one of the first eminent American painters. His portraits of contemporaries, especially Washington, have been used on many U.S. stamps.*

| CM226 | | MNHVF | UseVF |
|---|---|---|---|
| 1¢ | **emerald** *(54,389,510)* | .25 | .20 |
| | Plate block of 4 | 1.00 | |
| | FDC *(Sept. 5, 1940)* | | 4.00 |

CM227 *James Abbott McNeill Whistler (1834-1903), a brilliant American painter and etcher, made his success in Europe. His portrait of his mother (see CM127) is his best-known work.*

| CM227 | | MNHVF | UseVF |
|---|---|---|---|
| 2¢ | **carmine** *(53,636,580)* | .25 | .20 |
| | Plate block of 4 | 1.00 | |
| | FDC *(Sept. 5, 1940)* | | 4.00 |

CM228 *Augustus Saint-Gaudens (1848-1907), great Irish-born sculptor, is best known for his equestrian statue of Sherman in New York City and his statue of Lincoln.*

| CM228 | | MNHVF | UseVF |
|---|---|---|---|
| 3¢ | **bright purple** *(55,313,230)* | .25 | .20 |
| | Plate block of 4 | 1.25 | |
| | FDC *(Sept. 16, 1940)* | | 4.00 |

CM229 *Daniel Chester French (1850-1931), New Hampshire sculptor, created* The Minute Man *(CM69) on Lexington Green and the seated Abraham Lincoln in the Lincoln Memorial at Washington, DC.*

| CM229 | | MNHVF | UseVF |
|---|---|---|---|
| 5¢ | **gray blue** *(21,720,580)* | .75 | .30 |
| | Plate block of 4 | 11.00 | |
| | FDC *(Sept. 16, 1940)* | | 5.00 |

CM230 *Frederic Remington (1861-1909), was a painter, illustrator and sculptor, known for his depiction of lively action in Western scenes. His artwork on CM21, CM23, CM496 and CM993.*

| CM230 | | MNHVF | UseVF |
|---|---|---|---|
| 10¢ | **sepia** *(13,600,580)* | 2.00 | 1.75 |
| | Plate block of 4 | 35.00 | |
| | FDC *(Sept. 30, 1940)* | | 6.00 |

CM231 *Eli Whitney (1765-1825), revolutionized the cotton industry in 1793 by inventing the cotton gin, a machine which separated cotton seed from the fiber 50 times faster than it could be done by hand.*

| CM231 | | MNHVF | UseVF |
|---|---|---|---|
| 1¢ | **emerald** *(47,599,580)* | .25 | .20 |
| | Plate block of 4 | 2.00 | |
| | FDC *(Oct. 7, 1940)* | | 4.00 |

CM232 *Samuel F. B. Morse (1791-1872), a portrait painter, invented the electric telegraph (CM266) and the telegraphic alphabet known as Morse Code.*

| CM232 | | MNHVF | UseVF |
|---|---|---|---|
| 2¢ | **carmine** *(53,766,510)* | .25 | .20 |
| | Plate block of 4 | 1.25 | |
| | FDC *(Oct. 7, 1940)* | | 4.00 |

CM233 *Cyrus Hall McCormick (1809-84), in 1831 invented a reaping machine with all key features of the harvesting machines of today. It increased American farm output and settlement of the West.*

| CM233 | | MNHVF | UseVF |
|---|---|---|---|
| 3¢ | **bright purple** *(54,193,580)* | .25 | .20 |
| | Plate block of 4 | 2.00 | |
| | FDC *(Oct. 14, 1940)* | | 4.00 |

CM234 *Elias Howe (1819-67), invented the sewing machine in 1846, which revolutionized clothesmaking, lowered costs, increased quality and eventualy brought many women into American industry.*

| CM234 | | MNHVF | UseVF |
|---|---|---|---|
| 5¢ | **gray blue** *(20,264,580)* | 1.25 | .50 |
| | Plate block of 4 | 17.50 | |
| | FDC *(Oct. 14, 1940)* | | 7.50 |

CM234 *Alexander Graham Bell (1847-1922), whose interest in accoustics stemmed from his work in teaching the deaf, invented the telphone in 1876.*

| CM235 | | MNHVF | UseVF |
|---|---|---|---|
| 10¢ | **sepia** *(13,726,580)* | 15.00 | 3.25 |
| | Plate block of 4 | 3.50 | |
| | FDC *(Oct. 28, 1940)* | | 7.50 |

**1940. PONY EXPRESS ISSUE** marked the 80th anniversary of the Central Overland California and Pike's Peak Express Company, the "Pony Express" that carried letters at $5 an ounce from St. Joseph, MO, to Sacramento, CA. Using 80 young riders, 420 horses and 190 relay stations, it made the 1,900-mile trip in ten days (winter) or eight days (summer). *Intaglio, perforated 11 x 10 1/2.*

CM236 *Pony Express Rider.*

| CM236 | | MNHVF | UseVF |
|---|---|---|---|
| 3¢ | **chestnut** *(46,497,400)* | .35 | .20 |
| | Plate block of 4 | 3.50 | |
| | FDC *(April 3, 1940)* | | 7.50 |

**1940. PAN-AMERICAN UNION ISSUE** commemorated the 50th anniversary of the founding of the International Bureau of American Republics, now known as the Pan-American Union. It was created by the various republics of North, Central and South America for the development of trade relations and peace. *Intaglio, perforated 10 1/2 x 11.*

CM237 *Three Graces. From Bottivcelli's painting.* Spring.

| CM237 | | MNHVF | UseVF |
|---|---|---|---|
| 3¢ | **lilac** *(47,700,000)* | .30 | .20 |
| | Plate block of 4 | 4.25 | |
| | FDC *(April 14, 1940)* | | 5.00 |

**1940. IDAHO STATEHOOD ISSUE** commemorated the 50th aniversary of Idaho's admission as the 43rd state. The region, crossed by Lewis and Clark in 1806, was a part of the Oregon Territory (CM170) in 1848-63, before becoming Idaho Territory. *Intaglio, perforated 11 x 10 1/2.*

CM238 *State Capitol at Boise.*

**CM238**

| | | MNHVF | UseVF |
|---|---|---|---|
| 3¢ | **light reddish violet** *(50,618,150)* | .25 | .20 |
| | Plate block of 4 | 2.50 | |
| | FDC *(July 3, 1940)* | | 5.00 |

**1940. WYOMING STATEHOOD ISSUE** commemorated the 50th anniversary of Wyoming's admission as the 44th state. The state seal's central figure, a female on a pedestal under the banner "Equal Rights," is a reminder that in Wyoming Territory women were given the right to vote in 1869. *Intaglio, perforated 10 1/2 x 11.*

CM239 *Wyoming State Seal.*

**CM239**

| | | MNHVF | UseVF |
|---|---|---|---|
| 3¢ | **purple brown** *(50,034,400)* | .25 | .20 |
| | Plate block of 4 | 2.25 | |
| | FDC *(July 10, 1940)* | | 5.00 |

**1940. CORONADO EXPEDITION ISSUE** observed the 400th anniversary of the expedition by Francisco Vasquez de Coronado, seeking the fabled Seven Cities of Cibola. Coronado's men discovered the Grand Canyon, explored what is now southern California and the Rio Grande, captured Zuni Indian settlements in New Mexico, and crossed the Arkansas River into Kansas. *Intaglio, perforated 11 x 10 1/2.*

CM240 *Coronado and His Captains. Painting by Gerald Cassidy.*

**CM240**

| | | MNHVF | UseVF |
|---|---|---|---|
| 3¢ | **reddish lilac** *(60,943,700)* | .25 | .20 |
| | Plate block of 4 | 1.75 | |
| | FDC *(Sept. 7, 1940)* | | 5.00 |

**1940. NATIONAL DEFENSE ISSUE** focused attention upon the necessity for building an adequate national defense. Original sketches by President Roosevelt were the basis for the final designs. *Intaglio, perforated 11 x 10 1/2.*

CM241 *The Statue of Liberty, rising 305 feet above the waters of New York Harbor, is the work of Alsatian sculptor Frederic Auguste Bartholdi (CM1163), who conceived the idea on a visit to the United States. A Centennial Gift from the People of France, it was up to America to supply the funds to build the pedestal, which was completed ten years later in 1886, after the efforts of Pulitzer and his New York World newspaper. Its full name is "Liberty Enlightening the World"; and it has become a universal symbol of the freedom and security of democracy in America.*

**CM241**

| | | MNHVF | UseVF |
|---|---|---|---|
| 1¢ | **emerald** *(6,081,409,300)* | .25 | .20 |
| | Plate block of 4 | .50 | |
| | Cracked plate | — | |
| | Gripper cracks | — | |
| | Gutter pair | — | |
| | FDC *(Oct. 16, 1940)* | | 5.00 |
| | v. Horizontal pair, imperforate between | 35.00 | |
| | v1. Vertical pair, imperforate between | 500. | |

CM242 *90mm anti-aircraft gun.*

**CM242**

| | | MNHVF | UseVF |
|---|---|---|---|
| 2¢ | **rose** *(5,211,708,200)* | .25 | .20 |
| | Plate block of 4 | .50 | |
| | Gutter pair | — | |
| | FDC *(Oct. 16, 1940)* | | 5.00 |
| | v. Horizontal pair, imperforate between | 40.00 | |

CM243 *Torch Symbolizing Enlightenment.*

**CM243**

| | | MNHVF | UseVF |
|---|---|---|---|
| 3¢ | **light reddish violet** *(8,384,867,600)* | .25 | .20 |
| | Plate block of 4 | .75 | |
| | Gutter pair | — | |
| | FDC *(Oct. 16, 1940)* | | 5.00 |
| | v. Horizontal pair, imperforate between | 25.00 | |

**1940. THIRTEENTH AMENDMENT ISSUE** commemorated the abolition of slavery in the United States. President Lincoln's Emancipation Proclamation of 1863 freed only the slaves in states that had seceded from the Union, leaving the status of nearly a million others in northern and border states were unchanged. The Thirteenth Amendment, proclaimed in force December 18, 1865, abolished all involuntary servitude except as a punishment for crime. *Intaglio, perforated 10 1/2 x 11.*

CM244 *Emancipation Monument by Thomas Ball in Lincoln Park, Washington, D.C.*

**CM244**

| | | MNHVF | UseVF |
|---|---|---|---|
| 3¢ | **violet** *(44,389,550)* | .35 | .20 |
| | Plate block of 4 | 3.75 | |
| | FDC *(Oct. 20, 1940)* | | 7.50 |

**1941. VERMONT STATEHOOD ISSUE** commemorated the 150th anniversary of Vermont's admission into the Union as the 14th state. *Intaglio, perforated 11 x 10 1/2.*

CM245 *State Capitol at Montpelier, VT.*

**CM245**

| | | MNHVF | UseVF |
|---|---|---|---|
| 3¢ | **violet** *(54,574,550)* | .25 | .20 |
| | Plate block of 4 | 2.00 | |
| | FDC *(March 4, 1941)* | | 7.50 |

**1942. KENTUCKY STATEHOOD ISSUE** commemorated the 150th anniversary of its admission as the 15th state. Kentucky was explored in 1767 by Daniel Boone who in 1775 led a party of settlers through the Cumberland Gap and over the Wilderness Road to erect a fort at what later became Boonesborough. *Intaglio, perforated 11 x 10 1/2.*

CM246 *Daniel Boone and Frontiersmen. Mural by Gilbert White, State Capitol, Frankfort, KY.*

| CM246 | | MNHVF | UseVF |
|---|---|---|---|
| 3¢ | **reddish violet** *(63,558,400)* | .25 | .20 |
| | Plate block of 4 | 1.25 | |
| | FDC *(June 1, 1942)* | | 5.00 |

**1942. WIN THE WAR ISSUE** following Pearl Harbor, replaced the 3¢ National Defense stamp (CM243) and symbolized the nation's war effort and its goal of victory. *Intaglio, perforated 11 x 10 1/2.*

CM247 *Victory Eagle*

| CM247 | | MNHVF | UseVF |
|---|---|---|---|
| 3¢ | **violet** *(20,642,793,300)* | .25 | .20 |
| | light violet | .25 | .20 |
| | Plate block of 4 | .75 | |
| | Gutter pair | — | |
| | FDC *(July 4, 1942)* | | 5.00 |
| | a. purple | — | |

**1942. CHINESE COMMEMORATIVE ISSUE** honored five years of Chinese resistance to Japanese aggression. Chinese characters below the portrait of Sun Yat-sen, founder of the Republic, are Abraham Lincoln's words: "of the people, by the people, for the people." *Intaglio, perforated 11 x 10 1/2.*

CM248 *Abraham Lincoln, Map of China, Sun Yat-sen.*

| CM248 | | MNHVF | UseVF |
|---|---|---|---|
| 5¢ | **Prussian blue** *(21,272,800)* | .60 | .30 |
| | Plate block of 4 | 12.00 | |
| | FDC *(July 7, 1942)* | | 10.00 |

**1943. ALLIED NATIONS ISSUE** commemorated the strength and unity with which nations of the free world were fighting to establish peace and freedom. *Intaglio, perforated 11 x 10 1/2.*

CM249 *Nations United for Victory.*

| CM249 | | MNHVF | UseVF |
|---|---|---|---|
| 2¢ | **carmine** *(1,671,564,200)* | .25 | .20 |
| | Plate block of 4 | .50 | |
| | Gutter pair | — | |
| | FDC *(Jan. 14, 1943)* | | 5.00 |

**1943. FOUR FREEDOMS ISSUE** Symbolized principles enunciated by President Roosevelt in the 1941 State of the Union message to Congress: freedom of speech and expression, freedom of worship, freedom from want and freedom from fear. *Intaglio, perforated 11 x 10 1/2.*

CM250 *Liberty Bearing the Torch of Freedom and Enlightenment.*

| CM250 | | MNHVF | UseVF |
|---|---|---|---|
| 1¢ | **emerald** *(1,227,334,200)* | .25 | .20 |
| | Plate block of 4 | .60 | |
| | FDC *(Feb. 12, 1943)* | | 5.00 |

**1943-44. OVERRUN COUNTRIES SERIES** recognized the countries occupied by the Axis powers, which implied the free world's determination to liberate them.

For the first time since 1893, the Bureau of Engraving and Printing contracted with a private firm, the American Bank Note Co., so that the stamps could be printed in color. The frames of all values were engraved slate violet. The vignettes were printed by offset in two or three colors. *Flat-plate, intaglio, perforated 12.*

CM251 *Flag of Poland*

| CM251 | | MNHVF | UseVF |
|---|---|---|---|
| 5¢ | **slate violet, scarlet and black** *(19,999,646)* | .25 | .20 |
| | "Poland" block of 4 | 7.25 | |
| | "Poland" block of 6, w/guide markings | — | |
| | FDC *(June 22, 1943)* | | 5.00 |

CM252 *Flag of Czechoslovakia*

| CM252 | | MNHVF | UseVF |
|---|---|---|---|
| 5¢ | **slate violet, blue, scarlet and black** *(19,999,646)* | .25 | .20 |
| | "Czechoslovakia" block of 4 | 4.00 | |
| | "Czechoslovakia" block of 6 w/guide markings | — | |
| | FDC *(July 12, 1943)* | | 5.00 |

CM253 *Flag of Norway*

| CM253 | | MNHVF | UseVF |
|---|---|---|---|
| 5¢ | **slate violet, rose red, ultramarine and black** *(19,999,616)* | .25 | .20 |
| | "Norway" block of 4 | 1.75 | |
| | "Norway" block of 6, w/guide markings | — | |
| | FDC *(July 27, 1943)* | | 5.00 |

CM254 *Flag of Luxembourg*

| CM254 | | MNHVF | UseVF |
|---|---|---|---|
| 5¢ | **slate violet, rose red, light blue and black** | .25 | .20 |
| | *(19,999,646)* | | |
| | "Luxembourg" block of 4 | 1.75 | |
| | "Luxembourg" block of 6, w/guide markings | — | |
| | FDC *(Aug. 10, 1943)* | | 5.00 |

CM255 *Flag of Netherlands*

| CM255 | | MNHVF | UseVF |
|---|---|---|---|
| 5¢ | **slate violet, scarlet, blue and black** | .25 | .20 |
| | *(19,999,646)* | | |
| | "Netherlands" block of 4 | 1.75 | |
| | "Netherlands" block of 6, w/guide markings | — | |
| | FDC *(Aug. 24, 1943)* | | 5.00 |

CM256 *Flag of Belgium*

| CM256 | | MNHVF | UseVF |
|---|---|---|---|
| 5¢ | **slate violet, scarlet, greenish yellow and black** *(19,999,646)* | .25 | .20 |
| | "Belgium" block of 4 | 1.75 | |
| | "Belgium" block of 6, w/guide markings | — | |
| | FDC *(Sept. 14, 1943)* | | 5.00 |

CM257 *Flag of France*

| CM257 | | MNHVF | UseVF |
|---|---|---|---|
| 5¢ | **slate violet, blue, red and black** | .25 | .20 |
| | *(19,999,648)* | | |
| | "France" block of 4 | 1.75 | |
| | "France" block of 6, w/guide markings | — | |
| | FDC *(Sept. 28, 1943)* | | 5.00 |

CM258 *Flag of Greece*

| CM258 | | MNHVF | UseVF |
|---|---|---|---|
| 5¢ | **slate violet, pale light blue and black** | .50 | .20 |
| | *(14,999,646)* | | |
| | "Greece" block of 4 | 15.00 | |
| | "Greece" block of 6, w/guide markings | — | |
| | FDC *(Oct. 12, 1943)* | | 5.00 |

CM259 *Flag of Yugoslavia*

| CM259 | | MNHVF | UseVF |
|---|---|---|---|
| 5¢ | **slate violet, blue, rose red and black** | .30 | .20 |
| | *(14,999,646)* | | |
| | "Yugoslavia" block of 4 | 8.00 | |
| | "Yugoslavia" block of 6, w/guide markings | — | |
| | FDC *(Oct. 26, 1943)* | | 5.00 |

CM260 *Flag of Albania*

| CM260 | | MNHVF | UseVF |
|---|---|---|---|
| 5¢ | **slate violet, red and black** *(14,999,646)* | .30 | .20 |
| | "Albania" block of 4 | 8.00 | |
| | "Albania" block of 6, w/guide markings | — | |
| | FDC *(Nov. 9, 1943)* | | 5.00 |

CM261 *Flag of Austria*

| CM261 | | MNHVF | UseVF |
|---|---|---|---|
| 5¢ | **slate violet, red and black** *(14,999,646)* | .30 | .20 |
| | "Austria" block of 4 | 5.25 | |
| | "Austria" block of 6, w/guide markings | — | |
| | FDC *(Nov. 23, 1943)* | | 5.00 |

CM262 *Flag of Denmark*

| CM262 | | MNHVF | UseVF |
|---|---|---|---|
| 5¢ | **slate violet, scarlet and black** | .30 | .20 |
| | *(14,999,646)* | | |
| | "Denmark" block of 4 | 6.25 | |
| | "Denmark" block of 6, w/guide markings | — | |
| | FDC *(Dec. 7, 1943)* | | 5.00 |

CM263 *Flag of Korea*

| CM263 | | MNHVF | UseVF |
|---|---|---|---|
| 5¢ | **slate violet, scarlet, bright blue and gray** | .30 | .20 |
| | *(14,999,646)* | | |
| | "Korea" block of 4 | 5.25 | |
| | "Korea" block of 6, w/guide markings | — | |
| | FDC *(Nov. 2, 1944)* | | 5.00 |
| | v.  'KORPA' plate flaw | 27.50 | |

**1944. TRANSCONTINENTAL RAILROAD ISSUE** marks the 75th anniversary of the conpletion of the first transcontinental railroad. A golden spike driven at Promitory Point, near Ogden, Utah on May 10, 1869, marked the meeting of the Union Pacific tracks from the west with the Central Pacific from the east. *Intaglio, perforated 11 x 10 1/2.*

CM264 *Golden Spike Ceremony. Mural by John McQuarrie, Union Pacific Station, Salt Lake City, UT.*

| CM264 | | MNHVF | UseVF |
|---|---|---|---|
| 3¢ | **violet** *(61,303,000)* | .30 | .20 |
| | Plate block of 4 | 1.75 | |
| | FDC *(May 10, 1944)* | | 7.50 |

**1944. STEAMSHIP ISSUE** commemorated the 125th anniversary of the first steamship crossing of the Atlantic. The first-day date was National Maritime Day. The ship *Savannah,* sailing with an auxiliary steam engine, crossed from Savannah, Ga. to Liverpool, England, in 19 days. *Intaglio, perforated 11 x 10 1/2.*

CM265 *S.S. Savannah. From ship model, Marine Museum, Newport News, VA.*

| CM265 | | MNHVF | UseVF |
|---|---|---|---|
| 3¢ | **violet** *(61,001,450)* | .25 | .20 |
| | Plate block of 4 | 1.50 | |
| | FDC *(May 22, 1944)* | | 7.50 |

**1944. TELEGRAPH CENTENNIAL ISSUE** commemorated the 100th anniversary of the first message sent by telegraph. The inventor, Samuel F. B. Morse (CM232), sent the historic words, "What hath God wrought!" from Washington, DC, to Baltimore, MD, where they were received by his associate, Alfred Vail. *Intaglio, perforated 11 x 10 1/2.*

CM266 *Telegraph Wires and Posts.*

| CM266 | | MNHVF | UseVF |
|---|---|---|---|
| 3¢ | **bright purple** *(60,605,000)* | .25 | .20 |
| | Plate block of 4 | 1.00 | |
| | FDC *(May 24, 1944)* | | 7.50 |

**1944. CORREGIDOR ISSUE** paid tribute to the gallant resistance of Gen. Jonathan M. Wainwright's American and Philippine troops beseiged there by the Japanese in 1942. After the fall of Bataan, the surviving forces withdrew to Corregidor in Manila Bay and withstood the invaders for almost a month before surrendering May 6, 1942. *Intaglio, perforated 11 x 10 1/2.*

CM267 *Corregidor Island*

| CM267 | | MNHVF | UseVF |
|---|---|---|---|
| 3¢ | **violet** *(50,129,350)* | .25 | .20 |
| | Plate block of 4 | 1.25 | |
| | FDC *(Sept. 27, 1944)* | | 7.50 |

**1944. MOTION PICTURE ISSUE** commemorated the 50th anniversary of motion pictures and paid tribute to the cinema industry's contributions to the war effort. *Intaglio, perforated 11 x 10 1/2.*

CM268 *Motion Pictures for the Troops.*

| CM268 | | MNHVF | UseVF |
|---|---|---|---|
| 3¢ | **violet** *(53,479,400)* | .25 | .20 |
| | Plate block of 4 | 1.00 | |
| | FDC *(Oct. 31, 1944)* | | 7.50 |

**1945. FLORIDA CENTENNIAL ISSUE** marked the 100th anniversary of Florida's admission as the 27th state. Explored by Juan Ponce de Leon in 1513, Florida was not settled by Europeans until 1565 when Pedro Menendez de Aviles set up a colony at St. Augustine, now the oldest city in the United States. West Florida was seized by the United States in 1813; East Florida was ceded by Spain in 1819. *Intaglio, perforated 11 x 10 1/2.*

CM269 *Gates of St. Augustine, State Seal and State Capitol.*

| CM269 | | MNHVF | UseVF |
|---|---|---|---|
| 3¢ | **bright purple** *(61,617,350)* | .25 | .20 |
| | Plate block of 4 | .75 | |
| | FDC *(March 3, 1945)* | | 7.50 |

**1945. UNITED NATIONS CONFERENCE ISSUE** honored the conference in San Francisco at which the delegates of 50 nations met to draft the Charter of the United Nations Organization. President Roosevelt, who had invited them there, died 13 days before the conference. His words "Toward United Nations, April 25, 1945." were inscribed on the stamp as a memorial to him. *Intaglio, perforated 11 x 10 1/2.*

CM270 *"Toward United Nations, April 25, 1945"*

| CM270 | | MNHVF | UseVF |
|---|---|---|---|
| 5¢ | **ultramarine** *(75,500,000)* | .25 | .20 |
| | Plate block of 4 | .75 | |
| | FDC *(April 25, 1945)* | | 8.00 |

**1945-46. ROOSEVELT SERIES** paid tribute to President Franklin Delano Roosevelt (1882-1945), who died April 12, 1945. The only American for whom the "no third term" tradition was set aside, he was elected to the presidency four times. First taking office in a time of grave economic depression, he began the vast economic and social program known as the New Deal. He gave substantial support to Great Britain after the fall of France in 1940, wrote (with British Prime Minister Winston S. Churchill) the Atlantic Charter in 1941, defined the Four Freedoms (CM250), helped lead the fight to victory in World War II and called the conference which was to organize the United Nations. Thirteen days before it opened, he died of a cerebral hemorrhage at the 'Summer White House' in Warm Springs, GA (CM272), where he had set up a foundation for children who had, like himself, been stricken by infantile paralysis. He was buried in the garden of his home at Hyde Park, NY (CM271).

An ardent stamp collector for 56 years, Roosevelt added greatly to the popularity of the hobby and suggested the designs of a number of postage stamps issued during his presidency. "I owe my life to my hobbies," he said, "especially stamp collecting." Many countries have honored him on their postage stamps. *Intaglio, perforated 11 x 10 1/2.*

CM271 *Roosevelt and Hyde Park*

| CM271 | | MNHVF | UseVF |
|---|---|---|---|
| 1¢ | **blue green** *(128,140,000)* | .25 | .20 |
| | Plate block of 4 | .50 | |
| | FDC *(July 26, 1945)* | | 4.00 |
| | p.  printed on thin, translucent paper | — | |

CM272 *Roosevelt and "Little White House" at Warm Springs, Ga.*

| CM272 | | MNHVF | UseVF |
|---|---|---|---|
| 2¢ | **carmine red** *(67,255,000)* | .25 | .20 |
| | Plate block of 4 | .50 | |
| | FDC *(Aug. 24, 1945)* | | 4.00 |

CM273 *Roosevelt and the White House.*

| CM273 | | MNHVF | UseVF |
|---|---|---|---|
| 3¢ | **lilac** *(138,870,000)* | .25 | .20 |
| | Plate block of 4 | .50 | |
| | FDC *(June 27, 1945)* | | 4.00 |

CM274 *Roosevelt, Globe and Four Freedoms.*

| CM274 | | MNHVF | UseVF |
|---|---|---|---|
| 5¢ | **light blue** *(76,455,400)* | .25 | .20 |
| | Plate block of 4 | .75 | |
| | FDC *(Jan. 30, 1946)* | | 3.00 |

## 1945-46. Armed Forces Series

of five stamps paid tribute to the nation's fighting forces and Merchant Marine for their valiant efforts toward victory in World War II.

**1945. MARINE COMMEMORATIVE** honored the U.S. Marine Corps. The design is taken from the famous photograph by Joseph Rosenthal of the Associated Press, showing the Marines raising the American Flag on Mount Suribachi on the Japanese island of Iwo Jima. The color was intended to match that of the Marine uniform. *Intaglio, perforated 10 1/2 x 11.*

CM275 *U.S. Marines Raising the Flag on Mount Suribachi, Iwo Jima.*

| CM275 | | MNHVF | UseVF |
|---|---|---|---|
| 3¢ | **dark yellow green** *(137,321,000)* | .25 | .20 |
| | Plate block of 4 | .75 | |
| | FDC *(July 11, 1945)* | | 7.50 |

**1945. ARMY COMMEMORATIVE** honored the U.S. Army, particularly the infantry, in World War II. The design was devised from a group of photographs of the 28th Division marching through Paris. The color was selected to match the olive-drab uniform of the Army. *Intaglio, perforated 11 x 10 1/2.*

CM276 *U.S. Infantry, Bombers and L'Arc de Triomphe, Paris, France.*

| CM276 | | MNHVF | UseVF |
|---|---|---|---|
| 3¢ | **brown olive** *(128,357,750)* | .25 | .20 |
| | Plate block of 4 | .65 | |
| | FDC *(Sept. 28, 1945)* | | 7.50 |

**1945. NAVY COMMEMORATIVE** honored the U.S. Navy in World War II. The design reproduces an official Navy photograph made at the Corpus Christi Naval Air Station. The color was selected to match the blue uniform of the Navy. *Intaglio, perforated 11 x 10 1/2*

CM277 *U.S. Sailors*

| CM277 | | MNHVF | UseVF |
|---|---|---|---|
| 3¢ | **blue** *(138,863,000)* | .25 | .20 |
| | Plate block of 4 | .65 | |
| | FDC *(Oct. 27, 1945)* | | 7.50 |

**1945. COAST GUARD COMMEMORATIVE** honored the U.S. Coast Guard service in World War II. The nation's oldest uniformed service, the Coast Guard participated in every major invasion of the war. *Intaglio, perforated 11 x 10 1/2.*

CM278 *Coast Guard Landing Craft and Supply Ship.*

| CM278 | | MNHVF | UseVF |
|---|---|---|---|
| 3¢ | **blue green** *(111,616,700)* | .25 | .20 |
| | Plate block of 4 | .65 | |
| | FDC *(Nov. 10, 1945)* | | 7.50 |

**1946. MERCHANT MARINE COMMEMORATIVE** honored the achievements of the U.S. Merchant Marine in World War II. Photographs of two Liberty Ships, the *James Madison* and the *John W. Troy,* were used in the composite design. *Intaglio, perforated 11 x 10 1/2.*

CM279 *Liberty Ship and Goods.*

| CM279 | | MNHVF | UseVF |
|---|---|---|---|
| 3¢ | **blue green** *(135,927,000)* | .25 | .20 |
| | Plate block of 4 | .65 | |
| | FDC *(Feb. 26, 1946)* | | 7.50 |

**1945. ALFRED E. SMITH ISSUE** honored the colorful and popular American who rose from humble beginnings to serve four terms as governor of New York. Known as "The Happy Warrior," he was the Democratic candidate for president in 1928, but was defeated by Herbert Hoover. He died in 1944. *Intaglio, perforated 11 x 10 1/2.*

 CM280 *Alfred E. Smith*

| CM280 | | MNHVF | UseVF |
|---|---|---|---|
| 3¢ | dark lilac *(308,587,700)* | .25 | .20 |
| | Plate block of 4. | .55 | |
| | Gutter Pair | — | |
| | FDC *(Nov. 26, 1945)* | | 5.00 |

**1945. TEXAS STATEHOOD ISSUE** commemorated the 100th anniversary of Texas as the 28th state. A former Mexican state whose American settlers revolted in 1836 and set up a republic (CM166), Texas was granted Congressional authority to divide its vast territory into as many as 5 states of "convenient size" and "sufficient population" without further permission of Congress. *Intaglio, perforated 11 x 10 1/2.*

 CM281 *U.S. and Texas Flags and the "Lone Star".*

| CM281 | | MNHVF | UseVF |
|---|---|---|---|
| 3¢ | Prussian blue *(170,640,000)* | .25 | .20 |
| | Plate Block of 4 | .55 | |
| | FDC *(Dec. 29, 1945)* | | 5.00 |

**1946. HONORABLE DISCHARGE STAMP** honored the members of the armed forces who were returning to civilian life after having served their country in World War II. *Intaglio perforated 10 X 11 1/2.*

 CM282 *Honorable Discharge Emblem*

| CM282 | | MNHVF | UseVF |
|---|---|---|---|
| 3¢ | violet *(269,339,100)* | .25 | .20 |
| | Plate Block of 4 | .55 | |
| | FDC *(May 9, 1946)* | | 5.00 |

**1946. TENNESSEE STATEHOOD ISSUE** commemorated the 150th anniversary of Tennessee as the 16th state. First settled in 1757 as part of North Carolina, it was ceded in 1784 to the federal government, which gave it neither administration nor protection. Settlers under John Sevier set up the independent State of Franklin in 1785-88, and later served as first governor of Tennessee. *Intaglio, perforated 11 x 10 1/2.*

 CM283 *Capitol at Nashville, Andrew Jackson and John Sevier*

| CM283 | | MNHVF | UseVF |
|---|---|---|---|
| 3¢ | violet *(132,274,500)* | .25 | .20 |
| | Plate block of 4 | .55 | |
| | FDC *(June 1, 1946)* | | 3.00 |

**1946. IOWA STATEHOOD ISSUE** commemorated the 100th anniversary of Iowa's admission as the 29th state. *Intaglio, perforated 11 x 10 1/2.*

 CM284 *Iowa map and Flag*

| CM284 | | MNHVF | UseVF |
|---|---|---|---|
| 3¢ | Prussian blue *(132,430,000)* | .25 | .20 |
| | Plate Block of 4 | .55 | |
| | FDC *(Aug. 3, 1946)* | | 3.00 |

**1946. SMITHSONIAN INSTITUTION ISSUE** commemorated the 100th anniversary of its establishment at Washington, D.C. James Smithson, an English chemist, willed more than £100,000 as a gift to the United States for "an establishment for the increase and diffusion of knowledge among men." Today it includes a great library and several museums, including the National Postal Museum, (CM1589-92). *Intaglio, perforated 11 x 10 1/2.*

 CM285 *Smithsonian Institution*

| CM285 | | MNHVF | UseVF |
|---|---|---|---|
| 3¢ | brown purple *(139,209,500)* | .25 | .20 |
| | Plate Block of 4 | .55 | |
| | FDC *(Aug. 10, 1946)* | | 3.00 |

**1946. KEARNY EXPEDITION ISSUE** commemorated the 100th anniversary of the march of Gen. Stephen W. Kearny's Army of the West from Fort Leavenworth to New Mexico. Kearny's unopposed entry into Santa Fe on Aug. 18, 1846, ended the Mexican War and established New Mexico as a part of the United States. *Intaglio, perforated 11 x 10 1/2*

 CM286 *Capture of Santa Fe. From a painting by Kenneth M. Chapman.*

| CM286 | | MNHVF | UseVF |
|---|---|---|---|
| 3¢ | brown purple *(114,684,450)* | .25 | .20 |
| | Plate Block of 4 | .55 | |
| | FDC *(Oct. 16, 1946)* | | 3.00 |

**1947. THOMAS A. EDISON ISSUE** commemorated the 100th anniversary of the birth of America's greatest practical scientist. Thomas Alva Edison's more than 1,200 inventions include the incandescent electric bulb (CM85), the automatic telegraph repeater, teleprinter, mimeograph, phonograph, microphone, Ediphone, storage battery, electric dynamo, electric automobile, electric locomotive, carbon telephone transmitter, many motion picture developments, and telegraphic communication with moving trains. *Intaglio, perforated 10 1/2 x 11.*

 CM287 *Thomas A. Edison*

| CM287 | | MNHVF | UseVF |
|---|---|---|---|
| 3¢ | **bright purple** (156,540,510) | .25 | .20 |
| | Plate block of 4 | .55 | |
| | FDC (Feb. 11, 1947) | | 3.00 |

**1947. JOSEPH PULITZER ISSUE** commemorated the 100th anniversary of the birth of Joseph Pulitzer, the Hungarian-born journalist who published the *St. Louis Post-Dispatch* and the *New York World*. It was a drive by Pulitzer's *World* that raised the funds to build the base for the Statue of Liberty. He founded and endowed the Columbia School of Journalism, which awards annual Pulitzer Prizes in journalism and letters. *Intaglio, perforated 11 x 10 1/2.*

CM288 *Joseph Pulitzer and the Statue of Liberty.*

| CM288 | | MNHVF | UseVF |
|---|---|---|---|
| 3¢ | **dark lilac** (120,452,600) | .25.20 | |
| | Plate block of 4 | .55 | |
| | FDC (April 10, 1947) | | 3.00 |

**1947. POSTAGE STAMP CENTENARY ISSUE** marked the 100th anniversary of the first regular issue postage stamps. *Intaglio, perforated 11 x 10 1/2.*

CM289 *Washington and Franklin and New Methods of Carrying the Mail.*

| CM289 | | MNHVF | UseVF |
|---|---|---|---|
| 3¢ | **blue** (127,104,300) | .25 | .20 |
| | Plate block of 4 | .55 | |
| | FDC (May 17, 1947) | | 3.00 |

**1947. CIPEX SOUVENIR SHEET** was an imperforate, flat-plate souvenir sheet featuring reproductions of the 2 stamps of the 1847 issue produced for the Centenary International Philatelic Exhibition. Stamps cut out of the sheet are valid for postage and sometimes are mistaken for the 1847 originals by those who have not checked the colors. The reproduced 5¢ Franklin is light blue instead of the original red brown and 10¢ Washington reproduction is Venetian red instead of black. The sheet is inscribed in the margin:

"PRINTED BY THE TREASURY DEPARTMENT, BUREAU OF ENGRAVING AND PRINTING-UNDER AUTHORITY OF ROBERT E. HANNEGAN, POST- MASTER GENERAL-IN COMPLIMENT TO THE CENTENARY INTERNATIONAL PHILATELIC EXHIBITION. NEW YORK,N.Y., MAY 17-25, 1947." *Intaglio, imperforate*

CM290 *CIPEX Souvenir Sheet*

| CM290 | | MNHVF | UseVF |
|---|---|---|---|
| 15¢ | **complete sheet of 2 stamps** (10,299,600) | .75 | .65 |
| | a. 5¢ light blue, from sheet | .30 | .25 |
| | b. 10¢ Venetian red, from sheet | .45 | .25 |
| | FDC (May 19, 1947) | | 4.00 |

**1947. THE DOCTOR'S ISSUE** paid tribute to the physicians of America. *Intaglio, perforated 11 x 10 1/2.*

CM291 *The Doctor. From a painting by Sir Luke Fildes.*

| CM291 | | MNHVF | UseVF |
|---|---|---|---|
| 3¢ | **brown purple** (132,902,000) | .25 | .20 |
| | Plate block of 4 | .75 | |
| | FDC (June 9, 1947) | | 7.00 |

**1947. UTAH ISSUE** commemorated the 100th anniversary of the settlement of Utah by the Mormons under Brigham Young. Driven out of the Mid-West by religious persecution, members of the Church of Jesus Christ of Latter-Day Saints made a mass migration to the valley of the Great Salt Lake and founded a territory called Deseret, which in 1850 became the Utah Territory. *Intaglio, perforated 11 x 10 1/2.*

CM292 *Pioneers Entering the Valley of Great Salt Lake, Utah.*

| CM292 | | MNHVF | UseVF |
|---|---|---|---|
| 3¢ | **violet** (131,968,000) | .25 | .20 |
| | Plate block of 4 | .75 | |
| | FDC (July 24, 1947) | | 3.00 |

**1947. U.S. FRIGATE CONSTITUTION ISSUE** commemorated the 150th anniversary of the launching of the great fighting ship *Constitution*. Ordered dismantled in 1830, she was saved by public sentiment aroused by Oliver Wendell Holmes' poem *Old Ironsides*. *Intaglio, perforated 11 x 10 1/2.*

CM293 *Drawing of the U.S. frigate Constitution.*

| CM293 | | MNHVF | UseVF |
|---|---|---|---|
| 3¢ | **blue green** (131,488,000) | .25 | .20 |
| | Plate block of 4 | .55 | |
| | FDC (Oct. 21, 1947) | | 3.50 |

**1947. EVERGLADES NATIONAL PARK ISSUE** commemorated the dedication of the park on Dec 6. The park contains more than a million acres of subtropical land in southern Florida, with extensive watercourses and profuse bird life. *Intaglio, perforated 11 x 10 1/2.*

CM294 *Great White Heron and Map of Florida*

| CM294 | | MNHVF | UseVF |
|---|---|---|---|
| 3¢ | emerald *(122,362,000)* | .25 | .20 |
| | Plate block of 4 | .75 | |
| | FDC *(Dec. 5, 1947)* | | 3.00 |

**1948. GEORGE WASHINGTON CARVER ISSUE** memorialized the 5th anniversary of the death of the agricultural chemist. Born in slavery, and illiterate until he was almost 20, Dr. Carver spent 47 years as director of agricultural research at Tuskegee Institute, discovered hundreds of industrial uses for the peanut, sweet potato and soybean, aided Southern agriculture, and developed a new cotton strain known as Carver's Hybrid. *Intaglio, perfortated 10 1/2 x 11.*

CM295 *George Washington Carver*

| CM295 | | MNHVF | UseVF |
|---|---|---|---|
| 3¢ | bright purple *(121,548,000)* | .25 | .20 |
| | Plate block of 4 | .55 | |
| | FDC *Jan. 5, 1948)* | | 4.00 |

**1948. CALIFORNIA GOLD CENTENNIAL ISSUE** celebrated the 100th anniversary of the discovery of gold by James W. Marshall at Sutter's Mill in California. News of the discovery brought 100,000 gold-seeking "Forty-Niners," to the state from all parts of the world. *Intaglio, perforated 11 x 10 1/2.*

CM296 *Sutter's Mill, Calif.*

| CM296 | | MNHVF | UseVF |
|---|---|---|---|
| 3¢ | violet *(131,109,500)* | .25 | .20 |
| | Plate block of 4 | .55 | |
| | FDC *(Jan. 24, 1948)* | | 2.00 |

**1948. MISSISSIPPI TERRITORY ISSUE** commemorated the 150th anniversary of the establishment of the Mississippi Territory, comprising the present states of Mississippi and Alabama. Winthrop Sargent was its first governor. *Intaglio, perforated 11 x 10 1/2*

CM297 *Map and Original Seal of the Territory and Sargent*

| CM297 | | MNHVF | UseVF |
|---|---|---|---|
| 3¢ | brown purple *(122,650,500)* | .25 | .20 |
| | Plate block of 4 | .55 | |
| | FDC *(April 7, 1948)* | | 2.00 |

**1948. FOUR CHAPLAINS ISSUE** honored the heroic chaplain - George L. Fox, Clark V. Poling , John P. Washington and Alexander D. Goode - who sacrificed themselves for their comrades when the *S.S. Dorchester* sank on February 3, 1943. 2 ministers, a priest, and a rabbi, they gave up their life preservers so that others might live. *Intaglio, perforated 11 x 10 1/2.*

CM298 *Four chaplains and the Sinking S.S. Dorchester*

| CM298 | | MNHVF | UseVF |
|---|---|---|---|
| 3¢ | black *(121,953,500)* | .25 | .20 |
| | Plate block of 4 | .55 | |
| | FDC *(May 28, 1948)* | | 2.00 |

**1948. WISCONSIN CENTENNIAL ISSUE** commemorated the 100th anniversary of Wisconsin's admission as the 30th state. First explored by Jean Nicolet in 1634, it was surrendered by France to the British in 1760 and ceded by the British to the United States in 1783. It was part of the Northwest, Indiana, Illinois, and Michigan Territories before becoming the Wisconsin Territory in 1836. *Intaglio, perforated 11 x 10 1/2.*

CM299 *Scroll with Map of Wisconsin and State Capitol at Madison,*

| CM299 | | MNHVF | UseVF |
|---|---|---|---|
| 3¢ | violet *(115,250,000)* | .25 | .20 |
| | Plate block of 4 | .75 | |
| | FDC *(May 29, 1948)* | | 2.00 |

**1948. SWEDISH PIONEERS ISSUE** hailed the 100th anniversary of the arrival of Swedish pioneers in the Mid-west. The 12 stars on the stamp represent the 12 states in which the immigrants settled. *Intaglio, perforated 11 x 10 1/2.*

CM300 *Swedish Pioneer and Covered Wagon.*

| CM300 | | MNHVF | UseVF |
|---|---|---|---|
| 5¢ | blue *(64,198,500)* | .25 | .20 |
| | Plate block of 4 | .75 | |
| | FDC *(June 4, 1948)* | | 2.00 |

**1948. THE PROGRESS OF WOMEN ISSUE** observed the 100th anniversary of the first women's rights convention, held at Seneca Falls, NY, July 19-20, 1848. The convention, called by pioneer feminists Elizabeth Stanton and Lucretia Mott, began the women's suffrage movement to which both devoted the rest of their lives. Carie Chapman Catt led the suffrage campaign to its final victory in 1920, when the 19th Amendment gave women the vote. *Intaglio, perforated 11 x 10 1/2.*

CM301 *Elizabeth Stanton, Carrie Chapman Catt, and Lucretia Mott.*

| CM301 | | MNHVF | UseVF |
|---|---|---|---|
| 3¢ | violet *(117,642,500)* | .25 | .20 |
| | Plate block of 4 | .55 | |
| | FDC *(July 19, 1948)* | | 2.00 |

**1948. WILLIAM ALLEN WHITE ISSUE** honored the distinguished editor of the *Emporia Gazette,* from 1896, when his editorial "What's the Matter with Kansas?" attracted nationwide attention, until his death in 1944. White was known for his intellectual greatness and honesty, and he made the *Gazette* one of the most notable newspapers in American history. *Intaglio, perforated 10 1/2 x 11*

CM302 *William Allen White*

| CM302 | | MNHVF | UseVF |
|---|---|---|---|
| 3¢ | **bright purple** *(77,649,000)* | .25 | .20 |
| | Plate block of 4 | .55 | |
| | FDC *(July 31, 1948)* | | 2.00 |

**1948. UNITED STATES - CANADA FRIENDSHIP ISSUE** commemorated a century of friendship between the United States ad Canada. the 3,000-mile frontier between the 2 countries is the longest undefended border in the world. *Intaglio, perforated 11 x 10 1/2.*

CM303 *The Niagara Gorge Railway Suspension Bridge joining the United States and Canada*

| CM303 | | MNHVF | UseVF |
|---|---|---|---|
| 3¢ | **blue** *(113,474,500)* | .25 | .20 |
| | Plate block 4 | .55 | |
| | FDC *(Aug. 2, 1948)* | | 2.00 |

**1948. FRANCIS SCOTT KEY ISSUE** honored the author of our national anthem, *The Star Spangled Banner.* Negotiating the exchange of an American held by the British fleet off Baltimore, Key was detained aboard a warship while the British bombarded Fort McHenry on September 13, 1814. After the fort endured a 25- hour bombardment of more than 1,500 shells, Key was thrilled to see the American flag still flying over the parapet. The verses were written there on the back of an envelope, published as *The Defense of Fort McHenry,* and set to an old English tune, *To Anacreon in Heaven.* The song was made the U.S. national anthem March 3, 1931. *Intaglio, perforated 11 x 10 1/2.*

CM304 *Francis Scott Key and American Flags.*

| CM304 | | MNHVF | UseVF |
|---|---|---|---|
| 3¢ | **carmine** *(120,868,500)* | .25 | .20 |
| | Plate block of 4 | .55 | |
| | FDC *(Aug. 9, 1948)* | | 2.00 |

**1948. AMERICAN YOUTH ISSUE** paid tribute to the young people of America, and was a part of the celebration of Youth Month. *Intaglio, perforated 11 x 10 1/2.*

CM305 *Girl and Boy*

| CM305 | | MNHVF | UseVF |
|---|---|---|---|
| 3¢ | **blue** *(77,800,500)* | .25 | .20 |
| | Plate block of 4 | .55 | |
| | FDC *(Aug. 11, 1948)* | | 2.00 |

**1948. OREGON TERRITORY ISSUE** commemorated the 100th anniversary of the signing of the Oregon Bill by President James Polk. The bill, passed after 7 months' wrangling between slavery and anti-slavery elements in Congress, established a non-slaveholding Oregon Territory. Jason Lee, a Methodist minister, had petitioned Congress for territorial status as early as 1836. Dr. John McLoughlin, who founded Fort Vancouver in 1824 and for 22 years served as administrator for the Hudson's Bay company, is known as the "Father of Oregon." *Intaglio, perforated 11 x 10 1/2.*

CM306 *John McLoughlin, Jason Lee, and Wagon on Oregon Trail.*

| CM306 | | MNHVF | UseVF |
|---|---|---|---|
| 3¢ | **Venetian red** *(52,214,000)* | .25 | .20 |
| | Plate block of 4 | .55 | |
| | FDC *(Aug. 14, 1948)* | | |

**1948. HARLAN FISKE STONE ISSUE** honored the great American jurist, appointed to the U.S. Supreme Court by President Calvin Coolidge in 1925. Stone was named 12th chief justice of the United States by President Franklin D. Roosevelt in 1941, and served until his death in 1946. *Intaglio, perforated 10 1/2 x 11.*

CM307 *Harlan Fiske Stone*

| CM307 | | MNHVF | UseVF |
|---|---|---|---|
| 3¢ | **bright purple** *(53,958,100)* | .25 | .20 |
| | Plate block of 4 | .75 | |
| | FDC *(Aug. 25, 1948)* | | 2.00 |

**1948. PALOMAR MOUNTAIN OBSERVATORY ISSUE** commemorated the dedication of the world's largest telescope on Palomar Mountain, 66 miles north of San Diego, CA. The 200-inch reflecting telescope, named in honor of the astronomer George Ellery Hale, penetrates a billion light years into the sky. *Intaglio, perforated 10 1/2 x 11.*

CM308 *Palomar Mountain Observatory*

| CM308 | | MNHVF | UseVF |
|---|---|---|---|
| 3¢ | **blue** *(61,120,010)* | .25 | .20 |
| | Plate block of 4 | 1.00 | |
| | FDC *(Aug. 30, 1948)* | | 2.00 |
| | v. Vertical pair, imperforate between | 450. | |

**1948. CLARA BARTON ISSUE** honored the founder of the American Red Cross (CM96, CM358). A humanitarian, Miss Barton organized supply and nursing services for Union casualties in the Civil War (CM1723), successfully campaigned for an American society of the International Red Cross, and served as its first president, 1882-1904. *Intaglio, perforated 11 x 10 1/2.*

CM309 *Clara Barton and Red Cross*

**CM309**

| | | MNHVF | UseVF |
|---|---|---|---|
| 3¢ | **carmine** *(57,823,000)* | .25 | .20 |
| | Plate block of 4 | .60 | |
| | FDC *(Sept. 7, 1948)* | | 2.00 |

**1948. POULTRY INDUSTRY CENTENNIAL ISSUE** marked the 100th anniversary of the establishment of the American poultry industry. *Intaglio, perforated 11 x 10 1/2.*

CM310 *Light Brahma Rooster.*

**CM310**

| | | MNHVF | UseVF |
|---|---|---|---|
| 3¢ | **sepia** *(52,975,000)* | .25 | .20 |
| | Plate block of 4 | .60 | |
| | FDC *(Sept. 9, 1948)* | | 2.00 |

**1948. GOLD STAR MOTHERS ISSUE** honored mothers of those members of the armed forces who lost their lives in both World Wars. *Intaglio, perforated 10 1/2 X 11.*

CM311 *Gold Star and Palm Branch*

**CM311**

| | | MNHVF | UseVF |
|---|---|---|---|
| 3¢ | **yellow** *(77,149,000)* | .25 | .20 |
| | Plate block of 4 | .60 | |
| | FDC *(Sept. 21, 1948)* | | 2.00 |

**1948. FORT KEARNY ISSUE** commemorated the 100th anniversary of the establishment of Fort Kearny, Neb., an important frontier post in protecting settlers. *Intaglio, perforated 11 x 10 1/2.*

CM312 *Fort Kearny and Pioneers*

**CM312**

| | | MNHVF | UseVF |
|---|---|---|---|
| 3¢ | **violet** *(58,332,000)* | .25 | .20 |
| | Plate block of 4 | .60 | |
| | FDC *(Sept. 22, 1948)* | | 2.00 |

**1948. VOLUNTEER FIREMAN ISSUE** commemorated the 300th anniversary of the organization of America's first volunteer fire department in New Amsterdam (now New York City) by Peter Stuyvesant, director -general of the Dutch colony of New Netherland. *Intaglio, perforated 11 x 10 1/2.*

CM313 *Peter Stuyvesant and Fire Engines*

**CM313**

| | | MNHVF | UseVF |
|---|---|---|---|
| 3¢ | **rose carmine** *(56,228,000)* | .25 | .20 |
| | Plate block of 4 | .60 | |
| | FDC *(Oct. 4, 1948)* | | 2.00 |

**1948. INDIAN CENTENNIAL ISSUE** commemorated the arrival of the 5 Civilized Indian Tribes in the Indian Territory, which later became the State of Oklahoma. The Cherokee, Choctaw, Chickasaw, Muskogee (Creek), and Seminole tribes were called "civilized" because of their willingness to adopt the ways of white culture. *Intaglio, perforated 11 x 10 1/2.*

CM314 *Map of Oklahoma and the Seals of the Five Civilized Tribes.*

**CM314**

| | | MNHVF | UseVF |
|---|---|---|---|
| 3¢ | **brown** *(57,832,000)* | .25 | .20 |
| | Plate block of 4 | .60 | |
| | FDC *(Oct. 15, 1948)* | | 2.00 |

**1948. ROUGH RIDERS ISSUE** marked the 50th anniversary of the First U.S. Volunteer Calvary Regiment, composed of cowboys and adventurous young Easterners, and known as the Rough Riders.

Commanded by Col. Leonard Wood and Lt. Col. Theodore Roosevelt, they fought a spectacular dismounted action in the Battle of San Juan Hill, Cuba (July 1, 1898), seizing the heights and exposing Santiago and the Spanish fleet to artillery bombardment. Capt. William "Bucky" O'Neill, killed in the battle, was one of 1,572 American casualties. *Intaglio, perforated 11 x 10 1/2.*

CM315 *Capt. William O'Neill on Horse. From statue by Solon H. Borglum, Prescott, AZ.*

**CM315**

| | | MNHVF | UseVF |
|---|---|---|---|
| 3¢ | **brown purple** *(53,875,000)* | .25 | .20 |
| | Plate block of 4 | .60 | |
| | FDC *(Oct. 27, 1948)* | | 2.00 |

**1948. JULIETTE LOW ISSUE** honored the Girl Scouts of America and the memory of founder Juliette Gordon Low, who organized its first troop in Savannah, GA, in 1912. *Intaglio, perforated 11 x 10 1/2.*

CM316 *Juliette Gordon Low and Girl Scout Emblem.*

**CM316**

| | | MNHVF | UseVF |
|---|---|---|---|
| 3¢ | **blue green** *(63,834,000)* | .25 | .20 |
| | Plate block of 4 | .60 | |
| | FDC *(Oct. 9, 1948)* | | 1.00 |

**1948. WILL ROGERS ISSUE** memorialized America's beloved cowboy philosopher and humorist. A part-Indian native of Oklahoma, Rogers began as a vaudeville entertainer, delivering humorous monologues while doing lasso tricks. As a lecturer, movie actor and newspaper columnist, he was known for his shrewd but kindly comentary on current events. He died in an airplane crash at Point Barrow, Alaska, in 1935 with his friend Wiley Post (A96-97), holder of the 'round-the-world flight record. (See also CM929). *Intaglio, perforated 10 1/2 x 11.*

CM317 *Will Rogers*

| CM317 | | MNHVF | UseVF |
|---|---|---|---|
| 3¢ | **bright purple** *(67,162,200)* | .25 | .20 |
| | Plate block of 4 | .60 | |
| | FDC *(Nov. 4, 1948)* | | 1.00 |

**1948. FORT BLISS CENTENNIAL ISSUE** commemorated the 100th anniversary of Fort Bliss, TX, largest cavalry post in America and later a center for guided-missile training. *Intaglio, perforated 10 1/2 x 11.*

CM318 *Fort Bliss and Rocket Launch.*

| CM318 | | MNHVF | UseVF |
|---|---|---|---|
| 3¢ | **chestnut** *(64,561,000)* | .35 | .20 |
| | Plate block of 4 | 1.50 | |
| | FDC *(Nov. 5, 1948)* | | 1.00 |

**1948. MOINA MICHAEL ISSUE** honored the originator of the Memorial Poppy. John McCrae's poem. *In Flanders Fields,* spoke of wild poppies growing in the cemetaries of the dead of World War I. By an annual Memorial Day sale of poppies made by disabled veterans, Moina Michael used this symbol of the dead to assist the living. *Intaglio, perforated 11 x 10 1/2.*

CM319 *Moina Michael and Poppies*

| CM319 | | MNHVF | UseVF |
|---|---|---|---|
| 3¢ | **rose carmine** *(64,079,500)* | .25 | .20 |
| | Plate block of 4 | .55 | |
| | FDC *(Nov. 9, 1948)* | | 1.00 |

**1948. GETTYSBURG ADDRESS ISSUE** commemorated the 85th anniversary of the brief speech with which Abraham Lincoln, dedicated the military cemetery at Gettysburg, PA, (CM174), November 19, 1863. The 11 sentences, which Lincoln said "the world will little note nor long remember," have since been recognized as one of the noblest and most eloquent orations in the English language. *Intaglio, perforated 11 x 10 1/2.*

CM320 *Abraham Lincoln. From the statue by Daniel Chester French, State Capitol, Lincoln, Neb.*

| CM320 | | MNHVF | UseVF |
|---|---|---|---|
| 3¢ | **light blue** *(63,388,000)* | .25 | .20 |
| | Plate block of 4 | .55 | |
| | FDC *(Nov. 19, 1948)* | | 1.00 |

**1948. AMERICAN TURNERS ISSUE** recalled the centennial of the formation in Cincinnati, of an association of gymnasts and athletes, known as the American Turners Society, which comes from the German *"turnverein,"* meaning an exercise club. The organizer was Friedrich Hecker, a German refugee. *Intaglio, perforated 10 1/2 x 11.*

CM321 *American Turners Emblem*

| CM321 | | MNHVF | UseVF |
|---|---|---|---|
| 3¢ | **carmine** *(62,285,000)* | .25 | .20 |
| | Plate block of 4 | .80 | |
| | FDC *(Nov. 20, 1948)* | | 1.00 |

**1948. JOEL CHANDLER HARRIS ISSUE** commemorated the 100th anniversary of the birth of the Georgia journalist and author of *Uncle Remus* and *Br'er Rabbit.* His stories, written for children, also are treasured by adults for their insights into human nature. The richness of their background and humor make them the greatest works in the school of folk literature. *Intaglio, perforated 10 1/2 x 11.*

CM322 *Joel Chandler Harris*

| CM322 | | MNHVF | UseVF |
|---|---|---|---|
| 3¢ | **bright purple** *(57,492,610)* | .25 | .20 |
| | Plate block of 4 | .60 | |
| | FDC *(Dec. 9, 1948)* | | 1.00 |

**1949. MINNESOTA TERRITORY ISSUE** commemorated the 100th anniversary of the Minnesota Territory, with Alexander Ramsey as its first governor. It encompassed part of the Northwest Territory and part of the Louisiana Purchase. *Intaglio, perforated 11 x 10 1/2.*

CM323 *Pioneer and Ox Cart*

| CM323 | | MNHVF | UseVF |
|---|---|---|---|
| 3¢ | **blue green** *(99,190,000)* | .25 | .20 |
| | Plate block of 4 | .55 | |
| | FDC *(March 3, 1949)* | | 1.00 |

**1949. WASHINGTON AND LEE UNIVERSITY ISSUE** commemorated the 200th anniversary of the founding of Agusta Academy at Lexington, VA. In 1776, as a patriotic gesture, it was renamed Liberty Hall Academy. In 1798, endowed with $50,000 by George Washington it became Washington Academy. It was renamed Washington and Lee University in 1871 after the death of its president, Gen. Robert E. Lee (CM175). *Intaglio, perforated 11 x 10 1/2.*

CM324 *George Washington, University, and Robert E. Lee*

| CM324 | | MNHVF | UseVF |
|---|---|---|---|
| 3¢ | **bright blue** *(104,790,000)* | .25 | .20 |
| | Plate block of 4 | .55 | |
| | FDC *(April 12, 1949)* | | 1.00 |

**1949. PUERTO RICO ELECTION ISSUE** celebrated Puerto Rico's first gubernatorial election, November 2, 1948. Acquired from Spain in 1898, the island was an unorganized territory until 1917, when its residents were made U.S. citizens. A bill signed by President Harry Truman in 1947 gave it the right to choose its own chief executive by popular vote. Luis Muãoz Marin (927), its first elected governor, was sworn into office January 2, 1949. *Intaglio, perforated 11 x 10 1/2.*

CM325 *Puerto Rican Farmer with Cog Wheel and Ballot Box.*

| CM325 | | MNHVF | UseVF |
|---|---|---|---|
| 3¢ | **dull green** *(108,805,000)* | .25 | .20 |
| | Plate block of 4 | .55 | |
| | FDC *(April 27, 1949)* | | 1.00 |

**1949. ANNAPOLIS TERCENTENARY ISSUE** marked the 300th anniversary of the founding of Annapolis by the colonists of Lord Baltimore's Maryland Plantation (CM126). Named for Queen Anne of England, it is the site of the U.S. Naval Academy (CM181). *Intaglio, perforated 11 x 10 1/2.*

CM326 *Map of 1718 and Seal of Lord Baltimore.*

| CM326 | | MNHVF | UseVF |
|---|---|---|---|
| 3¢ | **turquoise green** *(107,340,000)* | .25 | .20 |
| | Plate block of 4 | .55 | |
| | FDC *(May 23, 1949)* | | 1.00 |

**1949. GAR ISSUE** commemorated the 83rd and final encampment, August 28 at Indianapolis, IN., of the Civil War Union-veterans' organization known as the Grand Army of the Republic. Founded in 1866 by Benjamin Frankin Stevenson, its members had included five presidents of the United States. *Intaglio, perforated 11 x 10 1/2.*

CM327 *Union Soldier and GAR Veteran*

| CM327 | | MNHVF | UseVF |
|---|---|---|---|
| 3¢ | **carmine** *(117,020,000)* | .25 | .20 |
| | Plate block of 4 | .55 | |
| | FDC *(Aug. 19, 1949)* | | 1.00 |

**1949. EDGAR ALLAN POE ISSUE** commemorated the 100th anniversary of the death of a world- renowned American writer. Born 1809 in Richmond, he was expelled from the University of Virginia for bad

debts and from the U.S. Military Academy for disobedience and neglect of duty, and went on to a brilliant but erratic career. Now recognized as one of the world's great lyric poets, he also was one of the originators of the modern detective story. *Intaglio, perforated 10 1/2 x 11.*

CM328 *Edgar Allan Poe*

| CM328 | | MNHVF | UseVF |
|---|---|---|---|
| 3¢ | **bright purple** *(122,633,000)* | .25 | .20 |
| | Plate block of 4 | .65 | |
| | Top inner frame line missing (position 42 of bottom-left pane of plate 24143) | — | |
| | FDC *(Oct. 7, 1949)* | | 1.00 |

**1950. AMERICAN BANKERS ASSOCIATION ISSUE** commemorates the 75th anniversary of its founding at Saratoga Springs, NY. The group made valuable contributions to the growth and development of American industry and life. *Intaglio, perforated 11 x 10 1/2.*

CM329 *Areas of Banking Service*

| CM329 | | MNHVF | UseVF |
|---|---|---|---|
| 3¢ | **green** *(130,960,000)* | .25 | .20 |
| | Plate block of 4 | .55 | |
| | FDC *(Jan. 3, 1950)* | | 1.00 |

**1950. SAMUEL GOMPERS ISSUE** commemorated the 100th anniversary of the birth of the British-born labor leader who helped to found the American Federation of Labor and served as its president from 1886 until his death in 1924. Acknowledged leader of the American labor movement, Gompers concentrated it on the betterment of wages, hours and working conditions. *Intaglio, perforated 10 1/2 x 11.*

CM330 *Samuel Gompers*

| CM330 | | MNHVF | UseVF |
|---|---|---|---|
| 3¢ | **bright purple** *(128,478,000)* | .25 | .20 |
| | Plate block of 4 | .55 | |
| | FDC *(Jan. 27, 1950)* | | 1.00 |

**1950. CAPITOL DOME STATUE OF FREEDOM ISSUE** Intaglio, perforated 10 1/2 x 11 (CM331) or 11 x 10 1/2 CM332-34).

CM331 *Capitol Dome's Statue of Freedom by Thomas Crawford.*

| CM331 | | MNHVF | UseVF |
|---|---|---|---|
| 3¢ | light blue *(132,090,000)* | .25 | .20 |
| | Plate block of 4 | .60 | |
| | FDC *(April 20, 1950)* | | 1.00 |

## 1950. EXECUTIVE MANSION ISSUE

CM332 *Executive Mansion, which Congress in 1902 officially designated The White House, was designed in 1792 by James Hoban (CM994-95) , who is believed to have patterned it after the Duke of Leinster's palace in Dublin . Its sandstone walls were painted white after the British burned it in 1814. It was enlarged by William Howard Taft and by both Roosevelts. In 1951-52, in bad disrepair, it was completely reconstructed with  in its original walls during the presidency of Harry Truman.*

| CM332 | | MNHVF | UseVF |
|---|---|---|---|
| 3¢ | dull green *(130,050,000)* | .25 | .20 |
| | Plate block of 4 | .65 | |
| | FDC *(June 12, 1950)* | | 1.00 |

## 1950. SUPREME COURT ISSUE

CM333 *The Supreme Court Building*

| CM333 | | MNHVF | UseVF |
|---|---|---|---|
| 3¢ | bluish violet *(131,350,000)* | .25 | .20 |
| | Plate block of 4 | .60 | |
| | FDC *(Aug. 2, 1950* | | 1.00 |

*Printed by intaglio, perforated 11 x 10 1/2.*

## 1950. U.S. CAPITOL ISSUE *Intaglio, perforated 11 x 10 1/2.*

CM334 *The U.S. Capitol is the seat of the Congress. Designed by William Thornton, it was built during 1793-1800, restored in 1814-17 after being burned by British troops in the War of 1812, and greatly enlarged in 1861-65, when the central dome was added.*

| CM334 | | MNHVF | UseVF |
|---|---|---|---|
| 3¢ | bright purple *(129,980,000)* | .25 | .20 |
| | Plate block of 4 | .80 | 1.00 |
| | Gripper cracks | — | |
| | FDC *(Nov. 22, 1950)* | | 1.00 |

## 1950. RAILROAD ENGINEERS ISSUE paid tribute to American railway and pictured the fabled hero, "Casey" Jones. Born John Luther Jones in 1864, he acquired the nickname "Casey" for having lived at one time in Cayce, KY. A railroader from boyhood, he spent the last 10 years of his life as an engineer with the Illinois Central Railroad. The "big eight-wheeler" in which he won his fame was a part of the Cannonball Express between Chicago and New Orleans, and Jones' run was between Canton Miss. and Memphis, Tenn. He was killed April 30, 1900, when his train crashed into the rear of a freight train near Vaughn, Miss. The ballad about the wreck is known throughout America. *Intaglio, perforated 11 x 10 1/2.*

CM335 *"Casey" Jones, Steam and Diesel Locomotives.*

| CM335 | | MNHVF | UseVF |
|---|---|---|---|
| 3¢ | brown purple *(122,315,000)* | .25 | .20 |
| | Plate block of 4 | .60 | |
| | FDC *(April 29, 1950)* | | 1.00 |

## 1950. KANSAS CITY CENTENNIAL ISSUE commemorated the 100th anniversary of the incorporation of Kansas City, MO. The "Gateway to the West," was first settled by a French fur trapper named Louis Barthelot. *Intaglio, perforated 11 x 10 1/2.*

CM336 *Kansas City in 1950 and Westport Landing in 1850.*

| CM336 | | MNHVF | UseVF |
|---|---|---|---|
| 3¢ | violet *(122,170,000)* | .25 | .20 |
| | Plate block of 4 | .55 | |
| | FDC *(June 3, 1950)* | | 1.00 |

## 1950. BOY SCOUT ISSUE honored the 40th anniversary of the Boy Scouts of America, and the 2nd National Jamboree at Valley Forge, Penn. The organization (CM454, CM1173) was incorporated Feb. 8, 1910, formed by uniting Ernest Thompson Seton's *Woodcraft Indians* with Daniel Beard's *Sons of Daniel Boone,* with ideas from the English program of Robert Baden-Powell. *Intaglio, perforated 11 x 10 1/2.*

CM337 *Scouts, Statue of Liberty, and Scout badge.*

| CM337 | | MNHVF | UseVF |
|---|---|---|---|
| 3¢ | sepia *(131,635,000)* | .25 | .20 |
| | Plate block of 4 | .60 | |
| | FDC *(June 30, 1950)* | | 1.00 |

## 1950. INDIANA TERRITORY SESQUICENTENNIAL ISSUE marked the 150th anniversary of the Indiana Territory. William Henry Harrison, later a military hero and 9th president, was the territory's first governor. *Intaglio, perforated 11 x 10 1/2.*

CM338 *Gov. William Henry Harrison and First Capitol at Vincennes.*

| CM338 | | MNHVF | UseVF |
|---|---|---|---|
| 3¢ | light blue *(121,860,000)* | .25 | .20 |
| | Plate block of 4 | .55 | |
| | FDC *(July 4, 1950)* | | 1.00 |

## 1950. CALIFORNIA STATEHOOD CENTENNIAL ISSUE commemorated the 100th anniversary of California's admission as the 31st state. First settled by the Spaniards under Gaspar de Portola, the territory was ceded to the United States by Mexico in 1848. Its development was greatly accelerated by the discovery of gold that year at Sutter's Mill (CM296). *Intaglio, perforated 11 x 10 1/2.*

CM339 *Gold Miner, Pioneers and S.S. Oregon*

**CM339**

| | | MNHVF | UseVF |
|---|---|---|---|
| 3¢ | **yellow** *(121,120,000)* | .25 | .20 |
| | Plate block of 4 | .55 | |
| | FDC *(Sept. 9, 1950)* | | 1.00 |

**1951. CONFEDERTE VETERANS ISSUE** commemorated the final re-union, May 30 at Norfolk, VA. of the Veterans of the Confederacy, organized in New Orleans in 1889. *Intaglio, perforated 11 x 10 1/2.*

CM340 *Confederate Soldier and Veteran*

**CM340**

| | | MNHVF | UseVF |
|---|---|---|---|
| 3¢ | **gray** *(119,120,000)* | .25 | .20 |
| | Plate block of 4 | .60 | |
| | FDC *(May 30, 1951)* | | 1.00 |

**1951. NEVADA CENTENNIAL ISSUE** commemorated the first settlement of Nevada in 1851. The discovery of the Comstock Lode in 1856 led to rapid development of the territory; by 1863 it had 40,000 inhabitants and was producing as much as $30,000,000 worth of silver a year. Nevada was admitted to statehood in 1864. *Intaglio, perforated 11 x 10 1/2.*

CM341 *Carson Valley Homestead*

**CM341**

| | | MNHVF | UseVF |
|---|---|---|---|
| 3¢ | **light olive green** *(112,125,000)* | .25 | .20 |
| | Plate block of 4 | .55 | |
| | FDC *(July 14, 1951)* | | 1.00 |

**1952. DETROIT ISSUE** noted the 250th anniversary of the landing of Antoine de la Mothe Cadillac, at what is now Detroit, with a charter from King Louis XIV of France. Established by Cadillac as a military post to protect his fur trade, Detroit became the automotive capital of the world. *Intaglio, perforated 11 x 10 1/2.*

CM342 *Landing of Cadillac at Detroit, Modern Skyline.*

**CM342**

| | | MNHVF | UseVF |
|---|---|---|---|
| 3¢ | **light blue** *(114,140,000)* | .25 | .20 |
| | Plate block of 4 | .55 | |
| | FDC *(July 24, 1951)* | | 1.00 |

**1951. COLORADO STATEHOOD ISSUE** commemorated the 75th anniversary of Colorado's admission as the 38th state. Formed of lands that were once part of the Louisiana Purchase and of the Texas and Mexican cessions, it became a territory in 1861. *Intaglio, perforated 11 x 10 1/2.*

CM343 *Capitol at Denver, Mount of the Holy Cross, Bronco Buster.*

**CM343**

| | | MNHVF | UseVF |
|---|---|---|---|
| 3¢ | **violet blue** *(114,490,000)* | .25 | .20 |
| | Plate block of 4 | .55 | |
| | FDC *(Aug. 1, 1951)* | | 1.00 |

**1951. AMERICAN CHEMICAL SOCIETY ISSUE** marks the 75th anniversary of the American Chemical Society. *Intaglio, perforated 11 x 10 1/2.*

CM344 *ACS Emblem, Industrial Chemical Equipment*

**CM344**

| | | MNHVF | UseVF |
|---|---|---|---|
| 3¢ | **brown purple** *(117,200,000)* | .25 | .20 |
| | Plate block of 4 | .55 | |
| | FDC *(Sept. 4, 1951)* | | 1.00 |

**1951. BATTLE OF BROOKLYN ISSUE** commemorated the 175th anniversary of the Battle of Long Island, August 27, 1776. British and Hessian troops, under Clinton, Howe, Percy, Cornwallis and DeHesiter, attacked the American fortifications at what is now Prospect Park in Brooklyn, overpowered the desperate Americans and captured their commander, Gen. John Sulivan (CM88). General Washington arrived late in the day with additional troops, saw the futility of making a stand, and withdrew the remaining American forces in a skillful night retreat. *Intaglio, perforated 11 x 10 1/2.*

CM345 *Gen. George Washington Evacuating the Army.*

**CM345**

| | | MNHVF | UseVF |
|---|---|---|---|
| 3¢ | **violet** *(16,130,000)* | .25 | .20 |
| | Plate block of 4 | .60 | |
| | FDC *(Dec. 10, 1951)* | | 1.00 |

**1952. BETSY ROSS ISSUE** celebrated the 200th birthday of Betsy Ross, the Philadelphia upholsterer, whom the Continental Congress engaged in 1777 to make the first American flag. The legend that she designed the original Stars and Stripes generally is disputed, and the credit given to Francis Hopkinson, one of the signers of the Declaration of Independence. *Intaglio, perforated 11 x 10 1/2.*

CM346 *Birth of Our Nation's Flag. From a painting by C.H. Weisgerber.*

**CM346**

| | | MNHVF | UseVF |
|---|---|---|---|
| 3¢ | **carime red** *(116,175,000)* | .25 | .20 |
| | Plate block of 4 | .55 | |
| | FDC *(Jan. 2, 1952)* | | 1.00 |

**1952. 4-H CLUB ISSUE** honored the farm youth organization whose emblem - the letter H on each leaf of a four-leaf-clover - signifies the 4-H pledge: "I pledge My Head to clear thinking. My Heart to great Loyalty. My Hands to larger service. My Health to better living, for my club, my community, and my country." *Intaglio, perforated 11 x 10 1/2.*

CM347 *American Farm, 4-H Emblem and Members*

**CM347**

| | | MNHVF | UseVF |
|---|---|---|---|
| 3¢ | **blue green** *(115,945,000)* | .25 | .20 |
| | Plate block of 4 | .55 | |
| | FDC *(Jan. 15, 1952)* | | 1.00 |

**1952. AMERICAN RAILROADS ISSUE** commemorated the 125th anniversary of the chartering of the B & O Railroad by the Maryland Legislature. The first passenger railroad in the United States, it was begun on July 4, 1828 with Charles Carroll of Carrollton in attendance, the last living signer of the Declaration of Independence. The first 14-mile section opened to horse-drawn traffic May 24, 1830. *Intaglio, perforated 11 x 10 1/2.*

CM348 *Charter, Horse-Drawn Car, Tom Thumb and Modern Diesel.*

| CM348 | | MNHVF | UseVF |
|---|---|---|---|
| 3¢ | light blue *(112,540,000)* | .25 | .20 |
| | Plate block of 4 | .55 | |
| | FDC *(Feb. 28, 1952)* | | 1.00 |

**1952. AAA ISSUE** commemorated the 50th anniversary of the American Automobile Association, (the Tripple-A) and honored its contribution to motoring safety and convenience. *Intaglio, perforated 11 x 10 1/2.*

CM349 *Children and Crossing Guard, Automobiles of 1902 and 1952.*

| CM349 | | MNHVF | UseVF |
|---|---|---|---|
| 3¢ | blue *(117,415,000)* | .25 | .20 |
| | Plate block of 4 | .55 | |
| | FDC *(March 4, 1952)* | | 1.00 |

**1952. NATO ISSUE** commemorated the third anniversary of the signing of the North Atlantic Treaty Organization, in which the United States, Canada and 10 Western European nations pledged that an armed attack against any of them would be considered an attack against all. *Intaglio, perforated 11 x 10 1/2.*

CM350 *The Torch of Liberty, Globe.*

| CM350 | | MNHVF | UseVF |
|---|---|---|---|
| 3¢ | violet *(2,899,580,000)* | .25 | .20 |
| | Plate block of 4 | .55 | |
| | FDC *(April 4, 1952)* | | 1.00 |
| | v.  thin, translucent paper | — | |

**1952. GRAND COULEE DAM ISSUE** commemorated 50 years of federal cooperation in developing western rivers, and paid tribute to the world's largest concrete dam, the Grand Coulee, built and operated by the Bureau of Reclamation on Washington's Columbia River. *Intaglio, perforated 11 x 10 1/2.*

CM351 *Grand Coulee Dam Spillway*

| CM351 | | MNHVF | UseVF |
|---|---|---|---|
| 3¢ | blue green *(114,540,000)* | .25 | .20 |
| | Plate block of 4 | .55 | |
| | FDC *(May 15, 1952)* | | 1.00 |

**1952. LAFAYETTE ISSUE** commemorated the 175th anniversary of the arrival in America of Marquis de Lafayette (CM409, CM866) to fight for American freedom. Commissioned a major general at 20 by the Continental Congress, he fought valiantly at Brandywine and Monmouth and in the Virginia campaign ending in the British surrender at Yorktown (CM97). After the war he was a significant figure in the French Revolution. He returned briefly to the United States in 1784 and again for a triumphant tour in 1824. *Intaglio, perforated 11 x 10 1/2.*

CM352 *Lafayette, Flags of the United States and France.*

| CM352 | | MNHVF | UseVF |
|---|---|---|---|
| 3¢ | bright blue *(113,135,000)* | .25 | .20 |
| | Plate block of 4 | .55 | |
| | FDC *(June 13, 1952)* | | 1.00 |

**1952. MOUNT RUSHMORE MEMORIAL ISSUE** marked the 25th anniversary of the dedication of the monument in the Black Hills of South Dakota. The first such memorial authorized by the government, it was financed by South Dakota. The sculptor Gutzon Borglum designed and carved the enormous heads of Washington, Jefferson, Lincoln and Roosevelt from the solid rock of the mountain. *Intaglio, perforated 11 x 10 1/2.*

CM353 *Mount Rushmore*

| CM353 | | MNHVF | UseVF |
|---|---|---|---|
| 3¢ | blue green *(116,255,000)* | .25 | .20 |
| | Plate block of 4 | .55 | |
| | FDC *(Aug. 11, 1952)* | | 1.00 |

**1952. ENGINEERING CENTENNIAL ISSUE** commemorated the 100th anniversary of the American Society of Civil Engineers. The George Washington Bridge in New York City, shown on the stamp, was chosen as a symbol of the great engineering projects for which society members are responsible. *Intaglio, perforated 11 x 10 1/2.*

CM354 *The George Washington Bridge and an Old Covered Bridge.*

| CM354 | | MNHVF | UseVF |
|---|---|---|---|
| 3¢ | ultramarine *(113,860,000)* | .25 | .20 |
| | Plate block of 4 | .55 | |
| | FDC *(Sept. 6, 1952)* | | 1.00 |

**1952. SERVICE WOMEN ISSUE** honors women in the U.S. armed services. More than 40,000 women served in World War II and contributed immeasurably to Allied victory. *Intaglio, perforated 11 x 10 1/2.*

CM355 *Marine Corp., Army, Navy and Air Force Service Women.*

**CM355**

| | | MNHVF | UseVF |
|---|---|---|---|
| 3¢ | blue *(124,260,000)* | .25 | .20 |
| | Plate block of 4 | .55 | |
| | FDC *(Sept. 11, 1952)* | | 1.00 |

**1952. GUTENBERG BIBLE ISSUE** commemorated the 500th anniversary of the first European book published from movable type, attributed to Johann Gutenberg of Mainz, Germany. Movable type replaced the tedious and costly process of hand copying. It made books available to many people, thus spreading knowledge on an unprecedented scale. *Intaglio, perforated 11 x 10 1/2.*

CM356 *Gutenberg Showing a Proof to the Elector of Mainz. From a mural by Edward Laning in the New York Public Library.*

**CM356**

| | | MNHVF | UseVF |
|---|---|---|---|
| 3¢ | violet *(115,735,000)* | .25 | .20 |
| | Plate block of 4 | .55 | |
| | FDC *(Sept. 30, 1952)* | | 1.00 |

**1952. NEWSPAPERBOYS OF AMERICA ISSUE** recognized the America's newsboys and the value of their early business training. It also complimented the meeting of the International Circulation Managers Association, at Philadelphia, PA, in October. *Intaglio, perforated 11 x 10 1/2.*

CM357 *Paperboy, Torch of "Free Enterprise" and Neighborhood.*

**CM357**

| | | MNHVF | UseVF |
|---|---|---|---|
| 3¢ | violet *(115,430,000)* | .25 | .20 |
| | Plate block of 4 | .55 | |
| | FDC *(Oct. 4, 1952)* | | 1.00 |

**1952. INTERNATIONAL RED CROSS ISSUE** honored the humanitarian society founded by Jean Henri Dunant and others in 1864. Its headquarters in Geneva, Switzerland, provides an exchange for all the Red Cross societies of the world. Maintaining strict neutrality, the organization extends relief to civilian victims of war, furnishes aid to war prisoners and monitors their treatment by their captors. (See also CM96, CM525 and CM969) *Intaglio, perforated 11 x 10 1/2.*

CM358 *Red Cross Enlightening the World.*

**CM358**

| | | MNHVF | UseVF |
|---|---|---|---|
| 3¢ | ultramarine and scarlet *(136,220,000)* | .25 | .20 |
| | Plate block of 4 | .55 | |
| | FDC *(Nov. 21, 1952)* | | 1.00 |

**1953. NATIONAL GUARD ISSUE** honors the oldest military organization in the United States, a service older than the nation itself (C110). The Guard, under state control except in war, has served with distinction in every national conflict. In peacetime, it aids in disasters such as floods, forest fires and hurricanes. *Intaglio, perforated 11 x 10 1/2.*

CM359 *National Guard in War and Peace*

**CM359**

| | | MNHVF | UseVF |
|---|---|---|---|
| 3¢ | light blue *(114,894,600)* | .25 | .20 |
| | Plate block of 4 | .55 | |
| | FDC *(Feb. 23, 1953)* | | 1.00 |

**1953. OHIO SESQUICENTENNIAL ISSUE** commemorated the 150th anniversry of Ohio as the 17th state. A part of the Northwest Territory, Ohio became a state March 1, 1803, with Chillicothe as its capital. Columbus has been the capital since 1817. Ohio has given the nation 8 presidents, and its history is reflected in many U.S. stamps. *Intaglio, perforated 11 x 10 1/2.*

CM360 *Ohio Map and Seal*

**CM360**

| | | MNHVF | UseVF |
|---|---|---|---|
| 3¢ | sepia *(117,706,000)* | .25 | .20 |
| | Plate block of 4 | .55 | |
| | FDC *(March 2, 1953)* | | 1.00 |

**1953. WASHINGTON TERRITORY ISSUE** commemorated the 100th anniversary of the Washington Territory. Visited by the Lewis and Clark Expedition in 1803, it was settled in 1811. *Intaglio, perforated 11 x 10 1/2.*

CM361 *Centennial Crest, Pioneer and Vista*

**CM361**

| | | MNHVF | UseVF |
|---|---|---|---|
| 3¢ | blue green *(114,190,000)* | .25 | .20 |
| | Plate block of 4 | .55 | |
| | FDC *(March 2, 1953)* | | 1.00 |

**1953. LOUISIANA PURCHASE ISSUE** commemorated the 150th anniversary of the Louisiana Purchase from France. (See CM32-CM36.) *Intaglio, perforated 11 x 10 1/2.*

CM362 *Monroe, Livingston and de Barbe-Marbois Signing Transfer. From the sculpture by Karl Bitter in the Jefferson Memorial, St. Louis Mo.*

**CM362**

| | | MNHVF | UseVF |
|---|---|---|---|
| 3¢ | brown purple *(113,990,000)* | .25 | .20 |
| | Plate block of 4 | .55 | |
| | FDC *(April 30, 1953)* | | 1.00 |

**1953. OPENING OF JAPAN ISSUE** commemorated the centennial of negotiations between Commodore Matthew C. Perry and representatives of the emperor of Japan, leading to the Treaty of Kanagawa in 1854. Japan, isolated since the early 17th century, agreed to open 2 ports to U.S. trade and make provision for shipwrecked American seamen. In 1858 Japan opened additional ports, granted residence rights to Americans, and exchanged diplomatic representatives. *Intaglio, perforated 11 x 10 1/2.*

CM363 *Commodore Perry and Vessels in Tokyo Bay.*

| CM363 | | MNHVF | UseVF |
|---|---|---|---|
| 5¢ | **blue green** *(89,289,600)* | .25 | .20 |
| | Plate block of 4 | .75 | |
| | FDC *(July 14, 1953)* | | 1.00 |

**1953. AMERICAN BAR ASSOCIATION ISSUE** honored the organization's 75th anniversary and its efforts in securing uniform state laws, promoting sound legislation and advancing the administration of justice. *Intaglio, perforated 11 x 10 1/2.*

CM364 *Wisdom, Justice, Divine Inspiration and Truth. Frieze on a wall of the Supreme Court.*

| CM364 | | MNHVF | UseVF |
|---|---|---|---|
| 3¢ | **light reddish violet** *(114,865,000)* | .25 | .20 |
| | Plate block of 4 | .75 | |
| | FDC *(Aug. 24, 1953)* | | 1.00 |

**1953. SAGAMORE HILL ISSUE** commemorated its dedication as a national shrine, June 14th. Sagamore Hill was the Oyster Bay, N.Y. home of Theodore Roosevelt and it was there that Roosevelt died on January 6, 1919. *Intaglio, perforated 11 x 10 1/2.*

CM365 *Sagamore Hill Home of Theodore Roosevelt*

| CM365 | | MNHVF | UseVF |
|---|---|---|---|
| 3¢ | **green** *(115,780,000)* | .25 | .20 |
| | Plate block of 4 | .55 | |
| | FDC *(Sept. 14, 1953)* | | 1.00 |

**1953. FUTURE FARMERS OF AMERICA ISSUE** honored the 25th anniversary of the founding of the Future Farmers of America under the auspices of the U.S. Office of Education. *Intaglio, perforated 11 x 10 1/2.*

CM366 *Future Farmer and Farmland*

| CM366 | | MNHVF | UseVF |
|---|---|---|---|
| 3¢ | **bright blue** *(115,224,600)* | .25 | .20 |
| | Plate block of 4 | .55 | |
| | FDC *(Oct. 13, 1953)* | | 1.00 |

**1953. TRUCKING INDUSTRY ISSUE** marked the 50th anniversary of the American Trucking Association and its convention in Los Angeles. *Intaglio, perforated 11 x 10 1/2.*

CM367 *Truck, Farm and City*

| CM367 | | MNHVF | UseVF |
|---|---|---|---|
| 3¢ | **violet** *(123,709,600)* | .25 | .20 |
| | Plate block of 4 | .55 | |
| | FDC *(Oct. 27, 1953)* | | 1.00 |

**1953. GENERAL PATTON ISSUE** honored Gen. George S. Patton, Jr., and the armred forces of the U.S. Army. Patton was a hero of the Battle of the Bulge in World War II. *Intaglio, perforated 11 x 10 1/2.*

CM368 *Gen. Patton and Patton Tanks in Action.*

| CM368 | | MNHVF | UseVF |
|---|---|---|---|
| 3¢ | **bluish violet** *(114,789,600)* | .25 | .20 |
| | Plate block of 4 | .65 | |
| | FDC *(Nov. 11, 1953)* | | 1.00 |

**1953. NEW YORK CITY TERCENTENARY ISSUE** commemorated the 300th anniversary of the incorporation of New Amsterdam as a city. Feb. 2, 1953. *Intaglio, perforated 11 x 10 1/2.*

CM369 *Dutch Ship and New Amsterdam, Modern New York City Skyline*

| CM369 | | MNHVF | UseVF |
|---|---|---|---|
| 3¢ | **bright purple** *(115,759,600)* | .25 | .20 |
| | Plate block of 4 | .55 | |
| | FDC *(Nov. 20, 1953)* | | 1.00 |

**1953. GADSDEN PURCHASE ISSUE** commemorated the 100th anniversary of the purchase of territory from Mexico to add territory to the states of Arizona and New Mexico and settle a dispute dating from the Guadelupe-Hildalgo Treaty of 1848. *Intaglio, perforated 11 x 10 1/2.*

CM370 *Gadsen Purchase Map and Pioneers*

| CM370 | | MNHVF | UseVF |
|---|---|---|---|
| 3¢ | **Venetian red** *(115,759,600)* | .25 | .20 |
| | Plate block of 4 | .55 | |
| | FDC *(Dec. 30, 1953)* | | 1.00 |

**1953. COLUMBIA UNIVERSITY ISSUE** commemorated the 200th anniversary of King's College, which closed during the Revolution to re-open as Columbia College. It now includes many colleges such as Teacher's College, Barnard College, and schools of medicine, pharmacy, engineering, law, architecture, and journalism among others. Located in New York City, it is one of the oldest and largest U.S. universities. *Intaglio, perforated 11 x 10 1/2.*

CM371 *Low Memorial Library*

| CM371 | | MNHVF | UseVF |
|---|---|---|---|
| 3¢ | **cobalt blue** *(118,540,000)* | .25 | .20 |
| | Plate block of 4 | .55 | |
| | FDC *(Jan. 4, 1954)* | | 1.00 |

**1954. NEBRASKA TERRITORIAL CENTENNIAL ISSUE** honors the centennial of the Nebraska Territory, under the Kansas-Nebraska Bill. *Intaglio, perforated 11 x 10 1/2.*

CM372 *Mitchell Pass, Scotts Bluff and The Sower. From a statue by Lee Lawrie from a painting by Millet.*

| CM372 | | MNHVF | UseVF |
|---|---|---|---|
| 3¢ | **violet** *(115,810,000)* | .25 | .20 |
| | Plate block of 4 | .55 | |
| | FDC *(May 7, 1954)* | | 1.00 |

**1954. KANSAS TERRITORIAL CENTENNIAL ISSUE** commemorated the centennial of the Kansas Territory from unorganized Indian reservations. The Kansas-Nebraska bill repealed the 1820 Missouri Compromise that had drawn a line north of which slavery could not exist. The politicians intended Kansas to be a slave state and Nebraska free, by "popular sovereignty." The rivalry for settling the status of these 2 new territories was one of the direct causes of the War Between the States. *Intaglio, perforated 11 x 10 1/2.*

CM373 *Wagon Train and Wheat Field*

| CM373 | | MNHVF | UseVF |
|---|---|---|---|
| 3¢ | **salmon** *(113,603,700)* | .25 | .20 |
| | Plate block of 4 | .55 | |
| | FDC *(May 31, 1954)* | | 1.00 |

**1954. GEORGE EASTMAN ISSUE** commemorated the 100th birthday of George Eastman at Waterville, NY. At an early age he went to Rochester where he gained fame as an inventor and philanthropist. His inventions made photography possible for virtually everyone, and his invention of transparent film created motion pictures. He gave $100 million to educational and musical institutions and dental clinics around the world. He was a proponent of the Community Chest, and profit sharing with employees. *Intaglio, perforated 10 1/2 x 11.*

CM374 *George Eastman*

| CM374 | | MNHVF | UseVF |
|---|---|---|---|
| 3¢ | **brown purple** *(121,100,000)* | .25 | .20 |
| | Plate block of 4 | .55 | |
| | FDC *(July 12, 1954)* | | 1.00 |

**1954. LEWIS AND CLARK EXPEDITION ISSUE** commemorated the trip made by Meriwether Lewis and William Clark, (brother of George Rogers Clark) at the request of President Jefferson to secure more information about the country west of the Mississippi. The party of 30 made its way overland to Oregon and the Pacific Ocean, leaving St. Louis in May 1804, and returning in 1806 after having been given up as lost. They owed much of the success of the venture to Sacagawea (Birdwoman), a Shoshone Indian woman who acted as their guide (CM1690). *Intaglio, perforated 11 x 10 1/2.*

CM375 *Lewis and Clark from a statue by Charles Keck at Charlottesville, Va., and Sacagawea from a statue by Leonard Crunekle at Bismark, ND.*

| CM375 | | MNHVF | UseVF |
|---|---|---|---|
| 3¢ | **brown** *(116,078,150)* | .25 | .20 |
| | Plate block of 4 | .55 | |
| | FDC *(July 28, 1954)* | | 1.00 |

**1955. PENNSYLVANIA ACADEMY OF FINE ARTS ISSUE** honored the 150th anniversary of that institution. The design of the stamp is a reproduction of the painting *Peale in his Museum*, a self-portrait of Charles Willson Peale (1741-1827), now in the collection of the Pennsylvania Academy, of which Peale was one of the founders. *Intaglio, perforated 10 1/2 X 11.*

CM376 *Charles Willson Peale in His Museum*

| CM376 | | MNHVF | UseVF |
|---|---|---|---|
| 3¢ | **brown purple** *(116,139,800)* | .25 | .20 |
| | Plate block of 4 | .55 | |
| | FDC *(Jan. 15, 1955)* | | 1.00 |

**1955. FIRST LAND-GRANT COLLEGE ISSUE** commemorated the centennial of the establishment of Michigan State University and Pennsylvania State University. Land grants, originally intended for settlers and homesteaders were extended in 1854 to various groups for services for the national welfare. *Intaglio, perforated 11 x 10 1/2.*

CM377 *Open Book and Symbols of Agriculture, Mining, Chemistry, Engineering.*

| CM377 | | MNHVF | UseVF |
|---|---|---|---|
| 3¢ | **emerald green** *(120,484,800)* | .25 | .20 |
| | Plate block of 4 | .55 | |
| | FDC *(Feb. 12, 1955)* | | 1.00 |

**1955. ROTARY INTERNATIONAL ISSUE** marked the 50th anniversary of the organization founded Feb. 23, 1905, by Chicago lawyer Paul P. Harris. Rotary became national in 1910, international in 1912. It is an organization of business and professional men founded to further the ideal of service to others in all relationships. *Intaglio, perforated 11 x 10 1/2.*

CM378 *Rotary Insignia, Globe and Torch.*

| CM378 | | MNHVF | UseVF |
|---|---|---|---|
| 8¢ | **deep blue** *(53,854,750)* | .25 | .20 |
| | Plate block of 4 | 1.95 | |
| | FDC *(Feb. 23, 1955)* | | 1.00 |

**1955. THE ARMED FORCES RESERVE ISSUE** honored the Reserves of all the U.S. armed forces. *Intaglio, perforated 11 x 10 1/2.*

CM379 *Marines, Coast Guard, Army, Navy and Air Force Reservists.*

| CM379 | | MNHVF | UseVF |
|---|---|---|---|
| 3¢ | **bright purple** *(176,075,000)* | .25 | .20 |
| | Plate block of 4 | .55 | |
| | FDC *(May 21, 1955)* | | 1.00 |

**1955. OLD MAN OF THE MOUNTAIN ISSUE** commemorated the sesquicentennial of the discovery of New Hampshire's famous landmark of that name (see also CM1312). Also called "The Great Stone Face," it was immortalized in prose by Hawthorne. *Intaglio, perforated 10 1/2 X 11.*

CM380 *Old Man of the Mountain (as seen from Franconia, N.H.*

| CM380 | | MNHVF | UseVF |
|---|---|---|---|
| 3¢ | **blue green** *(125,944,400)* | .25 | .20 |
| | Plate block of 4 | .55 | |
| | FDC *(June 21, 1955)* | | 1.00 |

**1955. SOO LOCKS CENTENNIAL ISSUE** was released in conjuction with the opening of the Soo Locks Exposition at Sault Ste. Marie, Mich., celebrating a century of Great Lakes transportation. *Intaglio, perforated 11 x 10 1/2.*

CM381 *Map of the Great Lakes and Freighter*

| CM381 | | MNHVF | UseVF |
|---|---|---|---|
| 3¢ | **blue** *(122,284,600)* | .25 | .20 |
| | Plate block of 4 | .55 | |
| | FDC *(June 28, 1955)* | | 1.00 |

**1955. ATOMS FOR PEACE ISSUE** symbolized the intention of the United States to put atomic energy to peaceful uses. The stamp features the words "To find the way by which the inventiveness of man shall be consecrated to his life" from President Eisenhower's speech before the U.N. General Assembly on Dec. 8, 1953. *Intaglio, perforated 11 x 10 1/2.*

CM382 *Atomic Emblem and Hemispheres*

| CM382 | | MNHVF | UseVF |
|---|---|---|---|
| 3¢ | **deep blue** *(133,638,850)* | .25 | .20 |
| | Plate block of 4 | .55 | |
| | FDC *(July 28, 1955)* | | 1.00 |

**1955. FORT TICONDEROGA BICENTENNIAL ISSUE** marked the building of the fort in 1755 by the French, who named it Fort Carillon. During the French & Indian War it was unsuccessfully attacked by Abercrombie in 1758, but a year later was captured by Lord Amherst. Ethan Allen and his Green Mountain Boys (see CM76) took the fort at the outbreak of the Revolution (1775). *Intaglio, perforated 11 x 10 1/2.*

CM383 *Plan of Fort Ticonderoga Officer and Cannon*

| CM383 | | MNHVF | UseVF |
|---|---|---|---|
| 3¢ | **dark red brown** *(118,664,600)* | .25 | .20 |
| | Plate block of 4 | .55 | |
| | FDC *(Sept. 18, 1955)* | | 1.00 |

**1955. ANDREW MELLON ISSUE** commemorated the 100th anniversary of the birth of Mellon (1855-1937), Secretary of the Treasury under Harding, Coolidge and Hoover. He negotiated the payments of war debts owed to the United States, and reduced internal debt and income taxes. He later served as ambassador to England. He donated a gallery and his very valuable art collection to the United States. *Intaglio, perforated 10 1/2 x 11.*

CM384 *Andrew W. Mellon, Portrait by O. Birely.*

| CM384 | | MNHVF | UseVF |
|---|---|---|---|
| 3¢ | **carmine red** *(112,434,000)* | .25 | .20 |
| | Plate block of 4 | .55 | |
| | FDC *(Dec. 20, 1955)* | | 1.00 |

**1956. FRANKLIN 250TH ANNIVERSARY ISSUE** commemorated the birth of the great inventor, writer and public official Benjamin Franklin (see 524). *Intaglio, perforated 10 1/2 X 11.*

CM385 *Franklin Taking Electricity from the Sky. Benjamin West painting.*

| CM385 | | MNHVF | UseVF |
|---|---|---|---|
| 3¢ | **carmine** *(129,384,550)* | .25 | .20 |
| | Plate block of 4 | .55 | |
| | FDC *(Jan. 17, 1956)* | | 1.00 |

**1956. BOOKER T. WASHINGTON ISSUE** commemorated the 100th anniversary of the great educator's birth (CM215). *Intaglio, perforated 11 x 10 1/2.*

CM386 *Log Cabin*

| CM386 | | MNHVF | UseVF |
|---|---|---|---|
| 3¢ | **deep blue** *(121,184,600)* | .25 | .20 |
| | Plate block of 4 | .55 | |
| | FDC *(April 5, 1956)* | | 1.00 |

**1956. FIPEX ISSUE** celebrated the 5th International Philatelic Exhibition (April 28 to May 6, 1956). Stamp, photography and auto exhibitions, held simultaneously, opened the New York Coliseum at Columbus Circle, New York City. *Intaglio, perforated 11 x 10 1/2.*

CM387 *New York Coliseum and Columbus Monument.*

| CM387 | | MNHVF | UseVF |
|---|---|---|---|
| 3¢ | **violet** *(119,784,200)* | .25 | .20 |
| | Plate block of 4 | .55 | |
| | FDC *(April 28, 1956)* | | 1.00 |

**1956. FIFTH INTERNATIONAL PHILATELIC EXHIBITION (FIPEX) SOUVENIR SHEET** pictured 2 oversize versions of stamps from the Liberty definitive series (see 573, 578) and measure 108 x 73mm. *Flat plate printing, intaglio, imperforate.*

CM388 *FIPEX Souvenir Sheet*

| CM388 | | MNHVF | UseVF |
|---|---|---|---|
| 11¢ | **Complete sheet of 2 stamps** *(9,802,025)* | 2.50 | 2.00 |
| | a. 3¢ dark violet, from sheet | | .80 |
| | b. 8¢ deep blue and rose, from sheet | | 1.00 |
| | FDC *(April 28, 1956)* | | 2.50 |

**1956. WILD TURKEY ISSUE** *Intaglio, perforated 11 x 10 1/2.*

| CM389 | | MNHVF | UseVF |
|---|---|---|---|
| 3¢ | **brown purple** *(123,159,400)* | .25 | .20 |
| | Plate block of 4 | .55 | |
| | FDC *(May 5, 1956)* | | 1.00 |

**1956. PRONGHORN ANTELOPE ISSUE**

CM390 *Pronghorn Antelope Buck and 2 Does. This species had dwindled to only 17,000, but multiplied rapidly under protection and now is widely hunted.*

| CM390 | | MNHVF | UseVF |
|---|---|---|---|
| 3¢ | **sepia** *(123,138,800)* | .25 | .20 |
| | Plate block of 4 | .55 | |
| | FDC *(June 22, 1956)* | | |

**1956. KING SALMON ISSUE**

CM391 *King Salmon Migrating to Spawning Ground. Construction of fish ladders and elevators, and elimination of log jams and high waterfalls aids salmon migration and reproduction.*

| CM391 | | MNHVF | UseVF |
|---|---|---|---|
| 3¢ | **blue green** *(109,275,000)* | .25 | .20 |
| | Plate block of 4 | .55 | |
| | FDC *(Nov. 9, 1956)* | | 1.00 |

**1956. PURE FOOD AND DRUG LAWS ISSUE** commemorated the 50th anniversary of their passage. Harvey W. Wiley (1844-1930) was a chemist and teacher who single- handedly devoted himself to the cause of pure food. While chief of the Bureau of Chemistry in the U.S. Department of Agriculture he secured passage of the 1906 laws, which required government inspection and accurate labeling of foods and drugs. Wiley was the author of hundreds of scientific papers and pamphlets. *Intaglio, perforated 10 1/2 x 11.*

CM392 *Harvey W. Wiley*

| CM392 | | MNHVF | UseVF |
|---|---|---|---|
| 3¢ | **blue green** *(112,932,200)* | .25 | .20 |
| | Plate block of 4 | .55 | |
| | FDC *(June 27, 1956)* | | 1.00 |

**1956. WHEATLAND ISSUE** honored President James Buchanan and his Pennsylvania home Wheatland. *Intaglio, perforated 11 x 10 1/2.*

CM393 *Wheatland, Lancaster, Pa.*

| CM393 | | MNHVF | UseVF |
|---|---|---|---|
| 3¢ | **black brown** *(125,475,000)* | .25 | .20 |
| | Plate block of 4 | .55 | |
| | FDC *(Aug. 5, 1956)* | | 1.00 |

**1956. LABOR DAY ISSUE** celebrated the national holiday honoring workers. The movement for a Labor Holiday was begun by the Knights of Labor, who paraded on the 1st Monday of Sept. in 1882-84. The holiday first was recognized by Oregon (1887) then by New York, New Jersey and Colorado, and by the U.S. Congress in 1894. *Intaglio, perforated 10 1/2 x 11.*

CM394 *"Labor is Life" Mural by L. Winter in AFL-CIO headquarters building, Washington, D.C.*

**CM394**

| | | MNHVF | UseVF |
|---|---|---|---|
| 3¢ | **deep blue** *(117,855,000)* | .25 | .20 |
| | Plate block of 4 | .55 | |
| | FDC *(Sept. 3, 1956)* | | 1.00 |

**1956. NASSAU HALL ISSUE** commemorated the 200th anniversary of the oldest building at Princeton University. Named for William of Nassau (later King William III of England), it was at its' completion the largest academic building in the American colonies. In 1783, in Nassau Hall, congress formally thanked George Washington for his leadership in the Revolutionary War. *Intaglio, perforated 11 x 10 1/2.*

CM395 *Nassau Hall. From the Dawkins engraving of 1764.*

**CM395**

| | | MNHVF | UseVF |
|---|---|---|---|
| 3¢ | **black on orange** *(122,100,00)* | .25 | .20 |
| | Plate block of 4 | .55 | |
| | FDC *(Sept. 22, 1956)* | | 1.00 |

**1956. DEVILS TOWER ISSUE** commemorated the 50th anniversary of the establishment of the 1,200-acre area as the first U.S. national monument. The natural 600-foot rock formation is the eroded core of a long-extinct volcano. *Intaglio, perforated 10 1/2 x 11.*

CM396 *Devils Tower National Monument, Wyoming*

**CM396**

| | | MNHVF | UseVF |
|---|---|---|---|
| 3¢ | **lilac** *(118,180,000)* | .25 | .20 |
| | Plate block of 4 | .55 | |
| | Gutter pair | | |
| | FDC *(Sept. 24, 1956)* | | 1.00 |

**1956. CHILDREN'S ISSUE** featured the theme "Friendship - The Key to World Peace," and promoted friendship among children throughout the world. The stamp design, by Ronald Dias, a 1956 high school graduate, was selected in a nationwide competition. *Intaglio, perforated 11 x 10 1/2.*

CM397 *Children of the World and Key of Friendship*

**CM397**

| | | MNHVF | UseVF |
|---|---|---|---|
| 3¢ | **blue** *(100,975,000)* | .25 | .20 |
| | Plate block of 4 | .55 | |
| | FDC *(Dec. 15, 1956)* | | 1.00 |

**1957. ALEXANDER HAMILTON BICENTENNIAL ISSUE** commemorated the 200th anniversary of the birth of this great patriot. The first secretary of the treasury and one of the signers of the Constitution. *Intaglio, perforated 11 x 10 1/2.*

CM398 *Alexander Hamilton and Federal Hall, New York, N.Y.*

**CM398**

| | | MNHVF | UseVF |
|---|---|---|---|
| 3¢ | **rose red** *(115,299,450)* | .25 | .20 |
| | Plate block of 4 | .55 | |
| | FDC *(Jan. 11, 1957)* | | 1.00 |

**1957. ANTI-POLIO ISSUE** is a tribute to those who helped fight this dreaded disease, from children who contributed pennies to scientists who devoted their lives to the battle against a terrifying affliction. Issue marked 20th anniversary of the National Foundation for Infantile Paralysis and the March of Dimes. *Intaglio, perforated 10 1/2 x 11.*

CM399 *Boy, Girl and Allegorical Figure with Shield Caduceus.*

**CM399**

| | | MNHVF | UseVF |
|---|---|---|---|
| 3¢ | **bright purple** *(186,949,250)* | .25 | .20 |
| | Plate block of 4 | .55 | |
| | FDC *(Jan. 15, 1957)* | | 1.00 |

**1957. COAST AND GEODETIC SURVEY ISSUE** commemorated the 150th anniversary of this government service, devoted to charting and surveying America's coasts and harbors and land masses. *Intaglio, perforated 11 x 10 1/2.*

CM400 *Coast and Geodestic Survey Flag and Ships*

**CM400**

| | | MNHVF | UseVF |
|---|---|---|---|
| 3¢ | **deep blue** *(115,235,000)* | .25 | .20 |
| | Plate block of 4 | .55 | |
| | FDC *(Feb. 11, 1957)* | | 1.00 |

**1957. ARCHITECTS OF AMERICA ISSUE** honored the centennial of the founding of the American Institute of Architects, and its members who create buildings, structures and communities of lasting beauty and usefulness. *Intaglio, perforated 11 x 10 1/2.*

CM401 *Corinthian Capitol and Modern Pillar.*

**CM401**

| | | MNHVF | UseVF |
|---|---|---|---|
| 3¢ | **rose lilac** *(106,647,500)* | .25 | .20 |
| | Plate block of 4 | .55 | |
| | FDC *(Feb. 23, 1957)* | | 1.00 |

**1957. STEEL INDUSTRY IN AMERICA ISSUE** marked the centennial of this great industry, which has contributed to our social progress, economic welfare and comforts in our daily lives. *Intaglio, perforated 10 1/2 x 11.*

CM402 *Eagle and Pouring Ladle*

**CM402**

| | | MNHVF | UseVF |
|---|---|---|---|
| 3¢ | **bright blue** *(112,010,000)* | .25 | .20 |
| | Plate block of 4 | .55 | |
| | FDC *(May 22, 1957)* | | 1.00 |

**1957. INTERNATIONAL NAVAL REVIEW ISSUE** commemorated the Jamestown Festival and the naval review. Its theme was "Freedom of the Seas," and it was the largest representation of nations in an event of this type. *Intaglio, perforated 11 x 10 1/2.*

CM403 *Aircraft Carrier and Jamestown Festival Emblem*

**CM403**

| | | MNHVF | UseVF |
|---|---|---|---|
| 3¢ | **blue green** *(118,399,600)* | .25 | .20 |
| | Plate block of 4 | .55 | |
| | FDC *(June 10, 1957)* | | 1.00 |

**1957. OKLAHOMA STATEHOOD ISSUE** celebrated the 50th anniversary of statehood, growth and progress of a land that was once the Indian Territory. *Intaglio, perforated 11 x 10 1/2.*

CM404 *Arrow, Atom and Oklahoma Map*

**CM404**

| | | MNHVF | UseVF |
|---|---|---|---|
| 3¢ | **bright blue** *(102,209,500)* | .25 | .20 |
| | Plate block of 4 | .55 | |
| | FDC *(June 14, 1957)* | | 1.00 |

**1957. TEACHERS OF AMERICA ISSUE** honored the National Education Association and the teaching profession that has contributed to the development of America through our school systems. *Intaglio, perforated 11 x 10 1/2.*

CM405 *Teacher, Students and Globe*

**CM405**

| | | MNHVF | UseVF |
|---|---|---|---|
| 3¢ | **brown purple** *(103,045,000)* | .25 | .20 |
| | Plate block of 4 | .55 | 1.00 |
| | FDC *(July 1, 1957)* | | 1.00 |

**1957. AMERICAN FLAG ISSUE** salutes "Old Glory," symbol of freedom throughout the world. *Intaglio (Giori Press), perforated 11.*

CM406 *48 Star American Flag*

**CM406**

| | | MNHVF | UseVF |
|---|---|---|---|
| 4¢ | **deep blue and carmine** *(84,054,400)* | .25 | .20 |
| | Plate block of 4 | .55 | |
| | FDC *(July 4, 1957)* | | 1.00 |

**1957. VIRGINIA OF SAGADAHOCK ISSUE** commemorated the 350th anniversary of shipbuilding in the United States, and featured the first American built ship to participate in world commerce. *Intaglio, perforated 10 1/2 x 11.*

CM407 *Virginia of Sagadahock and state Seal of Maine*

**CM407**

| | | MNHVF | UseVF |
|---|---|---|---|
| 3¢ | **violet** *(126,266,000)* | .25 | .20 |
| | Plate block of 4 | .55 | |
| | FDC *(Aug. 15, 1957)* | | 1.00 |

## Champions of Liberty Series

**1957. RAMON MAGSAYSAY ISSUE** was the first of a new five-year-long series honoring Champions of Liberty and freedom fighters of other nations. A man of humble birth, Magsaysay became president of the Philippines. (See also CM419-20, CM423-24, CM434-35, CM445-46, CM456-57, CM474-75, CM477-78 and CM483-84.) *Intaglio (Giori Press), perforated 11.*

CM408 *Ramon Magsaysay*

**CM408**

| | | MNHVF | UseVF |
|---|---|---|---|
| 8¢ | **scarlet, deep ultramarine and ocher** *(39,489,600)* | .25 | .20 |
| | Plate block of 4, 2 numbers | .75 | |
| | Plate block of 4, deep ultramarine number omitted | — | |
| | FDC *(Aug. 31, 1957)* | | 1.00 |

**1957. LAFAYETTE ISSUE** commemorated the 200th birthday of the French officer who came to America in 1777 and helped the fight for independence. *Intaglio, perforated 10 1/2 x 11.*

CM409 *Lafayette, Flintlock Rifle and Sword*

**CM409**

| | | MNHVF | UseVF |
|---|---|---|---|
| 3¢ | **brown purple** (122,990,000) | .25 | .20 |
| | Plate block of 4 | .55 | |
| | FDC (Sept. 6, 1957) | | 1.00 |

**1957. WILDLIFE CONSERVATION ISSUE** brought to the attention of the American public the need to protect and preserve wildlife resources. This, the 4th in the series (see CM389-CM391), portrays the whooping crane, which at the time was almost extinct. *Intaglio, (Giori Press), perforated 11.*

CM410 *Whooping Cranes*

**CM410**

| | | MNHVF | UseVF |
|---|---|---|---|
| 3¢ | **gray blue, yellow and blue green** (174,372,800) | .25 | .20 |
| | Plate block of 4 | .55 | |
| | FDC (Nov. 22, 1957) | | 1.00 |

**1957. FLUSHING REMONSTRANCE ISSUE** recalled a 1657 demonstration for religious freedom and liberty by the citizens of Flushing, NY. *Intaglio, perforated 10 1/2 x 11.*

CM411 *Bible, Hat, Pen and Inkwell*

**CM411**

| | | MNHVF | UseVF |
|---|---|---|---|
| 3¢ | **brown black** (114,365,000) | .25 | .20 |
| | Plate block of 4 | .55 | |
| | FDC (Dec. 27, 1957) | | 1.00 |

**1958. GARDEN AND HORTICULTURAL ISSUE** marked the 100th birthday of Liberty Hyde Bailey, famous botanist, author, and teacher whose horticultural achievements contributed to American prosperity. *Intaglio, perforated 10 1/2 x 11.*

CM412 *Allegory of the Good Earth with Horn of Plenty.*

**CM412**

| | | MNHVF | UseVF |
|---|---|---|---|
| 3¢ | **dull green** (122,765,200) | .25 | .20 |
| | Plate block of 4 | .55 | |
| | FDC (March 15, 1958) | | 1.00 |

**1958. BRUSSELS UNIVERSAL AND INTERNATIONAL EXHIBITION ISSUE** pays tribute to the World's Fair and U.S. participation in it. *Intaglio, perforated 11 x 10 1/2.*

CM413 *U.S. Fair Pavilion*

**CM413**

| | | MNHVF | UseVF |
|---|---|---|---|
| 3¢ | **brown purple** (113,660,200) | .25 | .20 |
| | Plate block of 4 | .55 | |
| | FDC (April 17, 1958) | | 1.00 |

**1958. JAMES MONROE ISSUE** commemorated the 200th birthday of the 5th president of the United States. *Intaglio, perforated 11 x 10 1/2.*

CM414 *James Monroe. From a portrait by Gilbert Stuart.*

**CM414**

| | | MNHVF | UseVF |
|---|---|---|---|
| 3¢ | **violet** (120,196,580) | .25 | .20 |
| | Plate block of 4 | .55 | |
| | FDC (April 28, 1958) | | 1.00 |

**1958. MINNESOTA STATEHOOD CENTENNIAL ISSUE** commemorated the 100th anniversary of Minnesota's admission as the 32nd state. *Intaglio, perforated 11 x 10 1/2.*

CM415 *Minnesota Lakes*

**CM415**

| | | MNHVF | UseVF |
|---|---|---|---|
| 3¢ | **emerald green** (120,805,200) | .25 | .20 |
| | Plate block of 4 | .55 | |
| | FDC (May 11, 1958) | | 1.00 |

**1958. INTERNATIONAL GEOPHYSICAL YEAR ISSUE** paid tribute to geophysicists in more than 60 countries who pool their knowledge for mankind's welfare in exploring outer space and the oceans and Earth. *Intaglio, (Giori Press), perforated 11.*

CM416 *Detail from Michelangelo's The Creation of Adam and Solar Surface.*

**CM416**

| | | MNHVF | UseVF |
|---|---|---|---|
| 3¢ | **black and red** (125,815,200) | .25 | .20 |
| | Plate block of 4 | .55 | |
| | FDC (May 31, 1958) | | 1.00 |

**1958. GUNSTON HALL BICENTENNIAL ISSUE** honors the completion of the home of George Mason, Revolutionary patriot and friend of George Washington. The house, about 15 miles south of Alexandria, Va., was opened to the public in 1952. *Intaglio, perforated 11 x 10 1/2.*

CM417 *Gunston Hall*

**CM417**

| | | | MNHVF | UseVF |
|---|---|---|---|---|
| 3¢ | **dull green** *(108,415,200)* | | .25 | .20 |
| | Plate block of 4 | | .55 | |
| | FDC *(June 12, 1958)* | | | 1.00 |

**1958. MACKINAC STRAITS BRIDGE ISSUE** marked the formal opening and dedication of the suspension span that connects St. Ignace and Mackinaw City, in Michigan's Upper and Lower Peninsulas. *Intaglio, perforated 10 1/2 x 11.*

CM418 *Ore Boat under Mackinac Bridge*

**CM418**

| | | | MNHVF | UseVF |
|---|---|---|---|---|
| 3¢ | **turquoise blue** *(107,195,200)* | | .25 | .20 |
| | Plate block of 4 | | .55 | |
| | FDC *(June 25, 1958)* | | | 1.00 |

**1958. SIMON BOLÍVAR ISSUE** The first 2-stamp installment in the Champions of Liberty series honors the South American freedom fighter known as "The Liberator" who dedicated his life to bringing happiness, social security and political stability to his countrymen. *Intaglio, perforated 10 1/2 x 11.*

CM419-20 *Simon Bolívar. From portrait by Acevedo Bernal.*

**CM419**

| | | | MNHVF | UseVF |
|---|---|---|---|---|
| 4¢ | **olive buff** *(115,745,280)* | | .25 | .20 |
| | Plate block of 4 | | .60 | |
| | FDC *(July 24, 1958)* | | | 1.00 |

**1958. SIMON BOLÍVAR ISSUE** *Intaglio, (Giori Press), perforated 11*

**CM420**

| | | | MNHVF | UseVF |
|---|---|---|---|---|
| 8¢ | **scarlet, deep ultramarine and deep ocher** *(39,743,640)* | | .25 | .20 |
| | Plate block of 4, 2 numbers | | — | |
| | v. Plate block of 4, ocher number only | | — | |
| | FDC *(July 25, 1958)* | | | 1.00 |

**1958. ATLANTIC CABLE CENTENNIAL ISSUE** commemorated the linking by cable of the eastern and western hemispheres in 1858. The first formal messages were exchanged by President Buchanan and Queen Victoria. *Intaglio, perforated 11 x 10 1/2.*

CM421 *Globe, Neptune and Mermaid*

**CM421**

| | | | MNHVF | UseVF |
|---|---|---|---|---|
| 4¢ | **red violet** *(114,570,200)* | | .25 | .20 |
| | Plate block of 4 | | .60 | |
| | FDC *(Aug. 15, 1958)* | | | 1.00 |

**1958. LINCOLN DOUGLAS DEBATE ISSUE** This 1st stamp marked the 100th anniversary of the Lincoln-Douglas debates held as part of the 1859 campaign for U.S. Senator. Although Douglas was re-elected, Lincoln gained national prominence and 2 years later was elected to the presidency. *Intaglio, perforated 11 x 10 1/2.*

CM422 *Lincoln and Douglas Debating*

**CM422**

| | | | MNHVF | UseVF |
|---|---|---|---|---|
| 4¢ | **brown** *(114,860,200)* | | .25 | .20 |
| | Plate block of 4 | | .85 | |
| | FDC *(Aug. 27, 1958)* | | | 1.00 |

**1958. LAJOS KOSSUTH ISSUE** The 3rd honoree in the Champions of Liberty Series honored the famous Hungarian patriot who fought to liberate Hungary from Austrian control. He lived in exile until his death in 1894, never giving up hope that some day his beloved country would be free. *Intaglio, perforated 10 1/2 x 11.*

CM423-24 *Lajos Kossuth. From a photo taken in the United States in 1852.*

**CM423**

| | | | MNHVF | UseVF |
|---|---|---|---|---|
| 4¢ | **dull green** *(120,561,280)* | | .25 | .20 |
| | Plate block of 4 | | .60 | |
| | FDC *(Sept. 19, 1958)* | | | 1.00 |

**1958. LAJOS KOSSUTH ISSUE** *Intaglio, (Giori Press), perforated 11*

**CM424**

| | | | MNHVF | UseVF |
|---|---|---|---|---|
| 8¢ | **scarlet, deep ultramarine and deep ochre** *(44,064,576)* | | .25 | .20 |
| | Plate block of 4 | | 1.30 | |
| | FDC *(Sept. 19, 1958)* | | | 1.00 |

**1958. JOURNALISM AND FREEDOM OF THE PRESS ISSUE** marked the 50th anniversary of the establishment of the world's 1st school of journalism at the University of Missouri. *Intaglio, perforated 10 1/2 x 11.*

CM425 *Symbols of a Free Press*

**CM425**

| | | | MNHVF | UseVF |
|---|---|---|---|---|
| 4¢ | **gray black** *(118,390,200)* | | .25 | .20 |
| | Plate block of 4 | | .60 | |
| | FDC *(Sept. 22, 1958)* | | | 1.00 |

**1958. OVERLAND MAIL CENTENNIAL ISSUE** honored the pioneer mail service established in 1858. "The Great Overland Mail Route" started its run from Memphis and St. Louis and went to San Francisco, it was important in the settlement of the Southwest. *Intaglio, perforated 11 x 10 1/2.*

CM426 *Overland Mail Coach and Map of Route.*

| CM426 | | MNHVF | UseVF |
|---|---|---|---|
| 4¢ | **orange red** *(125,770,200)* | .25 | .20 |
| | Plate block of 4 | .60 | |
| | FDC *(Oct. 10, 1958)* | | 1.00 |

**1958. NOAH WEBSTER BICENTENNIAL ISSUE** commemorated the 200th birthday of the noted lexicographer. He fought for American independence in the Revolutionary War, and his *Elementary Spelling Book* sold a million copies. *Intaglio, perforated 10 1/2 x 11.*

CM427 *Noah Webster. From a painting by James Herring.*

| CM427 | | MNHVF | UseVF |
|---|---|---|---|
| 4¢ | **magenta** *(114,114,280)* | .25 | .20 |
| | Plate block of 4 | .60 | |
| | FDC *(Oct. 16, 1958)* | | 1.00 |

**1958. FOREST CONSERVATION ISSUE** honored the 100th birthday of Theodore Roosevelt, one of the first leaders in the movement to preserve the nation's natural resources. *Intaglio, (Giori Press), perforated 11.*

CM428 *Forest and Deer*

| CM428 | | MNHVF | UseVF |
|---|---|---|---|
| 4¢ | **deep green, yellow and brown** *(156,600,200)* | .25 | .20 |
| | Plate block of 4 | .60 | |
| | FDC *(Oct. 27, 1958)* | | 1.00 |

**1958. FORT DUQUESNE BICENTENNIAL ISSUE** commemorated the 200th anniversary of the historic site that was so important in the conflict between England and France for control of North America. *Intaglio, perforated 11 x 10 1/2.*

CM429 *Composite drawing showing Gen. Forbes, Col. Washington, and Col. Henry Bouquet.*

| CM429 | | MNHVF | UseVF |
|---|---|---|---|
| 4¢ | **light blue** *(124,200,200)* | .25 | .20 |
| | Plate block of 4 | .60 | |
| | FDC *(Nov. 25, 1958)* | | 1.00 |

**1959. LINCOLN SESQUICENTENNIAL ISSUE**

CM430 Beardless Lincoln. *Painting by George P.A. Healy.*

| CM430 | | MNHVF | UseVF |
|---|---|---|---|
| 1¢ | **deep green** *(120,400,200)* | .25 | .20 |
| | Plate block of 4 | .45 | |
| | FDC *(Feb. 12, 1959)* | | 1.00 |

**1959. HEAD OF LINCOLN ISSUE**

CM431 Head of Lincoln. *Sculpture by Gutzon Borglum.*

| CM431 | | MNHVF | UseVF |
|---|---|---|---|
| 3¢ | **deep plum** *(91,160,200)* | .25 | .20 |
| | Plate block of 4 | .60 | |
| | FDC *(Feb. 27, 1959)* | | 1.00 |

**1959. LINCOLN STATUE ISSUE** *Intaglio, perforated 10 1/2 x 11.*

CM432 Lincoln Statue. *By Daniel Chester French, taken from a line and pastel drawing by Fritz Busse.*

| CM432 | | MNHVF | UseVF |
|---|---|---|---|
| 4¢ | **blue** *(126,500,000)* | .25 | .20 |
| | Plate block of 4 | 1.25 | |
| | FDC *(May 30, 1959)* | | 1.00 |

**1959. OREGON STATEHOOD ISSUE** commemorated the 100th anniversary of Oregon's admission as a state. *Intaglio, perforated 11 x 10 1/2.*

CM433 *Mount Hood and Covered Wagon*

| CM433 | | MNHVF | UseVF |
|---|---|---|---|
| 4¢ | **blue green** *(120,740,200)* | .25 | .20 |
| | Plate block of 4 | .60 | |
| | FDC *(Feb. 14, 1959)* | | 1.00 |

**1959. JOSÉ DE SAN MARTIN ISSUE** the 4th of the Champions of Liberty-paid tribute to the "hero of the Andes," a great general who fought for freedom in his native Argentina and other South American nations. *Intaglio, perforated 10 1/2 x 11.*

CM434-35 *Portrait of José de San Martin. From a print provided by the Library of Congress.*

| CM434 | | MNHVF | UseVF |
|---|---|---|---|
| 4¢ | **blue** *(113,623,280)* | .25 | .20 |
| | Plate block of 4 | .60 | |
| | FDC *(Feb. 25,1959)* | | 1.00 |
| | v. horizontal pair, imperforate between | 1250. | |

| CM435 | | MNHVF | UseVF |
|---|---|---|---|
| 8¢ | **carmine, blue and ocher** *(45,569,088)* | .25 | .20 |
| | Plate block of 4 | 1.25 | |
| | FDC *(Feb. 25, 1959)* | | 1.00 |

**1959. NATO ISSUE** honors the 10th anniversary of the North Atlantic Treaty Organization, binding 15 nations "to safeguard the freedom, common heritage and civilization of their people, founded on the principles of democracy, individual liberty and the rule of law." *Intaglio, perforated 10 1/2 x 11.*

CM436 *NATO Emblem*

| CM436 | | MNHVF | UseVF |
|---|---|---|---|
| 4¢ | **blue** *(122,493,280)* | .25 | .20 |
| | Plate block of 4 | .60 | |
| | FDC *(April 1, 1959)* | | 1.00 |

**1959. ARCTIC EXPLORATIONS ISSUE** marked the conquest of the north polar regions and commemorated the 50th anniversary of Adm. Peary's expedition. The nuclear-powered submarine, *USS Nautilis,* joined the anniversary celebration, making the first underwater crossing of the North Pole. *Intaglio, perforated 11 x 10 1/2.*

CM437 *Dog team and USS Nautilis.*

| CM437 | | MNHVF | UseVF |
|---|---|---|---|
| 4¢ | **turquoise blue** *(131,260,200)* | .25 | .20 |
| | Plate block of 4 | .60 | |
| | FDC *(April 6, 1959)* | | 1.00 |

**1959. PEACE THROUGH TRADE ISSUE** was released in association with the 17th Congress of the International Chamber of Commerce, held in Washington, D.C., from April 19 to 25. *Intaglio, perforated 11 x 10 1/2.*

CM438 *Globe and Laurel Spray*

| CM438 | | MNHVF | UseVF |
|---|---|---|---|
| 8¢ | **brown purple** *(47,125,200)* | .25 | .20 |
| | Plate block of 4 | .60 | |
| | FDC *(April 20, 1959)* | | 1.00 |

**1959. SILVER CENTENNIAL ISSUE** commemorated the 100th anniversary of the discovery of the Comstock Lode, which produced about $300,000,000 worth of silver in its first 20 years. *Intaglio, perforated 11 x 10 1/2.*

CM439 *Henry Comstock and miners*

| CM439 | | MNHVF | UseVF |
|---|---|---|---|
| 4¢ | **black** *(123,105,000)* | .25 | .20 |
| | Plate block of 4 | .60 | |
| | FDC *(June 8, 1959)* | | 1.00 |

**1959. ST. LAWRENCE SEAWAY ISSUE** commemorated the opening of a new link joining the United States and Canada in friendship and commerce, and providing a source of electric energy for both countries. Canada issued a commemorative stamp on the same day (Canada 480). Artists of both nations contributed to the design of both stamps, which are identical in design except for captions and denominations. *Intaglio, (Giori Press), perforated 11 .*

CM440 *Linked Eagle and Maple Leaf over Great Lakes.*

| CM440 | | MNHVF | UseVF |
|---|---|---|---|
| 4¢ | **blue and red** *(126,105,050)* | .25 | .20 |
| | Plate block of 4 | .60 | |
| | Gutter pair | — | |
| | FDC *(June 26, 1959)* | | 1.00 |

**1959. 49-STAR FLAG ISSUE** commemorated the admission of Alaska as the 49th state. *Intaglio, (Giori Press), perforated 11.*

CM441 *49 Star American Flag*

| CM441 | | MNHVF | UseVF |
|---|---|---|---|
| 4¢ | **deep blue and carmine** *(209,170,000)* | .25 | .20 |
| | Plate block of 4 | .60 | |
| | FDC *(July 4, 1959)* | | 1.00 |

**1959. SOIL CONSERVATION ISSUE** was a tribute to the effort to prevent erosion and conserve soil, vital to successful farming and ranching. *Intaglio, (Giori Press), perforated 11.*

CM442 *Soil Conservation Methods*

| CM442 | | MNHVF | UseVF |
|---|---|---|---|
| 4¢ | **blue green and yellow orange** *(120,835,000)* | .25 | .20 |
| | Plate block of 4 | .60 | |
| | FDC *(Aug. 26, 1959)* | | 1.00 |
| | v. Orange brown omitted | 5280. | |

**1959. PETROLEUM INDUSTRY CENTENNIAL Commemorative** marked the 100th anniversary of the completion of the first oil well at Titusville, Pa., by Edwin L. Drake. *Intaglio, perforated 10 1/2 x 11.*

CM443 *Oil Derrick*

| CM443 | | MNHVF | UseVF |
|---|---|---|---|
| 4¢ | brown *(115,715,000)* | .25 | .20 |
| | Plate block of 4 | .60 | |
| | FDC *(Aug. 27, 1959)* | | 1.00 |

**1959. DENTAL HEALTH ISSUE** honored the centennial of the American Dental Association. *Intaglio, perforated 11 x 10 1/2.*

CM444 *Children playing and smiling girl with feather-cut hair style.*

| CM444 | | MNHVF | UseVF |
|---|---|---|---|
| 4¢ | dark green *(118,445,000)* | .25 | .20 |
| | Plate block of 4 | .90 | |
| | FDC *(Sept. 14, 1959)* | | 1.00 |

**1959. ERNST REUTER ISSUE** 5th in the Champions of Liberty series - honored Ernst Reuter (1889-1953). He was persecuted and imprisoned by the Nazis, went into exile and after World War II returned to help rebuild his country. He was elected mayor of Berlin in 1947, holding that office until his death. *Intaglio, perforated 10 1/2 x 11.*

CM445-46 *Ernst Reuter*

| CM445 | | MNHVF | UseVF |
|---|---|---|---|
| 4¢ | black *(111,685,000)* | .25 | .20 |
| | Plate block of 4 | .60 | |
| | FDC *(Sept. 29, 1959)* | | 1.00 |

**1959. ERNST REUTER ISSUE** *Intaglio, (Giori Press), perforated 11.*

| CM446 | | MNHVF | UseVF |
|---|---|---|---|
| 8¢ | carmine, blue and ocher *(43,099,200)* | .25 | .20 |
| | Plate block of 4 | 1.25 | |
| | FDC *(Sept. 29, 1959)* | | 1.00 |

**1959. EPHRAIM MCDOWELL ISSUE** paid tribute to a famous American who performed the first successful abdominal operation of its kind in the world at Danville, Ky., in 1809. *Intaglio, perforated 10 1/2 x 11.*

CM447 *Ephraim McDowell*

| CM447 | | MNHVF | UseVF |
|---|---|---|---|
| 4¢ | brown purple *(115,444,000)* | .25 | .20 |
| | Plate block of 4 | .65 | |
| | FDC *(Dec. 3, 1959)* | | 1.00 |
| | v. Vertical pair, imperforate between | 500. | |
| | v1. Vertical pair, imperforate horizontally | 300. | |

**1960. GEORGE WASHINGTON ISSUE** *Intaglio, (Giori Press), perforated 11.*

CM448 *"Observe good faith and justice toward all nations."* George Washington

| CM448 | | MNHVF | UseVF |
|---|---|---|---|
| 4¢ | deep blue and carmine *(126,470,000)* | .25 | .20 |
| | Plate block of 4 | .65 | |
| | FDC *(Jan. 20, 1960)* | | 1.00 |

**1960. BENJAMIN FRANKLIN ISSUE**

CM449 *"Fear to do ill, and you need fear nought else."* Benjamin Franklin

| CM449 | | MNHVF | UseVF |
|---|---|---|---|
| 4¢ | brown bister and emerald *(124,460,000)* | .25 | .20 |
| | Plate block of 4 | .65 | |
| | FDC *(March 31, 1960)* | | 1.00 |

**1960. THOMAS JEFFERSON ISSUE**

CM450 *"I have sworn hostility against every form of tyranny over the mind of man."* Thomas Jefferson

| CM450 | | MNHVF | UseVF |
|---|---|---|---|
| 4¢ | gray and scarlet *(115,445,000)* | .25 | .20 |
| | Plate block of 4 | .65 | |
| | FDC *(May 18, 1960)* | | 1.00 |

**1960. FRANCIS SCOTT KEY**

CM451 *"And this be our motto, in God is our Trust."* Francis Scott Key

| CM451 | | MNHVF | UseVF |
|---|---|---|---|
| 4¢ | carmine red and deep blue *(122,060,000)* | .25 | .20 |
| | Plate block of 4 | .65 | |
| | FDC *(Sept. 14, 1960)* | | 1.00 |

**1960. ABRAHAM LINCOLN ISSUE**

CM452 *"Those who deny freedom to others deserve it not for themselves."* Abraham Lincoln

| CM452 | | MNHVF | UseVF |
|---|---|---|---|
| 4¢ | bright purple and green *(120,540,000)* | .25 | .20 |
| | Plate block of 4 | .90 | |
| | FDC *(Nov. 19, 1960)* | | 1.00 |

### 1960. PATRICK HENRY ISSUE

CM453 *"Give me liberty or give me death." Patrick Henry*

| CM453 | | MNHVF | UseVF |
|---|---|---|---|
| 4¢ | green and brown *(113,075,000)* | .25 | .20 |
| | Plate block of 4 | .90 | |
| | Gutter Pair | — | |
| | FDC *(Jan. 11, 1961)* | | 1.00 |

### 1960. BOY SCOUT ISSUE commemorated the 50th anniversary of the Boy Scout movement in America. Norman Rockwell designed the stamp. *Intaglio, (Giori Press), perforated 11.*

CM454 *Boy Scout Giving the Sign.*

| CM454 | | MNHVF | UseVF |
|---|---|---|---|
| 4¢ | red, deep blue and deep ocher *(139,325,000)* | .25 | .20 |
| | Plate block of 4 | .90 | |
| | FDC *(Feb. 8, 1960)* | | 1.00 |

### 1960. WINTER OLYMPIC GAMES ISSUE marked the 8th Winter Games at Squaw Valley, Ca. It was the 2nd time this important athletic contest was held in the United States (see CM110). *Intaglio, perforated 10 1/2 x 11.*

CM455 *Olympic Emblem and Snowflake*

| CM455 | | MNHVF | UseVF |
|---|---|---|---|
| 4¢ | turquoise blue *(124,445,000)* | .25 | .20 |
| | Plate block of 4 | .60 | |
| | FDC *(Feb. 18, 1960)* | | 1.00 |
| | Plate block of 4 | .60 | |
| | FDC *(Feb. 18. 1960)* | | 1.00 |

### 1960. TOMAS G. MASARYK ISSUE 6th in the Champions of Liberty series - honored the 1st president of Czechoslovakia, who rose from humble origin to lead the movement for an independent nation. The 2 stamps were issued on the 41st anniversary of the republic. *Intaglio, perforated 10 1/2 x 11.*

CM456-57 *Tomas G. Masaryk*

| CM456 | | MNHVF | UseVF |
|---|---|---|---|
| 4¢ | blue *(113,792,000)* | .25 | .20 |
| | Plate block of 4 | .60 | |
| | v. Vertical pair, imperforate between | 3250. | |
| | FDC *(March 7, 1960)* | | 1.00 |

| CM457 | | MNHVF | UseVF |
|---|---|---|---|
| 8¢ | carmine, deep blue and ocher *(44,215,200)* | .25 | .20 |
| | Plate block of 4 | 1.10 | |
| | v. Horizontal pair, imperforate between | — | |
| | FDC *(March 7, 1960)* | | 1.00 |

### 1960. WORLD REFUGEE YEAR ISSUE focused attention on the world's homeless and destitute; and the importance of universal participation in aiding them. *Intaglio, perforated 11 x 10 1/2.*

CM458 *Family Facing Doorway to a New Life.*

| CM458 | | MNHVF | UseVF |
|---|---|---|---|
| 4¢ | gray black *(113,195,000)* | .25 | .20 |
| | Plate block of 4 | .60 | |
| | FDC *(April 7, 1960)* | | 1.00 |

### 1960. WATER CONSERVATION ISSUE issued in conjunction with the Seventh National Watershed Congress, emphasized the importance of conserving this precious natural resource. *Intaglio, (Giori Press), perforated 11.*

CM459 *Watershed and Dependent Farm and Factories.*

| CM459 | | MNHVF | UseVF |
|---|---|---|---|
| 4¢ | blue, green and orange brown *(120,570,000)* | .25 | .20 |
| | Plate block of 4 | .60 | |
| | FDC *(April 18, 1960)* | | 1.00 |

### 1960. SEATO ISSUE commemorates the South East Asia Treaty Organization Conference (May 31-June 3) and the organization's efforts on behalf of peace and freedom. This defensive alliance of nations includes Australia, France, New Zealand, Pakistan, Philippines, Thailand, United Kingdom and the United States. *Intaglio, perforated 10 1/2 x 11.*

CM460 *SEATO Emblem*

| CM460 | | MNHVF | UseVF |
|---|---|---|---|
| 4¢ | blue *(115,353,000)* | .25 | .20 |
| | Plate block of 4 | .60 | |
| | FDC *(May 31, 1960)* | | 1.00 |
| | v. Vertical pair, imperforate between | 150. | |

### 1960. AMERICAN WOMEN ISSUE emphasized the important contributions American women have made to the social, spiritual, economic and political progress of our nation. *Intaglio, perforated 11 x 10 1/2.*

CM461 *Mother, Daughter, and Open Book*

| CM461 | | MNHVF | UseVF |
|---|---|---|---|
| 4¢ | **violet** *(111,080,000)* | .25 | .20 |
| | Plate block of 4 | .60 | |
| | FDC *(June 2, 1960)* | | 1.00 |

**1960. 50-STAR FLAG ISSUE** commemorated the admission of Hawaii as the 50th state. *Intaglio, (Giori Press), perforated 11.*

CM462 *50-Star American Flag*

| CM462 | | MNHVF | UseVF |
|---|---|---|---|
| 4¢ | **deep blue and scarlet** *(153,025,000)* | .25 | .20 |
| | Plate block of 4 | .60 | |
| | FDC *(July 4, 1960)* | | 1.00 |

**1960. PONY EXPRESS CENTENARY ISSUE** commemorated the contribution to our nation's progress by this pioneer transportation service, which provided a faster mail service vitally needed at the time. A stamped envelope (EN844) also was issued in conjunction with this event (See also CM236). *Intaglio, perforated 11 x 10 1/2.*

CM463 *Pony Express Rider and Map of Route.*

| CM463 | | MNHVF | UseVF |
|---|---|---|---|
| 4¢ | **sepia** *(119,665,000)* | .25 | .20 |
| | Plate block of 4 | .70 | |
| | FDC *(July 19, 1960)* | | 1.00 |

**1960. EMPLOY THE HANDICAPPED ISSUE** focused on the need to promote employment of physically handicapped people who could be trained for gainful activity in American industry. *Intaglio, perforated 10 1/2 x 11.*

CM464 *Drill Press Operator in Wheelchair*

| CM464 | | MNHVF | UseVF |
|---|---|---|---|
| 4¢ | **blue** *(117,855,000)* | .25 | .20 |
| | Plate block of 4 | .60 | |
| | FDC *(Aug. 28, 1960)* | | 1.00 |

**1960. FIFTH WORLD FORESTRY CONGRESS ISSUE** paid tribute to the 2,000 foresters from more than 60 nations who gathered to explore the many uses of forest land. The congress was sponsored by the Food and Agriculture Organization of the United Nations. *Intaglio, perforated 10 1/2 X 11.*

CM465 *Seal of World Forestry Congress*

| CM465 | | MNHVF | UseVF |
|---|---|---|---|
| 4¢ | **blue green** *(118,185,000)* | .25 | .20 |
| | Plate block of 4 | .60 | |
| | FDC *(Aug. 29, 1960)* | | 1.00 |

**1960. MEXICAN INDEPENDENCE ISSUE** marked the 150th anniversary of the Republic of Mexico. Mexico issued an identical stamp on the same day. (Mexico 1373) different only in captions and denomination. *Intaglio, (Giori Press), perforated 11.*

CM466 *Freedom Bell of the National Palace, Mexico City*

| CM466 | | MNHVF | UseVF |
|---|---|---|---|
| 4¢ | **deep green and carmine red** *(112,260,000)* | .25 | .20 |
| | Plate block of 4 | .60 | |
| | FDC *(Sept. 16, 1960)* | | 1.00 |

**1960. UNITED STATES OF AMERICA-JAPAN CENTENNIAL ISSUE** commemorated the 100th anniversary of the first treaty between the 2 countries to promote good will and understanding. *Intaglio, (Giori Press), perforated 11.*

CM467 *Washington Monument and Cherry Blossoms*

| CM467 | | MNHVF | UseVF |
|---|---|---|---|
| 4¢ | **light blue and carmine** *(125,010,000)* | .25 | .20 |
| | Plate block of 4 | .65 | |
| | FDC *(Sept. 28, 1960)* | | 1.00 |

**1960. IGNACE JAN PADEREWSKI ISSUE** 7th in the Champions of Liberty series - honored the world-famous statesman, pianist and Polish patriot. *Intaglio, perforated 10 1/2 x 11.*

CM468-69 *Ignace Jan Paderewski*

| CM468 | | MNHVF | UseVF |
|---|---|---|---|
| 4¢ | **blue** *(119,798,000)* | .25 | .20 |
| | Plate block of 4 | .60 | |
| | FDC *(Oct. 8, 1960)* | | 1.00 |

| CM469 | | MNHVF | UseVF |
|---|---|---|---|
| 8¢ | **red, blue and ocher** *(42,696,000)* | .25 | .20 |
| | Plate block of 4 | 1.10 | |
| | FDC *(Oct. 8, 1960)* | | 1.00 |

**1960. ROBERT A. TAFT ISSUE** honored the memory of a great American who served his country as a senator from 1939 until his death on July 31, 1953. A native of Ohio, he distinguished himself as Senate majority leader. *Intaglio, perforated 10 1/2 x 11.*

CM470 *Robert A. Taft*

| CM470 | | MNHVF | UseVF |
|---|---|---|---|
| 4¢ | **violet** *(115,171,000)* | .25 | .20 |
| | Plate block of 4 | .60 | |
| | FDC *(Oct. 10, 1960)* | | 1.00 |

**1960. WHEELS OF FREEDOM ISSUE** was issued as a tribute to the automotive industry. It was released in conjunction with the National Automobile Show in Detroit. *Intaglio, perforated 11 x 10 1/2.*

CM471 *Hemispheres and steering wheel, symbol of automobile industry.*

| CM471 | | MNHVF | UseVF |
|---|---|---|---|
| 4¢ | **blue** *(109,695,000)* | .25 | .20 |
| | Plate block of 4 | .60 | |
| | FDC *(Oct. 15, 1960)* | | 1.00 |

**1960. BOYS' CLUB OF AMERICA ISSUE** commemorated the 100th anniversary of the movement that provided excellent recreational facilities for the underprivileged. *Intaglio, (Giori Press), perforated 11.*

CM472 *American youth*

| CM472 | | MNHVF | UseVF |
|---|---|---|---|
| 4¢ | **deep blue, black and red** *(123,690,000)* | .25 | .20 |
| | Plate block of 4 | .60 | |
| | FDC *(Oct. 18, 1960)* | | 1.00 |

**1960. FIRST AUTOMATED POST OFFICE ISSUE** commemorated the establishment of the first fully automated post office at Providence, RI. Considered a milestone in postal progress, the specially created machinery was expected to speed mail delivery. *Intaglio, (Giori Press), perforated 11.*

CM473 *Automated post office*

| CM473 | | MNHVF | UseVF |
|---|---|---|---|
| 4¢ | **deep blue and scarlet** *(127,970,000)* | .25 | .20 |
| | Plate block of 4 | .60 | |
| | FDC *(Oct. 20, 1960)* | | 1.00 |

**1960. BARON KARL GUSTAF EMIL MANNERHEIM ISSUE** the 8th of the Champions of Liberty series - honored the great Finnish soldier, statesman and leader for his heroic devotion to his country, in peace and war. Born in Askainen, June 4, 1867, he rose to the rank of marshal and led Finnish forces 3 times in his country's struggle for independence. He served twice as Finland's chief of state.

CM474-75 *Karl Gustaf Emil Mannerheim*

| CM474 | | MNHVF | UseVF |
|---|---|---|---|
| 4¢ | **blue** *(124,796,000)* | .25 | .20 |
| | Plate block of 4 | .60 | |
| | FDC *(Oct. 26, 1960)* | | 1.00 |

| CM475 | | MNHVF | UseVF |
|---|---|---|---|
| 8¢ | **red, blue and ocher** *(42,076,800)* | .25 | .20 |
| | Plate block of 4 | 1.10 | |
| | FDC *(Oct. 26,1960)* | | 1.00 |

**1960. CAMPFIRE GIRLS ISSUE** commemorated the Golden Jubilee Convention celebration of the organization that was created in 1910 for girls 7 to 18 years of age. *Intaglio, (Giori Press), perforated 11.*

CM476 *Campfire Girls Insignia*

| CM476 | | MNHVF | UseVF |
|---|---|---|---|
| 4¢ | **blue and red** *(116,215,000)* | .25 | .20 |
| | Plate block of 4 | .60 | |
| | FDC *(Nov. 1, 1960)* | | 1.00 |

**1960. GIUSEPPE GARIBALDI ISSUE** the 9th of the Champions of Liberty series - commemorated Italy's great patriot and fighter for freedom. A born leader, Garibaldi helped unify Italy and fought for the cause of liberty in South America and Europe. *Intaglio, perforated 10 1/2 x 11.*

CM477-78 *Giuseppe Garibaldi*

**CM477**

| | | MNHVF | UseVF |
|---|---|---|---|
| 4¢ | **green** *(126,252,000)* | .25 | .20 |
| | Plate block of 4 | .60 | |
| | FDC *(Nov. 2, 1960)* | | 1.00 |

**CM478**

| | | MNHVF | UseVF |
|---|---|---|---|
| 8¢ | **red, blue and ocher** *(42,746,400)* | .25 | .20 |
| | Plate block of 4 | 1.10 | |
| | FDC *(Nov. 2, 1960)* | | 1.00 |

**1960. WALTER F. GEORGE ISSUE** honored the distinguished public servant who served as a senator from Georgia and as special assistant for President Eisenhower to NATO in 1957. *Intaglio, perforated 10 1/2 x 11.*

CM479 *Walter F. George*

**CM479**

| | | MNHVF | UseVF |
|---|---|---|---|
| 4¢ | **violet** *(124,117,000)* | .25 | .20 |
| | Plate block of 4 | .60 | |
| | FDC *(Nov. 5, 1960)* | | 1.00 |

**1960. JOHN FOSTER DULLES ISSUE** paid tribute to a famous American who died while serving as Secretary of State. His long distinguished career included service as secretary to the Hague Peace Conference in 1907 and as U.S. Senator from New York. *Intaglio, perforated 10 1/2 x 11.*

CM480 *John Foster Dulles*

**CM480**

| | | MNHVF | UseVF |
|---|---|---|---|
| 4¢ | **violet** *(177,187,000)* | .25 | .20 |
| | Plate block of 4 | .60 | |
| | FDC *(Dec. 6, 1960)* | | 1.00 |

**1960. ANDREW CARNEGIE ISSUE** honored the industrialist on his 125th birthday and the 50th anniversary of the establishment of the Carnegie Endowment for International Peace. Born in Scotland, Carnegie came to the United States as a young boy and became one of the great leaders of world industry. He devoted a good portion of his life and wealth to the cause of social and educational advancements and the promotion of international peace. In 1910, in an effort to abolish the horrors of war, he founded the Carnegie Endowment for International Peace with a gift of $10 million. *Intaglio, perforated 10 1/2 x 11.*

CM481 *Andrew Carnegie*

**CM481**

| | | MNHVF | UseVF |
|---|---|---|---|
| 4¢ | **claret** *(119,840,000)* | .25 | .20 |
| | Plate block of 4 | .60 | |
| | FDC *(Nov. 25, 1960)* | | 1.00 |

**1960. ECHO I SATELLITE ISSUE** commemorated the world's first communications satellite launched by NASA into orbit on Aug. 12, 1960. *Intaglio, perforated 11 x 10 1/2.*

CM482 *Echo I satellite in orbit.*

**CM482**

| | | MNHVF | UseVF |
|---|---|---|---|
| 4¢ | **violet** *(125,290,000)* | .25 | .20 |
| | Plate block of 4 | 1.00 | |
| | FDC *(Dec. 15, 1960)* | | 1.00 |

**1961. MAHATMA GANDHI ISSUE** the 10th and final Champions of Liberty issue - honored the Indian who led his country to freedom. A physically frail man, he endured many hardships that inspired his countrymen to work non-violently for independence, equality and social justice. *Intaglio, perforated 10 1/2 x 11.*

CM483-84 *Mahatma Gandhi*

**CM483**

| | | MNHVF | UseVF |
|---|---|---|---|
| 4¢ | **red orange** *(112,966,000)* | .25 | .20 |
| | Plate block of 4 | .60 | |
| | FDC *(Jan. 26, 1961)* | | 1.00 |

**CM484**

| | | MNHVF | UseVF |
|---|---|---|---|
| 8¢ | **red, blue and ocher** *(41,644,200)* | .25 | .20 |
| | Plate block of 4 | 1.20 | |
| | FDC *(Jan. 26.1961)* | | 1.00 |

**1961. RANGE CONSERVATION ISSUE** was released in conjunction with the annual meeting of the American Society of Range Management, devoted to conservation, forestry, livestock and land management. *Intaglio, (Giori Press), perforated 11.*

CM485 *Trail Boss and Cattle Grazing.*

**CM485**

| | | MNHVF | UseVF |
|---|---|---|---|
| 4¢ | **blue, orange and indigo** *(110,850,000)* | .25 | .20 |
| | Plate block of 4 | .60 | |
| | FDC *(Feb. 2, 1961)* | | 1.00 |

**1961. HORACE GREELEY ISSUE** honored the publisher and editor who advised the youth of America to "Go West, young man, go West." He established the *New York Tribune* in 1841. *Intaglio, perforated 10 1/2 x 11.*

CM486 *Horace Greeley*

**CM486**

| | | MNHVF | UseVF |
|---|---|---|---|
| 4¢ | **violet** *(98,616,000)* | .25 | .20 |
| | Plate block of 4 | .60 | |
| | FDC *(Feb. 3, 1961)* | | 1.00 |

## 1961-65. Civil War Centennial Series

saluted the 100th anniversary of the bloodiest conflict in the nation's history with 1 centennial stamp for each of the war's 5 years.

### 1961. FORT SUMTER ISSUE

marked the anniversary of the assault and capture of the Charleston fort. This attack committed the Confederate states to war. *Intaglio, perforated 10 1/2 x 11.*

CM487 *Costal Gun at Fort Sumter*

| CM487 | | MNHVF | UseVF |
|---|---|---|---|
| 4¢ | green *(101,125,000)* | .25 | .20 |
| | Plate block of 4 | 1.65 | |
| | FDC *(April 12, 1961)* | | 1.00 |

### 1962. BATTLE OF SHILOH ISSUE

commemorates the valiant stand of Confederate troops under Gen. Albert S. Johnston and Union soldiers under Gen. Ulysses S. Grant in the fields of Tennessee. (See also CM1725). *Intaglio, perforated 11 x 10 1/2.*

CM488 *Infantryman in Action*

| CM488 | | MNHVF | UseVF |
|---|---|---|---|
| 4¢ | black on pink *(124,865,000)* | .25 | .20 |
| | Plate block of 4 | 1.10 | |
| | FDC *(April 7, 1962)* | | 1.00 |

### 1963. BATTLE OF GETTYSBURG ISSUE

honored the heroes of one of the most important battles of the Civil War, which was fought July 1-3, 1863 in eastern Pennsylvania. (See CM1740). *Intaglio, (Giori Press), perforated 11.*

CM489 *Union and Confederate Soldiers Fighting*

| CM489 | | MNHVF | UseVF |
|---|---|---|---|
| 5¢ | gray and blue *(79,905,000)* | .25 | .20 |
| | Plate block of 4 | 1.75 | |
| | FDC *(July 1, 1963)* | | 1.00 |

### 1964. BATTLE OF THE WILDERNESS ISSUE

saluted the fierce battle between the armies of Grant and Lee that took place in densely wooded terrain near Fredericksburg, VA. *Intaglio, (Giori Press), perforated 11.*

CM490 *Artillery In Action*

| CM490 | | MNHVF | UseVF |
|---|---|---|---|
| 5¢ | brown, purple and black *(125,410,000)* | .25 | .20 |
| | Plate block of 4 | 1.50 | |
| | FDC *(May 5, 1964)* | | 1.00 |

### 1965. APPOMATTOX ISSUE

celebrated the end of the War between the States. It was at Appomattox Court House, VA., on Sunday, April 9, 1865, that the Confederate Army under the command of Gen. Robert E. Lee surrendered to Gen. Ulysses S. Grant and the Union forces. *Intaglio, (Giori Press), perforated 11.*

CM491 *Civil War Soldier and Rifles*

| CM491 | | MNHVF | UseVF |
|---|---|---|---|
| 5¢ | blue and black *(112,845,000)* | .25 | .20 |
| | Plate block of 4 | 3.75 | |
| | FDC *(April 9, 1965)* | | 1.00 |
| | v. Horizontal pair, imperforate vertically | | |

### 1961. KANSAS STATEHOOD CENTENNIAL ISSUE

marks 100 years of statehood for Kansas admitted in 1861 as the 34th state. *Intaglio, (Giori Press), perforated 11.*

CM492 *Sunflower, Pioneers and Fort*

| CM492 | | MNHVF | UseVF |
|---|---|---|---|
| 4¢ | brown, lake and green on yellow paper *(106,210,000)* | .25 | .20 |
| | Plate block of 4 | .60 | |
| | FDC *(May 10, 1961)* | | 1.00 |

### 1961. GEORGE WILLIAM NORRIS ISSUE

honors the Nebraska senator on his 100th birthday. Among his many achievements was a key role in the creation of the Tennessee Valley Authority. *Intaglio, perforated 11 x 10 1/2.*

CM493 *George W. Norris and Norris Dam*

| CM493 | | MNHVF | UseVF |
|---|---|---|---|
| 4¢ | blue green *(110,810,000)* | .25 | .20 |
| | Plate block of 4 | .60 | |
| | FDC *(July 11, 1961)* | | 1.00 |

### 1961. NAVAL AVIATION ISSUE

salutes the Golden Jubilee of the Navy's participation and development in aviation. *Intaglio, perforated 11 x 10 1/2.*

CM494 *Naval Air Wings and First Naval Airplane (1911 Curtis A-1)*

| CM494 | | MNHVF | UseVF |
|---|---|---|---|
| 4¢ | blue *(116,995,000)* | .25 | .20 |
| | Plate block of 4 | .65 | |
| | Gutter Pair | — | |
| | FDC *(Aug. 20, 1961)* | | 1.00 |

**1961. WORKMAN'S COMPENSATION ISSUE** marks the 50th anniversary of the first U.S. legislation to compensate workers injured on the job. The Wisconsin law of 1911 set a pattern that was followed by 9 other states that year. *Intaglio, perforated 10 1/2 x 11.*

CM495 *Factory and Family in Scales of Justice.*

| CM495 | | MNHVF | UseVF |
|---|---|---|---|
| 4¢ | **ultramarine on bluish paper** | .25 | .20 |
| | *(121,015,000)* | | |
| | Plate block of 4 | .60 | |
| | v. Plate block of 4, | | |
| | plate number inverted | — | |
| | FDC *(Sept. 4, 1961)* | | 1.00 |

## Fine Arts Series

**1961. FREDERIC REMINGTON ISSUE** first stamp in a continuing Fine Arts series, honored the 100th birthday of this American artist of the West (CM230) who won fame for his paintings and sculptures of North American Indians, U.S. soldiers and cowboys on the western plains. (See also CM993). *Intaglio, (Giori Press), perforated 11.*

CM496 *Detail from The Smoke Signal by Remington (left side of painting).*

| CM496 | | MNHVF | UseVF |
|---|---|---|---|
| 4¢ | **blue, red and yellow** *(111,600,000)* | .25 | .20 |
| | Plate block of 4 | .65 | |
| | FDC *(Oct. 4, 1961)* | | 1.00 |

**1961. 50TH ANNIVERSARY OF THE REPUBLIC OF CHINA ISSUE** bears the portrait of Sun Yat-sen (1866-1925), the founder of the republic who fought against dynastic rule for the freedom of China. (See also CM248). *Intaglio, perforated 10 1/2 x 11.*

CM497 *Sun Yat-Sen*

| CM497 | | MNHVF | UseVF |
|---|---|---|---|
| 4¢ | **blue** *(110,620,000)* | .25 | .20 |
| | Plate block of 4 | .85 | |
| | FDC *(Oct. 10, 1961)* | | 1.00 |

**1961. NAISMITH-BASKETBALL ISSUE** commemorated the 100th birthday of Dr. James A. Naismith (1861-1939), Canadian-born inventor of basketball. An athletic instructor at the YMCA, Naismith saw the need for a fast-moving, exciting indoor sport that could be played in the winter. In 1891 he founded the game, which today draws millions of participants and spectators. *Intaglio, perforated 10 1/2 x 11.*

CM498 *Basketball, Hand and Net*

| CM498 | | MNHVF | UseVF |
|---|---|---|---|
| 4¢ | **brown** *(109,110,000)* | .25 | .20 |
| | Plate block of 4 | 1.00 | |
| | FDC *(Nov. 6, 1961)* | | 1.00 |

**1961. NURSING ISSUE** honored the 100th anniversary of the nursing profession in the United States. An urgent need for skilled nurses was created by the Civil War. The training programs then established laid the foundations for the profession, which thousands of American women enter each year. *Intaglio, (Giori Press), perforated 11.*

CM499 *Nurse Lighting Candle*

| CM499 | | MNHVF | UseVF |
|---|---|---|---|
| 4¢ | **blue, black, orange and flesh** | .25 | .20 |
| | *(145,350,000)* | | |
| | Plate block of 4 | .60 | |
| | FDC *(Dec. 28, 1961)* | | 1.00 |

**1962. NEW MEXICO STATEHOOD ISSUE** commemorated the 50th anniversry of its admission as the 47th state. (See CM286). *Intaglio, (Giori Press), perforated 11.*

CM500 *Shiprock Mesa*

| CM500 | | MNHVF | UseVF |
|---|---|---|---|
| 4¢ | **light blue, bister and brown purple** | .25 | .20 |
| | *(112,870,000)* | | |
| | Plate block of 4 | .60 | |
| | FDC *(Jan. 6, 1962)* | | 1.00 |

**1962. ARIZONA STATEHOOD ISSUE** marks the 50th anniversary of the admission of the 48th state. *Intaglio, (Giori Press), perforated 11.*

CM501 *Giant Saguaro Cactus in Bloom at Night.*

| CM501 | | MNHVF | UseVF |
|---|---|---|---|
| 4¢ | **scarlet, deep blue and green** | .25 | .20 |
| | (121,820,000) | | |
| | Plate block of 4 | .60 | |
| | FDC *(Feb. 14, 1962)* | | 1.00 |

**1962. PROJECT MERCURY ISSUE** paid tribute to the successful 3-orbit flight of Lt. Col. John H. Glenn, Jr. The stamp was released at the moment the flight was completed - the first time the United States honored a historic event with an unannounced, simultaneous commemorative. Glenn, the first American astronaut to orbit the earth, traveled at 17,500 miles per hour in his Mercury capsule, *Friendship 7. Intaglio, (Giori Press), perforated 11.*

CM502 *Mercury Capsule Circling Earth*

| CM502 | | MNHVF | UseVF |
|---|---|---|---|
| 4¢ | **deep blue and yellow** (289,240,000) | .25 | .20 |
| | Plate block of 4 | .80 | |
| | FDC *(Feb. 20, 1962)* | | 1.00 |

**1962. MALARIA ERADICATION ISSUE** pledged U.S. support to the World Health Organization in its campaign to eliminate malaria, a disease that claims countless lives each year. *Intaglio, (Giori Press), perforated 11.*

CM503 *United States Seal and WHO Emblem*

| CM503 | | MNHVF | UseVF |
|---|---|---|---|
| 4¢ | **blue and bister** (120,155,000) | .25 | .20 |
| | Plate block of 4 | .60 | |
| | FDC *(March 30, 1962)* | | 1.00 |

**1962. CHARLES EVANS HUGHES ISSUE** honors the 100th birthday of this statesman-jurist (1862-1948). Hughes served as governor of New York, secretary of state under President Harding and as Chief Justice of the U.S. Supreme Court (1930-41). *Intaglio, perforated 10 1/2 x 11.*

CM504 *Charles Evans Hughes*

| CM504 | | MNHVF | UseVF |
|---|---|---|---|
| 4¢ | **black on yellow paper** (124,595,000) | .25 | .20 |
| | Plate block of 4 | .60 | |
| | FDC *(April 11, 1962)* | | 1.00 |

**1962. SEATTLE WORLD'S FAIR ISSUE** marks the International Exposition held in Seattle, WA. April 21-Oct. 21, 1962. This was America's first space-age world's fair, with the 550-foot-high Space Needle as its most distinctive structure and symbol. *Intaglio, (Giori Press), perforated 11.*

CM505 *Space Needle and Monorail*

| CM505 | | MNHVF | UseVF |
|---|---|---|---|
| 4¢ | **red and deep blue** (147,310,000) | .25 | .20 |
| | Plate block of 4 | .60 | |
| | FDC *(April 25, 1962)* | | 1.00 |

**1962. LOUISIANA STATEHOOD COMMEMORATIVE ISSUE** marks the 150th anniversary of the admission of Louisiana as the 18th state. *Intaglio, (Giori Press), perforated 11.*

CM506 *Mississippi Riverboat*

| CM506 | | MNHVF | UseVF |
|---|---|---|---|
| 4¢ | **gray green, blue and vermillion** | .25 | .20 |
| | (118,690,000) | | |
| | Plate block of 4 | .60 | |
| | FDC *(April 30, 1962)* | | 1.00 |

**1962. HOMESTEAD ACT ISSUE** commemorates the 100th anniversary of the act signed by Abraham Lincoln that opened the Great Plains to settlers. A homesteader couldacquire 160 acres by living and working on the land for 5 years. *Intaglio, perforated 11 1/4 x 10 1/2.*

CM507 *Sod Hut and Homesteaders*

| CM507 | | MNHVF | UseVF |
|---|---|---|---|
| 4¢ | **slate blue** (122,730,000) | .25 | .20 |
| | Plate block of 4 | .60 | |
| | FDC *(May 20, 1962)* | | 1.00 |

**1962. GIRL SCOUTS OF AMERICA ISSUE** commemorates the 50th anniversary of the movement, which has grown into an organization of millions. (See CM316). *Intaglio, perforated 11 1/4 X 10 1/2.*

CM508 *Girl Scout, American Flag*

| CM508 | | MNHVF | UseVF |
|---|---|---|---|
| 4¢ | **red** (126,515,000) | .25 | .20 |
| | Plate block of 4 | .60 | |
| | Gutter pair | — | |
| | FDC *(July 24, 1962)* | | 1.00 |

**1962. BRIEN MCMAHON ISSUE** pays tribute to the Connecticut senator who saw the vast potential of the atom for medical, industrial and scientific purposes. McMahon (1903-1952) succeeded in forming the Atomic Energy Commission. (See also CM382). *Intaglio, perforated 11 1/4 X 10 1/2.*

CM509 *James O'Brien McMahon and Atomic Symbol*

| CM509 | | MNHVF | UseVF |
|---|---|---|---|
| 4¢ | **violet** *(130,960,000)* | .25 | .20 |
| | Plate block of 4 | .60 | |
| | FDC *(July 28, 1962)* | | 1.00 |

**1962. NATIONAL APPRENTICESHIP ISSUE** marked the 25th anniversary of the program, under which the U.S. Department of Labor, unions and management join in sponsoring apprenticeship training. *Intaglio, perforated 11 1/4 X 10 1/2.*

CM510 *Young Hand Receiving Micrometer*

| CM510 | | MNHVF | UseVF |
|---|---|---|---|
| 4¢ | **black on buff** *(120,055,000)* | .25 | .20 |
| | Plate block of 4 | .60 | |
| | FDC *(Aug. 31, 1962)* | | 1.00 |

**1962. SAM RAYBURN ISSUE** honored the Texan who served as a Congressman from 1913 until 1961. Rayburn was Speaker of the House of Representatives for 17 years, longer than any other. *Intaglio, (Giori Press), perforated 11.*

CM511 *Sam Rayburn and Capitol Dome*

| CM511 | | MNHVF | UseVF |
|---|---|---|---|
| 4¢ | **brown and blue** *(120,715,000)* | .25 | .20 |
| | Plate block of 4 | .60 | |
| | FDC *(Sept. 16, 1962)* | | 1.00 |

**1962. DAG HAMMARSKJÖLD ISSUE** honored the secretary-general of the United Nations who lost his life while on a peace mission in Africa. *Intaglio, (Giori Press), perforated 11..*

CM512-13 *Dag Hammarskjöld and U.N. Building*

| CM512 | | MNHVF | UseVF |
|---|---|---|---|
| 4¢ | **black, brown and yellow** *(121,440,000)* | .25 | .20 |
| | Plate block of 4 | .60 | |
| | FDC *(Oct. 23, 1962)* | | 1.00 |

**1962. DAG HAMMARSKJÖLD SPECIAL ISSUE** Shortly after the commemorative was released, a yellow inverted error was discovered by collectors in New Jersey and Ohio. The Post Office Department deliberately reprinted this error - the 1st U.S. invert error since the 24¢ Jenny airmail of 1918. Only the yellow is inverted and there are 3 distinct varieties as noted below. *Intaglio, (Giori Press), perforated 11.*

| CM513 | | MNHVF | UseVF |
|---|---|---|---|
| 4¢ | **black, brown and yellow** *(40,270,000)* | | |
| | Type I, the non-yellow strip at left is 3.5mm wide | .55 | .25 |
| | Type II, the non-yellow strip at left is 11.5mm wide | .55 | .25 |
| | Type III, the non-yellow strip at left is 9.75mm wide | .55 | .25 |

**1962. HIGHER EDUCATION ISSUE** commemorated the centennial of the law creating land-grant colleges and universities and pointed out the role higher education has played in the development of the United States, (See also CM377). *Intaglio, (Giori Press), perforated 11.*

CM514 *Lamp of Learning and U.S. Map.*

| CM514 | | MNHVF | UseVF |
|---|---|---|---|
| 4¢ | **blue, green and black** *(120,035,000)* | .25 | .20 |
| | Plate block of 4 | .65 | |
| | FDC *(Nov. 14, 1962)* | | 1.00 |

**1962. WINSLOW HOMER ISSUE** honors the American artist who painted *Breezing Up,* on display in the National Gallery of Art in Washington, D.C. This is the 2nd issue in the Fine Arts series. *Intaglio, (Giori Press), perforated 11.*

CM515 Breezing Up *by Winslow Homer.*

| CM515 | | MNHVF | UseVF |
|---|---|---|---|
| 4¢ | **multicolored** *(117,870,000)* | .25 | .20 |
| | Plate block of 4 | .65 | |
| | v. Horizontal pair. imperforate between | 6750. | |
| | FDC *(Dec. 15, 1962)* | | 1.00 |

**1963. CAROLINA CHARTER ISSUE** commemeorates the 300th anniversary of the granting of the charter by Chrles II to 8 supporters who helped him regain the English throne. The land grant covered 1.5 million square miles. *Intaglio, (Giori Press), perforated 11.*

CM516 *Charter and Quill Pen*

| CM516 | | MNHVF | UseVF |
|---|---|---|---|
| 5¢ | **dark carmine and brown** *(129,445,000)* | .25 | .20 |
| | Plate block of 4 | .65 | |
| | FDC *(April 6, 1963)* | | 1.00 |

**1963. FOOD FOR PEACE ISSUE** pays tribute to the World Food Congress and joins nearly 150 other nations and territories in publicizing the international Freedom from Hunger campaign on stamps. *Intaglio, (Giori Press), perforated 11.*

CM517 *Stalk of Wheat*

**CM517**

| | | MNHVF | UseVF |
|---|---|---|---|
| 5¢ | green, yellow and red *(135,620,000)* | .25 | .20 |
| | Plate block of 4 | .65 | |
| | FDC *(June 4, 1963)* | | 1.00 |

**1963. WEST VIRGINIA STATEHOOD ISSUE** commemorated the 100th anniversary of the admission of the Mountain State to the union. *Intaglio, (Giori Press), perforated 11.*

CM518 *Map and State Capitol West Virginia*

**CM518**

| | | MNHVF | UseVF |
|---|---|---|---|
| 5¢ | green, red and black *(137,540,000)* | .25 | .20 |
| | Plate block of 4 | .65 | |
| | FDC *(June 20, 1963)* | | 1.00 |

**1963. EMANCIPATION PROCLAMATION ISSUE** commemorated the centennial of President Lincoln's action to abolish slavery in the United States. *Intaglio, (Giori Press), perforated 11.*

CM519 *Broken Chains*

**CM519**

| | | MNHVF | UseVF |
|---|---|---|---|
| 5¢ | bright blue, scarlet and indigo *(132,435,000)* | .25 | .20 |
| | Plate block of 4 | .85 | |
| | FDC *(Aug. 16, 1963)* | | 1.00 |

**1963. ALLIANCE FOR PROGRESS ISSUE** marks the second anniversary of an inter-American program for peaceful coexistence and economic improvement. Other members of the Organization of American States to issue stamps honoring the event include Argentina, Bolivia, Costa Rica, Uruguay and Canal Zone. *Intaglio, (Giori Press), perforated 11.*

CM520 *Torch of Progress*

**CM520**

| | | MNHVF | UseVF |
|---|---|---|---|
| 5¢ | bright blue and green *(135,520,000)* | .25 | .20 |
| | Plate block of 4 | .65 | |
| | FDC *(Aug. 17, 1963)* | | 1.00 |

**1963. CORDELL HULL ISSUE** paid tribute to the secretary of state during the administration of Franklin Roosevelt, from 1933 until 1944. He was awarded the Nobel Peace Prize in 1945. *Intaglio, perforated 10 1/2 X 11.*

CM521 *Cordell Hull*

**CM521**

| | | MNHVF | UseVF |
|---|---|---|---|
| 5¢ | blue green *(131,420,000)* | .25 | .20 |
| | Plate block of 4 | .65 | |
| | FDC *(Oct. 5, 1963)* | | 1.00 |

**1963. ELEANOR ROOSEVELT ISSUE** celebrates the 79th birthday of Franklin D. Roosevelt's widow who died in 1962. A champion of liberty and a formidable fighter for human rights. The likeness on the stamp was taken from a photograph she liked best. *Intaglio, perforated 11 X 10 1/2.*

CM522 *Eleanor Roosevelt*

**CM522**

| | | MNHVF | UseVF |
|---|---|---|---|
| 5¢ | purple *(133,170,000)* | .25 | .20 |
| | Plate block of 4 | .65 | |
| | FDC *(Oct. 11, 1963)* | | 1.00 |

**1963. NATIONAL ACADEMY OF SCIENCE ISSUE** saluted this organization on its 100th anniversary. Abraham Lincoln signed into law the legislation that created the academy, which was originally composed of 50 American scientists. *Intaglio, (Giori Press), perforated 11.*

CM523 *Astral Belt Over Globe*

**CM523**

| | | MNHVF | UseVF |
|---|---|---|---|
| 5¢ | turquoise, blue and black *(139,195,000)* | .25 | .20 |
| | Plate block of 4 | .65 | |
| | FDC *(Oct. 14, 1963)* | | 1.00 |

**1963. CITY MAIL DELIVERY ISSUE** marked the centennial of the service begun at the suggestion of Postmaster General Montgomery Blair, who convinced Congress to pass a law providing for the free delivery of city mail. Designed by Norman Rockwell, this commemorative is considered the first expression of humor on a U.S. stamp. It was also the 1st U.S. commerative issue tagged with an invisible compound of zinc-orthosilicate that glows green under ultraviolet light in automated mail handling equipment. *Intaglio, (Giori Press), perforated 11.*

CM524 *Postman flanked by boy and dog*

**CM524**

| | | MNHVF | UseVF |
|---|---|---|---|
| 5¢ | **red, gray and blue** tagged *(128,450,000)* | .25 | .20 |
| | Plate block of 4 | .65 | |
| | FDC *(Oct. 26, 1963)* | | 1.00 |
| | zo. Tagging omitted | — | |

**1963. INTERNATIONAL RED CROSS ISSUE** marks the centennial of the organization and salutes the Red Cross for its participation in the Cuban prisoner exchange program. *Intaglio, (Giori Press), perforated 11.*

CM525 *Cuban Refugees on S.S. Morning Light*

**CM525**

| | | MNHVF | UseVF |
|---|---|---|---|
| 5¢ | **deep gray and red** *(116,665,000)* | .25 | .20 |
| | Plate block of 4 | .65 | |
| | FDC *(Oct. 29, 1963)* | | 1.00 |

**1963. JOHN JAMES AUDUBON ISSUE** honors the great American artist and ornithologist. This is the 3rd in the Fine Arts series and is the 2nd time Audubon has been honored with a stamp (see CM216). *Intaglio, (Giori Press), perforated 11.*

CM526 *Audubon's Columbia Jays*

**CM526**

| | | MNHVF | UseVF |
|---|---|---|---|
| 5¢ | **multicolored** *(175,175,000)* | .25 | .20 |
| | Plate block of 4 | .80 | |
| | FDC *(Dec. 7, 1963)* | | 1.00 |

**1964. SAM HOUSTON ISSUE** salutes the 1st president of the Republic of Texas, commander of the army that defeated Santa Ana in 1836 and thus gained independence for the Lone Star state. This was the first use of the Mr. Zip marginal inscription. (See also CM166, CM168.) *Intaglio, perforated 10 1/2 X 11.*

CM527 *Sam Houston*

**CM527**

| | | MNHVF | UseVF |
|---|---|---|---|
| 5¢ | **black** *(125,995,000)* | .25 | .20 |
| | Plate block of 4 | .85 | |
| | FDC *(Jan. 10, 1964)* | | 1.00 |

**1964. CHARLES M. RUSSELL ISSUE** honors the 100th anniversary of the artist's birth with the 4th stamp in the Fine Arts series. Famous for his Western themes, Russell's art has themes of gunmen, longhorn steers, broncos and dancehall girls. *Intaglio, (Giori Press), perforated 11.*

CM528 *Russell's* Jerked Down

**CM528**

| | | MNHVF | UseVF |
|---|---|---|---|
| 5¢ | **multicolored** *(128,025,000)* | .25 | .20 |
| | Plate block of 4 | .85 | |
| | FDC *(March 19, 1964)* | | 1.00 |

**1964. NEW YORK WORLD'S FAIR ISSUE** commemorated the opening of the international exposition dedicated to "Peace Through Understanding." Approximately 175 separate pavilions and other structures presented the achievements of more than 509 nations, states and major industries. *Intaglio, perforated 11 x 10 1/2.*

CM529 *Unisphere and World Fair Mall*

**CM529**

| | | MNHVF | UseVF |
|---|---|---|---|
| 5¢ | **green** *(145,700,000)* | .25 | .20 |
| | Plate block of 4 | .85 | |
| | FDC *(April 22, 1964)* | | 1.00 |

**1964. JOHN MUIR ISSUE** honored the naturalist and conservationist whose efforts helped save California's priceless forests. *Intaglio, (Giori Press), perforated 11.*

CM530 *John Muir and Redwoods*

**CM530**

| | | MNHVF | UseVF |
|---|---|---|---|
| 5¢ | **brown, green, brownish gray and olive green** *(120,310,000)* | .25 | .20 |
| | Plate block of 4 | .85 | |
| | FDC *(April 29, 1964)* | | 1.00 |

**1964. JOHN F. KENNEDY MEMORIAL ISSUE** pays tribute to the 35th president of the United States, assassinated Nov. 22, 1963. Many nations mourned his passing and issued stamps in his memory. Although Boston was the official First Day city, the stamp was released nation wide that same day. *Intaglio, perforated 11 x 10 1/2.*

CM531 *John F. Kennedy and Eternal Flame*

**CM531**

| | | MNHVF | UseVF |
|---|---|---|---|
| 5¢ | **gray blue** *(500,000,000)* | .25 | .20 |
| | Plate block of 4 | 1.85 | |
| | FDC *(May 29, 1964)* | | 1.00 |

**1964. NEW JERSEY TERCENTENARY ISSUE** marks the 300th anniversary of the colonization of the Garden State by the British. The stamp was first issued in Elizabeth, the state's 1st capital and oldest city. *Intaglio, perforated 10 1/2 X 11.*

CM532 *Philip Carteret at Elizabethtown*

| CM532 | | MNHVF | UseVF |
|---|---|---|---|
| 5¢ | ultramarine *(123,845,000)* | .25 | .20 |
| | Plate block of 4 | .65 | |
| | FDC *(June 15, 1964)* | | 1.00 |

**1964. NEVADA STATEHOOD ISSUE** commemorates the centenary of the entry of Nevada as the 36th state. *Intaglio, (Giori Press), perforated 11.*

CM533 *Virginia City and Map of Nevada*

| CM533 | | MNHVF | UseVF |
|---|---|---|---|
| 5¢ | multicolored *(122,825,000)* | .25 | .20 |
| | Plate block of 4 | .65 | |
| | FDC *(July 22, 1964)* | | 1.00 |

**1964. REGISTER AND VOTE ISSUE** encourages all eligible Americans to take part in the forthcoming election and was endorsed by both the Democratic and Republican parties. *Intaglio, (Giori Press), perforated 11.*

CM534 *U.S. Flag*

| CM534 | | MNHVF | UseVF |
|---|---|---|---|
| 5¢ | blue and red *(325,000,000)* | .25 | .20 |
| | Plate block of 4 | .65 | |
| | FDC *(Aug. 1, 1964)* | | 1.00 |

**1964. WILLIAM SHAKESPEARE ISSUE** commemorates the 400th birthday of the Bard of Avon. His contribution to the world included such masterpieces as *Romeo & Juliet, Hamlet, Othello, Macbeth, and King Lear. Intaglio, perforated 10 1/2 X 11.*

CM335 *William Shakespeare*

| CM535 | | MNHVF | UseVF |
|---|---|---|---|
| 5¢ | brown on tan paper *(123,245,000)* | .25 | .20 |
| | Plate block of 4 | .65 | |
| | FDC *(Aug. 14, 1964)* | | 1.00 |

**1964. DOCTORS MAYO ISSUE** honors the birth of William J. Mayo and his brother Charles H. Mayo and the 50th anniversary of the founding of the world-famous Mayo Clinic in Rochester, MN. *Intaglio, perforated 10 1/2 X 11.*

CM536 *Statue of the Mayo Brothers*

| CM536 | | MNHVF | UseVF |
|---|---|---|---|
| 5¢ | green *(123,355,000)* | .25 | .20 |
| | Plate block of 4 | 1.50 | |
| | FDC *(Sept. 11, 1964)* | | 1.00 |

**1964. AMERICAN MUSIC ISSUE** commemorates the 50th anniversary of the American Society of Composers, Authors and Publishers. *Intaglio, (Giori Press), perforated 11.*

CM537 *Lute and Horn, Music Score, Oak and Laurel*

| CM537 | | MNHVF | UseVF |
|---|---|---|---|
| 5¢ | red, gray and blue on granite paper *(126,370,000)* | .25 | .20 |
| | Plate block of 4 | .85 | |
| | v. blue omitted | 1000. | |
| | FDC *(Oct. 15, 1964)* | | 1.00 |

**1964. HOMEMAKERS ISSUE** commemorates the 50th anniversary of the Smith-Lever Act that improved home life in America and was issued in conjunc tion with the annual meeting of the National Extension Homemakers Council. This is the first time the Bureau of Engraving and Printing combined offset and intaglio printing on a stamp, a method used by the American Bank Note Company to print the Overrun Countries stamps (CM251-63). *Intaglio, (Giori Press) and offset, perforated 11.*

CM538 *Needlepoint Sampler of American Farm Scene*

| CM538 | | MNHVF | UseVF |
|---|---|---|---|
| 5¢ | multicolored on buff *(121,250,000)* | .25 | .20 |
| | Plate block of 4 | .85 | |
| | FDC *(Oct. 26, 1964)* | | 1.00 |

**1964. VERRAZANO-NARROWS BRIDGE ISSUE** marks the dedication of what was the longest single suspension bridge in the world. Named for the Florentine explorer who discovered New York Bay in 1524, the span links Staten Island and Brooklyn, NY. *Intaglio, perforated 10 1/2 X 11.*

CM539 *Verrazano-Narrows Bridge and Map*

| CM539 | | MNHVF | UseVF |
|---|---|---|---|
| **5¢** | **green** *(125,005,000)* | .25 | .20 |
| | Plate block of 4 | .65 | |
| | FDC *(Nov. 21, 1964)* | | 1.00 |

**1964. ABSTRACT ART ISSUE** is the 5th in the series of Fine Arts commemoratives. It is based on a lithograph by the late Stuart Davis. *Intaglio, (Giori Press), perforated 11.*

CM540 *Melange of Squiggles by Stuart Davis.*

| CM540 | | MNHVF | UseVF |
|---|---|---|---|
| **5¢** | **blue, black and red** *(125,800,000)* | .25 | .20 |
| | Plate block of 4 | .65 | |
| | FDC *(Dec. 2, 1964)* | | 1.00 |

**1964. AMATEUR RADIO OPERATORS ISSUE** paid tribute to the nation's 250,000 "hams" and their long record of service to the country in emergencies and marks the 50th anniversary of the American Radio Relay League. *Intaglio, perforated 10 1/2 X 11.*

CM541 *Radio Dial and Wave*

| CM541 | | MNHVF | UseVF |
|---|---|---|---|
| **5¢** | **purple** *(122,230,000)* | .25 | .20 |
| | Plate block of 4 | .90 | |
| | FDC *(Dec. 15, 1964)* | | 1.00 |

**1965. BATTLE OF NEW ORLEANS ISSUE** salutes 150 years of peace between England and the United States and the sesquicentennial of the famous battle between American forces under Gen. Andrew Jackson and the British troops led by Sir Edward Packenham. *Intaglio, (Giori Press), perforated 11.*

CM542 *Gen. Andrew Jackson Leading Troops in Battle and Sesquicentennial Medal.*

| CM542 | | MNHVF | UseVF |
|---|---|---|---|
| **5¢** | **carmine, blue and slate** *(115,695,000)* | .25 | .20 |
| | Plate block of 4 | .65 | |
| | FDC *(Jan. 8, 1964)* | | 1.00 |

**1965. SOKOL CENTENNIAL - PHYSICAL FITNESS ISSUE** paid tribute to the program initiated by President Kennedy and the 100th an-

niversary of the Sokol educational and physical fitness organization. *Intaglio, (Giori Press), perforated 11.*

CM543 *Discus Thrower*

| CM543 | | MNHVF | UseVF |
|---|---|---|---|
| **5¢** | **lake and deep slate** *(115,095,000)* | .25 | .20 |
| | Plate block of 4 | .65 | |
| | FDC *(Feb. 15, 1965)* | | 1.00 |

**1965. CRUSADE AGAINST CANCER ISSUE** publicizes the importance of medical checkups and prompt treatment and salutes the efforts of those dedicated to the eradicating cancer. *Intaglio, (Giori Press), perforated 11.*

CM544 *Stethoscope and Microscope*

| CM544 | | MNHVF | UseVF |
|---|---|---|---|
| **5¢** | **reddish violet, black and red** *(116,560,000)* | .25 | .20 |
| | Plate block of 4 | .65 | |
| | FDC *(April 1, 1965)* | | 1.00 |

**1965. WINSTON CHURCHILL MEMORIAL ISSUE** honors the World War II British leader, (1874-1965). *Intaglio, perforated 10 1/2 X 11.*

CM545 *Winston Churchill*

| CM545 | | MNHVF | UseVF |
|---|---|---|---|
| **5¢** | **black** *(125,180,000)* | .25 | .20 |
| | Plate block of 4 | .65 | |
| | FDC *(May 13, 1965)* | | 1.00 |

**1965. MAGNA CARTA ISSUE** commemorates the 750th anniversary of the document by King John that became the 1st detailed statement of English feudal law esteemed by many as a cornerstone of later British and American law. *Intaglio, (Giori Press), perforated 11.*

CM546 Triumph of the People over the King. *Symbolic design by Brook Temple*

| CM546 | | MNHVF | UseVF |
|---|---|---|---|
| 5¢ | **black, yellow and reddish-violet** *(120,135,000)* | .25 | .20 |
| | Plate block of 4 (2 numbers) | .65 | |
| | v. Plate block of 4, black plate number omitted | — | |
| | FDC *(June 15, 1965)* | | 1.00 |

**1965. UN International Cooperation Year Issue** commemorates the 20th anniversary of the United Nations. The United States and other U.N. member nations, issued stamps dedicated to the theme, and the United Nations issued a set of 2 stamps and a souvenir sheet on the same day as this U.S. stamp. *Intaglio, (Giori Press), perforated 11.*

CM547 *International Cooperation Year Emblem*

| CM547 | | MNHVF | UseVF |
|---|---|---|---|
| 5¢ | **turquoise blue and slate** *(115,405,000)* | .25 | .20 |
| | Plate block of 4 | .65 | |
| | FDC *(June 26, 1965)* | | 1.00 |

**1965. Salvation Army Issue** marks the 100th anniversary of this non-sectarian international organization. Founded in London by William Booth in 1865, the Salvation Army was first established in the United States in 1880. *Intaglio, (Giori Press), perforated 11.*

CM548 *Salvation Army*

| CM548 | | MNHVF | UseVF |
|---|---|---|---|
| 5¢ | **red, black and deep blue** *(115,855,000)* | .25 | .20 |
| | Plate block of 4 | .65 | |
| | FDC *(July 2, 1965)* | | 1.00 |

**1965. Dante Alighieri Issue** marks the 700th birthday of Italy's poet who wrote *The Divine Comedy. Intaglio, perforated 10 1/2 X 11.*

CM549 *Dante Alighieri. Adopted from a 16th-century painting.*

| CM549 | | MNHVF | UseVF |
|---|---|---|---|
| 5¢ | **carmine red on light venetian red paper** *(115,340,000)* | .25 | .20 |
| | Plate block of 4 | .65 | |
| | FDC *(July 17, 1965)* | | 1.00 |

**1965. Herbert Hoover Issue** paid tribute to the 31st president of the United States who died Oct. 20, 1964. He was a talented mining engineer and served the country in many capacities, including secretary of commerce under Harding. *Intaglio, perforated 10 1/2 X 11.*

CM550 *Herbert Hoover*

| CM550 | | MNHVF | UseVF |
|---|---|---|---|
| 5¢ | **red** *(114,840,000)* | .25 | .20 |
| | Plate block of 4 | .65 | |
| | FDC *(Aug. 10, 1965)* | | 1.00 |

**1965. Robert Fulton Issue** commemorated the 200th birthday of the inventor who built the 1st successful steamship, *The Clermont,*in 1807. *Intaglio, (Giori Press), perforated 11.*

CM551 *Robert Fulton and The Clermont*

| CM551 | | MNHVF | UseVF |
|---|---|---|---|
| 5¢ | **blue and black** *(116,140,000)* | .25 | .20 |
| | Plate block of 4 | .65 | |
| | FDC *(Aug. 19, 1965)* | | 1.00 |

**1965. European Settlement Issue** commemorated the 400th anniversary of the establishment by Spanish colonists of a permanent settlement in Florida in September 1565. Spain released a joint issue marking this event (Spain 1715). *Intaglio, (Giori Press), perforated 11.*

CM552 *Spanish Explorer and Ships*

| CM552 | | MNHVF | UseVF |
|---|---|---|---|
| 5¢ | **yellow, red and black** *(116,900,000)* | .25 | .20 |
| | Plate block of 4 | .65 | |
| | v. Yellow omitted | 400. | |
| | FDC *(Aug. 28, 1965)* | | 1.00 |

**1965. Traffic Safety Issue** called attention to the urgent need to reduce automotive accidents. *Intaglio, (Giori Press), perforated 11.*

CM553 *Traffic Signal*

| CM553 | | MNHVF | UseVF |
|---|---|---|---|
| 5¢ | **green, black and red** *(114,085,000)* | .25 | .20 |
| | Plate block of 4 | .65 | |
| | FDC *(Sept. 3, 1965)* | | 1.00 |

**1965. John Singleton Copley Issue** is the 6th stamp in the Fine Arts series. Features a portrait of the artist's daughter, part of a family group painted in 1776 by Copley. The original now hangs in the National Gallery of Art, Washington, D.C. *Intaglio, (Giori Press), perforated 11.*

CM554 *Elizabeth Clarke Copley*

| CM554 | | MNHVF | UseVF |
|---|---|---|---|
| 5¢ | **black and tones of brown and olive** *(114,880,000)* | .25 | .20 |
| | Plate block of 4 | .65 | |
| | FDC *(Sept. 17, 1965)* | | 1.00 |

**1965. INTERNATIONAL TELECOMMUNICATION UNION ISSUE** commemorated the 100th anniversary of this international organization created in 1865 to develop electronic communication among nations. *Intaglio, (Giori Press), perforated 11.*

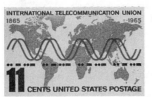

CM555 *World Map and Radio Wave*

| CM555 | | MNHVF | UseVF |
|---|---|---|---|
| 11¢ | **yellow, red and black** *(26,995,000)* | .25 | .20 |
| | Plate block of 4 | 5.50 | |
| | FDC *(Oct. 6, 1965)* | | 1.00 |

**1965. ADLAI STEVENSON ISSUE** pays tribute to the late U.S. ambassador to the United Nations and former presidential candidate. *Intaglio, (Giori Press), and offset perforated 11.*

CM556 *Adlai Stevenson, U.N. Wreath and U.S. Colors*

| CM556 | | MNHVF | UseVF |
|---|---|---|---|
| 5¢ | **light blue gray, black, red and blue** *(128,495,000)* | .25 | .20 |
| | Plate block of 4 | .65 | |
| | FDC *(Oct. 23, 1965)* | | 1.00 |

**1966. MIGRATORY BIRD TREATY ISSUE** marked the 50th anniversary of cooperation between the United States and Canada in protecting birds. *Intaglio, (Giori Press) perforated 11.*

CM557 *Birds Over the Great Lakes*

| CM557 | | MNHVF | UseVF |
|---|---|---|---|
| 5¢ | **red, blue and light blue** *(116,835,000)* | .25 | .20 |
| | Plate block of 4 | .65 | |
| | FDC *(March 16, 1966)* | | 1.00 |

**1966. HUMANE TREATMENT OF ANIMALS ISSUE** paid tribute to The American Society for the Prevention of Cruelty to Animals, founded in 1866 by Henry Bergh. *Intaglio, (Giori Press) and offset, perforated 11.*

CM558 *"Babe" the Dog*

| CM558 | | MNHVF | UseVF |
|---|---|---|---|
| 5¢ | **reddish brown and black** *(117,470,000)* | .25 | .20 |
| | Plate block of 4 | .65 | |
| | FDC *(April 9, 1966)* | | 1.00 |

**1966. INDIANA STATEHOOD ISSUE** marked the 150th anniversary of the admission to the union. The event was officially celebrated at Corydon, the 1st capital of Indiana. *Intaglio, (Giori Press), perforated 11.*

CM559 *Map of Indiana and Old Capitol*

| CM559 | | MNHVF | UseVF |
|---|---|---|---|
| 5¢ | **blue, yellow and brown** *(123,770,000)* | .25 | .20 |
| | Plate block of 4 | .65 | |
| | FDC *(April 16, 1966)* | | 1.00 |

**1966. AMERICAN CIRCUS ISSUE** saluted the Big Top and those who bring fun and thrills to audiences throughout the nation. *Intaglio, (Giori Press), perforated 11.*

CM560 *Circus Clown*

| CM560 | | MNHVF | UseVF |
|---|---|---|---|
| 5¢ | **red, blue, pink and black** *(131,270,000)* | .25 | .20 |
| | Plate block of 4 | .90 | |
| | FDC *(May 2, 1966)* | | 1.00 |

**1966. SIXTH INTERNATIONAL PHILATELIC EXHIBITION ISSUE** commemorated the show, held in Washington, D.C., May 21-30. This commemorative stamp, souvenir sheet and airmail postal card were issued to mark the event. *Intaglio (Giori Press) and offset, perforated 11.*

CM561 *Envelope with Stamps*

| CM561 | | MNHVF | UseVF |
|---|---|---|---|
| 5¢ | **multicolored** *(122,285,000)* | .25 | .20 |
| | Plate block of 4 | .65 | |
| | FDC *(May 21, 1966)* | | 1.00 |

**1966. SIPEX SOUVENIR SHEET** dedicated to stamp collectors also features the words "Discover America," the theme of President Johnson's program to stimulate travel and tourism in the United States. *Intaglio (Giori Press) and offset, imperforate.*

CM562 *Envelope and Capitol Scene*

**CM562**

| 5¢ | multicolored *(14,680,000)* | MNHVF | UseVF |
|---|---|---|---|
| | | .30 | .25 |
| | FDC *(May 23, 1966)* | | 1.00 |

**1966. BILL OF RIGHTS ISSUE** commemorated the 175th anniversary of the 1st 10 ammendments to the U.S. Constitution. The stamp was designated by Herbert L. Block, renowned editorial cartoonist. *Intaglio, (Giori Press), perforated 11.*

CM563 *"Freedom Conquers Tyranny"*

**CM563**

| 5¢ | red and blue *(114,160,000)* | MNHVF | UseVF |
|---|---|---|---|
| | | .25 | .20 |
| | Plate block of 4 | .65 | |
| | FDC *(July 1, 1966)* | | 1.00 |

**1966. POLISH MILLENNIUM ISSUE** commemorated the 1,000th anniversary of Poland and pays tribute to the longstanding friendship between Americans and the Polish people. *Intaglio, perforated 10 1/2 x 11.*

CM564 *Polish Eagle*

**CM564**

| 5¢ | red *(126,475,000)* | MNHVF | UseVF |
|---|---|---|---|
| | | .25 | .20 |
| | Plate block of 4 | .65 | |
| | FDC *(July 30, 1966)* | | 1.00 |

**1966. NATIONAL PARK SERVICE ISSUE** paid tribute to the 50th anniversary of the National Park Service. Although the national park system dates back to 1872, it was first established as a bureau under the Department of Interior August 25, 1916. *Intaglio (Giori Press) and offset, perforated 11.*

CM565 *National Park Emblem*

**CM565**

| 5¢ | multicolored *(119,535,000)* | MNHVF | UseVF |
|---|---|---|---|
| | | .25 | .20 |
| | Plate block of 4 | .80 | |
| | FDC *(Aug. 25, 1966)* | | 1.00 |
| | z. Tagged | .30 | .25 |
| | Plate block of 4, tagged | 2.00 | |
| | FDC, tagged *Aug. 26, 1966)* | — | 30.00 |
| | z1. Tagged after perforating | .30 | |
| | Plate block of 4, with untagged left margin | 2.00 | |
| | FDC (Washington D.C.) *(Aug. 26, 1966)* | | — |
| | z2. Tagging inverted | | |
| | Plate block of 4 | — | |
| | z3. Error (untagged), plate-block- side margin strip of 20 with plate, zip, with tagged and untagged erros on same piece | 1.40 | |

*Stamps tagged after perforation can be distinguished by a grid of tagging which connects the perforation holes on the gummed side of unused stamps and perforation-sized disc-like blemishes in the tagging on the face of the stamps. Untagged gripper margins, about 3/8-inch in width, were intended to appear in left sheet margins, but some sheets were put through the offset tagging press with the underlying design inverted, resulting in errors with tagging absent in the opposite margins.*

*Values shown for the untagged errors are for strips of at least five stamps with both tagged and untagged specimens on a single piece.*

*For more information on tagging, see the introduction.*

**1966. MARINE CORPS RESERVE ISSUE** celebrates the 50th anniversary of the military organization. *Intaglio (Giori Press) and offset, perforate.*

CM566 *U.S. Marines 1775-1966*

**CM566**

| 5¢ | black, olive, red and blue *(125,110,000)* | MNHVF | UseVF |
|---|---|---|---|
| | | .25 | .20 |
| | Plate block of 4 | .65 | |
| | FDC *(Aug. 29, 1966)* | | 1.00 |
| | z. Tagged | .30 | .25 |
| | Plate block of 4, tagged | 2.00 | |
| | FDC, tagged *(Aug. 29, 1966)* | | 30.00 |
| | z1. Error (untagged), strip of 5 showing both tagged and untagged on same piece. | — | |
| | v. Black and olive omitted | 15400. | |

**1966. GENERAL FEDERATION OF WOMEN'S CLUBS ISSUE** commemorated 75 years of service ranging from aiding school dropouts to aiding international understanding, and the millions of women who are members of the clubs and associate organizations. *Intaglio, (Giori Press), perforated 11.*

CM567 *Women of 1890's and 1960's*

**CM567**

| 5¢ | pink, blue and black *(114,853,000)* | MNHVF | UseVF |
|---|---|---|---|
| | | .25 | .20 |
| | Plate block of 4 | .65 | |
| | FDC *(Sept. 12, 1966)* | | 30.00 |
| | z. tagged | .30 | .25 |
| | Plate block of 4 | 2.00 | |
| | FDC *(Sept. 13, 1966)* | | 30.00 |

**1966. JOHNNY APPLESEED ISSUE** the inaugural stamp in the American Folklore series, honors John Chapman, eccentric nurseryman who devoted his life to planting apple trees in Pennsylvania, Ohio and Indiana. It is reputed that he covered over 100,000 square miles before his death in 1845. *Intaglio, (Giori Press), perforated 11.*

CM568 *Johnny Appleseed and Apple*

| CM568 | | MNHVF | UseVF |
|---|---|---|---|
| 5¢ | black, red and green *(124,290,000)* | .25 | .20 |
| | Plate block of 4 | .65 | |
| | FDC *(Sept. 24, 1966)* | | 1.00 |
| | z. tagged | .30 | .25 |
| | Plate block of 4 | 2.00 | |
| | FDC *(Sept. 26, 1966)* | | 1.00 |

**1966. BEAUTIFICATION OF AMERICA ISSUE** publicized the campaign to restore and enhance the beauty of the country. *Intaglio, (Giori Press), perforated 11.*

CM569 *Jefferson Memorial and Cherry Blossoms*

| CM569 | | MNHVF | UseVF |
|---|---|---|---|
| 5¢ | black, green and pink *(128,460,000)* | .25 | .20 |
| | Plate block of 4 | .65 | |
| | FDC *(Oct. 5, 1966)* | | 1.00 |
| | z. tagged | .30 | .25 |
| | Plate block of 4 | 2.00 | |
| | FDC *(Oct. 5, 1966)* | | 30.00 |
| | z1. Tagged after perforating | .30 | |
| | Plate block of 4, untagged right margin | 2.00 | |
| | z2. Tagged after perforating (error), untagged *left* margin | 1.75 | |
| | Plate block of 4 | 2.00 | |

**1966. GREAT RIVER ROAD ISSUE** publicizes the longest parkway in the world, stretching from Kenora, Canada southward to New Orleans, a distance of 5,600 miles. *Intaglio (Giori Press) and offset, imperforate.*

CM570 *Map of Mississippi River and Road*

| CM570 | | MNHVF | UseVF |
|---|---|---|---|
| 5¢ | salmon, blue, olive yellow and yellow green *(127,585,000)* | .25 | .20 |
| | Plate block of 4 | .65 | |
| | FDC *(Oct. 21, 1966)* | | 1.00 |
| | z. tagged | .30 | .25 |
| | Plate block of 4 | 2.00 | |
| | FDC *(Oct. 22, 1966)* tagged | | 30.00 |

**1966. U.S. SAVINGS BOND ISSUE** salutes 25 years of bond sales and also carries the message, "We Appreciate our Servicemen." *Intaglio (Giori Press) and offset, perforated 11.*

CM571 *Statue of Liberty and U.S. Flag*

| CM571 | | MNHVF | UseVF |
|---|---|---|---|
| 5¢ | red, blue and black *(115,875,000)* | .25 | .20 |
| | Plate block of 4 | .75 | |
| | FDC *(Oct. 26, 1966)* | | 1.00 |
| | v. Red, black and dark blue omitted | 5000. | |
| | v1. Dark blue omitted | 8000. | |
| | z. tagged | .30 | .25 |
| | Plate block of 4 | 2.00 | |
| | FDC *(Oct. 27, 1966)* tagged | | 30.00 |

**1966. MARY CASSATT ISSUE** the 7th in the Fine Arts series, pays tribute to the American painter whom many critics regard as the greatest female artist. She is the only American, besides Whistler, to have her work hang in the Louvre. *Intaglio, (Giori Press), perforated 11.*

CM572 *The Boating Party*

| CM572 | | MNHVF | UseVF |
|---|---|---|---|
| 5¢ | multicolored *(114,015,000)* | .25 | .20 |
| | Plate block of 4 | .75 | |
| | FDC *(Nov. 17, 1966)* | | 1.00 |
| | z. tagged | .30 | .25 |
| | Plate block of 4 | — | |
| | FDC *(Nov. 17, 1966)* tagged | | 30.00 |

**1967. NATIONAL GRANGE ISSUE** commemorates the 100th anniversary of the farmer's organization founded by Oliver H. Kelley to help farmers develope economically and culturally. Its sphere of activities has broadened and now include scholarships and aid to underdeveloped nations. *Intaglio, (Giori Press), perforated 11.*

CM573 *Grange Poster of 1870*

| CM573 | | MNHVF | UseVF |
|---|---|---|---|
| 5¢ | brownish orange, green, orange and black *(121,105,000)* | .25 | .20 |
| | Plate block of 4 | .65 | |
| | FDC *(April 17, 1967)* | | 1.00 |
| | zo. Tagging omitted | 3.50 | |

**1967. CANADA CENTENNIAL ISSUE** commemorated the anniversary of Canada's Confederation. The stamp was first sold at the U.S. pavilion at Expo '67 in Montreal. *Intaglio, (Giori Press), perforated 11.*

CM574 *Abstract Canadian Landscape*

| CM574 | | MNHVF | UseVF |
|---|---|---|---|
| 5¢ | blue, green, dark blue and olive green, tagged *(132,045,000)* | .25 | .20 |
| | Plate block of 4 | .65 | |
| | FDC *(May 26, 1967)* | | 1.00 |
| | zo. Tagging omitted | 4.50 | |

**1967. ERIE CANAL SESQUICENTENNIAL ISSUE** celebrates the engineering feat that linked Lake Erie with New York City. This 363-mile man-made waterway contributed to the economic development of the young nation. *Intaglio (Giori Press) and offset, perforate 11.*

CM575 *Canal Boat*

| CM575 | | MNHVF | UseVF |
|---|---|---|---|
| 5¢ | dark blue, light blue, black red, tagged *(118,780,000)* | .25 | .20 |
| | Plate block of 4 | .65 | |
| | FDC *(July 4, 1967)* | | 1.00 |
| | zo. Tagging omitted | 10.00 | |

**1967. LIONS INTERNATIONAL ISSUE** salutes the world's largest volunteer service organization on its 50th anniversary. The theme of the stamp, "Search for Peace," was that of an essay contest sponsored by the Lions. *Intaglio, (Giori Press), perforated 11.*

CM576 *Dove of Peace and Olive Branch*

| CM576 | | MNHVF | UseVF |
|---|---|---|---|
| 5¢ | red, blue and black on granite paper, tagged *(121,985,000)* | .25 | .20 |
| | Plate block of 4 | .80 | |
| | FDC *(July 5, 1967)* | | 1.00 |
| | zo. Tagging omitted | 4.00 | |

**1967. HENRY DAVID THOREAU ISSUE** honors the 19th-century essayist on his 150th birthday. His writings reflect his love of nature and his belief in the dignity of all man. *Intaglio, (Giori Press) and offset, perforated 11.*

CM577 *Henry David Thoreau*

| CM577 | | MNHVF | UseVF |
|---|---|---|---|
| 5¢ | red, black and green, tagged *(111,850,000)* | .25 | .20 |
| | Plate block of 4 | .65 | |
| | FDC *(July 12, 1967)* | | 1.00 |
| | zo. Tagging omitted | — | |

**1967. NEBRASKA STATEHOOD ISSUE** marks the centennial of the State's entry into the union. *Intaglio, (Giori Press), perforated 11.*

CM578 *Cattle and corn*

| CM578 | | MNHVF | UseVF |
|---|---|---|---|
| 5¢ | yellow, green and brown, tagged *(117,225,000)* | .25 | .20 |
| | Plate block of 4 | .65 | |
| | FDC *(July 29, 1967)* | | 1.00 |
| | zo. Tagging omitted | 5.00 | |

**1967. VOICE OF AMERICA ISSUE** pays tribute to the radio branch of the U.S. Information Agency on its 25th anniversary. *Intaglio, (Giori Press), perforated 11.*

CM579 *Radio Tower Transmitting*

| CM579 | | MNHVF | UseVF |
|---|---|---|---|
| 5¢ | red, blue and black, tagged *(111,515,000)* | .25 | .20 |
| | Plate block of 4 | .65 | |
| | FDC *(Aug. 1, 1967)* | | 1.00 |
| | zo. Tagging omitted | 5.00 | |

**1967. DAVY CROCKETT ISSUE** the 2nd stamp in the American Folklore series, honors the Tennessee backwoodsman who gained fame as a trapper, hunter, soldier, public official and died at the Alamo. *Intaglio, (Giori Press), perforated 11.*

CM580 *Davy Crockett*

| CM580 | | MNHVF | UseVF |
|---|---|---|---|
| 5¢ | green, black and yellow tagged *(114,270,000)* | .25 | .20 |
| | Plate block of 4 | .85 | |
| | FDC *(Aug. 17, 1967)* | | 1.00 |
| | v. Green omitted | — | |
| | v1. green and black omitted | — | |
| | v2. green and yellow omitted | — | |
| | v3. Vertical pair, imperforate betweem | 6000. | |
| | zo. Tagging omitted | 4.50 | |

**1967. SPACE TWINS ISSUE** salutes America's achievements in space. For the first time, the United States printed 2 se-tenant stamp that blend into 1 complete design. *Intaglio, (Giori Press)and offset, perforated 11.*

CM581-82 *Spacewalking Astronaut and Gemini Capsule*

| CM581 | | MNHVF | UseVF |
|---|---|---|---|
| 5¢ | dark blue, black and red tagged *(120,865,000)* | 1.00 | .35 |

**CM582**

| | | MNHVF | UseVF |
|---|---|---|---|
| 5¢ | **dark blue, red and blue green,** tagged | 1.00 | .35 |
| | Se-tenant pair, CM581-82 | 2.00 | 1.50 |
| | Plate block of 4 | 4.50 | |
| | FDC, single *(Sept. 29, 1967)* | | 5.00 |
| | FDC, pair | | 10.00 |
| | zo. Tagging omitted, any single | 5.00 | |
| | zoy.Tagging omitted, pair | 10.00 | |

**1967. URBAN PLANNING ISSUE** publicizes the need to improve and develop Americn cities. *Intaglio, (Giori Press), perforated 11.*

CM583 *Overhead View of Model City*

**CM583**

| | | MNHVF | UseVF |
|---|---|---|---|
| 5¢ | **dark blue, light blue and black,** tagged *(110,675,000)* | .25 | .20 |
| | Plate block of 4 | .65 | |
| | FDC *(Oct. 2, 1967)* | | 1.00 |
| | zo. Tagging omitted | — | |

**1967. FINLAND INDEPENDENCE ISSUE** Honors the 50th anniversary of Finnish sovereignty. *Intaglio, (Giori Press), perforated 11.*

CM584 *Finnish Coat of Arms*

**CM584**

| | | MNHVF | UseVF |
|---|---|---|---|
| 5¢ | **blue,** tagged *(110,670,000)* | .25 | .20 |
| | Plate block of 4 | .65 | |
| | FDC *(Oct. 6, 1967)* | | 1.00 |
| | zo. Tagging omitted | — | |

**1967. THOMAS EAKINS ISSUE** the 8th stamp in the Fine Arts series, honors an American artist who gained fame for his paintings of athletic events, portraits and early American life. A professor of anatomy at the Pennsylvania Academy of Fine Arts, Eakins' thorough knowledge of this subject is reflected in his works. The 1st U.S. postage stamp using the *gravure* method. The issue was printed by the Photogravure and Color Co., Moonachie, NJ. *Perforated 12.*

CM585 *The Biglin Brothers Racing*

**CM585**

| | | MNHVF | UseVF |
|---|---|---|---|
| 5¢ | **gold and multicolored,** tagged *(113,825,000)* | .25 | .20 |
| | Plate block of 4 | .65 | |
| | FDC *(Nov. 2, 1967)* | | 1.00 |
| | zo. Tagging omitted | 6.00 | |

**1967. MISSISSIPPI STATEHOOD ISSUE** honors the 150th anniversry of the Magnolia State's entry into the union. *Intaglio, (Giori Press), perforated 11.*

CM586 *Magnolia Blossom*

**CM586**

| | | MNHVF | UseVF |
|---|---|---|---|
| 5¢ | **green blue, blue green and brown** tagged *(113,330,000)* | .25 | .20 |
| | Plate block of 4 | .75 | |
| | FDC *(Dec. 11, 1967)* | | 1.00 |
| | zo. Tagging omitted | 5.00 | |

**1968. ILLINOIS STATEHOOD ISSUE** marks the 150th anniversry of the State's entry into the Union. *Intaglio, (Giori Press), perforated 11.*

CM587 *Illinois Farm Scene*

**CM587**

| | | MNHVF | UseVF |
|---|---|---|---|
| 6¢ | **multicolored** tagged *(141,350,000)* | .25 | .20 |
| | Plate block of 4 | .85 | |
| | FDC *(Feb. 12, 1968)* | | 1.00 |
| | zo. Tagging omitted | — | |

**1968. HEMISFAIR '68 ISSUE** celebrated the international exposition that opened in San Antonio, TX, April 6th. The theme was "The Confluence of Civilizations in the Americas," and the stamp also commemorated the 250th anniversary of San Antonio. *Intaglio (Giori Press) and offset, perforated 11.*

CM588 *North and South America with Lines converging on San Antonio.*

**CM588**

| | | MNHVF | UseVF |
|---|---|---|---|
| 6¢ | **blue, pink, and white** tagged *(117,470,600)* | .25 | .20 |
| | Plate block of 4 | .85 | |
| | FDC *(March 30, 1968)* | | 1.00 |
| | v. White omitted | 1400. | |

**1968. SUPPORT OUR YOUTH ISSUE** honored the Benevolent and Protectorate Order of Elks centennial year and the expansion of its youth service program. *Intaglio, (Giori Press), perforated 11.*

CM589 *Young Americans*

**CM589**

| | | MNHVF | UseVF |
|---|---|---|---|
| 6¢ | **red and blue,** tagged *(147,120,000)* | .25 | .20 |
| | Plate block of 4 | .85 | |
| | FDC *(May 1, 1968)* | | 1.00 |
| | zo. Tagging omitted | 5.00 | |

**1968. LAW AND ORDER ISSUE** publicized the work of the law enforcement officer as a protector and friend of the people. *Intaglio, (Giori Press), perforated 11.*

CM590 *Policeman and young friend*

| CM590 | | MNHVF | UseVF |
|---|---|---|---|
| 6¢ | **red, blue and black,** tagged *(130,125,000)* | .25 | .20 |
| | Plate block of 4 | .85 | |
| | FDC *(May 17, 1968)* | | 1.00 |
| | zo. Tagging omitted | — | |

**1968. REGISTER AND VOTE ISSUE** supports the efforts of the American Heritage Foundation and others in making the public aware of its civic obligation to vote. *Intaglio (Giori Press) and offset, perforated 11.*

CM591 *Eagle Weathervane*

| CM591 | | MNHVF | UseVF |
|---|---|---|---|
| 6¢ | **gold and black,** tagged *(158,070,000)* | .25 | .20 |
| | Plate block of 4 | .85 | |
| | FDC *(June 27, 1968)* | | 1.00 |
| | zo. Tagging omitted | — | |

**1968. HISTORIC FLAGS ISSUE** saluted 10 banners from America's struggle for independence. 9 of the flags were selected because of their important roles in the Revolutionary War period. 1 flag, the one flown at Fort McHenry, inspired Francis Scott Key to write the *Star Spangled Banner* during the War of 1812. *Intaglio (Giori Press) and offset, perforated 11.*

CM592 *Fort Moultrie Flag (1776)*

| CM592 | | MNHVF | UseVF |
|---|---|---|---|
| 6¢ | **blue,** tagged *(228,040,000)* | .40 | .30 |

CM593 *Fort McHenry Flag (1795-1818)*

| CM593 | | MNHVF | UseVF |
|---|---|---|---|
| 6¢ | **red and blue,** tagged | .40 | .30 |

CM594 *Washington's Cruisers Flag (1775)*

| CM594 | | MNHVF | UseVF |
|---|---|---|---|
| 6¢ | **green and blue,** tagged | .40 | .30 |

CM595 *Bennington Flag (1777)*

| CM595 | | MNHVF | UseVF |
|---|---|---|---|
| 6¢ | **red and blue,** tagged | .40 | .30 |

CM596 *Rhode Island Flag (1775)*

| CM596 | | MNHVF | UseVF |
|---|---|---|---|
| 6¢ | **gold and blue,** tagged | .40 | .30 |

CM597 *First Stars and Stripes (1777)*

| CM597 | | MNHVF | UseVF |
|---|---|---|---|
| 6¢ | **red and blue,** tagged | .40 | .30 |

CM598 *Bunker Hill Flag (1775)*

| CM598 | | MNHVF | UseVF |
|---|---|---|---|
| 6¢ | **red, green and blue,** tagged | .40 | .30 |

CM599 *Grand Union Flag (1776)*

| CM599 | | MNHVF | UseVF |
|---|---|---|---|
| 6¢ | **red and blue,** tagged | .40 | .30 |

CM600 *Philadelphia Light Horse Flag (1775)*

| CM600 | | MNHVF | UseVF |
|---|---|---|---|
| 6¢ | **multicolored,** tagged | .40 | .30 |

CM601 *First Navy Jack (1775)*

| CM601 | | MNHVF | UseVF |
|---|---|---|---|
| 6¢ | **red, gold and blue,** tagged | .40 | .30 |
| | Plate block of 20 | 7.50 | |
| | Se-tenant strip of 10 (CM592-60) | 3.50 | 4.00 |
| | FDC, any single *(July 4, 1968)* | | 1.00 |
| | zo. Tagging omitted, any single | — | |
| | zoy.Tagging omitted se-tenant strip of 10 | — | |

*Because the plate number is attached to a vertical column of 10 different stamps, plate block of 20 is listed.*

**1968. WALT DISNEY ISSUE** hails the creative genius who brought a new dimension to entertainment with his animated cartoons, full-length films and theme parks. The creator of Mickey Mouse, Donald Duck and other lovable characters, built a multi-million dollar entertainment empire. *Gravure by Achrovure Division of Union-Camp Corporation, Englewood, N.J., perforated 12.*

CM602 *Walt Disney and Cartoon Children*

| CM602 | | MNHVF | UseVF |
|---|---|---|---|
| 6¢ | **multicolored,** tagged *(153,015,000)* | .25 | .20 |
| | Plate block of 4 | 2.10 | |
| | FDC *(Sept. 11, 1968)* | | 1.00 |
| | v.  Horizontal pair, imperforate between | 5000. | |
| | v1. Imperforate pair | 675. | |
| | v2. Vertical pair, imperforate horizontally | 650. | |
| | v3. Black omitted | 2150. | |
| | v4. Blue omitted | 2150. | |
| | v5. Yellow omitted | 750. | |
| | zo. Tagging omitted | 7.50 | |

**1968. FATHER JACQUES MARQUETTE ISSUE** honors the French explorer-missionary (CM17) who in 1668 established what is considered the oldest permanent settlement in Michigan. *Intaglio (Giori Press) and offset, perforated 11.*

CM603 *Jacques Marquette and Louis Joliet in canoe*

| CM603 | | MNHVF | UseVF |
|---|---|---|---|
| 6¢ | **black, green and brown,** tagged | .25 | .20 |
| | *(132,560,000)* | | |
| | Plate block of 4 | .85 | |
| | FDC *(Sept. 20, 1968)* | | 1.00 |
| | zo. Tagging omitted | 6.00 | |

**1968. DANIEL BOONE ISSUE** the 3rd commemorative in the American Folklore series, recalls the frontiersman whose exploits inspired historians and fiction writers to record the remarkable achievements of this heroic hunter, trapper, soldier and public servant. *Intaglio (Giori Press) and offset, perforated 11.*

CM604 *Pipe Tomahawk, Powder Horn, Rifle, and Knife*

| CM604 | | MNHVF | UseVF |
|---|---|---|---|
| 6¢ | **red brown, brown, yellow and black** | .25 | .20 |
| | tagged *(130,385,000)* | | |
| | Plate block of 4 | .85 | |
| | FDC *(Sept. 26, 1968)* | | 1.00 |
| | zo. Tagging omitted | — | |

**1968. ARKANSAS RIVER NAVIGATION ISSUE** pays tribute to this important waterway and the economic potential of the $1.2 billion project. *Intaglio (Giori Press) and offset, perforated 11.*

CM605 *Ship's Wheel and Transmission Tower*

| CM605 | | MNHVF | UseVF |
|---|---|---|---|
| 6¢ | **blue, black and dark blue,** tagged | .25 | .20 |
| | *(132,265,000)* | | |
| | Plate block of 4 | .85 | |
| | FDC *(Oct. 1, 1968)* | | 1.00 |
| | zo. Tagging omitted | — | |

**1968. LEIF ERIKSON ISSUE** honored the 11th century Norseman, whose navigational skills and daring brought him to the Americas 500 years before Christopher Columbus. *Intaglio (Giori Press) and offset, perforated 11.*

CM606 *Statue of Leif Erikson by A. Stirling Calder*

| CM606 | | MNHVF | UseVF |
|---|---|---|---|
| 6¢ | **brown** *(128,710,000)* | .25 | .20 |
| | Plate block of 4 | .85 | |
| | FDC *(Oct. 9, 1968)* | | 1.00 |

**1968. CHEROKEE STRIP ISSUE** marks the 75th anniversary of the historic land run by more than 100,000 would-be homesteaders into northern Oklahoma, competing for the 40,000 available homesites. *Rotary press printing, perforated 11.*

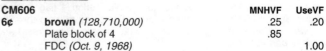

CM607 *Racing for Homesteads*

| CM607 | | MNHVF | UseVF |
|---|---|---|---|
| 6¢ | **brown,** tagged *(124,775,000)* | .25 | .20 |
| | Plate block of 4 | .85 | |
| | FDC *(Oct. 15 1968)* | | 1.00 |
| | zo. Tagging omitted | 5.00 | |

**1968. JOHN TRUMBULL ISSUE** 9th stamp in the Fine Arts series honors an artist noted for his paintings of Revolutionary War scenes. The design came from an original painting at Yale University, New Haven, CT. *Intaglio (Giori Press) and offset, perforated 11.*

CM608 *Liet. Thomas Grosvenor and Peter Salem. Detail from the Battle of Bunker's Hill.*

| CM608 | | MNHVF | UseVF |
|---|---|---|---|
| 6¢ | **multicolored,** tagged *(128,295,000)* | .25 | .20 |
| | Plate block of 4 | .90 | |
| | FDC *(Oct. 18, 1968)* | | 1.00 |
| | zo. Tgging omitted | 20.00 | |

**1968. WATERFOWL CONSERVATION ISSUE** pointed out the need for protecting waterfowl and their habitats. *Intaglio (Giori Press) and offset, perforated 11.*

CM609 *Wood Ducks in Flight*

| CM609 | | MNHVF | UseVF |
|---|---|---|---|
| 6¢ | **multicolored** *(142,245,000)* | .25 | .20 |
| | Plate block of 4 | 1.10 | |
| | FDC *(Oct. 24, 1968)* | | 1.00 |
| | v. Dark blue and red omitted | 1250. | |
| | v1. Vertical pair, imperforate between | 525. | |

**1968. CHIEF JOSEPH ISSUE** was released in conjunction with the dedication of the National Portrait Gallery in Washington, D.C. A portrait of the stamp subject, Chief Joseph, hangs in the gallery, which is part of the Smithsonian Institution. *Intaglio and offset, perforated 11.*

CM610 *Chief Joseph. Painting by Cyrenius Hall*

| CM610 | | MNHVF | UseVF |
|---|---|---|---|
| 6¢ | **multicolored,** tagged *(125,100,000)* | .25 | .20 |
| | Plate block of 4 | 1.10 | |
| | FDC *(Nov. 4, 1968)* | | 1.00 |
| | zo. Tagging omitted | — | |

**1969. BEAUTIFICATION OF AMERICA ISSUE** encouraged the participation of all Americans in a nationwide natural beauty campaign. 4 se-tenant stamp designs appear in the same pane of 50 stamps. *Intaglio, (Giori Press), perforated 11.*

CM611 *Azaleas, Tulips and Capitol Building*

CM612 *Daffodils, Washington Monument and Potomac River*

CM613 *Highway, Poppies and Lupines*

CM614 *Flowering Crabapples on Tree-Lined Street*

| CM611 | | MNHVF | UseVF |
|---|---|---|---|
| 6¢ | **multicolored,** tagged *(102,570,000)* | | |

| CM612 | | MNHVF | UseVF |
|---|---|---|---|
| 6¢ | **multicolored,** tagged | .30 | .25 |

| CM613 | | MNHVF | UseVF |
|---|---|---|---|
| 6¢ | **multicolored,** tagged | .30 | .25 |

| CM614 | | MNHVF | UseVF |
|---|---|---|---|
| 6¢ | **multicolored,** tagged | .30 | .25 |
| | Plate block of 4 | 2.50 | |
| | Se-tenant block of 4 | 2.00 | |
| | FDC *(Jan. 16, 1969)* | | 1.00 |
| | zo. Tagging omitted, any single | | |
| | zoy.Tagging omitted, se-tenant block of 4 | — | |

**1969. AMERICAN LEGION ISSUE** saluted the 50th anniversary of the veterans' organization incorporated by an Act of Congress and signed by Woodrow Wilson on Sept. 16, 1919. *Intaglio (Giori Press) and offset, perforated 11.*

CM615 *Eagle with Olive Branch, from the Great Seal of the United States.*

| CM615 | | MNHVF | UseVF |
|---|---|---|---|
| 6¢ | **red, black and blue,** tagged *(148,770,000)* | .25 | .20 |
| | Plate block of 4 | .85 | |
| | FDC *(March 15, 1969)* | | 1.00 |
| | zo. Tagging Omitted | 5.00 | |

**1969. GRANDMA MOSES ISSUE** honored the grand old lady of American painting, who took up art at the age of 76 and continued until her death at 101. *Intaglio (Giori Press) and offset, perforated 11.*

CM616 *July 4th. Detail from a Grandma Moses painting.*

| CM616 | | MNHVF | UseVF |
|---|---|---|---|
| 6¢ | **multicolored,** tagged *(139,475,000)* | .25 | .20 |
| | Plate block of 4 | .85 | |
| | FDC *May 1, 1969)* | | 1.00 |
| | v. Black and Prussian blue omitted | 850. | |
| | v1. Horizontal pair, imperforate between | 225. | |
| | zo. Tagging omitted | — | |

**1969. APOLLO 8 ISSUE** commemorated a vital space mission prior to the moon landing. *Intaglio, (Giori Press), perforated 11.*

CM617 *Earth Rising Over Lunar Surface*

**CM617**

| | | MNHVF | UseVF |
|---|---|---|---|
| 6¢ | **gray, deep blue and blue,** tagged | .25 | .20 |
| | *(187,165,000)* | | |
| | Plate block of 4 | 1.30 | |
| | FDC *(May 5, 1969)* | | 1.00 |
| | zo. Tagging omitted | — | |

*Note: Imperforate varieties, from printer's waste, exist.*

**1969. W.C. HANDY ISSUE** honored the memory of the great African-American composer and jazz musician who composed such immortal hits as *The St. Louis Blues, The Memphis Blues*and *The Beale Street Blues. Intaglio (Giori Press) and offset, perforated 11.*

CM618 *W.C. Handy and Horn*

**CM618**

| | | MNHVF | UseVF |
|---|---|---|---|
| 6¢ | **multicolored,** tagged *(125,555,000)* | .25 | .20 |
| | Plate block of 4 | 1.30 | |
| | FDC *(May 17, 1969)* | | 1.00 |
| | zo. Tagging omitted | 6.00 | |

**1969. SETTLEMENT OF CALIFORNIA ISSUE** commemorated the 200th anniversary of European settlement in the state. On July 16, 1769, a Spanish expedition led by Capt. Gasper de Portola entered San Diego, which became the 1st European settlement in California. *Intaglio (Giori Press) and offset, perforated 11.*

CM619 *Mission Bells at Carmel, Calif.*

**CM619**

| | | MNHVF | UseVF |
|---|---|---|---|
| 6¢ | **multicolored,** tagged *(144,425,000)* | .25 | .20 |
| | Plate block of 4 | .85 | |
| | FDC *(July 16, 1969)* | | 1.00 |
| | zo. Tagging omitted | 5.50 | |

**1969. JOHN WESLEY POWELL ISSUE** honored the eminent geologist, who in 1869 explored the Colorado River. *Intaglio (Giori Press) and offset, perforated 11.1*

CM620 *Maj. Powell Leading Colorado River Expedition*

**CM620**

| | | MNHVF | UseVF |
|---|---|---|---|
| 6¢ | **multicolored,** tagged *(133,100,000)* | .25 | .20 |
| | Plate block of 4 | .85 | |
| | FDC *(Aug. 1, 1969)* | | 1.00 |
| | zo. Tagging omitted | 4.50 | |

**1969. ALABAMA STATEHOOD ISSUE** marked the 150th anniversary of the entry of Alabama into the Union. *Intaglio (Giori Press) and offset, perforated 11.*

CM621 *Camelia and Yellow- Shafted Flicker*

**CM621**

| | | MNHVF | UseVF |
|---|---|---|---|
| 6¢ | **multicolored,** tagged *(136,900,000)* | .25 | .20 |
| | Plate block of 4 | .85 | |
| | FDC *(Aug. 2, 1969)* | | 1.00 |
| | zo. Tagging omitted | — | |

**1969. 11TH INTERNATIONAL BOTANICAL CONGRESS ISSUE** saluted the 1st international meeting of botanists held in the United States. 4 se-tenant stamp designs appear in the same pane of 50 stamps, each design represents a region of the country. *Intaglio (Giori Press) and offset, perforated 11.*

CM622 *Douglas Fir*

CM623 *Lady's-Slipper*

CM624 *Ocotillo*

CM625 *Franklinia*

**CM622**

| | | MNHVF | UseVF |
|---|---|---|---|
| 6¢ | **multicolored,** tagged *(158,695,000)* | .30 | .25 |

**CM623**

| | | MNHVF | UseVF |
|---|---|---|---|
| 6¢ | **multicolored,** tagged | .30 | .25 |

**CM624**

| | | MNHVF | UseVF |
|---|---|---|---|
| 6¢ | **multicolored,** tagged | .30 | .25 |

**CM625**

| | | MNHVF | UseVF |
|---|---|---|---|
| 6¢ | **multicolored,** tagged | .30 | .25 |
| | Plate block of 4 | 2.75 | |
| | y. Se-tenant block of 4 | 2.25 | 2.50 |
| | FDC *(Aug. 23, 1969)* | | 1.00 |

**1969. DARTMOUTH COLLEGE CASE ISSUE** commemorated the 150th anniversary of the legal decision that protected college charters and reasserted the sanctity of contracts. Daniel Webster won the case before the U.S. Supreme Court. *Intaglio, perforated 10 1/2 X 11.*

CM626 *Daniel Webster and Dartmouth Hall*

**CM626**

| | | MNHVF | UseVF |
|---|---|---|---|
| 6¢ | **green,** tagged *(124,075,000)* | .25 | .20 |
| | Plate block of 4 | .95 | |
| | FDC *(Sept. 22, 1969)* | | 1.00 |

**1969. PROFESSIONAL BASEBALL ISSUE** marked the 100th anniversary of the use of salaried players on a baseball team. The Red Stocking of Cincinnati, Ohio, in 1869 became the 1st club to pay its team members. *Intaglio (Giori Press) and offset, perforated 11.*

CM627 *Player at bat*

**CM627**

| | | MNHVF | UseVF |
|---|---|---|---|
| 6¢ | **yellow, red, black and green** *tagged* | 1.25 | .20 |
| | *(129,925,000)* | | |
| | Plate block of 4 | 4.95 | |
| | FDC *(Sept. 24, 1969)* | | 1.00 |
| | v. Black omitted | 950. | |

**1969. INTERCOLLEGIATE FOOTBALL ISSUE** celebrated the 100th anniversary of the popular college sport that started Nov. 6, 1869, when Rutgers defeated Princeton. *Intaglio and offset, perforated 11.*

CM628 *Coach and Football Player*

**CM628**

| | | MNHVF | UseVF |
|---|---|---|---|
| 6¢ | **red and green,** *tagged (129,860,000)* | .45 | .20 |
| | Plate block of 4 | 2.00 | |
| | FDC *(Sept. 26, 1969)* | | 1.00 |
| | zo. Tagging omitted | — | |

*The intaglio portion of CM628 was printed on a rotary press normally used for currency.*

**1969. DWIGHT D. EISENHOWER ISSUE** paid tribute to the West Point graduate who went on to become a 5-star general and the Supreme Allied Commander in Europe during World War II. He also served as the 34th president. *Intaglio, (Giori Press), perforated 11.*

CM629 *Dwight D. Eisenhower and flag*

**CM629**

| | | MNHVF | UseVF |
|---|---|---|---|
| 6¢ | **blue, black and reddish purple,** tagged | .25 | .20 |
| | *(138,976,000)* | | |
| | Plate block of 4 | .85 | |
| | FDC *(Oct. 14, 1969)* | | 1.00 |
| | zo. Tagging omitted | — | |

**1969. HOPE FOR THE CRIPPLED ISSUE** encouraged aid in research and therapy for the handicapped. *Intaglio (Giori Press) and offset, perforated 11.*

CM630 *Child Rising from Wheelchair*

**CM630**

| | | MNHVF | UseVF |
|---|---|---|---|
| 6¢ | **multicolored** tagged *(124,565,000)* | .25 | .20 |
| | Plate block of 4 | .85 | |
| | FDC *(Nov. 20, 1969)* | | 1.00 |
| | zo. Tagging omitted | — | |

**1969. WILLIAM M. HARNETT ISSUE** honored an artist noted for his realistic work. *Intaglio (Giori Press) and offset, perforated 11.*

CM631 *Still life Old Models*

**CM631**

| | | MNHVF | UseVF |
|---|---|---|---|
| 6¢ | **multicolored,** tagged *(124,729,000)* | .25 | .20 |
| | Plate block of 4 | .85 | |
| | FDC *(Dec. 3, 1969)* | | 1.00 |

**1970. NATURAL HISTORY ISSUE** commemorated the centenary of the American Museum of Natural History in New York City. 4 se-tenant stamp designs appear in the same 32-image pane. *Intaglio (Giori Press) and offset, perforated 11.*

CM632 *American Bald Eagle.* Detail from a display in The American Museum of Natural History CM633 *Herd of African Elephants.* A display in Carl Akeley Memorial Hall CM634 *Northwest Coast Canoe (Haida Indians).* The figures in the canoe represent a Tlingit chief and his party on their way to a marriage ceremony. CM635 *Jurassic Dinosaurs.* From a mural at Yale University's Peabody Museum of Natural History

**CM632**

| | | MNHVF | UseVF |
|---|---|---|---|
| 6¢ | **multicolored,** tagged *(201,794,600)* | .25 | .20 |

**CM633**

| | | MNHVF | UseVF |
|---|---|---|---|
| 6¢ | **multicolored,** tagged | .25 | .20 |

**CM634**

| | | MNHVF | UseVF |
|---|---|---|---|
| 6¢ | **multicolored,** tagged | .25 | .20 |

**CM635**

| | | MNHVF | UseVF |
|---|---|---|---|
| 6¢ | **multicolored** tagged | .25 | .20 |
| | Plate block of 4 | 1.00 | |
| | y. Se-tenant block of 4 (CM632-35) | | |
| | FDC *(May 6, 1970)* | | 1.00 |
| | zo. Tagging omitted, any single | — | |
| | zoy. Tagging omitted, block of 4 | — | |

**1970. MAINE STATEHOOD ISSUE** honored the 150th anniversary of its entry into the Union. *Intaglio (Giori Press) and offset, perforated 11.*

CM636 *The Lighthouse at Two Lights, Painted by Edward Hopper's oil painting in New York's Metropolitan Museum of Art*

| CM636 | | MNHVF | UseVF |
|---|---|---|---|
| 6¢ | **multicolored,** *(171,850,000)* | .25 | .20 |
| | Plate block of 4 | 1.00 | |
| | FDC *(July 9, 1970)* | | 1.00 |
| | zo. Tagging omitted | — | |

**1970. WILDLIFE CONSERVATION ISSUE** reminds Americans of the continuing need to protect wildlife. Issued in Custer, S.D., near Custer State Park, home to the largset buffalo herd in the country. *Intaglio, perforated 11 x 10 1/2.*

CM637 *American Bison*

| CM637 | | MNHVF | UseVF |
|---|---|---|---|
| 6¢ | **black on tan** *(142,205,000)* | .25 | .20 |
| | Plate block of 4 | 1.00 | |
| | FDC *(July 20, 1970)* | | 1.00 |

**1970. EDGAR LEE MASTERS ISSUE** 1st in an American Poets series, paid tribute to the author of *Spoon River Anthology.* Its ruthless exposure of small-town mores won instant acclaim as well as outraged criticism. *Intaglio (Giori Press) and offset, perforated 11.*

CM638 *Edgar Lee Masters*

| CM638 | | MNHVF | UseVF |
|---|---|---|---|
| 6¢ | **black,** tagged *(137,660,000)* | .25 | .20 |
| | Plate block of 4 | .85 | |
| | FDC *(Aug. 22, 1970)* | | 1.00 |
| | zo. Tagging omitted | — | |

**1970. THE 50TH ANNIVERSARY OF WOMAN SUFFRAGE ISSUE** celebrated the ratification of the 19th Amendment which gave women the right to vote. *Intaglio, (Giori Press), perforated 11.*

CM639 *Suffragrettes of 1920 and Modern Voters*

| CM639 | | MNHVF | UseVF |
|---|---|---|---|
| 6¢ | **blue,** tagged *(135,125,000)* | .25 | .20 |
| | Plate block of 4 | .85 | |
| | FDC *(Aug. 25, 1970)* | | 1.00 |

**1970. SOUTH CAROLINA ISSUE** marks the 300th anniversary of the state's 1st permanent European settlement, established by the English at Charles Town (now Charleston). *Intaglio (Giori Press) and offset, perforated 11.*

CM640 *Aspects of South Carolina*

| CM640 | | MNHVF | UseVF |
|---|---|---|---|
| 6¢ | **brown, black and red,** tagged *(135,895,000)* | .25 | .20 |
| | Plate block of 4 | .85 | |
| | FDC *(Sept. 12, 1970)* | | 1.00 |

**1970. STONE MOUNTAIN ISSUE** commemorated the Georgia granite carving that has become one of the great wonders of the world. The memorial carving shows the mounted figures of Robert E. Lee, Jefferson Davis and Stonewall Jackson. *Intaglio, (Giori Press), perforated 11.*

CM641 *Stone Mountain Memorial*

| CM641 | | MNHVF | UseVF |
|---|---|---|---|
| 6¢ | **gray black,** tagged *(132,675,000)* | .25 | .20 |
| | Plate block of 4 | 1.10 | |
| | FDC *(Sept. 19, 1970)* | | 1.00 |

**1970. FORT SNELLING SESQUICENTENNIAL ISSUE** commemorates the importance of this outpost in settling the Northwestern United States. The fort was named after Col. Joshiah Snelling. *Intaglio (Giori Press) and offset, perforated 11.*

CM642 *Fort Snelling and surrounding area*

| CM642 | | MNHVF | UseVF |
|---|---|---|---|
| 6¢ | **multicolored,** tagged *(134,795,000)* | .25 | .20 |
| | Plate block of 4 | .85 | |
| | FDC *(Oct. 17, 1970)* | | 1.00 |
| | zo. Tagging omitted | — | |

**1970. ANTI-POLLUTION ISSUE** emphasizes the importance of our ecology. 4 se-tenant designs appear in the pane. *Printed in gravure by the Bureau of Engraving and Printing at Guilford Graphics, Inc., perforated 11 x 10 1/2.*

CM643 *Save Our Soil* CM644 *Save Our Cities* CM645 *Save Our Water* CM646 *Save Our Air*

| CM643 | | MNHVF | UseVF |
|---|---|---|---|
| 6¢ | **multicolored,** tagged *(161,600,000)* | .25 | .20 |

| CM644 | | MNHVF | UseVF |
|---|---|---|---|
| 6¢ | **multicolored,** tagged | .25 | .20 |

| CM645 | | MNHVF | UseVF |
|---|---|---|---|
| 6¢ | **multicolored,** tagged | .25 | .20 |

| CM646 | | MNHVF | UseVF |
|---|---|---|---|
| 6¢ | **multicolored,** tagged | .25 | .20 |
| | Plate block of 4 | 3.50 | |
| | Se-tenant block of 4 | — | |
| | FDC *(Oct. 28, 1970)* | | 1.00 |

**1970. UNITED NATIONS ISSUE** marks the 25th anniversary of the international organization, chartered in San Francisco on June 26, 1945. *Intaglio (Giori Press) and offset, perforated 11.*

CM647 *"Peace, Justice, and Progress"*

United Nations 25th Anniversary

| CM647 | | MNHVF | UseVF |
|---|---|---|---|
| 6¢ | **black, red and blue,** tagged *(127,610,000)* | .25 | .20 |
| | Plate block of 4 | .85 | |
| | Gutter pair | — | |
| | FDC *(Nov. 20, 1970)* | | 1.00 |
| | zo. Tagging omitted | — | |

**1970. LANDING OF THE PILGRIMS ISSUE** commemorates the 350th anniversary of the arrival of the *Mayflower* and the landing of the Pilgrims at Plymouth, MA. *Intaglio (Giori Press) and offset, perforated 11.*

CM648 *Mayflower and Pilgrims*

| CM648 | | MNHVF | UseVF |
|---|---|---|---|
| 6¢ | **multicolored,** tagged *(129,785,000)* | .25 | .20 |
| | Plate block of 4 | .85 | |
| | FDC *(Nov. 21, 1970)* | | 1.00 |
| | v. Orange and yellow omitted | 950. | |

**1970. U.S. SERVICEMEN ISSUE** pays tribute to the Disabled American Veterans, Prisoners of War and those missing and killed in action. 2 se-tenant stamp designs alternate in the pane. *Intaglio (Giori Press) and offset, perforated 11.*

| CM649 | | MNHVF | UseVF |
|---|---|---|---|
| 6¢ | **multicolored,** tagged *(134,380,000)* | .25 | .20 |

| CM650 | | MNHVF | UseVF |
|---|---|---|---|
| 6¢ | **dark blue, black and red,** tagged | .25 | .20 |
| | Plate block of 4 | 1.30 | |
| | y. Se-tenant pair | .50 | |
| | FDC *(Nov. 24, 1970)* | | 1.00 |
| | zo. Tagging omitted, single | — | |
| | zoy. Tagging omitted, se-tenant pair | — | |

**1971. AMERICAN WOOL ISSUE** commemorates the 450th anniversry of the introduction of sheep in America. *Intaglio (Giori Press) and offset, perforated 11.*

CM651 *Ewe and Lamb*

| CM651 | | MNHVF | UseVF |
|---|---|---|---|
| 6¢ | **multicolored,** tagged *(135,305,000)* | .25 | .20 |
| | Plate block of 4 | .85 | |
| | FDC *(Jan. 19, 1971)* | | 1.00 |
| | zo. Tagging omitted | 5.00 | |

**1971. DOUGLAS MACARTHUR ISSUE** honors the soldier who rose to the rank of 5-star general and was supreme commander in Tokyo for the Allied Powers. *Intaglio, (Giori Press), perforated 11.*

CM652 *Douglas MacArthur*

| CM652 | | MNHVF | UseVF |
|---|---|---|---|
| 6¢ | **red, blue and black,** tagged *(134,840,000)* | .25 | .20 |
| | Plate block of 4 | .85 | |
| | FDC *(Jan. 26, 1971)* | | 1.00 |
| | zo. Tagging omitted | — | |

**1971. BLOOD DONORS ISSUE** points out the need for more Americans to increase their participation. *Intaglio (Giori Press) and offset, perforated 11.*

CM653 *Giving Blood Saves Lives*

| CM653 | | MNHVF | UseVF |
|---|---|---|---|
| 6¢ | **red and blue,** tagged *(130,975,000)* | .25 | .20 |
| | Plate block of 4 | .85 | |
| | FDC *(March 12, 1971)* | | 1.00 |
| | zo. Tagging omitted | 5.00 | |

**1971. MISSOURI STATEHOOD ISSUE** honors the 150th anniversary of entry into the Union of the "Show Me" state. *Gravure (Andreotti Press), perforated 11 x 10 1/2.*

CM654 Independence and the Opening of the West. *Detail of a mural by Thomas Hart Benton.*

| CM654 | | MNHVF | UseVF |
|---|---|---|---|
| 8¢ | **multicolored,** tagged *(161,235,000)* | .25 | .20 |
| | Plate block of 12 | 3.25 | |
| | FDC *(May 8, 1971)* | | 1.00 |
| | zo. Tagging omitted | — | |

**1971. WILDLIFE CONSERVATION ISSUE** stressed the importance of preserving nature's creations from extinction. 4 different representatives of wildlife are featured in the sheet of 32 stamps. *Intaglio (Giori Press) and offset, perforated 11.*

CM655 *Polar bear* CM656 *Condor* CM657 *Alligator* CM658 *Trout*

| CM655 | | MNHVF | UseVF |
|---|---|---|---|
| 8¢ | **multicolored,** tagged *(175,680,000)* | .25 | .20 |

| CM656 | | MNHVF | UseVF |
|---|---|---|---|
| 8¢ | **multicolored,** tagged | .25 | .20 |

| CM657 | | MNHVF | UseVF |
|---|---|---|---|
| 8¢ | **multicolored,** tagged | .25 | .20 |

| CM658 | | MNHVF | UseVF |
|---|---|---|---|
| 8¢ | **multicolored,** tagged | .25 | .20 |
| | Plate block of 4 | 1.20 | |
| | Se-tenant block of 4 | .75 | |
| | FDC *(June 12, 1971)* | | 1.00 |
| | v.  Red omitted, block of 4 | 9500. | |
| | v.  Light green and dark green omitted, block of 4 | 4500. | |
| | xo. Tagging omitted, any single | — | |
| | xoy. Tagging omitted, se-tenant block of 4 | — | |

**1971. ANTARCTIC TREATY ISSUE** marked the 10th anniversary of the treaty that pledged 12 nations to scientific cooperation and peaceful use of Antartica: Argentina, Australia, Belgium, Chile, France, Japan, New Zealand, Norway, South Africa, Soviet Union, United Kingdom and United States. *Intaglio, (Giori Press), perforated 11.*

CM659 *Antarctic Treaty Emblem*

| CM659 | | MNHVF | UseVF |
|---|---|---|---|
| 8¢ | **red and dark blue,** tagged *(138,700,000)* | .25 | .20 |
| | Plate block of 4 | 1.00 | |
| | FDC *(June 23, 1971)* | | 1.00 |
| | zo. Tagging omitted | 5.00 | |

**1971. AMERICAN REVOLUTION BICENTENNIAL ISSUE** commemorates the struggle that led to the birth of the United States, and is the 1st in a series of stamps to pay tribute to the men, women, places nd events of the Revolutionary War. *Intaglio (Giori Press) and offset, perforated 11.*

CM660 *American Revolution Bicentennial Symbol*

| CM660 | | MNHVF | UseVF |
|---|---|---|---|
| 8¢ | **gray, red, blue and black,** tagged *(138,165,000)* | .25 | .20 |
| | Plate block of 4 | 1.10 | |
| | FDC *(July 4, 1971)* | | 1.00 |
| | v.  Gray (top legend) omitted | 1250. | |
| | v1. Black and gray omitted | 700. | |

**1971. SPACE ACHIEVEMENTS DECADE ISSUE** marks 10 years of extraordinary accomplishments in space. With a Se-tenant pair. *Intaglio (Giori Press) and offset, perforated 11.*

CM661 *Landing Craft On Moon's surface* CM662 *Astronauts in Lunar Rover.*

| CM661 | | MNHVF | UseVF |
|---|---|---|---|
| 8¢ | **multicolored,** tagged *(176,295,000)* | .25 | .20 |
| | v.  Blue and red omitted | 600. | |

| CM662 | | MNHVF | UseVF |
|---|---|---|---|
| 8¢ | **multicolored,** tagged | .25 | .20 |
| | y.  Se-tenant pair, CM661-62 | .50 | |
| | Plate block of 4 | 1.15 | |
| | FDC *(Aug. 2, 1971)* | | 1.00 |
| | v.  Blue and red omitted | 600. | |
| | y.  Se-tenant pair, blue and red omitted | 1500. | |
| | zo. Tagging omitted, any single | 6.00 | |
| | zoy. Se-tenant pair, tagging omitted | 22.50 | |

**1971. JOHN SLOAN ISSUE** honors the artist on the centennial of his birth at Lock Haven, PA. *Intaglio (Giori Press) and offset, perforated 11.*

CM663 *The Wake of the Ferry, Phillips Gallery, Washington, D.C.*

| CM663 | | MNHVF | UseVF |
|---|---|---|---|
| 8¢ | **multicolored,** tagged *(152,125,000)* | .25 | .20 |
| | Plate block of 4 | 1.00 | |
| | FDC *(Aug. 2, 1971)* | | 1.00 |
| | zo. Tagging omitted | — | |

**1971. EMILY DICKINSON ISSUE** honors this poet (1830-86), who was born in Amherst, MA. Only after she died was her works widely published and acclaimed. *Intaglio (Giori Press) and offset, perforated 11.*

CM664 *Emily Dickinson*

| CM664 | | MNHVF | UseVF |
|---|---|---|---|
| 8¢ | **multicolored,** tagged *(142,845,000)* | .25 | .20 |
| | Plate block of 4 | 1.00 | |
| | FDC *(Aug. 28, 1971)* | | 1.00 |
| | v.  Black and olive omitted | 850. | |
| | v1. Pale rose omitted | 7500. | |
| | zo. Tagging omitted | — | |

**1971. SAN JUAN ISSUE** marked the 450th anniversary of the founding of the Puerto Rican city. *Intaglio (Giori Press) and offset, perforated 11.*

CM665 *Battlement at El Morro Castle*

| CM665 | | MNHVF | UseVF |
|---|---|---|---|
| 8¢ | **multicolored,** tagged *(148,755,000)* | .25 | .20 |
| | Plate block of 4 | 1.00 | |
| | FDC *(Sept. 12, 1971)* | | 1.00 |
| | zo. Tagging omitted | 6.00 | |

**1971. PREVENT DRUG ABUSE ISSUE** publicizes drug addiction as a national menace of concern to every American. *Gravure (Andreotti Press), perforated 10 1/2 x 11.*

CM666 *Drug Addict*

| CM666 | | MNHVF | UseVF |
|---|---|---|---|
| 8¢ | **blue, deep blue and black,** tagged *(139,080,000)* | .25 | .20 |
| | Plate block of 6 | 1.50 | |
| | FDC *(Oct. 4, 1971)* | | 1.00 |
| | zo. Tagging omitted | — | |

**1971. CARE ISSUE** honors the 25th anniversary of the American-Canadian Cooperative for American Relief Everywhere. *Intaglio, (Giori Press), perforated 11.*

CM667 *Hands and CARE Emblem*

| CM667 | | MNHVF | UseVF |
|---|---|---|---|
| 8¢ | **black, blue, violet and red lilac,** tagged *(130,755,000)* | .25 | .20 |
| | Plate block of 8 | 1.95 | |
| | FDC *(Oct. 27, 1971)* | | 1.00 |
| | a. Black omitted | | 4750. |
| | zo. Tagging omitted | 4.00 | |

**1971. HISTORIC PRESERVATION ISSUE** pays tribute to important artifacts of America's past. *Intaglio (Giori Press) and offset, perforated.*

CM668 *Decatur House, Washington, D.C.* CM669 *Whaling Ship Charles W. Morgan, Mystic, Conn.* CM670 *Cable Car, San Francisco, Calif.* CM671 *San Xavier del Bac Mission, Tucson, AZ*

| CM668 | | MNHVF | UseVF |
|---|---|---|---|
| 8¢ | **brown and dark beige on buff,** tagged *(170,208,000)* | .25 | .20 |

| CM669 | | MNHVF | UseVF |
|---|---|---|---|
| 8¢ | **brown and dark beige on buff,** tagged | .25 | .20 |

| CM670 | | MNHVF | UseVF |
|---|---|---|---|
| 8¢ | **brown and dark beige on buff,** tagged | .25 | .20 |

| CM671 | | MNHVF | UseVF |
|---|---|---|---|
| 8¢ | **brown and dark beige on buff,** tagged | .25 | .20 |
| | Plate block of 4 | 1.20 | |
| | y. Se-tenant block of 4 (CM668-71) | .75 | |
| | FDC *(Oct. 29, 1971)* | | 1.00 |
| | v. Brown omitted (any single) | — | |
| | v1. Dark beige omitted (any single) | — | |
| | vy. Brown omitted, se-tenant block of 4 | 2600. | |
| | vly.Dark beige omitted, se-tenant block of 4 | — | |
| | zo. Tagging omitted, any single | — | |
| | voy.Tagging omitted, se-tenant block of 4 | 50.00 | |

**1972. AMERICAN POETS ISSUE** honors Sidney Lanier, who had a distinguished career as a lawyer, teacher, musician and poet. Born in Macon, GA., he died at the age of 39. *Intaglio, (Giori Press), perforated 11.*

CM672 *Sidney Lanier*

| CM672 | | MNHVF | UseVF |
|---|---|---|---|
| 8¢ | **black, reddish brown and blue,** tagged *(137,355,000)* | .25 | .20 |
| | Plate block of 4 | 1.00 | |
| | FDC *(Feb. 3, 1972)* | | 1.00 |
| | zo. Tagging omitted | 12.50 | |

**1972. PEACE CORPS ISSUE** pays tribute to a government organization created to aid developing countries. *Gravre (Andreotti Press), perforated 10 1/2 x 11.*

CM673 *Flag and Doves, from poster by David Battle.*

**CM673**

| | | MNHVF | UseVF |
|---|---|---|---|
| 8¢ | **dark blue, light blue and red,** tagged *(150,400,000)* | .25 | .20 |
| | Plate block of 6 | 1.60 | |
| | FDC *(Feb. 11, 1972)* | | 1.00 |
| | zo. Tagging omitted | 4.00 | |

## National Parks Centennial Series

released over a 5-month period consists of 8 stamps (one is is an airmail stamp, A82).

**1972. YELLOWSTONE PARK ISSUE** Marks the centennial of the establishment of the first national park in the world, located in Western Wyoming. *Intaglio (Giori Press) and offset, perforated 11.*

CM674 *Old Faithful, Yellowstone Park*

**CM674**

| | | MNHVF | UseVF |
|---|---|---|---|
| 8¢ | **multicolored,** tagged *(164,096,000)* | .25 | .20 |
| | Plate block of 4 | 1.00 | |
| | FDC *(March 1, 1972)* | | 1.00 |
| | zo. Tagging omitted | 14.00 | |

**1972. CAPE HATTERAS ISSUE**

CM675-78 *Cape Hatteras National Seashore*

**CM675**

| | | MNHVF | UseVF |
|---|---|---|---|
| 2¢ | **multicolored,** tagged *(172,730,000)* | .25 | .20 |

**CM676**

| | | MNHVF | UseVF |
|---|---|---|---|
| 2¢ | **multicolored,** tagged | .25 | .20 |

**CM677**

| | | MNHVF | UseVF |
|---|---|---|---|
| 2¢ | **multicolored,** tagged | .25 | .20 |

**CM678**

| | | MNHVF | UseVF |
|---|---|---|---|
| 2¢ | **multicolored,** tagged | .25 | .20 |
| | Plate block of 4 | .60 | |
| | y. Se-tenant block of 4 (CM675-78) | | |
| | FDC *(April 5, 1972)* | | 1.00 |
| | v. Black omitted (any single) | — | |
| | vy. Black omitted, se-tenant block of 4 | 2750. | |
| | zo. Tagging omitted, any single | — | |
| | zoy. Tagging omitted, se-tenant block of 4 | — | |

**1972. WOLF TRAP FARM ISSUE**

CM679 *Theater at Wolf Trap Farm, VA.*

**CM679**

| | | MNHVF | UseVF |
|---|---|---|---|
| 6¢ | **multicolored,** tagged *(104,090,000)* | .25 | .20 |
| | Plate block of 4 | .85 | |
| | FDC *(June 26, 1972)* | | 1.00 |
| | zo. Tagging omitted | 6.00 | |

**1972. MOUNT MCKINLEY ISSUE**

CM680 *Mount McKinley, Alaska*

**CM680**

| | | MNHVF | UseVF |
|---|---|---|---|
| 15¢ | **multicolored,** tagged *(53,920,000)* | .25 | .20 |
| | Plate block of 4 | 1.90 | |
| | FDC *(July 28, 1972)* | | 1.00 |
| | zo. Tagging omitted | 19.00 | |

**1972. FAMILY PLANNING ISSUE** reminds people of the need for planning to have a better America and a better world. *Intaglio, (Giori Press), perforated 11.*

CM681 *Planned Family*

**CM681**

| | | MNHVF | UseVF |
|---|---|---|---|
| 8¢ | **multicolored,** tagged *(153,025,000)* | .25 | .20 |
| | Plate block of 4 | 1.10 | |
| | FDC *(March 18, 1972)* | | 1.00 |
| | v. Dark brown omitted | 9350. | |
| | v1. Dark brown and olive omitted | — | |
| | v2. Yellow omitted | 1650. | |
| | zo. Tagging omitted | — | |

**1972. COLONIAL CRAFTSMEN, GLASSMAKER ISSUE** commemorates the contributions of Colonial artisans to the early development of America. *Intaglio, perforated 11 x 10 1/2.*

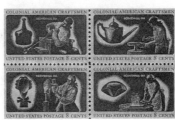

CM682 *Glassmaker*
CM683 *Silversmith*
CM684 *Wigmaker*
CM685 *Hatter*

**CM682**

| | | MNHVF | UseVF |
|---|---|---|---|
| 8¢ | **deep brown on buff paper,** tagged *(201,890,000)* | .25 | .20 |

**1972. COLONIAL CRAFTSMEN, SILVERSMITH ISSUE**

| CM683 | | MNHVF | UseVF |
|---|---|---|---|
| 8¢ | **deep brown on buff paper,** tagged | .25 | .20 |

**1972. COLONIAL CRAFTSMEN, WIGMAKER ISSUE**

| CM684 | | MNHVF | UseVF |
|---|---|---|---|
| 8¢ | **deep brown on buff paper,** tagged | .25 | .20 |

**1972. COLONIAL CRAFTSMEN, HATTER ISSUE**

| CM685 | | MNHVF | UseVF |
|---|---|---|---|
| 8¢ | **deep brown on buff paper,** tagged | .25 | .20 |
| | Plate block of 4 | 1.25 | |
| | y. Se-tenant block of 4, (CM682-85) | .75 | |
| | FDC *(July 4, 1972)* | | 1.00 |
| | Tagging omitted, any single | — | |
| | zo. Tagging omitted, se-tenant block of 4 | — | |

**1972. OLYMPIC GAMES ISSUE** saluted international athletic meets in Sapporo, Japan (Winter Games) and Munich, Germany (Summer Games) (See also A837). *Gravure (Andreotti Press), perforated 11 x 10 1/2. (See A83).*

CM686 *Cycling*

| CM686 | | MNHVF | UseVF |
|---|---|---|---|
| 6¢ | **multicolored,** tagged *(67,335,000)* | .25 | .20 |
| | Plate block of 10 | 2.10 | |
| | Plate flaw, broken red ring (position 43 of top-left pane of plate No. 33313) | 7.50 | |
| | FDC *(Aug. 17, 1972)* | | 1.00 |

CM687 *Bobsled Racing*

| CM687 | | MNHVF | UseVF |
|---|---|---|---|
| 8¢ | **multicolored,** tagged *(96,240,000)* | .25 | .20 |
| | Plate block of 10 | 2.75 | |
| | FDC *(Aug. 17, 1972)* | | 1.00 |
| | zo. Tagging omitted | 5.00 | |

CM688 *Foot Racing*

| CM688 | | MNHVF | UseVF |
|---|---|---|---|
| 15¢ | **multicolored,** tagged *(46,340,000)* | .25 | .20 |
| | Plate block of 10 | 5.25 | |
| | FDC *(Aug. 17, 1972)* | | 1.00 |

**1972. PARENT-TEACHERS ASSOCIATION ISSUE** salutes the 75th anniversary of an organization dedicated to improving eduational methods furthering development of young minds. *Gravure (Andreotti Press), perforated 11 x 10 1/2.*

CM689 *Blackboard, symbol of education*

| CM689 | | MNHVF | UseVF |
|---|---|---|---|
| 8¢ | **yellow and black,** tagged *(180,155,000)* | .25 | .20 |
| | Plate block of 4 | 1.00 | |
| | Plate block, yellow inverted | — | |
| | FDC *(Sept. 15, 1972)* | | 1.00 |
| | zo. Tagging omitted | — | |

**1972. WILDLIFE CONSERVATION ISSUE** showcases the importance and beauty of nature's creatures. *Intaglio (Giori Press) and offset, perforated 11.*

CM690 *Fur Seal* CM691 *Cardinal* CM692 *Brown Pelican* CM693 *Bighorn Sheep*

| CM690 | | MNHVF | UseVF |
|---|---|---|---|
| 8¢ | **multicolored** tagged *(198,364,800)* | .25 | .20 |

| CM691 | | MNHVF | UseVF |
|---|---|---|---|
| 8¢ | **multicolored** tagged | .25 | .20 |

| CM692 | | MNHVF | UseVF |
|---|---|---|---|
| 8¢ | **multicolored** tagged | .25 | .20 |

| CM693 | | MNHVF | UseVF |
|---|---|---|---|
| 8¢ | **multicolored,** tagged | .25 | .20 |
| | Plate block of 4 | 1.10 | |
| | y. Se-tenant block of 4 (CM690-93) | | |
| | FDC *(Sept. 20, 1972)* | | 1.00 |
| | v. Brown omitted | — | |
| | vy. Se-tenant block of 4 brown omitted | 4500. | |
| | v1. Green and blue omitted | — | |
| | v1y. Se-tenant block of 4, green and blue omitted | 4500. | |
| | v2. Red and brown omitted | — | |
| | v2y. Se-tenant block of 4, red and brown omitted | 4500. | |

**1972. MAIL ORDER CENTENNIAL ISSUE** marked the 100th anniversary of the introduction of the merchandising by mail. *Gravure (Andreotti Press), perforated 11 x 10 1/2.*

CM694 *Rural Post Office Store*

| CM694 | | MNHVF | UseVF |
|---|---|---|---|
| 8¢ | **multicolored,** tagging *(185,490,000)* | .25 | .20 |
| | Plate block of 12 | 3.00 | |
| | FDC *(Sept. 27, 1972)* | | 1.00 |

*Tagging on this issue typically consists of a vertical bar, 10 mm wide.*

**1972. OSTEOPATHIC MEDICINE ISSUE** marks the 75th anniversary of the American Osteopathic Association established by Dr. Andrew Still. *Gravure (Andreotti Press), perforated 10 1/2 x 11.*

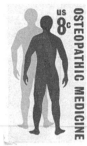

CM695 *Osteopathic Medicine*

| CM695 | | MNHVF | UseVF |
|---|---|---|---|
| 8¢ | **multicolored,** tagged *(162,335,000)* | .25 | .20 |
| | Plate block of 6 | 1.60 | |
| | FDC *(Oct, 9, 1972)* | | 1.00 |

**1972. TOM SAWYER ISSUE** the 4th stamp in the American Folklore Series, recalls the exciting, carefree adventures of the fictional mischievous boy created by Mark Twain (see CM205). *Intaglio (Giori Press) and offset, perforated 11.*

CM696 *Tom Sawyer, Painted by Norman Rockwell*

| CM696 | | MNHVF | UseVF |
|---|---|---|---|
| 8¢ | **multicolored,** tagged *(162,789,950)* | .25 | .20 |
| | Plate block of 4 | 1.10 | |
| | FDC *(Oct. 13, 1972)* | | 1.00 |
| | v.  Black and red omitted | 2250. | |
| | v1. Yellow and tan omitted | 2100. | |
| | v2. Horizontal pair, imperforate between | 5500. | |
| | zo. Tagging omitted | 15.00 | |

**1972. PHARMACY ISSUE** saluted the nation's druggists and their contribution to keeping Americans healthy. *Intaglio (Giori Press) and offset, perforated 11.*

CM697 *Bowl of Hygeia, Mortar and Pestle*

| CM697 | | MNHVF | UseVF |
|---|---|---|---|
| 8¢ | **multicolored,** tagged *(165,895,000)* | .25 | .20 |
| | Plate block of 4 | 1.75 | |
| | FDC *(Nov. 10, 1972)* | | 1.00 |
| | v.  Blue omitted | 2000. | |
| | v1. Blue and orange omitted | 875. | |
| | v2. Orange omitted | 2000. | |
| | zo. Tagging omitted | — | |

**1972. STAMP COLLECTING ISSUE** paid tribute to the nation's stamp collectors and the hobby of philately. *Intaglio (Giori Press) and offset, perforated 11.*

CM698 *First U.S. Stamp under magnifying glass*

| CM698 | | MNHVF | UseVF |
|---|---|---|---|
| 8¢ | **multicolored,** tagged *(166,508,000)* | .25 | .20 |
| | Plate block of 4 | 1.00 | |
| | FDC *(Nov. 17, 1972)* | | 1.00 |
| | v.  Black omitted | 900. | |
| | zo. Tagging omitted | — | |

**1973. RISE OF THE SPIRIT OF INDEPENDENCE ISSUE** remarks   on the role of communications in spurring the American revolution. *Intaglio (Giori Press) and offset, perforated 11.*

CM700 *Pamphlets Printed by Press*

| CM700 | | MNHVF | UseVF |
|---|---|---|---|
| 8¢ | **blue, greenish black and red,** tagged *(166,005,000)* | .25 | .20 |
| | Plate block of 4 | 1.00 | |
| | FDC *(Feb. 16, 1973)* | | 1.00 |
| | zo. Tagging omitted | 12.50 | |

**1973. RISE OF THE SPIRIT OF INDEPENDENCE ISSUE** remarks   on the role of communications in spurring the American revolution. *Intaglio (Giori Press) and offset, perforated 11.*

CM701 *Posting a Broadside*

| CM701 | | MNHVF | UseVF |
|---|---|---|---|
| 8¢ | **black, orange and ultramarine,** tagged *(163,050,000)* | .25 | .20 |
| | Plate block of 4 | 1.00 | |
| | FDC *(April 13, 1973)* | | 1.00 |
| | Gutter Pair | — | |
| | zo. Tagging omitted | — | |

CM702 *Colonial Post Rider*

| CM702 | | MNHVF | UseVF |
|---|---|---|---|
| 8¢ | **blue, black, red and green,** tagged *(159,005,000)* | .25 | .20 |
| | Plate block of 4 | 1.00 | |
| | FDC *(June 22, 1973)* | | 1.00 |
| | zo. Tagging omitted | — | |

CM703 *Drummer Summoning Minutemen*

| CM703 | | MNHVF | UseVF |
|---|---|---|---|
| 8¢ | **blue, black, yellow and red,** tagged *(147,295,000)* | .25 | .20 |
| | Plate block of 4 | 1.00 | |
| | FDC *(Sept. 28, 1973)* | | 1.00 |
| | zo. Tagging omitted | — | |

**1973. GEORGE GERSHWIN ISSUE** honors the American composer who created music for over 400 songs, including *Rhapsody in Blue* and *Porgy and Bess* (CM1586), a folk opera. *Gravure (Andreotti Press), perforated 11.*

CM704 *George Gershwin and Porgy and Bess Montage*

| CM704 | | MNHVF | UseVF |
|---|---|---|---|
| **8¢** | **multicolored** *(139,152,000)* | .25 | .20 |
| | Plate block of 12 | 3.25 | |
| | FDC *(Feb. 28, 1973)* | | 1.00 |
| | v. Vertical pair, imperforate horizontally | 225. | |

**1973. NICOLAUS COPERNICUS ISSUE** pays tribute to the father of modern astronomy on the 500th anniversary of his birth. *Intaglio (Giori Press) and offset, perforated 11.*

CM705 *Nicolaus Copernicus*

| CM705 | | MNHVF | UseVF |
|---|---|---|---|
| **8¢** | **black and yellow,** tagged *(159,475,000)* | .25 | .20 |
| | Plate block of 4 | 1.10 | |
| | FDC *(April 23, 1973)* | | 1.00 |
| | v. Engraved black omitted | 1300. | |
| | v1. Yellow omitted | 1000. | |
| | zo. Tagging omitted | 15.00 | |

*The yellow may be removed chemically. Competent expertization is recommended of CM705v1.*

**1973. POSTAL SERVICE EMPLOYEE ISSUE** saluted the 700,000 employees of the U.S. Postal Service. 10 different stamps in a pane of 50 depict some of the services performed by postal employees, with text describing those activities printed on the reverse side of the stamp, under the gum, a U.S. stamp 1st. *Gravure (Andreotti Press), perforated 10 1/2 x 11.*

CM706-CM715 *Postal people performing services*

| CM706 | | MNHVF | UseVF |
|---|---|---|---|
| **8¢** | **multicolored,** tagged *(486,020,000)* | .25 | .20 |

| CM707 | | MNHVF | UseVF |
|---|---|---|---|
| **8¢** | **multicolored,** tagged | .25 | .20 |

| CM708 | | MNHVF | UseVF |
|---|---|---|---|
| **8¢** | **multicolored,** tagged | .25 | .20 |

| CM709 | | MNHVF | UseVF |
|---|---|---|---|
| **8¢** | **multicolored,** tagged | .25 | .20 |

| CM710 | | MNHVF | UseVF |
|---|---|---|---|
| **8¢** | **multicolored,** tagged | .25 | .20 |

| CM711 | | MNHVF | UseVF |
|---|---|---|---|
| **8¢** | **multicolored,** tagged | .25 | .20 |

| CM712 | | MNHVF | UseVF |
|---|---|---|---|
| **8¢** | **multicolored,** tagged | .25 | .20 |

| CM713 | | MNHVF | UseVF |
|---|---|---|---|
| **8¢** | **multicolored,** tagged | .25 | .20 |

| CM714 | | MNHVF | UseVF |
|---|---|---|---|
| **8¢** | **multicolored,** tagged | .25 | .20 |

| CM715 | | MNHVF | UseVF |
|---|---|---|---|
| **8¢** | **multicolored,** tagged | .25 | .20 |
| | Plate block of 20 | 5.50 | |
| | y. Se-tenant strip of 10, (CM706-15) | 4.00 | |
| | FDC *(April 30, 1973)* | | 3.00 |
| | zo. Tagging omitted, any single | — | |
| | zoy. Tagging omitted, se-tenant strip of 10 | — | |

*Tagging consists of a 1/2 inch high horizontal band.*

**1973. HARRY S TRUMAN ISSUE** honors the 33rd president of the United States, who died December 26, 1972. *Intaglio, (Giori Press), perforated 11.*

CM716 *Harry S Truman, from a photograph by Leo Stern*

| CM716 | | MNHVF | UseVF |
|---|---|---|---|
| **8¢** | **red, black and blue,** tagged *(157,052,800)* | .25 | .25 |
| | Plate block of 4 | 1.10 | |
| | FDC *(May 8, 1973)* | | 1.00 |
| | zo. Tagging omitted | 5.00 | |

**1973. BOSTON TEA PARTY ISSUE** uses 4 different se-tenant designs to form a single scene depicting this historical event that preceded the war of independence. *Intaglio (Giori Press) and offset, perforated 11.*

CM717-20 *Boston Tea Party*

| CM717 | | MNHVF | UseVF |
|---|---|---|---|
| **8¢** | **multicolored,** tagged *(196,275,000)* | .25 | .20 |

CM706-CM715 *Postal people performing services*

**CM718**

| | MNHVF | UseVF |
|---|---|---|
| **8¢** **multicolored,** tagged | .25 | .20 |

**CM719**

| | MNHVF | UseVF |
|---|---|---|
| **8¢** **multicolored,** tagged | .25 | .20 |

**CM720**

| | MNHVF | UseVF |
|---|---|---|
| **8¢** **multicolored,** tagged | .25 | .20 |
| Plate block of 4 | 1.15 | |
| y. Se-tenant block of 4, (CM717-20) | .75 | |
| FDC *(July 4, 1973)* | | 2.00 |
| vy. Se-tenant block of 4, intaglio black omitted | 1500. | |
| vy1.Se-tenant block of 4, intaglio black omitted | 500. | |
| zo. Tagging omitted, any single | — | |
| zoy.Se-tenant block of 4, tagging omitted | — | |

**1973. PROGRESS IN ELECTRONICS ISSUE** commemorates advances and developments in electronic communications. (See also A84). *Intaglio (Giori Press) and offset, perforated 11.*

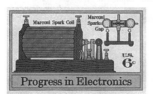

CM721 *Marconi Spark Coil and Gap*

**CM721**

| | MNHVF | UseVF |
|---|---|---|
| **6¢** **multicolored,** tagged *(53,005,000)* | .25 | .20 |
| Plate block of 4 | .85 | |
| FDC *(July 10, 1973)* | | 1.00 |
| zo. Tagging omitted | — | |

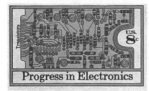

CM722 *Transistors and Electronic Circuit*

**CM722**

| | MNHVF | UseVF |
|---|---|---|
| **8¢** **multicolored,** tagged *(159,775,000)* | .25 | .20 |
| Plate block of 4 | 1.00 | |
| FDC *(July 10, 1973)* | | 1.00 |
| a. Black (inscription) omitted | 650. | |
| b. Lilac and tan (background) omitted | 1300. | |
| zo. Tagging omitted | — | |

CM723 *Radio and Television Components*

**CM723**

| | MNHVF | UseVF |
|---|---|---|
| **15¢** **multicolored,** tagged *(39,005,000)* | .25 | .20 |
| Plate block of 4 | 1.85 | |
| FDC *(July 10, 1973)* | | 1.00 |
| v. Black omitted | 1500. | |

**1973. ROBINSON JEFFERS ISSUE** pays tribute to the poet whose works were mainly allegories influenced by his love of the classical Greek and Roman tragedies. *Gravure (Andreotti Press), perforated*

CM724 *Robinson Jeffers and Children with Burro*

**CM724**

| | MNHVF | UseVF |
|---|---|---|
| **8¢** **multicolored,** tagged *(128,048,000)* | .25 | .20 |
| Plate block of 12 | 3.00 | |
| FDC *(Aug. 13, 1973)* | | 1.00 |
| v. Vertical pair, imperforate horizontally | 250. | |

**1973. LYNDON B. JOHNSON ISSUE** honored the 36th president of the United States, who died January 22, 1973. *Gravure (Andreotti Press), perforated 11.*

CM725 *Lyndon B. Johnson*

**CM725**

| | MNHVF | UseVF |
|---|---|---|
| **8¢** **multicolored** *(152,624,000)* | .25 | .20 |
| Plate block of 12 | 3.50 | |
| FDC *(Aug. 27, 1973)* | | 1.00 |
| v. Horizontal pair, imperforate vertically | 350. | |

**1973. HENRY O. TANNER ISSUE** salutes the artist who studied art under Thomas Eakins. Many of his works were based on Biblical themes. *Gravure (Andreotti Press), perforated 11.*

CM726 *Henry O. Tanner, Palette and Rainbow*

**CM726**

| | MNHVF | UseVF |
|---|---|---|
| **8¢** **multicolored,** tagged *(146,008,000)* | .25 | .20 |
| Plate block of 12 | 3.00 | |
| FDC *(Sept. 10, 1973)* | | 1.00 |

**1973. WILLA CATHER ISSUE** salutes a novelist who won a 1922 Pulitzer Prize. *Gravure (Andreotti Press), perforated 11.*

CM727 *Willa Cather, Pioneers and Covered Wagon*

**CM727**

| | MNHVF | UseVF |
|---|---|---|
| **8¢** **multicolored,** tagged *(139,608,000)* | .25 | .20 |
| Plate block of 12 | 3.00 | |
| FDC *(Sept. 20, 1973)* | | 1.00 |
| v. Vertical pair, imperforate horizontally | 275. | |

## Rural America Series

**1973. ANGUS CATTLE ISSUE** 1st of a series of 3 stamps honoring rural America, saluted the 100th anniversary of the introduction of Aberdeen Angus cattle into the United States (See also CM751-52F). *Intaglio (Giori Press) and offset, perforated 11.*

CM728 *Angus Cattle and Longhorn Cattle on Prairie*

| CM728 | | MNHVF | UseVF |
|---|---|---|---|
| 8¢ | **multicolored,** tagged *(145,430,000)* | .25 | .20 |
| | Plate block of 4 | 1.00 | |
| | FDC *(Oct. 5, 1973)* | | 1.00 |
| | v. Green and red brown omitted | 975. | |
| | v1. Vertical pair, imperforate between | 4500. | |
| | zo. Tagging omitted | 14.00 | |

**1974. VETERANS OF FOREIGN WARS ISSUE** saluted the men and women in America's military service since the Revolutionary War. *Intaglio, (Giori Press), perforated 11.*

CM729 *VFW Emblem*

| CM729 | | MNHVF | UseVF |
|---|---|---|---|
| 10¢ | **red and blue,** tagged *(145,430,000)* | .25 | .20 |
| | Plate block of 4 | 1.30 | |
| | FDC *(March 11, 1974)* | | 1.00 |
| | zo. Tagging omitted | 5.00 | |

**1974. ROBERT FROST ISSUE** honors the New England poet (1873-1963) and 4-time winner of the Pulitzer Prize. *Intaglio, perforated 10 1/2 x 11.*

CM730 *Robert Frost*

| CM730 | | MNHVF | UseVF |
|---|---|---|---|
| 10¢ | **black,** tagged *(145,235,000)* | .25 | .20 |
| | Plate block of 4 | 1.30 | |
| | FDC *(March 26, 1974)* | | 1.00 |

**1974. EXPO '74 WORLD'S FAIR ISSUE** featured the theme "Preserve the Environment," magically rendered by Peter Max in his images Cosmic Jumper and Smiling Sage. *Gravure (Andreotti Press), perforated 11.*

CM731 *Expo '74*

| CM731 | | MNHVF | UseVF |
|---|---|---|---|
| 10¢ | **multicolored,** tagged *(135,052,000)* | .25 | .20 |
| | Plate block of 12 | 4.25 | |
| | FDC *(April 18, 1974)* | | 1.00 |

**1974. HORSE RACING ISSUE** commemorates the 100th running of the Kentucky Derby. *Gravure (Andreotti Press), perforated 11 x 10 1/2.*

CM732 *Horses at the Turn*

| CM732 | | MNHVF | UseVF |
|---|---|---|---|
| 10¢ | **multicolored,** tagged *(156,750,000)* | .25 | .20 |
| | Plate block of 12 | 3.75 | |
| | FDC *(May 4, 1974)* | | 1.00 |
| | v. Blue "Horse Racing" omitted | 900. | |
| | b. Red "U.S. Postage 10 cents" omitted | — | |
| | zo. Tagging omitted | 15.00 | |

*Beware of stamps with minute traces of red being offered as CM732b. They are printing freeks, and do not have comparable value to a full color-omitted error.*

**1974. SKYLAB PROJECT ISSUE** paid tribute to the Skylab I program, devoted to experimentation in space.

CM733 *Skylab*

| CM733 | | MNHVF | UseVF |
|---|---|---|---|
| 10¢ | **multicolored,** tagged *(164,670,000)* | .25 | .20 |
| | Plate block of 4 | 1.30 | |
| | FDC *(May 14, 1974)* | | 1.00 |
| | v. Vertical pair, imperforate between | — | |
| | zo. Tagging omitted | 750. | |

**1974. UNIVERSAL POSTAL UNION ISSUE** marked the centenary of the international organization that helped standardize mail rates and expedite mail delivery worldwide. *Gravure (Andreotti Press), perforated 11.*

CM734 Lady Writing a Letter *by Terboch* CM735 Still Life *by Chardin* CM736 Mrs. John Douglas *by Gainsborough* CM737 Don Antonio Noriega *Goya* CM738 Portrait of Michelangelo *by Raphael* CM739 5 Feminine Virtues *by Hokusai* CM740 Old Scraps (Old Letter Rack) *by Peto* CM741 The Lovely Reader *by Liotard*

| CM734 | | MNHVF | UseVF |
|---|---|---|---|
| 10¢ | **multicolored,** tagged *(190,154,680)* | .25 | .20 |

| CM735 | | MNHVF | UseVF |
|---|---|---|---|
| 10¢ | **multicolored** tagged | .25 | .20 |

| CM736 | | MNHVF | UseVF |
|---|---|---|---|
| 10¢ | **multicolored,** tagged | .25 | .20 |

| CM737 | | MNHVF | UseVF |
|---|---|---|---|
| 10¢ | **multicolored,** tagged | .25 | .20 |

| CM738 | | MNHVF | UseVF |
|---|---|---|---|
| 10¢ | **multicolored,** tagged | .25 | .20 |

| CM739 | | MNHVF | UseVF |
|---|---|---|---|
| 10¢ | multicolored, tagged | .25 | .20 |

| CM740 | | MNHVF | UseVF |
|---|---|---|---|
| 10¢ | multicolored, tagged | .25 | .20 |

| CM741 | | MNHVF | UseVF |
|---|---|---|---|
| 10¢ | multicolored, tagged | .25 | .20 |
| | Plate block of 10 | 3.50 | |
| | Se-tenant block or strip of 8, CM734-41 | 2.00 | |
| | FDC (June 6, 1974) | | 1.00 |
| | v. Se-tenant block or strip of 8 imperforate vertically | 7500. | |

**1974. MINERAL HERITAGE ISSUE** focused attention to the outstanding contributions minerals have made to making the United States a leader among nations. *Intaglio (Giori Press) and offset, perforated 11.*

CM742 *Amethyst*

CM743 *Petrified Wood*

CM744 *Rhodochrosite*

CM745 *Tourmaline*

| CM742 | | MNHVF | UseVF |
|---|---|---|---|
| 10¢ | multicolored, tagged (167,212,800) | .25 | .20 |
| | v. Light blue and yellow omitted | — | |

| CM743 | | MNHVF | UseVF |
|---|---|---|---|
| 10¢ | multicolored, tagged | .25 | .20 |
| | v. Light blue and yellow omitted | — | |

| CM744 | | MNHVF | UseVF |
|---|---|---|---|
| 10¢ | multicolored, tagged | .25 | .20 |
| | v. Light blue omitted | — | |
| | v1. Black and red omitted | — | |

| CM745 | | MNHVF | UseVF |
|---|---|---|---|
| 10¢ | multicolored, tagged | .25 | .20 |
| | v. Light blue and omitted | — | |
| | v1. Black and purple omitted | — | |
| | Plate block of 4 | | 1.00 |
| | Se-tenant block or strip of 4 | — | |
| | FDC (June 13, 1974) | | |
| | vy. Se-tenant block or strip of 4, light blue & yellow omitted | | |
| | zo. Tagging omitted, any single | — | |
| | zoy.Se-tenant block or strip of 4, tagging omitted | 58.00 | |

**1974. SETTLEMENT OF KENTUCKY ISSUE** saluted the 200th anniversary of the founding of Fort Harrod, the 1st British settlement west of the Allegheny Mountains. *Intaglio (Giori Press) and offset, perforated 11.*

CM746 *Settlers at Fort Harrod*

| CM746 | | MNHVF | UseVF |
|---|---|---|---|
| 10¢ | multicolored, tagged (156,265,000) | .25 | .20 |
| | Plate block of 4 | 1.30 | |
| | FDC (June 15, 1974) | | 1.00 |
| | v. Offset dull black omitted | 800. | |
| | v1. Green & black (Intaglio & offset) & blue omitted | 4250. | |
| | v2. Green intaglio & offset black omitted | — | |
| | v3. Intaglio green omitted | — | |
| | zo. Tagging omitted | 10.00 | |

**1974. FIRST CONTINENTAL CONGRESS ISSUE** commemorated the 200th anniversary of the assemblage that paved the way for the creation of the United States. *Intaglio, (Giori Press), perforated 11.*

CM747 *Carpenters' Hall* CM748 *Independence Hall* CM749 *Quote from 1st Continental Congress* CM750 *Quote from Declaration of Independence*

| CM747 | | MNHVF | UseVF |
|---|---|---|---|
| 10¢ | dark blue and red, tagged (195,585,000) | .25 | .20 |

| CM748 | | MNHVF | UseVF |
|---|---|---|---|
| 10¢ | red and dark blue, tagged | .25 | .20 |

| CM749 | | MNHVF | UseVF |
|---|---|---|---|
| 10¢ | gray, dark blue and red, tagged | .25 | .20 |

| CM750 | | MNHVF | UseVF |
|---|---|---|---|
| 10¢ | gray, dark blue and red, tagged | .25 | .20 |
| | Plate block of 4 | 1.40 | |
| | y. Se-tenant block of 4, CM747-50 | .75 | |
| | FDC (July 4, 1974) | | 1.00 |
| | zo. Tagging omitted, any single | — | |
| | zoy.Se-tenant block of 4, tagging omitted | 50.00 | |

**1974. CHAUTAUQUA TENT ISSUE** the 2nd and 3rd stamps completing this series, commemorated the 100th anniversary of the founding of the Chautauqua Institution, which developed into a teachers' training center for Sunday school and, later, public school, and also marked the 100th anniversary of hard winter wheat. *Intaglio (Giori Press) and offset, perforated 11.*

CM751 *Chautauqua Tent*

| CM751 | | MNHVF | UseVF |
|---|---|---|---|
| 10¢ | multicolored, tagged (151,335,000) | .25 | .20 |
| | Plate block of 4 | 1.30 | |
| | FDC (Aug. 6, 1974) | | 1.00 |

**1974. WINTER WHEAT AND TRAIN ISSUE**

CM752 *Winter Wheat and Train*

| CM752 | | MNHVF | UseVF |
|---|---|---|---|
| 10¢ | **multicolored,** tagged *(141,085,000)* | .25 | .20 |
| | Plate block of 4 | 1.30 | |
| | FDC *(Aug. 16, 1974)* | | 1.00 |
| | v. Black and intaglio blue omitted | 875. | |
| | zo. Tagging omitted | 15.00 | |

**1974. ENERGY CONSERVATION ISSUE** focused attention upon the national fuel shortage and the need to save energy. *Intaglio (Giori Press) and offset, perforated 11.*

CM753 *Energy Conservation*

| CM753 | | MNHVF | UseVF |
|---|---|---|---|
| 10¢ | **multicolored,** tagged *(148,850,000)* | .25 | .20 |
| | Plate block of 4 | 1.30 | |
| | FDC *(Sept. 23, 1974)* | | 1.00 |
| | v. Blue and orange omitted | 950. | |
| | v1. Green omitted | 875. | |
| | c2. Orange and green omitted | 800. | |
| | zo. Tagging omitted | 5.00 | |

**1974. LEGEND OF SLEEPY HOLLOW ISSUE** is the 5th in the American Folklore series and commemorates Washington Irving's *Legend of Sleepy Hollow. Intaglio (Giori Press) and offset, perforated 11.*

CM754 *Headless Horseman pursuing Ichabod Crane*

| CM754 | | MNHVF | UseVF |
|---|---|---|---|
| 10¢ | **dark blue, black, orange, and yellow,** tagged *(157,270,000)* | .25 | .20 |
| | Plate block of 4 | 1.30 | |
| | FDC *(Oct. 10, 1974)* | | 1.00 |

**1974. HELP FOR RETARDED CHILDREN ISSUE** encourages efforts to help mentally retarded persons. *Intaglio, (Giori Press), perforated 11.*

CM755 *Retarded Girl and Helping Hand*

| CM755 | | MNHVF | UseVF |
|---|---|---|---|
| 10¢ | **light and dark brown,** tagged *(150,245,000)* | .25 | .20 |
| | Plate block of 4 | 1.30 | |
| | FDC *(Oct. 12, 1974)* | | 1.00 |
| | zo. Tagging omitted | 6.00 | |

**1975. BENJAMIN WEST ISSUE** the final stamp in The American Arts series begun in 1961 (CM496) commemorated Benjamin West, 1st American-born painter to gain an international reputation working abroad. *Gravure (Andreotti Press), perforated 10 1/2 x 11.*

CM756 *Self Portrait, Benjamin West*

| CM756 | | MNHVF | UseVF |
|---|---|---|---|
| 10¢ | **multicolored,** tagged *(156,995,000)* | .25 | .20 |
| | Plate block of 10 | 3.25 | |
| | FDC *(Feb. 10, 1975)* | | 1.00 |

**1975. PIONEER SPACE ISSUE** salutes the unmanned Pioneer space mission, which probed the planet Jupiter in 1973-74. *Intaglio (Giori Press) and offset, perforated 11.*

CM757 *Pioneer 10 and Jupiter*

| CM757 | | MNHVF | UseVF |
|---|---|---|---|
| 10¢ | **dark blue, yellow and red,** tagged *(173,685,000)* | .25 | .20 |
| | Plate block of 4 | 1.30 | |
| | FDC *(Feb. 28, 1975)* | | 1.00 |
| | v. Intaglio blue omitted | 950. | |
| | v1. Red and yellow omitted | 1350. | |
| | zo. Tagging omitted | 7.50 | |

*Imperforate varieties came from printer's waste.*

**1975. COLLECTIVE BARGAINING ISSUE** commemorated the 40th anniversary of collective bargaining law in the Wagner Act, which stabilized labor-management relations in the United States. *Gravure (Andreotti Press), perforated 11.*

CM758 *Collective Bargaining*

| CM758 | | MNHVF | UseVF |
|---|---|---|---|
| 10¢ | **multicolored,** tagged *(153,355,000)* | .25 | .20 |
| | Plate block of 8 | 2.50 | |
| | FDC *(March 13, 1975)* | | 1.00 |
| | Imperforate pair | 350. | |

*Imperforate varieties came from printer's waste.*

**1975. CONTRIBUTORS TO THE CAUSE ISSUE** honors 4 heroes of the American Revolution. Emerald green inscriptions on the back of the stamp telling the story of each individual are printed under the gum. *Gravure (Andreotti Press), perforated 11 x 10 1/2.)*

CM759 *Sybil Ludington, Youthful Heroine*

| CM759 | | MNHVF | UseVF |
|---|---|---|---|
| 10¢ | **multicolored,** tagged *(63,205,000)* | .25 | .20 |
| | Plate block of 10 | 2.50 | |
| | FDC *(March 25, 1975)* | | 1.00 |
| | v. Inscription on back omitted | 250. | |

CM760 *Salem Poor, Gallant Soldier*

| CM760 | | MNHVF | UseVF |
|---|---|---|---|
| 10¢ | **multicolored,** tagged *(157,865,000)* | .25 | .20 |
| | Plate block of 10 | 3.25 | |
| | FDC *(March 25, 1975)* | | 1.00 |
| | v. Inscription on back omitted | 250. | |

CM761 *Haym Solomon, Financial Hero*

| CM761 | | MNHVF | UseVF |
|---|---|---|---|
| 10¢ | **multicolored,** tagged *(166,810,000)* | .25 | .20 |
| | Plate block of 10 | 3.25 | |
| | FDC *(March 25, 1975)* | | 1.00 |
| | v. Inscription on back omitted | 250. | |
| | v1. Red omitted | 275. | |

CM762 *Peter Francisco, Fighter Extraordinary*

| CM762 | | MNHVF | UseVF |
|---|---|---|---|
| 18¢ | **multicolored,** tagged *(44,825,000)* | .25 | .20 |
| | Plate block of 10 | 6.25 | |
| | FDC *(March 25, 1975)* | | 1.00 |

**1975. MARINER SPACE ISSUE** honored the Mariner 10 unmanned space mission to Venus and Mercury. *Intaglio (Giori Press) and offset, perforated 11.*

CM763 *Mariner 10, Venus and Mercury*

| CM763 | | MNHVF | UseVF |
|---|---|---|---|
| 10¢ | **black, red, ultramarine and bister,** tagged *(158,600,000)* | .25 | .20 |
| | Plate block of 4 | 1.30 | |
| | FDC *(April 4, 1975)* | | 1.00 |
| | v. Red omitted | 575. | |
| | v1. Ultramarine and bister omitted | 1750. | |
| | zo. Tagging omitted | 7.50 | |

**1975. LEXINGTON AND CONCORD ISSUE** commemorated these 1775 battles, the 1st of the Revolutionary war. *Gravure (Andreotti Press), perforated 11.*

CM764 *Lexington and Concord, Based on painting* Birth of Liberty *by Henry Sandham.*

| CM764 | | MNHVF | UseVF |
|---|---|---|---|
| 10¢ | **multicolored,** tagged *(114,028,000)* | .25 | .20 |
| | Plate block of 12 | 3.75 | |
| | FDC *(April 19, 1975)* | | 1.00 |
| | v. Vertical pair, imperforate horizontally | 425. | |

**1975. PAUL LAURENCE DUNBAR ISSUE** honors the African-American poet. *Gravure (Andreotti Press), perforated 11.*

CM765 *Paul Lawrence Dunbar*

| CM765 | | MNHVF | UseVF |
|---|---|---|---|
| 10¢ | **multicolored,** tagged *(146,365,000)* | .25 | .20 |
| | Plate block of 10 | 3.25 | |
| | FDC *(May 1, 1975)* | | 1.00 |
| | v. Imperforate pair | 1300. | |

**1975. D.W. GRIFFITH ISSUE** of the American Art series and commemorates motion picture pioneer D.W. Griffith. *Intaglio (Giori Press) and offset, perforated 11.*

CM766 *D.W. Griffith Motion Picture Camera*

| CM766 | | MNHVF | UseVF |
|---|---|---|---|
| 10¢ | **multicolored,** tagged *(148,805,000)* | .25 | .20 |
| | Plate block of 4 | 1.30 | |
| | FDC *(May 27, 1975)* | | 1.00 |
| | v. Intaglio dark brown omitted | 650. | |

**1975. BUNKER HILL ISSUE** commemorates the 200th anniversary of the Battle of Bunker Hill. *Gravure (Andreotti Press), perforated 11.*

CM767 *Detail from the painting* The Battle of Bunker Hill *by John Trumbull*

| CM767 | | MNHVF | UseVF |
|---|---|---|---|
| 10¢ | **multicolored,** tagged *(139,928,000)* | .25 | .20 |
| | Plate block of 12 | 3.75 | |
| | FDC *(June 17, 1975)* | | 1.00 |

**1975. MILITARY SERVICES BICENTENNIAL ISSUE** honored the 200th anniversary year of the U.S. military services. Designs depict uniforms worn by the Continental Army, Navy, Marines and Militia during the Revolutionary War. *Gravure (Andreotti Press), perforated 11.*

CM768 *Soldier*
CM769 *Sailor*
CM770 *Marine*
CM772 *Militiaman*

| CM768 | | MNHVF | UseVF |
|---|---|---|---|
| 10¢ | multicolored, tagged *(179,855,000)* | .25 | .20 |

| CM769 | | MNHVF | UseVF |
|---|---|---|---|
| 10¢ | multicolored, tagged | .25 | .20 |

| CM770 | | MNHVF | UseVF |
|---|---|---|---|
| 10¢ | multicolored, tagged | .25 | .20 |

| CM771 | | MNHVF | UseVF |
|---|---|---|---|
| 10¢ | multicolored, tagged | .25 | .20 |
| | Plate block of 12 | 4.25 | |
| | y. Se-tenant block of 4, CM768-71 | .75 | |
| | FDC *(July 4, 1975)* | | 1.00 |

**1975. APOLLO SOYUZ ISSUE** honored the 1st combined space mission between the United States and Soviet Union. The se-tenant designs used by both nations are identical except for language and denomination (Russia Nos. 4472-4473). *Gravure (Andreotti Press), perforated 11.*

CM772
*Spacecraft in Docked Position*

| CM772 | | MNHVF | UseVF |
|---|---|---|---|
| 10¢ | multicolored, tagged *(161,863,200)* | .25 | .20 |

CM773
*Spacecraft Prior to Docking*

| CM773 | | MNHVF | UseVF |
|---|---|---|---|
| 10¢ | multicolored, tagged | .25 | .20 |
| | Plate block of 12 | 4.00 | |
| | y. Se-tenant pair, CM772-73 | .45 | |
| | Gutter pair | — | |
| | FDC *(July 15, 1975)* | | 1.00 |
| | v. Vertical pair, imperforate horizontally | 2500. | |
| | zo. Tagging omitted, either single | — | |
| | zoy.Se-tenant pair, tagging omitted | 25.00 | |

**1975. WORLD PEACE THROUGH LAW ISSUE** was a prelude to the 7th World Law Conference of the World Peace Through Law Center and commemorates man's effort toward the universal goal of a peaceful world order with justice. *Intaglio (Giori Press), perforated 11.*

CM774 *Olive Branch, Globe, Gavel and Law Book*

| CM774 | | MNHVF | UseVF |
|---|---|---|---|
| 10¢ | green, gray blue and brown, tagged *(146,615,000)* | .25 | .20 |
| | Plate block of 4 | 1.35 | |
| | FDC *(Sept. 29, 1975)* | | 1.00 |
| | v. Horizontal pair, imperforate vertically (only 1 plate block) | 14000. | |
| | zo. Tagging omitted | 6.00 | |

**1975. INTERNATIONAL WOMEN'S YEAR ISSUE** celebrated the significance of women. *Gravure (Andreotti Press), perforated 11 x 10 1/2.*

CM775 *Stylized Dove, Globe and Gender Sign*

| CM775 | | MNHVF | UseVF |
|---|---|---|---|
| 10¢ | blue, orange and dark blue, tagged *(145,640,000)* | .25 | .20 |
| | Plate block of 6 | 1.90 | |
| | FDC *(Aug. 26, 1975)* | | 1.00 |

**1975. U.S. POSTAL SERVICE BICENTENNIAL ISSUE** commemorated the 200th anniversary of Postal Service in the U.S. *Gravure (Andreotti Press), perforated 11 x 10 1/2.*

CM776 *Stagecoach and Modern Trailer Truck* CM777 *Early and Modern Locomotives* CM778 *Early Mail Plane and Jumbo Jet* CM779 *Satelite for Mailgram Transmittions*

| CM776 | | MNHVF | UseVF |
|---|---|---|---|
| 10¢ | multicolored, tagged *(168,655,000)* | .25 | .20 |

| CM777 | | MNHVF | UseVF |
|---|---|---|---|
| 10¢ | multicolored, tagged | .25 | .20 |

| CM778 | | MNHVF | UseVF |
|---|---|---|---|
| 10¢ | multicolored, tagged | .25 | .20 |
| | | .25 | .20 |

| CM779 | | MNHVF | UseVF |
|---|---|---|---|
| 10¢ | multicolored, tagged | .25 | .20 |
| | Plate block of 12 | 4.25 | |
| | y. Se-tenant block of 4 CM776-79 | 1.25 | |
| | FDC *(Sept. 3, 1975)* | | 1.00 |
| | vy. Se-tenant block of 4, red "10¢" omitted | 7500. | |

**1975. BANKING AND COMMERCE ISSUE** focused on the importance of these commercial activities in the nation's development. *Intaglio (Giori Press) and offset, perforated 11.*

CM780 *Coins and Currency Motif* CM781 *Coins and Currency Motif*

| CM780 | | MNHVF | UseVF |
|---|---|---|---|
| 10¢ | **multicolored,** tagged *(146,196,000)* | .25 | .20 |

| CM781 | | MNHVF | UseVF |
|---|---|---|---|
| 10¢ | **multicolored,** tagged | .25 | .20 |
| | Plate block of 4 | 1.50 | |
| | y. Se-tenant pair, CM780-81 | .75 | .50 |
| | FDC *(Oct. 6, 1975)* | | 2.00 |
| | vy. Se-tenant pair, brown and blue (offset) omitted | 2500. | |
| | vly. Se-tenant pair, brown, blue and yellow (offset) omitted | 2750. | |

**1976. SPIRIT OF '76 ISSUE** reproduces a classic image of the American Revolution. *Gravure (Andreotti Press), perforated 11.*

CM782-84 *Revolutionary War fife and drum trio, printing by Archibald M. Willard*

| CM782 | | MNHVF | UseVF |
|---|---|---|---|
| 13¢ | **multicolored,** tagged *(219,455,000)* | .25 | .20 |

| CM783 | | MNHVF | UseVF |
|---|---|---|---|
| 13¢ | **multicolored,** tagged | .25 | .20 |

| CM784 | | MNHVF | UseVF |
|---|---|---|---|
| 13¢ | **multicolored,** tagged | .25 | .20 |
| | Plate block of 12 | 5.00 | |
| | y. Se-tenant strip of 3, CM782-84 | .75 | 1.00 |
| | FDC *(Jan. 1, 1976)* | | 1.00 |
| | v. Vertical pair, CM784, imperforate | 900. | |
| | v1. Se-tenant strip of 3, imperforate | 1300. | |

**1976. INTERPHIL ISSUE** commemorates the 7th International Philatelic Exhibition. May 29-June 6, 1976, in Philadelphia, PA. *Intaglio (Giori Press) and offset, perforated 11.*

CM785 *Interphil 76*

| CM785 | | MNHVF | UseVF |
|---|---|---|---|
| 13¢ | **blue, red and ultramarine,** tagged *(157,825,000)* | .25 | .20 |
| | Plate block of 4 | 1.60 | |
| | FDC *(Jan. 17, 1976)* | | 1.00 |

**1976. 50-STATE FLAG ISSUE** included in 1 sheet the flag of every state, arranged in order of its admission to the union. *Gravure (Andreotti Press), perforated 11, all stamps multicolored.*

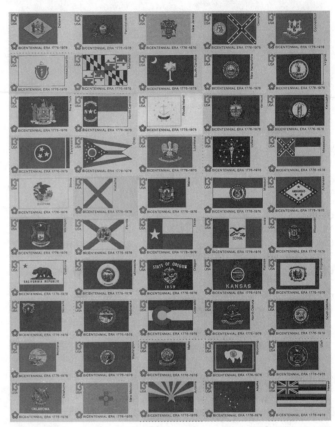

CM786-CM835 *State Flags*

| CM786 | | MNHVF | UseVF |
|---|---|---|---|
| 13¢ | **Delaware,** tagged *(436,005,000)* | .55 | .40 |

| CM787 | | MNHVF | UseVF |
|---|---|---|---|
| 13¢ | **Pennsylvania,** tagged | .55 | .40 |

| CM788 | | MNHVF | UseVF |
|---|---|---|---|
| 13¢ | **New Jersey,** tagged | .55 | .40 |

| CM789 | | MNHVF | UseVF |
|---|---|---|---|
| 13¢ | **Georgia,** tagged | .55 | .40 |

| CM790 | | MNHVF | UseVF |
|---|---|---|---|
| 13¢ | **Connecticut,** tagged | .55 | .40 |

| CM791 | | MNHVF | UseVF |
|---|---|---|---|
| 13¢ | **Massachusetts,** tagged | .55 | .40 |

| CM792 | | MNHVF | UseVF |
|---|---|---|---|
| 13¢ | **Maryland,** tagged | .55 | .40 |

| CM793 | | MNHVF | UseVF |
|---|---|---|---|
| 13¢ | **South Carolina,** tagged | .55 | .40 |

| CM794 | | MNHVF | UseVF |
|---|---|---|---|
| 13¢ | **New Hampshire,** tagged | .55 | .40 |

| CM795 | | MNHVF | UseVF |
|---|---|---|---|
| 13¢ | **Virginia,** tagged | .55 | .40 |

| CM796 | | MNHVF | UseVF |
|---|---|---|---|
| 13¢ | **New York,** tagged | .55 | .40 |

| CM797 | | MNHVF | UseVF |
|---|---|---|---|
| 13¢ | **North Carolina,** tagged | .55 | .40 |

| CM798 | | MNHVF | UseVF |
|---|---|---|---|
| 13¢ | **Rhode Island,** tagged | .55 | .40 |

| CM799 | | MNHVF | UseVF |
|---|---|---|---|
| 13¢ | **Vermont,** tagged | .55 | .40 |

| CM800 | | MNHVF | UseVF |
|---|---|---|---|
| 13¢ | **Kentucky,** tagged | .55 | .40 |

| CM801 | | MNHVF | UseVF |
|---|---|---|---|
| 13¢ | **Tennessee,** tagged | .55 | .40 |

| CM802 | | MNHVF | UseVF |
|---|---|---|---|
| 13¢ | **Ohio,** tagged | .55 | .40 |

| CM803 | | MNHVF | UseVF |
|---|---|---|---|
| 13¢ | **Louisiana,** tagged | .55 | .40 |

| CM804 | | MNHVF | UseVF |
|---|---|---|---|
| 13¢ | **Indiana,** tagged | .55 | .40 |

| CM805 | | MNHVF | UseVF |
|---|---|---|---|
| 13¢ | **Mississippi,** tagged | .55 | .40 |

| CM806 | | MNHVF | UseVF |
|---|---|---|---|
| 13¢ | **Illinois,** tagged | .55 | .40 |

| CM807 | | MNHVF | UseVF |
|---|---|---|---|
| 13¢ | **Alabama,** tagged | .55 | .40 |

| CM808 | | MNHVF | UseVF |
|---|---|---|---|
| 13¢ | **Maine,** tagged | .55 | .40 |

| CM809 | | MNHVF | UseVF |
|---|---|---|---|
| 13¢ | **Missouri,** tagged | .55 | .40 |

| CM810 | | MNHVF | UseVF |
|---|---|---|---|
| 13¢ | **Arkansas,** tagged | .55 | .40 |

| CM811 | | MNHVF | UseVF |
|---|---|---|---|
| 13¢ | **Michigan,** tagged | .55 | .40 |

| CM812 | | MNHVF | UseVF |
|---|---|---|---|
| 13¢ | **Florida,** tagged | .55 | .40 |

| CM813 | | MNHVF | UseVF |
|---|---|---|---|
| 13¢ | **Texas,** tagged | .55 | .40 |

| CM814 | | MNHVF | UseVF |
|---|---|---|---|
| 13¢ | **Iowa,** tagged | .55 | .40 |

| CM815 | | MNHVF | UseVF |
|---|---|---|---|
| 13¢ | **Wisconsin,** tagged | .55 | .40 |

| CM816 | | MNHVF | UseVF |
|---|---|---|---|
| 13¢ | **California,** tagged | .55 | .40 |

| CM817 | | MNHVF | UseVF |
|---|---|---|---|
| 13¢ | **Minnesota,** tagged | .55 | .40 |

| CM818 | | MNHVF | UseVF |
|---|---|---|---|
| 13¢ | **Oregon,** tagged | .55 | .40 |

| CM819 | | MNHVF | UseVF |
|---|---|---|---|
| 13¢ | **Kansas,** tagged | .55 | .40 |

| CM820 | | MNHVF | UseVF |
|---|---|---|---|
| 13¢ | **West Virginia,** tagged | .55 | .40 |

| CM821 | | MNHVF | UseVF |
|---|---|---|---|
| 13¢ | **Nevada,** tagged | .55 | .40 |

| CM822 | | MNHVF | UseVF |
|---|---|---|---|
| 13¢ | **Nebraska,** tagged | .55 | .40 |

| CM823 | | MNHVF | UseVF |
|---|---|---|---|
| 13¢ | **Colorado,** tagged | .55 | .40 |

| CM824 | | MNHVF | UseVF |
|---|---|---|---|
| 13¢ | **North Dakota,** tagged | .55 | .40 |

| CM825 | | MNHVF | UseVF |
|---|---|---|---|
| 13¢ | **South Dakota,** tagged | .55 | .40 |

| CM826 | | MNHVF | UseVF |
|---|---|---|---|
| 13¢ | **Montana,** tagged | .55 | .40 |

| CM827 | | MNHVF | UseVF |
|---|---|---|---|
| 13¢ | **Washington,** tagged | .55 | .40 |

| CM828 | | MNHVF | UseVF |
|---|---|---|---|
| 13¢ | **Idaho,** tagged | .55 | .40 |

| CM829 | | MNHVF | UseVF |
|---|---|---|---|
| 13¢ | **Wyoming,** tagged | .55 | .40 |

| CM830 | | MNHVF | UseVF |
|---|---|---|---|
| 13¢ | **Utah,** tagged | .55 | .40 |

| CM831 | | MNHVF | UseVF |
|---|---|---|---|
| 13¢ | **Oklahoma,** tagged | .55 | .40 |

| CM832 | | MNHVF | UseVF |
|---|---|---|---|
| 13¢ | **New Mexico,** tagged | .55 | .40 |

| CM833 | | MNHVF | UseVF |
|---|---|---|---|
| 13¢ | **Arizona,** tagged | .55 | .40 |

| CM834 | | MNHVF | UseVF |
|---|---|---|---|
| 13¢ | **Alaska,** tagged | .55 | .40 |

| CM835 | | MNHVF | UseVF |
|---|---|---|---|
| 13¢ | **Hawaii,** tagged | .55 | .40 |
| | FDC, any single *(Feb. 23, 1976)* | | 1.00 |
| | FDC, pane of 50 | | 15.00 |

**1976. TELEPHONE CENTENNIAL ISSUE** honored the 100th anniversary of the 1st telephone call by Alexander Graham Bell (CM235). *Intaglio (Giori Press), perforated 11.*

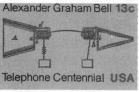

CM836 *Patent Application of Bell's 1876 Telephone*

| CM836 | | MNHVF | UseVF |
|---|---|---|---|
| 13¢ | **black, purple and red on tan paper** tagged *(159,915,000)* | .25 | .20 |
| | Plate block of 4 | 1.60 | |
| | FDC *(March 10, 1976)* | | 1.00 |

**1976. COMMERCIAL AVIATION ISSUE** saluted the 50th anniversary of the 1st contract airmail flights. The stamp depicts a Ford-Pullman monoplane and a Laird Swallow biplane. *Gravure (Andreotti Press), perforated 11.*

CM837 *Early Contract Airmail Planes*

| CM837 | | MNHVF | UseVF |
|---|---|---|---|
| 13¢ | **multicolored,** tagged *(156,960,000)* | .25 | .20 |
| | Plate block of 10 | 4.70 | |
| | FDC *(March 19, 1976)* | | 1.00 |

**1976. CHEMISTRY ISSUE** pays tribute to that science and salutes the 100th anniversary of the American Chemical Society. *Gravure (Andreotti Press), perforated 11.*

CM838 *Laboratory Flasks, Computer Tape*

| CM838 | | MNHVF | UseVF |
|---|---|---|---|
| 13¢ | **multicolored,** tagged *(158,470,000)* | .25 | .20 |
| | Plate block of 12 | 4.70 | |
| | Gutter pair | | |
| | FDC *(April 6, 1976)* | | 1.00 |

**1976. BICENTENNIAL SOUVENIR SHEETS,** issued to coincide with the 7th International Philatelic Exhibition, held in Philadelphia, PA, May 29-June 6. Each contained 5 stamps of the same denomination. *Offset, perforated 11.*

CM839 *Surrender of Cornwallis at Yorktown by John Trumbull (five 13¢ stamps)*

**CM839**

| | | | MNHVF | UseVF |
|---|---|---|---|---|
| 65¢ | **multicolored,** tagged *(1,990,500)* | | 4.75 | 4.50 |
| | a. 13c 2 British officers | | .95 | .90 |
| | b. 13c Gen. Benjamin Lincoln | | .95 | .90 |
| | c. 13c Gen. George Washington | | .95 | .90 |
| | d. 13c John Trumbull, Col. Cobb, von Steuben, Lafayette & Thomas Nelson | | .95 | .90 |
| | e. Alexander Hamilton, John Laurens & Walter Stewart | | .95 | .90 |
| | FDC *(May 29, 1976)* | | | 10.00 |
| | v. "USA/13c" omitted on CM839b, CM839c & CM839d, imperforate | | 500. | |
| | v1. "USA/13c" omitted on CM839b, CM839c & CM839d | | 900. | |
| | v2. "USA/13c" omitted on CM839a & CM839e | | 500. | |
| | v3. "USA/13c" omitted on CM839c & CM838d | | 500. | |
| | v4. "USA/13c" omitted on CM839e | | 600. | |
| | v5. "USA/13c" double on CM839b | | — | |
| | v6. Tagging and "USA/13c" omitted imperforate | | — | |
| | zo. Tagging omitted | | — | |
| | zov. Tagging omitted, imperforate | | 2250. | |

CM840 *Declaration of Independence by John Trumbull (five 18¢ stamps*

**CM840**

| | | | MNHVF | UseVF |
|---|---|---|---|---|
| 90¢ | **multicolored,** tagged *(1,983,000)* | | 6.00 | 5.75 |
| | a. 18c John Adams, Roger Sherman, & Robert Livingston | | 1.35 | 1.30 |
| | b. 18c Jefferson and Franklin | | 1.35 | 1.30 |
| | c. 18c Thomas Nelson, Jr., Francis Lewis, John Whitherspoon & Samuel Huntington | | 1.35 | 1.30 |
| | d. 18c John Hancock and Charles Thompson | | 1.35 | 1.30 |
| | e. 18c George Read, John Dickenson & Edward Rutledge | | 1.35 | 1.30 |
| | FDC *(May 29, 1976)* | | | 10.00 |
| | v. Black omitted in design | | 1250. | |
| | v1. Design and marginal inscriptions omitted | | — | |
| | v2. "USA/18c" and tagging omitted, imperforate | | — | |
| | v3. "USA/18c" omitted on CM840a & CM840c | | 600. | |
| | v4. "USA/18c" omitted on CM840b, CM840d & CM840e | | 500. | |
| | v5. "USA/18c" omitted on CM840d | | 550. | |
| | v6. "USA/18c" omitted on CM840b & CM840e | | 550. | |
| | zo. Tagging omitted | | — | |

CM841 *Washington crossing the Delaware by E. Leutze and E. Johnson (five 24¢ stamps)*

**CM841**

| | | | MNHVF | UseVF |
|---|---|---|---|---|
| $1.20 | **multicolored,** tagged *(1,953,000)* | | 8.25 | 8.00 |
| | a. 24c Boatsman | | 1.80 | 1.70 |
| | b. 24c Gen. George Washington | | 1.80 | 1.70 |
| | c. 24c Flag bearer | | 1.80 | 1.70 |
| | d. 24c Men in boat | | 1.80 | 1.70 |
| | e. 24c Men on shore | | 1.80 | 1.70 |
| | FDC *(May 29, 1976)* | | | |
| | v. Design & marginal inscription omitted | | 3250. | |
| | v1. "USA/24c" omitted, imperforate | | — | |
| | v2. "USA/24c" omitted on CM841a, CM841b & CM841C | | 600. | |
| | v3. "USA/24c" omitted on CM841d & CM841e | | 550. | |
| | v4. "USA/24c" of CM841d & CM841e inverted | | 500. | |
| | zo. Tagging omitted | | — | |
| | zov. Tagging omitted, imperforate | | 2500. | |

CM842 *Washington Reviewing Army at Valley Forge by William T. Trego (five 31¢ stamps)*

**CM842**

| | | | MNHVF | UseVF |
|---|---|---|---|---|
| $1.55 | **multicolored,** tagged *(1,903,000)* | | 10.75 | 10.50 |
| | a. 31c 2 officers | | 2.25 | 2.15 |
| | b. 31c Gen. George Washington | | 2.15 | 2.15 |
| | c. 31c Officer on black horse | | 2.25 | 2.15 |
| | d. 31c Officer and white horse | | 2.25 | 2.15 |
| | e. 31c 3 foot soldiers | | 2.25 | 2.15 |
| | FDC *(May 29, 1976)* | | | |
| | v. Black omitted in design | | — | |
| | v1. "USA/31c" omitted, imperforate | | 2500. | |
| | v2. "USA/31c" omitted on CM842a, CM842b & CM842e | | — | |
| | v3. "USA/31c" and tagging omitted on CM842a, CM842b & CM842c, imperforate | | — | |
| | v4. "USA/31c" omitted on CM842a & CM842c | | 550. | |
| | v5. "USA/31c" and tagging omitted on CM842a & CM842c, imperforate | | — | |
| | v6. "USA/31c"omitted on CM842b, CM842d & CM842e | | — | |
| | v7. "USA/31c" and tagging omitted on CM842b, CM842d & CM842e, imperforate | | 2500. | |
| | v8. "USA/31c" omitted on CM842b & CM842d | | — | |
| | v9. "USA/31c" omitted on CM842d & CM842e | | 1250. | |
| | v10. "USA/31c" omitted on CM842e | | 550. | |
| | z11. tagging omitted, imperforate | | 2250. | |

**1976. BENJAMIN FRANKLIN ISSUE** honors America's 1st postmaster general, appointed by the Continental Congress, *Intaglio (Giori Press) and offset, perforated 11.*

CM843 *Benjamin Franklin and map of North America.*

**CM843**

| | | MNHVF | UseVF |
|---|---|---|---|
| 13¢ | **multicolored,** tagged *(164,890,000)* | .25 | .20 |
| | Plate block of 4 | 1.60 | |
| | FDC *June 1, 1976)* | | 1.00 |
| | v. Light blue omitted | 275. | |
| | zo. Tagging omitted | 4.00 | |

**1976. DECLARATION OF INDEPENDENCE ISSUE** celebrates the anniversary of the approval of the document on July 4, 1776, by the members of the Continental Congress. *Gravure (Andreotti Press), perforated 11.*

CM844-47 The Declaration of Independence, *painting by John Trumbull*

**CM844**

| | | MNHVF | UseVF |
|---|---|---|---|
| 13¢ | **multicolored,** tagged *(208,035,000)* | .25 | .20 |

**CM845**

| | | MNHVF | UseVF |
|---|---|---|---|
| 13¢ | **multicolored,** tagged | .25 | .20 |

**CM846**

| | | MNHVF | UseVF |
|---|---|---|---|
| 13¢ | **multicolored,** tagged | .25 | .20 |

**CM847**

| | | MNHVF | UseVF |
|---|---|---|---|
| 13¢ | **multicolored,** tagged | .25 | .20 |
| | Plate block of 16 | 11.00 | |
| | y. Se-tenant strip of 4, | | |
| | CM844-47 | 1.00 | 1.00 |
| | FDC *(July 4, 1976)* | | 2.00 |
| | FDC, any single | | 1.00 |

**1976. OLYMPIC GAMES ISSUE** salutes the 1976 Winter Games in Innsbruck, Austria and the Summer Games in Montreal, Canada. *Gravure (Andreotti Press), perforated 11.*

CM848 *Diving*

**CM848**

| | | MNHVF | UseVF |
|---|---|---|---|
| 13¢ | **multicolored,** tagged *(185,715,000)* | .25 | .20 |

CM849 *Skiing*

**CM849**

| | | MNHVF | UseVF |
|---|---|---|---|
| 13¢ | **multicolored,** tagged | .25 | .20 |

CM850 *Running*

**CM850**

| | | MNHVF | UseVF |
|---|---|---|---|
| 13¢ | **multicolored,** tagged | .25 | .20 |

CM851 *Skating*

**CM851**

| | | MNHVF | UseVF |
|---|---|---|---|
| 13¢ | **multicolored,** tagged | .25 | .20 |
| | Plate block of 12 | 6.50 | |
| | y. Se-tenant block of 4 | 1.25 | 1.50 |
| | FDC *(July 16, 1976)* | | 1.00 |
| | v. Imperforate se-tenant block of of 4 | 750. | |
| | vl. Imperforate pair (either) | 275. | |

**1976. CLARA MAASS ISSUE** honors the 100th birthday of the nurse who gave her life during yellow fever research. *Gravure (Andreotti Press), perforated 11.*

CM852 *Nurse Clara Maass and Hospital Pin*

**CM852**

| | | MNHVF | UseVF |
|---|---|---|---|
| 13¢ | **multicolored,** tagged *(130,592,000)* | .25 | .20 |
| | Plate block of 12 | 5.75 | |
| | FDC *(Aug. 18, 1976)* | | 1.00 |
| | v. Horizontal pair, imperforate vertically | 500. | |

**1976. ADOLPH S. OCHS ISSUE** commemorates the 125th anniversary of *The New York Times.* Ochs was the publisher of the *Times* from 1896 until his death in 1935. *Intaglio (Giori Press), perforated 11.*

CM853 *Adolph S. Ochs from portrait by S.J. Woolf.*

**CM853**

| | | MNHVF | UseVF |
|---|---|---|---|
| 13¢ | **gray and black,** tagged *(158,332,800)* | .25 | .20 |
| | Plate block of 4 | 1.60 | |
| | FDC *(Sept. 18, 1976)* | | 1.00 |

**1977. WASHINGTON AT PRINCETON ISSUE** commemorates the American victory at Princeton, NJ, over the British lead by Lord Cornwallis. *Gravure (Andreott Press), perforated 11.*

CM854 *George Washington Painting by Charles Willson Peale*

**CM854**

| | | MNHVF | UseVF |
|---|---|---|---|
| 13¢ | **multicolored,** tagged *(150,328,000)* | .25 | .20 |
| | Plate block of 10 | 3.95 | |
| | FDC *(Jan. 3, 1977)* | | 1.00 |
| | v. Horizontal pair, imperforate vertically | 550. | |

**1977. SOUND RECORDING ISSUE** pays tribute to a century of progress in the field of sound recording. *Intaglio (Giori Press) and offset, perforated 11.*

CM855 *Early Sound Recorder*

**CM855**

| | | MNHVF | UseVF |
|---|---|---|---|
| 13¢ | **multicolored,** tagged *(176,830,000)* | .25 | .20 |
| | Plate block of 4 | 1.60 | |
| | FDC *(March 23, 1977)* | | 1.00 |

**1977. PUEBLO INDIAN ART ISSUE** first installment in the all se-tenant American Folk Art series showcases the artistic achievements of the Pueblo Indians in the craft of pottery. *Gravure (Andreotti Press), perforated 11.*

CM856 *Zia Pueblo*

CM857 *San Ildefonso Pueblo*

CM858 *Hopi Pueblo*

CM859 *Acoma Pueblo*

**CM856**

| | | MNHVF | UseVF |
|---|---|---|---|
| 13¢ | **multicolored,** tagged *(195,976,000)* | .25 | .20 |

**CM857**

| | | MNHVF | UseVF |
|---|---|---|---|
| 13¢ | **multicolored,** tagged | .25 | .20 |

**CM858**

| | | MNHVF | UseVF |
|---|---|---|---|
| 13¢ | **multicolored,** tagged | .25 | .20 |

**CM859**

| | | MNHVF | UseVF |
|---|---|---|---|
| 13¢ | **multicolored,** tagged | .25 | .20 |
| | Plate block of 10 | 4.50 | |
| | y. Se-tenant block or strip of 4 | .75 | |
| | FDC *(April 13, 1977)* | | 1.00 |
| | v. Se-tenant block or strip of 4, imperforate vertically | 2500. | |

**1977. 50TH ANNIVERSARY OF TRANSATLANTIC FLIGHT ISSUE** commemorated the epic solo flight of Charles A. Lindbergh's across the Atlantic Ocean (see A10). *Gravure (Andreotti Press), perforated 11.*

CM860 *The Spirit of St. Louis over the Atlantic Ocean*

**CM860**

| | | MNHVF | UseVF |
|---|---|---|---|
| 13¢ | **multicolored,** tagged *(208,820,000)* | .25 | .20 |
| | Plate block of 12 | 4.75 | |
| | FDC *(May 20, 1977)* | | 1.00 |
| | v. Imperforate pair | 1250. | |

*Privately applied overprints on this stamp have no official status.*

**1977. COLORADO STATEHOOD ISSUE** celebrates the centennial of Colorado's entry into the union as the 38th state. *Gravure (Andreotti Press), perforated 11.*

CM861 *Columbine and Mountain Peak*

**CM861**

| | | MNHVF | UseVF |
|---|---|---|---|
| 13¢ | **multicolored,** tagged *(190,005,000)* | .25 | .20 |
| | Plate block of 12 | 4.75 | |
| | FDC *(May 21, 1977)* | | 1.00 |
| | v. Horizontal pair, imperforate between | 900. | |
| | v1. Horizontal pair, imperforate vertically | 900. | |
| | v2. Perforated 11 1/4 | .35 | |

**1977. BUTTERFLY ISSUE** commemoratives display representatives of different regions of the United States. *Gravure (Andreotti Press), perforated 11.*

CM862 *Swallowtail*

CM863 *Checkerspot*

CM864 *Dogface*

CM865 *Orange-Tip*

**CM862**

| | | MNHVF | UseVF |
|---|---|---|---|
| 13¢ | **multicolored,** tagged *(219,830,000)* | .25 | .20 |

**CM863**

| | | MNHVF | UseVF |
|---|---|---|---|
| 13¢ | **multicolored,** tagged | .25 | .20 |

**CM864**

| | | MNHVF | UseVF |
|---|---|---|---|
| 13¢ | **multicolored,** tagged | .25 | .20 |

**CM865**

| | | MNHVF | UseVF |
|---|---|---|---|
| 13¢ | **multicolored,** tagged | .25 | .20 |
| | Plate block of 12 | 5.50 | |
| | y. Se-tenant block of 4, CM1712-1715 | 1.00 | .80 |
| | FDC *(June 6, 1977)* | | 2.00 |
| | v. Se-tenant block of 4, imperforate horizontally | 13000. | |

**1977. LAFAYETTE ISSUE** marks the 200th anniversary of Marquis de Lafayette's landing on the coast of South Carolina, north of Charleston. *Intaglio, (Giori Press), perforated 11.*

CM866 *Marquis de Lafayette*

**CM866**

| | | MNHVF | UseVF |
|---|---|---|---|
| 13¢ | **blue, black and red** *(159,852,000)* | .25 | .20 |
| | Plate block of 4 | 1.60 | |
| | FDC *(June 13, 1977)* | | 1.00 |

**1977. SKILLED HANDS OF INDEPENDENCE ISSUE** salutes representatives of 4 American industries - blacksmiths, wheelwrights, leatherworkers and seamstresses - who contributed to winning the Revolutionary War. *Gravure (Andreotti Press), perforated 11.*

CM867 *Seamstress*
CM868 *Blacksmith*
CM869 *Wheelwright*
CM870 *Leatherworker*

**CM867**

| | | MNHVF | UseVF |
|---|---|---|---|
| 13¢ | **multicolored,** tagged *(188,310,000)* | .25 | .20 |

**CM868**

| | | MNHVF | UseVF |
|---|---|---|---|
| 13¢ | **multicolored,** tagged | .25 | .20 |

**CM869**

| | | MNHVF | UseVF |
|---|---|---|---|
| 13¢ | **multicolored,** tagged | .25 | .20 |

**CM870**

| | | MNHVF | UseVF |
|---|---|---|---|
| 13¢ | **multicolored** | .25 | .20 |
| | Plate block of 12 | 5.50 | |
| | y. Se-tenant block of 4, CM1717-1720 | 1.00 | .80 |
| | FDC *(July 4, 1977)* | | 1.00 |

**1977. PEACE BRIDGE ISSUE** marked the 50th anniversary of the Peace Bridge between Buffalo (Fort Porter) NY, and Fort Erie, Ontario, Canada. *Intaglio, perforated 11 x 10 1/2.*

CM871 *Dove Over Peace Bridge*

**CM871**

| | | MNHVF | UseVF |
|---|---|---|---|
| 13¢ | **blue,** tagged *(163,625,000)* | .25 | .20 |
| | Plate block of 4 | 1.60 | |
| | FDC *(Aug. 4, 1977)* | | 1.00 |

**1977. HERKIMER AT ORISKANY ISSUE** honors Gen. Nicholas Herkimer's contribution to the American War for Independence and the 200th anniversary of the Battle of Oriskany. *Gravure (Andreotti Press), perforated 11.*

CM872 *Wounded Gen. Herkimer at Battle of Oriskany*

**CM872**

| | | MNHVF | UseVF |
|---|---|---|---|
| 13¢ | **multicolored,** tagged *(156,296,000)* | .25 | .20 |
| | Plate block of 10 | 3.95 | |
| | FDC *(Aug. 6, 1977)* | | 1.00 |

**1977. ALTA CALIFORNIA ISSUE** commemorates the bicentennial of the 1st Spanish civil settlement in Alta (northern) California. *Intaglio (Giori Press) and offset, perforated 11.*

CM873 *Spanish Colonial Farms*

**CM873**

| | | MNHVF | UseVF |
|---|---|---|---|
| 13¢ | **multicolored,** tagged *(154,495,000)* | .25 | .20 |
| | Plate block of 4 | 1.60 | |
| | FDC *(Sept. 9, 1977)* | | 1.00 |

**1977. ARTICLES OF CONFEDERATION ISSUE** marked the 200th anniversary of the drafting of the Articles of Confederation in 1777. *Intaglio (Giori Press), perforated 11.*

CM874 Drafting the Articles of Confederation

**CM874**

| | | MNHVF | UseVF |
|---|---|---|---|
| 13¢ | **red and dark brown on cream paper,** tagged *(168,050,000)* | .25 | .20 |
| | Plate block of 4 | 1.60 | |
| | FDC *(Sept. 30, 1977)* | | 1.00 |
| | zo. Tagging omitted | 10.00 | |

**1977. TALKING PICTURES ISSUE** marks 50 years since the introduction of sound in films. *The Jazz Singer,* starring Al Jolson, is accepted as the 1st feature-length talking picture. *Intaglio (Giori Press) and offset, perforated 11.*

CM875 *Early Projector and Phonograph*

**CM875**

| | | MNHVF | UseVF |
|---|---|---|---|
| 13¢ | **multicolored,** tagged *(156,810,000)* | .25 | .20 |
| | Plate block of 4 | 1.60 | |
| | FDC *(Oct. 6, 1977)* | | 1.00 |

**1977. SURRENDER AT SARATOGA** marked the surrender of British Gen. John Burgoyne to Gen. Horatio Gates in 1777 (See CM77). *Gravure (Andreotti Press), perforated 11.*

CM876 *Surrender of Burgoyne, Painted by John Trumbell*

| CM876 | | MNHVF | UseVF |
|---|---|---|---|
| 13¢ | **multicolored** *(153,736,000)* | .25 | .20 |
| | Plate block of 10 | 4.00 | |
| | FDC *(Oct. 7, 1977)* | | 1.00 |

**1977. ENERGY ISSUE** stresses the importance of conserving energy and developing new sources. *Gravure (Andreotti Press), perforated 11.*

CM876A *"Conservation"*

CM876B *"Development"*

| CM876A | | MNHVF | UseVF |
|---|---|---|---|
| 13¢ | **13c multicolored,** tagged | .25 | .20 |
| | Plate block of 12 | 5.00 | |
| | *(Oct. 20, 1977)* | .25 | .20 |
| | y. Se-tenant pair CM876A & CM876B | .50 | |

| CM876B | | MNHVF | UseVF |
|---|---|---|---|
| 13¢ | **multicolored,** tagged | .25 | .20 |
| | *(Oct. 20, 1977)* | | |
| | Plate block of 12 | 5.00 | |
| | y. Se-tenant pair CM876A and CM876B | .50 | |

**1978. CARL SANDBURG ISSUE** honored "The Poet of the People" on the 100th anniversary of his birth. He won the Pulitzer Prize 3 times for his works. *Intaglio (Giori Press), perforated 11.*

CM877 *Carl Sandburg*

| CM877 | | MNHVF | UseVF |
|---|---|---|---|
| 13¢ | **brown and black,** tagged *(156,560,000)* | .25 | .20 |
| | Plate block of 4 | 1.60 | |
| | FDC *(Jan. 6, 1978)* | | 1.00 |
| | v. Brown omitted | | |

**1978. CAPTAIN COOK ISSUE** featuring two stamps oriented differently in the same sheet, marks the 200th anniversary of the explorer's arrival in Hawaii and Alaska. *Intaglio (Giori Press), perforated 11.*

CM878 *Capt. James Cook*

CM879 *Cook's ships Resolution and Discovery*

| CM878 | | MNHVF | UseVF |
|---|---|---|---|
| 13¢ | **blue,** tagged *(202,155,000)* | .25 | .20 |
| | FDC *(Jan. 20, 1978)* | | 1.00 |

| CM879 | | MNHVF | UseVF |
|---|---|---|---|
| 13¢ | **green,** tagged | .25 | .20 |
| | Plate block of 4, CM878 & CM879 | 1.60 | |
| | Plate block of 20, 10 each CM878-79 | 5.25 | |
| | Se-tenant pair CM878-79 | .50 | |
| | FDC *(Jan. 20, 1978)* | | 1.00 |
| | FDC, Se-tenant pair | | 2.00 |
| | v. Se-tenant pair, imperforate between | 4250. | |
| | v1. Vertical pair (CM879), imperforate horizontally | — | |

**1978. HARRIET TUBMAN ISSUE** first stamp in the long-running Black Heritage Series, honors the woman known as the "Moses of her People." Born into slavery, she is credited with helping more than 300 slaves to escape via the "Underground Railway." (See also CM1731) *Gravure (Andreotti Press), perforated 10 1/2 x 11.*

CM880 *Harriet Tubman*

| CM880 | | MNHVF | UseVF |
|---|---|---|---|
| 13¢ | **multicolored,** tagged *(156,525,000)* | .25 | .20 |
| | Plate block of 12 | 6.50 | |
| | FDC *(Feb. 1, 1978)* | | 1.00 |

**1978. AMERICAN QUILTS ISSUE** the 2nd se-tenant set in the American Folk Art Series, shows 4 different basket design quilt patterns. *Gravure (Andreotti Press), perforated 11.*

CM881-884 *Basket Design, Designed by Christopher Pullman after 1875 quilt made in New York City. Illustration slightly reduced.*

| CM881 | | MNHVF | UseVF |
|---|---|---|---|
| 13¢ | **multicolored,** tagged *(165,182,000)* | .25 | .20 |

| CM882 | | MNHVF | UseVF |
|---|---|---|---|
| 13¢ | **multicolored,** tagged | .25 | .20 |

| CM883 | | MNHVF | UseVF |
|---|---|---|---|
| 13¢ | **multicolored,** tagged | .25 | .20 |

| CM884 | | MNHVF | UseVF |
|---|---|---|---|
| 13¢ | **multicolored,** tagged | .25 | .20 |
| | Plate block of 12 | 5.50 | |
| | Se-tenant block of 4, CM881-84 | 1.00 | .95 |
| | FDC *(May 8, 1978)* | | 2.00 |

**1978. AMERICAN DANCE ISSUE** celebrates various styles of popular dancing. *Gravure (Andreotti Press), perforated 11.*

CM885 *Ballet*

CM886 *Theater*

CM887 *Folk*

CM888 *Modern*

| CM885 | | MNHVF | UseVF |
|---|---|---|---|
| 13¢ | **multicolored,** tagged *(157,598,400)* | .25 | .20 |

| CM886 | | MNHVF | UseVF |
|---|---|---|---|
| 13¢ | **multicolored,** tagged | .25 | .20 |

| CM887 | | MNHVF | UseVF |
|---|---|---|---|
| 13¢ | **multicolored,** tagged | .25 | .20 |

| CM888 | | MNHVF | UseVF |
|---|---|---|---|
| 13¢ | **multicolored,** tagged | .25 | .20 |
| | Plate block of 12 | 5.50 | |
| | Se-tenant block of 4, CM885-88 | 1.50 | .95 |
| | FDC *(April 26, 1978)* | | 2.00 |

**1978. FRENCH ALLIANCE ISSUE** marks the 200th anniversary of the signing of the French Alliance in 1778. *Intaglio (Giori Press) and offset, perforated 11.*

CM889 *King Louis XVI and Benjamin Franklin. Porcelain statuette by Charles Gabriel Sauvage.*

| CM889 | | MNHVF | UseVF |
|---|---|---|---|
| 13¢ | **blue, black, and red,** tagged *(102,856,000)* | .25 | .20 |
| | Plate block of 4 | 1.60 | |
| | FDC *(May 4, 1978)* | | 1.00 |

**1978. GEORGE PAPANICOLAOU ISSUE** commemorates the noted cancer researcher for his development of an early cancer detection procedure, the use of which has saved the lives of thousands of women. *Intaglio, perforated 10 1/2 x 11.*

CM890 *Dr. Papanicolaou and Microsope.*

| CM890 | | MNHVF | UseVF |
|---|---|---|---|
| 13¢ | **brown,** tagged *(152,270,000)* | .25 | .20 |
| | Plate block of 4 | 2.10 | |
| | FDC *(May 13, 1978)* | | 1.00 |

## Performing Artists Series

**1978. JIMMIE RODGERS ISSUE** the 1st stamp in the Performing Artists Series, commemorates the country and western singer known as the "Singing Brakeman" and "Father of Country Music". Rodgers was the 1st person inducted into the Country Music Hall of Fame in 1967. *Gravure (Andreotti Press), perforated 11.*

CM891 *Jimmie Rodgers*

| CM891 | | MNHVF | UseVF |
|---|---|---|---|
| 13¢ | **Multicolored,** tagged *(94,600,000)* | .25 | .20 |
| | Plate block of 12 | 5.00 | |
| | FDC *(May 24, 1978)* | | 1.00 |

**1978. CANADIAN INTERNATIONAL PHILATELIC EXHIBITION** Souvenir Sheet commemorates the 1978 CAPEX stamp shown in Toronto, Canada. The souvenir sheet contains 8 perforated stamps depicting animals and birds indigenous to the United States and Canada . *Intaglio (Giori Press) and offset, perforated 11.*

CM892 *CAPEX souvenir sheet*

| CM892 | | MNHVF | UseVF |
|---|---|---|---|
| $1.04 | **multicolored** *(10,400,000)* | 2.75 | 2.00 |
| | Souvenir sheet w/ plate number attached | 3.25 | 2.25 |
| | a. 13¢ Cardinal, tagged | .25 | .20 |
| | b. 13¢ Mallard, tagged | .25 | .20 |
| | c. 13¢ Canada Goose, tagged | .25 | .20 |
| | d. 13¢ Blue Jay, tagged | .25 | .20 |
| | e. 13¢ Moose, tagged | .25 | .20 |
| | f. 13¢ Chipmunk, tagged | .25 | .20 |
| | g. 13¢ Red Fox, tagged | .25 | .20 |
| | h. 13¢ Raccoon, tagged | .25 | .20 |
| | y. Se-tenant block of 8 CM892 a-h | 3.00 | |
| | FDC *(June 6, 1978)* | | |
| | v. Yellow, green, red, brown, blue & offset black omitted | 7000. | |
| | v1. Strip of 4 (a-d), imperforate vertically | 7500. | |
| | v2. Strip of 4 (e-h), imperforate vertically | 6500. | |

**1978. PHOTOGRAPHY ISSUE** celebrates the colorful, popular art form. *Gravure (Andreotti Press), perforated 11.*

CM893 *Camera, Filters and Photo Equipment.*

Photography USA 15c

| CM893 | | MNHVF | UseVF |
|---|---|---|---|
| 15¢ | **multicolored,** tagged *(161,228,000)* | .30 | .20 |
| | Plate block of 12 | 5.75 | |
| | FDC *(June 26, 1978)* | | 1.00 |

**1978. GEORGE M. COHAN ISSUE** 2nd stamp in the Performing Artists Series, marked the 100th birthday of George M. Cohan, a patriotic and world-renowned actor, popular song writer, playwright and producer. Gravure (Andreotti Press), perforated 11.

CM894 *George M. Cohan*

| CM894 | | MNHVF | UseVF |
|---|---|---|---|
| 15¢ | **multicolored,** tagged *(151,570,000)* | .30 | .20 |
| | Plate block of 12 | 5.75 | |
| | FDC *(July 3, 1978)* | | 1.00 |

**1978. VIKING MISSIONS ISSUE** commemorates the historic Viking space voyages; issued on the 2nd anniversary of the landing of Viking 1 on Mars. *Intaglio (Giori Press) and offset, perforated 11.*

CM895 *Viking I lander and Mars.*

| CM895 | | MNHVF | UseVF |
|---|---|---|---|
| 15¢ | **multicolored,** tagged *(158,880,000)* | .30 | .20 |
| | Plate block of 4 | 2.25 | |
| | FDC *(July 20, 1978)* | | 1.00 |

**1978. WILDLIFE CONSERVATION ISSUE** features 4 species of owls native to the United States. *Intaglio (Giori Press) and offset, perforated 11.*

CM896 *Great Gray Owl*

CM897 *Saw Whet Owl*

CM898 *Barred Owl*

CM899 *Great Horned Owl*

| CM896 | | MNHVF | UseVF |
|---|---|---|---|
| 15¢ | Great Gray Owl, tagged *(186,550,000)* | .30 | .20 |

| CM897 | | MNHVF | UseVF |
|---|---|---|---|
| 15¢ | Saw Whet Owl, tagged | .30 | .20 |

| CM898 | | MNHVF | UseVF |
|---|---|---|---|
| 15¢ | Barred Owl, tagged | .30 | .20 |

| CM899 | | MNHVF | UseVF |
|---|---|---|---|
| 15¢ | Great Horned Owl, tagged | .30 | .20 |
| | Plate block of 4 | 2.00 | |
| | y. Se-tenant block of 4 CM896-99 | 1.50 | 1.00 |
| | FDC *(Aug. 26, 1978)* | | 2.00 |

**1978. AMERICAN TREES ISSUE** highlighted 4 different trees native to the United States and reflected a variety in both appearance and geographic location. *Gravure, perforated 11.*

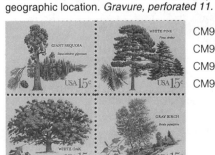

CM900 *Giant Sequoia*

CM901 *Eastern White Pine*

CM902 *White Oak*

CM903 *Gray Birch*

| CM900 | | MNHVF | UseVF |
|---|---|---|---|
| 15¢ | Giant Sequoia, tagged *(168,136,000)* | .30 | .20 |

| CM901 | | MNHVF | UseVF |
|---|---|---|---|
| 15¢ | Eastern White Pine, tagged | .30 | .20 |

| CM902 | | MNHVF | UseVF |
|---|---|---|---|
| 15¢ | White Oak, tagged | .30 | .20 |

| CM903 | | MNHVF | UseVF |
|---|---|---|---|
| 15¢ | Gray Birch, tagged | .30 | .20 |
| | Plate block of 12 | 6.00 | |
| | y. Se-tenant block of 4, CM900-03 | 1.25 | 1.00 |
| | FDC *(Oct. 9, 1978)* | | 2.00 |
| | vy. Se-tenant block of 4, imperforate horizontally | 12250. | |

**1979. ROBERT F. KENNEDY ISSUE** honors the assassinated U.S. senator and presidential hopeful. *Intaglio, perforated 11.*

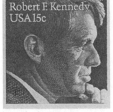

CM904 *Robert F. Kennedy*

| CM904 | | MNHVF | UseVF |
|---|---|---|---|
| 15¢ | **blue,** tagged *(159,297,000)* | .30 | .20 |
| | Plate block of 4 | 1.80 | |
| | FDC *(Jan. 12, 1979)* | | 1.00 |
| | za. Tagging omitted | — | |

**1979. MARTIN LUTHER KING JR. ISSUE** honors the civil rights leader and his role in the struggle for racial equality. Black Heritage Series. *Gravure Andreotti Press), perforated 11.*

CM905 *Martin Luther King Jr.*

**CM905**

| | | MNHVF | UseVF |
|---|---|---|---|
| **15¢** | **multicolored,** tagged *(166,435,000)* | .30 | .20 |
| | Plate block of 12 | 6.25 | |
| | FDC *(Jan. 13, 1979)* | | 1.00 |
| | v. Imperforate pair | 1750. | |

**1979. INTERNATIONAL YEAR OF THE CHILD ISSUE** commemorates the declaration by the U.N. General Assembly of 1979 as a year of concern for the condition and well being of the children of the world. *Intaglio, perforated 11.*

CM906 *Portraits of 4 Children.*

**CM906**

| | | MNHVF | UseVF |
|---|---|---|---|
| **15¢** | **light and dark brown,** tagged | .30 | .20 |
| | *(162,535,000)* | | |
| | Plate block of 4 | 1.80 | |
| | FDC *(Feb. 15, 1979)* | | 1.00 |

**1979. JOHN STEINBECK ISSUE** the first release in the Literary Arts Series, honors the novelist who won the Pulitzer Prize in 1940 and the Nobel Prize for Literature in 1962. *Intaglio, perforated 10 1/2 x 11.*

CM907 *John Steinbeck. From photograph by Philippe Halsman.*

**CM907**

| | | MNHVF | UseVF |
|---|---|---|---|
| **15¢** | **dark blue,** tagged *(155,000,000)* | .30 | .20 |
| | Plate block of 4 | 1.80 | |
| | FDC *(Feb. 27, 1979)* | | 1.00 |

**1979. ALBERT EINSTEIN ISSUE** honors the physicist, philosopher and humanitarian who is best known as the creator of the special and general theories of relativity. *Intaglio, perforated 10 1/2 x 11.*

CM908 *Albert Einstein. From photograph by Hermann Landshoff.*

**CM908**

| | | MNHVF | UseVF |
|---|---|---|---|
| **15¢** | **brown,** tagged *(157,310,000)* | .30 | .20 |
| | Plate block of 4 | 1.80 | |
| | Gutter pair, vertical | — | |
| | FDC *(March 4, 1979)* | | 1.00 |

**1979. PENNSYLVANIA TOLEWARE ISSUE** the 3rd se-tenant installment in the American Folk Art Series, depicts 4 of Pennsylvania Toleware, work well known for its colorful design motifs. *Gravure (Andreotti Press), perforated 11, multicolored.*

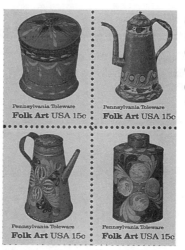

CM909 *Coffee Pot w/ Straight Spout*

CM910 *Tea Caddy*

CM911 *Sugar Bowl w/ Lid*

Cm912 *Coffee Pot w/ Gooseneck Spout*

**CM909**

| | | MNHVF | UseVF |
|---|---|---|---|
| **15¢** | Coffee pot w/straight spout *(174,096,000)* | .30 | .20 |

**CM910**

| | | MNHVF | UseVF |
|---|---|---|---|
| **15¢** | Tea caddy | .30 | .20 |

**CM911**

| | | MNHVF | UseVF |
|---|---|---|---|
| **15¢** | Sugar bowl and lid | .30 | .20 |

**CM912**

| | | MNHVF | UseVF |
|---|---|---|---|
| **15¢** | Coffee pot w/gooseneck spout | .30 | .20 |
| | Plate block of 12 | 5.00 | |
| | y. Se-tenant block of 4, CM909-12 | 1.50 | 1.00 |
| | FDC *(April 19, 1979)* | | 2.00 |
| | vy. Se-tenant block of 4, imperforate horizontally | 4250. | |

**1979. AMERICAN ARCHITECTURE ISSUE** the 1st of 4 se-tenant quartets on this subject designed by Walter D. Richards, commemorates successful early American architecture of enduring beauty, strength and usefulness. *Intaglio (Giori Press), perforated 11, multicolored.*

CM913 *Virginia Rotunda, designed by Thomas Jefferson.*

CM914 *Baltimore Cathedral, designed by Benjamin Latrobe.*

CM915 *Boston State House, designed by Charles Bulfinch.*

CM916 *Philadelphia Exchange, designed by William Strickland.*

**CM913**

| | | MNHVF | UseVF |
|---|---|---|---|
| **15¢** | University of Virginia Rotunda, tagged | .30 | .20 |
| | *(164,793,000)* | | |

**CM914**

| | | MNHVF | UseVF |
|---|---|---|---|
| **15¢** | Baltimore Cathedral, tagged | .30 | .20 |

**CM915**

| | | MNHVF | UseVF |
|---|---|---|---|
| **15¢** | Bostom State House, tagged | .30 | .20 |

**CM916**

| | | MNHVF | UseVF |
|---|---|---|---|
| **15¢** | Philadelphia Exchange, tagged | .30 | .20 |
| | Plate block of 4 | 2.50 | |
| | Se-tenant block of 4 CM913-16 | 1.50 | 1.00 |
| | FDC *(June 4, 1979)* | | 2.00 |

**1979. ENDANGERED FLORA ISSUE** portrays 4 of the more than 1,700 plant species in the United States that are seriously threatened with extinction. *Gravure (Andreotti Press), perforated 11, multicolored.*

CM917 *Persistent Trillium*

CM918 *Hawaiian Wild Broadbean*

CM919 *Contra Costa Wallflower*

CM920 *Antioch Dunes Evening Primrose*

| CM917 | | MNHVF | UseVF |
|---|---|---|---|
| 15¢ | Persistent Trillium, tagged *(163,055,000)* | .30 | .20 |

| CM918 | | MNHVF | UseVF |
|---|---|---|---|
| 15¢ | Hawaiian Wild Broadbeam, tagged | .30 | .20 |

| CM919 | | MNHVF | UseVF |
|---|---|---|---|
| 15¢ | Contra Costa wallflower, tagged | .30 | .20 |

| CM920 | | MNHVF | UseVF |
|---|---|---|---|
| 15¢ | Antioch Dunes Evening Primrose , tagged | .30 | .20 |
| | Plate block of 12 | 6.50 | |
| | FDC *(June 7, 1979)* | | 1.00 |
| | Horizontal gutter block of 4 | — | |
| | y.  Se-tenant block of 4 CM917-20 | 2.00 | 1.00 |
| | vy. Imperforate se-tenant block of 4 | 600. | |

**1979. SEEING EYE DOG ISSUE** commemorates the 50th anniversary of the 1st guide dog program in the United States, founded by Dorothy Harrison. *Gravure (Combination Press), perforated 11.*

CM921 *German Shepherd Leading Man.*

| CM921 | | MNHVF | UseVF |
|---|---|---|---|
| 15¢ | multicolored, tagged *(161,860,000)* | .30 | .20 |
| | Plate block of 20 | 9.00 | |
| | FDC *(June 15, 1979)* | | 1.00 |
| | v.  Imperforate pair | 425. | |
| | zo. Tagging omitted | 6.00 | |

**1979. SPECIAL OLYMPICS ISSUE** honors the international program of sports training, physical fitness and athletic competition for mentally retarded children and adults. *Gravure (Andreotti Press), perforated 11.*

CM922 *Child with Special Olympic Medal.*

| CM922 | | MNHVF | UseVF |
|---|---|---|---|
| 15¢ | multicolored, tagged *(165,775,000)* | .30 | .20 |
| | Plate block of 10 | 4.50 | |
| | FDC *(Aug. 9, 1979)* | | 1.00 |

**1979. SUMMER GAMES ISSUE** *Gravure, perforated 11, multicolored.*

| CM923 | | MNHVF | UseVF |
|---|---|---|---|
| 10¢ | multicolored, tagged *(67,195,000)* | .25 | .25 |
| | Plate block of 12 | 4.50 | |
| | FDC *(Sept. 5, 1979)* | | 1.00 |

**1979. JOHN PAUL JONES ISSUE** honors the naval hero of the American Revolution. On the 200th anniversary of his victory over the British in the 1779 battle between *Bonhomme Richard* and *HMS Serapis*. This stamp was the 1st to be printed privately under terms of a contract awarded by the U.S. Postal Service in 1978. *Gravure by J.W. Fergusson and Sons, Richmond, Va., with perforating, cutting and final processing by Americn Bank Note Co., New York, N.Y. perforated 11 x 12.*

CM924, 24B *John Paul Jones. Based on portrait by Charles Willson Peale.*

| CM924 | | MNHVF | UseVF |
|---|---|---|---|
| 15¢ | multicolored, tagged *(160,000,000, all perforation types)* | .30 | .20 |
| | Plate block of 10 | 4.50 | |
| | FDC *(Sept. 23, 1979)* | | 1.00 |
| | v.  Vertical pair, imperforate horizontally | 65.00 | |

*Imperforate errors are from printer's waste.*

| CM924A | | MNHVF | UseVF |
|---|---|---|---|
| 15¢ | multicolored, tagged | .75 | .25 |
| | Plate block of 10 | 8.50 | |
| | FDC *(Sept. 23, 1979)* | | 1.00 |
| | v.  Vertical pair, imperforate horizontally | 140. | |

| CM924B | | MNHVF | UseVF |
|---|---|---|---|
| 15¢ | multicolored, tagged | 2300. | 1000. |
| | v.  Vertical pair, imperforate horizontally | 175. | |

**1979. SUMMER GAMES ISSUE** *Gravure, perforated 11, multicolored.*

CM925 *Women Runners*

CM926 *Women Swimmers*

CM927 *Pair of Rowers*

Cm928 *Horse and Rider*

| CM925 | | MNHVF | UseVF |
|---|---|---|---|
| **15¢** | Women runners, tagged *(186,905,000)* | .25 | .20 |

| CM926 | | MNHVF | UseVF |
|---|---|---|---|
| **15¢** | Women swimmers, tagged | .25 | .20 |

| CM927 | | MNHVF | UseVF |
|---|---|---|---|
| **15¢** | Pair of rowers, tagged | .25 | .20 |

| CM928 | | MNHVF | UseVF |
|---|---|---|---|
| **15¢** | Horse and Rider, tagged | .25 | .20 |
| | Plate block of 12 | 6.50 | |
| | y. Se-tenant block of 4 CM925-28 | 1.50 | 1.10 |
| | FDC *(Sept. 28, 1979)* | | 2.00 |
| | vy. Se-tenant block of 4, imperorate | 1500. | |
| | v1. Vertical pair, imperforate (either) | 650. | |

**1979. WILL ROGERS ISSUE** 3rd stamp in the series, honors the American humorist on the 100th anniversary of his birth. (See also CM267.) *Gravure (Andreotti Press), perforated 11.*

CM929 *Will Rogers*

| CM929 | | MNHVF | UseVF |
|---|---|---|---|
| **15¢** | **multicolored,** tagged *(161,290,000)* | .30 | .20 |
| | Plate block of 12 | 6.00 | |
| | FDC *(Nov. 4, 1979)* | | 1.00 |
| | v. Imperforate pair | 200. | |

**1979. VIETNAM VETERANS ISSUE** pays tribute to the veterans of the war in Southeast Asia. *Gravure (Andreotti Press), perforated 11.*

CM930 *Vietnam Service Ribbon.*

| CM930 | | MNHVF | UseVF |
|---|---|---|---|
| **15¢** | **multicolored,** tagged *(172,740,000)* | .30 | .20 |
| | Plate block of 10 | 5.95 | |
| | FDC *(Nov. 11, 1979)* | | 1.00 |

**1980. W.C. FIELDS ISSUE** 4th stamp in the series honors the juggler, actor and comedian on the 100th anniversary of his birth. *Gravure, perforated 11.*

CM931 *W.C. Fields*

| CM931 | | MNHVF | UseVF |
|---|---|---|---|
| **15¢** | **multicolored,** tagged *(168,995,000)* | .30 | .20 |
| | Plate block of 12 | 6.00 | |
| | FDC *(Jan. 29, 1980)* | | 1.00 |
| | v. Imperforate pair | — | |

**1980. WINTER GAMES ISSUE** includes 4 commemoratives for events from the Winter Games, and honors the 13th Winter Games at Lake Placid, N.Y. *Gravure, perforated 11 x 10 1/2, multicolored.*

CM932, CM932A *Speed Skater*

CM933, CM933A *Ski Jumper*

CM934, CM934A *Downhill Skier*

CM935, CM935A *Hockey Goaltender*

| CM932 | | MNHVF | UseVF |
|---|---|---|---|
| **15¢** | Speedskater, tagged *(208,295,000)* (both perforation types) | .30 | .20 |

| CM933 | | MNHVF | UseVF |
|---|---|---|---|
| **15¢** | Ski jumper, tagged | .30 | .20 |

| CM934 | | MNHVF | UseVF |
|---|---|---|---|
| **15¢** | Downhill skier, tagged | .30 | .20 |

| CM935 | | MNHVF | UseVF |
|---|---|---|---|
| **15¢** | Hockey Goaltender, tagged | .30 | .20 |
| | Plate block of 12 | 6.50 | |
| | Se-tenant block of 4 CM932-35 | 1.50 | 1.10 |
| | FDC *(Feb. 1, 1980)* | | 2.00 |

1988 Winter Games, *perforated 11.*

| CM935A | | MNHVF | UseVF |
|---|---|---|---|
| **15¢** | Speed Skater, tagged | .80 | .75 |

| CM935B | | MNHVF | UseVF |
|---|---|---|---|
| **15¢** | Ski jumper, tagged | .80 | .75 |

| CM935C | | MNHVF | UseVF |
|---|---|---|---|
| **15¢** | Downhill skier, tagged | .80 | .75 |

| CM935D | | MNHVF | UseVF |
|---|---|---|---|
| **15¢** | Hockey goaltender, tagged | .80 | .75 |
| | Plate block of 12 | 14.00 | |
| | Se-tenant block of 4 CM935A- 935C | 4.00 | 4.00 |

## Black Heritage Series

**1980. BENJAMIN BANNEKER ISSUE** honors a pioneer American scientist and mathematician. Born free in 1731, he became both a noted astronomer and surveyor. *Gravure by J.W. Fergusson and Sons for American Bank Note Co., perforated 11.*

CM936 *Benjamin Banneker*

| CM936 | | MNHVF | UseVF |
|---|---|---|---|
| **15¢** | **multicolored,** tagged *(160,000,000)* | .30 | .20 |
| | Plate block of 12 | 5.50 | |
| | FDC *(Feb. 15, 1980)* | | 1.00 |
| | v. Horizontal pair, imperforate vertically | 50.00 | |
| | v1. Imperforate pair | 750. | |

*Imperforates with misregistered colors from printers' waste, and have been fraudulently perforated to simulate CM936v. Genuine examples of this error have colors correctly registered. Expert certification recommended.*

**1980. NATIONAL LETTER WRITING ISSUE** focuses attention on the importance of letter writing. Three sets of vertical pairs. *Gravure, perforated 11, multicolored.*

CM937-38 *"Letters Preserve Memories" and "P.S. Write Soon."*

CM939-40 *"Letters Lift Spirits" and "P.S. Write Soon."*

CM41-42 *"Letters Shape Opinions" and "P.S. Write Soon."*

| CM937 | | MNHVF | UseVF |
|---|---|---|---|
| 15¢ | "Letters Preserve Memories" *(232,134,000)* | .30 | .20 |

| CM938 | | MNHVF | UseVF |
|---|---|---|---|
| 15¢ | "Write Soon", tagged | .30 | .20 |

| CM939 | | MNHVF | UseVF |
|---|---|---|---|
| 15¢ | "Letters Lift Spirits", tagged | .30 | .20 |

| CM940 | | MNHVF | UseVF |
|---|---|---|---|
| 15¢ | "Write Soon", tagged | .30 | .20 |

| CM941 | | MNHVF | UseVF |
|---|---|---|---|
| 15¢ | "Letters Shape Opinions", tagged | .30 | .20 |

| CM942 | | MNHVF | UseVF |
|---|---|---|---|
| 15¢ | "Write Soon", tagged | .30 | .20 |
| | Plate block of 36 | 19.50 | |
| | Se-tenant vertical strip of 6 CM937-42 | 2.00 | |
| | FDC *(Feb. 25, 1980)* | | 2.00 |

**1980. FRANCES PERKINS ISSUE** honors the 1st woman to serve as a member of a U.S. presidential cabinet. Perkins served as Franklin Roosevelt's Secretary of Labor. *Intaglio, perforated 10 1/2 x 11.*

CM943 *Frances Perkins*

| CM943 | | MNHVF | UseVF |
|---|---|---|---|
| 15¢ | blue, tagged *(163,510,000)* | .30 | .20 |
| | Plate block of 4 | 1.95 | |
| | FDC *(April 10, 1980)* | | 1.00 |

**1980. EMILY BISSELL ISSUE** celebrates the crusader against tuberculosis who introduced Christmas seals to the United States. *Intaglio, perforated 11.*

CM945 *Emily Bissell*

| CM944 | | MNHVF | UseVF |
|---|---|---|---|
| 15¢ | black and red, tagged *(95,695,000)* | .30 | .20 |
| | Plate block of 4 | 1.80 | |
| | FDC *(May 31, 1980)* | | 1.00 |
| | v. Vertical pair, imperforate horizontally | 375. | |

**1980. HELEN KELLER AND ANNE SULLIVAN ISSUE** commemorates blind, deaf author and lecturer Helen Keller, and her teacher, Anne Sullivan. *Offset and Intaglio, perforated 11.*

CM945 *Helen Keller and Anne Sullivan.*

| CM945 | | MNHVF | UseVF |
|---|---|---|---|
| 15¢ | multicolored, tagged *(153,975,000)* | .30 | .20 |
| | Plate block of 4 | 1.80 | |
| | FDC *(June 27, 1980)* | | 1.00 |

**1980. VETERANS ADMINISTRATION ISSUE** marks the 50th anniversary of the Veterans Administration. *Gravure by J.W. Fergusson and Sons for American Bank Note Co., perforated 11.*

CM946 *Veterans Administration Emblem.*

| CM946 | | MNHVF | UseVF |
|---|---|---|---|
| 15¢ | red and dark blue, tagged *(160,000,000)* | .30 | .20 |
| | Plate block of 4 | 1.80 | |
| | FDC *(July 21, 1980)* | | 1.00 |
| | v. Horizontal pair, imperforate vertically | 475. | |

**1980. BERNARDO DE GALVEZ ISSUE** honors Gen. de Galvez, governor of Spanish Louisiana during the American Revolution, and a major contributor to the winning of the war. *Intaglio and offset, perforated 11.*

CM947 *Bernardo de Golvez from statue in Spanish Plaza, Mobile, AL.*

| CM947 | | MNHVF | UseVF |
|---|---|---|---|
| 15¢ | multicolored, tagged *(103,850,000)* | .30 | .20 |
| | Plate block of 4 | 1.80 | |
| | FDC *(July 23, 1980)* | | 1.00 |
| | v. Blue, brown, red & yellow omitted | 13.50 | |
| | v1. Red, brown & blue omitted | 7.50 | |

**1980. CORAL REEFS ISSUE** showcases corals found in the waters of the United States, its territories and possessions. *Gravure, perforated 11, multicolored.*

CM948 *Brain Coral, U.S. Virgin Islands.*

CM949 *Elkhorn Coral, Florida.*

CM950 *Chalice Coral, American Samoa.*

CM951 *Finger Coral, Hawaii.*

| **CM948** | | **MNHVF** | **UseVF** |
|---|---|---|---|
| 15¢ | Brain Coral, tagged *(204,715,000)* | .30 | .20 |

| **CM949** | | **MNHVF** | **UseVF** |
|---|---|---|---|
| 15¢ | Elkhorn Coral, tagged | .30 | .20 |

| **CM950** | | **MNHVF** | **UseVF** |
|---|---|---|---|
| 15¢ | Chalice Coral, tagged | .30 | .20 |

| **CM951** | | **MNHVF** | **UseVF** |
|---|---|---|---|
| 15¢ | Finger Coral, tagged | .30 | .20 |
| | Plate block of 12 | 6.00 | |
| | y. Se-tenant block of 4 CM948-51 | 1.50 | |
| | FDC *(Aug. 26, 1980)* | | 2.00 |
| | v. Se-tenant block of 4, imperforate | 1200. | |
| | v1. Se-tenant block of 4, imperforate between vertically | 3750. | |
| | v2. Se-tenant block of 4, imperforate vertically | 3000. | |

**1980. ORGANIZED LABOR ISSUE** honors the American labor movement, an integral part of the history of democracy and freedom in the United States. *Gravure, perforated 11.*

CM952 *Bald Eagle*

| **CM952** | | **MNHVF** | **UseVF** |
|---|---|---|---|
| 15¢ | **multicolored,** tagged *(166,545,000)* | .30 | .20 |
| | Plate block of 12 | 5.50 | |
| | FDC *(Sept. 1, 1980)* | | 1.00 |
| | v. Imperforate pair | 375. | |

## Literary Arts Series

**1980. EDITH WHARTON ISSUE** honors the Pulitzer Prize-winning author of *The Age of Innocence* and other novels, as well as short stories and poetry. *Intaglio, perforated 10 1/2 x 11.*

CM953 *Edith Wharton*

| **CM953** | | **MNHVF** | **UseVF** |
|---|---|---|---|
| 15¢ | **purple,** tagged *(163,310,000)* | .30 | .20 |
| | Plate block of 4 | 2.00 | |
| | FDC *(Sept. 5, 1980)* | | 1.00 |

**1980. EDUCATION IN AMERICA ISSUE** commemorates American education and calls attention to the newly established U.S. Education Department. *Gravure by J.W. Fergusson and Sons for the American Bank Note Co., perforated 11.*

CM954 Homage to the Square: Glow. *Acrylic printing by Josef Albers.*

| **CM954** | | **MNHVF** | **UseVF** |
|---|---|---|---|
| 15¢ | **multicolored,** tagged *(160,000,000)* | .30 | .20 |
| | Plate block of 6 | 3.50 | |
| | FDC *(Sept. 12, 1980)* | | 1.00 |
| | v. Vertical pair, imperforate vertically | 225. | |

## American Folk Art Series

**1980. PACIFIC NORTHWEST MASKS ISSUE** features 4 carved masks representing the craftsmanship of tribes in the Pacific Northwest coastal region. *Gravure, perforated 11.*

CM955 *Heiltsuk Bella Bella Mask*

CM956 *Chilkat Tlingit Mask*

CM957 *Tlingit Mask*

CM958 *Bella Coola Mask*

| **CM955** | | **MNHVF** | **UseVF** |
|---|---|---|---|
| 15¢ | Heiltsuk Bella Bella Mask, tagged *(152,404,000)* | .30 | .20 |

| **CM956** | | **MNHVF** | **UseVF** |
|---|---|---|---|
| 15¢ | Chikat Tlingit Mask, tagged | .30 | .20 |

| CM957 | | MNHVF | UseVF |
|---|---|---|---|
| 15¢ | Tlingit Mask, tagged | .30 | .20 |

| CM958 | | MNHVF | UseVF |
|---|---|---|---|
| 15¢ | Bella Coola Mask, tagged | .30 | .20 |
| | Plate block of 10 | 7.00 | |
| | y. Se-tenant block of 4 CM955-58 | 2.25 | 1.50 |
| | FDC (Sept. 24, 1980) | | 2.00 |

**1980. AMERICAN ARCHITECTURE ISSUE** second of four se-tenant quartets, representing 19th-century architecture of enduring beauty, strength and usefulness. *Intaglio (Giori Press), perforated 11.*

CM959 *Smithsonian Institution in Washington, D.C., designed by James Renwick.*

CM960 *Trinity Church in Boston, designed by Henry Hobson Richardson.*

CM961 *Pennsylvania Academy of Fine Arts in Philadelphia, designed by Frank Furness.*

CM962 *Lyndhurst at Tarry town, New York, designed by Alexander Jackson Davis*

| CM959 | | MNHVF | UseVF |
|---|---|---|---|
| 15¢ | Smithsonian Institution, tagged | .30 | .20 |
| | (152,720,000) | | |

| CM960 | | MNHVF | UseVF |
|---|---|---|---|
| 15¢ | Trinity Church, tagged | .30 | .20 |

| CM961 | | MNHVF | UseVF |
|---|---|---|---|
| 15¢ | Pennsylvania Academy of Art, tagged | .30 | .20 |

| CM962 | | MNHVF | UseVF |
|---|---|---|---|
| 15¢ | Lyndhurst, tagged | .30 | .20 |
| | Plate block of 4 | 2.50 | |
| | y. Se-tenant block of 4 CM959-62 | 2.25 | 1.50 |
| | FDC (Oct. 9, 1980) | | 2.00 |

**1981. EVERETT DIRKSEN ISSUE** commemorates a public servant first elected from Illinois to the U.S. House of Representatives in 1932, then to the U.S. Senate in 1950, where he served until his death in 1969. Dirksen was noted for his oratory and attention to legislative detail. *Intaglio, perforated 11.*

CM963 *Everett Dirksen*

| CM963 | | MNHVF | UseVF |
|---|---|---|---|
| 15¢ | gray, tagged (160,155,000) | .30 | .20 |
| | Plate block of 4 | 2.50 | |
| | FDC (Jan. 4, 1981) | | 1.00 |

**1981. WHITNEY MOORE YOUNG ISSUE** Black Heritage Series honors the noted civil rights leader who was executive director of the National Urban League at his death. Young was an author, former dean of the Atlanta School of Social Work and a recipient of the Medal of Freedom. *Gravure, perforated 11.*

CM964 *Whitney M. Young*

| CM964 | | MNHVF | UseVF |
|---|---|---|---|
| 15¢ | multicolored, tagged (159,505,000) | .30 | .20 |
| | Plate block of 4 | 1.80 | |
| | FDC (Jan. 30, 1981) | | 1.00 |

**1981. FLOWER ISSUE** features the designs of 4 flowers cultivated in the United States, reproduced from original paintings by Lowell Nesbitt in se-tenant form. *Gravure, perforated 11, multicolored.*

CM965 *Rose*

CM966 *Camellia*

CM967 *Dahlia*

CM968 *Lily*

| CM965 | | MNHVF | UseVF |
|---|---|---|---|
| 18¢ | Rose, tagged (210,633,000) | .30 | .20 |

| CM966 | | MNHVF | UseVF |
|---|---|---|---|
| 18¢ | Camellia, tagged | .30 | .20 |

| CM967 | | MNHVF | UseVF |
|---|---|---|---|
| 18¢ | Dahlia, tagged | .30 | .20 |

| CM968 | | MNHVF | UseVF |
|---|---|---|---|
| 18¢ | Lily, tagged | .30 | .20 |
| | Plate block of 4 | 2.60 | |
| | y. Se-tenant block of 4 CM965-68 | 2.00 | 1.50 |
| | FDC (April 23, 1981) | | 2.00 |

**1981. AMERICAN RED CROSS ISSUE** marks the centennial of the organization and honors the thousands of Red Cross volunteers who have given freely of their time to help people throughout the country. *Gravure, perforated 10 1/2 x 11.*

CM969 *Nurse and Baby.*

| CM969 | | MNHVF | UseVF |
|---|---|---|---|
| 18¢ | multicolored, tagged (165,175,000) | .30 | .20 |
| | Plate block of 4 | 2.80 | |
| | FDC (May 1, 1981) | | 1.00 |

**1981. SAVINGS AND LOAN ISSUE** marks the sesquicentennial of the 1st savings and loan organization in the United States, and emphasizes the importance of thrift and home ownership. *Gravure, perforated 11.*

CM970 *Savings and Loan Building Coin Bank.*

| CM970 | | MNHVF | UseVF |
|---|---|---|---|
| 18¢ | **multicolored,** tagged *(107,240,000)* | .30 | .20 |
| | Plate block of 4 | 2.50 | |
| | FDC *(May 8, 1981)* | | 1.00 |

**1981. SPACE ACHIEVEMENT ISSUE** salutes the U.S. accomplishments and technology in space research. *Gravure, perforated 11, multicolored.*

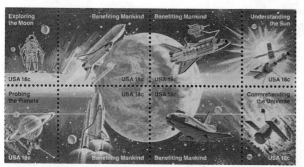

CM971 *Astronaut on Moon.* CM972 *Pioneer II and Saturn* CM973 *Skylab and Sun.* CM974 *Hubble Space Telescope.* CM975 *Space Shuttle In Orbit* CM976 *Space Shuttle with Arm Deployed.* CM977 *Space Shuttle at Launch.* CM978 *Space Shuttle prior to Landing*

| CM971 | | MNHVF | UseVF |
|---|---|---|---|
| 18¢ | Astronaut on Moon, tagged *(337,819,000)* | .30 | .20 |
| CM972 | | MNHVF | UseVF |
| 18¢ | Pioneer II and Saturn, tagged | .30 | .20 |
| CM973 | | MNHVF | UseVF |
| 18¢ | Skylab and Sun, tagged | .30 | .20 |
| CM974 | | MNHVF | UseVF |
| 18¢ | Hubble Space Telescope, tagged | .30 | .20 |
| CM975 | | MNHVF | UseVF |
| 18¢ | Space Shuttle in Orbit, tagged | .30 | .20 |
| CM976 | | MNHVF | UseVF |
| 18¢ | Space Shuttle with Arm Deployed, tagged | .30 | .20 |
| CM977 | | MNHVF | UseVF |
| 18¢ | Space Shuttle at launch, tagged | .30 | .20 |
| CM978 | | MNHVF | UseVF |
| 18¢ | Space Shuttle at landing, tagged | .30 | .20 |
| | Plate block of 8 | 6.00 | |
| | y. Se-tenant block of 8 CM971-78 | 5.00 | 4.00 |
| | FDC *(May 5, 1981)* | | |
| | v. Se-tenant block of 8, imperforate | 9500. | |

**1981. PROFESSIONAL MANAGEMENT ISSUE** marks the 100th anniversary of professional management education in the United States, and honored Joseph Wharton, founder of the Wharton School of Business. *Gravure, perforated 11.*

CM979 *Joseph Wharton*

| CM979 | | MNHVF | UseVF |
|---|---|---|---|
| 18¢ | **blue and black,** tagged *(99,420,000)* | .30 | .20 |
| | Plate block of 4 | 2.40 | |
| | FDC *(June 18, 1981)* | | 1.00 |

**1981. SAVE WILDLIFE HABITATS ISSUE** focuses on the necessity for the preservation of the natural environment of our native birds and mammals. *Gravure, perforated 11, multicolored.*

CM980 *Blue Heron*
CM981 *Badger*
CM982 *Grizzly Bear*
CM983 *Ruffed Grouse*

| CM980 | | MNHVF | UseVF |
|---|---|---|---|
| 18¢ | Blue Heron, tagged *(178,930,000)* | .30 | .20 |
| CM981 | | MNHVF | UseVF |
| 18¢ | Badger, tagged | .30 | .20 |
| CM982 | | MNHVF | UseVF |
| 18¢ | Grizzly Bear, tagged | .30 | .20 |
| CM983 | | MNHVF | UseVF |
| 18¢ | Ruffed Grouse, tagged | .30 | .20 |
| | Plate block of 4 | 2.50 | |
| | y. Se-tenant block of 4 CM980-83 | 2.25 | 1.50 |
| | FDC *(June 26, 1981)* | | 2.00 |

**1981. DISABLED PERSONS ISSUE** hails the UN's International Year of Disabled Persons, and the worldwide effort to promote education, prevention of impairments and rehabilitation. *Gravure, perforated 11.*

CM984 *Disabled Man Using Microscope.*

| CM984 | | MNHVF | UseVF |
|---|---|---|---|
| 18¢ | **multicolored,** tagged *(100,265,000)* | .30 | .20 |
| | Plate block of 4 | 2.40 | |
| | FDC *(June 29, 1981)* | | 1.00 |
| | v. Vertical pair, imperforate horizontally | 2750. | |

**1981. EDNA ST. VINCENT MILLAY ISSUE** honors the poet and author who received, among other awards, the Pulitzer Prize for Poetry in 1923. *Offset and Intaglio, perforated 11.*

CM985 *Edna St. Vincent Millay. From miniature painting by Glenora Case Richards.*

| CM985 | | MNHVF | UseVF |
|---|---|---|---|
| 18¢ | **multicolored,** tagged *(99,615,000)* | .30 | .25 |
| | Plate block of 4 | 2.40 | |
| | FDC *(July 10, 1981)* | | 1.00 |
| | v. Intaglio block (inscriptions) omitted | 525. | |

**1981. BEAT ALCOHOLISM ISSUE** conveys the message that alcoholism is a treatable disease. *Intaglio, perforated 11.*

 CM986 *Alcoholism - You Can Beat It !*

| CM986 | | MNHVF | UseVF |
|---|---|---|---|
| 18¢ | **blue and black,** tagged *(97,535,000)* | .65 | .20 |
| | Plate block of 20 | 40.00 | |
| | FDC *(Aug. 19, 1981)* | | 1.00 |
| | v. Imperforate pair | 425. | |
| | v1. Vertical pair, imperforate horizontally | 1850. | |

**1981. AMERICAN ARCHITECTURE ISSUE** the third of four quartets or se-tenant this subject, features examples of successful work by late 19th and early 20th century American architects. *Intaglio, perforated 11, multicolored.*

CM987 *New York University Library*

CM988 *Biltmore House*

CM989 *Palace of Arts*

CM990 *Bank Building*

| CM987 | | MNHVF | UseVF |
|---|---|---|---|
| 18¢ | N.Y. University Library, tagged *(167,308,000)* | .30 | .20 |

| CM988 | | MNHVF | UseVF |
|---|---|---|---|
| 18¢ | Biltmore House, tagged | .30 | .20 |

| CM989 | | MNHVF | UseVF |
|---|---|---|---|
| 18¢ | Palace of Arts, tagged | .30 | .20 |

| CM990 | | MNHVF | UseVF |
|---|---|---|---|
| 18¢ | Bank Building, tagged | .30 | .20 |
| | Plate block of 4 | 3.00 | |
| | y. Se-tenant block of 4 CM987-90 | 2.75 | |
| | FDC *(Aug. 28, 1981)* | | 2.00 |

**1981. BOBBY JONES ISSUE** inaugurated the American Sports Series honoring famous American athletes. In 1930 Bobby Jones became the only golfer in history to win the Grand Slam of Golf. *Intaglio, perforated 10 1/2 x 11.*

 CM991 *Bobby Jones*

| CM991 | | MNHVF | UseVF |
|---|---|---|---|
| 18¢ | **green,** tagged *(99,170,000)* | .30 | .20 |
| | Plate block of 4 | 7.75 | |
| | FDC *(Sept. 22, 1981)* | | 1.00 |

**1981. BABE ZAHARIAS ISSUE** Babe Zaharias, one of the greatest athletes of the first half of the 20th century, won virtually every women's golf title, both as an amateur and as a professional. *Intaglio, perforated 10 1/2 x 11.*

 CM992 *Babe Zaharias*

| CM992 | | MNHVF | UseVF |
|---|---|---|---|
| 18¢ | **light violet,** tagged *(101,625,000)* | .30 | .20 |
| | Plate block of 4 | 4.00 | |
| | FDC *(Sept. 22, 1981)* | | 1.00 |

**1981. FREDERIC REMINGTON ISSUE** honors the American painter, illustrator and sculptor. *Offset and intaglio, perforated 11.*

 CM993 *Frederic Remington's* Coming Through the Rye Sculpture.

| CM993 | | MNHVF | UseVF |
|---|---|---|---|
| 18¢ | **multicolored,** tagged *(101,155,000)* | .30 | .20 |
| | Plate block of 4 | 2.40 | |
| | FDC *(Oct. 9, 1981)* | | 1.00 |
| | v. Brown omitted | 550. | |
| | v1. Vertical pair, imperforate between | 250. | |

**1981. JAMES HOBAN ISSUE** honors the Irish-American architect of the White House. The Irish Postal Administration and the U.S. Postal Service jointly issued stamps identical in design except for country designation and denomination (Ireland 528). The issue was released by the USPS in 2 denominations: the lower to accommodate the then current first-class letter rate; and the higher to accommodate the rate that went into effect a little more than 2 weeks following the release of the stamps. *Gravure, perforated 11.*

 CM994-95 *James Hoban and White House*

| CM994 | | MNHVF | UseVF |
|---|---|---|---|
| 18¢ | **multicolored,** tagged *(101,200,000)* | .30 | .20 |
| | Plate block of 4 | 2.40 | |
| | FDC *(Oct. 13, 1981)* | | 1.00 |

| CM995 | | MNHVF | UseVF |
|---|---|---|---|
| 20¢ | **multicolored,** tagged *(167,360,000)* | .30 | .20 |
| | Plate block of 4 | 2.50 | |
| | FDC *(Oct. 13, 1981)* | | 1.00 |

**1981. BATTLE OF YORKTOWN AND THE VIRGINIA CAPES ISSUE** commemorates the bicentennial of the 2 battles. The Battle of the Virginia Capes of Sept. 6, 1781, prevented the British fleet from aiding British troops, a critical turning point in the Revolutionary War. The Battle of Yorktown, Oct. 16-19, ending with the surrender of the British, marked the end of the final battle of the war. *Intaglio and offset, perforated 11.*

CM996 *Map of Yorktown Capes*  CM997 *Map of Virginia Capes*

| CM996 | | MNHVF | UseVF |
|---|---|---|---|
| 18¢ | **multicolored,** tagged *(162,420,000)* | .30 | .20 |
| | v. Intaglio back (inscriptions) omitted | 175. | |
| | zo. Tagging omitted | — | |

| CM997 | | MNHVF | UseVF |
|---|---|---|---|
| 18¢ | **multicolored,** tagged | .30 | .20 |
| | Plate block of 4 | 3.00 | |
| | y. Se-tenant pair CM996-97 | | |
| | FDC *(Oct. 16, 1981)* | | 1.00 |
| | v. Intaglio black (inscriptions) omitted | 175. | |
| | vy. Se-tenant pair, Intaglio black, (inscriptions) omitted | 425. | |
| | zo. Tagging omitted | — | |
| | zoy. Se-tenant pair, tagging omitted | — | |

**1981. John Hanson Issue** commemorates the American Revolutionary leader elected 1s president of the Continental Congress Nov. 5, 1781. Elected "President of the United States in congress Assembled," and often considered the 1st president of the United States, Hanson was a congressional presiding officer and had none of the powers of the president under the Constitution. *Gravure, perforated 11.*

CM998 *John Hanson*

| CM998 | | MNHVF | UseVF |
|---|---|---|---|
| 20¢ | **multicolored,** tagged *(167,130,000)* | .30 | .20 |
| | FDC *(Nov. 5, 1981)* | | 1.00 |

**1981. Desert Plants Issue** depicts 4 plants that grow in the arid American West. 3 are in the cactus family, and the agave is a succulent plant of the amaryllis family. *Intaglio, perforated 11, multicolored.*

CM999 *Barrel cactus,* CM1000 *Agave,* CM1001 *Beavertail cactus,* CM1002 *Saguaro*

| CM999 | | MNHVF | UseVF |
|---|---|---|---|
| 20¢ | Barrel Cactus, tagged *(191,560,000)* | .35 | .20 |

| CM1000 | | MNHVF | UseVF |
|---|---|---|---|
| 20¢ | Agave, tagged | .35 | .20 |

| CM1001 | | MNHVF | UseVF |
|---|---|---|---|
| 20¢ | Beavertail Cactus, tagged | .35 | .20 |

| CM1002 | | MNHVF | UseVF |
|---|---|---|---|
| 20¢ | Saguaro, tagged | .35 | .20 |
| | Plate block of 4 | 3.25 | |
| | FDC *(Dec. 11, 1981)* | | 2.00 |
| | v. Vertical pair (CM1002), imperforate | 6500. | |
| | y. Se-tenant block of 4 C999-1002 | 2.00 | |
| | vy. Se-tenant block of 4, intaglio brown omitted | 8000. | |

**1982. Franklin D. Roosevelt Issue** commemorates the 100th birthday of the 32nd president of the United States, the only president to be elected 4 times, roosevelt was inaugurated in 1933 and served as president through the New Deal era and World War II until his death in April 1945. *Intaglio, perforated 11.*

CM1003 *Franklin D. Roosevelt*

| CM1003 | | MNHVF | UseVF |
|---|---|---|---|
| 20¢ | **blue,** tagged *(163,939,200)* | .35 | .20 |
| | Plate block of 4 | 2.50 | |
| | FDC *(Jan. 3, 1982)* | | 1.00 |

**1982. Love Issue** celebrates special occasions, such as birthdays, anniversaries, weddings and other special sentiments. Flowers form the letters "L": miniature poppy; "O": painted daisies and miniature pansies; "V": cornflower; "E": corabells. *Gravure, perforated 11.*

CM1004-04A

| CM1004 | | MNHVF | UseVF |
|---|---|---|---|
| 20¢ | **multicolored,** tagged | .35 | .20 |
| | Plate block of 4 | 3.25 | |

**1982. LOVE Issue** *Gravure, perforated 11 x 10 1/2.*

| CM1004A | | MNHVF | UseVF |
|---|---|---|---|
| 20¢ | **multicolored,** tagged | 1.00 | .25 |
| | Plate block of 4 | 5.50 | |
| | FDC *(Feb. 1, 1982)* | | 1.00 |
| | v. Blue omitted | 225. | |
| | v1. Imperforate pair | 275. | |

**1982. George Washington Issue** commemorates the 250th anniversary of his birth. *Gravure, perforated 11.*

CM1005 *George Washington*

| CM1005 | | MNHVF | UseVF |
|---|---|---|---|
| 20¢ | **multicolored,** tagged *(180,700,000)* | .35 | .20 |
| | Plate block of 4 | 2.75 | |
| | FDC *(Feb. 22, 1982)* | | 1.00 |

**1982. STATE BIRDS AND FLOWERS (PERFORATED 10 1/2 x 11)** commemorates the official birds and flowers of all 50 states . Arranged in alphabetical order in the pane, from top-left to bottom right, these stamps were designed by the father- and-son team of Arthur and Alan Singer. Arthur, the father, created the birds designs and Alan contributed the flower designs. *Gravure, perforated 10 1/2 x 11.*

| | | MNHVF | UseVF |
|---|---|---|---|
| CM1021 | | MNHVF | UseVF |
| 20¢ | Kansas, multicolored, tagged | 1.00 | .50 |
| CM1022 | | MNHVF | UseVF |
| 20¢ | Kentucky, multicolored, tagged | 1.00 | .50 |
| CM1023 | | MNHVF | UseVF |
| 20¢ | Louisiana, multicolored, tagged | 1.00 | .50 |

| | | MNHVF | UseVF | | | | MNHVF | UseVF |
|---|---|---|---|---|---|---|---|---|
| CM1006 | | MNHVF | UseVF | | CM1024 | | MNHVF | UseVF |
| 20¢ | Alabama, multicolored, tagged (666,950,000) | 1.00 | .50 | | 20¢ | Maine, multicolored, tagged | 1.00 | .50 |
| CM1007 | | MNHVF | UseVF | | CM1025 | | MNHVF | UseVF |
| 20¢ | Alaska, multicolored, tagged | 1.00 | .50 | | 20¢ | Maryland, multicolored, tagged | 1.00 | .50 |
| CM1008 | | MNHVF | UseVF | | CM1026 | | MNHVF | UseVF |
| 20¢ | Arizona, multicolored, tagged | 1.00 | .50 | | 20¢ | Massachusetts, multicolored, tagged | 1.00 | .50 |
| CM1009 | | MNHVF | UseVF | | CM1027 | | MNHVF | UseVF |
| 20¢ | Arkansas, multicolored, tagged | 1.00 | .50 | | 20¢ | Michigan, multicolored, tagged | 1.00 | .50 |
| CM1010 | | MNHVF | UseVF | | CM1028 | | MNHVF | UseVF |
| 20¢ | California, multicolored, tagged | 1.00 | .50 | | 20¢ | Minnesota, multicolored, tagged | 1.00 | .50 |
| CM1011 | | MNHVF | UseVF | | CM1029 | | MNHVF | UseVF |
| 20¢ | Colorado, multicolored, tagged | 1.00 | .50 | | 20¢ | Mississippi, multicolored, tagged | 1.00 | .50 |
| CM1012 | | MNHVF | UseVF | | CM1030 | | MNHVF | UseVF |
| 20¢ | Connecticut, multicolored, tagged | 1.00 | .50 | | 20¢ | Missouri, multicolored, tagged | 1.00 | .50 |
| CM1013 | | MNHVF | UseVF | | CM1031 | | MNHVF | UseVF |
| 20¢ | Delaware, multicolored, tagged | 1.00 | .50 | | 20¢ | Montana, multicolored, tagged | 1.00 | .50 |
| CM1014 | | MNHVF | UseVF | | CM1032 | | MNHVF | UseVF |
| 20¢ | Florida, multicolored, tagged | 1.00 | .50 | | 20¢ | Nebraska, multicolored, tagged | 1.00 | .50 |
| CM1015 | | MNHVF | UseVF | | CM1033 | | MNHVF | UseVF |
| 20¢ | Georgia, multicolored, tagged | 1.00 | .50 | | 20¢ | Nevada, multicolored, tagged | 1.00 | .50 |
| CM1016 | | MNHVF | UseVF | | CM1034 | | MNHVF | UseVF |
| 20¢ | Hawaii, multicolored, tagged | 1.00 | .50 | | 20¢ | New Hampshire multicolored, tagged | 1.00 | .50 |
| CM1017 | | MNHVF | UseVF | | CM1035 | | MNHVF | UseVF |
| 20¢ | Idaho, multicolored, tagged | 1.00 | .50 | | 20¢ | New Jersey, multicolored, tagged | 1.00 | .50 |
| CM1018 | | MNHVF | UseVF | | CM1036 | | MNHVF | UseVF |
| 20¢ | Illinois, multicolored, multicolored, tagged | 1.00 | .50 | | 20¢ | New Mexico, multicolored, tagged | 1.00 | .50 |
| CM1019 | | MNHVF | UseVF | | CM1037 | | MNHVF | UseVF |
| 20¢ | Indiana, multicolored, tagged | 1.00 | .50 | | 20¢ | New York multicolored, tagged | 1.00 | .50 |
| CM1020 | | MNHVF | UseVF | | CM1038 | | MNHVF | UseVF |
| 20¢ | Iowa, multicolored, tagged | 1.00 | .50 | | 20¢ | North Carolina, multicolored, tagged | 1.00 | .50 |

| | | MNHVF | UseVF | | | | MNHVF | UseVF |
|---|---|---|---|---|---|---|---|---|
| **CM1039** | | | | | **CM1055AM** | | | |
| 20¢ | North Dakota, **multicolored,** tagged | 1.00 | .50 | | 20¢ | Illinois, **multicolored,** tagged | 1.00 | .50 |
| **CM1040** | | | | | **CM1055AN** | | | |
| 20¢ | Ohio, **multicolored,** tagged | 1.00 | .50 | | 20¢ | Indiana, **multicolored,** tagged | 1.00 | .50 |
| **CM1041** | | | | | **CM1055AO** | | | |
| 20¢ | Oklahoma, **multicolored,** tagged | 1.00 | .50 | | 20¢ | Iowa, **multicolored,** tagged | 1.00 | .50 |
| **CM1042** | | | | | **CM1055AP** | | | |
| 20¢ | Oregon, **multicolored,** tagged | 1.00 | .50 | | 20¢ | Kansas, **multicolored,** tagged | 1.00 | .50 |
| **CM1043** | | | | | **CM1055AQ** | | | |
| 20¢ | Pennsylvania, **multicolored,** tagged | 1.00 | .50 | | 20¢ | Kentucky, **multicolored,** tagged | 1.00 | .50 |
| **CM1044** | | | | | **CM1055AR** | | | |
| 20¢ | Rhode Island, **multicolored,** tagged | 1.00 | .50 | | 20¢ | Louisiana, **multicolored,** tagged | 1.00 | .50 |
| **CM1045** | | | | | **CM1055AS** | | | |
| 20¢ | Rhode Island, **multicolored,** tagged | 1.00 | .50 | | 20¢ | Maine, **multicolored,** tagged | 1.00 | .50 |
| **CM1046** | | | | | **CM1055AT** | | | |
| 20¢ | South Dakota, **multicolored,** tagged | 1.00 | .50 | | 20¢ | Maryland, **multicolored,** tagged | 1.00 | .50 |
| **CM1047** | | | | | **CM1055AU** | | | |
| 20¢ | Tennessee, **multicolored,** tagged | 1.00 | .50 | | 20¢ | Massachusetts, **multicolored,** tagged | 1.00 | .50 |
| **CM1048** | | | | | **CM1055AV** | | | |
| 20¢ | Texas **multicolored,** tagged | 1.00 | .50 | | 20¢ | Michigan, **multicolored,** tagged | 1.00 | .50 |
| **CM1049** | | | | | **CM1055AW** | | | |
| 20¢ | Utah, **multicolored,** tagged | 1.00 | .50 | | 20¢ | Minnesota, **multicolored,** tagged | 1.00 | .50 |
| **CM1050** | | | | | **CM1055AX** | | | |
| 20¢ | Vermont, **multicolored,** tagged | 1.00 | .50 | | 20¢ | Mississippi, **multicolored,** tagged | 1.00 | .50 |
| **CM1051** | | | | | **CM1055AY** | | | |
| 20¢ | Virginia, **multicolored,** tagged | 1.00 | .50 | | 20¢ | Missouri, **multicolored,** tagged | 1.00 | .50 |
| **CM1052** | | | | | **CM1055AZ** | | | |
| 20¢ | Washington, **multicolored,** tagged | 1.00 | .50 | | 20¢ | Montana, **multicolored,** tagged | 1.00 | .50 |
| **CM1053** | | | | | **CM1055BA** | | | |
| 20¢ | West Virginia, **multicolored,** tagged | 1.00 | .50 | | 20¢ | Nebraska, **multicolored,** tagged | 1.00 | .50 |
| **CM1054** | | | | | **CM1055BB** | | | |
| 20¢ | Wisconsin, **multicolored,** tagged | 1.00 | .50 | | 20¢ | Nevada, **multicolored,** tagged | 1.00 | .50 |
| **CM1055** | | | | | **CM1055BC** | | | |
| 20¢ | Wyoming, **multicolored,** tagged | 1.00 | .50 | | 20¢ | New Hampshire, **multicolored,** tagged | 1.00 | .50 |
| | y. Se-tenant pane of 50 | 45.00 | | | **CM1055BD** | | | |
| | FDC *(April 14, 1982)* | | 1.00 | | 20¢ | New Jersey, **multicolored,** tagged | 1.00 | .50 |
| | FDC, pane of 50 | | 15.00 | | **CM1055BE** | | | |
| | v. Imperforate pane of 50 | 23000. | | | 20¢ | New Mexico, **multicolored,** tagged | 1.00 | .50 |

*Because most plate block collectors consider that a plate block contains at lease 1 copy of each stamp in the issue, a plate block of the State Birds and Flowers Issue is considered to be a full pane of 50 stamps.*

### 1982. STATE BIRDS AND FLOWERS ISSUE (PERFORATED 11)

| | | MNHVF | UseVF | | | | MNHVF | UseVF |
|---|---|---|---|---|---|---|---|---|
| **CM1055AA** | | | | | **CM1055BF** | | | |
| 20¢ | Wyoming, **multicolored,** tagged | 1.00 | .50 | | 20¢ | New York, **multicolored,** tagged | 1.00 | .50 |
| | y. Se-tenant pane of 50 | 47.50 | | | **CM1055BG** | | | |
| **CM1055AB** | | | | | 20¢ | North Carolina, **multicolored,** tagged | 1.00 | .50 |
| 20¢ | Alaska, **multicolored,** tagged | 1.00 | .50 | | **CM1055BH** | | | |
| **CM1055AC** | | | | | 20¢ | North Dakota, **multicolored,** tagged | 1.00 | .50 |
| 20¢ | Arizona, **multicolored,** tagged | 1.00 | .50 | | **CM1055BI** | | | |
| **CM1055AD** | | | | | 20¢ | Ohio, **multicolored,** tagged | 1.00 | .50 |
| 20¢ | Arkansas, **multicolored,** tagged | 1.00 | .50 | | **CM1055BJ** | | | |
| **CM1055AE** | | | | | 20¢ | Oklahoma, **multicolored,** tagged | 1.00 | .50 |
| 20¢ | California, **multicolored,** tagged | 1.00 | .50 | | **CM1055BK** | | | |
| **CM1055AF** | | | | | 20¢ | Oregon, **multicolored,** tagged | 1.00 | .50 |
| 20¢ | Colorado, **multicolored,** tagged | 1.00 | .50 | | **CM1055BL** | | | |
| **CM1055AG** | | | | | 20¢ | Pennsylvania, **multicolored,** tagged | 1.00 | .50 |
| 20¢ | Connecticut, **multicolored,** tagged | 1.00 | .50 | | **CM1055BM** | | | |
| **CM1055AH** | | | | | 20¢ | Rhode Island, **multicolored,** tagged | 1.00 | .50 |
| 20¢ | Delaware, **multicolored,** tagged | 1.00 | .50 | | **CM1055BN** | | | |
| **CM1055AI** | | | | | 20¢ | South Carolina, **multicolored,** tagged | 1.00 | .50 |
| 20¢ | Florida, **multicolored,** tagged | 1.00 | .50 | | **CM1055BO** | | | |
| **CM1055AJ** | | | | | 20¢ | South Dakota, **multicolored,** tagged | 1.00 | .50 |
| 20¢ | Georgia, **multicolored,** tagged | 1.00 | .50 | | **CM1055BP** | | | |
| **CM1055AK** | | | | | 20¢ | Tennessee, **multicolored,** tagged | 1.00 | .50 |
| 20¢ | Hawaii, **multicolored,** tagged | 1.00 | .50 | | **CM1055BQ** | | | |
| **CM1055AL** | | | | | 20¢ | Texas, **multicolored,** tagged | 1.00 | .50 |
| 20¢ | Idaho, **multicolored,** tagged | 1.00 | .50 | | **CM1055BR** | | | |
| | | | | | 20¢ | Utah, **multicolored,** tagged | 1.00 | .50 |
| | | | | | **CM1055BS** | | | |
| | | | | | 20¢ | Vermont, **multicolored,** tagged | 1.00 | .50 |

| CM1055BT | | MNHVF | UseVF |
|---|---|---|---|
| 20¢ | **Virginia, multicolored,** tagged | 1.00 | .50 |

| CM1055BU | | MNHVF | UseVF |
|---|---|---|---|
| 20¢ | **Washington, multicolored,** tagged | 1.00 | .50 |

| CM1055BV | | MNHVF | UseVF |
|---|---|---|---|
| 20¢ | **West Virginia, multicolored,** tagged | 1.00 | .50 |

| CM1055BW | | MNHVF | UseVF |
|---|---|---|---|
| 20¢ | **Wisconsin, multicolored,** tagged | 1.00 | .50 |

| CM1055BX | | MNHVF | UseVF |
|---|---|---|---|
| 20¢ | **Alabama, multicolored,** tagged | 1.00 | .50 |

**1982. NETHERLANDS ISSUE** marks the 200th anniversary of Netherlands' diplomatic recognition of the United States. The Netherlands released 2 stamps at the same time as this one (Netherlands 1365-66). *Gravure, perforated 11.*

CM1056 *200th Anniversary of Netherlands Diplomatic Recognition of the United States.*

| CM1056 | | MNHVF | UseVF |
|---|---|---|---|
| 20¢ | **orange, red, blue and dark gray,** tagged *(109,245,000)* | .35 | .20 |
| | Plate block of 6 | 13.95 | |
| | FDC *(April 20, 1982)* | | 1.00 |
| | v. Imperforate pair | 300. | |

**1982. LIBRARY OF CONGRESS ISSUE** salutes the library for the services and information it provides to Congress and many other organizations and researchers who use it every year. *Intaglio, perforated 11.*

CM1057 *Library of Congress*

| CM1057 | | MNHVF | UseVF |
|---|---|---|---|
| 20¢ | **black and red,** tagged *(112,535,000)* | .35 | .20 |
| | Plate block of 4 | 2.50 | |
| | FDC *(April 21, 1982)* | | 1.00 |

**1982. KNOXVILLE WORLD'S FAIR ISSUE** commemorates the Knoxville, Tenn. World's Fair, the theme of which was energy. 4 stamps depict solar, fossil, nuclear and synthetic fuel energy sources. *Gravure, perforated 11, multicolored.*

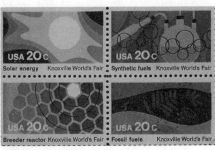

CM1058 *Solar Energy*

CM1059 *Synthetic Fuels*

CM1060 *Reactor*

CM1061 *Fossil Fuels*

| CM1058 | | MNHVF | UseVF |
|---|---|---|---|
| 20¢ | Solar Energy, tagged *(124,640,000)* | .35 | .20 |

| CM1059 | | MNHVF | UseVF |
|---|---|---|---|
| 20¢ | Synthetic Fuels, tagged | .35 | .20 |

| CM1060 | | MNHVF | UseVF |
|---|---|---|---|
| 20¢ | Reactor, tagged | .35 | .20 |

| CM1061 | | MNHVF | UseVF |
|---|---|---|---|
| 20¢ | Fossil Fuels, tagged | .35 | .20 |
| | Plate block of 4 | 3.25 | |
| | y. Se-tenant block of 4 CM1058-61 | 2.00 | 1.50 |
| | FDC *(April 29, 1982),* Block of 4 | | 2.00 |

**1982. HORATIO ALGER ISSUE** honors the 150th birthday of Alger, a best-selling author of books for boys, with more than 100 of his works published during his lifetime. Alger's *Phil the Fiddler,* or *The Story of a Young Street Musician* is credited with bringing public and legislative attention to forced child labor. *Intaglio, perforated 11.*

CM1062 *Horatio Alger. Frontispiece from Ragged Dick series by Alger.*

| CM1062 | | MNHVF | UseVF |
|---|---|---|---|
| 20¢ | **red and black on tan paper,** tagged *(107,605,000)* | .35 | .20 |
| | Plate block of 4 | 2.50 | |
| | FDC *(April 30, 1982)* | | 1.00 |
| | v. Red and black omitted | — | |

**1982. AGING TOGETHER ISSUE** honors the elderly and heightens awareness that older persons enrich society with their wealth of experience and creative energy. *Intaglio, perforated 11.*

CM1063 *Aging Together*

| CM1063 | | MNHVF | UseVF |
|---|---|---|---|
| 20¢ | **brown,** tagged *(173,160,000)* | .35 | .20 |
| | Plate block of 4 | 2.50 | |
| | FDC *(May 21, 1982)* | | 1.00 |

**1982. BARRYMORE FAMILY ISSUE** honors the distinguished American theatrical family, featur ing likenesses of Ethel, John, and Lionel Barrymore. Perform ing Artists series. *Gravure, perforated 11.*

CM1064 *Ethel, John and Lionel Barrymore*

| CM1064 | | MNHVF | UseVF |
|---|---|---|---|
| 20¢ | **multicolored,** tagged *(107,285,000)* | .35 | .20 |
| | Plate block of 4 | 2.50 | |
| | FDC *(June 8, 1982)* | | 1.00 |

**1982. MARY WALKER ISSUE** commemorates the Civil War surgeon who gave care and treatme nt to the sick and the wounded. *Gravure, perforated 11.*

CM1065 *Dr. Mary Walker*

| CM1065 | | MNHVF | UseVF |
|---|---|---|---|
| 20¢ | **multicolored,** tagged *(109,040,000)* | .35 | .20 |
| | Plate block of 4 | 3.00 | |
| | FDC *(June 10, 1982)* | | 1.00 |

**1982. INTERNATIONAL PEACE GARDEN ISSUE** recognizes the 50th anniversary of the garden shared by Dunseith, N.D., and Boissevain, Manitoba. A symbol of more than 150 years of peace and friendship between the United States and Canada. *Offset and intaglio, perforated 11.*

CM1066 *Maple Leaf and Rose*

| CM1066 | | MNHVF | UseVF |
|---|---|---|---|
| 20¢ | **multicolored,** tagged *(183,270,000)* | .35 | .20 |
| | Plate block of 4 | 2.50 | |
| | FDC *(June 30, 1982)* | | 1.00 |
| | v. Black & intaglio green omitted | 275. | |

**1982. AMERICA'S LIBRARIES ISSUE** honors the contribution of libraries to the growth and development of the United States. *Intaglio, perforated 11*

CM1067 *America's Libraries*

| CM1067 | | MNHVF | UseVF |
|---|---|---|---|
| 20¢ | **red and black,** tagged *(169,495,000)* | .35 | .20 |
| | Plate block of 4 | 2.50 | |
| | FDC *(July 13, 1982)* | | 1.00 |
| | v. Vertical pair, imperforate horizontally | 325. | |
| | zo. Tagging omitted | 6.00 | |

**1982. JACKIE ROBINSON ISSUE** honors the athlete who broke major league baseball's racial barrier in 1947. Hired to play for the Dodgers' top farm team and then for the Dodgers in 1947, he withstood racial hostility to become one of the most exciting baseball players of his era. Black Heritage series. *Gravure, perforated 10 1/2 x 11.*

CM1068 *Jackie Robinson*

| CM1068 | | MNHVF | UseVF |
|---|---|---|---|
| 20¢ | **multicolored,** tagged *(164,235,000)* | 2.50 | .20 |
| | Plate block of 4 | 11.00 | |
| | FDC *(Aug. 2, 1982)* | | 2.00 |

**1982. TOURO SYNAGOGUE ISSUE** honors the oldest existing synagogue in the United States. Designated a National Historical Site in 1946, the synagogue was built principally by Sephardic Jews from Spain and Portugal who fled the Inquisition and found religious freedom in the Rhode Island colony. *Gravure and intaglio, perforated 11.*

CM1069 *Touro Synagogue*

| CM1069 | | MNHVF | UseVF |
|---|---|---|---|
| 20¢ | **multicolored,** tagged *(110,130,000)* | .35 | .20 |
| | Plate block of 20 | 13.75 | |
| | FDC *(Aug. 22, 1982)* | | 1.00 |
| | v. Imperforate pair | 2750. | |

**1982. WOLF TRAP FARM ISSUE** salutes the Wolf Trap Farm Park for the Performing Arts, a theater in wooded surroundings and part of the National Park System since 1971. (See also CM679.) *Gravure, perforated 11.*

CM1070 *Wolf Trap Farm Park*

| CM1070 | | MNHVF | UseVF |
|---|---|---|---|
| 20¢ | **multicolored,** tagged *(110,995,000)* | .35 | .20 |
| | Plate block of 4 | 2.50 | |
| | FDC *(Sept. 1, 1982)* | | 1.00 |

**1982. AMERICAN ARCHITECTURE ISSUE** the 4th and final installment in the series, which honors key structures and architects of the 20th century. *Intaglio, perforated 11.*

CM1071 *Fallingwater, Mill Run, Pa., designed by Frank Lloyd Wright.*
CM1072 *Illimois Institute of Technology, Chicago, Ill., designed by Ludwig Mies van der Rohe.* CM1073 *Gropius House, Lincoln, Mass., designed by Walter Gropius in collaboration with Marcel Breuer.* CM1074 *Dulles International Airport, Washington, D.C. designed by Eero Saarinen.*

| CM1071 | | MNHVF | UseVF |
|---|---|---|---|
| 20¢ | Falling Water, tagged *(165,340,000)* | .35 | .20 |

| CM1072 | | MNHVF | UseVF |
|---|---|---|---|
| 20¢ | Illinois Intitute of Technology, tagged | .35 | .20 |

| CM1073 | | MNHVF | UseVF |
|---|---|---|---|
| 20¢ | Gropius House, tagged | .35 | .20 |

| CM1074 | | MNHVF | UseVF |
|---|---|---|---|
| 20¢ | Washington International Airport, tagged | .35 | .20 |
| | Plate block of 4 | 4.25 | |
| | y. Se-tenant block of 4 CM1071-74 | 2.00 | |
| | FDC *(Sept. 30, 1982)* | | 2.00 |

**1982. FRANCIS OF ASSISI ISSUE** honors the 800th birthday of the man whose compassion earned him reverence transcending religious bounds. He formed the Franciscan Order in 1209, the members of which still minister to the sick and needy. *Gravure by J.W. Fergusson and Sons for American Bank Note Co., perforated 11.*

CM1075 *Francis of Assisi*

| CM1075 | | MNHVF | UseVF |
|---|---|---|---|
| 20¢ | **multicolored,** tagged *(174,180,000)* | .35 | .20 |
| | Plate block of 4 | 2.75 | |
| | FDC *(Oct. 7, 1982)* | | 1.00 |

**1982. PONCE DE LEON ISSUE** honors the Spaniard who explored Puerto Rico in 1508-09 and Florida in 1513. *Gravure (Combination Press), perforated 11.*

CM1076 *Ponce de Leon*

| CM1076 | | MNHVF | UseVF |
|---|---|---|---|
| 20¢ | **multicolored,** tagged *(110,261,000)* | .35 | .20 |
| | Plate block of 6 | 16.00 | |
| | FDC *(Oct. 12, 1982)* | | 1.00 |
| | v. Imperforate pair | 500. | |
| | v1. Vertical pair, imperforate between | — | |

**1983. SCIENCE AND INDUSTRY ISSUE** salutes their contributions to the growth and development of the United States. *Offset and intaglio, perforated 11.*

CM1077 *Science and Industry*

| CM1077 | | MNHVF | UseVF |
|---|---|---|---|
| 20¢ | **multicolored,** tagged *(118,555,000)* | .35 | .20 |
| | Plate block of 4 | 2.50 | |
| | FDC *(Jan. 19, 1983)* | | 1.00 |
| | a. Intaglio black omitted | 1400. | |

**1983. SWEDEN ISSUE** marks the 200th anniversary of the signing of the Treaty of Amity and Commerce between Sweden and the United States. A stamp of similar design was issued simultaneously by Sweden (Sweden 1247). *Intaglio, perforated 11.*

CM1078 *Benjamin Franklin and Treaty Seal*

| CM1078 | | MNHVF | UseVF |
|---|---|---|---|
| 20¢ | **multicolored,** tagged *(118,225,000)* | .30 | .20 |
| | Plate block of 4 | 2.50 | |
| | FDC *(March 24, 1983)* | | 1.00 |

**1983. BALLOONING ISSUE** honors the sport of hot air balloons. Balloons were invented in June 1783 by 2 brothers, Joseph and Jacques Montgolfier, in France. Used for surveillance and scientific research over the years. they are today enjoyed by thousands of recreational enthusiasts. *Gravure, perforated 11.*

CM1079 *Intrepid 1861* CM1080 *Hot air balloon* CM1081 *Hot air ballooning* CM1082 *Explorer II, of 1935*

| CM1079 | | MNHVF | UseVF |
|---|---|---|---|
| 20¢ | Intrepid, tagged *(226,128,000)* | .35 | .20 |
| **CM1080** | | **MNHVF** | **UseVF** |
| 20¢ | Hot Air Baloon, tagged | .35 | .20 |
| **CM1081** | | **MNHVF** | **UseVF** |
| 20¢ | Hot Air Balooning, tagged | .35 | .20 |
| **CM1082** | | **MNHVF** | **UseVF** |
| 20¢ | Explorer II, tagged | .35 | .20 |
| | Plate block of 4 | 3.00 | |
| | y. Se-tenant block of 4 CM1079-82 | 2.00 | |
| | FDC *(March 31, 1983)*, any single | | 2.00 |
| | vy. Se-tenant block of 4, imperforate | 5500. | |

**1983. CIVILIAN CONSERVATION CORPS ISSUE** honors the 50th anniversary of the Great Depression programs , which recruited thousands of unemployed young men to develop and conserve the nation's natural resources. *Gravure, perforated 11.*

CM1083 *Civilian Conservation Corps*

| CM1083 | | MNHVF | UseVF |
|---|---|---|---|
| 20¢ | **multicolored,** tagged *(114,290,000)* | .35 | .20 |
| | Plate block of 4 | 2.50 | |
| | FDC *(April 5, 1983)* | | 1.00 |
| | v. Imperforate pair | 2750. | |

**1983. JOSEPH PRIESTLEY ISSUE** commemorates the clergyman and chemist (1733-1804) who discovered oxygen. *Gravure, perforated 11.*

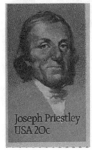

CM1084 *Joseph Priestley*

| CM1084 | | MNHVF | UseVF |
|---|---|---|---|
| 20¢ | **multicolored,** tagged *(165,000,000)* | .35 | .20 |
| | Plate block of 4 | 3.00 | |

**1983. VOLUNTEER ISSUE** recognizes the contribution volunteers have made to the development of the United States. *Intaglio, perforated 11.*

CM1085 *Helping Hand*

**CM1085**

| | | MNHVF | UseVF |
|---|---|---|---|
| 20¢ | **red and black,** tagged *(120,430,000)* | .35 | .20 |
| | Plate block of 20 | 13.95 | |
| | FDC *(April 20, 1983)* | | 1.00 |
| | v. Imperforate pair | 800. | |

**1983. GERMAN CONCORD ISSUE** honors the 300th anniversary of the arrival of the 1st German immigrants to the United States. A stamp of similar design was issued on May 5th, 6 days after the U.S. issue by West Germany (2363). *Intaglio, perforated 11.*

CM1086 *Concord 1683, German Immigration Tricentenn ial.*

**CM1086**

| | | MNHVF | UseVF |
|---|---|---|---|
| 20¢ | **brown,** tagged *(117,025,000)* | .35 | .20 |
| | Plate block of 4 | 2.50 | |
| | FDC *(April 29, 1983)* | | 1.00 |

**1983. PHYSICAL FITNESS ISSUE** salutes physical fitness activities for maintaining good physical health. *Gravure (Combination Press), perforated 11.*

CM1087 *Physical Fitness*

**CM1087**

| | | MNHVF | UseVF |
|---|---|---|---|
| 20¢ | **multicolored,** tagged *(111,775,000)* | .35 | .20 |
| | Plate block of 20 | 13.95 | |
| | FDC *(May 14, 1983)* | | 1.00 |

**1983. BROOKLYN BRIDGE ISSUE** honors the 100th anniversary of the completion of the bridge, created by 19-century civil engineer John A. Roebling, and his son Washington. It opened on May 24, 1883. *Intaglio, perforated 11.*

CM1088 *Brooklyn Bridge*

**CM1088**

| | | MNHVF | UseVF |
|---|---|---|---|
| 20¢ | **blue,** tagged *(181,700,000)* | .35 | .20 |
| | Plate block of 4 | 2.50 | |
| | FDC *(May 17, 1983)* | | 1.00 |
| | zo. Tagging omitted | | |

**1983. TENNESSEE VALLEY AUTHORITY ISSUE** marks the 50th anniversary of its establishment, providing flood control through a system of dams and locks, developing the natural resources of the area and creating new industry. *Gravure and intaglio (Combination Press), perforated 11.*

CM1089 *Norris Hydroelectric Dam*

**CM1089**

| | | MNHVF | UseVF |
|---|---|---|---|
| 20¢ | **multicolored,** tagged *(114,250,000)* | .35 | .20 |
| | Plate block of 20 | 13.95 | |
| | FDC *(May 18, 1983)* | | 1.00 |

**1983. MEDAL OF HONOR ISSUE** salutes the United States highest military award and all those who have been awarded the medal. It is awarded for "courage above and beyond the call of duty." *Offset and intaglio, perforated 11.*

CM1090 *Medal of Honor*

**CM1090**

| | | MNHVF | UseVF |
|---|---|---|---|
| 20¢ | **multicolored,** tagged *(108,820,000)* | .35 | .20 |
| | Plate block of 4 | 3.00 | |
| | FDC *(June 7, 1983)* | | 1.00 |
| | v. Red omitted | 325. | |

**1983. SCOTT JOPLIN ISSUE** honors the ragtime composer who successfully combined the charm of late Victorian music and the lively qualities of pioneer American folk song and dance. *Gravure, perforated 11.*

CM1091 *Scott Joplin*

**CM1091**

| | | MNHVF | UseVF |
|---|---|---|---|
| 20¢ | **multicolored,** tagged *(115,200,000)* | .35 | .20 |
| | Plate block of 4 | 3.00 | |
| | FDC *(June 9, 1983)* | | 1.00 |
| | v. Imperforate pair | 550. | |

## American Sports Series

**1983. BABE RUTH ISSUE** commemorates the great baseball player and Hall of Fame member George Herman Ruth (1895-1948). *Intaglio, perforated 10 1/2 x 11.*

CM1092 *George Herman "Babe" Ruth*

**CM1092**

| | | MNHVF | UseVF |
|---|---|---|---|
| 20¢ | **blue,** tagged *(184,950,000)* | .35 | .20 |
| | Plate block of 4 | 9.75 | |
| | FDC *(July 6, 1983)* | | 1.00 |

**1983. NATHANIEL HAWTHORNE ISSUE** honors the American author of the novel, *The House of Seven Gables.* A master at writing tales, Hawthorne was one of the 1st American writers who built his stories around the New England of his forefathers. *Gravure, perforated 11.*

 CM1093 *Nathaniel Hawthorne*

**CM1093**

| | | MNHVF | UseVF |
|---|---|---|---|
| 20¢ | **multicolored,** tagged *(110,925,000)* | .35 | .20 |
| | Plate block of 4 | 2.50 | |
| | FDC *(July 8, 1983)* | | 1.00 |

**1983. 1984 OLYMPIC ISSUE** was the 1st of an array of postal paper designed by Robert Peak, commemorating the Summer Games in Los Angeles and the Winter Games in Sarajevo, Yugoslavia. (see also CM1111-14, CM1126-29, A101-12, ALS19, PC96 and PC98.) *Gravure, perforated 11, multicolored.*

CM1094 *Discus*
CM1095 *High Jump*
CM1096 *Archery*
CM1097 *Boxing*

**CM1094**

| | | MNHVF | UseVF |
|---|---|---|---|
| 13¢ | Discus, tagged *(395,424,000)* | .25 | .20 |

**CM1095**

| | | MNHVF | UseVF |
|---|---|---|---|
| 13¢ | High Jump, tagged | .25 | .20 |

**CM1096**

| | | MNHVF | UseVF |
|---|---|---|---|
| 13¢ | Archery, tagged | .25 | .20 |

**CM1097**

| | | MNHVF | UseVF |
|---|---|---|---|
| 13¢ | Boxing, tagged | .25 | .20 |
| | Plate block of 4 | 3.75 | |
| | y. Se-tenant block of 4 CM1094-97 | 2.00 | |
| | FDC *(July 28, 1983)* | | 2.00 |

**1983. TREATY OF PARIS ISSUE** marks the 200th anniversary of the Treaty of Paris, which officially ended the American Revolution and was signed by John Adams, Benjamin Franklin, and John Jay. The treaty established the boundaries of the new nation at the Great Lakes, the Mississippi River and the northern border of Florida. *Gravure, perforated 11.*

 CM1098 *Treaty of Paris*

**CM1098**

| | | MNHVF | UseVF |
|---|---|---|---|
| 20¢ | **multicolored,** tagged *(104,340,000)* | .35 | .20 |
| | Plate block of 4 | 2.75 | |
| | FDC *(Sept. 2, 1983)* | | 1.00 |

**1983. CIVIL SERVICE ISSUE** marks 100 years of federal civil service. *Gravure and intaglio, perforated 11.*

 CM1099 *Civil Service*

**CM1099**

| | | MNHVF | UseVF |
|---|---|---|---|
| 20¢ | **beige, blue and red,** tagged *(114,725,000)* | .35 | .20 |
| | Plate block of 20 | 13.95 | |
| | FDC *(Sept. 9, 1983)* | | 1.00 |

**1983. METROPOLITAN OPERA ISSUE** celebrates the centennial of the Metropolitan Opera in New York, combining features from the original Metropolitan Opera (the proscenium arch above the stage) and the new building at Lincoln Center (the five-arched entrance). *Offset and intaglio, perforated 11.*

 CM1100 *Metropolitan Opera*

**CM1100**

| | | MNHVF | UseVF |
|---|---|---|---|
| 20¢ | **dark carmine and yellow orange,** tagged | .35 | .20 |
| | *(112,525,000)* | | |
| | Plate block of 4 | 2.75 | |
| | FDC *(Sept. 14, 1983)* | | 1.00 |
| | zo. Tagging omitted | 7.00 | |

**1983. AMERICAN INVENTOR'S ISSUE** honors Charles Steinmetz, Edwin Armstrong, Nikola Tesla, and Philo T. Farnsworth. Steinmetz pioneered research on alternating current and high-voltage power. Armstrong's crowning achievement is wide-band frequency modulation, now used in FM radio. Tesla, creator of more than 700 inventions, is best known for the induction motor. Farnsworth, with more than 300 inventions in television and related fields, is most famous for the first all-electronic television transmission in 1927. *Offset and intaglio, perforated 11, multicolored.*

CM1101 *Charles Steinmetz*
CM1102 *Edwin Armstrong*
CM1103 *Nikola Tesla*
CM1104 *Philo T. Farnsworth*

**CM1101**

| | | MNHVF | UseVF |
|---|---|---|---|
| 20¢ | Charles Steinmetz, tagged *(193,055,000)* | .35 | .20 |

**CM1102**

| | | MNHVF | UseVF |
|---|---|---|---|
| 20¢ | Edwin Armstrong, tagged | .35 | .20 |

**CM1103**

| | | MNHVF | UseVF |
|---|---|---|---|
| 20¢ | Nikola Tesla, tagged | .35 | .20 |

**CM1104**

| | | MNHVF | UseVF |
|---|---|---|---|
| 20¢ | Philo T. Farnsworth, tagged | .35 | .20 |
| | Plate block of four | 4.25 | |
| | Se-tenant block of 4 CM1101-04 | 2.00 | |
| | FDC *(Sept. 21, 1983)* | | 2.00 |
| | vy. Block of 4, black (engraved) omitted | 425. | |
| | vy1.Black (engraved) omitted, any single | 100. | |

**1983. STREETCAR ISSUE** pays tribute to the evolution of importance of the streetcar in the United States. *Offset and intaglio, perforated 11.*

CM1105 *1st American streetcar New York City, 1832.* CM1106 *Early electric streetcar, Montgomery, Alabama, 1886.* CM1107 *"Bobtail" horse car, Sulphur Rock, Arkansas, 1926.* CM1108 *St. Charles streetcar, New Orleans, Louisiana, 1923.*

| CM1105 | | MNHVF | UseVF |
|---|---|---|---|
| 20¢ | NYC's First Horsecar, tagged | .35 | .20 |

| CM1106 | | MNHVF | UseVF |
|---|---|---|---|
| 20¢ | Montgomery electric, tagged | .35 | .20 |

| CM1107 | | MNHVF | UseVF |
|---|---|---|---|
| 20¢ | "Bobtail" Horse Car, tagged | .35 | .20 |

| CM1108 | | MNHVF | UseVF |
|---|---|---|---|
| 20¢ | St. Charles Streetcar, tagged | .35 | .20 |
| | Plate block of 4 | 4.25 | |
| | y. Se-tenant block of 4 CM1105-08 | 2.00 | |
| | FDC *(Oct. 8, 1983)* | | 2.00 |
| | vy. Block of 4 black (engraved) omitted | 425. | |
| | vyl.Black (engraved) omitted, any single | 75.00 | |

**1983. MARTIN LUTHER ISSUE** commemorates the 500th birthday of religious reformer Martin Luther. *Gravure (American Bank Note Co.), perforated 11.)*

 CM1109 *Martin Luther*

| CM1109 | | MNHVF | UseVF |
|---|---|---|---|
| 20¢ | **multicolored,** tagged *(165,000,000)* | .35 | .20 |
| | Plate block of 4 | 2.50 | |
| | FDC *(Nov. 10, 1983)* | | 1.00 |

**1984. ALASKA STATEHOOD ISSUE** honors the 25th anniversary of the 49th state. *Gravure by J.W. Fergusson and Sons for the American Bank Note Co., perforated 11.*

 CM110 *Alaska Statehood*

| CM1110 | | MNHVF | UseVF |
|---|---|---|---|
| 20¢ | **multicolored,** tagged *(120,000,000)* | .35 | .20 |
| | Plate block of 4 | 2.50 | |
| | FDC *(Jan. 3, 1984)* | | 1.00 |

**1984. WINTER OLYMPICS ISSUE** features events from the games in Sarajevo, Yugoslavia. Designed by Robert Peak. *Gravure, perforated 10 1/2 x 11.*

CM1111 *Ice Dancing*

CM1112 *Alpine Skiing*

CM1113 *Cross-country Skiing*

CM1114 *Ice Hockey*

| CM1111 | | MNHVF | UseVF |
|---|---|---|---|
| 20¢ | Ice Dancing, tagged *(319,675,000)* | .35 | .20 |

| CM1112 | | MNHVF | UseVF |
|---|---|---|---|
| 20¢ | Alpine Skiing, tagged | .35 | .20 |

| CM1113 | | MNHVF | UseVF |
|---|---|---|---|
| 20¢ | Cross Country Skiing, tagged | .35 | .20 |

| CM1114 | | MNHVF | UseVF |
|---|---|---|---|
| 20¢ | Ice Hockey, tagged | .35 | .20 |
| | Plate block of 4 | 4.25 | |
| | y. Se-tenant block of 4 CM1111-14 | 2.00 | |
| | FDC *(Jan. 6, 1984)* | | 2.00 |

**1984. FEDERAL DEPOSIT INSURANCE CORPORATION ISSUE** honors the 50th anniversary of the institution, which gives bank depositors limited protection in the event of bank insolvency. *Gravure, perforated 11.*

 CM1115 *Federal Deposit Insurance Corporation*

| CM1115 | | MNHVF | UseVF |
|---|---|---|---|
| 20¢ | **multicolored,** tagged *(103,975,000)* | .35 | .20 |
| | Plate block of 4 | 2.50 | |
| | FDC *(Jan. 12, 1984)* | | 1.00 |

**1984. LOVE ISSUE** for use on Valentine's Day as well as other special occasions. From a design by Bradbury Thompson. *Gravure and intaglio (Combination Press), perforated 11 x 10 1/2.*

 CM1116 *Love*

| CM1116 | | MNHVF | UseVF |
|---|---|---|---|
| 20¢ | **multicolored,** tagged *(554,675,000)* | .35 | .20 |
| | Plate block of 20 | 14.50 | |
| | FDC *(Jan. 31, 1984)* | | 1.00 |
| | v.  Horizontal pair, imperforate vertically | 175. | |
| | zo. Tagging omitted | 5.00 | |

## Black Heritage Series

**1984. CARTER G. WOODSON ISSUE** honors the African-American historian, teacher and administrator, as well as editor of the *Journal of Negro History. Gravure by American Bank Note Co., perforated 11.*

CM1117 *Carter G. Woodson*

| CM1117 | | MNHVF | UseVF |
|---|---|---|---|
| 20¢ | **multicolored,** tagged *(120,000,000)* | .35 | .20 |
| | Plate block of 4 | 2.75 | |
| | FDC *(Feb. 1, 1984)* | | 1.00 |
| | v.  Horizontal pair, imperforate vertically | 1750. | |

**1984. SOIL AND WATER CONSERVATION ISSUE** recognizes the 50th anniversary of government efforts to abate soil erosion and conserve water resources. *Gravure, perforated 11.*

CM1118 *Soil and Water Conservation*

| CM1118 | | MNHVF | UseVF |
|---|---|---|---|
| 20¢ | **multicolored,** tagged *(106,975,000)* | .35 | .20 |
| | Plate block of 4 | 2.50 | |
| | FDC *(Feb. 6, 1984)* | | 1.00 |

**1984. CREDIT UNION ACT OF 1934 ISSUE** honors the 50th anniversary of the act that enabled "credit unions to be organized everywhere in the United States under charters from the federal government." *Gravure, perforated 11.*

CM1119 *Credit Union Act of 1934*

| CM1119 | | MNHVF | UseVF |
|---|---|---|---|
| 20¢ | **multicolored,** tagged *(107,325,000)* | .35 | .20 |
| | Plate block of 4 | 2.50 | |
| | FDC *(Feb. 10, 1984)* | | 1.00 |

**1984. ORCHIDS ISSUE** featured 4 different native American orchids: the wild pink orchid is of Florida; yellow lady's slipper of the Midwest; spreading pogonia of the Northeast; and the Pacific calypso found along the Pacific Coast. *Gravure, perforated 11.*

CM1120 *Wild Pink*
CM1121 *Yellow Lady's Slipper*
CM1122 *Spreading Pogonia*
CM1123 *Pacific Calypso*

| CM1120 | | MNHVF | UseVF |
|---|---|---|---|
| 20¢ | Wild Pink Orchid, tagged *(306,912,000)* | .35 | .20 |

| CM1121 | | MNHVF | UseVF |
|---|---|---|---|
| 20¢ | Lady's Slipper Orchid, tagged | .35 | .20 |

| CM1122 | | MNHVF | UseVF |
|---|---|---|---|
| 20¢ | Spreading Pogonia, tagged | .35 | .20 |

| CM1123 | | MNHVF | UseVF |
|---|---|---|---|
| 20¢ | Pacific Calypso Orchid, tagged | .35 | .20 |
| | Plate block of 4 | 3.50 | |
| | y.  Se-tenant block of 4 CM1120-23 | 2.00 | |
| | FDC *(March 6, 1984)* | | 2.00 |

**1984. HAWAII STATEHOOD ISSUE** honors the 25th anniversary of Hawaii statehood. Hawaii was admitted as the 50th state Aug. 21, 1959. *Gravure by American Bank Note Co., perforated 11.*

CM1124 *Hawaii Statehood*

| CM1124 | | MNHVF | UseVF |
|---|---|---|---|
| 20¢ | **multicolored,** tagged *(120,000,000)* | .35 | .20 |
| | Plate block of 4 | 2.75 | |
| | FDC *(March 12, 1984)* | | 1.00 |

**1984. NATIONAL ARCHIVES ISSUE** marks the 50th anniversary of the National Archives in Washington, D.C., which preserves the Declaration of Independence, the Constitution of the United States, the Bill of Rights and other treasures of America's past such as photographs, maps, sound recordings of film. *Gravure, perforated 11.*

CM1125 *National Archives*

| CM1125 | | MNHVF | UseVF |
|---|---|---|---|
| 20¢ | **multicolored,** tagged *(108,000,000)* | .35 | .20 |
| | Plate block of 4 | 2.75 | |
| | FDC *(April 16, 1984)* | | 1.00 |

**1984. SUMMER OLYMPICS ISSUE** featured events from the Los Angeles Summer Games. *Gravure, perforated 11.*

CM1126 *Men's diving*

CM1127 *Women's long jump*

CM1128 *Wrestling*

CM1129 *Women's kyacking*

| CM1126 | | MNHVF | UseVF |
|---|---|---|---|
| 20¢ | Men's diving, tagged *(313,350,000)* | .35 | .20 |

| CM1127 | | MNHVF | UseVF |
|---|---|---|---|
| 20¢ | Women's long jump, tagged | .35 | .20 |

| CM1128 | | MNHVF | UseVF |
|---|---|---|---|
| 20¢ | Wrestling, tagged | .35 | .20 |

| CM1129 | | MNHVF | UseVF |
|---|---|---|---|
| 20¢ | Women's kyacking, tagged | .35 | .20 |
| | Plate block of 4 | 5.50 | |
| | y. Se-tenant block of 4 CM1126-29 | 2.00 | |
| | FDC *(May 4, 1984)* | | 2.00 |

**1984. LOUISIANA WORLD EXPOSITION ISSUE** honors the exposition that celebrated fresh water, spotlighting rivers and ports of the world through displays and exhibitions. *Gravure, perforated 11.*

CM1130 *Louisiana World Exposition*

| CM1130 | | MNHVF | UseVF |
|---|---|---|---|
| 20¢ | multicolored, tagged *(130,320,000)* | .35 | .20 |
| | Plate block of 4 | 2.75 | |
| | FDC *(May 11, 1984)* | | 1.00 |

**1984. HEALTH RESEARCH ISSUE** hails the professionals who have worked to prevent disease and prolong life. *Gravure by American Bank Note Co., perforated 11.*

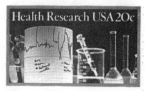

CM1131 *Health Research*

| CM1131 | | MNHVF | UseVF |
|---|---|---|---|
| 20¢ | multicolored, tagged *(120,000,000)* | .35 | .20 |
| | Plate block of 4 | 3.00 | |
| | FDC *(May 17, 1984)* | | 1.00 |

**1984. DOUGLAS FAIRBANKS ISSUE** recalls the actor as part of the Performing Artist series. Together with Charlie Chaplin, D.W. Griffith and Mary Pickford, in 1919 Fairbanks formed United Artists Corp. *Gravure and intaglio (Combination Press), perforated 11.*

CM1132 *Douglas Fairbanks*

| CM1132 | | MNHVF | UseVF |
|---|---|---|---|
| 20¢ | multicolored, tagged *(117,050,000)* | .35 | .20 |
| | Plate, block of 20 | 17.50 | |
| | FDC *(May 23, 1984)* | | 1.00 |
| | v. Horizontal pair, imperforate vertically | — | |
| | zo. Tagging omitted | 7.50 | |

## American Sports Series

**1984. JIM THORPE ISSUE** salutes the American athlete whose feats on the track, base- ball and football fields are legendary. In 1912, at the Summer Olympics in Stockholm, Thorpe became the 1st athlete to win both the pentathlon and the decathlon. Later, he was stripped of his medals when it ws learned that he had briefly played semi-professional baseball in 1910. In 1938, the International Olympic Committee returned replicas of Thorpe's 1912 medals to his family, restoring his place in Olympic history. *Intaglio, perforated 11.*

CM1133 *Jim Thorpe*

| CM1133 | | MNHVF | UseVF |
|---|---|---|---|
| 20¢ | dark brown, tagged *(115,725,000)* | .75 | .20 |
| | Plate block of 4 | 3.00 | |
| | FDC *(May 24, 1984)* | | 1.00 |

## Performing Artists Series

**1984. JOHN McCORMACK ISSUE** honored the 100th birthday of the Irish-American singer and world-famous tenor who sang with the outstanding opera companies in North America, as well as performing Irish folk songs and ballads in major cities of the world. This stamp was released jointly with an Irish stamp (Ireland 622). *Gravure, perforated 11.*

CM1134 *John McCormack*

| CM1134 | | MNHVF | UseVF |
|---|---|---|---|
| 20¢ | multicolored, tagged *(116,600,000)* | .35 | .20 |
| | Plate block of 4 | 2.50 | |
| | FDC *(June 6, 1984)* | | 1.00 |

**1984. St. Lawrence Seaway Issue** commemorates the 25th anniversary of the opening of the seaway, which stretches from the Atlantic Ocean to Duluth, Minn. This was a joint issue with Canada (Canada 1085). *Gravure by American Bank Note Co., perforated 11.*

CM1135 *St. Lawrence Seaway*

| CM1135 | | MNHVF | UseVF |
|---|---|---|---|
| 20¢ | **multicolored,** tagged *(120,000,000)* | .35 | .20 |
| | Plate block of 4 | 2.50 | |
| | FDC *(June 26, 1984)* | | 1.00 |

**1984. Wetlands Preservation Issue** marks the 50th anniversary of the Migratory Bird Hunting and Conservation Stamp Act, enacted in 1934 as a result of a proposal by conservationist Jay Norwood ("Ding") Darling for a federal revenue stamp required to be purchased by waterfowl hunters. Funds from the sale of these stamps go to buy and lease waterfowl habitats. *Intaglio, perforated 11.*

CM1136 Mallards Dropping In, *by Jay Norwood Darling*

| CM1136 | | MNHVF | UseVF |
|---|---|---|---|
| 20¢ | **blue,** tagged *(123,575,000)* | .35 | .20 |
| | Plate block of 4 | 4.50 | |
| | FDC *(July 2, 1984)* | | 1.00 |
| | v. Horizontal pair, imperforate vertically | 400. | |

**1984. Roanoke Voyages Issue** commemorates the 400th anniversary of the establishment of an English colony in the New World. An expedition landed in 1584 on what is now the coast of North Carolina and took possession of the new land in the name of Queen Elizabeth. 2 groups landed in 1585, and 1587. In 1590, the crew of a ship carrying supplies to the colony landed and could find no evidence of the colonists, whose fate remains a mystery. *Gravure by American Bank Note Co., perforated 11.*

CM1137 *Roanoke Voyages*

| CM1137 | | MNHVF | UseVF |
|---|---|---|---|
| 20¢ | **multicolored,** tagged *(120,000,000)* | .35 | .20 |
| | Plate block of 4 | 2.80 | |
| | Gutter Pair | — | |
| | FDC *(July 13, 1984)* | | 1.00 |

## Literary Arts Series

**1984. Herman Melville Issue** honors the 19th century American author of *Moby Dick. Intaglio, perforated 11.*

CM1138 *Herman Melville*

| CM1138 | | MNHVF | UseVF |
|---|---|---|---|
| 20¢ | **blue green,** tagged *(117,125,000)* | .35 | .20 |
| | Plate block of 4 | 2.50 | |
| | FDC *(Aug. 1, 1984)* | | 1.00 |

**1984. Horace Moses Issue** salutes the man who created Junior Achievement because of his interest in career-oriented educational opportunities for city youth. *Intaglio (Combination Press), perforated 11.*

CM1139 *Horace Moses*

| CM1139 | | MNHVF | UseVF |
|---|---|---|---|
| 20¢ | **orange and dark brown,** tagged *(117,225,000)* | .35 | .20 |
| | Plate block of 20 | 17.00 | |
| | FDC *(Aug. 6, 1984)* | | 1.00 |

**1984. Smokey Bear Issue** celebrates the symbol for forest fire prevention used by the Forest Service of the U.S. Department of Agriculture. *Combination of offset and intaglio, perforated 11.*

CM1140 *Smokey and Bear Cub*

| CM1140 | | MNHVF | UseVF |
|---|---|---|---|
| 20¢ | **multicolored,** tagged *(95,525,000)* | .35 | .20 |
| | Plate block of 4 | 3.00 | |
| | FDC *(Aug. 13, 1984)* | | 1.00 |
| | v. Horizontal pair, imperforate between | 275. | |
| | v1. Horizontal pair, imperforate vertically | 1750. | |
| | v2. Vertical pair, imperforate between | 225. | |
| | v3. Block of 4, imperforate between horizontally & vertically | 6000. | |

**1984. Roberto Clemente Issue** commemorates the 18-year Pittsburgh Pirates veteran inducted into the Baseball Hall of Fame in 1973, the year following his untimely death while on a volunteer humanitarian mission *Gravure, perforated 11.*

CM1141 *Roberto Clemente*

| CM1141 | | MNHVF | UseVF |
|---|---|---|---|
| 20¢ | **multicolored,** tagged *(119,125,000)* | 3.50 | .20 |
| | Plate block of 4 | 12.75 | |
| | FDC *(Aug. 17, 1984)* | | 1.00 |
| | v. Horizontal pair, imperforate vertically | 2000. | |

**1984. AMERICAN DOGS ISSUE** depicted 8 pedigreed dogs that represent the types most often bred in the United States. The stamps were issued in conjuction with the American Kennel Club's centennial. *Gravure, perforated 11.*

CM1142 *Beagle, Boston Terrier*

CM1143 *Chesapeake Bay Retriever, Cocker Spaniel*

CM1144 *Alaskan Malamute, Collie*

CM1145 *Black and Tan Coonho und, American Foxhound*

| CM1142 | | MNHVF | UseVF |
|---|---|---|---|
| 20¢ | Beagle & Terrier, tagged *(216,260,000)* | .35 | .20 |

| CM1143 | | MNHVF | UseVF |
|---|---|---|---|
| 20¢ | Retriever & Cocker Spaniel, tagged | .35 | .20 |

| CM1144 | | MNHVF | UseVF |
|---|---|---|---|
| 20¢ | Malamute & Collie, tagged | .35 | .20 |

| CM1145 | | MNHVF | UseVF |
|---|---|---|---|
| 20¢ | Coonhound & Foxhound, tagged | .35 | .20 |
| | Plate block of 4 | 4.25 | |
| | y. Se-tenant block of 4 CM1142-45 | 2.00 | |
| | FDC *(Sept. 7, 1984)* | | 1.00 |

**1984. CRIME PREVENTION ISSUE** depicts McGruff, the Crime Dog, popularlized to boost public confidence and encourage participation in citizen crime prevention activities. *Gravure by American Bank Note Co., perforated 11.*

CM1146 *McGruff, the Crime Dog.*

| CM1146 | | MNHVF | UseVF |
|---|---|---|---|
| 20¢ | **multicolored,** tagged *(120,000,000)* | .35 | .20 |
| | Plate block of 4 | 2.50 | |
| | FDC *(Sept. 26, 1984)* | | 1.00 |

**1984. FAMILY UNITY ISSUE** was designed by high school student Molly LaRue. *Gravure and intaglio (Combination Press), perforated 11.*

CM1147 *STick-Figure Family*

| CM1147 | | MNHVF | UseVF |
|---|---|---|---|
| 20¢ | **multicolored,** tagged *(117,625,000)* | .35 | .20 |
| | Plate block of 20 | 17.75 | |
| | FDC *(Oct. 1, 1984)* | | 1.00 |
| | v. Horizontal pair, imperforate vertically | 525. | |
| | v1. Vertical pair, imperforate between | — | |
| | zo. Tagging omitted | 4.00 | |

**1984. ELEANOR ROOSEVELT ISSUE** honors the woman who distinguished herself both as the First Lady, and as a humanitarian who fought for human rights as a delegate to the United Nations. *Intaglio, perforated 11.*

CM1148 *Eleanor Roosevelt*

| CM1148 | | MNHVF | UseVF |
|---|---|---|---|
| 20¢ | **blue,** tagged *(112,896,000)* | .35 | .20 |
| | Plate block of 4 | 2.50 | |
| | FDC *(Oct. 11, 1984)* | | 1.00 |

**1984. NATION OF READERS ISSUE** recognizes the importance of reading in American society, including the traditions of public education and the public library. *Intaglio, perforated 11.*

CM1149 *Abraham Lincoln and Son Tad. From a daguerreotype by Mathew Brady.*

| CM1149 | | MNHVF | UseVF |
|---|---|---|---|
| 20¢ | **brown and dark red,** tagged, *(116,500,000)* | .35 | .20 |
| | Plate block of 4 | 2.95 | |
| | FDC *(Oct. 16, 1984)* | | 1.00 |

**1984. HISPANIC AMERICANS ISSUE** honors Hispanic Americans and their contribution to national defense. Many have received the nation's highest honors and awards for gallantry in the armed services. *Gravure, perforated 11.*

CM1150 *Hispanic Americans*

| CM1150 | | MNHVF | UseVF |
|---|---|---|---|
| 20¢ | **multicolored,** tagged *(108,140,000)* | .35 | .20 |
| | Plate block of 4 | 2.50 | |
| | FDC *(Oct. 31, 1984)* | | 1.00 |
| | v. Vertical pair, imperforate horizontally | 1850. | |

**1984. VIETNAM VETERANS MEMORIAL ISSUE** commemorates the 2nd anniversary of the dedication of the Vietnam Veterans Memorial. The Washington D.C. memorial contains the names of 57,939 Americans killed or missing in action during the war. *Intaglio, perforated 10 1/2.*

CM1151 *Vietnam Veterans Memorial*

| CM1151 | | MNHVF | UseVF |
|---|---|---|---|
| 20¢ | **multicolored,** tagged *(105,300,000)* | .35 | .20 |
| | Plate block of 4 | 4.25 | |
| | FDC *(Nov. 10, 1984)* | | 1.00 |
| | zo. Tagging omitted | | |

**1985. JEROME KERN ISSUE** Performing Artists Series celebrated the 100th birthday of the composer who wrote more than 108 complete theatrical scores, over 1,000 songs and earned 2 Academy Awards. He perhaps is best known for *Show Boat. Gravure by American Bank Note Co., perforated 11.*

CM1152 *Jerome Kern*

| CM1152 | | MNHVF | UseVF |
|---|---|---|---|
| 22¢ | **multicolored,** tagged *(124,500,000)* | .35 | .20 |
| | Plate block of 4 | 3.00 | |
| | FDC *(Jan. 23, 1985)* | | 1.00 |
| | zo. Tagging omitted | 7.00 | |

**1985. MARY MCLEOD BETHUNE ISSUE** Black Heritage Series commemorates the noted educator and social activist. *Gravure by American Bank Note Co., perforated 11.*

CM1153 *Mary McLeod Bethune*

| CM1153 | | MNHVF | UseVF |
|---|---|---|---|
| 22¢ | **multicolored,** tagged *(120,000,000)* | .35 | .20 |
| | Plate block of 4 | 3.25 | |
| | FDC *(March 5, 1985)* | | 1.00 |

## American Folk Art Series

**1985. DUCK DECOYS ISSUE** has designs based on actual decoys: a broadbill decoy carved by Ben Holmes of Stratford, Conn. in 1890; a mallard decoy by Percy Grant of Osbornville, N.J. , in 1900; a canvasback by Bob McGraw of Havre de Grace, Md. , 1929; and a redhead by Keyes Chadwick of Martha's Vineyard , Mass., in 1925. *Gravure by American Bank Note Co., perforated 11.*

CM1154 *Broadbill Decoy*

CM1155 *Mallard Decoy*

CM1156 *Canvasback*

CM1157 *Redhead Decoy*

| CM1154 | | MNHVF | UseVF |
|---|---|---|---|
| 22¢ | Broadbull decoy, tagged *(300,000,000)* | .40 | .20 |

| CM1155 | | MNHVF | UseVF |
|---|---|---|---|
| 22¢ | Mallard decoy, tagged | .40 | .20 |

| CM1156 | | MNHVF | UseVF |
|---|---|---|---|
| 22¢ | Canvasback decoy, tagged | .40 | .20 |

| CM1157 | | MNHVF | UseVF |
|---|---|---|---|
| 22¢ | Redhead decoy, tagged | .40 | .20 |
| | Plate block of 4 | 12.00 | |
| | y. Se-tenant block of 4 CM1154-57 | 2.00 | 1.50 |
| | FDC *(March 22, 1985)* | | 1.00 |

**1985. SPECIAL OLYMPICS ISSUE** salutes the largest program of sports training and athletic competition for mentally retarded people in the world. With assistance of 550,000 volunteers worldwide, more than 1 million children and adults participate. *Gravure, perforated 11.*

CM1158 *Winter Special Olympics*

| CM1158 | | MNHVF | UseVF |
|---|---|---|---|
| 22¢ | **multicolored,** tagged *(120,580,000)* | .35 | .20 |
| | Plate block of 4 | 2.95 | |
| | FDC *(March 25, 1985)* | | 1.00 |
| | v. Vertical pair, imperforate horizontally | 575. | |

**1985. LOVE ISSUE** was a special issue for use on many occasions throughout the year. Color lines by Corita Kent. *Gravure, perforated 11.*

CM1159 *Love*

| CM1159 | | MNHVF | UseVF |
|---|---|---|---|
| 22¢ | **multicolored,** tagged *(729,700,000)* | .35 | .20 |
| | Plate block of 4 | 3.25 | |
| | FDC *(April 17, 1985)* | | 1.00 |
| | v. Imperforate pair | 1500. | |

**1985. RURAL ELECTRIFICATION ADMINISTRATION ISSUE** marks the 50th anniversary of the organization, which has served as a lending agency as well as developing programs for rural electrification. *Gravure and intaglio (Combination Press), perforated 11.*

CM1160 *Rural Electrificatio n Administration*

| CM1160 | | MNHVF | UseVF |
|---|---|---|---|
| 22¢ | **multicolored,** tagged *(124,750,000)* | .35 | .20 |
| | Plate block of 20 | 32.50 | |
| | FDC *(May 11, 1985)* | | 1.00 |
| | v. Vertical pair, imperforate between | — | |

**1985. AMERIPEX 86 ISSUE** honors the 1986 international stamp show hosted by the United States in suburban Chicago, Ill. The stamp depicted is the 1 cent National Bank Note of 1870 (No. 97). *Offset and intaglio, perforated 11.*

CM1161 *Ameripex 86*

| CM1161 | | MNHVF | UseVF |
|---|---|---|---|
| 22¢ | **multicolored,** tagged *(203,496,000)* | .35 | .20 |
| | Plate block of 4 | 2.75 | |
| | 260 *(May 25, 1985)* | | 1.00 |
| | v. Red omitted | 2250. | |
| | v1. Red and black omitted | 1250. | |
| | v2. Black, blue, and red omitted | 200. | |

**1985. ABIGAIL ADAMS ISSUE** honors the wife of John Adams, 2nd president of the United States. She acted as adviser to her husband, maintained the family estate, raised 4 children (son John Quincy Adams became the 6th president of the United States), and distinguished herself as one of the leading women writers of her era. *Gravure, perforated 11.*

CM1162 *Abigail Adams*

| CM1162 | | MNHVF | UseVF |
|---|---|---|---|
| 22¢ | **multicolored,** tagged *(126,325,000)* | .35 | .20 |
| | Plate block of 4 | 2.75 | |
| | FDC *(June 14, 1985)* | | 1.00 |
| | v. Imperforate pair | 250. | |

*Examples exist with minute traces of the intaglio black remaining, which are worth far less than a complete color-omitted error. Competent expertizing is required.*

**1985. FREDERIC AUGUSTE BARTHOLDI ISSUE** salutes the sculptor of the Statue of Liberty. *Offset and intaglio, perforated 11.*

F.A. Bartholdi, Statue of Liberty Sculptor

CM1163 *F.A. Bartholdi and Statue of Liberty.*

| CM1163 | | MNHVF | UseVF |
|---|---|---|---|
| 22¢ | **multicolored,** tagged *(130,000,000)* | .35 | .20 |
| | Plate block of 4 | 2.75 | |
| | FDC *(July 18, 1985)* | | 1.00 |
| | v. Intaglio black omitted | — | |

**1985. KOREAN WAR VETERANS ISSUE** honors Americans who served during the Korean War of 1950-53 , the 1st conflict in which U.S. troops fought under the flag of the United Nations. *Intaglio, perforated 11.*

CM1164 *Troops Marching, from a photograph by David Duncan.*

| CM1164 | | MNHVF | UseVF |
|---|---|---|---|
| 22¢ | **gray green and rose red,** tagged *(119,975,000)* | .35 | .20 |
| | Plate block of 4 | 3.50 | |
| | FDC *(July 26, 1985)* | | 1.00 |

**1985. SOCIAL SECURITY ACT ISSUE** marks the 50th anniversary of the Social Security Act, which , along with later amendments, brought workers essential protection. These include old age, survivor, disability, and health insurance; compensation for unemployment; public assistance; and health and welfare services. *Gravure by American Bank Note Co., perforated 11.*

CM1165 *Social Security Act*

| CM1165 | | MNHVF | UseVF |
|---|---|---|---|
| 22¢ | **dark blue and light blue,** tagged *(120,000,000)* | .35 | .20 |
| | Plate block of 4 | 3.50 | |
| | FDC *(Aug. 14, 1985)* | | 1.00 |

**1985. WORLD WAR I VETERANS ISSUE** honoring American sacrifice in "the War to End all Wars," is based on drawing *The Battle of the Marne* by Capt. Harvey Dunn, one of 8 official artists for the American Expeditionary Force. *Intaglio, perforated 11.*

CM1166 *The Battle of the Marne.*

| CM1166 | | MNHVF | UseVF |
|---|---|---|---|
| 22¢ | **green and red,** tagged *(119,975,000)* | .35 | .20 |
| | Plate block of 4 | 3.50 | |
| | FDC *(Aug. 26, 1985)* | | 1.00 |

**1985. AMERICAN HORSES ISSUE** featured 4 breeds of horses representing the many types of horses, mules and donkeys in North America. *Gravure, perforated 11.*

CM1167 *Quarter Horse*

CM1168 *Morgan*

CM1169 *Saddlebred*

CM1170 *Appaloosa*

| CM1167 | | MNHVF | UseVF |
|---|---|---|---|
| 22¢ | Quarter horse, tagged *(147,940,000)* | 2.75 | .20 |

| CM1168 | | MNHVF | UseVF |
|---|---|---|---|
| 22¢ | Morgan, tagged | 2.75 | .20 |

| CM1169 | | MNHVF | UseVF |
|---|---|---|---|
| 22¢ | Saddlebred, tagged | 2.75 | .20 |

| CM1170 | | MNHVF | UseVF |
|---|---|---|---|
| 22¢ | Appaloosa, tagged | 2.75 | .20 |
| | Plate block of 4 | 15.00 | |
| | y. Se-tenant block of 4 CM1167-70 | 13.00 | 6.50 |
| | FDC *(Sept. 25, 1985)* | | 4.00 |

**1985. PUBLIC EDUCATION ISSUE** recognizes the importance of public education in the development of America. *Gravure by American Bank Note Co., perforated 11.*

CM1171 *Pen and Inkwell, Glasses, Penmanship Drill.*

| CM1171 | | MNHVF | UseVF |
|---|---|---|---|
| 22¢ | **multicolored,** tagged *(120,000,000)* | .35 | .20 |
| | Plate block of 4 | 6.50 | |
| | FDC *(Oct. 1, 1985)* | | 1.00 |

**1985. INTERNATIONAL YOUTH YEAR ISSUE** honors youth groups with outdoor scenes and representative individuals from each group. *Gravure by American Bank Note Co., perforated 11.*

CM1172 *YMCA Youth camping*

CM1173 *Boy Scouts*

CM1174 *Big Brothers/Big Sisters*

CM1175 *Camp Fire*

| CM1172 | | MNHVF | UseVF |
|---|---|---|---|
| 22¢ | YMCA, tagged *(130,000,000)* | 1.00 | .20 |

| CM1173 | | MNHVF | UseVF |
|---|---|---|---|
| 22¢ | Boy Scouts, tagged | 1.00 | .20 |

| CM1174 | | MNHVF | UseVF |
|---|---|---|---|
| 22¢ | Big Brothers/Sisters, tagged | 1.00 | .20 |

| CM1175 | | MNHVF | UseVF |
|---|---|---|---|
| 22¢ | Campfire, tagged | 1.00 | .20 |
| | Plate block of 4 | 8.00 | |
| | y. Se-tenant block of 4 CM1172-75 | 3.50 | 3.00 |
| | FDC *(Oct. 7, 1985)* | | 1.00 |

**1985. HELP END HUNGER ISSUE** focuses on the plight of millions suffering from hunger worldwide. *Gravure by American Bank Note Co., perforated 11.*

CM1176 *Help End Hunger*

| CM1176 | | MNHVF | UseVF |
|---|---|---|---|
| 22¢ | **multicolored,** tagged *(129,000,000)* | .35 | .20 |
| | Plate block of 4 | 3.00 | |
| | FDC *(Oct. 15, 1985)* | | 1.00 |

**1986. ARKANSAS STATEHOOD ISSUE** marks the 150th anniversary of Arkansas' entry into the Union as the 25th state. *Gravure by American Bank Note Co., perforated 11.*

CM1177 *Old State House, Little Rock, Ark.*

| CM1177 | | MNHVF | UseVF |
|---|---|---|---|
| 22¢ | **multicolored,** tagged | .35 | .20 |
| | Plate block of 4 | 3.00 | |
| | FDC *(Jan. 3, 1986)* | | 1.00 |
| | v. Vertical pair, imperforate horizontally | — | |

**1986. STAMP COLLECTING BOOKLET ISSUE** celebrates philately. This 1st booklet of commemorative stamps was issued by the U.S. Postal Service on the same day as a booklet about stamp collecting was issued by the postal administration of Sweden (Sweden 1368). The U.S. also paid tribute to the centennial of the Smithsonian Institution's 1st acceptance of philatelic items and to the centennial year of the American Philatelic Society. The cover of the U.S. stamp collecting booklet was an acceptable admission ticket to the international stamp show, AMERIPEX '86. *Offset and intaglio, perforated 10 vertically.*

CM1178 *Handstamp, Magnifying glass, 1883 stamps* CM1179 *Boy with his Stamp Collection* CM1180 *2 Swedish Stamps and U.S. CM191* CM1181 *First-day cover of 1986 Presidents Souvenir Sheet*

| CM1178 | | MNHVF | UseVF |
|---|---|---|---|
| 22¢ | covers & handstamp, tagged *(67,996,800)* | .40 | .20 |

| CM1179 | | MNHVF | UseVF |
|---|---|---|---|
| 22¢ | youth w/albums, tagged | .40 | .20 |

| CM1180 | | MNHVF | UseVF |
|---|---|---|---|
| 22¢ | magnifier & stamp, tagged | .40 | .20 |

| CM1181 | | MNHVF | UseVF |
|---|---|---|---|
| 22¢ | AMERIPEX '86 souvenir sheet, tagged | .40 | .20 |
| | FDC *(Jan. 23, 1986)* | | 2.00 |
| | n. Se-tenant booklet pane of 4 CM1178-1181 | 2.00 | |
| | nv. Booklet pane with black omitted CM1178 & CM1181 | 45.00 | 150. |
| | nv1.Booklet pane with blue omitted CM1178-CM1180 | 2500. | |
| | nv2.Booklet pane with light brown omitted | — | |

*The complete booklet contains 2 panes.*

**1986. LOVE STAMP ISSUE** was the 5th U.S. Love stamp. *Gravure, perforated 11.*

CM1182 *Puppy*

| CM1182 | | MNHVF | UseVF |
|---|---|---|---|
| 22¢ | **multicolored,** tagged *(947,450,000)* | .35 | .20 |
| | Plate block of 4 | 3.50 | |
| | FDC *(Jan. 30, 1986)* | | 1.00 |
| | zo. Tagging omitted | | |

**1986. SOJOURNER TRUTH ISSUE** Black Heritage Series honors the woman who, after acquiring her freedom, dedicated her life to the enfranchisement and education of freed slaves and to the cause of human rights. *Gravure by American Bank Note Co., perforated 11.*

CM1183 *Sojourner Truth*

| CM1183 | | MNHVF | UseVF |
|---|---|---|---|
| 22¢ | **multicolored,** tagged *(130,000,000)* | .35 | .20 |
| | Plate block of 4 | 3.50 | |
| | FDC *(Feb. 4, 1986)* | | 1.00 |

**1986. REPUBLIC OF TEXAS ISSUE** commemorates the 150th anniversary of Texan independence from Mexico. *Gravure by American Bank Note Co., perforated 11.*

CM1184 *Spur on Texas State*

| CM1184 | | MNHVF | UseVF |
|---|---|---|---|
| 22¢ | **dark blue dark red, and dark gray,** tagged *(136,500,000)* | .35 | .20 |
| | Plate block of 4 | 3.50 | |
| | FDC *(March 2, 1986)* | | 1.00 |
| | v. Dark red omitted | 2550. | |
| | v1. Horizontal pair, imperforate vertically | 1100. | |

**1986. FISH BOOKLET ISSUE** featured 5 fish common to the U.S. waters. *Gravure, perforated 10 horizontally.*

CM1185 *Muskellunge*

CM1186 *Atlantic cod*

CM1187 *Largemouth bass*

CM1188 *Bluefin tuna*

CM1189 *Catfish*

| CM1185 | | MNHVF | UseVF |
|---|---|---|---|
| 22¢ | Muskellunge, tagged *(219,990,000)* | 1.75 | .20 |

| CM1186 | | MNHVF | UseVF |
|---|---|---|---|
| 22¢ | Atlantic Cod, tagged | 1.75 | .20 |

| CM1187 | | MNHVF | UseVF |
|---|---|---|---|
| 22¢ | Largemouth bass, tagged | 1.75 | .20 |

| CM1188 | | MNHVF | UseVF |
|---|---|---|---|
| 22¢ | Bluefin tuna, tagged | 1.75 | .20 |

| CM1189 | | MNHVF | UseVF |
|---|---|---|---|
| 22¢ | Catfish, tagged | 1.75 | .20 |
| | FDC *(March 21, 1986)* | | 2.00 |
| | n. Se-tenant booklet pane of 5 CM1185-89 | 8.50 | |

*The complete booklet contains 2 panes.*

**1986. PUBLIC HOSPITALS ISSUE** honors U.S. public hospitals that trace their history back to Philadelphia General Hospital, which opened about 1731 (closed in 1977). *Gravure by American Bank Note Co., perforated 11.*

CM1190 *Public Hospitals*

| CM1190 | | MNHVF | UseVF |
|---|---|---|---|
| 22¢ | **multicolored,** tagged *(130,000,000)* | .35 | .20 |
| | Plate block of 4 | 3.25 | |
| | FDC *(April 11, 1986)* | | 1.00 |
| | v. Horizontal pair, imperforate vertically | 1250. | |
| | v1. Vertical pair, imperforate horizontally | 325. | |

**1986. DUKE ELLINGTON ISSUE** Performing Artists Series
pays homage to the renowned jazz composer on the 75th anniversary
of his birth. Edward Kennedy Ellington was a creative master of jazz
composition, songwriting, film scoring, ballet and sacred music alike.
*Gravure by American Bank Note Co., perforated 11.*

CM1191 *Duke Ellington*

| CM1191 | | MNHVF | UseVF |
|---|---|---|---|
| 22¢ | **multicolored,** tagged *(130,000,000)* | .35 | .20 |
| | Plate block of 4 | 3.00 | |
| | FDC *(April 29, 1986)* | | 1.00 |
| | v. Vertical pair, imperforate horizontally | 900. | 375. |

**1986. PRESIDENTS SOUVENIR SHEETS** honor U.S. presidents on 4
souvenir sheets of 9 stamps (one for each president and one featuring
the White House). The sheets were issued in conjuction with Ameripex '86, in Chicago. *Intaglio, perforated 11.*

CM1192

CM1193

Presidents of
the United States: II

AMERIPEX 86
International
Stamp Show
Chicago, Illinois
May 22-June 1, 1986

| CM1193 | | MNHVF | UseVF |
|---|---|---|---|
| $1.98 | **souvenir sheet of 9** *(5,825,050)* | 5.25 | 4.50 |
| | a.  22¢ John Tyler, tagged | .50 | .40 |
| | b.  22¢ James K. Polk, tagged | .50 | .40 |
| | c.  22¢ Zachary Taylor, tagged | .50 | .40 |
| | d.  22¢ Millard Fillmore, tagged. | .50 | .40 |
| | e.  22¢ Franklin Pierce, tagged | .50 | .40 |
| | f.  22¢ James Buchanan, tagged | .50 | .40 |
| | g.  22¢ Abraham Lincoln, tagged | .50 | .40 |
| | h.  22¢ Andrew Johnson, tagged | .50 | .40 |
| | i.  22¢ Ulysses S. Grant, tagged | .50 | .40 |
| | FDC *(May 22, 1986)* | | 8.00 |
| | v.  Black (inscription) omitted | 3000. | |

CM1194

Presidents of
the United States: III

AMERIPEX 86
International
Stamp Show
Chicago, Illinois
May 22-June 1, 1986

AMERIPEX 86
International
Stamp Show
Chicago, Illinois
May 22-June 1, 1986

| CM1192 | | MNHVF | UseVF |
|---|---|---|---|
| $1.98 | **souvenir sheet of 9** *(5,825,050)* | 5.25 | 4.50 |
| | a.  22¢ George Washington, tagged. | | |
| | b.  22¢ John Adams, tagged | .50 | .40 |
| | c.  22¢ Thomas Jefferson, tagged. | | |
| | d.  22¢ James Madison, tagged | .50 | .40 |
| | e.  22¢ James Monroe, tagged | .50 | .40 |
| | f.  22¢ John Quincy Adams, tagged | | |
| | g.  22¢ Andrew Jackson, tagged | .50 | .40 |
| | h.  22¢ Martin Van Buren, tagged | | |
| | i.  22¢ William Henry Harrison, tagged | .50 | .40 |
| | FDC *(May 22, 1986)* | | 8.00 |
| | v.  Black (inscription) omitted | 2000. | — |
| | v1. Intaglio blue omitted | 3500. | |
| | v2. Imperforate, pane of 0 | 10500. | |

**CM1194**

| | | MNHVF | UseVF |
|---|---|---|---|
| $1.98 | souvenir sheet of 9 *(5,825,050)* | 5.25 | 4.50 |
| | a. 22¢ Rugherford B. Hayes, tagged | .50 | .40 |
| | b. 22¢ James A. Garfield, | .50 | .40 |
| | c. 22¢ Chester A. Arthur, tagged | .50 | .40 |
| | d. 22¢ Grover Cleveland, tagged | .50 | .40 |
| | e. 22¢ Benjamin Harrison, tagged | .50 | .40 |
| | f. 22¢ William McKinley, tagged | .50 | .40 |
| | g. 22¢ Theodore Roosevelt, tagged | .50 | .40 |
| | h. 22¢ William H. Taft, tagged | .50 | .40 |
| | i. 22¢ Woodrow Wilson, tagged | .50 | .40 |
| | FDC *(May 22, 1986)* | | 8.00 |
| | v. Black (inscription) omitted | — | |
| | v1. Intaglio brown omitted | 2750. | |

CM1195

Presents of
the United States: IV

AMERIPEX 86
International
Stamp Show
Chicago, Illinois
May 22-June 1, 1986

**CM1195**

| | | MNHVF | UseVF |
|---|---|---|---|
| $1.98 | souvenir sheet of 9 *(5,825,050)* | | |
| | a. 22¢ Warren G. Harding, tagged | .50 | .40 |
| | b. 22¢ Calvin Coolidge, tagged | .50 | .40 |
| | c. 22¢ Herbert C. Hoover, tagged | .50 | .40 |
| | d. 22¢ Franklin D. Roosevelt, tagged | .50 | .40 |
| | e. 22¢ White House, tagged | .50 | .40 |
| | f. 22¢ Harry S. Truman, tagged | .50 | .40 |
| | g. 22¢ Dwight D. Eisenhower, tagged | .50 | .40 |
| | h. 22¢ John F. Kennedy, tagged | .50 | .40 |
| | i. 22¢ Lyndon B. Johnson, tagged | .50 | .40 |
| | FDC *(May 22, 1986)* | | 8.00 |
| | v. Intaglio blue black inscripton omitted on 6 stamps at left (a-b, d-e, g-h) | 2250. | |
| | zo. Tagging omitted on 3 stamps at right (c.f.i) | — | |

**1986. ARCTIC EXPLORERS ISSUE** honors 5 pioneers of polar exploration who accomplished a variety of geographical, anthropological, mapping, and other scientific work. *Gravure, perforated 11.*

CM1196 *Elisha Kent Kane*

CM1197 *Adolphus W. Greely*

CM1198 *Vihjalmur Stefansson*

CM1199 *Robert E. Peary and Matthew Henson*

**CM1196**

| | | MNHVF | UseVF |
|---|---|---|---|
| 22¢ | E.K. Kane *(130,000,000)* | 1.10 | .20 |

**CM1197**

| | | MNHVF | UseVF |
|---|---|---|---|
| 22¢ | A.W. Greely | 1.10 | .20 |

**CM1198**

| | | MNHVF | UseVF |
|---|---|---|---|
| 22¢ | V. Stefansson | 1.10 | .20 |

**CM1199**

| | | MNHVF | UseVF |
|---|---|---|---|
| 22¢ | R.E. Peary & M. Henson | 1.10 | .20 |
| | Plate block of 4 | 8.00 | |
| | y. Se-tenant block of 4 CM1196-99 | 5.50 | 3.75 |
| | FDC *(May 28, 1986)* | | 2.00 |
| | vy. Se-tenant block of 4, engraved black omitted | 11550. | |
| | vy1.Se-tenant block of 4, engraved black omitted from CM1196-97 only | — | |

**1986. STATUE OF LIBERTY ISSUE** commemorates the 100th anniversary of this sculpture, a gift to the United States from the people of France as a demonstration of their sympathy with the nation's founding principles. France simultaneously released a 2.20-franc stamp with matching design. *Intaglio, perforated 11.*

CM1200 *Statue of Liberty*

**CM1200**

| | | MNHVF | UseVF |
|---|---|---|---|
| 22¢ | red and blue *(220,725,000)* | .35 | .20 |
| | Plate block of 4 | 4.00 | |
| | FDC *(July 4, 1986)* | | 1.00 |

**1986. NAVAJO ART ISSUE** depicts 4 Navajo blankets. This issue is the third Folk Art celebrating native American handicrafts. *Offset and intalio, perforated 11.*

CM1201, CM1202, CM1203, CM1204
*Navajo blankets*

**CM1201**

| | | MNHVF | UseVF |
|---|---|---|---|
| 22¢ | multicolored *(240,525,000)* | .40 | .20 |

**CM1202**

| | | MNHVF | UseVF |
|---|---|---|---|
| 22¢ | multicolored | .40 | .20 |

**CM1203**

| | | MNHVF | UseVF |
|---|---|---|---|
| 22¢ | multicolored | .40 | .20 |

**CM1204**

| | | MNHVF | UseVF |
|---|---|---|---|
| 22¢ | multicolored | .40 | .20 |
| | Plate block of 4 | 6.00 | |
| | y. Se-tenant block of 4 CM1201-04 | 3.00 | 1.50 |
| | FDC *(Sept. 4, 1986)* | | 2.00 |
| | vy. Se-tenant block of 4 (engraved) black omitted | 375. | |

## Literary Arts Series

**1986. T.S. ELIOT ISSUE** commemorates Thomas Sterns Eliot, prominent poet, critic, editor, and dramatist, awarded the Nobel Prize for Literature. *Gravure, perforated 11.*

CM1205 *T.S. Eliot*

| CM1205 | | MNHVF | UseVF |
|---|---|---|---|
| 22¢ | **copper red** *(131,700,000)* | .35 | .20 |
| | Plate block of 4 | 2.75 | |
| | FDC *(Sept. 26, 1986)* | | 1.00 |

**1986. WOODCARVED FIGURINES ISSUE** Since Colonial times, woodcarved figurines frequently served as advertisements by merchants displayed outside their shop doors. *Gravure by American Bank Note Co., perforated 11.*

CM1206 *Highlander Figure*

CM1207 *Ship Figurehead*

CM1208 *Nautical Figure*

CM1209 *Cigar Store Figure*

| CM1206 | | MNHVF | UseVF |
|---|---|---|---|
| 22¢ | Highlander figure, tagged *(240,000,000)* | .40 | .20 |

| CM1207 | | MNHVF | UseVF |
|---|---|---|---|
| 22¢ | Ship figurehead, tagged | .40 | .20 |

| CM1208 | | MNHVF | UseVF |
|---|---|---|---|
| 22¢ | Nautical figure, tagged | .40 | .20 |

| CM1209 | | MNHVF | UseVF |
|---|---|---|---|
| 22¢ | Cigar Store figure, tagged | .40 | .20 |
| | Plate block of 4 | 4.50 | |
| | y. Se-tenant block of 4 CM1206-09 | 3.25 | 1.50 |
| | FDC *(Oct. 1, 1986)* | | 1.00 |
| | vy. Block of 4, imperforate vertically | 1450. | |
| | vy1.Pair, any, imperforate, vertically | 300. | |

**1987. MICHIGAN STATEHOOD ISSUE** honors the 150th anniversary of Michigan's admission as the 26th state of the Union. *Gravure, perforated 11.*

CM1210 *White Pine*

| CM1210 | | MNHVF | UseVF |
|---|---|---|---|
| 22¢ | **multicolored,** tagged *(167,430,000)* | .35 | .20 |
| | Plate block of 4 | 2.75 | |
| | Gutter pair | | |
| | FDC *(Jan. 26, 1987)* | | 1.00 |

**1987. PAN-AMERICAN GAMES ISSUE** commemorates the international sports competition held every 4 years since 1957. *Gravure, perforated 11.*

CM1211 *Runners*

| CM1211 | | MNHVF | UseVF |
|---|---|---|---|
| 22¢ | **multicolored,** tagged *(166,555,000)* | .35 | .20 |
| | Plate block of 4 | 2.75 | |
| | FDC *(Jan. 29, 1987)* | | 1.00 |
| | v. metallic silver omitted | 1600. | |

**1987. LOVE STAMP ISSUE** *Gravure, perforated 11 1/2 x 11.*

CM1212 *Love*

| CM1212 | | MNHVF | UseVF |
|---|---|---|---|
| 22¢ | **multicolored,** tagged *(811,560,000)* | .35 | .20 |
| | Plate block of 4 | 2.75 | |
| | FDC *(Jan. 30, 1987)* | | 1.00 |

## Black Heritage Series

**1987. JEAN-BAPTISTE DU SABLE ISSUE** honors the founder of Chicago in the year of that city's sesquicentennial. Du Sable played an active role in the frontier settlement on the Chicago River as a general merchant, fur trader, farmer and Indian overseer. *Gravure, perforated 11.*

CM1213 *Jean-Baptiste du Sable*

| CM1213 | | MNHVF | UseVF |
|---|---|---|---|
| 22¢ | **multicolored,** tagged *(142,905,000)* | .35 | .20 |
| | Plate block of 4 | 3.25 | |
| | FDC *(Feb. 20, 1987)* | | 1.00 |

## Performing Artists Series

**1987. ENRICO CARUSO ISSUE** honors one of the most popular opera performers of all time and the world's highest paid performer in his day. *Gravure by American Bank Note Co., perforated 11.*

CM1214 *Enrico Caruso*

| CM1214 | | MNHVF | UseVF |
|---|---|---|---|
| 22¢ | **multicolored,** tagged *(130,000,000)* | .35 | .20 |
| | Plate block of 4 | 2.75 | |
| | FDC *(Feb. 27, 1987)* | | 1.00 |
| | v. Intaglio black omitted | 5000. | |

**1987. GIRL SCOUTS ISSUE** marks the 75th anniversary of the Girl Scouts. Juliette Low (CM316) formed the 1st Girl Scout troop in the United States, patterned after the English Girl Guides. *Intaglio (Giori Press), perforated 11.*

 CM1215 *Girl Scout Badges*

| CM1215 | | MNHVF | UseVF |
|---|---|---|---|
| 22¢ | **multicolored,** tagged *(149,980,000)* | .35 | .20 |
| | Plate block of 4 | 3.25 | |
| | FDC *(March 12, 1987)* | | 1.00 |
| | v. Black, yellow, magenta, cyan & green omitted | 2750. | |

**1987. SPECIAL OCCASIONS ISSUE** consists of 8 designs (CM1216 and CM1221) each are repeated once in a booklet pane of 10. The stamps were intended for use on greeting cards and other special personal mail. *Gravure, perforated 10.*

CM1216 *Congratulations!*

CM1217 *Get Well!*

CM1218 *Thank You!*

CM1219 *Love You, Dad!*

CM1220 *Best Wishes!*

CM1221 *Happy Birthday!*

CM1222 *Love You, Mother!*

CM1223 *Keep in Touch!*

| CM1216 | | MNHVF | UseVF |
|---|---|---|---|
| 22¢ | Congratulations, tagged *(610,425,000)* | 1.75 | .40 |

| CM1217 | | MNHVF | UseVF |
|---|---|---|---|
| 22¢ | Get Well, tagged | 1.75 | .40 |

| CM1218 | | MNHVF | UseVF |
|---|---|---|---|
| 22¢ | Thank You, tagged | 1.75 | .40 |

| CM1219 | | MNHVF | UseVF |
|---|---|---|---|
| 22¢ | Love You Dad, tagged | 1.75 | .40 |

| CM1220 | | MNHVF | UseVF |
|---|---|---|---|
| 22¢ | Best Wishes, tagged | 1.75 | .40 |

| CM1221 | | MNHVF | UseVF |
|---|---|---|---|
| 22¢ | Happy Birthday, tagged | 1.75 | .40 |

| CM1222 | | MNHVF | UseVF |
|---|---|---|---|
| 22¢ | Love You Mother, tagged | 1.75 | .40 |

| CM1223 | | MNHVF | UseVF |
|---|---|---|---|
| 22¢ | Keep in Touch, tagged | 1.75 | .40 |
| | FDC *(April 20, 1987) any single* | | 1.00 |
| | n. Booklet pane of 10 | 16.00 | 12.00 |
| | FDC | | 5.00 |

*Numbers CM1224 and CM1225 were not assigned.*

**1987. UNITED WAY ISSUE** celebrated the community-based charity's 100th anniversary. *Offset and intaglio, perforated 11.*

 CM1226 *Faces In Profile*

| CM1226 | | MNHVF | UseVF |
|---|---|---|---|
| 22¢ | **multicolored,** tagged *(156,995,000)* | .35 | .20 |
| | Plate block of 4 | 2.75 | |
| | FDC *(April 28, 1987)* | | 1.00 |

**1987. AMERICAN WILDLIFE ISSUE** 50 different stamps se-tenant in one pane released during Capex 87 in Toronto, Canada. Stamps feature animals indigenous to North America and Hawaii. *Gravure, perforated 11.*

| CM1227 | | MNHVF | UseVF |
|---|---|---|---|
| 22¢ | **Barn Swallow,** tagged | 1.50 | .55 |

| CM1228 | | MNHVF | UseVF |
|---|---|---|---|
| 22¢ | **Monarch Butterfly,** tagged | 1.50 | .55 |

| CM1229 | | MNHVF | UseVF |
|---|---|---|---|
| 22¢ | **Bighorn Sheep,** tagged | 1.50 | .55 |

| CM1230 | | MNHVF | UseVF |
|---|---|---|---|
| 22¢ | **Broad-tailed Hummingbird,** tagged | 1.50 | .55 |

| CM1231 | | MNHVF | UseVF |
|---|---|---|---|
| 22¢ | **Cottontail,** tagged | 1.50 | .55 |

| CM1232 | | MNHVF | UseVF |
|---|---|---|---|
| 22¢ | **Osprey,** tagged | 1.50 | .55 |

| CM1233 | | MNHVF | UseVF |
|---|---|---|---|
| 22¢ | **Mountain Lion,** tagged | 1.50 | .55 |

| CM1234 | | MNHVF | UseVF |
|---|---|---|---|
| 22¢ | **Luna Moth,** tagged | 1.50 | .55 |

| CM1235 | | MNHVF | UseVF |
|---|---|---|---|
| 22¢ | **Mule Deer,** tagged | 1.50 | .55 |

| CM1236 | | MNHVF | UseVF |
|---|---|---|---|
| 22¢ | **Gray Squirrel,** tagged | 1.50 | .55 |

| CM1237 | | MNHVF | UseVF |
|---|---|---|---|
| 22¢ | **Armadillo,** tagged | 1.50 | .55 |

| CM1238 | | MNHVF | UseVF |
|---|---|---|---|
| 22¢ | **Eastern Chipmunk,** tagged | 1.50 | .55 |

| CM1239 | | MNHVF | UseVF |
|---|---|---|---|
| 22¢ | **Moose,** tagged | 1.50 | .55 |

| CM1240 | | MNHVF | UseVF |
|---|---|---|---|
| 22¢ | **Black Bear,** tagged | 1.50 | .55 |

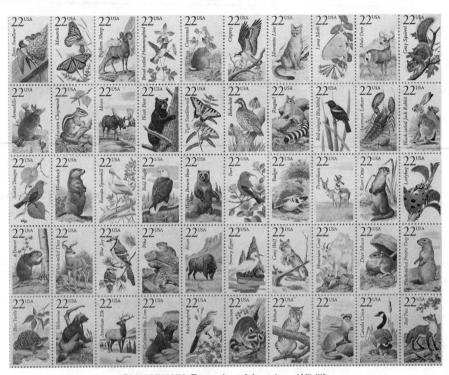

CM1227-1276 *Examples of American Wildlife*

| | | MNHVF | UseVF |
|---|---|---|---|
| **CM1241** | | MNHVF | UseVF |
| 22¢ | **Tiger Swallowtail,** tagged | 1.50 | .55 |
| **CM1242** | | MNHVF | UseVF |
| 22¢ | **Bobwhite,** tagged | 1.50 | .55 |
| **CM1243** | | MNHVF | UseVF |
| 22¢ | **Ringtail,** tagged | 1.50 | .55 |
| **CM1244** | | MNHVF | UseVF |
| 22¢ | **Red-winged Blackbird,** tagged | 1.50 | .55 |
| **CM1245** | | MNHVF | UseVF |
| 22¢ | **American Lobster,** tagged | 1.50 | .55 |
| **CM1246** | | MNHVF | UseVF |
| 22¢ | **Black-tailed Jack Rabbit,** tagged | 1.50 | .55 |
| **CM1247** | | MNHVF | UseVF |
| 22¢ | **Scarlet Tanager,** tagged | 1.50 | .55 |
| **CM1248** | | MNHVF | UseVF |
| 22¢ | **Woodchuck,** tagged | 1.50 | .55 |
| **CM1249** | | MNHVF | UseVF |
| 22¢ | **Roseate Spoonbill,** tagged | 1.50 | .55 |
| **CM1250** | | MNHVF | UseVF |
| 22¢ | **Bald Eagle,** tagged | 1.50 | .55 |
| **CM1251** | | MNHVF | UseVF |
| 22¢ | **Alaskan Brown Bear,** tagged | 1.50 | .55 |
| **CM1252** | | MNHVF | UseVF |
| 22¢ | **Iiwi,** tagged | 1.50 | .55 |
| **CM1253** | | MNHVF | UseVF |
| 22¢ | **Badger,** tagged | 1.50 | .55 |
| **CM1254** | | MNHVF | UseVF |
| 22¢ | **Pronghorn,** tagged | 1.50 | .55 |
| **CM1255** | | MNHVF | UseVF |
| 22¢ | **River Otter,** tagged | 1.50 | .55 |
| **CM1256** | | MNHVF | UseVF |
| 22¢ | **Ladybug,** tagged | 1.50 | .55 |
| **CM1257** | | MNHVF | UseVF |
| 22¢ | **Beaver,** tagged | 1.50 | .55 |
| **CM1258** | | MNHVF | UseVF |
| 22¢ | **White-tailed Deer,** tagged | 1.50 | .55 |
| **CM1259** | | MNHVF | UseVF |
| 22¢ | **Blue Jay,** tagged | 1.50 | .55 |

| | | MNHVF | UseVF |
|---|---|---|---|
| **CM1260** | | MNHVF | UseVF |
| 22¢ | **Pika,** tagged | 1.50 | .55 |
| **CM1261** | | MNHVF | UseVF |
| 22¢ | **Bison,** tagged | 1.50 | .55 |
| **CM1262** | | MNHVF | UseVF |
| 22¢ | **Snowy Egret,** tagged | 1.50 | .55 |
| **CM1263** | | MNHVF | UseVF |
| 22¢ | **Gray Wolf,** tagged | 1.50 | .55 |
| **CM1264** | | MNHVF | UseVF |
| 22¢ | **Mountain Goat,** tagged | 1.50 | .55 |
| **CM1265** | | MNHVF | UseVF |
| 22¢ | **Deer Mouse,** tagged | 1.50 | .55 |
| **CM1266** | | MNHVF | UseVF |
| 22¢ | **Black-tailed Prairie Dog,** tagged | 1.50 | .55 |
| **CM1267** | | MNHVF | UseVF |
| 22¢ | **Box Turtle,** tagged | 1.50 | .55 |
| **CM1268** | | MNHVF | UseVF |
| 22¢ | **Wolverine,** tagged | 1.50 | .55 |
| **CM1269** | | MNHVF | UseVF |
| 22¢ | **American Elk,** tagged | 1.50 | .55 |
| **CM1270** | | MNHVF | UseVF |
| 22¢ | **California Sea Lion,** tagged | 1.50 | .55 |
| **CM1271** | | MNHVF | UseVF |
| 22¢ | **Mockingbird,** tagged | 1.50 | .55 |
| **CM1272** | | MNHVF | UseVF |
| 22¢ | **Raccoon,** tagged | 1.50 | .55 |
| **CM1273** | | MNHVF | UseVF |
| 22¢ | **Bobcat,** tagged | 1.50 | .55 |
| **CM1274** | | MNHVF | UseVF |
| 22¢ | **Black-footed Ferret,** tagged | 1.50 | .55 |
| **CM1275** | | MNHVF | UseVF |
| 22¢ | **Canada Goose,** tagged | 1.50 | .55 |
| **CM1276** | | MNHVF | UseVF |
| 22¢ | **Red Fox,** tagged | 1.50 | .55 |
| | Pane of 50 | 65.00 | 20.00 |
| | FDC *(June 13, 1987),* full pane | | 25.00 |
| | v. Red omitted, any single | — | |

**1987. DELAWARE STATEHOOD ISSUE** was the 1st stamp in a series commemorating the bicentennial of the ratification of the Constitution. Delaware was the 1st state to vote for ratification. *Offset and intaglio by BEP, perforated 11.*

CM1277 *Delaware State Seal*

| CM1277 | | MNHVF | UseVF |
|---|---|---|---|
| 22¢ | multicolored, tagged *(166,725,000)* | .35 | .20 |
| | Plate block of 4 | 3.00 | |
| | FDC *(July 4, 1987)* | | 1.00 |

**1987. FRIENDSHIP WITH MOROCCO ISSUE** marks the bicentennial of diplomatic relations between the United States and Morocco. Morocco issued a stamp at the same time (Morocco 1281). *Intaglio (Giori Press), perforated 11.*

CM1278 *Arbesque from door of Dar Batha Palace, Fez, Morocco.*

| CM1278 | | MNHVF | UseVF |
|---|---|---|---|
| 22¢ | red and black, tagged *(157,475,000)* | .35 | .20 |
| | Plate block of 4 | 2.75 | |
| | FDC *(July 17, 1987)* | | 1.00 |
| | v. Intaglio black omitted | 350. | |

**1987. WILLIAM FAULKNER ISSUE** Literary Arts Series honors the Nobel Prize-winning novelist and poet, noted for his writings about life in the South. *Intaglio, perforated 11.*

CM1279 *William Faulkner*

| CM1279 | | MNHVF | UseVF |
|---|---|---|---|
| 22¢ | green, tagged *(156,225,000)* | .35 | .20 |
| | Plate block of 4 | 2.75 | |
| | FDC *(Aug. 3, 1987)* | | 1.00 |
| | v. Imperforate single | | |

NOTE: Imperforate singles are untagged and from printer's waste.

## American Folk Art Series

**1987. LACEMAKING ISSUE** featuring 4 different designs of delicate needlework. *Offset and intaglio, perforated 11.*
Intaglio white ink was printed on top of offset blue to achieve the lace effect.

CM1280 *Squash Blossoms*

CM1281 *Floral Design*

CM1282 *Floral Lace*

CM1283 *Dogwood Blossoms*

| CM1280 | | MNHVF | UseVF |
|---|---|---|---|
| 22¢ | Squash Blossoms, tagged *(163,980,000)* | .40 | .20 |

| CM1281 | | MNHVF | UseVF |
|---|---|---|---|
| 22¢ | Floral Design, tagged | .40 | .20 |

| CM1282 | | MNHVF | UseVF |
|---|---|---|---|
| 22¢ | Floral Design, tagged | .40 | .20 |

| CM1283 | | MNHVF | UseVF |
|---|---|---|---|
| 22¢ | Dogwood Blossoms, tagged | .40 | .20 |
| | Plate block of 4 | 5.00 | |
| | y. Se-tenant block of 4 CM1280-83 | 2.50 | 1.50 |
| | FDC *(Aug. 14, 1987)* | | 1.00 |
| | vy. Se-tenant block of 4, white omitted | 900. | |
| | vy1.White omitted, any single | 165. | |

## Constitution Ratification Bicentennial Series

**1987. PENNSYLVANIA STATEHOOD ISSUE** The Keystone State ratified the U.S. Constitution on Dec. 12, 1787. *Gravure by American Bank Note Co., perforated 11.*

CM1284 *Independence Hall, Philadelphia*

| CM1284 | | MNHVF | UseVF |
|---|---|---|---|
| 22¢ | multicolored, tagged *(186,575,000)* | .35 | .20 |
| | Plate block of 4 | 3.95 | |
| | FDC *(Aug. 26, 1987)* | | |

**1987. CONSTITUTION BICENTENNIAL ISSUE** released in booklet format, commemorates the 200th anniversary of the drafting of the U.S. Constitution with excerpts from the preamble. *Gravure, perforated 10 horizontally.*

CM1285-89

**CM1285**

| 22¢ | Constitution Bicentennial, tagged | MNHVF | UseVF |
|---|---|---|---|
| | (584,340,000) | .75 | .25 |

**CM1286**

| 22¢ | We The People..., tagged | MNHVF | UseVF |
|---|---|---|---|
| | | .75 | .25 |

**CM1287**

| 22¢ | Establish Justice..., tagged | MNHVF | UseVF |
|---|---|---|---|
| | | .75 | .25 |

**CM1288**

| 22¢ | Secure Liberty..., tagged | MNHVF | UseVF |
|---|---|---|---|
| | | .75 | .25 |

**CM1289**

| 22¢ | Ordain..., tagged | MNHVF | UseVF |
|---|---|---|---|
| | | .75 | .25 |
| | FDC (Aug. 28, 1987), any single | | 1.00 |
| | n. Se-tenant booklet pane of 5 CM1285-89 | 4.25 | 3.50 |
| | FDC | | 2.00 |

**1987. NEW JERSEY STATEHOOD ISSUE** Constitution Ratification Bicentennial Series *Gravure by American Bank Note Co., perforated 11.*

CM1290 *Farmer Carrying Produce*

**CM1290**

| 22¢ | multicolored, tagged (184,325,000) | MNHVF | UseVF |
|---|---|---|---|
| | | .35 | .20 |
| | Plate block of 4 | 3.50 | |
| | FDC (Sept. 11, 1987) | | 1.00 |
| | v. Intaglio black omitted | 6500. | |

**1987. CONSTITUTION BICENTENNIAL ISSUE** honors the 200th anniversary of the signing of the document. *Offset and intaglio, perforated 11.*

CM1291 *Constitution and feather pen*

**CM1291**

| 22¢ | multicolored, tagged (168,995,000) | MNHVF | UseVF |
|---|---|---|---|
| | | .35 | .20 |
| | Plate block of 4 | 3.25 | |
| | FDC (Sept. 17, 1987) | | 1.00 |

**1987. CERTIFIED PUBLIC ACCOUNTANTS ISSUE** honors the centennial of the accounting profession in the United States. *Intaglio, perforated 11.*

CM1292 *Spreadsheet and Pen*

**CM1292**

| 22¢ | multicolored, tagged (163,120,000) | MNHVF | UseVF |
|---|---|---|---|
| | | .35 | .20 |
| | Plate block of 4 | | |
| | FDC (Sept. 21, 1987) | | 1.00 |
| | v. Intaglio black omitted | 900. | |

**1987. STEAM LOCOMOTIVE ISSUE** a 5-stamp booklet, pays tribute to the steam locomotives that drove the railroad revolution in America. *Offset and intaglio, perforated 10, horizontally.*

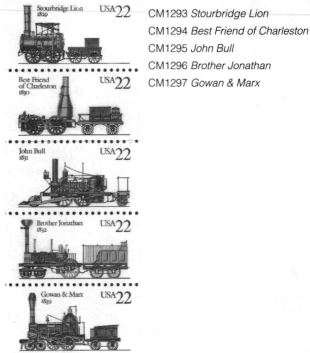

CM1293 *Stourbridge Lion*

CM1294 *Best Friend of Charleston*

CM1295 *John Bull*

CM1296 *Brother Jonathan*

CM1297 *Gowan & Marx*

**CM1293**

| 22¢ | Stourbridge Lion, tagged | MNHVF | UseVF |
|---|---|---|---|
| | | .75 | .25 |

**CM1294**

| 22¢ | Best Friend of Charleston, tagged | MNHVF | UseVF |
|---|---|---|---|
| | | .75 | .25 |

**CM1295**

| 22¢ | John Bull, tagged | MNHVF | UseVF |
|---|---|---|---|
| | | .75 | .25 |

**CM1296**

| 22¢ | Brother Jonathan, tagged | MNHVF | UseVF |
|---|---|---|---|
| | | .75 | .25 |
| | v. Red omitted | 1100. | |

**CM1297**

| 22¢ | Gowan & Marx, tagged | MNHVF | UseVF |
|---|---|---|---|
| | | .75 | .25 |
| | Blue omitted | — | |
| | FDC (Oct. 1, 1993), any single | | 1.00 |
| | n. Se-tenant booklet pane of 5, CM1293-97 | 3.75 | 2.50 |
| | FDC | | 5.00 |
| | vn. Booklet pane of 5, black omitted | — | |

**1988. GEORGIA STATEHOOD ISSUE** Constitution Ratification Bicentennial Series *Gravure, perforated 11.*

CM1298 *Live Oak and Atlanta skyline*

**CM1298**

| | | MNHVF | UseVF |
|---|---|---|---|
| 22¢ | **multicolored,** tagged *(165,845,000)* | .35 | .20 |
| | Plate block of 4 | 3.50 | |
| | FDC *(Jan. 6, 1988)* | | 1.00 |

**1988. CONNECTICUT STATEHOOD ISSUE** Constitution Ratification Bicentennial Series
*Offset and intaglio, perforated 11.*

CM1299 *Harbor Scene*

**CM1299**

| | | MNHVF | UseVF |
|---|---|---|---|
| 22¢ | **multicolored,** tagged *(155,170,000)* | .35 | .20 |
| | Plate block of 4 | 3.50 | |
| | FDC *(Jan. 9, 1988)* | | 1.00 |

**1988. WINTER OLYMPICS ISSUE** honors the 1988 Winter Games at Calgary, Alberta, Canada. *Gravure by American Bank Note Co., perforated 11.*

CM1300 *Alpine Skier*

**CM1300**

| | | MNHVF | UseVF |
|---|---|---|---|
| 22¢ | **multicolored,** tagged *(158,870,000)* | .35 | .20 |
| | Plate block of 4 | 3.25 | |
| | FDC *(Jan. 10, 1988)* | | 1.00 |

**1988. AUSTRALIA BICENTENNIAL ISSUE** marked the 200th anniversary of the 1st European settlement in Australia. The stamp was issued at the same time as one by Australia (Australia 1175), and is the 19th U.S. joint issue. *Gravure, perforated 11.*

CM1301 *Cartoon of Australian Koala and American Bald Eagle*

**CM1301**

| | | MNHVF | UseVF |
|---|---|---|---|
| 22¢ | **multicolored,** tagged *(145,560,000)* | .35 | .20 |
| | Plate block of 4 | 2.75 | |
| | FDC *(Jan. 26, 1988)* | | 1.00 |

**1988. JAMES WELDON JOHNSON ISSUE** Black Heritage Series honors the educator, diplomat, lawyer, author and lyricist. *Gravure by American Bank Note Co., perforated 11.*

CM1302 *James Weldon Johnson*

**CM1302**

| | | MNHVF | UseVF |
|---|---|---|---|
| 22¢ | **multicolored,** tagged *(97,300,000)* | .35 | .20 |
| | Plate block of 4 | 3.00 | |
| | FDC *(Feb. 2, 1988)* | | 1.00 |

**1988. CATS ISSUE** depicts 8 popular feline breeds. *Gravure by American Bank Note Co., perforated 11.*

CM1303 *Siamese, Exotic Shorthair*

CM1304 *Abyssinian, Himalayan*

CM1305 *Maine Coon Cat, Burmese*

CM1306 *American Shorthair Cat, Persian*

**CM1303**

| | | MNHVF | UseVF |
|---|---|---|---|
| 22¢ | Siamese, Exotic Shorthair, tagged | 1.00 | .20 |
| | *(158,556,000)* | | |

**CM1304**

| | | MNHVF | UseVF |
|---|---|---|---|
| 22¢ | Abyssinian, Himalayan, tagged | 1.00 | .20 |

**CM1305**

| | | MNHVF | UseVF |
|---|---|---|---|
| 22¢ | Maine Coon Cat, Burmese, tagged | 1.00 | .20 |

**CM1306**

| | | MNHVF | UseVF |
|---|---|---|---|
| 22¢ | American Shorthair, Persian, tagged | 1.00 | .20 |
| | Plate block of 4 | 5.75 | |
| | y. Se-tenant block of 4 CM1303-06 | 4.50 | 2.50 |
| | FDC *(Feb. 5, 1988)* any single | 1.00 | |

**1988. MASSACHUSETTS STATEHOOD ISSUE** Massachusetts' own constitution was a model for the federal document. *Intaglio, perforated 11.*

CM1307 *Old Statehouse*

**CM1307**

| | | MNHVF | UseVF |
|---|---|---|---|
| 22¢ | **dark blue and dark red,** tagged | .35 | .20 |
| | *(102,100,000)* | | |
| | Plate block of 4 | 3.50 | |
| | FDC *(Feb. 6, 1988)* | | 1.00 |

**1988. MARYLAND STATEHOOD ISSUE** *Offset and intaglio, perforated 11.*

CM1308 *Skipjack Sailboat and Annapolis*

| CM1308 | | MNHVF | UseVF |
|---|---|---|---|
| 22¢ | **multicolored,** tagged *(103,325,000)* | .35 | .20 |
| | Plate block of 4 | 3.50 | |
| | FDC *(Feb. 15, 1988)* | | 1.00 |

## American Sports Series

**1988. KNUTE ROCKNE ISSUE** honors the famed player and Notre Dame University football coach credited with developing the forward pass. *Offset and intaglio, perforated 11.*

CM1309 *Knute Rockne*

| CM1309 | | MNHVF | UseVF |
|---|---|---|---|
| 22¢ | **multicolored,** tagged *(97,300,000)* | .35 | .20 |
| | Plate block of 4 | 3.95 | |
| | FDC *(March 9, 1988)* | | 1.00 |

**1988. SOUTH CAROLINA STATEHOOD ISSUE** Constitution Ratification Bicentennial Series
the 1st commemorative stamp paying the 25-cent first-class rate. *Gravure by American Bank Note Co., perforated 11.*

CM1310 *Palmetto Trees*

| CM1310 | | MNHVF | UseVF |
|---|---|---|---|
| 25¢ | **multicolored,** tagged *(162,045,000)* | .40 | .20 |
| | Plate block of 4 | 3.95 | |
| | FDC *(May 23, 1988)* | | 1.00 |
| v. | Horizontal strip of 3, vertically imperforate between | 10450. | |

**1988. FRANCIS OUIMET ISSUE** honors the 75th anniversary of his victory at the U.S. Open Golf Championship, which made him the 1st amateur to win the event. *Gravure by American Bank Note Co., perforated 11.*

CM1311 *Francis Ouimet*

| CM1311 | | MNHVF | UseVF |
|---|---|---|---|
| 25¢ | **multicolored,** tagged *(153,045,000)* | .40 | .20 |
| | Plate block of 4 | 5.75 | |
| | FDC *(June 13, 1988)* | | 1.00 |

## Constitution Ratification Bicentennial Series

**1988. NEW HAMPSHIRE STATEHOOD ISSUE** (See also CM380.) *Gravure by American Bank Note Co., perforated 11.*

CM1312 *Old Man of the Mountain*

| CM1312 | | MNHVF | UseVF |
|---|---|---|---|
| 25¢ | **multicolored,** tagged *(153,295,000)* | .40 | .20 |
| | Plate block of 4 | 3.95 | |
| | FDC *(June 21, 1988)* | | 1.00 |

**1988. VIRGINIA STATEHOOD ISSUE** Constitution Ratification Bicentennial Series
(See also CM380.) *Offset and intaglio, perforated 11.*

CM1313 *Old Capitol Building , Williamsburg*

| CM1313 | | MNHVF | UseVF |
|---|---|---|---|
| 25¢ | **multicolored,** tagged *(153,295,000)* | .40 | .20 |
| | Plate block of 4 | 3.95 | |
| | FDC *(June 25, 1988)* | | 1.00 |

**1988. LOVE ISSUE** 7th in the series begun in 1982, featured a rose and was released in Pasadena, Calif., home of the annual Rose Bowl. *Gravure, perforated 11.*

CM1314 *Rose*

| CM1314 | | MNHVF | UseVF |
|---|---|---|---|
| 25¢ | **multicolored,** tagged *(841,240,000)* | .40 | .20 |
| | Plate block of 4 | 3.25 | |
| | FDC *(July 4, 1988)* | | 1.00 |
| | v. Imperforate pair | 2750. | |

**1988. NEW YORK STATEHOOD ISSUE** Constitution Ratification Bicentennial Series
Offset and intaglio, perforated 11.

CM1315 *Federal Hall, Wall Street and Trinity Church Steeple.*

| CM1315 | | MNHVF | UseVF |
|---|---|---|---|
| 25¢ | **multicolored,** tagged *(183,290,000)* | .40 | .20 |
| | Plate block of 4 | 3.25 | |
| | FDC *(July 26, 1988)* | | 1.00 |

**1988. LOVE ISSUE** the 2nd of the year, this one in a 45-cent different denomination, was released to cover the postal rate for 2 ounces of first-class mail (such as a standard wedding invitation and R.S.V.P. envelope). *Gravure, perforated 11.*

CM1316 *Roses*

| CM1316 | | MNHVF | UseVF |
|---|---|---|---|
| 45¢ | **multicolored,** tagged *(169,765,000)* | 1.35 | .20 |
| | Plate block of 4 | 5.75 | |
| | FDC *(Aug. 8, 1988)* | | 1.00 |

**1988. SUMMER OLYMPIC GAMES ISSUE** honors the 14th Summer Games in Seoul, Korea. *Gravure, perforated 11.*

CM1317 *Gymnast on rings*

| CM1317 | | MNHVF | UseVF |
|---|---|---|---|
| 25¢ | **multicolored,** tagged *(157,215,000)* | .40 | .20 |
| | Plate block of 4 | 3.50 | |
| | FDC *(Aug. 19, 1988)* | | 1.00 |

**1988. CLASSIC CARS ISSUE** featured 5 automobiles of 1925-42 in se-tenant booklet pane. *Offset and intaglio, perforated 10 horizontally.*

CM1318-CM1322

| CM1318 | | MNHVF | UseVF |
|---|---|---|---|
| 25¢ | Locomobile, tagged *(635,238,000)* | 2.00 | .50 |

| CM1319 | | MNHVF | UseVF |
|---|---|---|---|
| 25¢ | Pierce-Arrow, tagged | 2.00 | .50 |

| CM1320 | | MNHVF | UseVF |
|---|---|---|---|
| 25¢ | Cord, tagged | 2.00 | .50 |

| CM1321 | | MNHVF | UseVF |
|---|---|---|---|
| 25¢ | Packard, tagged | 2.00 | .50 |

| CM1322 | | MNHVF | UseVF |
|---|---|---|---|
| 25¢ | Duesenberg, tagged | 2.00 | .50 |
| | FDC *(Aug. 25, 1988),* any single | | 1.00 |
| | n. Se-tenant booklet pane of 5, CM1318-22 | 10.00 | |
| | FDC | | 3.75 |

**1988. ANTARCTIC EXPLORERS ISSUE** salutes 4 men who first explored the vast ice-capped continent of Antarctica. *Gravure by American Bank Note Co., perforated 11.*

CM1323 *Nathaniel Palmer*

CM1324 *Lt. Charles Wilkes*

CM1325 *Richard E. Byrd*

CM1326 *Lincoln Ellsworth*

| CM1323 | | MNHVF | UseVF |
|---|---|---|---|
| 25¢ | Nathanel Palmer, tagged *(162,142,500)* | 1.00 | .20 |

| CM1324 | | MNHVF | UseVF |
|---|---|---|---|
| 25¢ | Lt. Charles Wilkes, tagged | 1.00 | .20 |

| CM1325 | | MNHVF | UseVF |
|---|---|---|---|
| 25¢ | R.E. Byrd, tagged | 1.00 | .20 |

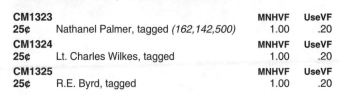

**CM1326**

| | | MNHVF | UseVF |
|---|---|---|---|
| **25¢** | Lincoln Ellsworth, tagged | 1.00 | .20 |
| | Plate block of 4 | 8.00 | |
| | y.  Se-tenant block of 4 CM1323-26 | 4.75 | 3.00 |
| | FDC *(Sept. 14, 1988)* | | 2.00 |
| | v.  Block of 4, intaglio black omitted | 1500. | |
| | v1. Block of 4, imperforate horizontally | 3000. | |

## Folk Art Series

**1988. CAROUSEL ANIMAL ISSUE** presents examples of a popular art form. *Offset and intaglio, perforated 11.*

CM1327 *Deer*

CM1328 *Horse*

CM1329 *Camel*

CM1330 *Goat*

**CM1327**

| | | MNHVF | UseVF |
|---|---|---|---|
| **25¢** | Deer, tagged *(305,015,000)* | 1.00 | .20 |

**CM1328**

| | | MNHVF | UseVF |
|---|---|---|---|
| **25¢** | Horse, tagged | 1.00 | .20 |

**CM1329**

| | | MNHVF | UseVF |
|---|---|---|---|
| **25¢** | Camel, tagged | 1.00 | .20 |

**CM1330**

| | | MNHVF | UseVF |
|---|---|---|---|
| **25¢** | Goat, tagged | 1.00 | .20 |
| | Plate block of 4 | 6.00 | |
| | y.  Se-tenant block of 4 CM1327-30 | 4.75 | 2.00 |
| | FDC *(Oct. 1, 1988)* | | 2.00 |

**1988. SPECIAL OCCASIONS ISSUE** has 4 different designs. Each booklet pane contains 6 stamps, 3 each of 2 designs. The two different panes bring the total to 12 stamps (3 of each design). *Gravure by American Bank Note Co., perforated 11.*

CM1331 *Happy Birthday*

**CM1331**

| | | MNHVF | UseVF |
|---|---|---|---|
| **25¢** | **multicolored,** tagged *(480,000,000)* | 1.00 | .20 |

CM1332 *Best Wishes*

**CM1332**

| | | MNHVF | UseVF |
|---|---|---|---|
| **25¢** | **multicolored,** tagged | 1.00 | .20 |
| | n.  Booklet pane of 6, 3 each CM1331 & | 5.00 | 4.00 |
| | CM1332 with a gutter between | | |

CM1333 *Thinking of You*

**CM1333**

| | | MNHVF | UseVF |
|---|---|---|---|
| **25¢** | **multicolored,** tagged | 1.00 | .20 |

CM1334 *Love You*

**CM1334**

| | | MNHVF | UseVF |
|---|---|---|---|
| **25¢** | **multicolored,** tagged | 1.00 | .20 |
| | n.  Booklet pane of 6, 3 each CM1333 & | 5.00 | 4.00 |
| | CM1334 with a gutter between | | |
| | nv. As above, imperforate horizontally | — | |
| | FDC *(Oct. 22, 1988)* any single | — | |

**1989. MONTANA STATEHOOD ISSUE** commemorates the state's centennial with a design by artist Charles Russell (see also CM528). *Offset and intaglio, perforated 11.*

CM1335 *C.M. Russell and Friends*

**CM1335**

| | | MNHVF | UseVF |
|---|---|---|---|
| **25¢** | **multicolored,** tagged | .40 | .20 |
| | Plate block of 4 | 4.00 | |
| | FDC *(Jan. 15, 1989)* | | 1.00 |

## Black Heritage Series

**1989. A. PHILIP RANDOLPH ISSUE** honors a prominent, respected and indefatigable voice for the rights of minority labor. *Gravure, perforated 11.*

CM1336 *A. Philip Randolph*

**CM1336**

| | | MNHVF | UseVF |
|---|---|---|---|
| **25¢** | **multicolored,** tagged *(151,675,000)* | .40 | .20 |
| | Plate block of 4 | 3.75 | |
| | FDC *(Feb. 3, 1989)* | | 1.00 |

**1989. NORTH DAKOTA STATEHOOD ISSUE** marks the centennial of the 39th state to enter the Union. *Gravure by American Bank Note Co., perforated 11.*

CM1337 *Grain Elevator*

| CM1337 | | MNHVF | UseVF |
|---|---|---|---|
| 25¢ | multicolored, tagged *(163,000,000)* | .40 | .20 |
| | Plate block of 4 | 3.50 | |
| | FDC *(Feb. 21, 1989)* | | 1.00 |

**1989. WASHINGTON STATEHOOD ISSUE** marks the centennial of the 40th state to enter the Union. *Gravure by American Bank Note Co., perforated 11.*

CM1338 *Mount Rainier*

| CM1338 | | MNHVF | UseVF |
|---|---|---|---|
| 25¢ | multicolored, tagged *(264,625,000)* | .75 | .20 |
| | Plate block of 4 | 1.90 | |
| | FDC *(Feb. 22, 1989)* | | 1.00 |

**1989. STEAMBOATS ISSUE** a se-tenant 5-stamp booklet issue depicts 5 of America's earliest and most innovative craft. *Offset and intaglio, perforated 11.*

CM1339 *Experiment*

CM1340 *Phoenix*

CM1341 *New Orleans*

CM1342 *Washington*

CM1343 *Walk in the Water*

| CM1339 | | MNHVF | UseVF |
|---|---|---|---|
| 25¢ | Experiment, tagged *(204,984,000)* | .75 | .20 |

| CM1340 | | MNHVF | UseVF |
|---|---|---|---|
| 25¢ | Phoenix, tagged | .75 | .20 |

| CM1341 | | MNHVF | UseVF |
|---|---|---|---|
| 25¢ | New Orleans, tagged | .75 | .20 |

| CM1342 | | MNHVF | UseVF |
|---|---|---|---|
| 25¢ | Washington, tagged | .75 | .20 |

| CM1343 | | MNHVF | UseVF |
|---|---|---|---|
| 25¢ | Walk in the Water, tagged | .75 | .20 |
| | FDC *(March 3, 1989), any single* | | 1.00 |
| | n. Se-tenant booklet pane CM1339-43 | 3.60 | 1.00 |
| | FDC | | 2.00 |

**1989. WORLD STAMP EXPO '89 ISSUE** honors the first-ever international stamp show to be sponsored by the U.S. Postal Service. The stamp depicted is the 90-cent Lincoln from the 1869 Pictorial series (No. 96). *Offset and intaglio, perforated 11.*

CM1344 *World Stamp Expo '89*

| CM1344 | | MNHVF | UseVF |
|---|---|---|---|
| 25¢ | red, gray and black *(103,835,000)* | .40 | .20 |
| | Plate block of 4 | 3.00 | |
| | FDC *(March 16, 1989)* | | 1.00 |

**1989. ARTURO TOSCANINI ISSUE** saluted a man who many consider the greatest conductor of all time. *Gravure by American Bank Note Co., perforated 11.*

CM1345 *Arturo Toscanini*

| CM1345 | | MNHVF | UseVF |
|---|---|---|---|
| 25¢ | multicolored, tagged *(152,250,000)* | .40 | .20 |
| | Plate block of 4 | 3.50 | |
| | FDC *(March 25, 1989)* | | 1.00 |

**1989. HOUSE OF REPRESENTATIVES ISSUE** is 1st in a series of 4 stamps honoring the 3 branches of government set by the U.S. Constitution. *Offset and intaglio, perforated 11.*

CM1346 *Car of History. From a marble work clock by Carlo Franzoni.*

| CM1346 | | MNHVF | UseVF |
|---|---|---|---|
| 25¢ | **multicolored,** tagged *(138,760,000)* | .40 | .20 |
| | Plate block of 4 | 3.75 | |
| | FDC *(April 4, 1989)* | | 1.00 |

**1989. SENATE ISSUE** honors the bicentennial of the U.S. Senate, the series honors branches of government established by the U.S. Constitution. *Offset and intaglio, perforated 11.*

 CM1347 *Old Senate Chamber Eagle and Shield*

| CM1347 | | MNHVF | UseVF |
|---|---|---|---|
| 25¢ | **multicolored,** tagged *(137,985,000)* | .40 | .20 |
| | Plate block of 4 | 3.75 | |
| | FDC *(April 6, 1989)* | | 1.00 |

## Branches of Government Series

**1989. EXECUTIVE BRANCH ISSUE** honors George Washington as the 1st person to head this government branch. *Offset and intaglio, perforated 11.*

 CM1348 *George Washington*

| CM1348 | | MNHVF | UseVF |
|---|---|---|---|
| 25¢ | **multicolored,** tagged *(138,580,000)* | .40 | .20 |
| | Plate block of 4 | 4.25 | |
| | FDC *(April 16, 1989)* | | 1.00 |

**1989. SOUTH DAKOTA STATEHOOD ISSUE** honors the centennial of the 41st state. *Gravure by American Bank Note Co., perforated 11.*

 CM1349 *Pasque flower, Pioneer Woman and Sod House.*

| CM1349 | | MNHVF | UseVF |
|---|---|---|---|
| 25¢ | **multicolored,** tagged *(164,680,000)* | .40 | .20 |
| | Plate block of 4 | 3.00 | |
| | FDC *(May 3, 1989)* | | 1.00 |

## American Sports Series

**1989. LOU GERHIG ISSUE** recognizes one of baseball's immortals, the "Iron Horse" of the New York Yankees. *Gravure by American Bank Note Co., perforated 11.*

 CM1350 *Lou Gehrig*

| CM1350 | | MNHVF | UseVF |
|---|---|---|---|
| 25¢ | **multicolored,** tagged *(138,760,000)* | 1.10 | .20 |
| | Plate block of 4 | 5.25 | |
| | FDC *(June 10, 1989)* | | 1.00 |

## Literary Arts Series

**1989. ERNEST HEMINGWAY ISSUE** honors the Nobel Prize-winning author of *The Sun Also Rises* and *For Whom The Bell Tolls. Gravure by American Bank Note Co., perforated 11.*

 CM1351 *Ernest Hemingway*

| CM1351 | | MNHVF | UseVF |
|---|---|---|---|
| 25¢ | **multicolored,** tagged *(191,755,000)* | .40 | .20 |
| | Plate block of 4 | 3.00 | |
| | FDC *(July 17, 1989)* | | 1.00 |

**1989. MOON LANDING ANNIVERSARY ISSUE** commemorates the 20th anniversary of man's first steps on the Moon. The stamp was the 1st to meet the basic Priority Mail rate. *Offset and intaglio, perforated 11.*

 CM1352 *Astronauts and Flag on Moon.*

| CM1352 | | MNHVF | UseVF |
|---|---|---|---|
| $2.40 | **multicolored,** tagged | 6.00 | 2.25 |
| | Plate block of 4 | 28.50 | |
| | FDC *(July 20, 1989)* | | 4.00 |
| | v. Intaglio black omitted | 2750. | |
| | v1. Offset black omitted | 4500. | |
| | v2. Imperforate pair | 900. | |

**1989. NORTH CAROLINA STATEHOOD ISSUE** Gravure by American Bank Note Co., perforated 11.

November 21, 1789

North Carolina

CM1353 *Dogwood*

| CM1353 | | MNHVF | UseVF |
|---|---|---|---|
| 25¢ | **multicolored,** tagged *(179,800,000)* | .40 | .20 |
| | Plate block of 4 | 3.95 | |
| | FDC *(Aug. 22, 1989)* | | 1.00 |

**1989. LETTER CARRIERS ISSUE** pays tribute to those who carry America's mail to over 100 million delivery points. *Gravure by American Bank Note Co., perforated 11.*

CM1354 *Letter Carrier Caricatures*

| CM1354 | | MNHVF | UseVF |
|---|---|---|---|
| 25¢ | **multicolored,** tagged *(188,400,000)* | .40 | .20 |
| | Plate block of 4 | 3.95 | |
| | FDC *(Aug. 30, 1989)* | | 1.00 |

**1989. BILL OF RIGHTS ISSUE** commemorates the freedoms guaranteed in the 1st ten Amendments to the Constitution. *Offset and intaglio, perforated 11.*

CM1355 *Eagle, Stars and Stripes*

| CM1355 | | MNHVF | UseVF |
|---|---|---|---|
| 25¢ | **multicolored,** tagged *(191,860,000)* | .40 | .20 |
| | Plate block of 4 | 5.50 | |
| | FDC *(Sept. 25, 1989)* | | 1.00 |
| | v. Intaglio black omitted | 350. | |

**1989. DINOSAURS ISSUE** celebrates the great prehistoric beasts, kicked off Stamp Collecting Month and served as a promotional tie-in with the videocassette release of the movie *The Land Before Time*. *Intaglio (Giori Press), perforated 11.*

CM1356 *Tyrannosaurus*

CM1357 *Pteranodon*

CM1358 *Stegosaurus*

CM1359 *Apatosaurus* ("*Brotosaurus*")

| CM1356 | | MNHVF | UseVF |
|---|---|---|---|
| 25¢ | Turannosaurus, tagged | 1.25 | .20 |

| CM1357 | | MNHVF | UseVF |
|---|---|---|---|
| 25¢ | Pteranodon, tagged | 1.25 | .20 |

| CM1358 | | MNHVF | UseVF |
|---|---|---|---|
| 25¢ | Stegosaurus, tagged | 1.25 | .20 |

| CM1359 | | MNHVF | UseVF |
|---|---|---|---|
| 25¢ | Apatosaurus, tagged | 1.25 | .20 |
| | Plate block of 4 | 5.75 | |
| | y. Se-tenant block of 4 CM1356-59 | 4.50 | 2.50 |
| | FDC *(Oct. 1, 1989)* | | 1.00 |
| | vy. Block of 4, intaglio black omitted | 1600. | |
| | vy1.Any single - intaglio black omitted | 175. | |

**1989. AMERICA ISSUE** honors the customs, images and traditions of native Americans prior to Columbus. Part of a 1989-91 Columbian series by members of the Postal Union of the Americas and Spain (PUAS). *Gravure by American Bank Note Co., perforated 11.*

CM1360 *Southwest Carved Figure*

| CM1360 | | MNHVF | UseVF |
|---|---|---|---|
| 25¢ | **multicolored,** tagged *(137,410,000)* | .40 | .20 |
| | Plate block of 4 | 3.00 | |
| | FDC *(Oct. 12, 1989)* | | 1.00 |

**1989. WORLD STAMP EXPO '89 SOUVENIR SHEET** features a reproduction of the 90¢ stamp from the 1869 Pictorials (No. 96) and three trial color proofs on a single imperforate sheet. *Offset and intaglio, perforated 11.*

CM1361 *World Stamp Expo '89 Souvenir Sheet*

| CM1361 | | MNHVF | UseVF |
|---|---|---|---|
| $3.60 | **souvenir sheet of four** *(2,017,225)* | 18.75 | 13.50 |
| | a. 90¢ like No. 96, Carmine frame, black vignette | 2.50 | 2.00 |
| | b. 90¢ blue frame, brown vignette | 2.50 | 2.00 |
| | c. 90¢ green frame, blue vignette | 2.50 | 2.00 |
| | d. 90¢ scarlet frame, blue vignette | 2.50 | 2.00 |
| | FDC *(Nov. 17, 1989)* | | 5.00 |

**1989. CLASSIC MAIL TRANSPORTATION ISSUE** honors vehicles that delivered mail from the 19th and the early 20th century. Issued in conjunction with the 20th UPU Congress. *Offset and intaglio, perforated 11.*

CM1362, 1366a *Stagecoach*

CM1363, 1366b *Steamboat*

CM1364, 1366c *Biplane*

CM1365, 1366d *Early Automobile*

| CM1362 | | MNHVF | UseVF |
|---|---|---|---|
| 25¢ | Stagecoach, tagged (163,824,000) | .75 | .20 |

| CM1363 | | MNHVF | UseVF |
|---|---|---|---|
| 25¢ | Steamboat, tagged | .75 | .20 |

| CM1364 | | MNHVF | UseVF |
|---|---|---|---|
| 25¢ | Biplane, tagged | .75 | .20 |

| CM1365 | | MNHVF | UseVF |
|---|---|---|---|
| 25¢ | Early Automobile, tagged | .75 | .20 |
| | Plate block of 4 | 6.00 | |
| | y. Se-tenant block of 4 CM1362-65 | 3.00 | 2.00 |
| | FDC (Nov. 19, 1989) | | 4.00 |
| | vy. Block of 4, intaglio dark blue omitted | 1250. | |
| | vy1.Any single - intaglio blue omitted | 200. | |

**1989. CLASSIC MAIL TRANSPORTATION SOUVENIR SHEET ISSUE**

 CM1366

| CM1366 | | MNHVF | UseVF |
|---|---|---|---|
| $1 | multicolored souvenir sheet, tagged | 5.00 | 4.00 |
| | a. 25¢ like CM1362 | 1.25 | .75 |
| | b. 25¢ like CM1363 | 1.25 | .75 |
| | c. 25¢ like CM1364 | 1.25 | .75 |
| | d. 25¢ like CM1365 | 1.25 | .75 |
| | FDC (Nov. 19, 1989), any single | | 1.00 |
| | v. Souvenir sheet, dark blue & gray ommited | 5500. | |

**1990. IDAHO STATEHOOD ISSUE** honors its centennial as the 43rd state to join the Union. *Gravure, American Bank Note Co., perforated 11.*

 CM1367 *Mountain Bluebird and Sawtooth Mountains*

| CM1367 | | MNHVF | UseVF |
|---|---|---|---|
| 25¢ | multicolored, tagged | .40 | .20 |
| | Plate block of 4 | 3.00 | |
| | FDC (Jan. 6, 1990) | | 1.00 |

**1990. LOVE ISSUE** is the 1st to include a booklet version of the winning Pennsylvania Dutch-inspired design, which came from a design project for Yale University graduate students. *Gravure, U.S. Banknote Corp. (sheet) and BEP (booklet).*

 CM1368-69 *Lovebirds*

| CM1368 | | MNHVF | UseVF |
|---|---|---|---|
| 25¢ | multicolored, tagged perforated 12 x 13 | .40 | .20 |
| | Plate block of 4 | 3.00 | |
| | FDC (Jan. 18, 1990) | | 1.00 |
| | v. Imperforate pair | 800. | |

| CM1369 | | MNHVF | UseVF |
|---|---|---|---|
| 25¢ | multicolored, tagged, perforated 11 1/2 on 2 or 3 sides | .40 | .20 |
| | FDC (Jan. 18, 1990) | | 1.00 |
| | v. Pink omitted, single | 250. | |
| | n. Booklet pane of 10 | 300. | |
| | nv. Pane of 10, pink omitted | 2000. | |

**1990. IDA B. WELLS ISSUE** Black Heritage Series honors the civil rights activist who was born a slave, and spent her life educating others about the horrors of discrimination and lynching. *Gravure, American Bank Note Co., perforated 11.*

 CM1370 *Ida B. Wells*

| CM1370 | | MNHVF | UseVF |
|---|---|---|---|
| 25¢ | multicolored, tagged | .40 | .20 |
| | Plate block of 4 | 3.75 | |
| | FDC (Feb. 1, 1990) | | 1.00 |

**1990. SUPREME COURT ISSUE** Branches of Government Series 4th and final stamp in the set honoring the 3 branches of the Federal government, honors the 200th anniversary of the judicial branch. *Offset and intaglio, perforated 11.*

 CM1371 *John Marshall*

| CM1371 | | MNHVF | UseVF |
|---|---|---|---|
| 25¢ | multicolored, tagged | .40 | .20 |
| | Plate block of 4 | 4.00 | |
| | FDC (Feb. 2, 1990) | | 1.00 |

**1990. WYOMING STATEHOOD ISSUE** commemorates the centennial of the state's entry into the Union. *Offset and intaglio, perforated 11.*

CM1372 *High Mountain Meadows by Conrad Schwiering.*

| CM1372 | | MNHVF | UseVF |
|---|---|---|---|
| 25¢ | **multicolored,** tagged | .40 | .20 |
| | Plate block of 4 | 3.85 | |
| | FDC *(Feb. 23, 1990)* | | 1.00 |
| | v. Intaglio black omitted | 2500. | |

**1990. CLASSIC FILMS ISSUE** showcases 4 works of Hollywood's Golden Era on the 50th anniversary of their nomination for the Academy Award. *Gravure, American Bank Note Co., perforated 11.*

CM1373 *Judy Garland and Toto, The Wizard of Oz.*

CM1374 *Clark Gable and Vivien Leigh, Gone with the Wind.*

CM1375 *Gary Cooper, Beau Geste*

CM1376 *John Wayne, Stagecoach*

| CM1373 | | MNHVF | UseVF |
|---|---|---|---|
| 25¢ | Wizard of Oz, tagged | 2.00 | .20 |

| CM1374 | | MNHVF | UseVF |
|---|---|---|---|
| 25¢ | Gone with The Wind, tagged | 2.00 | .20 |

| CM1375 | | MNHVF | UseVF |
|---|---|---|---|
| 25¢ | Beau Geste, tagged | 2.00 | .20 |

| CM1376 | | MNHVF | UseVF |
|---|---|---|---|
| 25¢ | Stagecoach, tagged | 2.00 | .20 |
| | Plate block of 4 | 10.00 | |
| | y. Se-tenant block of 4 CM1373-76 | 9.00 | |
| | FDC *(March 23, 1990)* block of 4 | | 5.00 |

**1990. MARIANNE MOORE ISSUE** Literary Arts Series pays tribute to the Pulitzer Prize-winning poet. *Gravure, American Bank Note Co., perforated 11.*

CM1377 *Marianne Moore*

| CM1377 | | MNHVF | UseVF |
|---|---|---|---|
| 25¢ | **multicolored,** tagged | .40 | .20 |
| | Plate block of 4 | 3.00 | |
| | FDC *(April 18, 1990)* | | 1.00 |

**1990. AMERICAN LIGHTHOUSES ISSUE** a se-tenant booklet issue of 5 designs, portrays ocean lighthouses. *Offset and intaglio, perforated 10, vertically.*

CM1378 *Admiralty Head, Wash.* CM1379 *Cape Hatteras, N.C.* CM1380 *West Quoddy Head, Maine* CM1381 *American Shoals, Fla.* CM1382 *Sandy Hook, N.J.*

| CM1378 | | MNHVF | UseVF |
|---|---|---|---|
| 25¢ | Admiralty Head, tagged | .40 | .20 |
| | v. White ("25 / USA") omitted | .15 | |

| CM1379 | | MNHVF | UseVF |
|---|---|---|---|
| 25¢ | Cape Hatteras, tagged | .40 | .20 |
| | v. White ("25 / USA") omitted | .15 | |

| CM1380 | | MNHVF | UseVF |
|---|---|---|---|
| 25¢ | West Quoddy Head, tagged | .40 | .20 |
| | v. White ("25 / USA") omitted | .15 | |

| CM1381 | | MNHVF | UseVF |
|---|---|---|---|
| 25¢ | American Shoals, tagged | .40 | .20 |
| | v. White ("25 / USA") omitted | .15 | |

| CM1382 | | MNHVF | UseVF |
|---|---|---|---|
| 25¢ | Sandy Hook, tagged | .40 | .20 |
| | FDC *(April 26, 1990)* | | 1.00 |
| | v. White ("25 / USA") omitted | .15 | |
| | n. Se-tenant booklet pane of 5 CM1378-82 | 400. | |
| | FDC | | |
| | nv. Booklet pane of 5, white omitted | 75.00 | |

**1990. RHODE ISLAND STATEHOOD ISSUE** is the final stamp in the Constitution Ratification Bicentennial Series. *Offset and intaglio, perforated 11.*

CM1383 *Slater Mill, R.I.*

| CM1383 | | MNHVF | UseVF |
|---|---|---|---|
| 25¢ | **multicolored,** tagged | .40 | .20 |
| | Plate block of 4 | 3.95 | |
| | FDC *(May 29, 1990)* | | 1.00 |

**1990. OLYMPIC ATHLETES ISSUE** honors 5 of the greatest U.S. Olympic athletes of the 1st half of the 20th century. *Gravure, American Bank Note Co., perforated 11.*

CM1384 *Jesse Owens* CM1385 *Ray Ewry* CM1386 *Hazel Wightman* CM1387 *Eddie Eagan* CM1388 *Helene Madison*

| CM1384 | | MNHVF | UseVF |
|---|---|---|---|
| 25¢ | Jesse Owens, tagged | .40 | .20 |

**CM1385**

| | | MNHVF | UseVF |
|---|---|---|---|
| 25¢ | Ray Ewry, tagged | .40 | .20 |

**CM1386**

| | | MNHVF | UseVF |
|---|---|---|---|
| 25¢ | Hazel Wightman, tagged | .40 | .20 |

**CM1387**

| | | MNHVF | UseVF |
|---|---|---|---|
| 25¢ | Eddie Eagan, tagged | .40 | .20 |

**CM1388**

| | | MNHVF | UseVF |
|---|---|---|---|
| 25¢ | Helene Madison, tagged | .40 | .20 |
| | Plate block of 10 | | |
| | y.  Se-tenant strip of 5 CM1384-88 | | |
| | FDC *(July 6, 1990)* | | 1.00 |

**1990. AMERICAN INDIAN HEADDRESSES ISSUE** features 5 different native headdresses or war bonnets. Folk Art series. *Offset and intaglio, perforated 11.*

CM1389 *Assiniboine* CM1390 *Cheyenne* CM1391 *Commanche* CM1392 *Flathead* CM1393 *Shoshone*

**CM1389**

| | | MNHVF | UseVF |
|---|---|---|---|
| 25¢ | Assiniboine, tagged | .40 | .20 |

**CM1390**

| | | MNHVF | UseVF |
|---|---|---|---|
| 25¢ | Cheyenne, tagged | .40 | .20 |

**CM1391**

| | | MNHVF | UseVF |
|---|---|---|---|
| 25¢ | Commanche, tagged | .40 | .20 |

**CM1392**

| | | MNHVF | UseVF |
|---|---|---|---|
| 25¢ | Flathead, tagged | .40 | .20 |

**CM1393**

| | | MNHVF | UseVF |
|---|---|---|---|
| 25¢ | Shoshone, tagged | .40 | .20 |
| | FDC *(Aug. 17, 1990)* any single | | 1.75 |
| | v.  Any single, intaglio black omitted | 300. | |
| | y.  Se-tenant strip of 5 CM1389-93 | 8.50 | 7.50 |
| | FDC strip of 5 | | 8.00 |
| | vy. Strip of 5, intaglio black omitted | 15000. | |
| | n.  Booklet of 10, 2 each CM1389-93 | 14.00 | |
| | nv. Booklet of 10, intaglio black omitted | 3850. | |

**1990. MICRONESIA AND MARSHALL ISLANDS ISSUE** commemorates the relationship between the United States and the Federated States of Micronesia and the Republic of the Marshall Islands. This was a joint issue among the three postal administrations (Micronesia 188-190, Marshall Islands 300). *Offset and intaglio, perforated 11.*

CM1394 *Micronesia flag* CM1395 *Marshall Islands flag*

**CM1394**

| | | MNHVF | UseVF |
|---|---|---|---|
| 25¢ | Micronesia, tagged | .40 | .20 |
| | v.  Intaglio black omitted | 1000. | |

**CM1395**

| | | MNHVF | UseVF |
|---|---|---|---|
| 25¢ | Marshall Island, tagged | .40 | .20 |
| | Plate block of 4 | 3.85 | |
| | Intaglio, black omitted | 1000. | |
| | FDC *(Sept. 28, 1990)* | | 1.00 |
| | y.  Se-tenant pair CM1394-95 | 1.00 | 1.00 |
| | vy. Se-tenant pair, intaglio black omitted | 4250. | |

**1990. SEA MAMMALS ISSUE** a joint release by the United States and the Soviet Union (Russia 6228-6231), focuses on the beauty and significance of marine mammals. *Offset and intaglio, perforated 11.*

CM1396 *Killer Whales*

CM1397 *Northern Sea Lions*

CM1398 *Sea Otter*

CM1399 *Dolphin*

**CM1396**

| | | MNHVF | UseVF |
|---|---|---|---|
| 25¢ | Killer Whale, tagged *(278,264,000)* | .75 | .20 |

**CM1397**

| | | MNHVF | UseVF |
|---|---|---|---|
| 25¢ | Northern Sea Lion, tagged | .75 | .20 |

**CM1398**

| | | MNHVF | UseVF |
|---|---|---|---|
| 25¢ | Sea Otter, tagged | .75 | .20 |

**CM1399**

| | | MNHVF | UseVF |
|---|---|---|---|
| 25¢ | Dolphin, tagged | .75 | .20 |
| | Plate block of 4 | 3.95 | |
| | FDC *(Oct. 3, 1990)* | | 3.00 |
| | zo. Tagging omitted, any single | | |
| | y.  Se-tenant block of 4 CM1396-99 | 3.00 | 2.00 |
| | vy. Block of 4, intaglio black omitted | 1900. | |
| | vyl.Any single intaglio black omitted | 250. | |
| | zoy.Block of 4, tagging omitted | | |

**1990. AMERICA ISSUE** honors natural wonders of the Americas as part of the joint release by the 24 participating postal administrations of PUAS. (See also A127.) *Gravure, American Bank Note Co., perforated 11.*

CM1400 *Grand Canyon*

**CM1400**

| | | MNHVF | UseVF |
|---|---|---|---|
| 25¢ | **multicolored,** tagged *(143,995,000)* | .40 | .20 |
| | Plate block of 4 | 3.00 | |
| | FDC *(Oct. 12, 1990)* | | 1.00 |

**1990. DWIGHT D. EISENHOWER ISSUE** pays tribute to the 34th president and the supreme commander of Allied Forces in Europe during World War II. *Gravure by American Bank Note Co., perforated 11.*

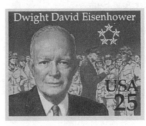

CM1401 *Dwight D. Eisenhower*

**CM1401**

| | | MNHVF | UseVF |
|---|---|---|---|
| 25¢ | **multicolored,** tagged *(142,692,000)* | .45 | .20 |
| | Plate block of 4 | 5.00 | |
| | FDC *(Oct. 13, 1990)* | | 1.00 |
| | v.  Imperforate pair | 2300. | |

**1991. SWITZERLAND 700TH ANNIVERSARY ISSUE** honors the small country founded in 1291. Switzerland issued a matching stamp at the same time (Switzerland 1579). *Gravure by American Bank Note Co., perforated 11.*

CM1402 *U.S. Capitol, Swiss Federal Palace*

| CM1402 | | MNHVF | UseVF |
|---|---|---|---|
| 50¢ | **multicolored,** tagged *(103,648,000)* | .75 | .35 |
| | Plate block of 4 | 6.50 | |
| | FDC *(Feb. 22, 1991)* | | 1.30 |

**1991. VERMONT STATEHOOD ISSUE** marks the bicentennial of the Green Mountain State, which remained an independent republic until admitted to the Union as the 14th state. *Gravure by American Bank Note Co., perforated 11.*

CM1403 *Vermont Farmland*

| CM1403 | | MNHVF | UseVF |
|---|---|---|---|
| 29¢ | **multicolored,** tagged *(179,990,000)* | .45 | .20 |
| | Plate block of 4 | 3.50 | |
| | FDC *(Mar. 1, 1991)* | | 1.00 |

**1991. U.S. SAVINGS BOND ISSUE** honors the 50th anniversary of the E-Series Savings Bond. *Gravure, perforated 11.*

CM1404 *Bald Eagle*

| CM1404 | | MNHVF | UseVF |
|---|---|---|---|
| 29¢ | **multicolored,** tagged *(150,560,000)* | .45 | .20 |
| | Plate block of 4 | 3.95 | |
| | FDC *(April 30, 1991)* | | 1.00 |

**1991. LOVE ISSUE** Gravure (29¢ sheet by U.S. Banknote Co., 29¢ booklet by BEP, 52¢ sheet by American Bank Note Co.)

CM1405-06 *Heart-shaped Earth*

| CM1405 | | MNHVF | UseVF |
|---|---|---|---|
| 29¢ | **multicolored,** tagged, perforated 12 1/2 x 13 | .45 | .20 |
| | Plate block of 4 | 3.75 | |
| | FDC *(May 9, 1991)* | | 1.00 |
| | v. Imperforated pair | 2500. | |

| CM1405A | | MNHVF | UseVF |
|---|---|---|---|
| 29¢ | **multicolored,** tagged, perforated 11 | .45 | .20 |
| | Plate block of 4 | 5.00 | |

| CM1406 | | MNHVF | UseVF |
|---|---|---|---|
| 29¢ | **multicolored,** tagged, perforated 11 or 2 or 3 sides | .45 | .20 |
| | FDC *(May 9, 1991)* | | 1.00 |
| | n. Booklet pane of 10 | 7.50 | |

CM1407 *Fischer's Lovebirds*

| CM1407 | | MNHVF | UseVF |
|---|---|---|---|
| 52¢ | **multicolored,** tagged | .75 | .35 |
| | Plate block of 4 | 5.75 | |
| | FDC *(May 9, 1991)* | | 1.00 |

## Literary Arts Series

**1991. WILLIAM SAROYAN ISSUE** honors the Armenian-American novelist, playwright and short story writer. This was a joint issue with Russia (Russia 6300). *Gravure, J.W. Fergusson Co. for the American Bank Note Co., perforated 11.*

CM1408 *William Saroyan*

| CM1408 | | MNHVF | UseVF |
|---|---|---|---|
| 29¢ | **multicolored,** tagged *(161,498,000)* | .45 | .20 |
| | Plate block of 4 | 3.50 | |
| | FDC *(May 22, 1991)* | | 1.00 |

**1991. FISHING FLIES ISSUE** shows 5 classic and carefully crafted lures in a 5 stamp se-tenant booklet format. *Gravure by American Bank Note Co., perforated 11.*

CM1409 *Royal Wulff*

CM1410 *Jock Scott*

CM1411 *Apte Tarpon Fly*

CM1412 *Lefty's Deceiver*

CM1413 *Muddler Minnow*

| CM1409 | | MNHVF | UseVF |
|---|---|---|---|
| 29¢ | Royal Wulff, tagged *(744,918,000)* | .45 | .20 |
| | v.  Black omitted | — | |

| CM1410 | | MNHVF | UseVF |
|---|---|---|---|
| 29¢ | Jack Scott, tagged | .45 | .20 |
| | v.  Black omitted | — | |

| CM1411 | | MNHVF | UseVF |
|---|---|---|---|
| 29¢ | Apte Tarpon, tagged | .45 | .20 |
| | v.  Black omitted | — | |

| CM1412 | | MNHVF | UseVF |
|---|---|---|---|
| 29¢ | Lefty's Deceiver, tagged | .45 | .20 |

| CM1413 | | MNHVF | UseVF |
|---|---|---|---|
| 29¢ | Muddler Minnow, tagged | .45 | .20 |
| | FDC *(May 31, 1991)* any single | | 1.00 |
| | n.  Se-tenant booklet pane of 5 CM1409-13 | 5.50 | 3.25 |
| | FDC | | 4.00 |

**1991. COLE PORTER ISSUE** honors the 20th-century composer. Performing Arts series. *Gravure by American Bank Note Co., perforated 11.*

CM1414 *Cole Porter*

| CM1414 | | MNHVF | UseVF |
|---|---|---|---|
| 29¢ | **multicolored,** tagged *(149,848,000)* | .45 | .20 |
| | Plate block of 4 | 3.75 | |
| | FDC *(June 8, 1991)* | | 1.00 |
| | v.  Vertical pair, imperforate between | 600. | |

**1991. DESERT SHIELD-DESERT STORM ISSUE** pays tribute to those who served in the Gulf War. *Gravure (sheet version by J.W. Fergusson and Sons for Stamp Venturers, perforated 11.*

CM1415-16 *Southwest Asia Service Medal*

| CM1415 | | MNHVF | UseVF |
|---|---|---|---|
| 29¢ | **multicolored,** tagged *(200,003,000)* | .45 | .20 |
| | Plate block of 4 | 3.50 | |
| | FDC *(July 2, 1991)* | | 1.00 |
| | v.  Vertical pair, imperforate horizontally | 2000. | |

**1991. DESERT SHIELD-DESERT STORM BOOKLET ISSUE** by the Multi-color Corp. for the American Bank Note Co., perforated 11 on 1 or 2 sides.

| CM1416 | | MNHVF | UseVF |
|---|---|---|---|
| 29¢ | **multicolored,** tagged *(200,000,000)* | .45 | .20 |
| | FDC *(July 2, 1991)* | | 1.00 |
| | n.  Booklet pane of 5 | 4.00 | |
| | FDC | | 2.00 |

**1991. OLYMPIC TRACK AND FIELD ISSUE** promoted the USPS sponsorship of the 1992 Winter and Summer Olympics. *Gravure by American Bank Note Co., perforated 11.*

CM1417 *Pole Vault* CM1418 *Discus* CM1419 *Women's Sprint* CM1420 *Javelin* CM1421 *Women's Hurdles*

| CM1417 | | MNHVF | UseVF |
|---|---|---|---|
| 29¢ | Pole vault, tagged *(170,025,000)* | .45 | .20 |

| CM1418 | | MNHVF | UseVF |
|---|---|---|---|
| 29¢ | Discus, tagged | .45 | .20 |

| CM1419 | | MNHVF | UseVF |
|---|---|---|---|
| 29¢ | Women's sprint, tagged | .45 | .20 |

| CM1420 | | MNHVF | UseVF |
|---|---|---|---|
| 29¢ | Javelan, tagged | .45 | .20 |

| CM1421 | | MNHVF | UseVF |
|---|---|---|---|
| 29¢ | Women's hurdles, tagged | .45 | .20 |
| | Plate block of 10 | 9.75 | |
| | y.  Se-tenant strip of 5, CM1417-21 | | |
| | FDC *(July 12, 1991)* any single | | 1.00 |
| | FDC, strip of 5 | | 4.50 |

**1991. NUMISMATICS ISSUE** salutes the hobby of coin and currency collecting. *Offset and intaglio, perforated 11.*

CM1422 *Coins and Banknotes*

| CM1422 | | MNHVF | UseVF |
|---|---|---|---|
| 29¢ | **multicolored,** tagged *(150,310,000)* | .45 | .20 |
| | Plate block of 4 | 4.50 | |
| | FDC *(Aug. 13, 1991)* | | 1.00 |

**1991. BASKETBALL CENTENNIAL ISSUE** commemorates the 100th anniversary of one of the world's most popular sports. Many basketball fans pointed out the design looks like an illegal goaltend. *Gravure, perforated 11.*

CM1423 *Hands above Basketball Hoop*

| CM1423 | | MNHVF | UseVF |
|---|---|---|---|
| 29¢ | **multicolored,** tagged *(149,810,000)* | .45 | .20 |
| | Plate block of 4 | 4.50 | |
| | FDC *(Aug. 28, 1991)* | | 1.00 |

**1991. AMERICAN COMEDIANS ISSUE** showcases comedians and teams of the 1st half of the 20th century. The stamps were the first designed by the famed caricaturist Al Hirschfeld. *Offset and intaglio, perforated 11.*

CM1424 *Stan Laurel, Oliver Hardy* CM1425 *Edgar Bergen, Charlie McCarthy* CM1426 *Jack Benny* CM1427 *Fanny Brice* CM1428 *Bud Abbott, Lou Costello*

| CM1424 | | MNHVF | UseVF |
|---|---|---|---|
| 29¢ | Laurel & Hardy, tagged *(699,978,000)* | .45 | .20 |

| CM1425 | | MNHVF | UseVF |
|---|---|---|---|
| 29¢ | Bergen & McCarthy, tagged | .45 | .20 |

| CM1426 | | MNHVF | UseVF |
|---|---|---|---|
| 29¢ | Jack Benny, tagged | .45 | .20 |

| CM1427 | | MNHVF | UseVF |
|---|---|---|---|
| 29¢ | Fanny Brice, tagged | .45 | .20 |

| CM1428 | | MNHVF | UseVF |
|---|---|---|---|
| 29¢ | Abbott & Costello, tagged | .45 | .20 |
| | y. Se-tenant strip of 5 CM1424-28 | 3.00 | |
| | FDC *(Aug. 28, 1991)* | | 1.00 |
| | a. Intaglio purple & red omitted, any single | — | |
| | n. Booklet pane of 10, 2 each CM1424-28 | 600. | |
| | vn. Booklet pane, intaglio purple & red omitted | 850. | |

**1991. 1941 A World at War Issue** is the first in an annual series issued through 1995. *Offset and intaglio, perforated 11.*

CM1429 *1941: A World at War*

| CM1429 | | MNHVF | UseVF |
|---|---|---|---|
| $2.90 | **Commemorative sheet** | | |
| | a. 29¢ Military Vehicles, tagged | .80 | .45 |
| | b. 29¢ Draft Recruits, tagged | .80 | .45 |
| | c. 29¢ Dockside View, tagged | .80 | .45 |
| | d. 29¢ Roosevelt and Churchill, tagged | .80 | .45 |
| | e. 29¢ Tank, tagged | .80 | .45 |
| | f. 29¢ Sinking of *Reuben Janes,* tagged | .80 | .45 |
| | g. 29¢ Gas Mask and Helmet, tagged | .80 | .45 |
| | h. 29¢ Liberty Ship, tagged | .80 | .45 |
| | i. 29¢ Pearl Harbor, tagged | .80 | .45 |
| | j. 29¢ Congress Declares War, tagged | .80 | .45 |
| | FDC *(Sept. 3, 1991)* any single | | 1.00 |
| | FDC Complete sheet | | 6.50 |
| | v. Black omitted, complete sheet of 20 | 12650. | |

**1991. District of Columbia Bicentennial Issue** marks the 100th anniversary of the federal district selected by Washington as a site for the permanent capital. *Offset and intaglio, perforated 11.*

CM1430 *Early View up Pennsylvania Avenue.*

| CM1430 | | MNHVF | UseVF |
|---|---|---|---|
| 29¢ | **multicolored,** tagged *(699,978,000)* | .45 | .20 |
| | Plate block of 4 | 3.50 | |
| | FDC *(Sept. 7, 1991)* | | 1.00 |
| | a. Intaglio black omitted | 150. | |
| | av. Plate block of 4, intaglio black omitted | 650. | |

## Black Heritage Series

**1991. Jan E. Matzeliger Issue** honors the man who patented a machine for shaping shoes, which revolutionized shoe manufacturing in the United States. *Gravure, J.W. Fergusson & Sons for the American Bank Note Co., perforated 11.*

CM1431 *Jan E. Matzeliger*

| CM1431 | | MNHVF | UseVF |
|---|---|---|---|
| 29¢ | **multicolored,** tagged *(148,973,000)* | .45 | .20 |
| | Plate block of 4 | 4.25 | |
| | FDC *(Sept. 15, 1991)* | | 1.00 |
| | v. Horizontal pair, imperforate vertically | 1750. | |
| | v1. Vertical pair, imperforate horizontally | 1600. | |
| | v2. Imperforate pair | 2500. | |

CM1429 *1941: A World at War*

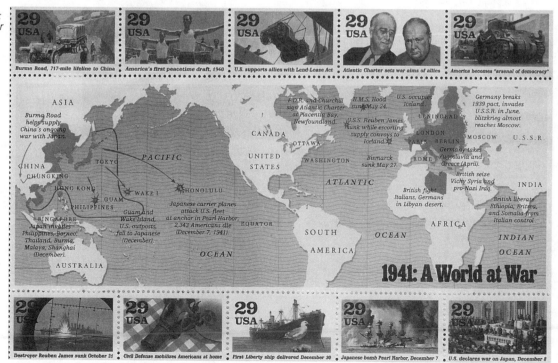

CM1432 *Mercury, Mariner 10* CM1433 *Venus, Mariner 2* CM1434 *Earth, Landsat* CM1435 *Moon, Lunar Orbiter* CM1436 *Mars, Viking Orbiter* CM1437 *Jupiter, Pioneer II* CM1438 *Saturn, Voyager 2* CM1439 *Uranus, Voyager 2* CM1440 *Neptune, Voyager 2* CM1441 *Pluto*

**1991. SPACE EXPLORATION ISSUE** a se-tenant 10-stamp booklet pane features unmanned spacecraft launched to the Earth's moon and each of the 9 planets that orbit the sun, with the exception of Pluto, which is depicted as well. *Gravure, perforated 11 on 2 or 3 sides.*

| | | MNHVF | UseVF |
|---|---|---|---|
| **CM1432** | | **MNHVF** | **UseVF** |
| 29¢ | Mercury, tagged *(333,948,000)* | .45 | .20 |
| **CM1433** | | **MNHVF** | **UseVF** |
| 29¢ | Venus, tagged | .45 | .20 |
| **CM1434** | | **MNHVF** | **UseVF** |
| 29¢ | Earth, tagged | .45 | .20 |
| **CM1435** | | **MNHVF** | **UseVF** |
| 29¢ | Moon, tagged | .45 | .20 |
| **CM1436** | | **MNHVF** | **UseVF** |
| 29¢ | Mars, tagged | .45 | .20 |
| **CM1437** | | **MNHVF** | **UseVF** |
| 29¢ | Jupiter, tagged | .45 | .20 |
| **CM1438** | | **MNHVF** | **UseVF** |
| 29¢ | Saturn, tagged | .45 | .20 |
| **CM1439** | | **MNHVF** | **UseVF** |
| 29¢ | Uranus, tagged | .45 | .20 |
| **CM1440** | | **MNHVF** | **UseVF** |
| 29¢ | Neptune, tagged | .45 | .20 |
| **CM1441** | | **MNHVF** | **UseVF** |
| 29¢ | Pluto, tagged | .45 | .20 |
| | FDC *(Oct. 1, 1991)* | | 1.00 |
| | Booklet pane (CM1432-41) | 8.75 | |
| | FDC | | 2.00 |

**1992. WINTER OLYMPICS ISSUE** honors 5 of the fastest sporting events of the games held in Albertville, France. *Gravure, J.W. Fergusson for Stamp Venturers, perforated 11.*

CM1442 *Ice Hockey*

| **CM1442** | | **MNHVF** | **UseVF** |
|---|---|---|---|
| 29¢ | **multicolored,** tagged | .45 | .20 |

CM1443 *Figure Skating*

| **CM1443** | | **MNHVF** | **UseVF** |
|---|---|---|---|
| 29¢ | **multicolored,** tagged | .45 | .20 |

CM1444 *Speed Skating*

| **CM1444** | | **MNHVF** | **UseVF** |
|---|---|---|---|
| 29¢ | **multicolored,** tagged | .45 | .20 |

CM1445 *Skiing*

| **CM1445** | | **MNHVF** | **UseVF** |
|---|---|---|---|
| 29¢ | **multicolored,** tagged | .45 | .20 |

CM1446 *Bobsledding*

| **CM1446** | | **MNHVF** | **UseVF** |
|---|---|---|---|
| 29¢ | **multicolored,** tagged | .45 | .20 |
| | Plate block of 10 | 9.75 | |
| | y. Se-tenant strip (CM1442-46) | 3.00 | |
| | FDC *(Jan. 11, 1992)* any single | | 1.00 |
| | FDC, strip of 5 | | 2.00 |

**1992. WORLD COLUMBIAN STAMP EXPO '92 ISSUE** promotes the international stamp show in Chicago. The stamp shows a detail from the 1869 15¢ Pictorial (No. 92). *Offset and intaglio, perforated 11.*

CM1447 *World Columbian Stamp Expo.*

**CM1447**

| | | MNHVF | UseVF |
|---|---|---|---|
| 29¢ | **multicolored,** tagged | .45 | .20 |
| | Plate block of 4 | 3.50 | |
| | FDC *(Jan. 24, 1992)* | | 1.00 |
| | zo. Tagging omitted | — | |

**1992. W.E.B. Du Bois Issue** Black Heritage Series honors the noted writer, historian critic, scholar and educator. The Niagara Movement he founded in 1905 evolved into the NAACP. *Offset and intaglio, perforated 11.*

CM1448 *W.E.B. Du Bois*

**CM1448**

| | | MNHVF | UseVF |
|---|---|---|---|
| 29¢ | **multicolored,** tagged | .45 | .20 |
| | Plate block of 4 | 3.75 | |
| | FDC *(Jan. 31, 1992)* | | 1.00 |

**1992. Love Issue** *Gravure, U.S. Bank Note Co., perforated 11.*

CM1449 *Heart*

**CM1449**

| | | MNHVF | UseVF |
|---|---|---|---|
| 29¢ | **multicolored,** tagged | .45 | .20 |
| | Plate block of 4 | 3.50 | |
| | FDC *(Feb. 6, 1992)* | | 1.00 |
| | v. Horizontal pair, imperforate between | 800. | |

**1992. Olympic Baseball Issue** commemorates the acceptance of baseball as an official Olympic sport. *Gravure, perforated 11.*

CM1450 *Player Sliding into Home.*

**CM1450**

| | | MNHVF | UseVF |
|---|---|---|---|
| 29¢ | **multicolored,** tagged | 1.00 | .20 |
| | Plate block of 4 | 4.75 | |
| | FDC *(April 3, 1992)* | | 1.00 |

**1992. Voyage of Columbus Issue** a joint issue with Italy (Italy 2416-2419), honors the explorer's historic 1st voyage to the New World with 4 related se-tenant designs. *Offset and intaglio, , perforated 11.*

CM1451 *Seeking Queen Isabella's support.*

CM1452 *Crossing the Atlantic*

CM1453 *Approaching Land*

CM1454 *Coming ashore*

**CM1451**

| | | MNHVF | UseVF |
|---|---|---|---|
| 29¢ | Seeking Support, tagged | 1.00 | .20 |

**CM1452**

| | | MNHVF | UseVF |
|---|---|---|---|
| 29¢ | Atlantic Crossing, tagged | 1.00 | .20 |

**CM1453**

| | | MNHVF | UseVF |
|---|---|---|---|
| 29¢ | Approaching land, tagged | 1.00 | .20 |

**CM1454**

| | | MNHVF | UseVF |
|---|---|---|---|
| 29¢ | Coming ashore, tagged | 1.00 | .20 |
| | Plate block of 4 | 4.75 | |
| | y. Se-tenant block of 4 (CM1451-54) | 4.00 | 3.00 |
| | FDC *(April 24, 1992)* any single | | 1.00 |
| | FDC, se-tenant block of 4 | | 4.00 |

**1992. New York Stock Exchange Issue** commemorates the bicentennial of the exchange, originally formed by 24 brokers and dealers who met regularly under a tree. *Offset and intaglio by Jeffries Bank Note Co. for the American Bank Note Co., perforated 11.*

CM1455 *Stock Certificate*

**CM1455**

| | | MNHVF | UseVF |
|---|---|---|---|
| 29¢ | **multicolored,** tagged | .45 | .20 |
| | Plate block of 4 | 3.50 | |
| | FDC *(May 17, 1992)* | | 1.00 |

**1992. Columbian Souvenir Sheets** were a joint issue with Italy, Portugal and Spain at the World Columbian Expo '92 (Italy 2423-28, Portugal 2102-07, Spain 3177-82). Stamps depicted on the sheets are close in appearance to the original Columbian commemoratives of 1893 (CM1-16), but are inscribed "1992" at upper right. *Offset and intaglio by American Bank Note Co., perforated 10 1/2.*

CM1456 *Seeking Royal Support*

**CM1456**

| | | MNHVF | UseVF |
|---|---|---|---|
| 85¢ | **sheet of three** | 3.00 | |
| | a. 5¢ brown like CM5 | | .75 |
| | b. 30¢ orange brown like CM10 | | 1.00 |
| | c. 50¢ slate black like CM11 | | 1.00 |
| | FDC *(May 22, 1992)* | | 4.00 |
| | v. Imperforate souvenir sheet | — | |

*NOTE: Imperforate souvenir sheets are very probably the result of printer's waste.*

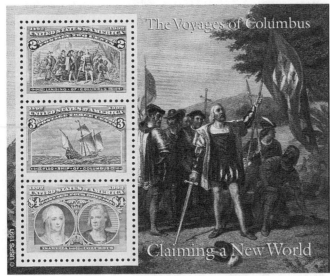

CM1457 *First Sighting of Land*

CM1458 *Reporting Discoveries*

CM1459 *Royal Favor Restored*

| CM1457 | | MNHVF | UseVF |
|---|---|---|---|
| $1.05 | **sheet of three** | 2.50 | |
| | a. 1¢ deep blue like CM1 | | .50 |
| | b. 4¢ gray blue like CM4 | | .75 |
| | c. $1 Venetian red like CM12 | | 2.50 |
| | FDC *(May 22, 1992)* | | 4.00 |
| | v. Imperforate souvenir sheet | — | |
| **CM1458** | | **MNHVF** | **UseVF** |
| $2.25 | **sheet of three** | 5.00 | |
| | a. 10¢ black brown like CM8 | | .75 |
| | b. 15¢ deep bluish green like CM9 | | .75 |
| | c. $2 brown red like CM13 | | 4.50 |
| | FDC *(May 22, 1992)* | | 6.00 |
| | v. Imperforate souvenir sheet | — | |
| **CM1459** | | **MNHVF** | **UseVF** |
| $3.14 | **sheet of three** | 8.50 | |
| | a. 6¢ dark lilac like CM6 | | 1.00 |
| | b. 8¢ brown purple like CM7 | | 1.00 |
| | c. $3 bronze green like CM14 | | 5.50 |
| | v. Imperforate souvenir sheet | — | |
| | FDC *(May 22, 1992)* | | 8.00 |
| **CM1460** | | **MNHVF** | **UseVF** |
| $4.07 | **sheet of three** | 9.00 | |
| | a. 2¢ dull purple like CM2 | | .75 |
| | b. 3¢ dark bluish green like CM3 | | .75 |
| | c. $4 deep rose like CM15 | | 7.00 |
| | FDC *(May 22, 1992)* | | 9.00 |
| | v. Imperforate souvenir sheet | — | |

CM1460 *Claiming a New World*

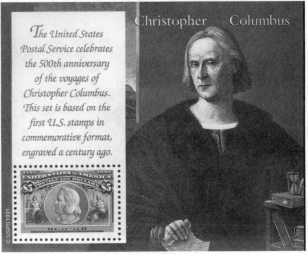

CM1461 *Christopher Columbus*

**CM1461**

| | | MNHVF | UseVF |
|---|---|---|---|
| $5 | **sheet of one.** Black like CM15. | 12.00 | 8.50 |
| | FDC *(May22, 1992)* | | |
| | Full set of 6 s/s | 40.00 | 37.50 |

**1992. SPACE ACHIEVEMENTS ISSUE** a joint issue with Russia (Russia 6376-79), honors a broad spectrum of space exploration by the 2 countries. *Gravure, perforated 11.*

CM1462 *Space Shuttle*

CM1463 *Astronaut, Space Shuttle, Space Station*

CM1464 *Lunar Lander, Apollo and Vostok Spacecraft, Sputnik*

CM1465 *Soyuz, Mercury and Gemini Spacecraft*

**CM1462**

| | | MNHVF | UseVF |
|---|---|---|---|
| 29¢ | Space Shuttle, tagged | 1.00 | .20 |

**CM1463**

| | | MNHVF | UseVF |
|---|---|---|---|
| 29¢ | Space Station, tagged | 1.00 | .20 |

**CM1464**

| | | MNHVF | UseVF |
|---|---|---|---|
| 29¢ | Apollo & Vostok Craft, tagged | 1.00 | .20 |

**CM1465**

| | | MNHVF | UseVF |
|---|---|---|---|
| 29¢ | Soyuz, Mercury & Gemini Craft, tagged | 1.00 | .20 |
| | Plate block of 4 | 4.50 | |
| | Se-tenant block of 4, (CM1462-65) | 4.00 | 2.50 |
| | FDC *(May 29, 1992)* any single | | 1.00 |
| | FDC, block of 4 | | 4.00 |

**1992. ALASKA HIGHWAY ISSUE** marks the 50th anniversary of the completion of the 1,500- mile route connecting army installations in Alaska and the United States during World War II. *Offset and intaglio, perforated 11.*

CM1466 *Alaska Highway*

**CM1466**

| | | MNHVF | UseVF |
|---|---|---|---|
| 29¢ | **multicolored,** tagged | .45 | .20 |
| | Plate block of 4 | 3.50 | |
| | FDC *(May 30, 1992)* | | 1.00 |
| | a. Intaglio black omitted | 900. | |

**1992. KENTUCKY STATEHOOD ISSUE** celebrates the bicentennial of the entry of the Bluegrass State into the Union. *Gravure, J.W. Fergusson & Sons for Stamp Venturers, perforated 11.*

CM1467 *My Old Kentucky Home State Park*

**CM1467**

| | | MNHVF | UseVF |
|---|---|---|---|
| 29¢ | **multicolored,** tagged | .45 | .20 |
| | Plate block of 4 | 3.50 | |
| | FDC *(June 1, 1992)* | | 1.00 |

**1992. SUMMER OLYMPIC GAMES ISSUE** presents 5 events contested in the quadrennial games held in Barcelona, Spain. *Gravure, J.W. Fergusson & Sons for Stamp Venturers.*

**CM1468**

| | | MNHVF | UseVF |
|---|---|---|---|
| 29¢ | Soccer, tagged | .45 | .20 |

**CM1469**

| | | MNHVF | UseVF |
|---|---|---|---|
| 29¢ | Gymnastics, tagged | .45 | .20 |

**CM1470**

| | | MNHVF | UseVF |
|---|---|---|---|
| 29¢ | Vollyball, tagged | .45 | .20 |

**CM1471**

| | | MNHVF | UseVF |
|---|---|---|---|
| 29¢ | Boxing, tagged | .45 | .20 |

**CM1472**

| | | MNHVF | UseVF |
|---|---|---|---|
| 29¢ | Swimming, tagged | .45 | .20 |
| | Plate block of 10 | 10.00 | |
| | Se-tenant strip of 5 | 8.00 | |
| | FDC *(June 11, 1992)* any single | | 1.00 |
| | FDC, strip of 5 | | 4.00 |

**1992. HUMMINGBIRDS ISSUE** a popular booklet release, featured 5 varieties of these colorful birds. *Gravure, Multi-Color Corp. for the American Bank Note Co., perforated 11.*

CM1473 *Ruby-throated hummingbird* CM1474 *Broad-billed hummingbird* CM1475 *Costa's hummingbird* CM1476 *Rufous hummingbird* CM1477 *Calliope hummingbird*

**CM1473**

| | | MNHVF | UseVF |
|---|---|---|---|
| 29¢ | Ruby Throated, tagged | .45 | .20 |

**CM1474**

| | | MNHVF | UseVF |
|---|---|---|---|
| 29¢ | Broad Billed, tagged | .45 | .20 |

**CM1475**

| | | MNHVF | UseVF |
|---|---|---|---|
| 29¢ | Costa's, tagged | .45 | .20 |

**CM1476**

| | | MNHVF | UseVF |
|---|---|---|---|
| 29¢ | Rufous, tagged | .45 | .20 |

**CM1477**

| | | MNHVF | UseVF |
|---|---|---|---|
| 29¢ | Calliope, tagged | .45 | .20 |
| | FDC *(June 15,1992)* any single | | 1.00 |
| | n. Booklet pane of 5 (CM1473-77) | 4.50 | |
| | FDC | | 4.00 |

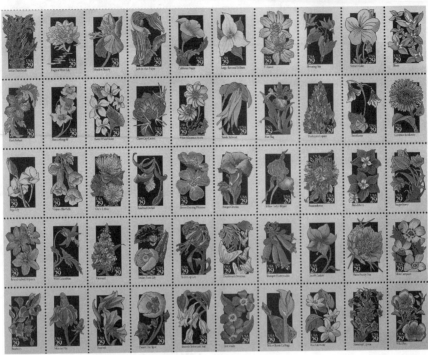

CM1478-1527 *Wildflowers from around the nation*

**1992. WILDFLOWERS ISSUE** showcased 50 colorful, blooming native plants. While no specific states are attached to each flower, 1 or more of the flowers are found in each of the states. *Offset, Ashton-Potter America, Inc., perforated 11.*

*Two simultaneous printings were produced, one with four panes (plate number positions) per sheet and the other with six panes (plate number positons) per sheet. Stamps from the four-pane press were assigned odd plate numbers and stamps from the six-pane press were assigned even plate numbers. Further, an illustration is found in the selvage of each pane depicting an uncut sheet and the location of the specific pane in hand.*

| | | MNHVF | UseVF |
|---|---|---|---|
| CM1478 | | MNHVF | UseVF |
| 29¢ | **Indian Paintbrush,** tagged | .95 | .60 |
| CM1479 | | MNHVF | UseVF |
| 29¢ | **Fragrant Water Lily,** tagged | .95 | .60 |
| CM1480 | | MNHVF | UseVF |
| 29¢ | **Meadow Beauty,** tagged | .95 | .60 |
| CM1481 | | MNHVF | UseVF |
| 29¢ | **Jack-In-The-Pulpit,** tagged | .95 | .60 |
| CM1482 | | MNHVF | UseVF |
| 29¢ | **California Poppy,** tagged | .95 | .60 |
| CM1483 | | MNHVF | UseVF |
| 29¢ | **Large-Flowered Trillium,** tagged | .95 | .60 |
| CM1484 | | MNHVF | UseVF |
| 29¢ | **Tickseed,** tagged | .95 | .60 |
| CM1485 | | MNHVF | UseVF |
| 29¢ | **Shooting Star,** tagged | .95 | .60 |
| CM1486 | | MNHVF | UseVF |
| 29¢ | **Stream Violet,** tagged | .95 | .60 |
| CM1487 | | MNHVF | UseVF |
| 29¢ | **Bluets,** tagged | .95 | .60 |
| CM1488 | | MNHVF | UseVF |
| 29¢ | **Herb Robert,** tagged | .95 | .60 |
| CM1489 | | MNHVF | UseVF |
| 29¢ | **Marsh Marigold,** tagged | .95 | .60 |
| CM1490 | | MNHVF | UseVF |
| 29¢ | **Sweet White Violet,** tagged | .95 | .60 |
| CM1491 | | MNHVF | UseVF |
| 29¢ | **Claret Cup Cactus,** tagged | .95 | .60 |
| CM1492 | | MNHVF | UseVF |
| 29¢ | **White Mountain Avens,** tagged | .95 | .60 |
| CM1493 | | MNHVF | UseVF |
| 29¢ | **Sessile Bellwort,** tagged | .95 | .60 |
| CM1494 | | MNHVF | UseVF |
| 29¢ | **Blue Flag,** tagged | .95 | .60 |
| CM1495 | | MNHVF | UseVF |
| 29¢ | **Harlequin Lupine,** tagged | .95 | .60 |
| CM1496 | | MNHVF | UseVF |
| 29¢ | **Twinflower,** tagged | .95 | .60 |
| CM1497 | | MNHVF | UseVF |
| 29¢ | **Common Sunflower,** tagged | .95 | .60 |
| CM1498 | | MNHVF | UseVF |
| 29¢ | **Sego Lily,** tagged | .95 | .60 |
| CM1499 | | MNHVF | UseVF |
| 29¢ | **Virginia Bluebells,** tagged | .95 | .60 |
| CM1500 | | MNHVF | UseVF |
| 29¢ | **Ohi'a Lehua,** tagged | .95 | .60 |
| CM1501 | | MNHVF | UseVF |
| 29¢ | **Rosebun Orchid,** tagged | .95 | .60 |
| CM1502 | | MNHVF | UseVF |
| 29¢ | **Showy Evening Primrose,** tagged | .95 | .60 |
| CM1503 | | MNHVF | UseVF |
| 29¢ | **Fringed Gentian,** tagged | .95 | .60 |
| CM1504 | | MNHVF | UseVF |
| 29¢ | **Yellow Lady's Slipper,** tagged | .95 | .60 |
| CM1505 | | MNHVF | UseVF |
| 29¢ | **Passionflower,** tagged | .95 | .60 |
| CM1506 | | MNHVF | UseVF |
| 29¢ | **Bunchberry,** tagged | .95 | .60 |
| CM1507 | | MNHVF | UseVF |
| 29¢ | **Pasqueflower,** tagged | .95 | .60 |
| CM1508 | | MNHVF | UseVF |
| 29¢ | **Round-Lobed Hepatica,** tagged | .95 | .60 |
| CM1509 | | MNHVF | UseVF |
| 29¢ | **Wild Columbine,** tagged | .95 | .60 |
| CM1510 | | MNHVF | UseVF |
| 29¢ | **Fireweed,** tagged | .95 | .60 |

| CM1511 | | MNHVF | UseVF |
|---|---|---|---|
| 29¢ | **Indian Pond Lily,** tagged | .95 | .60 |

| CM1512 | | MNHVF | UseVF |
|---|---|---|---|
| 29¢ | **Turk's Cap Lily,** tagged | .95 | .60 |

| CM1513 | | MNHVF | UseVF |
|---|---|---|---|
| 29¢ | **Dutchman's Breeches,** tagged | .95 | .60 |

| CM1514 | | MNHVF | UseVF |
|---|---|---|---|
| 29¢ | **Trumpet Honeysuckle,** tagged | .95 | .60 |

| CM1515 | | MNHVF | UseVF |
|---|---|---|---|
| 29¢ | **Jacob's Ladder,** tagged | .95 | .60 |

| CM1516 | | MNHVF | UseVF |
|---|---|---|---|
| 29¢ | **Plains Prickly Pear,** tagged | .95 | .60 |

| CM1517 | | MNHVF | UseVF |
|---|---|---|---|
| 29¢ | **Moss Champion,** tagged | .95 | .60 |

| CM1518 | | MNHVF | UseVF |
|---|---|---|---|
| 29¢ | **Bearberry,** tagged | .95 | .60 |

| CM1519 | | MNHVF | UseVF |
|---|---|---|---|
| 29¢ | **Mexican Hat,** tagged | .95 | .60 |

| CM1520 | | MNHVF | UseVF |
|---|---|---|---|
| 29¢ | **Harebell,** tagged | .95 | .60 |

| CM1521 | | MNHVF | UseVF |
|---|---|---|---|
| 29¢ | **Desert five Spot,** tagged | .95 | .60 |

| CM1522 | | MNHVF | UseVF |
|---|---|---|---|
| 29¢ | **Smooth Solomon's Seal,** tagged | .95 | .60 |

| CM1523 | | MNHVF | UseVF |
|---|---|---|---|
| 29¢ | **Red Maids,** tagged | .95 | .60 |

| CM1524 | | MNHVF | UseVF |
|---|---|---|---|
| 29¢ | **Yellow Skunk Cabbage,** tagged | .95 | .60 |

| CM1525 | | MNHVF | UseVF |
|---|---|---|---|
| 29¢ | **Rue Anemone,** tagged | .95 | .60 |

| CM1526 | | MNHVF | UseVF |
|---|---|---|---|
| 29¢ | **Standing Cypress,** tagged | .95 | .60 |

| CM1527 | | MNHVF | UseVF |
|---|---|---|---|
| 29¢ | **Wild Flax,** tagged | .95 | .60 |
| | Pane of 50 (CM1478-1527) | 42.50 | |
| | FDC *(July 24, 1992)* any single | | 1.00 |
| | FDC, pane of 50 | | 30.00 |

**1992. 1942: Into The Battle Issue** includes a map and stamps showing events of the war in 1942. *Offset and intaglio, perforated 11.*

| CM1528 | | MNHVF | UseVF |
|---|---|---|---|
| $2.90 | **Sheet of ten** | | |
| | a. 29¢ B-25 Raid on Tokyo, tagged | .75 | .45 |
| | b. 29¢ Ration Stamps, tagged | .75 | .45 |
| | c. 29¢ Carrier Crewman & fighter tagged | .75 | .45 |
| | d. 29¢ Prisoners of War, tagged | .75 | .45 |
| | e. 29¢ Attack on Aleutian Islands, tagged | .75 | .45 |
| | f. 29¢ Coded Message, tagged | .75 | .45 |
| | g. 29¢ *USS Yorktown,* tagged | .75 | .45 |
| | h. 29¢ Woman Defense Worker, tagged | .75 | .45 |
| | i. 29¢ Marines at Guadalcanal, tagged | .75 | .45 |
| | j. 29¢ Tank in Desert, tagged | .75 | .45 |
| | Block of 10 (CM1528a-j) | 18.25 | |
| | FDC *(Aug. 17, 1992)* any single | | 1.00 |
| | FDC, complete sheet | | 8.00 |
| | v. Red omitted | 6000. | |

## Literary Arts Series

**1992. Dorothy Parker Issue** honors the writer, poet and critic. *Gravure by J.W. Fergusson & Sons for Stamp Venturers, perforated 11.*

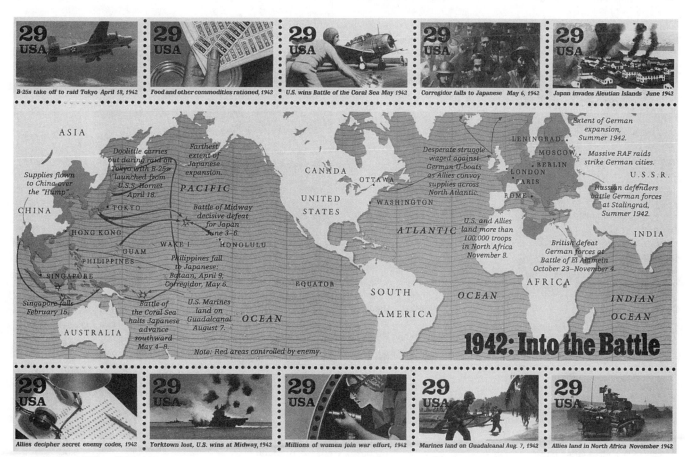

CM1528 *World Ware II 1942 Events.*

CM1529 *Dorothy Parker*

| CM1529 | | MNHVF | UseVF |
|---|---|---|---|
| 29¢ | **multicolored,** tagged | .45 | .20 |
| | Plate block of 4 | 3.50 | |
| | FDC *(Aug. 22, 1992)* | | .75 |

**1992. Theodore von Kármán Issue** pays tribute to the aerospace scientist credited with establishing the center for rocket research that now is the Jet Propulsion Laboratory at the California Institute of Technology. *Grauvure, J.W. Fergusson & Sons for Stamp Venturers, perforated 11.*

CM1530 *Theodore von Kármán*

| CM1530 | | MNHVF | UseVF |
|---|---|---|---|
| 29¢ | **multicolored,** tagged | .45 | .20 |
| | Plate block of 4 | 3.50 | |
| | FDC *(Aug. 31, 1992)* | | 1.00 |

**1992. Minerals Issue** featured speciments from the Smithsonian Institution's National Museum of Natural History collection. *Offset and intaglio, perforated 11.*

CM1531 *Azurite*

CM1532 *Copper*

CM1533 *Variscite*

CM1534 *Wulfenite*

| CM1531 | | MNHVF | UseVF |
|---|---|---|---|
| 29¢ | Azurite, tagged | .45 | .20 |

| CM1532 | | MNHVF | UseVF |
|---|---|---|---|
| 29¢ | Copper, tagged | .45 | .20 |

| CM1533 | | MNHVF | UseVF |
|---|---|---|---|
| 29¢ | Variscite, tagged | .45 | .20 |

| CM1534 | | MNHVF | UseVF |
|---|---|---|---|
| 29¢ | Wulfenite, tagged | .45 | .20 |
| | Plate block of 4 | 4.50 | |
| | y. Se-tenant block or strip of 4, (CM1531-34) | 3.00 | |
| | FDC *(Sept. 17, 1992) any single* | | 1.00 |
| | FDC, block or strip of 4 | | 2.00 |
| | v. silver omitted | — | |

**1992. Juan Rodríguez Cabrillo Issue** recalls the Spanish explorer who named San Miguel Harbor, later the site of San Diego, Calif. *Printed by The Press and J.W. Fergusson & Sons for Stamp Venturers, perforated 11.*

CM1535 *Juan Rodríguez Cabrillo*

| CM1535 | | MNHVF | UseVF |
|---|---|---|---|
| 29¢ | **multicolored,** tagged | .45 | .20 |
| | Plate block of 4 | 3.50 | |
| | FDC *(Sept. 28, 1992)* | | 1.00 |

**1992. Wild Animals Issue** depicts 4 popular animals in U.S. zoos. *Gravure, J.W. Fergusson & Sons for Stamp Venturers, perforated 11 horizontally.*

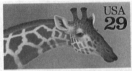

CM1536 *Giraffe*

CM1537 *Giant Panda*

CM1538 *Flamingo*

CM1539 *King Penguins*

CM1540 *White Bengal Tiger*

| CM1536 | | MNHVF | UseVF |
|---|---|---|---|
| 29¢ | Giraffe, tagged | .45 | .20 |

| CM1537 | | MNHVF | UseVF |
|---|---|---|---|
| 29¢ | Giant Panda, tagged | .45 | .20 |

| CM1538 | | MNHVF | UseVF |
|---|---|---|---|
| 29¢ | Flamingo, tagged | .45 | .20 |

| CM1539 | | MNHVF | UseVF |
|---|---|---|---|
| 29¢ | King Penguins, tagged | .45 | .20 |
| | n. Pane of 5 | 3.50 | |
| | v. Imperforate pane of 5 | 3500. | |

**CM1540**

| | | MNHVF | UseVF |
|---|---|---|---|
| 29¢ | White Bengal Tiger, tagged | .45 | .20 |
| | FDC *(Oct. 1, 1992)* any single | | 1.00 |
| | n. Booklet pane of 5 (CM1536-40) | | |
| | FDC | | 2.00 |

**1992. NEW YEAR ISSUE** was the 1st U.S. stamp to honor the Asian lunar holiday. *Offset and intaglio, American Bank Note Co., perforated 11.*

CM1541 *Rooster and Chinese Characters*

**CM1541**

| | | MNHVF | UseVF |
|---|---|---|---|
| 29¢ | **multicolored,** tagged | .45 | .20 |
| | Plate block of 4 | 3.95 | |
| | FDC *(Dec. 30, 1992)* | | 1.00 |

**1993. ELVIS PRESLEY ISSUE** of 500 million stamps represented a massive press run for a single commemorative, reflecting the interest in the rock 'n roll entertainer. The public in a write-in poll voted for the designing of this stamp over a second design showing an older-looking portrait of the pop icon. This stamp is also the 1st in a lengthy and electric American Music series. *Gravure, perforated 11.*

CM1542 *Elvis Presley*

**CM1542**

| | | MNHVF | UseVF |
|---|---|---|---|
| 29¢ | **multicolored,** tagged | .45 | .20 |
| | Plate block of 4 | 3.50 | |
| | FDC *(Jan. 8, 1993)* | | 1.00 |

**1993. SPACE FANTASY ISSUE** reminiscent of the 1930's vision of space travel made popular in movie and comic-book adventure. *Gravure, perforated 11 vertically.*

CM1543 CM1544 CM1545 CM1546 CM1547

**CM1543**

| | | MNHVF | UseVF |
|---|---|---|---|
| 29¢ | Saturn Rings, tagged | .45 | .20 |

**CM1544**

| | | MNHVF | UseVF |
|---|---|---|---|
| 29¢ | Two oval crafts, tagged | .45 | .20 |

**CM1545**

| | | MNHVF | UseVF |
|---|---|---|---|
| 29¢ | Spacement & Jet Pack, tagged | .45 | .20 |

**CM1546**

| | | MNHVF | UseVF |
|---|---|---|---|
| 29¢ | Craft & lights, tagged | .45 | .20 |

**CM1547**

| | | MNHVF | UseVF |
|---|---|---|---|
| 29¢ | Three craft, tagged | .45 | .20 |
| | FDC *(Jan. 25, 1993)* any single | | 1.00 |
| | n. Booklet pane of 5 (CM1541-45) | 5.50 | |
| | FDC | | 2.00 |

## Black Heritage Series

**1993. PERCY LAVON JULIAN ISSUE** honors the research chemist who synthesized cortisone for treatment of arthritis. *Offset and intaglio, perforated 11.*

CM1548 *Percy Lavon Julian*

**CM1548**

| | | MNHVF | UseVF |
|---|---|---|---|
| 29¢ | **multicolored,** tagged | .45 | .20 |
| | Plate block of 4 | 3.50 | |
| | FDC *(Jan. 29, 1993)* | | 1.00 |

**1993. OREGON TRAIL ISSUE** recalled the 2,000-mile stretch from Independence, Mo., to Oregon City, Ore. that was a popular route used by settlers traveling west. *Offset and intaglio, perforated 11.*

CM1549 *The Oregon Trail*

**CM1549**

| | | MNHVF | UseVF |
|---|---|---|---|
| 29¢ | **multicolored,** tagged | .45 | .20 |
| | Plate block of 4 | 3.50 | |
| | FDC *(Feb. 12, 1993)* | | 1.00 |
| | zo. Tagging omitted | — | |

*The official first day city was Salem, Ore. but the stamp was available February 12 at 36 cities along the Trail.*

**1993. WORLD UNIVERSITY GAMES ISSUE** celebrates the 1st time this biennial competition was held in the United States. *Gravure, perforated 11.*

CM1550 *World University Games*

**CM1550**

| | | MNHVF | UseVF |
|---|---|---|---|
| 29¢ | **multicolored,** tagged | .45 | .20 |
| | Plate block of 4 | 4.00 | |
| | FDC *(Feb. 25, 1993)* | | 1.00 |

**1993. GRACE KELLY ISSUE** memorializes the American actress who became Princess of Monaco. Monaco and the United States jointly issued similar stamps (Monaco 2127). *Intaglio, Stamp Venturers, perforated 11.*

CM1551 *Grace Kelly*

| CM1551 | | MNHVF | UseVF |
|---|---|---|---|
| 29¢ | **blue,** tagged | .45 | .20 |
| | Plate block of 4 | 3.50 | |
| | FDC *(March 24, 1993)* | | 1.00 |

**1993. OKLAHOMA! ISSUE** paid tribute to the landmark American musical. The stamp was available for sale in every post office in the state on its 1st day, rather than at a single outlet. American Music Series.*Gravure, perforated 10.*

CM1552 *Oklahoma*

| CM1552 | | MNHVF | UseVF |
|---|---|---|---|
| 29¢ | **multicolored,** tagged | .45 | .20 |
| | Plate block of 4 | 3.50 | |
| | FDC *(March 30, 1993)* | | 1.00 |

**1993. CIRCUS ISSUE** honored the 200th anniversary of the 1st circus performance in America. *Offset, Ashton Potter America, perforated 11.*

CM1553 *Trapeze Artist*

CM1554 *Elephant*

CM1555 *Clown*

CM1556 *Ringmaster*

| CM1553 | | MNHVF | UseVF |
|---|---|---|---|
| 29¢ | Trapeze Artist, tagged | .45 | .20 |

| CM1554 | | MNHVF | UseVF |
|---|---|---|---|
| 29¢ | Elephant, tagged | .45 | .20 |

| CM1555 | | MNHVF | UseVF |
|---|---|---|---|
| 29¢ | Clown, tagged | .45 | .20 |

| CM1556 | | MNHVF | UseVF |
|---|---|---|---|
| 29¢ | Ring Master, tagged | .45 | .20 |
| | Plate block of 6 | 6.75 | |
| | Plate block of 4 | 4.00 | |
| | y. Se-tenant block of 4 (CM1553-56) | 3.00 | |
| | FDC *(April 6, 1993)* | | 2.00 |

**1993. CHEROKEE STRIP LAND RUN CENTENNIAL ISSUE** commemorates the events of Sept. 16, 1893, when more than 100,000 pioneers raced to stake out land claims in the 8 million acre parcel of land known as the "Cherokee Strip". *Offset and intaglio, by American Bank Note Co., perforated 11.*

CM1557

| CM1557 | | MNHVF | UseVF |
|---|---|---|---|
| 29¢ | **multicolored,** tagged | .45 | .20 |
| | Plate block of 4 | 3.50 | |
| | FDC *(April 17, 1993)* | | 1.00 |

**1993. DEAN ACHESON ISSUE** honors the former U.S. secretary of state. *Intaglio, Stamp Venturers, perforated 11.*

CM1558 *Dean Acheson*

| CM1558 | | MNHVF | UseVF |
|---|---|---|---|
| 29¢ | **multicolored,** tagged | .45 | .20 |
| | Plate block of 4 | 3.50 | |
| | FDC *(April 21, 1993)* | | 1.00 |

**1993. SPORTING HORSES ISSUE** commemorates 4 equestrian events. *Offset and intaglio, Stamp Venturers, perforated 11.*

CM1559 *Steeplechase*

CM1560 *Thoroughbred Racing*

CM1561 *Harness Racing*

CM1562 *Polo*

| CM1559 | | MNHVF | UseVF |
|---|---|---|---|
| 29¢ | Stepple Chase, tagged | .45 | .20 |

| CM1560 | | MNHVF | UseVF |
|---|---|---|---|
| 29¢ | Thoroughbred Racing, tagged | .45 | .20 |

| CM1561 | | MNHVF | UseVF |
|---|---|---|---|
| 29¢ | Harness Racing, tagged | .45 | .20 |

| CM1562 | | MNHVF | UseVF |
|---|---|---|---|
| 29¢ | Polo, tagged | .45 | .20 |
| | Plate block of 4 | 4.25 | |
| | FDC *(May 1, 1993)* | — | |
| | y. Se-tenant block of 4 (CM1559-62) | — | |
| | vy. Block of 4, intaglio black omitted | 1650. | |
| | vyl.Any single, intaglio, black omitted | 375. | |

**1993. GARDEN FLOWERS ISSUE** show an array of popular blooms in a booklet format. *Offset and intaglio, perforated 11 vertically.*

CM1563 *Hyacinth* CM1564 *Daffodil* CM1565 *Tulip* CM1566 *Iris* CM1567 *Lilac*

| CM1563 | | MNHVF | UseVF |
|---|---|---|---|
| 29¢ | Hyacinth, tagged | .45 | .20 |

| CM1564 | | MNHVF | UseVF |
|---|---|---|---|
| 29¢ | Daffodil, tagged | .45 | .20 |

| CM1565 | | MNHVF | UseVF |
|---|---|---|---|
| 29¢ | Tulip, tagged | .45 | .20 |

| CM1566 | | MNHVF | UseVF |
|---|---|---|---|
| 29¢ | Iris, tagged | .45 | .20 |

| CM1567 | | MNHVF | UseVF |
|---|---|---|---|
| 29¢ | Lilac, tagged | .45 | .20 |
| | FDC *(May 15, 1993)* | 1.00 | |
| | n. Booklet pane of 5 (CM1563-67) | 5.50 | |
| | FDC | | 2.00 |
| | v. Booklet pane, imperforated | 2750. | |
| | v1. Booklet pane, black omitted | 350. | |

**1993. WORLD WAR II 1943: TURNING THE TIDE ISSUE** includes
a map and stamps showing events of the war in 1943. *Offset and intaglio,
perforated 11.*

| CM1568 | | MNHVF | UseVF |
|---|---|---|---|
| $2.90 | **Sheet of ten** | 8.75 | 7.00 |
| | a. Allied Escort ships, tagged | .75 | .45 |
| | b. Military Medics, tagged | .75 | .45 |
| | c. Sicily Attacked, tagged | .75 | .45 |
| | d. B-24's Hit Ploesti, tagged | .75 | .45 |
| | e. V-mail Delivers Letters, tagged | .75 | .45 |
| | f. Italy Invaded (PT boat), tagged | .75 | .45 |
| | g. War Bonds & Stamps, tagged | .75 | .45 |
| | h. "Willie and Joe", tagged | .75 | .45 |
| | i. Gold Stars Marks losses, tagged | .75 | .45 |
| | j. Marines Assault Tarawa, tagged | .75 | .45 |
| | FDC *(May 31, 1993)* any single | | 1.00 |
| | FDC, complete sheet | | 10.00 |

**1993. HANK WILLIAMS ISSUE** honored the country singer and composer credited with integrating country music and rock 'n Roll. *Gravure, Stamp Venturers, perforated 11.*

CM1569 *Hank Williams*

| CM1569 | | MNHVF | UseVF |
|---|---|---|---|
| 29¢ | **multicolored,** tagged | .45 | .20 |
| | Plate block of 4 | 3.50 | |
| | FDC *(June 9, 1993)* | | 1.00 |

**1993. ROCK 'N ROLL - RHYTHM & BLUES ISSUE** honored 7 stars
in a continuation of the American Music series, including a 2nd Elvis
Presley stamp that spells out his last name. Additional personalities
featured in this issue are Buddy Holly, Ritchie Valens, Bill Haley, Dinah Washington, Otis Redding, and Clyde McPhatter. The stamps
were released in a pane of 35 stamps and a booklet of 20 stamps.
The booklet consists of 2 panes of 8 (with 6 of 7 honorees appearing
once and Elvis Presley appearing twice), and 1 pane of 4 (the bottom
4 stamps of the pane of 8).

Although the stamp designs are similar, the stamps in the booklet
panes are printed in magenta, cyan,, yellow, and black, while the
commemorative sheet is printed in those 4 colors plus additional blue
and red inks. The sheet stamps are 31.5mm high and booklet stamps
are 31.1mm high. *Gravure, Stamp Venturers, perforated 10 on 4
sides.*

Allied forces battle German U-boats, 1943 · Military medics treat the wounded, 1943 · Sicily attacked by Allied forces, July 1943 · B-24s hit Ploesti refineries, August 1943 · V-mail delivers letters from home, 1943

1943: Turning the Tide

Italy invaded by Allies, September 1943 · Bonds and stamps help war effort, 1943 · "Willie and Joe" keep spirits high, 1943 · Gold Stars mark World War II losses, 1943 · Marines assault Tarawa, November 1943

CM1568 *1943: Turning the Tide*

CM1570, CM1577 *Elvis Presley*

CM1571, CM1582 *Buddy Holly*

CM1572, CM1580 *Ritchie Valens*

CM1573, CM1578 *Bill Haley*

CM1574, CM1583 *Dinah Washington*

CM1575, CM1581 *Otis Redding*

CM1576, CM1579 *Clyde McPhatter*

| | | MNHVF | UseVF |
|---|---|---|---|
| **CM1570** | | MNHVF | UseVF |
| 29¢ | Elvis Presley, tagged | .45 | .20 |
| **CM1571** | | MNHVF | UseVF |
| 29¢ | Buddy Holly, tagged | .45 | .20 |
| **CM1572** | | MNHVF | UseVF |
| 29¢ | Richie Valenz, tagged | .45 | .20 |
| **CM1573** | | MNHVF | UseVF |
| 29¢ | Bill Haley, tagged | .45 | .20 |
| **CM1574** | | MNHVF | UseVF |
| 29¢ | Dinah Washington, tagged | .45 | .20 |
| **CM1575** | | MNHVF | UseVF |
| 29¢ | Otis Redding, tagged | .45 | .20 |
| **CM1576** | | MNHVF | UseVF |
| 29¢ | Clyde McPhatter, tagged | .45 | .20 |
| | Commemorative sheet of 35 (includes 4 plate nos.) | | |
| | FDC *(June 16, 1993)* any single | | 1.75 |

*Gravure, Multi-Color Corp. Perforated 11 on one or two sides.*

| | | MNHVF | UseVF |
|---|---|---|---|
| **CM1577** | | MNHVF | UseVF |
| 29¢ | **multicolored,** tagged | .45 | .20 |

| | | MNHVF | UseVF |
|---|---|---|---|
| **CM1578** | | MNHVF | UseVF |
| 29¢ | **multicolored,** tagged | .45 | .20 |
| **CM1579** | | MNHVF | UseVF |
| 29¢ | **multicolored,** tagged | .45 | .20 |
| **CM1580** | | MNHVF | UseVF |
| 29¢ | **multicolored,** tagged | .45 | .20 |
| **CM1581** | | MNHVF | UseVF |
| 29¢ | **multicolored,** tagged | .45 | .20 |
| **CM1582** | | MNHVF | UseVF |
| 29¢ | **multicolored,** tagged | .45 | .20 |
| **CM1583** | | MNHVF | UseVF |
| 29¢ | **multicolored,** tagged | .45 | .20 |
| | FDC *(June 16, 1993)* any single | | 1.75 |
| | n. Pane of 8, (2 of CM1577, 1 each of CM-1578-83) | | |
| | FDC, pane of 8 | | 3.00 |
| | n1. Pane of 4, (CM1577 & CM1581-83, plus tab) | | 2.50 |

*The vertically oriented pane of eight consists of the following stamps, from top to bottom: CM1577, CM1578, CM1579, CM1580, CM1581, CM1582, CM1583, CM1577. The vertically oriented pane of four consists of the following stamps, from top to bottom: CM1581, CM1582, CM1583, CM1584. A complete booklet consists of two panes of eight and one pane of four.*

**1993. JOE LOUIS ISSUE** honors the heavyweight boxing champion and was issued on the 55th anniversary of his knockout win over Max Schmeling. *Offset and intaglio, perforated 11.*

CM1584 *Joe Louis*

| | | MNHVF | UseVF |
|---|---|---|---|
| **CM1584** | | MNHVF | UseVF |
| 29¢ | **multicolored,** tagged | .45 | .20 |
| | Plate block of 4 | 4.75 | |
| | FDC *(June 22, 1993)* | | 1.00 |

## American Music Series

**1993. BROADWAY MUSICALS ISSUE** Honored are 4 of the most celebrated musicals in American theater. Gravure, Multi-Color Corp. for the American Bank Note Co., perforated 11 horizontally.

CM1585 *Showboat*

CM1586 *Porgy & Bess*

CM1587 *Oklahoma!*

CM1588 *My Fair Lady*

**CM1585**

| | | MNHVF | UseVF |
|---|---|---|---|
| 29¢ | Showboat, tagged | .45 | .20 |

**CM1586**

| | | MNHVF | UseVF |
|---|---|---|---|
| 29¢ | Porgy & Bess, tagged | .45 | .20 |

**CM1587**

| | | MNHVF | UseVF |
|---|---|---|---|
| 29¢ | Oklahoma, tagged | .45 | .20 |

**CM1588**

| | | MNHVF | UseVF |
|---|---|---|---|
| 29¢ | My Fair Lady, tagged | .45 | .20 |
| | FDC *(July 14, 1993)* any single | | 1.00 |
| | n. Booklet pane of 4 | 4.95 | |
| | FDC, booklet pane | | |

**1993. NATIONAL POSTAL MUSEUM ISSUE** marked the opening of the Washington, D.C., facility, part of the Smithsonian Institution. *Offset and intaglio, American Bank Note Co., perforated 11.*

CM1589 *Benjamin Franklin, Liberty Hall, Printing Press.*

CM1590 *Civil War Soldier Writing Letter, Stagecoach.*

CM1591 *Air Mail Plane, Charles Lindbergh, Railway Mail Car and Mail Truck.*

CM1592 *Miner's Letter, Stamps, Barcode and Date stamp*

**CM1589**

| | | MNHVF | UseVF |
|---|---|---|---|
| 29¢ | Benjamin Franklin, tagged | .45 | .20 |

**CM1590**

| | | MNHVF | UseVF |
|---|---|---|---|
| 29¢ | Civil War Soldier writing letter | .45 | .20 |

**CM1591**

| | | MNHVF | UseVF |
|---|---|---|---|
| 29¢ | Charles Lindbergh, tagged | .45 | .20 |

**CM1592**

| | | MNHVF | UseVF |
|---|---|---|---|
| 29¢ | Letters & date stamp, tagged | .45 | .20 |
| | Plate block of 4 | 4.25 | |
| | FDC *(July 30, 1993)* any single | | 3.00 |
| | v. Imperforate, block of 4 | 3500. | |

**1993. AMERICAN SIGN LANGUAGE/RECOGNIZING DEAFNESS ISSUE** shows non-verbal communication used with the hearing impaired. Both stamps show the sign for "I love you." *Gravure, Stamp Venturers, perforated 11.*

CM1593-CM1594 *"I Love You"*

**CM1593**

| | | MNHVF | UseVF |
|---|---|---|---|
| 29¢ | Mother and child, tagged | .45 | .20 |

**CM1594**

| | | MNHVF | UseVF |
|---|---|---|---|
| 29¢ | Sign "I love you" | .45 | .20 |
| | y. Se-tenant pair (CM1593-94) | | |
| | Plate block of 4 | 3.95 | |
| | FDC *(Sept. 20, 1993)* | 2.00 | |

**1993. COUNTRY MUSIC ISSUE** American Music Series
An earlier design featured Hank Williams (CM1569), here joined by The Carter Family, Patsy Cline and Bob Willis. The stamps were available, a 20-stamp pane with a large title across the top, or a booklet

with each stamp appearing once on each of the 5 panes. Although the designs and sizes are identical, the sheet stamps used burgundy and blue in addition to yellow, magenta, cyan, and black, while the booklet stamps were produced using pink and line black in addition to the 4 process colors. *Gravure, Stamp Venturers, perforated 10 on 4 sides.*

CM1595, CM1599 *Hank Williams*

CM1596, CM1600 *The Carter Family*

CM1597, CM1601 *Patsy Cline*

CM1598, CM1602 *Bob Willis*

**CM1595**

| | | MNHVF | UseVF |
|---|---|---|---|
| 29¢ | Hank Williams, tagged | .45 | .20 |

**CM1596**

| | | MNHVF | UseVF |
|---|---|---|---|
| 29¢ | The Carter Family, tagged | .45 | .20 |

**CM1597**

| | | MNHVF | UseVF |
|---|---|---|---|
| 29¢ | Patsy Cline, tagged | .45 | .20 |

**CM1598**

| | | MNHVF | UseVF |
|---|---|---|---|
| 29¢ | Bob Willis, tagged | .45 | .20 |
| | Plate block of 4 | 3.95 | |
| | y. Se-Tenant block or strip of 4 (CM1595-98) | 2.50 | |
| | FDC *(Sept. 25, 1993)* | | 2.00 |

*Gravure by American Bank Note Co., perforated 11 on 1 or 2 sides, from booklet panes.*

**CM1599**

| | | MNHVF | UseVF |
|---|---|---|---|
| 29¢ | Hank Williams, tagged | .45 | .20 |

**CM1600**

| | | MNHVF | UseVF |
|---|---|---|---|
| 29¢ | The Carter Family, tagged | .45 | .20 |

**CM1601**

| | | MNHVF | UseVF |
|---|---|---|---|
| 29¢ | Patsy Cline, tagged | .45 | .20 |

**CM1602**

| | | MNHVF | UseVF |
|---|---|---|---|
| 29¢ | Bob Wills, tagged | .45 | .20 |
| | FDC *(Sept. 25, 1993)* any single | | 1.75 |
| | Pane of 4, (CM1599-1602) | 4.95 | |
| | FDC, full page | | 5.00 |
| | n. Imperforate, booklet pane | — | |

**1993. YOUTH CLASSICS ISSUE** is a se-tenant block of 4 honoring 4 of the best-loved and popular stories for young readers. Louisa May Alcott's *Little Women* was published in 2 volumes in 1868-69. Kate Douglas Smith Wiggin's *Rebecca of Sunnybrook Farm,* the story of a fatherless little girl who goes to live with her maiden aunts, was a bestseller in 1903. Laura Ingalls Wilder drew upon her own childhood and travels on the frontier as inspiration for her books, including *Little*

*House on the Prairie,* published in 1935. *The Adventures of Huckleberry Finn* also is a peek into the childhood of its author, Samuel Clemens (Mark Twain). *Offset and Itaglio by American Bank Note Co., perforated 11.*

 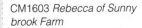 

CM1603 *Rebecca of Sunny brook Farm*

CM1604 *Little House on the Prairie*

CM1605 *The Adventures of Huckleberry Finn*

CM1606 *Little Women*

| CM1603 | | MNHVF | UseVF |
|---|---|---|---|
| 29¢ | Rebecca, tagged | .45 | .20 |

| CM1604 | | MNHVF | UseVF |
|---|---|---|---|
| 29¢ | Little House, tagged | .45 | .20 |

| CM1605 | | MNHVF | UseVF |
|---|---|---|---|
| 29¢ | Huck Finn, tagged | .45 | .20 |

| CM1606 | | MNHVF | UseVF |
|---|---|---|---|
| 29¢ | Little Women, tagged | .45 | .20 |
| | Plate block of 4 | 4.50 | |
| | y. Se-tenant block or strip of 4 (CM1603-06) | 3.50 | |
| | FDC *(Oct. 23, 1993)* any single | | 1.75 |
| | FDC, block of 4 | | 4.00 |
| | v. Imperforate, block of 4 | 3000. | |

**1993. COMMONWEALTH OF THE NORTHERN MARIANA ISLANDS ISSUE** salutes a group of 16 islands in the western Pacific Ocean administered by the United States following World War II as part of the U.N. Trust Territorries of the Pacific Islands. In 1978, following a referendum, the Archipelago became a self-governing entity in union with the United States. Mail to and from the Mariana Islands is sent at domestic U.S. postage rates from a U.S. post office. *Offset and intaglio, perforated 11.*

CM1607 *Flag and Limestone Pillars*

| CM1607 | | MNHVF | UseVF |
|---|---|---|---|
| 29¢ | **multicolored,** tagged | .45 | .20 |
| | Plate block of 4 | 3.50 | |
| | FDC *(Nov. 4, 1993)* | | 1.00 |

**1993. COLUMBUS LANDING IN PUERTO RICO ISSUE** marks the 500th anniversary of the arrival of Columbus.

CM1608 *Caravels in Boqueron Bay*

| CM1608 | | MNHVF | UseVF |
|---|---|---|---|
| 29¢ | **multicolored,** tagged | .45 | .20 |
| | Plate block of 4 | 3.50 | |
| | FDC *(Nov. 19, 1993)* | | 1.00 |

**1993. AIDS AWARENESS ISSUE** symbolizes compassion and awareness for those afflicted by this disease. The stamps were sold nationwide on their 1st day of issue, and were available in sheet form or in 10- stamp booklets. *Gravure.*

CM1609

| CM1609 | | MNHVF | UseVF |
|---|---|---|---|
| 29¢ | **red and black,** tagged | .45 | .20 |
| | Plate block of 4 | 4.00 | |

| CM1609A | | MNHVF | UseVF |
|---|---|---|---|
| 29¢ | | | |
| | a. Perforated 11 vertically on 1 or 2 sides | .75 | .25 |
| | n. Booklet pane of 10 perforated 11 vertically | 4.50 | |

**1994. WINTER OLYMPICS ISSUE** honors the 1994 Winter Games. *Offset, Ashton-Potter, perforated 11.*

CM1610 *Downhill Skiing* CM1611 *Luge* CM1612 *Figure Skating*
CM1613 *Cross Country Skiing* CM1614 *Hockey*

| CM1610 | | MNHVF | UseVF |
|---|---|---|---|
| 29¢ | Downhill skiing, tagged | .45 | .20 |

| CM1611 | | MNHVF | UseVF |
|---|---|---|---|
| 29¢ | Luge, tagged | .45 | .20 |

| CM1612 | | MNHVF | UseVF |
|---|---|---|---|
| 29¢ | Figure skating, tagged | .45 | .20 |

| CM1613 | | MNHVF | UseVF |
|---|---|---|---|
| 29¢ | Cross Country Skiing, tagged | .45 | .20 |

| CM1614 | | MNHVF | UseVF |
|---|---|---|---|
| 29¢ | Hockey, tagged | .45 | .20 |
| | Plate block of 10 | 7.50 | |
| | y. Se-tenant strip of 5 (CM-1610-14) | 3.00 | |
| | FDC *(Jan. 6, 1994)* any single | | 1.00 |

**1994. EDWARD R. MURROW ISSUE** honors the broadcast journalist who joined CBS in 1935 and directed its European bureau through World War II. In 1945 he was made CBS vice president in charge of news, education and discussion programs. *Intaglio, perforated 11.*

CM1615 *Edward R. Murrow*

| CM1615 | | MNHVF | UseVF |
|---|---|---|---|
| 29¢ | **brown,** tagged | .45 | .20 |
| | Plate block of 4 | 3.50 | |
| | FDC *(Jan. 21, 1994)* | | 1.00 |

**1994. LOVE ISSUE** a self-adhesive stamp, one of three 1994 stamps with this theme. (See CM1619-20). *Offset and intaglio, imperforate (die cut).*

 CM1616 *Love - Heart*

| CM1616 | | MNHVF | UseVF |
|---|---|---|---|
| 29¢ | **multicolored,** tagged | .45 | .20 |
| | FDC *(Jan. 27, 1994)* | | 1.00 |
| | n. Booklet pane of 18 | 6.00 | |

## Black Heritage Series

**1994. DR. ALLISON DAVIS ISSUE** honors the influential social anthropologist and educator who challenged the cultural bias of standardized intelliegen ce tests and helped end racial segregation. *Intaglio by Stamp Venturers, perforated 11.*

BLACK HERITAGE CM1617 *Dr. Allison Davis*

| CM1617 | | MNHVF | UseVF |
|---|---|---|---|
| 29¢ | **red brown and brown,** tagged | .45 | .20 |
| | Plate block of 4 | 4.00 | |
| | FDC *(Feb. 1, 1994)* | | 1.00 |

## Asian Lunar New Year Series

**1994. NEW YEAR ISSUE** the 2nd in the series, features the royal dog of China, a Pekinese, and marks the Year of the Dog. *Gravure, perforated 11.*

 CM1618 *Lunar New Year*

| CM1618 | | MNHVF | UseVF |
|---|---|---|---|
| 29¢ | **multicolored,** tagged | .45 | .20 |
| | Plate block of 4 | 3.75 | |
| | FDC *(Feb. 5, 1994)* | | 1.00 |

## Love Series

**1994. LOVE ISSUES** are 2 lick-and-stick stamps released on Valentine's Day, complimenting the earlier self-adhesive issue, CM1616. (See also CM1642.) *Gravure, and intaglio, perforated 10 3/4 by 11 on 2 or 3 sides.*

LOVE CM1619 *Love-Dove and Roses*

| CM1619 | | MNHVF | UseVF |
|---|---|---|---|
| 29¢ | **multicolored,** tagged | .45 | .20 |
| | FDC *(Feb. 14, 1994)* | | 1.00 |
| | n. Pane of 10 | 6.00 | |
| | FDC, pane of 10 | | 5.00 |
| | v. Imperforate pair | — | |
| | v1. Horizontal pair, imperforate between | — | |

 CM1620 *Love*

| CM1620 | | MNHVF | UseVF |
|---|---|---|---|
| 52¢ | **multicolored,** tagged | 1.50 | .35 |
| | Plate block of 4 | 7.00 | |
| | FDC *(Feb. 14, 1994)* | | 1.00 |

**1994. BUFFALO SOLDIERS ISSUE** honored the U.S. Army's regiments that played a major role on the settlement of the American West. Predominantly black cavalry and infantry. Black troops of the Buffalo Soldier regiments were the 1st authorized to serve on the U.S. Army during peace-time. *Offset and intaglio, perforated 11 1/2 x 11.*

 CM1621 *Buffalo Soldiers*

| CM1621 | | MNHVF | UseVF |
|---|---|---|---|
| 29¢ | **multicolored,** tagged | .45 | .20 |
| | Plate block of 4 | 1.25 | |
| | FDC *(April 22, 1994)* | | 1.00 |

**1994. SILENT SCREEN STARS ISSUE** featured 10 early film stars, drawn by Al Hirschfeld. Theda Bara's work in *The Vampire* led to the term "vamp". Film star Clara Bow first arrived in Hollywood as the result of a high school beauty contest. Lon Chaney used his incredible make-up and characterization in *The Hunchback of Notre Dame, Phantom of the Opera* and *The Unholy Three.* Charlie Chaplin's "Little Tramp" character became famous worldwide. John Gilbert began with a stage career that led to romantic roles in such films as *The Merry Widow, The Big Parade* and *Flesh and the Devil.* Buster Keaton is known for slapstick comedy and his deadpan stare. Mack Sennett's Keystone Cops kept audiences laughing through many short films of 1914-20. Comedian Harold Lloyd made more than 500 movies, beginning in 1914. Zasu Pitts began as an extra, moving to both comedy and dramatic roles. Rudolf Valentino is one of the world's best-known film stars remembered for *The Four Horsemen of the Apocalypse, The Sheik,* and *Blood and Sand. Offset and intaglio, perforated 11.*

CM1622 *Rudolf Valentino* CM1623 *Clara Bow* CM1624 *Charlie Chaplin*
CM1625 *Lon Chaney* CM1626 *John Gilbert* CM1627 *Zasu Pitts*
CM1628 *Harold Lloyd* CM1629 *Keystone Cops* CM1630 *Theda Bara*
CM1631 *Buster Keaton*

| CM1622 | | MNHVF | UseVF |
|---|---|---|---|
| 29¢ | Rudolf Valentino, tagged | .45 | .20 |

| CM1623 | | MNHVF | UseVF |
|---|---|---|---|
| 29¢ | Clara Bow, tagged | .45 | .20 |

| CM1624 | | MNHVF | UseVF |
|---|---|---|---|
| 29¢ | Charlie Chaplin, tagged | .45 | .20 |

| CM1625 | | MNHVF | UseVF |
|---|---|---|---|
| 29¢ | Lon Chaney, tagged | .45 | .20 |

| CM1626 | | MNHVF | UseVF |
|---|---|---|---|
| 29¢ | John Gilbert, tagged | .45 | .20 |

| CM1627 | | MNHVF | UseVF |
|---|---|---|---|
| 29¢ | Zasu Pitts, tagged | .45 | .20 |

| CM1628 | | MNHVF | UseVF |
|---|---|---|---|
| 29¢ | Harold Lloyd, tagged | .45 | .20 |

| CM1629 | | MNHVF | UseVF |
|---|---|---|---|
| 29¢ | Keystone Cops, tagged | .45 | .20 |

| CM1630 | | MNHVF | UseVF |
|---|---|---|---|
| 29¢ | Theda Bara, tagged | .45 | .20 |

| CM1631 | | MNHVF | UseVF |
|---|---|---|---|
| 29¢ | Buster Keaton, tagged | .45 | .20 |
| | Plate block of 10 | 9.00 | |
| | y.  Se-tenant block of 10 (CM1622-31) | 8.00 | |
| | vy. Block of 10, offset black omitted | — | |
| | vy1.Block of 10, offset black & intaglio red & purple omitted | — | |

**1994. GARDEN FLOWERS ISSUE** the 2nd such 5-stamp booklet showing bright and popular flowers that bloom in summer. *Offset and intaglio, perforated 11.*

CM1632 *Lily* CM1633 *Zinnia* CM1634 *Gladiola* CM1635 *Marigold* CM1636 *Rose*

| CM1632 | | MNHVF | UseVF |
|---|---|---|---|
| 29¢ | Lilly, tagged | .45 | .20 |

| CM1633 | | MNHVF | UseVF |
|---|---|---|---|
| 29¢ | Zinnia, tagged | .45 | .20 |

| CM1634 | | MNHVF | UseVF |
|---|---|---|---|
| 29¢ | Gladiola, tagged | .45 | .20 |

| CM1635 | | MNHVF | UseVF |
|---|---|---|---|
| 29¢ | Marigold, tagged | .45 | .20 |

| CM1636 | | MNHVF | UseVF |
|---|---|---|---|
| 29¢ | Rose, tagged | .45 | .20 |
| | FDC *(April 28, 1994)*, any single | | 2.00 |
| | n.  Booklet pane of 5 (CM1632-36) | 4.50 | |
| | FDC *(April 28, 1994)*, pane of 5 | | 4.00 |
| | vn. Pane of 5, intaglio black omitted | 375. | |
| | vn1.Imperforate pane of 5 | 2250. | |

**1994. WORLD CUP SOCCER CHAMPIONSHIP ISSUE** of three stamps and a souvenir sheet honors the 1st time the United States hosted the final rounds of soccer's quadrennial World Cup. Stamps issued in panes of 20 were printed on phosphorcoated paper; those within the souvenir sheet are block tagged. The 50¢ stamp in the souvenir sheet (CM1640c) has part of the yellow map from the sheet in the lower-right corner of its design. *Gravure, perforated 11.*

| CM1637 | | MNHVF | UseVF |
|---|---|---|---|
| 29¢ | **multicolored,** phosphored paper | .75 | .20 |
| | Plate block of 4 | 4.00 | |
| | FDC *(May 29, 1994)* | | 1.00 |

| CM1638 | | MNHVF | UseVF |
|---|---|---|---|
| 40¢ | **multicolored,** phosphored paper | 1.00 | .35 |
| | Plate block of 4 | 5.50 | |
| | FDC *(May 26, 1994)* | | 1.00 |

| CM1639 | | MNHVF | UseVF |
|---|---|---|---|
| 50¢ | **multicolored,** phosphored paper | 1.50 | .50 |
| | Plate block of 4 | 6.50 | |
| | FDC *(May 26, 1994)* | | 1.00 |

| CM1640 | | MNHVF | UseVF |
|---|---|---|---|
| $1.19 | **Souvenir Sheet** | 3.75 | 3.00 |
| | a.  29¢ like CM1637, block tagged | | .75 |
| | b.  40¢ like CM1638, block tagged | | 1.00 |
| | c.  50¢ like CM1639, block tagged | | 1.25 |

CM1640 *World Cup Souvenir Sheet*

Allied forces retake New Guinea, 1944

P-51s escort B-17s on bombing raids, 1944

Allies in Normandy, D-Day, June 6, 1944

Airborne units spearhead attacks, 1944

Submarines shorten war in Pacific, 1944

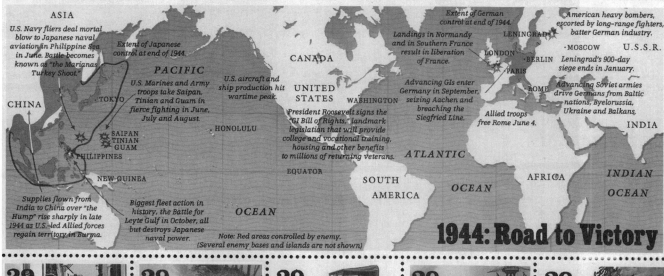

Allies free Rome, June 4; Paris, Aug. 25, 1944

U.S. troops clear Saipan bunkers, 1944

Red Ball Express speeds vital supplies, 1944

Battle for Leyte Gulf, October 23-26, 1944

Bastogne and Battle of the Bulge, Dec. 1944

CM1641 *1944: WWII-Road to Victory*

**1994. 1944: ROAD TO VICTORY ISSUE** includes map and stamps showing events of the war in 1944. *Offset and intaglio, perforated 11.*

| CM1641 | | MNHVF | UseVF |
|---|---|---|---|
| $2.90 | **Sheet of ten,** tagged | 8.75 | 7.00 |
| | a. **29¢** Forces Retake New Guinea | .75 | .70 |
| | b. **29¢** P51s escort B017s | .75 | .70 |
| | c. **29¢** Allies Free Normady | .75 | .70 |
| | d. **29¢** Airborn Units | .75 | .70 |
| | e. **29¢** Submarines | .75 | .70 |
| | f. **29¢** Allies Free Rome, Paris | .75 | .70 |
| | g. **29¢** U.S. Troops clear Saipan | .75 | .70 |
| | h. **29¢** Red Ball Express | .75 | .70 |
| | i. **29¢** Battle of Leyte Gulf | .75 | .70 |
| | j. **29¢** Bastogne and The Buldge | .75 | .70 |
| | FDC *(June 6, 1994)* any single | | 1.00 |
| | FDC sheet of 10 | | 10.00 |

**1994. LOVE ISSUE** is a slightly longer sheet version of the 29¢ booklet stamp (CM1620) released on Valentine's Day. *Offset and intaglio, perforated 11.*

CM1642 *Love*

| CM1642 | | MNHVF | UseVF |
|---|---|---|---|
| **29¢** | **multicolored,** tagged | .50 | .20 |
| | Plate block of 4 | 3.50 | |
| | FDC *(June 11, 1994)* | | 1.00 |

**1994. NORMAN ROCKWELL ISSUE** honors the artist best known as a chronicler of 20th century America for more than 4,000 works, including 321 original *Saturday Evening Post* covers between 1916 and 1963. The commemoration consisted of a single stamp and a commemorative sheet of 4 stamps depicting Franklin D. Roosevelt's Four Freedoms. *Offset and intaglio, perforated 11.*

CM1643 *Norman Rockwell*

| CM1643 | | MNHVF | UseVF |
|---|---|---|---|
| **29¢** | **multicolored,** tagged | .50 | .20 |
| | Plate block of 4 | 3.50 | |
| | FDC *(July 1, 1994)* | | 1.00 |

# Norman Rockwell

From our doughboys in WWI to our astronauts striding across the moon, Norman Rockwell's artwork has captured America's traditional values along with the characteristic optimism of its people. Rockwell loved people, and people loved him. He was an enormously skilled technician and, according to several new reassessments, a true artist. He had a genius for capturing the emotional content of the commonplace. ☞ © USPS ☞ 1993

1894
1994

CM1644a *Freedom from Want*

CM1644b *Freedom from Fear*

CM1644c *Freedom of Speech*

CM1644d *Freedom of Worship*

| CM1644 |  | MNHVF | UseVF |
|---|---|---|---|
| $2 | **multicolored,** tagged | 6.00 | 5.00 |
|  | a. 50¢ Freedom from Want | 1.00 | 1.00 |
|  | b. 50¢ Freedom from Fear | 1.00 | 1.00 |
|  | c. 50¢ Freedom of Speech | 1.00 | 1.00 |
|  | d. 50¢ Freedom of Worship | 1.00 | 1.00 |

**1994. MOON LANDING ANNIVERSARY ISSUE** released in special 12-stamp sheetlets, celebrates the 25th anniversary of man's 1st landing on the Moon. (See also No. 1045). *Gravure, by Stamp Venturers, perforated 11.*

CM1645 *Moon Landing, 25th Anniversary*

First Moon Landing, 1969

| CM1645 |  | MNHVF | UseVF |
|---|---|---|---|
| 29¢ | **multicolored,** tagged | .50 | .25 |
|  | FDC *(July 20, 1994)* |  | 1.00 |
|  | n. Sheetlet of 12 | 9.00 | 7.50 |

**1994. LOCOMOTIVES ISSUE** a 5-stamp booklet, depicts historically significant locomotives. (See also CM1293-97.) *Gravure, by J.W. Ferguson & Sons for Stamp Venturers, perforated 11 horizontally.*

CM1646 *General*

CM1647 *Jupiter*

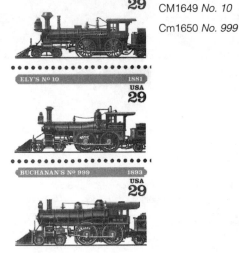

CM1648 *No. 242*

CM1649 *No. 10*

Cm1650 *No. 999*

| CM1646 |  | MNHVF | UseVF |
|---|---|---|---|
| 29¢ | Hudson's General, tagged | .75 | .50 |

| CM1647 |  | MNHVF | UseVF |
|---|---|---|---|
| 29¢ | McQueen's Jupiter, tagged | .75 | .50 |

| CM1648 |  | MNHVF | UseVF |
|---|---|---|---|
| 29¢ | Eddy's No. 242, tagged | .75 | .50 |

| CM1649 |  | MNHVF | UseVF |
|---|---|---|---|
| 29¢ | Ely's No. 10, tagged | .75 | .50 |

| CM1650 |  | MNHVF | UseVF |
|---|---|---|---|
| 29¢ | Buchannan's No. 999, tagged | .75 | .50 |
|  | FDC *(July 29, 1994),* any singe |  | 1.00 |
|  | n. Booklet pane of 5 (CM1646-50) | 4.50 |  |
|  | FDC |  | 4.50 |
|  | v. Imperforate pane of 5 | — |  |

**1994. GEORGE MEANY ISSUE** honors one of the most influential labor leaders in American history, president of the American Federation of Labor (AFL) from 1952-55 and 1st president of the AFL and Congress of Industrial Organizations (CIO) from 1955 until his retirement in 1979. *Intaglio, perforated 11.*

CM1651 *George Meany*

**CM1651**

| | | MNHVF | UseVF |
|---|---|---|---|
| 29¢ | **blue,** tagged | .50 | .20 |
| | Plate block of 4 | 3.50 | |
| | FDC *(Aug. 16, 1994)* | | 1.00 |

## American Music Series

**1994. POPULAR SINGERS ISSUE** honors five showstoppers of this century. *Gravure by J.W. Fergusson & Sons for Stamp Venturers, perforated 11.*

CM1652 *Al Jolson*

CM1653 *Bing Crosby*

CM1654 *Ethel Waters*

CM1655 *Nat 'King' Cole*

CM1656 *Ethel Merman*

**CM1652**

| | | MNHVF | UseVF |
|---|---|---|---|
| 29¢ | Al Jolson, tagged | .75 | .50 |

**CM1653**

| | | MNHVF | UseVF |
|---|---|---|---|
| 29¢ | Bing Crosby, tagged | .75 | .50 |

**CM1654**

| | | MNHVF | UseVF |
|---|---|---|---|
| 29¢ | Ethel Waters, tagged | .75 | .50 |

**CM1655**

| | | MNHVF | UseVF |
|---|---|---|---|
| 29¢ | Nat "King" Cole, tagged | .47 | .50 |

**CM1656**

| | | MNHVF | UseVF |
|---|---|---|---|
| 29¢ | Ethel Merman, tagged | .75 | .50 |
| | Plate block of 6 (vertical) | 6.00 | |
| | Plate block of 12 (horizontal) | 11.00 | |
| | FDC *(Sept. 1, 1994)* any single | | 1.00 |
| | a. Pane of 20 | 17.50 | |

## Literary Arts Series

**1994. JAMES THURBER ISSUE** hails the author, humorist, playwright and cartoonist whose 31 books gave humorous views of life in America. *Offset and intaglio, perforated 11.*

CM1657 *James Thurber*

**CM1657**

| | | MNHVF | UseVF |
|---|---|---|---|
| 29¢ | **multicolored,** tagged | .50 | .20 |
| | Plate block of 4 | 3.50 | |
| | FDC *(Sept. 10. 1994)* | | 1.00 |

**1994. BLUES AND JAZZ SINGERS ISSUE** American Music Series honors seminal artists in these distinctive American musical genres. *Offset by Manhardt-Alexander for Ashton-Potter (USA) Ltd., perforated 11 x 10 3/4.*

CM1658 *Bessie Smith*

CM1659 *Muddy Watters*

CM1660 *Billie Holiday*

CM1661 *Robert Johnson*

CM1662 *Jimmy Rushing*

CM1663 *'Ma' Rainy*

CM1664 *Mildred Barley*

CM1665 *Howlin' Wolf*

| CM1658 | | MNHVF | UseVF |
|---|---|---|---|
| 29¢ | Bessie Smith, tagged | .50 | .25 |

| CM1659 | | MNHVF | UseVF |
|---|---|---|---|
| 29¢ | Muddy Waters, tagged | .50 | .25 |

| CM1660 | | MNHVF | UseVF |
|---|---|---|---|
| 29¢ | Billie Holiday, tagged | .50 | .25 |

| CM1661 | | MNHVF | UseVF |
|---|---|---|---|
| 29¢ | Robert Johnson, tagged | .50 | .25 |

| CM1662 | | MNHVF | UseVF |
|---|---|---|---|
| 29¢ | Jimmy Rushing, tagged | .50 | .25 |

| CM1663 | | MNHVF | UseVF |
|---|---|---|---|
| 29¢ | "Ma" Rainy, tagged | .50 | .25 |

| CM1664 | | MNHVF | UseVF |
|---|---|---|---|
| 29¢ | Mildred Barley, tagged | .50 | .25 |

| CM1665 | | MNHVF | UseVF |
|---|---|---|---|
| 29¢ | Howelin' Wolf, tagged | .50 | .25 |
| | Plate block of 10 | 9.00 | |
| | y.  Se-tenant block of 9, plus 1 extra stamp, (CM-1658-65) | 8.50 | |
| | FDC *(Sept. 17, 1994)* any single | | 1.00 |
| | a.  Pane of 35 | 27.50 | |

**1994. WONDERS OF THE SEAS ISSUE** uses 4 se-tenant stamps to form a single underwater fantasy scene. *Offset by Barton Press for the Banknote Corp., of America, perforated 11.*

CM1666 *Porcupine Fish*

CM1667 *Dolphin*

CM1668 *Nautilus and Ship's Wheel*

CM1669 *Fish and Coral*

| CM1666 | | MNHVF | UseVF |
|---|---|---|---|
| 29¢ | Porcupine fish, tagged | .75 | .25 |

| CM1667 | | MNHVF | UseVF |
|---|---|---|---|
| 29¢ | Dolphin, tagged | .75 | .25 |

| CM1668 | | MNHVF | UseVF |
|---|---|---|---|
| 29¢ | Nautilus and Ship's Wheel, tagged | .75 | .25 |

| CM1669 | | MNHVF | UseVF |
|---|---|---|---|
| 29¢ | Fish and Coral, tagged | .75 | .25 |
| | Plate block of 4 | 4.00 | |
| | y.  Se-tenant block of 4 (CM1666-69) | 3.00 | |
| | FDC *(Oct. 3, 1994),* any single | | 1.00 |
| | vy.  Imperforate block of 4 | 2500. | |

**1994. CRANES ISSUE** depicts 2 of the world's rarest birds, the North American whooping crane and the Chinese black-necked crane. A joint issue of the United States and the People's Republic of China, the issues of the 2 countries show the same designs, with the Chinese issue as 2 separate stamps and the U.S. issue as a se-tenant pair. *Offset and intaglio by Barton Press for the Banknote Corp. of America, perforated 11.*

CM1670 *Black-necked Crane*

CM1671 *Whooping Crane*

| CM1670 | | MNHVF | UseVF |
|---|---|---|---|
| 29¢ | Black-necked crane, tagged | .45 | .20 |

| CM1671 | | MNHVF | UseVF |
|---|---|---|---|
| 29¢ | Whooping crane, tagged | .45 | .20 |
| | Plate block of 4 | 1.25 | |
| | y.  Se-tenant pair (CM1670-71) | | |
| | FDC *(Oct. 9, 1994)* pair | | 2.00 |
| | v.  Se-tenant pair, black and red omitted | — | |

**1993-1994. LEGENDS OF THE WEST ISSUE** Late in 1993, the Postal Service printed more than 5 million Legends of the West panes and forwarded them to postal distribution centers and post offices throughout the country , even though the stamps were not scheduled to be issued until 1994. These stamps were to be the 1st in a new series fromatted by USPS as "Classic Collections" - special panes of 20 different first-class letter rate stamps with explanatory text on the back of each and a banner across the top of the pane describing its collective subject - in this case, legendary personalities and themes from the early days of the Western frontier.

A total of a least 183 of these panes inadvertently were sold at 4 post offices long before the planned 1st day of issue, beginning with a full pane that was purchased and used to frank a parcel mailed in Bend, Ore., Dec. 14, 1993.

At about the same time, USPS learned that 1 stamp in the original pane, purported to have depicted black cowboy and rodeo showman Bill Pickett, was actually a portrait of his brother, Ben. Bill Pickett's descendants demanded that the Postal Service withdraw and destroy panes with the incorrect portrait and print new ones with an accurate portrait of Bill Pickett, and USPS agreed to do so.

However, the early release and use of the panes from the original printing containing the stamp with the incorrect portrait made that impossible.

After a great deal of public and private debate as to the best solution (including 2 lawsuits), the Postal Service decided to print a 2nd Legends of the West pane as promised, with a revised, accurate portrait of Bill Pickett, but also to offer 150,000 original Legends of the West panes with the Ben Pickett portrait to collectors in a special lottery. The remainder of the original Legends of the West - about 5 million panes - would then be destroyed.

The USPS stuck to this plan despite considerable criticism from stamp collectors, even when it was revealed that, in the revised pane, 16 of the 20 stamps in the pane different from those in the original pane. (The red framelines around the stamps portraying people in the original pane are about half the thickness of those in the revised pane.) *Gravure by J.W. Fergusson & Sons for Stamp Venturers, perforated 11.*

| CM1671A | | MNHVF | UseVF |
|---|---|---|---|
| $5.80 | **Legends of the West commemorative pane,** tagged *(earliest known use Dec. 14, 1993)* | 195. | |

| CM1671Aa | | |
|---|---|---|
| 29¢ | Home on the Range | |

| CM1671Ab | | |
|---|---|---|
| 29¢ | Buffalo Bill | |

| CM1671Ac | | |
|---|---|---|
| 29¢ | Jim Bridger | |

| CM1671Ad | | |
|---|---|---|
| 29¢ | Annie Oakley | |

| CM1671Ae | | |
|---|---|---|
| 29¢ | Native American Culture | |

| CM1671Af | | |
|---|---|---|
| 29¢ | Chief Joseph | |

| CM1671Ag | | |
|---|---|---|
| 29¢ | Ben Pickett | |

| CM1671Ah | | |
|---|---|---|
| 29¢ | Bat Masterson | |

| CM1671Ai | | |
|---|---|---|
| 29¢ | John Fremont | |

| CM1671Aj | | |
|---|---|---|
| 29¢ | Wyatt Earp | |

CM1671A *Legends of the West commemorative pane (original version).* CM1671Ag *Ben Pickett (incorrect portrait in original pane).*

**CM1671Ak**
29¢    Nellie Cashman

**CM1671Al**
29¢    Charles Goodnight

**CM1671Am**
29¢    Geronimo

**CM1671An**
29¢    Kit Carson

**CM1671Ao**
29¢    Wild Bill Hickok

**CM1671Ap**
29¢    Western Wildlife

**CM1671Aq**
29¢    Jim Beckwourth

**CM1671Ar**
29¢    Bill Tilghman

**CM1671As**
29¢    Sacagawea

**CM1671At**
29¢    Overland Mail

**1994. REVISED LEGENDS OF THE WEST ISSUE** with a stamp showing an accurate portrait of Bill Pickett and thicker red framelines around his portrait and the portraits on the other 15 stamps in the pane that depict individuals. Because the overwhelming majority of the 150,000 original Legends of the West commemorative panes that were sold to collectors at a premium by lottery were retained as panes

by collectors, it has been listed as a single number (CM1672), with the individual stamps as minor varieties of that number. Because the revised panes were sold at face value, and stamps from them were used relatively more extensively on mail, stamps from the revised pane are listed and numbered individually. *Gravure by J.W. Fergusson & Sons for Stamp Venturers, perforated 11.*

| | | MNHVF | UseVF |
|---|---|---|---|
| **CM1672** | | **MNHVF** | **UseVF** |
| 29¢ | Home on the Range, tagged | .45 | .20 |
| **CM1673** | | **MNHVF** | **UseVF** |
| 29¢ | Buffalo Bill, tagged | .45 | .20 |
| **CM1674** | | **MNHVF** | **UseVF** |
| 29¢ | Jim Bridger, tagged | .45 | .20 |
| **CM1675** | | **MNHVF** | **UseVF** |
| 29¢ | Annie Oakley, tagged | .45 | .20 |
| **CM1676** | | **MNHVF** | **UseVF** |
| 29¢ | Native American Culture, tagged | .45 | .20 |
| **CM1677** | | **MNHVF** | **UseVF** |
| 29¢ | Chief Joseph, tagged | .45 | .20 |
| **CM1678** | | **MNHVF** | **UseVF** |
| 29¢ | Bill Pickett, tagged | .45 | .20 |
| **CM1679** | | **MNHVF** | **UseVF** |
| 29¢ | Bat Masterson, tagged | .45 | .20 |
| **CM1680** | | **MNHVF** | **UseVF** |
| 29¢ | John Fremont, tagged | .45 | .20 |
| **CM1681** | | **MNHVF** | **UseVF** |
| 29¢ | Wyatt Earp, tagged | .45 | .20 |

CM1691a *Legends of the West commemorative pane (revised version).* CM1678 *Bill Pickett (correct portrait in revised pane).*

| CM1682 | | MNHVF | UseVF |
|---|---|---|---|
| 29¢ | Nellie Cashan, tagged | .45 | .20 |
| CM1683 | | MNHVF | UseVF |
| 29¢ | Charles Goodnight, tagged | .45 | .20 |
| CM1684 | | MNHVF | UseVF |
| 29¢ | Geronimo, tagged | .45 | .20 |
| CM1685 | | MNHVF | UseVF |
| 29¢ | Kit Carson, tagged | .45 | .20 |
| CM1686 | | MNHVF | UseVF |
| 29¢ | Wild Bill Hickok, tagged | .45 | .20 |
| CM1687 | | MNHVF | UseVF |
| 29¢ | Western Wildlife, tagged | .45 | .20 |
| CM1688 | | MNHVF | UseVF |
| 29¢ | Jim Beckwourth, tagged | .45 | .20 |
| CM1689 | | MNHVF | UseVF |
| 29¢ | Bill Tilghman, tagged | .45 | .20 |
| CM1690 | | MNHVF | UseVF |
| 29¢ | Sacagawea, tagged | .45 | .20 |
| CM1691 | | MNHVF | UseVF |
| 29¢ | Overland Mail, tagged | .45 | .20 |
| | FDC *(Oct. 18, 1994)* | | 10.00 |
| | y.  Se-tenant pane of 20 | 16.00 | 14.00 |
| | Six pane press sheet | 125. | |

*Because this issue also was made available to collectors in full six-pane printing sheets, gutter pairs and blocks and cross-gutter multiples also exist.*

**1994. BUREAU OF ENGRAVING AND PRINTING CENTENNIAL SOUVENIR ISSUE** marks the 100th anniversary of the national security printer with a souvenir sheet containing four, $2.00 James Madison definitives of a design 1st used almost a century before (185), when BEP first began printing U.S. stamps. *Offset and intaglio, perforated 11.*

CM1692 *BEP Centennial Souvenir Sheet*

| CM1692 | | MNHVF | UseVF |
|---|---|---|---|
| $8 | **multicolored,** tagged *(Nov. 3, 1994)* | 20.00 | 14.50 |
| | a.  single stamp | 5.00 | 3.50 |
| | Major double transfer on right $2 stamp in sheet of 4 | — | |
| | Major double transfer, single $2 stamp | — | |
| | Minor double transfer on $2 stamp in sheet of 4 | — | |
| | Minor double transfer, single $2 stamp | — | |

*Listings for minor double transfers refer to any of approximately 10 different ones that are known.*

**1994. NEW YEAR ISSUE** Asian Lunar New Year Series
for the Year of the Boar is the 3rd installment. This stamp was released oly 2 days before the first-class letter rate increased from 29¢ to 32¢. *Gravure by Stamp Venturers, perforated 11.*

CM1693 *Lunar New Year, Boar*

| CM1693 | | MNHVF | UseVF |
|---|---|---|---|
| 29¢ | **multicolored,** tagged | .50 | .20 |
| | Plate block of 4 | 3.50 | |
| | FDC *(Dec. 30, 1994)* | | 1.00 |

**1995. LOVE ISSUE** Love Series
features non-denominated conventional and self-adhesive stamps depicting a cherub from the 16th-century *Sistine Madonna* by Raphael. *Offset and intaglio (BEP), perforated 11 1/2.*

CM21694 *Love Cherub, tall design*

| CM1694 | | MNHVF | UseVF |
|---|---|---|---|
| 32¢ | **multicolored,** phosphored paper | .50 | .20 |
| | Plate block of 4 | 1.25 | |
| | FDC *(Feb. 1, 1995)* | | 1.00 |

*Self-adhesive booklet, offset and intaglio by Banknote Corp. of America, imperforate (die cut).*

CM1695 *Love Cherub, short design*

| CM1695 | | MNHVF | UseVF |
|---|---|---|---|
| 32¢ | **multicolored,** phosphored paper | .50 | .20 |
| | FDC *(Feb. 1, 1995)* | | 1.00 |
| | n. Booklet pane of 20, plus label | 16.00 | |
| | vn. Booklet pane of 20, intaglio red (inscriptions) omitted | 1000. | |

**1995. FLORIDA SESQUICENTENNIAL ISSUE** marked the 150th anniversary of Florida statehood. *Offset by Sterling Sommer for Ashton-Potter (USA) Ltd., perforated 11.*

CM1696 *Florida Statehood Sesquicentennial*

| CM1696 | | MNHVF | UseVF |
|---|---|---|---|
| 32¢ | **multicolored,** phosphored paper | .50 | .20 |
| | Plate block of 4 | 3.50 | |
| | FDC *(March 3, 1995)* | | 1.00 |

**1995. EARTH DAY ISSUE** showcased the 4 winning designs created by children in a nationwide contest to produce stamps for the 25th anniversary of Earth Day. The winning quartet was issued in a pane of 16 (4 se-tenant blocks of 4) with a "Kids Care!" banner across selvage at the top of the pane and the details of the contest in the selvage at the floor of the pane. *Offset by Sterling Sommer for Ashton-Potter (USA) Ltd., perforated 11.*

CM1697 *Clean Earth*

CM1698 *Solar Power*

CM1699 *Tree Planting*

CM1670 *Clean Beaches*

| CM1697 | | MNHVF | UseVF |
|---|---|---|---|
| 32¢ | Clear Earth, phosphored paper | .50 | .20 |

| CM1698 | | MNHVF | UseVF |
|---|---|---|---|
| 32¢ | Solar Power, phosphored paper | .50 | .20 |

| CM1699 | | MNHVF | UseVF |
|---|---|---|---|
| 32¢ | Tree Planting, phosphored paper | .50 | .20 |

| CM1700 | | MNHVF | UseVF |
|---|---|---|---|
| 32¢ | Clean Beaches, phosphored paper | .50 | .20 |
| | Plate block of 4 | 3.50 | |
| | y. Se-tenant block of 4 | 2.00 | |
| | FDC *(April 20, 1995)* | | 2.00 |
| | a. Pane of 20 | 13.50 | |

**1995. RICHARD M. NIXON ISSUE** marks the death on April 22, 1994, of the 37th president of the United States, Richard Milhous Nixon, (1913-1994). *Offset and intaglio by Barton Press and Banknote Corp. of America, perforated 11.*

CM1701 *Richard M. Nixon*

| CM1701 | | MNHVF | UseVF |
|---|---|---|---|
| 32¢ | **multicolored,** phosphored paper | .50 | .20 |
| | Plate block of 4 | 3.50 | |
| | FDC *(April 26, 1995)* | | 1.00 |
| | v. Intaglio red ("Richard Nixon") omitted | 1250. | |

**1995. BESSIE COLEMAN ISSUE** commemorates the 1st African-American woman aviator, who traveled to France to learn the language in order to earn her pilot's license there in 1921 after American flying schools had refused to admit her. *Intaglio by BEP, perforated 11.*

CM1702 *Bessie Coleman*

**CM1702**

| | | MNHVF | UseVF |
|---|---|---|---|
| 32¢ | **red and black,** phosphored paper | .50 | .20 |
| | Plate block of 4 | 3.50 | |
| | FDC (April 27, 1995) | | 1.00 |

**1995. LOVE ISSUE** Love Series
added stamps with a 32¢ face value in matching designs to follow the non-denominated versions issued in Feb. (CM1695 -96), along with 55¢ stamps showing the cherub on the right in the same Raphael painting, paying the rate for letters under 2 ounces (such as most wedding invitations with response cards and envelopes enclosed). *Offset and intaglio, by BEP. Perforated 11 1/4.*

CM1703 *Love Cherub*

**CM1703**

| | | MNHVF | UseVF |
|---|---|---|---|
| 32¢ | **multicolored,** phosphored paper | .50 | .20 |
| | Plate block of 4 | 2.50 | |
| | FDC (May 12, 1995) | | 1.00 |

**1995. LOVE BOOKLET ISSUE** Love Series
perforated 9 3/4 x 11 on 2 or 3 sides.

CM1704 *Love Cherub*

**CM1704**

| | | MNHVF | UseVF |
|---|---|---|---|
| 32¢ | **multicolored,** phosphored paper | .50 | .20 |
| | FDC (May 12, 1995) | | 1.00 |
| | n.  Booklet pane of 10 | 5.50 | |

Cm1705 *Love Cherub*

**CM1705**

| | | MNHVF | UseVF |
|---|---|---|---|
| 55¢ | **multicolored,** phosphored paper | 1.00 | .35 |
| | Plate block of 4 | 5.00 | |
| | FDC (May 12, 1995) | | 1.50 |

**1995. LOVE SELF-ADHESIVE BOOKLET ISSUE** Love Series
printed in offset and intaglio by Banknote Corp. of America, imperforate (die cut).

CM1706 *Love Cherub*

**CM1706**

| | | MNHVF | UseVF |
|---|---|---|---|
| 55¢ | **multicolored,** phosphored paper | 1.00 | .35 |
| | FDC (May 12, 1995) | | 1.50 |
| | n.  Booklet pane of 20, plus label | 22.50 | |

**1995. RECREATIONAL SPORTS ISSUE** depicts popular American pastimes in 5 se-tenant designs. *Offset by Barton Press for Banknote Corp. of America, perforated 11 x 11 1/4.*

CM1707 *Bowling*

CM1708 *Tennis*

CM1709 *Golf*

CM1710 *Volleyball*

CM1711 *Baseball*

**CM1707**

| | | MNHVF | UseVF |
|---|---|---|---|
| 32¢ | Bowling, phosphored paper | .50 | .20 |

**CM1708**

| | | MNHVF | UseVF |
|---|---|---|---|
| 32¢ | Tennis, phosphored paper | .50 | .20 |

**CM1709**

| | | MNHVF | UseVF |
|---|---|---|---|
| 32¢ | Golf, phosphored paper | .50 | .20 |

**CM1710**

| | | MNHVF | UseVF |
|---|---|---|---|
| 32¢ | Volleyball, phosphored paper | .50 | .20 |

**CM1711**

| | | MNHVF | UseVF |
|---|---|---|---|
| 32¢ | Baseball, phosphored paper | .50 | .20 |
| | Plate block of 10 | 8.50 | |
| | y.  Se-tenant vertical strip of 5 (CM1708-12) | 3.00 | |
| | FDC (May 20, 1995) any single | | 1.00 |
| | a.  Sheetlet of 20 | 16.00 | |
| | vy. Imperforate strip of 5 | 2750. | |
| | vy1.Vertical strip of 5, yellow omitted | 2500. | |
| | vy2.Vertical strip of 5, yellow, cyan & magenta omitted | 2500. | |

**1995. POW & MIA ISSUE** salutes personnel in the U.S. armed forces who were prisoners of war or who were unaccounted for after the end of hostilities. *Offset by Sterling Sommer for Ashton- Potter (USA) Ltd., perforated 11.*

CM1712 *POW/MIA'S*

**CM1712**

| | | MNHVF | UseVF |
|---|---|---|---|
| 32¢ | **multicolored,** phosphored paper | .50 | .20 |
| | Plate block of 4 | 3.50 | |
| | FDC (May 29, 1995) | | 1.00 |
| | Sheetlet of 20 | 14.50 | |

**1995. MARILYN MONROE ISSUE** 1st installment in the USPS Legends of Hollywood series, got under way with a pane of 20 (each stamp having its corner perforations in the shape of a star, bearing the likeness and facsimile autograph of Marily Monroe (1926-1962 ), with the large all-around selvage in the commemorative pane of 20 showing an enlargement of a portrait of the movie star near the height of her powers. *Gravure by J.W. Fergusson & Sons for Stmp Venturers, perforated 11.*

CM1713 *Marilyn Monroe*

| CM1713 | | MNHVF | UseVF |
|---|---|---|---|
| 32¢ | **multicolored,** block tagged | .75 | .20 |
| | Plate block of 4 | 3.50 | |
| | FDC *(June 1, 1995)* | | 1.00 |
| a. | Pane of 20 | 14.50 | |
| v. | Imperforate pair | 625. | |
| | Six pane press sheets | 125. | |

*Because this issue also was made available to collectors in full six-pane printing sheets, gutter pairs and blocks and cross-gutter multiples also exist.*

**1995. TEXAS SESQUICENTENNIAL ISSUE** - marks the 150th anniversary of Texas statehood. *Offset by Sterling Sommer for Ashton-Potter (USA) Ltd., perforated 11.*

CM1714 *Texas Statehood Sesquicentennial*

| CM1714 | | MNHVF | UseVF |
|---|---|---|---|
| 32¢ | **multicolored,** phosphored paper | .50 | .20 |
| | Plate block of 4 | 3.50 | |
| | FDC *(June 16, 1995)* | | 1.00 |

**1995. LIGHTHOUSES ISSUE** uses the same format and designer as the 1990 Lighthouses issue (CM1378-82) to create a boklet showcasing lighthouses of the Great Lakes. *Gravure by J.W. Ferguson & Sons for Stamp Venturers, perforated 11 vertically on one or two sides.*

CM1715 *Split Rock* CM1716 *St. Joseph* CM1617 *Spectacle Reef*
CM1618 *Marblehead* CM1619 *Thirty Mile Point*

| CM1715 | | MNHVF | UseVF |
|---|---|---|---|
| 32¢ | Split Rock, phosphored paper | .50 | .20 |

| CM1716 | | MNHVF | UseVF |
|---|---|---|---|
| 32¢ | St. Joseph, phosphored paper | .50 | .20 |

| CM1717 | | MNHVF | UseVF |
|---|---|---|---|
| 32¢ | Spectacle Reef, phosphored paper | .50 | .20 |

| CM1718 | | MNHVF | UseVF |
|---|---|---|---|
| 32¢ | Marblehead, phosphored paper | .50 | .20 |

| CM1719 | | MNHVF | UseVF |
|---|---|---|---|
| 32¢ | Thiry Mile Point, phosphored paper | .50 | .20 |
| | FDC *(June 17, 1995)* | | 2.00 |
| | Booklet pane of 5 CM1715-19 | 4.00 | |

**1995. UNITED NATIONS ISSUE** marks the 50th anniversary of that organization. *Intaglio by Banknote Co. of America, perforated 11 1/4 x 11.*

CM1720 *United Nations*

| CM1720 | | MNHVF | UseVF |
|---|---|---|---|
| 32¢ | **blue,** phosphored paper | .50 | .20 |
| | Plate block of 4 | 3.00 | |
| | FDC *(June 26, 1995)* | | 1.00 |

**1995. CIVIL WAR ISSUE** was the 2nd release in the USPS Classic Collections series to showcase 20 stamps on a single theme in a pane with a colorful banner across the top selvage identifying the subject - in this case, the Civil War. As on the 1994 Legends of the West pane that introduced the concept, the 4 corner stamps detail events (battles, in this instance) while the other 16 stamps are painstakingly researched portraits of individuals who played a significant role in the era, while text printed on the back of the stamps provides information on the subject of each. *Gravure by J.W. Fergusson & Sons for Stamp Venturers, perforated 10 1/4 x 10. Multicolored, block tagged (June 29, 1995).*

| CM1721 | | MNHVF | UseVF |
|---|---|---|---|
| 32¢ | Monitor and Virgina | .75 | .50 |

| CM1722 | | MNHVF | UseVF |
|---|---|---|---|
| 32¢ | Robert E. Lee | .75 | .50 |

| CM1723 | | MNHVF | UseVF |
|---|---|---|---|
| 32¢ | Clara Barton | .75 | .50 |

| CM1724 | | MNHVF | UseVF |
|---|---|---|---|
| 32¢ | Ulysses S. Grant | .75 | .50 |

| CM1725 | | MNHVF | UseVF |
|---|---|---|---|
| 32¢ | Battle of Shiloh | .75 | .50 |

| CM1726 | | MNHVF | UseVF |
|---|---|---|---|
| 32¢ | Jefferson Davis | .75 | .50 |

| CM1727 | | MNHVF | UseVF |
|---|---|---|---|
| 32¢ | David Farragut | .75 | .50 |

| CM1728 | | MNHVF | UseVF |
|---|---|---|---|
| 32¢ | Frederick Douglass | .75 | .50 |

| CM1729 | | MNHVF | UseVF |
|---|---|---|---|
| 32¢ | Raphael Semmes | .75 | .50 |

| CM1730 | | MNHVF | UseVF |
|---|---|---|---|
| 32¢ | Abraham Lincoln | .75 | .50 |

| CM1731 | | MNHVF | UseVF |
|---|---|---|---|
| 32¢ | Harriet Tubman | .75 | .50 |

| CM1732 | | MNHVF | UseVF |
|---|---|---|---|
| 32¢ | Stand Watie | .75 | .50 |

| CM1733 | | MNHVF | UseVF |
|---|---|---|---|
| 32¢ | Joseph E. Johnston | .75 | .50 |

CM1721 *Monitor & Virginia*

CM1722 *Robert E. Lee*

CM1723 *Clara Barton*

CM1724 *Ulysses S. Grant*

CM1725 *Battle of Shiloh*

CM1726 *Jefferson Davis*

CM1727 *David Farragut*

CM1728 *Federick Douglass*

CM1729 *Raphael Semmes*

CM1730 *Abraham Lincoln*

CM1731 *Harriet Tubman*

CM1732 *Stand Watie*

CM1733 *Joseph E. Johnston*

CM1734 *Winfield Hancock*

CM1735 *Mary Chesnut*

CM1736 *Battle of Chancellor sville*

CM1737 *William T. Sherman*

CM1738 *Phoebe Pember*

CM1739 *Stonewall Jackson*

CM1740 *Battle of Gettysburg*

| CM1734 | | MNHVF | UseVF |
|---|---|---|---|
| 32¢ | Winfield Hancock | .75 | .50 |
| **CM1735** | | **MNHVF** | **UseVF** |
| 32¢ | Mary Chesnut | .75 | .50 |
| **CM1736** | | **MNHVF** | **UseVF** |
| 32¢ | Battle of Chancellorsville | .75 | .50 |
| **CM1737** | | **MNHVF** | **UseVF** |
| 32¢ | William T. Sherman | .75 | .50 |
| **CM1738** | | **MNHVF** | **UseVF** |
| 32¢ | Phoebe Pember | .75 | .50 |
| **CM1739** | | **MNHVF** | **UseVF** |
| 32¢ | Stonewall Jackson | .75 | .50 |
| **CM1740** | | **MNHVF** | **UseVF** |
| 32¢ | Battle of Gettysburg | .75 | .50 |
| | y.  pane of 20 (CM1721-40) | 16.00 | 14.00 |
| | vy. Imperforate pane of 20 | — | |
| | v1y.Pane with CM1721-25 imperforated, (CM1726-30) part perforated | — | |
| | v2y.Pane with CM1731-35 imperforated, (CM1736-40) part perforated | — | |
| | v3. Block of 9 (CM1726-28, CM1731-33, CM1736-38), imperforate vertically | — | |
| | Six pane press sheet | 150. | |

*Because this issue also was made available to collectors in full six-pane printing sheets, gutter pairs and blocks and cross-gutter multiples also exist.*

## American Folk Art Series

**1995. Carousel Horses Issue** uses the same designer and much the same format and subjects s the popular 1988 Carousel Animals issue (CM1327-30) in portraying 4 stalwart steed from the classical American carnival ride. *Offset by Sterling Sommer for Ashton-Potter (USA) Ltd., perforated 11.*

CM1741 *Golden Horse*

CM1742 *Black Horse*

CM1743 *Armored Horse*

CM1744 *Brown Horse*

**CM1741**
| | | MNHVF | UseVF |
|---|---|---|---|
| 32¢ | Golden horse, phosphored paper | .50 | .20 |

**CM1742**
| | | MNHVF | UseVF |
|---|---|---|---|
| 32¢ | Black horse, phosphored paper | .50 | .20 |

**CM1743**
| | | MNHVF | UseVF |
|---|---|---|---|
| 32¢ | Armored horse, phosphored paper | .50 | .20 |

**CM1744**
| | | MNHVF | UseVF |
|---|---|---|---|
| 32¢ | Brown horse, phosphored paper | .50 | .20 |
| | Plate block of 4 | 3.75 | |
| | Se-tenant block of 4 | 2.00 | |
| | FDC *(July 21, 1995)* any single | | 1.00 |

**1995. WOMENS SUFFRAGE ISSUE** memorialized the 75th anniversary of Aug. 18 1920, ratification of the 19th Amendment to the Constitution: "The right of citizens of the United States to vote will not be denied or abridged by the United States or by any state on account of sex."*Offset and intaglio by Ashton Potter (USA) Ltd., perforated 11.*

CM1745 *U.S. Constitution's 19th Amendment*

**CM1745**
| | | MNHVF | UseVF |
|---|---|---|---|
| 32¢ | **multicolored,** phosphored paper | .50 | .20 |
| | Plate block of 4 | 3.50 | |
| | FDC *(Aug. 26, 1995)* | | 1.00 |
| | v. Imperforate pair | 1600. | |
| | v1. Intaglio black omitted | 450. | |

**1995. LOUIS ARMSTRONG ISSUE** honors the New Orleans-born trumpet player, composer, improviser and unofficial U.S. goodwill ambassador who made giant contributions to jazz. *Offset by Sterling Sommer for Ashton-Potter (USA) Ltd., perforated 11.*

CM1746 *Louis Armstrong*

**CM1746**
| | | MNHVF | UseVF |
|---|---|---|---|
| 32¢ | **multicolored,** phosphored paper | .50 | .20 |
| | Plate block of 4 | 3.50 | |
| | FDC *(Sept. 1, 1995)* | | 1.00 |

*For a similar design with "32" in white, see CM1749.*

**1995. 1945 VICTORY AT LAST PANE ISSUE** the final installment in this 5-year, 50-stamp series, features a map and stamps covering events of the war in 1945. *Offset and intaglio by BEP, perforated 11.*

**CM1747**
| | | MNHVF | UseVF |
|---|---|---|---|
| $3.20 | **pane of ten,** overall tagged | 9.00 | 8.00 |
| | a. 32¢ Flag raised on Iwo Jima | .80 | .75 |
| | b. 32¢ Manila freed | .80 | .75 |
| | c. 32¢ Okinawa | .80 | .75 |
| | d. 32¢ U.S. & Soviets at Elbe | .80 | .75 |
| | e. 32¢ Liberate Camps | .80 | .75 |
| | f. 32¢ Germany surrenders | .80 | .75 |
| | g. 32¢ Displaced persons | .80 | .75 |
| | h. 32¢ Japan surrenders | .80 | .75 |
| | i. 32¢ News of victory | .80 | .75 |
| | j. 32¢ Hometowns honor verterans | .80 | .75 |

CM1747 *1945: Victory at Last*

## American Music Series

**1995. JAZZ MUSICIANS ISSUE** a se-tenant pane of 20 stamps depicting 10 jazz greats including a 2nd version of the Louis Armstrong commemorative released Sept. 1, continues the American Music series that began in 1993.*Offset by Sterling Sommer for Ashton-Potter (USA) Ltd., perforated 11.*

CM1748 *Coleman Hawkins*

CM1749 *Louis Armstrong*

CM1750 *James P. Johnston*

CM1751 *'Jelly Roll' Morton*

CM1752 *Charlie Parker*

CM1753 *Eubie Blake*

CM1754 *Charles Mingus*

CM1755 *Thelonious Monk*

CM1756 *John Coltrane*

CM1757 *Erroll Garner*

| CM1748 | | MNHVF | UseVF |
|---|---|---|---|
| 32¢ | Coleman Hawkins, phosphored paper | .50 | .20 |
| **CM1749** | | **MNHVF** | **UseVF** |
| 32¢ | Louis Armstrong, phosphored paper | .50 | .20 |
| **CM1750** | | **MNHVF** | **UseVF** |
| 32¢ | James P. Johnston, phosphored paper | .50 | .20 |
| **CM1751** | | **MNHVF** | **UseVF** |
| 32¢ | "Jelly Roll" Morton, phosphored paper | .50 | .20 |
| **CM1752** | | **MNHVF** | **UseVF** |
| 32¢ | Charles Parker, phosphored paper | .50 | .20 |
| **CM1753** | | **MNHVF** | **UseVF** |
| 32¢ | Eubie Blake, phosphored paper | .50 | .20 |
| **CM1754** | | **MNHVF** | **UseVF** |
| 32¢ | Charlie Mingus, phosphored paper | .50 | .20 |
| **CM1755** | | **MNHVF** | **UseVF** |
| 32¢ | Thelonious Monk, phosphored paper | .50 | .20 |
| **CM1756** | | **MNHVF** | **UseVF** |
| 32¢ | John Coltrane, phosphored paper | .50 | .20 |
| **CM1757** | | **MNHVF** | **UseVF** |
| 32¢ | Erroll Garner, phosphored paper | .50 | .20 |
| | Plate block of 10 | 8.50 | |
| | FDC *(Sept. 16, 1995)* any single | | 2.00 |
| | y. Se-tenant vertical block of 10 (CM1748-57) | 9.50 | |
| | a. Pane of 20 | 25.00 | |
| | va. Pane of 20, dark blue omitted | — | |

**1995. GARDEN FLOWERS ISSUE** is the 4th in an annual series of colorful and popular se-tenant 5-stamp booklets, this one depicting late summer and early autumn blooms. *Offset and intaglio by BEP, perforated 11 vertically on 1 or 2 sides.*

CM1758 *Aster* CM1759 *Chrysanthemum* CM1760 *Dahlia* CM1761 *Hydrangea* CM1762 *Rudbeckia*

| CM1758 | | MNHVF | UseVF |
|---|---|---|---|
| 32¢ | Aster, overall tagged | .50 | .20 |
| **CM1759** | | **MNHVF** | **UseVF** |
| 32¢ | Chrysanthemum, overall tagged | .50 | .20 |
| **CM1760** | | **MNHVF** | **UseVF** |
| 32¢ | Dahlia, overall tagged | .50 | .20 |
| **CM1761** | | **MNHVF** | **UseVF** |
| 32¢ | Hydranzzea, overall tagged | .50 | .20 |
| **CM1762** | | **MNHVF** | **UseVF** |
| 32¢ | Rudbeckia, overall tagged | .50 | .20 |
| | FDC *(Sept. 19, 1995)* any single | | 1.00 |
| | n. Booklet pane of 5 | 4.00 | |
| | FDC | | 3.00 |
| | vn. Imperforate pane of 5 | — | |

**1995. REPUBLIC OF PALAU ISSUE** celebrates the 1st anniversary of independence for this former U.S. trust territory of the western Pacific Ocean, which released a joint issue almost identical in design on Oct. 1. This stamp also is complimentary in design to those of earlier U.S. issues honoring each of the other three territories previously administered by the United States: Marshall Islands (CM1394); Micronesia (CM1395); and the Northern Mariana Islands (CM1607). *Offset by Sterling Sommer for Ashton Potter (USA) Ltd., perforated 11.*

CM1763 *Republic of Palau*

| CM1763 | | MNHVF | UseVF |
|---|---|---|---|
| 32¢ | **multicolored,** phosphored paper | .50 | .20 |
| | Plate block of 4 | 3.50 | |
| | FDC *(Sept. 29, 1995)* | | 1.00 |

**1995. COMIC STRIP CLASICS ISSUE** is the 3rd USPS Classic Collection of 20 stamps on a single theme in a se-tenant pane with a header across the top and explanatory text on the back of each stamp. This issue takes as its subject influential U.S. comic strips, and it was issued to mark the 100th anniversary of *The Yellow Kid* , which appeared in the *New York World* in May 1895 and is recognized as one of the 1st modern comic strip characters. *Gravure by J.W. Fergusson & Sons for Stamp Venturers, perforated 10 1/4 x 10. Multicolored, block tagged (Oct. 1, 1995)*

| CM1764 | | MNHVF | UseVF |
|---|---|---|---|
| 32¢ | The Yellow Kid | .75 | .50 |
| **CM1765** | | **MNHVF** | **UseVF** |
| 32¢ | Katzenjammer Kids | .75 | .50 |
| **CM1766** | | **MNHVF** | **UseVF** |
| 32¢ | Little Nemo in Slumberland | .75 | .50 |
| **CM1767** | | **MNHVF** | **UseVF** |
| 32¢ | Bringing Up Father | .75 | .50 |

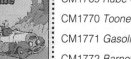

CM1764 *The Yellow Kid*

CM1765 *Katzenjammer Kids*

CM1766 *Little Nemo in Slumberland*

CM1767 *Bringing Up Father*

CM1768 *Krazy Kat*

CM1769 *Rube Goldberg's Inventions*

CM1770 *Toonerville Folks*

CM1771 *Gasoline Alley*

CM1772 *Barney Google*

CM1773 *Little Orphan Annie*

CM1774 *Popeye*

CM1775 *Blondie*

CM1776 *Dick Tracy*

CM1777 *Alley Oop*

CM1778 *Nancy*

CM1779 *Flash Gordon*

CM1780 *Li'l Abner*

CM1781 *Terry and the Pirates*

CM1782 *Prince Valiant*

CM1783 *Brenda Starr, Reporter*

| CM1768 | | MNHVF | UseVF |
|---|---|---|---|
| 32¢ | Krazy Kat | .75 | .50 |
| CM1769 | | MNHVF | UseVF |
| 32¢ | Rube Goldberg's Inventions | .75 | .50 |
| CM1770 | | MNHVF | UseVF |
| 32¢ | Toonerville Folks | .75 | .50 |
| CM1771 | | MNHVF | UseVF |
| 32¢ | Gasoline Alley | .75 | .50 |
| CM1772 | | MNHVF | UseVF |
| 32¢ | Barney Google | .75 | .50 |
| CM1773 | | MNHVF | UseVF |
| 32¢ | Little Orphan Annie | .75 | .50 |
| CM1774 | | MNHVF | UseVF |
| 32¢ | Popeye | .75 | .50 |
| CM1775 | | MNHVF | UseVF |
| 32¢ | Blondie | .75 | .50 |
| CM1776 | | MNHVF | UseVF |
| 32¢ | Dick Tracy | .75 | .50 |
| CM1777 | | MNHVF | UseVF |
| 32¢ | Alley Oop | .75 | .50 |
| CM1778 | | MNHVF | UseVF |
| 32¢ | Nancy | .75 | .50 |
| CM1779 | | MNHVF | UseVF |
| 32¢ | Flash Gordon | .75 | .50 |
| CM1780 | | MNHVF | UseVF |
| 32¢ | Li'l Abner | .75 | .50 |
| CM1781 | | MNHVF | UseVF |
| 32¢ | Terry and the Pirates | .75 | .50 |
| CM1782 | | MNHVF | UseVF |
| 32¢ | Prince Valiant | .75 | .50 |
| CM1783 | | MNHVF | UseVF |

| 32¢ | Brenda Star | .75 | .50 |
|---|---|---|---|
| | y. Se-tenant pane of 20 (CM1764-83) | 15.00 | 14.00 |
| | v. Imperforate pane of 20 | — | |
| | v1. Pane with CM1764-71 imperforate, CM1772-75 part perforated | — | |
| | Six pane press sheets | 125. | |

*Because this issue also was made available to collectors in full 6-pane printing sheets, gutter pairs and blocks and cross-gutter multiples also exist.*

**1995. U.S. NAVAL ACADEMY ISSUE** marks the 150th anniversary of the Annapolis, Md., institution with a stamp showing the racing sloop *Swift* crewed by academy midshipmen. *Offset by Sterling Sommer for Ashton-Potter (USA) Ltd., perforated 11.*

CM1784 *U.S. Naval Academy Sesquicentennial*

| CM1784 | | MNHVF | UseVF |
|---|---|---|---|
| 32¢ | **multicolored,** phosphored paper | .50 | .20 |
| | Plate block of 4 | 3.50 | |
| | FDC (Oct. 10, 1995) | | 1.00 |

## Literary Arts Series

**1995. TENNESSEE WILLIAMS ISSUE** memorializes the Mississippi-born playwright and author. Williams (1911-83) was among the most influential U.S. dramatists of the 20th century, including such powerful works as *The Glass Menagerie, Suddenly Last Summer* and *A Street-car Named Desire. Offset by Sterling Sommer for Ashton-Potter (USA) Ltd., perforated 11.*

CM1785 *Tennessee Williams*

| **CM1785** | | | | **MNHVF** | **UseVF** |
|---|---|---|---|---|---|
| **32¢** | **multicolored,** phosphored paper | | | .50 | .20 |
| | Plate block of 4 | | | 3.50 | |
| | FDC *(Oct. 13, 1995)* | | | | 1.00 |

**1995. JAMES K. POLK ISSUE** with its frame design adapted from the 1932 1/2¢ Washington Bicentennial stamp (CM98). This issue commemorates the 200th birthday of the 11th president of the United States. *Intaglio by Banknote Corp. of American, perforated 11 1/4 x 11.*

CM1786 *James A. Polk*

| **CM1786** | | **MNHVF** | **UseVF** |
|---|---|---|---|
| **32¢** | **reddish brown,** phosphored paper | .50 | .20 |
| | Plate block of 4 | 3.50 | |
| | FDC *(Nov. 2, 1995)* | | 1.00 |

**1995. ANTIQUE AUTOMOBILES ISSUE** depicts in a se-tenant pane of 25 stamps 5 of the earliest types of automobiles made in the United States at the turn of the century. *Gravure by J.W. Fergusson & Sons for Stamp Venturers, perforated 10 x 11.*

CM1787 *Duryea*

CM1788 *Haynes*

CM1789 *Columbia*

CM1790 *Winton*

CM1791 *White*

| **CM1787** | | **MNHVF** | **UseVF** |
|---|---|---|---|
| **32¢** | Duryea, phosphored paper | .75 | .50 |
| **CM1788** | | **MNHVF** | **UseVF** |
| **32¢** | Haynes, phosphored paper | .75 | .50 |
| **CM1789** | | **MNHVF** | **UseVF** |
| **32¢** | Columbia, phosphored paper | .75 | .50 |
| **CM1790** | | **MNHVF** | **UseVF** |
| **32¢** | Winton, phosphored paper | .75 | .50 |
| **CM1791** | | **MNHVF** | **UseVF** |
| **32¢** | White, phosphored paper | .75 | .50 |
| | Plate block of 10 | 9.00 | |
| | y. Se-tenant strip of 5 (CM1787-91) | 4.00 | |
| | FDC *(Nov. 3, 1995)* any single | | 1.00 |

**1996. UTAH CENTENNIAL ISSUE** marks the 100th anniversary of Utah statehood with a color ful rendering of a natural rock formation from the state's Arches National Park, inscribed "Utah 1896." *Offset by Sterling Sommer for Ashton-Potter (USA) Ltd., perforated 11.*

CM1792 *Utah State Centennial*

| **CM1792** | | **MNHVF** | **UseVF** |
|---|---|---|---|
| **32¢** | **multicolored,** tagged *(120,000,000)* | .50 | .20 |
| | Plate block of 4 | 3.50 | |
| | FDC *(Jan. 4, 1996)* | | 1.00 |

**1996. GARDEN FLOWERS ISSUE** is the 4th in the popular series of colorful 5-stamp pane booklets, this one depicting blooms that appear at various locations in the United States during the winter months. *Offset and intaglio by BEP, perforated 11 vertically on 1 or 2 sides.*

CM1793 *Crocus* CM1794 *Winter Aconite* CM1795 *Pansy* CM1796 *Snowdrop* CM1797 *Anemone*

| **CM1793** | | **MNHVF** | **UseVF** |
|---|---|---|---|
| **32¢** | Crocus, phosphored paper *(160,000,000)* | .50 | .20 |
| **CM1794** | | **MNHVF** | **UseVF** |
| **32¢** | Winter Aconite, phosphored paper | .50 | .20 |
| **CM1795** | | **MNHVF** | **UseVF** |
| **32¢** | Pansy, phosphored paper | .50 | .20 |
| **CM1796** | | **MNHVF** | **UseVF** |
| **32¢** | Snowdrop, phosphored paper | .50 | .20 |
| **CM1797** | | **MNHVF** | **UseVF** |
| **32¢** | Anemone, phosphored paper | .50 | .20 |
| | FDC *(Jan. 19, 1996)* any single | | 1.00 |
| | n. Booklet pane of CM1793-97 | 4.00 | |
| | FDC | | 3.50 |
| | nv. Imperforate pane of 5 | — | |

**1996. LOVE ISSUE** is slightly reformatted self-adhesive version of the 32¢ Cherub design (CM1703-04) in booklet form. *Offset and intaglio by Banknote Corp. of America, serpent ine die cut 11 1/4.*

CM1798 *Love*

| **CM1798** | | **MNHVF** | **UseVF** |
|---|---|---|---|
| **32¢** | **multicolored,** tagged *(2,550,000,000)* | .50 | .20 |
| | FDC *Jan. 20, 1996)* | | 1.00 |
| | n. Booklet pane of 20 plus label | 16.50 | |
| | n1. Booklet pane of 15 plus label | 10.00 | |
| | v. Red omitted | — | |

## Black Heritage Series

**1996. ERNEST E. JUST ISSUE** honors marine biologist, scientist and professor Ernest Everett Just (1883-1941) whose research on abnormal cell development contributed to understanding leukemia, sickle- cell anemia and cancer. *Offset by Banknote Corp. of America, perforated 11.*

CM1799 *Ernest E. Just*

| CM1799 | | MNHVF | UseVF |
|---|---|---|---|
| 32¢ | **black and gray,** tagged *(92,100,000)* | .50 | .20 |
| | Plate block of 4 | 3.50 | |
| | FDC *(Feb. 1, 1996)* | | 1.00 |

**1996. SMITHSONIAN INSTITUTION SESQUICENTENNIAL ISSUE** marks the 150th anniversary of the national museum, begun in 1829 with a $508,318 bequest from a British chemist named Smithson, "to found at Washington...an establishment for the increase & diffusion of knowledge among men." (See also CM285 and CM959). *Offset by Sterling Sommer for Ashton-Potter (USA) Ltd., perforated 11.*

CM1800 *Smithsonian Institution Sesquicentennial*

| CM1800 | | MNHVF | UseVF |
|---|---|---|---|
| 32¢ | **multicolored,** tagged *(115,600,000)* | .50 | .20 |
| | Plate block of 4 | 3.50 | |
| | FDC *(Feb. 7, 1996)* | | 1.00 |

## Asian Lunar New Year Series

**1996. NEW YEARS ISSUE** for the Year of the Ox is the 5th in the on going series celebrating the Asian lunar holiday. *Gravure by Stamp Venturers, perforated 11 1/4.*

CM1801 *Lunar New Year Rat*

| CM1801 | | MNHVF | UseVF |
|---|---|---|---|
| 32¢ | **multicolored,** tagged *(93,150,000)* | .50 | .20 |
| | Plate block of 4 | 3.50 | |
| | FDC *(Feb. 8, 1996)* | | 1.00 |
| | v. Imperforate single | — | |
| | v1. Imperforate pair | — | |
| | v2. Imperforate plate block | — | |

**1996. PIONEERS OF COMMUNICATIONS ISSUE** salutes a quartet of 19th-century innovators in photographic and print technology. Eadweard Muybridge (1830-1904) pioneered the conversion of photographs to moving images. Ottmar Mergenthaler (1854-99) invented Linotype, which vastly reduced the cost of printing newspapers and boosted circulation. Chief among the many inventions of Frederic E. Ives (1856-1937) was the half-tone printing process, which enabled newspapers to reproduce photographs. William Kennedy Laurie Dickson (1860-1935), an Edison employee, devised the kinetoscope, in which precise synchronization gives motion pictures the illusion of movement. *Offset by Ashton-Potter (USA) Ltd., perforated 11.*

CM1802 *Eadweard MuyBridge*

CM1803 *Ottman Mergenthaler*

CM1804 *Frederic Eives*

CM1805 *William Dickson*

| CM1802 | | MNHVF | UseVF |
|---|---|---|---|
| 32¢ | Eadweard MuyBridge, phosphored paper *(23,292,500)* | .50 | .20 |

| CM1803 | | MNHVF | UseVF |
|---|---|---|---|
| 32¢ | Ottman Mergenthaler, phosphored paper | .50 | .20 |

| CM1804 | | MNHVF | UseVF |
|---|---|---|---|
| 32¢ | Frederic Eives, phosphored paper | .50 | .20 |

| CM1805 | | MNHVF | UseVF |
|---|---|---|---|
| 32¢ | William Dickson, phosphored paper | .50 | .20 |
| | Plate block of 4 | 3.50 | |
| | y. Se-tenant block or strip of CM1802-05 | 3.00 | 2.50 |
| | FDC *(Feb. 22, 1996)* | | 2.00 |

**1996. FULBRIGHT SCHOLARSHIPS ISSUE** marks the 50th anniversary of the annual awards, named for Arkansas Senator and long-time Foreign Relations Committee Chairman J. William Fulbright, sponsor of the 1946 act that created the program. To date, about a quarter million Fulbright scholars either have traveled from the United States to study abroad or have come from abroad to study in the United States. *Offset and intaglio by BEP, perforated 11.*

CM1806 *Fulbright Scholarships*

| CM1806 | | MNHVF | UseVF |
|---|---|---|---|
| 32¢ | **multicolored,** tagged *(111,000,000)* | .50 | .20 |
| | Plate block of 4 | 3.50 | |
| | FDC *(Feb. 28, 1996)* | | 1.00 |

**1996. MARATHON ISSUE** salutes the 100th running of the annual 26.2-mile Boston Marathon. *Offset by Banknote Corp. of America, perforated 11.*

CM1807 *Marathon*

| CM1807 | | MNHVF | UseVF |
|---|---|---|---|
| 32¢ | **multicolored,** tagged *(209,450,000)* | .50 | .20 |
| | Plate block of 4 | 3.50 | |
| | FDC *(April 11, 1996)* | | 1.00 |

**1996. ATLANTA 1996 CENTENNIAL OLYMPIC GAMES ISSUE** is the 4th USPS Classic Collection of 20 stamps on a single theme in a se-tenant pane with a header across the top and descriptive text on the back of each stamp. This issue celebrates the 100th anniversary of the 1st modern Olympiad. *Gravure by J.W. Fergusson & Sons for Stamp Venturers, perforated 10 1/4 x 10. Multicolored, block tagged (May 2, 1996)*

| | | MNHVF | UseVF |
|---|---|---|---|
| **CM1808** | | | |
| 32¢ | Javelin | .75 | .50 |
| **CM1809** | | MNHVF | UseVF |
| 32¢ | Whitewater Canoeing | .75 | .50 |
| **CM1810** | | MNHVF | UseVF |
| 32¢ | Women's Running | .75 | .50 |
| **CM1811** | | MNHVF | UseVF |
| 32¢ | Women's Platform Diving | .75 | .50 |
| **CM1812** | | MNHVF | UseVF |
| 32¢ | Men's Cycling | .75 | .50 |
| **CM1813** | | MNHVF | UseVF |
| 32¢ | Freestyle Wrestling | .75 | .50 |
| **CM1814** | | MNHVF | UseVF |
| 32¢ | Women's Gymnastics | .75 | .50 |
| **CM1815** | | MNHVF | UseVF |
| 32¢ | Women's Sailboarding | .75 | .50 |
| **CM1816** | | MNHVF | UseVF |
| 32¢ | Men's Shot Put | .75 | .50 |
| **CM1817** | | MNHVF | UseVF |
| 32¢ | Women's Soccer | .75 | .50 |
| **CM1818** | | MNHVF | UseVF |
| 32¢ | Beach Volleyball | .75 | .50 |

| | | MNHVF | UseVF |
|---|---|---|---|
| **CM1819** | | MNHVF | UseVF |
| 32¢ | Men's Rowing | .75 | .50 |
| **CM1820** | | MNHVF | UseVF |
| 32¢ | Men's Sprinting Events | .75 | .50 |
| **CM1821** | | MNHVF | UseVF |
| 32¢ | Women's Swimming | .75 | .50 |
| **CM1822** | | MNHVF | UseVF |
| 32¢ | Women's Softball | .75 | .50 |
| **CM1823** | | MNHVF | UseVF |
| 32¢ | Men's Hurdles | .75 | .50 |
| **CM1824** | | MNHVF | UseVF |
| 32¢ | Men's Swimming (Backstroke) | .75 | .50 |
| **CM1825** | | MNHVF | UseVF |
| 32¢ | Men's Gymnastics (Pommel Horse) | .75 | .50 |
| **CM1826** | | MNHVF | UseVF |
| 32¢ | Equestrian Events | .75 | .50 |
| **CM1827** | | MNHVF | UseVF |
| 32¢ | Men's Basketball | .75 | .50 |
| | FDC *(May 2, 1996)* any single | | 1.00 |
| | y.  Pane of CM1808-27 | 14.00 | |
| | vy. Imperforate pane of 20 | — | |
| | vy1.Partially perforated pane of 20 | — | |
| | Six pane press sheet | 150. | |

*Because this issue also was made available to collectors in full 6-pane printing sheets, gutter pairs and blocks and cross-gutter multiples also exist.*

CM1808 *Javelin*

CM1809 *Whitewater Canoeing*

CM1810 *Women's Running*

CM1811 *Platform Diving*

CM1812 *Men's Cycling*

CM1813 *Freestyle Wrestling*

CM1814 *Women's Gymnastics*

CM1815 *Sailboarding*

CM1816 *Shot Put*

CM1817 *Soccer*

CM1818 *Beach Volleyball*

CM1819 *Men's Rowing*

CM1820 *Men's Sprint*

CM1821 *Women's Swimming*

CM1822 *Women's Softball*

CM1823 *Men's Hurdles*

CM1824 *Men's Swimming*

CM1825 *Pommel Horse*

CM1826 *Equestrian Events*

CM1827 *Men's Basketball*

**1996. GEORGIA O'KEEFFE ISSUE** commemorates the artist whose distinctive, vibrant presentation of images from nature in abstract, creative settings marked her as a true American original. One of 200 early flower paintings created by O'Keeffe (1887-1986) was reproduced in a 15-stamp commemorative pane with selvage picturing the painter and a quotation by her. *Gravure by J.W. Fergusson & Sons for Stamp Venturers, perforated 11 1/2.*

CM1828 *Georgia O'Keeffe's flower*

| CM1828 | | MNHVF | UseVF |
|---|---|---|---|
| 32¢ | **multicolored,** tagged (156,300,000) | .50 | .20 |
| | Plate block of 4 | 3.50 | |
| | Pane of 20 | 16.00 | |
| | FDC (May 23, 1996) | | 1.00 |
| | v. Imperforate pair | 200. | |

**1996. TENNESSEE BICENTENNIAL ISSUE** marks the 200th anniversary of Tennessee entering the Union as the 13th state. It is the 1st conventional commemorative issued simultaneously both in lick-and-stick panes and self- adhesive booklets. *Gravure by J.W. Fergusson & Sons for Stamp Venturers, perforated 11.*

CM1829-30 *Tennessee Statehood*

| CM1829 | | MNHVF | UseVF |
|---|---|---|---|
| 32¢ | **multicolored,** tagged (100,000,000) | .50 | .20 |
| | Plate block of 4 | 3.25 | |
| | FDC (May 31, 1996) | | 1.00 |

**1996. TENNESSEE BICENTENNIAL BOOKLET ISSUE** *Serpentine die cut 10 x 10 3/4.*

| CM1830 | | MNHVF | UseVF |
|---|---|---|---|
| 32¢ | **multicolored,** tagged (60,120,000) | .75 | .20 |
| | FDC (May 31, 1996) | | 1.00 |
| | n. Booklet pane of 20 | 16.00 | |
| | v. Horizontal pair, imperforate (no die cutting) between | — | |

**1996. AMERICAN INDIAN DANCES ISSUE** pictures an important component of native American culture and ritual in a 20-stamp commemorative pane. *Gravure by Ashton-Potter (USA) Ltd., perforated 11.*

CM1831 *Fancy Dance* CM1832 *Butterfly Dance* CM1833 *Traditional Dance* CM1834 *Raven Dance* CM1835 *Hoop Dance*

| CM1831 | | MNHVF | UseVF |
|---|---|---|---|
| 32¢ | Fancy Dance, tagged (27,850,000) | .75 | .50 |

| CM1832 | | MNHVF | UseVF |
|---|---|---|---|
| 32¢ | Butterfly Dance, tagged | .75 | .50 |

| CM1833 | | MNHVF | UseVF |
|---|---|---|---|
| 32¢ | Traditional Dance, tagged | .75 | .50 |

| CM1834 | | MNHVF | UseVF |
|---|---|---|---|
| 32¢ | Raven Dance, tagged | .75 | .50 |

| CM1835 | | MNHVF | UseVF |
|---|---|---|---|
| 32¢ | Hoop Dance, tagged | .75 | .50 |
| | Plate block of 10 | 8.00 | |
| | y. Se-tenant strip of CM1831-53 | 3.50 | |
| | FDC (June 7, 1996) any single | | 1.00 |
| | Pane of 20 | 14.50 | |

**1996. PREHISTORIC ANIMALS ISSUE** features dramatic portraits of 4 important North American representatives of the Cenozoic Era (or Age of Mammals), comprising the last 65 million years. *Offset by Ashton-Potter (USA) Ltd., perforated 11.*

CM1836 *Eohippus*

CM1837 *Wooly Mammoth*

CM1838 *Mastodon*

CM1839 *Saber-tooth Cat*

| CM1836 | | MNHVF | UseVF |
|---|---|---|---|
| 32¢ | Eohippus, tagged (22,218,000) | .75 | .50 |

| CM1837 | | MNHVF | UseVF |
|---|---|---|---|
| 32¢ | Woolly Mammoth, tagged | .75 | .50 |

| CM1838 | | MNHVF | UseVF |
|---|---|---|---|
| 32¢ | Mastodon, tagged | .75 | .50 |

| CM1839 | | MNHVF | UseVF |
|---|---|---|---|
| 32¢ | Saber-tooth Cat, tagged | .75 | .50 |
| | Plate block of 4 | 3.50 | |
| | y. Se-tenant block or strip of CM1836-39 | 3.00 | |
| | FDC (June 8, 1996) any single | | 1.00 |

**1996. BREAST CANCER AWARENESS ISSUE** takes note of a serious health risk to American women to raise awreness and encourage early detection. Special postmarks, clinics and screening in conjunction with this stamp across the nation increased public attention, and helped spark Congress to request a breast cancer semipostal stamp in 1998. *Offset by Ashton-Potter (USA) Ltd., perforated 11.*

CM1840 *Breast Cancer Awareness*

| CM1840 | | MNHVF | UseVF |
|---|---|---|---|
| 32¢ | **multicolored,** tagged (95,600,000) | .50 | .20 |
| | Plate block of 4 | 3.25 | |
| | FDC (June 15, 1996) | | 1.00 |

**1996. JAMES DEAN ISSUE** the 2nd in the Legends of Hollywood series, again consisted of a 20-stamp commemorative pane with star-shaped corner perforations and a large area of selvage displaying an enlargement of the actor. Dean (1931-55) had enormous impact in 3 films -- *East of Eden, Rebel Without a Cause* and *Giant* -- before his death in a car crash at the age of 24. *Gravure by J.W. Fergusson & Sons for Stamp Venturers, perforated 11.*

CM1841 *James Dean*

| CM1841 | | MNHVF | UseVF |
|---|---|---|---|
| 32¢ | **multicolored,** tagged *(300,000,000)* | .50 | .20 |
| | Plate block of 4 | 3.25 | |
| | FDC *(June 24, 1996)* | | 1.00 |
| | a. Pane of 20 | 14.50 | |
| | Six pane press sheet | | |
| | v. Imperforate pair | — | 495. |
| | v1. Imperforate pane | — | |
| | v2. Partially perforate pane | — | |

*Because this issue also was made available to collectors in full six-pane printing sheets, gutter pairs and blocks and cross-gutter multiples also exist.*

**1996. FOLK HEROES ISSUE** features bold portraits of larger-than-life characters made famous in popular American fiction: Mighty Casey, whose turn at the bat in Ernest L. Thayer's 188 poem tragically came to naught; legendary lumberjack Paul Bunyan, who transformed America together with Babe, his giant blue ox; John Henry, the "steel drivin,man" who beat a steam drill in carving out a West Virginia railway tunnel, but perished in the attempt; and the cyclone-taming Texas cowboy Pecos Bill, who wears a rattlesnake for a scarf on the stamp. *Offset by Ashton-Potter (USA) Ltd., perforated 11.*

CM1842 *Mighty Casey*

CM1843 *Paul Bunyan*

CM1844 *John Henry*

CM1845 *Pecos Bill*

| CM1842 | | MNHVF | UseVF |
|---|---|---|---|
| 32¢ | Mighty Casey, tagged *(23,681,250)* | .50 | .20 |

| CM1843 | | MNHVF | UseVF |
|---|---|---|---|
| 32¢ | Paul Bunyan, tagged | .50 | .20 |

| CM1844 | | MNHVF | UseVF |
|---|---|---|---|
| 32¢ | John Henry, tagged | .50 | .20 |

| CM1845 | | MNHVF | UseVF |
|---|---|---|---|
| 32¢ | Pecos Bill, tagged | .50 | .20 |
| | Plate block of 4 | 3.50 | |
| | y. Se-tenant block or strip of CM1842-45 | 3.00 | |
| | FDC *(July 11, 1996)* any single | | 1.00 |

**1996. OLYMPIC GAMES CENTENNIAL ISSUE** was another single-design 20-stamp commemorative pane to mark the 100th anniversary of the 1st modern Olympiad in 1896 in Athens, Greece. Left margin selvage showed an enlargement of *Discobolus*, after the original bronze created by the Greek sculptor Myron in the 5th century B.C. *Offset and intaglio by Ashton-Potter (USA) Ltd., perforated 11.*

CM1846 *Discus Thrower, Centennial Olympics*

| CM1846 | | MNHVF | UseVF |
|---|---|---|---|
| 32¢ | **brown,** tagged *(133,613,000)* | .50 | .20 |
| | Plate block of 4 | 3.00 | |
| | FDC *(July 19, 1996)* | | 1.00 |
| | Pane of 20 | 14.00 | |

**1996. IOWA SESQUICENTENNIAL ISSUE** marks the 150th anniversary of Iowa entering the Union as the 29th state. The conventional commemorative was available throughout the country, whereas the self-adhesive booklet version of the stamp was sold only in Iowa and at philatelic centers out of state. *Perforated 11, Offset by Ashton-Potter (USA) Ltd.*

| CM1847 | | MNHVF | UseVF |
|---|---|---|---|
| 32¢ | **multicolored,** tagged *(103,400,000)* | .50 | .20 |
| | Plate block of 4 | 3.00 | |
| | FDC *(Aug. 1, 1996)* | | 1.00 |

**1996. IOWA SESQUICENTENNIAL SELF ADHESIVE ISSUE** Serpentine die cut 10 x 10 3/4.

| CM1848 | | MNHVF | UseVF |
|---|---|---|---|
| 32¢ | **multicolored,** tagged *(60,000,000)* | .75 | .30 |
| | FDC *(Aug. 1, 1996)* | | 1.00 |
| | n. Booklet pane of 20 | 16.00 | |

**1996. RURAL FREE DELIVERY CENTENNIAL ISSUE** saluted a century of the service that brought mail for the 1st time directly to the homes of America's farmers and other rural residents. *Offset and intaglio by BEP, perforated 11.*

CM1849 *Rural Free Delivery*

| CM1849 | | MNHVF | UseVF |
|---|---|---|---|
| 32¢ | **multicolored,** tagged *(134,000,000)* | .50 | .20 |
| | Plate block of 4 | 3.00 | |
| | FDC *(Aug. 7, 1996)* | | 1.00 |

**1996. RIVERBOATS ISSUE** is a se-tenant presentation of 5 self-adhesive stamps saluting historic 19th-century steamboats that carried passengers and important cargo on the inland waterways of America. *Gravure by Avery Dennison Security Printing Division, serpentine die cut 11.*

CM1850 *Robert E. Lee*

CM1851 *Sylvan Dell*

CM1852 *Far West*

CM1853 *Rebecca Everingham*

CM1854 *Bailey Gatzert*

| CM1850 | | MNHVF | UseVF |
|---|---|---|---|
| 32¢ | Robert E. Lee, tagged *(32,000,000)* | .75 | .50 |
| CM1851 | | MNHVF | UseVF |
| 32¢ | Sylvan Dell, tagged | .75 | .50 |
| CM1852 | | MNHVF | UseVF |
| 32¢ | Forwest, tagged | .75 | .50 |
| CM1853 | | MNHVF | UseVF |
| 32¢ | Rebecca Everingham, tagged | .75 | .50 |
| CM1854 | | MNHVF | UseVF |
| 32¢ | Bailey Gatzert, tagged | .75 | .50 |
| | Plate block of 10 | 8.00 | |
| | y. Se-tenant vertical strip of CM1850-54 | 3.50 | |
| | v. Die Cut through backing full pane | 35.00 | |
| | FDC *(Aug. 22, 1996)* any single | | 1.00 |

**1996. Big Band Leaders Issue** honored outstanding orchestra leaders of the Big Band era, whot popularized the Swing music that had its heyday in the 1930s and 40s. Count Basie (1904-84), a brilliant composer whose bands for almost 50 years featured many of the nation's finest jazz soloists, is best remembered for tunes including *One O'Clock Jump, Swingin' the Blues* and *Jumpin' at the Woodside.* The Dorsey Brothers, clarinetist Jimmy (1904-57) and trombonist Tommy (1905-56), headed dance bands separately and together, notable for melodies such as *Tangerine* and *I'm Sentimental Over You.* Glenn Miller (1904-44), a gifted trombonist and arranger presided over 1 of the most successful Swing er a orchestras, the distinctive sound of which is recognizable in classics such as *In the Mood, Kalamazoo,* and *Sunrise Serenade.* Benny Goodman (1909-86), known as the "King of Swing", was a clarinet prodigy and a perfectionist as band leader, with *King Porter Stomp, Don't Be That Way* and *Sing, Sing, Sing* among his hits. *Offset by Ashton-Potter (USA) Ltd., perforated 11.*

CM1855 *Count Basie*

CM1856 *Tommy & Jimmy Dorsey*

CM1857 *Glenn Miller*

CM1858 *Benny Goodman*

| CM1855 | | MNHVF | UseVF |
|---|---|---|---|
| 32¢ | Count Basie, tagged *(23,025,000)* | .50 | .20 |
| CM1856 | | MNHVF | UseVF |
| 32¢ | Tommy & Jimmy Dorsey, tagged | .50 | .20 |
| CM1857 | | MNHVF | UseVF |
| 32¢ | Glenn Miller, tagged | .50 | .20 |
| CM1858 | | MNHVF | UseVF |
| 32¢ | Benny Goodman, tagged | .50 | .20 |
| | Plate block of 4 | 3.50 | |
| | y. Se-tenant block or strip of CM1855-58 | 3.00 | |
| | FDC *(Sept. 11, 1996)* any single | | 1.00 |
| | Pane of 20 | 14.00 | |

**1996. Songwriters Issue** honored 4 of the finest songwriters of the 20th century. Harold Arlen (1905-86) is best known for his scores for 2 Judy Garland films, *The Wizard of OZ* (co-written with Yip Harburg) and *A Star is Born* (co-written with Ira Gershwin), and tunes written for Harlem's renowned Cotton Club including *Stormy Weather.* Songwriter, singer and Capitol Records founder Johnny Mercer (1909-76) penned the lyrics to more than 1,000 songs, from *I'm an Old Cowhand* to *Moon River.* The nation's finest female songwriter, Dorothy Fields (1905-74) credits include *Sunny Side of the Street, The Way You Look Tonight,* and *A Fine Romance.* Hoagy Carmichael (1899-1981) may be most closely associated with *Stardust,* but authored many other great songs as well, including *Heart and Soul* and *Georgia on My Mind. Offset by Ashton-Potter (USA) Ltd., perforated 11.*

CM1859 *Harold Arlen*

CM1860 *Johnny Mercer*

CM1861 *Dorothy Fields*

CM1862 *Hoagy Carmichael*

| CM1859 | | MNHVF | UseVF |
|---|---|---|---|
| 32¢ | Harold Arlen, tagged *(23,025,000)* | .50 | .20 |
| CM1860 | | MNHVF | UseVF |
| 32¢ | Johnny Mercer, tagged | .50 | .20 |
| CM1861 | | MNHVF | UseVF |
| 32¢ | Dorothy Fields, tagged | .50 | .20 |
| CM1862 | | MNHVF | UseVF |
| 32¢ | Hoagy Carmichael, tagged | .50 | .20 |
| | Plate block of 4 | 3.50 | |
| | y. Se-tenant block or strip of CM1859-62 | 3.00 | |
| | FDC *(Sept. 11, 1996)* any single | | 1.00 |
| | Pane of 20 | 14.00 | |

**1996. F. Scott Fitzgerald Issue** celebrated the 100th birthday of the novelist (1896-1940) who immortalized the Jazz Age of the 1920s in such works as *The Beautiful and the Damned, The Great Gatsby* and *Tender is the Night.* The stamp prepays the 23¢ fee for each additional ounce over the basic 32¢ first-class letter rate. *Gravure by BEP, perforated 11.*

CM1863 *F. Scott Fitzgerald*

| CM1863 | | MNHVF | UseVF |
|---|---|---|---|
| 32¢ | **multicolored,** tagged *(300,000,000)* | .50 | .20 |
| | Plate block of 4 | 2.75 | |
| | FDC *(Sept. 27, 1996)* | | 1.00 |

# Endangered Species

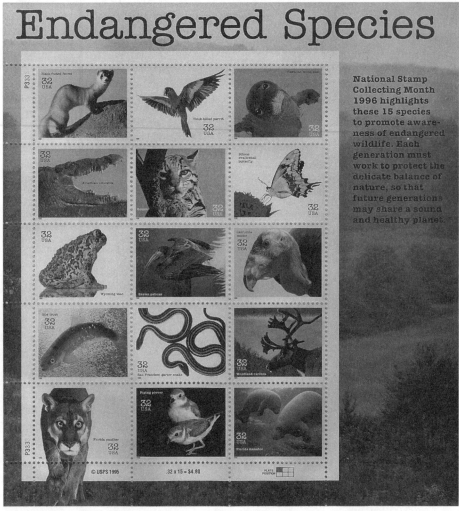

National Stamp Collecting Month 1996 highlights these 15 species to promote awareness of endangered wildlife. Each generation must work to protect the delicate balance of nature, so that future generations may share a sound and healthy planet.

CM1864 *Black-footed Ferret*

CM 1865 *Thick-billed Ferret*

CM1866 *Hawaiian Monk Seal*

CM1867 *American Crocodile*

CM1868 *Ocelot*

CM1869 *Schaus Swallowtail Butterfly*

CM1870 *Wyoming Toad*

CM1871 *Brown Pelican*

CM1872 *California Condor*

CM1873 *Gila Trout*

CM1874 *San Francisco Garter Snake*

CM1875 *Woodland Caribou*

CM1876 *Florida Panther*

CM1877 *Piping Plover*

CM188 *Florida Manatee*

**1996. ENDANGERED SPECIES ISSUE** was a 15-stamp se-tenant commemorative pane with a banner and marginal text, each stamp featuring an indigenous American animal currently threatened with extinction. Although not a joint issue technically speaking, a pane of 24 stamps depicting native endangered species was issued simultaneously by Mexico. *Offset (14,910,000 panes) by Sterling Sommer for Ashton-Potter (USA) Ltd., perforated 11. Multicolored, block tagged (Oct 2, 1996).*

| | | MNHVF | UseVF |
|---|---|---|---|
| **CM1864** | | | |
| 32¢ | Black-footed Ferret | .50 | .20 |
| **CM1865** | | MNHVF | UseVF |
| 32¢ | Thick-billed Parrot | .50 | .20 |
| **CM1866** | | MNHVF | UseVF |
| 32¢ | Hawaiian Monk Seal | .50 | .20 |
| **CM1867** | | MNHVF | UseVF |
| 32¢ | American Crocodile | .50 | .20 |
| **CM1868** | | MNHVF | UseVF |
| 32¢ | Ocelot | .50 | .20 |
| **CM1869** | | MNHVF | UseVF |
| 32¢ | Schaus Swallowtail Butterfly | .50 | .20 |
| **CM1870** | | MNHVF | UseVF |
| 32¢ | Wyoming Toad | .50 | .20 |
| **CM1871** | | MNHVF | UseVF |
| 32¢ | Brown Pelican | .50 | .20 |
| **CM1872** | | MNHVF | UseVF |
| 32¢ | California Condor | .50 | .20 |
| **CM1873** | | MNHVF | UseVF |
| 32¢ | Gila Trout | .50 | .20 |

| | | MNHVF | UseVF |
|---|---|---|---|
| **CM1874** | | MNHVF | UseVF |
| 32¢ | San Francisco Garter Snake | .50 | .20 |
| **CM1875** | | MNHVF | UseVF |
| 32¢ | Woodland Caribou | .50 | .20 |
| **CM1876** | | MNHVF | UseVF |
| 32¢ | Florida Panther | .50 | .20 |
| **CM1877** | | MNHVF | UseVF |
| 32¢ | Piping Plover | .50 | .20 |
| **CM1878** | | MNHVF | UseVF |
| 32¢ | Florida Manatee | .50 | .20 |
| | FDC *(Oct. 2, 1996)* any single | | 1.00 |
| | y.  Se-tenant pane of CM1864-78 | 11.00 | |

**1996. COMPUTER TECHNOLOGY ISSUE** marks the 50th anniversary of the Electronic Numerical Integrator and Calculator (ENIAC), regarded widely as the 1st general-purpose electronic digital computer, forerunner to the millions in use today. *Offset and intaglio, by Ashton-Potter (USA) Ltd., perforated 11.*

CM1879 *Computer Technology*

| CM1879 | | MNHVF | UseVF |
|---|---|---|---|
| 32¢ | **multicolored,** tagged *(93,612,000)* | .50 | .20 |
| | Plate block of 4 | 3.00 | |
| | FDC *(Oct. 8, 1996)* | | 1.00 |

**1996. HANUKKAH ISSUE** 1st stamp in what USPS announced as a Holiday Celebration series, honors the Jewish Festival of Lights and shares its design with a joint issue from Isreal. The self-adhesive stamp shows a stylized menorah and the colorful candles with which Jews mark the eight-day observance. Due to its popularity, it was reprinted in 1997 with no major differences. *Gravure by Avery Dennison Security Printing Division, serpentine die cut 11.*

 CM1880 *Hanukkah*

| CM1880 | | MNHVF | UseVF |
|---|---|---|---|
| 32¢ | **multicolored,** tagged *(103,520,000)* | .75 | .20 |
| | Plate block of 4 | 3.00 | |
| | FDC *(Oct. 22, 1996)* | | 1.00 |
| | n. Booklet pane of 20 | 12.50 | |

**1996. CYCLING SOUVENIR SHEET** was chiefly issued, according to *Linn's U.S. Stamp Yearbook,* so that the Postal Service would "have an item it could sell at international cycling meets in which the USPS Pro Cycling Team competed, to help defray the team's $1 million annual subsidy." *Gravure by J.W. Fergusson & Sons for Stamp Venturers, perforated 11.*

 CM1881

| CM1881 | | MNHVF | UseVF |
|---|---|---|---|
| 50¢ | **multicolored,** tagged *(20,000,000)* | 2.50 | 1.00 |
| | a. **50¢** multicolored & orange | 1.50 | 1.00 |
| | b. **50¢** multicolored & blue green | 1.50 | 1.00 |
| | FDC *(Nov. 1, 1996)* | | 1.00 |

## Asian Lunar New Year Series

**1997. NEW YEARS ISSUE** for the Year of the Ox is the 5th in the on going series celebrating the Asian lunar holiday. *Gravure by Stamp Venturers, perforated 11 1/4.*

 CM1882 *Year of the Ox*

| CM1882 | | MNHVF | UseVF |
|---|---|---|---|
| 32¢ | **multicolored,** tagged *(160,000,000)* | .50 | .20 |
| | Plate block of 4 | 3.00 | |
| | FDC *(Jan. 5, 1997)* | | 1.00 |

## Black Heritage Series

**1997. BENJAMIN O. DAVIS ISSUE** salutes with a self-adhesive stamp the nation's 1st black brigadier general, a soldier began as a private and rose through the ranks in a 50-year career to become both a force for and a symbol of integration in America's military. *Offset by Banknote Corp. of America, serpentine die cut 11 1/2.*

 CM1883 *Benjamin O. Davis, Sr.*

| CM1883 | | MNHVF | UseVF |
|---|---|---|---|
| 32¢ | **gray, green and black,** phosphored paper *(112,000,000)* | .50 | .20 |
| | Plate block of 4 | 3.00 | |
| | FDC *(Jan. 28, 1997)* | | 1.00 |

**1997. LOVE ISSUE** used bilaterally symmetrical profiles of 2 elegant swans outlining a heart in 2 self-adhesive booklets paying the 32¢ standard first-class 1-ounce letter rate and the 55¢ rate for 2-ounce letters (useful for wedding invitations containing reply cards and envelopes), respectively. Serpentine die cut 11 3/4 x 11 1/2 on 2, 3, or 4 sides. *Offset by Banknote Corp. of American.*

 CM1884 *32¢ Love Swans*

| CM1884 | | MNHVF | UseVF |
|---|---|---|---|
| 32¢ | **multicolored,** tagged | .50 | .20 |
| | FDC *(Feb. 7, 1997)* | | 1.00 |
| | n. Booklet pane of 20 plus label | 13.00 | |
| | v. Imperforate pair (no die cutting) | 275. | |
| | vn. Imperforate pane of 20 (no die cutting) | — | |

**1997. LOVE ISSUE** Serpentine die cut 11 1/2 x 11 3/4 on 2, 3, or 4 sides.

 CM1885 *55¢ Love Swans*

| CM1885 | | MNHVF | UseVF |
|---|---|---|---|
| 55¢ | **multicolored,** tagged | 1.00 | .30 |
| | FDC *(Feb. 7, 1997)* | | 1.00 |
| | n. Booklet pane of 20 plus label | 22.50 | |

**1997. HELPING CHILDREN LEARN ISSUE** a self-adhesive stamp, calls attentin to the developmental importance and simple pleasure of reading as an activity for adults to share with children, and coincides with the centennial of the PTA, the nation's oldest and largest volunteer association working for children. *Gravure by Avery Dennison Security Printing Division, serpentine die cut 11 1/2 x 11 3/4.*

 CM1886 *Helping Children Learn*

**CM1886**

| | | MNHVF | UseVF |
|---|---|---|---|
| 32¢ | **multicolored,** tagged | .50 | .20 |
| | Plate block of 4 | 3.00 | |
| | FDC *(Feb. 18, 1997)* | | 1.00 |

**1997. PACIFIC '97 ISSUE** The 1st triangular stamps in U.S. philatelic history, uses 2 early means of moving the mail -- the stagecoach and the clipper ship -- to promote the Pacific 97 International Philatelic Exhibition May 29 to June 8 in San Francisco, Calif. *Intaglio by Banknote Corp. of America, perforated 11 1/4.*

CM1887 *Stagecoach*

**CM1887**

| | | MNHVF | UseVF |
|---|---|---|---|
| 32¢ | **red,** phosphored paper *(65,000,000)* | .50 | .20 |

CM1888 *Clipper Ship*

**CM1888**

| | | MNHVF | UseVF |
|---|---|---|---|
| 32¢ | **blue,** phosphored paper | .50 | .20 |
| | Plate block of 4 | 3.00 | |
| | y. Se-tenant pair (CM1887-88) | 1.25 | |
| | FDC *(March 13, 1997)* | | 2.00 |
| | Six pane press sheets | 150. | |

*Because this issue also was made available in full 96- subject printing sheets of 6 16-stamp panes, gutter pairs and blocks and cross-gutter multiples also exist.*

**1997. THORNTON WILDER ISSUE** celebrated the 100th birthday of the 3-time Pulitzer Prize- winning author (1897-1975) of the novel *The Bridge of San Luis Rey* and the plays *Our Town*(symbolically depicted on the stamp) and *The Skin of Our Teeth. Offset by Ashton-Potter (USA) Ltd., perforated 11.*

CM1889 *Thornton Wilder*

**CM1889**

| | | MNHVF | UseVF |
|---|---|---|---|
| 32¢ | **multicolored,** tagged *(97,500,000)* | .50 | .20 |
| | Plate block of 4 | 3.00 | |
| | FDC *(April 17, 1997)* | | 1.00 |

**1997. RAOUL WALLENBERG ISSUE** commemorates the Swedish diplomat who in 1944 risked his own life to save over 20,000 Hungarian Jews from Nazi genocide by issuing them falsified Swedish passports. In 1945, Wallenberg was taken prisoner by the Soviets, who only in 1957 announced that he had died a decade earlier, of a purported heart attack, while in Moscow's Lubyanka Prison. *Offset by Sterling Sommer for Ashton-Potter (USA) Ltd., perforated 11.*

CM1890 *Wallenberg and Refugees*

**CM1890**

| | | MNHVF | UseVF |
|---|---|---|---|
| 32¢ | **multicolored,** tagged *(96,000,000)* | .50 | .20 |
| | Plate block of 4 | 3.00 | |
| | FDC *(April 24, 1997)* | | 1.00 |

**1997. THE WORLD OF DINOSAURS ISSUE** a 15-stamp pane, showcases 2 panoramic dioramas of life in the age of the giant reptiles: a scene in Colorado 150 million years ago in the top panel; and a 75-

CM1891 *The World of Dinosaurs*

million-year- old scene from Montana in the bottom panel of the pane. The pane portrays many species never before shown on stamps. *Offset by Sterling Sommer for Ashton-Potter (USA) Ltd., perforated 11.*

| CM1891 | | MNHVF | UseVF |
|---|---|---|---|
| $4.80 | **sheet of 15,** tagged *(14,600,000)* | 15.00 | 9.50 |
| | a. **32¢** Ceratosaurus | .75 | .50 |
| | b. **32¢** Camptosaurus | .75 | .50 |
| | c. **32¢** Camarasaurus | .75 | .50 |
| | d. **32¢** Brachiosaurus | .75 | .50 |
| | e. **32¢** Goniopholis | .75 | .50 |
| | f. **32¢** Stegosaurus | .75 | .50 |
| | g. **32¢** Allosaurus | .75 | .50 |
| | h. **32¢** Opisthias | .75 | .50 |
| | i. **32¢** Edmontonia | .75 | .50 |
| | j. **32¢** Einiosaurus | .75 | .50 |
| | k. **32¢** Daspletosaurus | .75 | .50 |
| | l. **32¢** Palaeosaniwa | .75 | .50 |
| | m. **32¢** Corythosaurus | .75 | .50 |
| | n. **32¢** Ornithomimus | .75 | .50 |
| | o. **32¢** Parasaurolophus | .75 | .50 |
| | FDC *(May 1, 1997)* any single | | 2.00 |
| | FDC pane of 15 | | 12.50 |
| | v. All colors omitted, untagged | — | |
| | v1. Perforations inverted | — | |
| | v2. Perforate CM1891 a-g, Imperforate CM1891 h-o | — | |

**1997. Bugs Bunny Commemorative Pane** 1st in an announced Warner Brothers Cartoon Characters series, showcases in 2 types of self-adhesive 10-stamp pane (rouletted vertically through the middle of the pane) the wisecracking "Oscar-winning rabbit" with the Brooklyn accent who has been a fixture on American movie and television screens for more than half a century. *Gravure by Avery Dennision Security Printing Division.*

CM1892 *Bugs Bunny*

| CM1892 | | MNHVF | UseVF |
|---|---|---|---|
| $3.20 | **pane of ten,** tagged | 7.50 | |
| | n. Right half of pane (single die cut CM1892a superimposed on enlarged image in right selvage) | 1.00 | |
| | n1. Left half of pane (block of 9 CM1892a) | 5.00 | |
| | a. 32c single | .75 | .25 |
| | FDC *(May 22, 1997)* | | 1.00 |

*Serpentine die cut 11 through stamps and backing.*

| CM1893 | | MNHVF | UseVF |
|---|---|---|---|
| $3.20 | **pane of ten,** tagged | 200. | |
| | n. Right half of pane (single imperforate CM1893a on enlarged image in right selvage) | 150. | |
| | n1. Left half of pane (block of 9 CM1893a) | 5.00 | |
| | a. 32c single | .75 | .25 |

*This issue also was made available in top and bottom half printing sheets of six 10-stamp panes each. A single plate number, trimmed away on individual panes, appears adjacent to the bottom-left pane in the bottom half of the printing sheet only. Value of plate number half at press time is $225 .*

*A gummed, non-denominated, untagged item similar to CM1893n on the same backing paper as the normal stamps lacks Bug's "autograph" and single stamp, the latter of which is replace d by "32 USA" as on the*

*issued stamp. Though printed for the USPS, this item was an advertising piece and was not postally valid.*

**1997. George Halas Issue** recalls the longtime coach of the Chicago Bears, a member of the Pro Football Hall of Fame, with a stamp issued in Chicago, Ill., similar to CM1920 but with a red bar over Halas' name. *Printed by Sterling Sommer for Ashton-Potter (USA) Ltd., perforated 11.*

CM1894 *Benjamin Franklin Souvenir Sheet*

| CM1894 | | MNHVF | UseVF |
|---|---|---|---|
| $6 | **pane of 12,** tagged | 11.50 | 9.00 |
| | a. 50¢ single | 1.00 | .50 |
| | FDC *(May 29, 1997)* | | 1.00 |

**1997. Pacific '97 U.S. Stamp Sesquicentennial** mark the 150th anniversary of the 1st regular-issue U.S. postage stamps (Minkus 1-2, depicted in the selvage of the souvenir sheets) and hail the opening of the Pacific 1997 International Philatelic Exhibition in San Francisco, Calif. The souvenir sheets were sold only during the 11 days of the show. *Offset and intaglio by BEP, perforated 10 1/2.*

CM1895 *George Washington Souvenir Sheet*

| CM1895 | | MNHVF | UseVF |
|---|---|---|---|
| $7.20 | **pane of 12,** tagged | 12.50 | 10.00 |
| | a. 60¢ single | 1.25 | .75 |
| | FDC *(May 29, 1997)* | | 1.00 |
| | Six subject press sheets (3 each of CM1894 & CM1895) | 150. | |

*Because this issue also was made available to collectors in full six-pane printing sheets, gutter pairs and blocks and cross-gutter multiples also exist.*

**1997. Marshall Plan 50th Anniversary Issue** saluted the post-World War II European Recovery Program unveiled in 1947 by Gen. George C. Marshall (1880-1959). The U.S. backed multi-billion-dollar plan to help a devastated Western Europe regain its economic health and halt the expansion of Soviet influence earned Marshall the Nobel Peace Prize. *Offset and Intaglio by Stevens Security Press for Ashton- Potter (USA) Ltd., perforated 11.*

CM1896 *The Marshall Plan*

| CM1896 | | MNHVF | UseVF |
|---|---|---|---|
| 32¢ | **multicolored,** tagged *(45,250,000)* | .50 | .20 |
| | Plate block of 4 | 3.50 | |
| | FDC *(June 4, 1997)* | | 1.00 |

**1997. Classic American Aircraft Issue** is the 5th USPS , 20- se-tenant single- theme stamps in a pane with a header across the top and descriptive text on the back of each stamp. This issue showcases

20 U.S. aircraft of the 1st half-century of powered flight. *Gravure (8,050,000 panes) by Stamp Ventures, perforated 10. Multicolored, block tagged (July 19, 1997)*

| CM1897 | | MNHVF | UseVF |
|---|---|---|---|
| 32¢ | North American P-51 Mustang fighter | .75 | .50 |

| CM1898 | | MNHVF | UseVF |
|---|---|---|---|
| 32¢ | Wright Model B Flyer | .75 | .50 |

| CM1899 | | MNHVF | UseVF |
|---|---|---|---|
| 32¢ | Piper J-3 Cub | .75 | .50 |

| CM1900 | | MNHVF | UseVF |
|---|---|---|---|
| 32¢ | Lockheed Vega | .75 | .50 |

| CM1901 | | MNHVF | UseVF |
|---|---|---|---|
| 32¢ | *Northrop Alpha* | .75 | .50 |

| CM1902 | | MNHVF | UseVF |
|---|---|---|---|
| 32¢ | Martin B-10 bomber | .75 | .50 |

| CM1903 | | MNHVF | UseVF |
|---|---|---|---|
| 32¢ | Chance Vought Corsair F4U fighter | .75 | .50 |

| CM1904 | | MNHVF | UseVF |
|---|---|---|---|
| 32¢ | Boeing B-47 Stratojet bomber | .75 | .50 |

| CM1905 | | MNHVF | UseVF |
|---|---|---|---|
| 32¢ | Gee Bee Super-Sportster | .75 | .50 |

| CM1906 | | MNHVF | UseVF |
|---|---|---|---|
| 32¢ | Beech Model C17L Staggerwing | .75 | .50 |

| CM1907 | | MNHVF | UseVF |
|---|---|---|---|
| 32¢ | Boeing B-17 Flying Fortress Bomber | .75 | .50 |

| CM1908 | | MNHVF | UseVF |
|---|---|---|---|
| 32¢ | Stearman PT-13 training aircraft | .75 | .50 |

| CM1909 | | MNHVF | UseVF |
|---|---|---|---|
| 32¢ | Lockheed Constellation | .75 | .50 |

| CM1910 | | MNHVF | UseVF |
|---|---|---|---|
| 32¢ | Lockheed P-38 Lightning fighter | .75 | .50 |

| CM1911 | | MNHVF | UseVF |
|---|---|---|---|
| 32¢ | Boeing P-26 Peashooter fighter | .75 | .50 |

| CM1912 | | MNHVF | UseVF |
|---|---|---|---|
| 32¢ | Ford Tri-Motor | .75 | .50 |

| CM1913 | | MNHVF | UseVF |
|---|---|---|---|
| 32¢ | Douglas DC-3 passenger plane | .75 | .50 |

| CM1914 | | MNHVF | UseVF |
|---|---|---|---|
| 32¢ | Boeing 314 Clipper flying boat | .75 | .50 |

| CM1915 | | MNHVF | UseVF |
|---|---|---|---|
| 32¢ | Curtiss JN-4 Jenny training aircraft | .75 | .50 |

| CM1916 | | MNHVF | UseVF |
|---|---|---|---|
| 32¢ | Grumman F4F Wildcat fighter | .75 | .50 |
| | FDC *(July 19, 1997)* | | 1.00 |
| | y. Se-tenant pane of CM1897-1906 | 15.00 | |
| | FDC | | 10.00 |
| | Six pane press sheets | 150. | |

*Because this issue also was made available to collectors in full 6-pane printing sheets, gutter pairs and blocks and cross-gutter multiples also exist.*

CM1897 - 1908

**1997. Legendary Football Coaches Issue** recalls 4 of the greatest who ever coached the game in a se-tenant issue released at Canton, Ohio, home of the professional Football Hall of Fame. Slightly revised designs of all 4 stamps were issued in August in the states where the coaches made their names (CM1937-40). *Offset by Sterling Sommer for Ashton-Potter (USA) Ltd., perforated 11.*

CM1917 *Paul "Bear" Bryant*

CM1918 *Glenn "Pop" Warner*

CM1919 *Vince Lombardi*

CM1920 *George Halas*

| CM1917 | | MNHVF | UseVF |
|---|---|---|---|
| 32¢ | Paul "Bear" Bryant, tagged *(22,500,000)* | .50 | .20 |
| **CM1918** | | **MNHVF** | **UseVF** |
| 32¢ | Glen "Pop" Warner, tagged | .50 | .20 |
| **CM1919** | | **MNHVF** | **UseVF** |
| 32¢ | Vince Lombardi, tagged | .50 | .20 |
| **CM1920** | | **MNHVF** | **UseVF** |
| 32¢ | George Halas, tagged | .50 | .20 |
| | Plate block of 4 | 3.50 | |
| | y. Se-tenant block or strip of CM1917-20 | 2.00 | |
| | FDC *(July 25, 1997)* | | 2.00 |

**1997. Classic American Dolls Issue** depicts these beloved toys of childhood (and, increasingly, collectibles for adults) dating from as far back as the 1850s up to the 1960s in a commemorative 15-stamp pane with a banner and descriptions in the margins. *Offset (7,000,000 pane) by Sterling Sommer for Ashton-Potter (USA) Ltd., perforated 11. Multicolored, tagged (July 28m 1997)*

| CM1921 | | MNHVF | UseVF |
|---|---|---|---|
| 32¢ | "Alabama Baby" and Martha Chase Doll | .75 | .50 |
| **CM1922** | | **MNHVF** | **UseVF** |
| 32¢ | Rutta Sisters "The Columbian Doll" | .75 | .50 |
| **CM1923** | | **MNHVF** | **UseVF** |
| 32¢ | Johnny Gruelle's "Raggedy Ann" | .75 | .50 |
| **CM1924** | | **MNHVF** | **UseVF** |
| 32¢ | Martha Chase Cloth Doll | .75 | .50 |
| **CM1925** | | **MNHVF** | **UseVF** |
| 32¢ | Effanbee Doll Co. "American Child" | .75 | .50 |
| **CM1926** | | **MNHVF** | **UseVF** |
| 32¢ | Ideal Novelty & Toy Co. "Baby Coos" | .75 | .50 |
| **CM1927** | | **MNHVF** | **UseVF** |
| 32¢ | Plains Indian Doll 1920s | .75 | .50 |
| **CM1928** | | **MNHVF** | **UseVF** |
| 32¢ | Izannah Walker Oil-Painted Cloth Doll | .75 | .50 |
| **CM1929** | | **MNHVF** | **UseVF** |
| 32¢ | All-Cloth "Babland Rag" Doll | .75 | .50 |
| **CM1930** | | **MNHVF** | **UseVF** |
| 32¢ | Rose O'Neill "Scootles" Doll | .75 | .50 |
| **CM1931** | | **MNHVF** | **UseVF** |
| 32¢ | Ludwig Greiner First U.S. Patent Doll | .75 | .50 |

CLASSIC
*American Dolls*

CM1921-1935

"Alabama Baby" and Martha Chase "Baby Coos" Ludwig Greiner

"The Columbian Doll" Plains Indian "Betsy McCall"

Johnny Gruelle's "Raggedy Ann" Izannah Walker Percy Crosby's "Skippy"

Martha Chase "Babyland Rag" "Maggie Mix-up"

"American Child" "Scootles" Albert Schoenhut

The above names include doll makers, designers, trade names and common names.

| CM1932 | | MNHVF | UseVF |
|---|---|---|---|
| 32¢ | "Betsy McCall" American Character Doll | .75 | .50 |

| CM1933 | | MNHVF | UseVF |
|---|---|---|---|
| 32¢ | Percy Crosby's "Skippy" | .75 | .50 |

| CM1934 | | MNHVF | UseVF |
|---|---|---|---|
| 32¢ | Alexander Doll Co. "Maggie Mix | .75 | .50 |

| CM1935 | | MNHVF | UseVF |
|---|---|---|---|
| 32¢ | Schoenut "All Word Perfection Art Dolls" | .75 | .50 |
| | FDC (July 28, 1997) any single | | 1.00 |
| | y. Se-tenant pane of CM1921-35 | 12.50 | |
| | y. FDC, pane of 15 | | 10.00 |

**1997. HUMPHREY BOGART ISSUE** 3rd in the Legends of Hollywood series, is a 20-stamp commemorative pane with a large area of selvage displaying an enlargement of the portrait of the actor on the stamp. Bogart was 1 of the giants of American film in the 1930s and '40s in such movies as *Casablanca, The Maltese Falcon* and *To Have and Have Not.* Bogart was nominated for an Academy Award for *Treasure of the Sierra Madre* and *The Caine Mutiny,* and finally won an Oscar for *The African Queen. Gravure by Stamp Venturers, perforated 11.*

CM1936 *Humphrey Bogart*

| CM1936 | | MNHVF | UseVF |
|---|---|---|---|
| 32¢ | **multicolored,** tagged *(195,000,000)* | .50 | .20 |
| | FDC (July 31, 1997) | | 1.00 |
| | Plate block of 4 | 3.50 | |
| | Pane of 20 | 8.00 | |
| | Six subject press sheet | 125. | |

*Because this issue also was made available to collectors in full 6-pane printing sheets, gutter pairs and blocks and cross-gutter multiples also exist.*

**1997. VINCE LOMBARDI ISSUE** recalls the legendary coach of the Green Bay Packers, a member of the Pro Football Hall of Fame, with a stamp issued in Green Bay, Wis., similar to CM1917 but with a red bar over Lombardi's name. *Printed by Sterling Sommer for Ashton-Potter (USA) Ltd., perforated 11.*

CM1937 *Vince Lombardi*

| CM1937 | | MNHVF | UseVF |
|---|---|---|---|
| 32¢ | **multicolored,** tagged *(20,000,000)* | .50 | .20 |
| | FDC (Aug. 5, 1997) | | 1.00 |
| | Plate block of 4 | 3.50 | |
| | y. Pane of 20 | 10.00 | |

**1997. PAUL "BEAR" BRYANT ISSUE** honors the fabled coach of the University of Alabama -- in Bryant's heyday, "the Crimson Tide" -- with a stamp issued in Tuscaloosa, Ala., similar to CM1918 but with a red bar over Bryant's name. *Printed by Sterling Sommer for Ashton-Potter (USA) Ltd., perforated 11.*

CM1938 *Paul "Bear" Bryant*

| CM1938 | | MNHVF | UseVF |
|---|---|---|---|
| 32¢ | **multicolored,** tagged *(20,000,000)* | .50 | .20 |
| | FDC (Aug. 7, 1997) | | 1.00 |
| | Plate block of 4 | 3.50 | |
| | y. Pane of 20 | 10.50 | |

**1997. GLEN "POP" WARNER ISSUE** commemorates the outstanding LaSalle University coach who gave his name to the nationwide Pop Warner Youth Football League with a stamp issued in Philadelphia, Pa., similar to CM1919 but with a red bar over Warner's name. *Printed by Sterling Sommer for Ashton-Potter (USA) Ltd., perforated 11.*

CM1939 *Glen "Pop" Warner*

| CM1939 | | MNHVF | UseVF |
|---|---|---|---|
| 32¢ | **multicolored,** tagged *(10,000,000)* | .50 | .20 |
| | FDC (Aug. 8, 1997) | | 1.00 |
| | Plate block of 4 | 3.50 | |
| | y. Pane of 20 | 10.00 | |

**1997. GEORGE HALAS ISSUE** recalls the longtime coach of the Chicago Bears, a member of the Pro Football Hall of Fame, with a stamp issued in Chicago, Ill., similar to CM1920 but with a red bar over Halas' name. *Printed by Sterling Sommer for Ashton-Potter (USA) Ltd., perforated 11.*

CM1940 *George Halas*

| CM1940 | | MNHVF | UseVF |
|---|---|---|---|
| 32¢ | **multicolored,** tagged *(10,000,000)* | .50 | .20 |
| | FDC (Aug. 16, 1997) | | 1.00 |
| | Plate block of 4 | 3.50 | |
| | y. Pane of 20 | 10.00 | |

**1997. "THE STARS AND STRIPES FOREVER" ISSUE** salutes the centennial of the premiere of *The Stars and Stripes Forver!,* arguably the best-loved and most frequently played composition of John Philip Sousa (CM222), the celebrated "March King." *Gravure by BEP, perforated 11 1/2.*

CM1941 *The Stars and Stripes Forever!*

| CM1941 | | MNHVF | UseVF |
|---|---|---|---|
| 32¢ | **multicolored, tagged** *(323,000,000)* | .50 | .20 |
| | Plate block of 4 | 3.50 | |
| | FDC (Aug. 21, 1997) | | 1.00 |

**1997. OPERA SINGERS ISSUE** is a se-tenant quartet of renowned vocalists in costumes from their greatest roles, celebrating the 400th anniversary of their art, which originated in 16th-century Florence, Italy. Lily Pons (1898-1976), a diminuative coloratura, made her debut at New York's Metropolitan Opera in 1931 as the heroine of *Lucia di Lammermoor.* Tenor Richard Tucker (1913-75), depicted in foreground of his stamp as the Duke in Verdi's *Rigoletto,* enjoyed a 30-year career at the Met and was regarded as the nation's foremost opera performer of the postwar era. Baritone Lawrence Tibbett (1896-1960) celebrated as the 1st American male to achieve operatic stardom in his own right, is portrayed as the Toreador in *Carmen,* one of many roles in which he excelled. A 21-year-old soprano, Rosa Ponselle (1897-1981) held her own opposite Caruso at the Met's premiere of Verdi's *La Forza del destino,* much to the delight of critics and audiences as well, and is pictured in her costume from *Norma.* American Music series. *Offset by Ashton-Potter (USA) Ltd., perforated 11.*

CM1942-1945

| CM1942 | | MNHVF | UseVF |
|---|---|---|---|
| 32¢ | Lily Pons, tagged *(21,500,000)* | .50 | .20 |
| **CM1943** | | **MNHVF** | **UseVF** |
| 32¢ | Richard Tucker, tagged | .50 | .20 |
| **CM1944** | | **MNHVF** | **UseVF** |
| 32¢ | Lawrence Tibbett, tagged | .50 | .20 |
| **CM1945** | | **MNHVF** | **UseVF** |
| 32¢ | Rosa Ponselle, tagged | .50 | .20 |
| | Plate block of 4 | 3.50 | |
| | FDC *(Sept. 10, 1997)* any single | | 1.00 |
| | y. Se-tenant block or strip of CM1942-45 | 3.50 | |
| | FDC | | 3.00 |
| | Pane of 20 | 8.00 | |

**1997. CLASSICAL COMPOSERS AND CONDUCTORS ISSUE** celebrates 4 composers and 4 conductors in a se-tenant 20- stamp pane. Leopold Stokowski began conducting the Cincinnati Symphony at the age of 27, and in 1912 moved to Philadelphia where he was to weild the baton for more than 25 years, making that city's symphony orchestra one of the finest in the world. Arthur Fiedler, who began as a viola player in the Boston Symphony, gained world fame and brought classical music to vast new audiences as conductor of the Boston Pops Orchestra. George Szell fashioned the Cleveland Orchestra into one of the finest in the nation. Eugene Ormandy was musical director of the Philadelphia Symphony for over 35 years, and in 1948 conducted the 1st symphony concert on American television. Composer Samuel Barber won the Pulitzer Prize for his operas *Vanessa* and his *Piano Concerto.* Composer, pianist and arrange r Ferde Grofe brilliantly scored Gershwin's *Rhapsody In Blue* for the symphony in 1924, and merged jazz and simpl e ballads with equal creativity in his own compositions. Charles Ives was an innovative composer who used daring techniques to mold hymns and folk tunes into unusual symphonies. Louis moreau Gottschalk gained international celebrity as a dazzling pianist whose compositions were built on the Creole rhythms of his native New Orleans. American Music series. *Offset by Sterling Sommer for Ashton-Potter (USA) Ltd., perforated 11.*

| CM1946 | | MNHVF | UseVF |
|---|---|---|---|
| 32¢ | Leopold Stokowski, tagged *(4,300,000)* 20-stamp panes | .50 | .20 |
| **CM1947** | | **MNHVF** | **UseVF** |
| 32¢ | Arthur Fiedler, tagged | .50 | .20 |
| **CM1948** | | **MNHVF** | **UseVF** |
| 32¢ | George Szell, tagged | .50 | .20 |
| **CM1949** | | **MNHVF** | **UseVF** |
| 32¢ | Eugene Ormandy, tagged | .50 | .20 |
| **CM1950** | | **MNHVF** | **UseVF** |
| 32¢ | Samuel Barber, tagged | .50 | .20 |
| **CM1951** | | **MNHVF** | **UseVF** |
| 32¢ | Ferde Grofe, tagged | .50 | .20 |
| **CM1952** | | **MNHVF** | **UseVF** |
| 32¢ | Charles Ives, tagged | .50 | .20 |
| **CM1953** | | **MNHVF** | **UseVF** |
| 32¢ | Louis Moreau Gottschalk,tagged | .50 | .20 |
| | Plate block of 10 | 5.00 | |
| | FDC *(Sept. 12, 1997)* any single | | 1.00 |
| | y. Se-tenant block of CM1946-53 | 4.00 | |
| | FDC | | 3.50 |
| | Pane of 20 | 8.00 | |

**1997. PADRE FELIX VARELA ISSUE** memorializes the priest, educator and social reformer whose humanitarian works for more than 30 years earned him high esteem. Varela (1788-1853) was educated in Cuba but is best known for his work in New York City beginning in the 1820s, when he concentrated on helping the poor, organized the New York Catholic Temperance Association, founded nurseries and orphanages and risked infection during an 1832 cholera epidemic. He also founded the 1st Hispanic newspaper in the United States, which chronicled social injustice, urged religious and ethnic tolerence and promoted the importance of education. The stamp is notable for its use of the microprinted letters "USPS" to form Varela's portrait. *Offset by Sterling Sommer for Ashton-Potter (USA) Ltd., perforated 11 3/4.*

CM1946-1953

CM1954 *Padre Felix Varela*

| CM1954 | | MNHVF | UseVF |
|---|---|---|---|
| 32¢ | **purple,** tagged *(25,250,000)* | .50 | .20 |
| | FDC *(Sept. 15, 1997)* | | 1.00 |
| | Plate block of 4 | 3.50 | |
| | y.  Pane of 20 | 7.50 | |

**1997. U.S. DEPARTMENT OF THE AIR FORCE ISSUE** marks    the 50th anniversary of the youngest branch of the U.S. armed forces as a separate military department. The stamp shows the Thunderbirds USAF demonstration team flying its custom-painted F-18 jet fighters in close "Diamond-Four" formation. This also was the 1st U.S. issue to include hidden images in the background of the stamp, designs visible only with a special USPS "Stamp Decoder." *Offset by Sterling Sommer for Ashton-Potter (USA) Ltd., perforated 11.*

CM1955 *U.S. Department of the Air Force*

| CM1955 | | MNHVF | UseVF |
|---|---|---|---|
| 32¢ | **multicolored,** tagged *(45,250,000)* | .50 | .20 |
| | FDC *(Sept. 18, 1997)* | | 1.00 |
| | Plate block of 4 | 3.50 | |
| | y.  Pane of 20 | 7.50 | |

**1997. CLASSIC MOVIE MONSTERS ISSUE** a 20-stamp pane with a banner across the top released for National Stamp Collecting Month, saluted monsters from Universal Studios films of the 1920s, '30s, and '40s and the actors who brought them to life. Includes hidden images to viewed with the USPS decoder. *Gravure by Stamp Venturers, perforated 10.*

| CM1956 | | MNHVF | UseVF |
|---|---|---|---|
| 32¢ | Lon Chaney, tagged *(29,000,000)* | .50 | .20 |

| CM1957 | | MNHVF | UseVF |
|---|---|---|---|
| 32¢ | Bela Lugosi, tagged | .50 | .20 |

| CM1958 | | MNHVF | UseVF |
|---|---|---|---|
| 32¢ | Boris Karloff, Frankenstein, tagged | .50 | .20 |

| CM1959 | | MNHVF | UseVF |
|---|---|---|---|
| 32¢ | Boris Karloff, Mummy, tagged | .50 | .20 |

| CM1960 | | MNHVF | UseVF |
|---|---|---|---|
| 32¢ | Lon Chaney Jr., tagged | .50 | .20 |
| | Plate block of 10 | 5.00 | |
| | FDC *(Sept. 30, 1997)* any single | | 1.00 |
| | y.  Se-tenant strip of CM1956-60 | 4.00 | |
| | FDC | | 4.00 |
| | Nine subject press sheet | 150. | |

*Because this issue also was made available to collectors in full nine-pane printing sheets, gutter pairs and blocks and cross-gutter multiples also exist.*

**1997. FIRST SUPERSONIC FLIGHT ISSUE** a    self-adhesive stamp, hails the 50th anniversary of the historic 1947 flight at Edward's Air Force Base in which a Bell X-1 rocket aircraft piloted by Chuck Yeager became the 1st to break the sound barrier and travel faster than Mach 1. *Offset by Banknote Corp. of America, serpentine roulette 11 1/2.*

CM1961 *First Supersonic Flight*

| CM1961 | | MNHVF | UseVF |
|---|---|---|---|
| 32¢ | **multicolored,** tagged *(173,000,000)* | .50 | .20 |
| | FDC *(Oct. 14, 1997)* | | 1.00 |
| | Plate block of 4 | 3.50 | |
| | y.  Pane of 20 | 7.50 | |

**1997. WOMEN IN MILITARY SERVICE ISSUE** salutes the nearly 2 million women who have served in the U.S. armed forces in conjunction with the Oct. 18 dedication of the Women in Military Service for America Memorial in Arlington National Cemetery near Washington, D.C. (See also CM355). *Offset by Banknote Corp. of America, perforated 11.*

CM1962 *Women in Military Service*

| CM1962 | | MNHVF | UseVF |
|---|---|---|---|
| 32¢ | **multicolored,** tagged *(37,000,000)* | .50 | .20 |
| | FDC *(Oct. 18, 1997)* | | 1.00 |
| | Plate block of 4 | 3.50 | |
| | y.  Pane of 20 | | |

**1997. KWANZAA ISSUE** a colorful self-adhesive design and the 2nd annual installme nt in the Postal Service's announced Holiday Celebration series, honors the non-sectarian African-American festival of family, community and culture that takes its name from the Swahili phrase meaning "first fruits." Available in panes of 50 or booklets of 15. *Gravure by Avery Dennison Security Printing Division, serpentine die cut 11.*

CM1963 *Kwanzaa*

| CM1963 | | MNHVF | UseVF |
|---|---|---|---|
| 32¢ | **multicolored,** tagged *(133,000,000)* | .50 | .20 |
| | FDC *(Oct. 22, 1997)* | | 1.00 |
| | Plate block of 4 | 3.50 | |
| | n.  Booklet of 15 | | |
| | Six subject press sheet | 150. | |

*Because this issue also was made available to collectors in full six-pane printing sheets, gutter pairs and blocks and cross-gutter multiples also exist.*

CM1956-1960

**1998. YEAR OF THE TIGER NEW YEARS ISSUE** The sixth of the on-going series celebrating the Asian Lunar holiday. *Gravure by Stamp Venturers, perforated 11.*

CM1964 *Year of The Tiger*

| CM1964 | | MNHVF | UseVF |
|---|---|---|---|
| 32¢ | **multicolored, tagged** | .50 | .20 |
| | FDC *(Jan. 5, 1998)* | | 1.50 |
| | Plate block of 4 | 2.00 | |
| | y. Pane of 20 | | |

**1998. WINTER SPORTS ISSUE** celebrates alpine skiing. The USPS circumvented the exhorbant licensing fee to the International Olympic Committee for use of the 5-rings to go, and still was able to honor the winter olympic games held in Nagano, Japan, thus this is a substitute Winter Olympic stamp for Nagano, Japan. Banknote Corporation of American, perforated 11.

CM1965 *Winter Sports - Alpine Skier.*

| CM1965 | | MNHVF | UseVF |
|---|---|---|---|
| 32¢ | **multicolored, tagged** | .50 | .20 |
| | FDC *(Jan. 22, 2998)* | | 1.50 |
| | Plate block of 4 | 2.00 | 1.50 |
| | y. Pane of 20 | 7.50 | |

**1997. MADAM C.J. WALKER ISSUE** salutes with a self adhesive stamp the successful cosmetic and hair-care products businesswomen of the early 20th century. She earned praise as a philanthropist champion such causes as the NAACP and Tuskegee Institute. The portrait photo is from the Scurlock Studio. Black Heritage Series. *Offset, Banknote Corporation of America. Serpentine die cut.*

CM1966 *Madam C.J. Walker*

| CM1966 | | MNHVF | UseVF |
|---|---|---|---|
| 32¢ | **tagged** | .50 | .20 |
| | Plate block of 4 | 2.00 | |
| | y. Pane of 20 | 7.50 | |
| | FDC *(Jan. 28, 1998)* | | 1.50 |

**1998. CELEBRATE THE CENTURY 1900'S ISSUE** *Offset and intaglio. Ashton-Potter USA.* A group of 15 stamps having each decade of the 20th Century. Arts, sciences, sports, inventors are all honored.

CM1967a-CM1967o

Historical text is printed on the back of each stamp. *Offset and Intaglio, printed by Ashton-Potter USA, perforated 11 3/4.*

| CM1967 | | MNHVF | UseVF |
|---|---|---|---|
| $4.80 | **Pane of 15,** tagged | 12.50 | 9.50 |
| | a. Model T Ford | .50 | .50 |
| | b. President Theodore Roosevelt | .50 | .50 |
| | c. The Great Train Robbery | .50 | .50 |
| | d. Crayola Crayons | .50 | .50 |
| | e. 1904 St. Louis Worlds Fair | .50 | .50 |
| | f. 1906 Pure Food and Drugs Act | .50 | .50 |
| | g. Kitty Hawk (1903) | .50 | .50 |
| | h. Ash Can Painters | .50 | .50 |
| | i. Immigrants Arrive | .50 | .50 |
| | j. John Muir Preservationist | .50 | .50 |
| | k. "Teddy" Bear Created | .50 | .50 |
| | l. W.E.B. DuBois, Social Activist | .50 | .50 |
| | m. Gibson Girl | .50 | .50 |
| | n. First World Series | .50 | .50 |
| | o. Robie House, Chicago | .50 | .50 |
| | FDC *(Feb. 3, 1998)* any single | | 2.00 |

**1998. CELEBRATE THE CENTURY 1910'S ISSUE** The second group of 15 stamps in the series. *Offset and intaglio. Ashton-Potter USA, perforated 11 3/4.*

| CM1968 | | MNHVF | UseVF |
|---|---|---|---|
| $4.80 | **Pane of 15,** tagged | 12.50 | 9.50 |
| | a. Charlie Chaplin | .50 | .50 |
| | b. Federal Reserve | .50 | .50 |
| | c. George Washington Carver | .50 | .50 |
| | d. Armory Show | .50 | .50 |
| | e. Transcontinental Phone Line | .50 | .50 |
| | f. Panama Canal | .50 | .50 |

| | | | |
|---|---|---|---|
| g. | Jim Thorp | .50 | .50 |
| h. | Grand Canyon | .50 | .50 |
| i. | World War I | .50 | .50 |
| j. | Scounting | .50 | .50 |
| k. | Woodrow Wilson | .50 | .50 |
| l. | Crossword Puzzle | .50 | .50 |
| m. | Jack Dempsey | .50 | .50 |
| n. | Construction toys | .50 | .50 |
| o. | Child Labor | .50 | .50 |
| | FDC *(Feb. 3, 1998)* any single | | 2.00 |

**1998. SPANISH AMERICAN WAR ISSUE** marks the centennial of this very short hostility which began after the sinking of the battleship Maine in Havana harbor. *Printed by BEP, perforated 11 1/4.*

CM1969 *Battleship Maine*

| CM1969 | | MNHVF | UseVF |
|---|---|---|---|
| 32¢ | **red and black,** tagged | .50 | .20 |
| | Plate block of 4 | 2.00 | |
| | y. Pane of 20 | 7.50 | |
| | FDC *(Feb. 15, 1998)* | | 1.50 |

**1998. FLOWERING TREE ISSUE** highlights in self-adhesive form these native North American trees. *Offset, serpentine die cut 11 1/4, printed by Banknote Corporation of America.*

CM1968a-CM1968o

CM1970 *Southern Magnolia*

**CM1970**

| | | MNHVF | UseVF |
|---|---|---|---|
| 32¢ | Southern Magnolia, tagged | .50 | .20 |

CM1971 *Blue Palonerde*

**CM1971**

| | | MNHVF | UseVF |
|---|---|---|---|
| 32¢ | Blue Paloverde, tagged | .50 | .20 |

CM1972 *Yellow Popular*

**CM1972**

| | | MNHVF | UseVF |
|---|---|---|---|
| 32¢ | Yellow Poplar, tagged | .50 | .20 |

CM1973 *Prairie Crab Apple*

**CM1973**

| | | MNHVF | UseVF |
|---|---|---|---|
| 32¢ | Prairie Crab Apple, tagged | .50 | .20 |

CM1974 *Pacific Dogwood*

**CM1974**

| | | MNHVF | UseVF |
|---|---|---|---|
| 32¢ | Pacific Dogwood, tagged | .50 | .20 |
| | FDC *March 19, 1998)* any single | | 1.50 |
| | a. Strip of 5 (CM1970-74) | 3.00 | |
| | y. Pane of 20 | 7.50 | |
| | Plate block of 10 | 5.50 | |

**1998. ALEXANDER CALDER ISSUE** honors the sculptor/artist on the centennial of his birth. *Gravure, Stamp Ventures, perforated 10 1/4.*

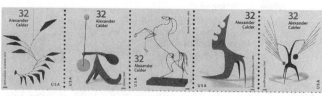

CM1975-79 *Calder Sculpture*

**CM1975**

| | | MNHVF | UseVF |
|---|---|---|---|
| 32¢ | Black Cascade, 13 verticals, | .50 | .20 |

**CM1976**

| | | MNHVF | UseVF |
|---|---|---|---|
| 32¢ | Untitled, tagged | .50 | .20 |

**CM1977**

| | | MNHVF | UseVF |
|---|---|---|---|
| 32¢ | Rearing Stallion, tagged | .50 | .20 |

**CM1978**

| | | MNHVF | UseVF |
|---|---|---|---|
| 32¢ | Portrait of a young man, tagged | .50 | .20 |

**CM1979**

| | | MNHVF | UseVF |
|---|---|---|---|
| 32¢ | Un Effect du Japonais, tagged | .50 | .20 |
| | FDC *(March 25, 1998)* any single | | 1.50 |
| | Plate block of 10 | 4.50 | |
| | a. Strip of 5 (CM1975-79) | 2.00 | |
| | y. Pane of 20 | 7.50 | |

**1998. CINCO DE MAYO ISSUE** honors the Festival of Mexican Heritage commemorating the Mexican victory over French Invaders at the Battle of Puebla in 1862. Featured a couple dancing in traditional costumes. It was a joint issue with Mexico. *Self-adhesive, Gravure, Stamp Ventures, Serpentine die cut 11 3/4 x 11.*

CM1980 *Cinco de Mayo Festival.*

**CM1980**

| | | MNHVF | UseVF |
|---|---|---|---|
| 32¢ | **multicolored** | .50 | .20 |
| | FDC *(April 16, 1998)* | | 1.50 |
| | Plate block of 4 | 2.00 | |
| | Pane of 20 | 7.50 | |

**1998. SYLVESTER AND TWEETIE ISSUE** The second issue in the Warner Brothers series. *Self-adhesive, Gravure, printed by Avery Dennison, Serpentine die cut 11 1/4 x 11.*

CM1981 *Sylvester and Tweetie*

**CM1981**

| | MNHVF | UseVF |
|---|---|---|
| **$3.20** | .50 | .25 |
| FDC *(April 27, 1998)* single | | 1.50 |
| y.  Pane of 10 | 5.00 | |
| 6 pane top press sheet | 175. | |
| 6 pane bottom press sheet | 225. | |

### 1998. SYLVESTER AND TWEETIE ISSUE

**CM1981a.**

| | MNHVF | UseVF |
|---|---|---|
| **$3.20**  Pane of 10, tagged | 5.00 | |
| n.  right half of pane (single die cut CM1981a superimposed on enlarged image in right selvege) | 1.00 | |
| n1.left half of pane (Block of 9 (CM1981a) | 5.00 | |
| a.  32¢ single | | |

### 1998. SYLVESTER AND TWEETIE ISSUE Self-adhesive - Gravure, printed by Avery Dennison, 9 stamps Serpentine die cut, and one imperforate on right panel.

**CM1982**

| | MNHVF | UseVF |
|---|---|---|
| **$3.20**  Pane of ten, tagged | 150. | |
| n.  right half of pane (angle imperforate CM1893a) enlarged image in right selvege | 125. | |
| n1.left half of pane (block of 9 CM1893a) | 5.50 | |
| a.  32¢ single | .50 | |

### 1998. CELEBRATE THE CENTURY, 1920'S ISSUE Third in the series honoring each decade of the 20th Century. Offset and intaglio, printed by Ashton Potter USA, perforated 11 3/4.

**CM1983**

| | MNHVF | UseVF |
|---|---|---|
| **$4.80**  **Sheetlet of 15, tagged** | 15.00 | 9.50 |
| a.  Babe Ruth | .75 | .50 |
| b.  The Gatsby Style | .75 | .50 |
| c.  Prohibition Enforced | .75 | .50 |
| d.  Electric toy trains | .75 | .50 |
| e.  19th Amendment | .75 | .50 |
| f.  Emily Post's Etiquette | .75 | .50 |
| g.  Margaret Mead, Anthropologist | .75 | .50 |
| h.  Flappers do the Charleston | .75 | .50 |
| i.  Radio Entertains America | .75 | .50 |
| j.  Art deco style | .75 | .50 |
| k.  Jazz flourishes | .75 | .50 |
| l.  Four Horsemen of Notre Dame | .75 | .50 |
| m. Lindbergh Flies Atlantic | .75 | .50 |
| n.  American Realism | .75 | .50 |
| o.  Stock Market Crash of 1929 | .75 | .50 |
| FDC *(May 28, 1998)* any single | | 2.00 |

### 1998. WISCONSIN STATEHOOD SESQUICENTENIAL ISSUE honors the 1848 entry into the union of the state of Wisconsin. *Self-adhesive, printed by American Packaging Corp. for SSP, serpentine die cut 11.*

CM1984 *Door County farm scene.*

**CM1984**

| | MNHVF | UseVF |
|---|---|---|
| **32¢**  **multicolored** | .50 | .20 |
| Plate block of 4 | 1.50 | |
| Pane of 20 | 7.50 | |
| FDC *(May 29, 1998)* | | 1.50 |

### 1998. TRANS-MISSISSIPPI COLOR ISSUE highlighting nine views of westward expansion. Orginally issued in one color for the 1898 Trans-Mississippi Exposition held in Omaha, Nebraska. *Gravure, printed by Banknote Corp. of America, perforated 12 1/4 x 12 1/2.*

**CM1985**

| | MNHVF | UseVF |
|---|---|---|
| **$3.80**  **Pane of 9** | 7.50 | 3.50 |
| a.  **1¢** dk. green & black | .25 | .20 |
| b.  **2¢** copper red & black | .25 | .20 |
| c.  **4¢** orange & black | .25 | .20 |
| d.  **5¢** dk. blue & black | .25 | .20 |
| e.  **8¢** dk. lilac & black | .25 | .20 |
| f.  **10¢** purple & black | .50 | .50 |
| g.  **50¢** olive & black | 1.50 | .50 |
| h.  **$1.00** red & black | 2.00 | .50 |
| i.  **$2.00** brown & black | 3.00 | 1.00 |
| FDC *(June 18, 1998)* any single | | 1.50 |
| FDC full pane of 9 | | 5.00 |
| Uncut press sheet 3-9 design CM1985a-i | 50.00 | |

**CM1986**

| | MNHVF | UseVF |
|---|---|---|
| **$9**  **Pane,** 9 examples of CM1985 | 15.00 | |
| FDC *(June 18, 1998)* | | 15.00 |
| Uncut press sheet 3-9 cattle CM1986 | 50.00 | |

### 1998. BERLIN AIRLIFT ISSUE commemorates the 50th Anniversary of the U.S. Air Force operation to assist the citizens of war ravaged Berlin from a land and water blockaide set up by the Soviets. The flights of C-47s and C-54s lasted from June 26, 1948 through September 30, 1949. *Offset by Banknote Corporation of America, perforated 11.*

CM1987 *Berliners watching arriving C-54.*

**CM1987**

| | MNHVF | UseVF |
|---|---|---|
| **32¢**  **multicolored** | .50 | .20 |
| Plate block of 4 | 1.50 | |
| y.  Pane of 20 | 7.50 | |
| FDC *(June 26, 1998)* | | 1.50 |

### 1998. FOLK MUSICIANS ISSUE *Gravure, American Packaging Corp. for Sennett Sucurity Products, perforated 10 1/4.*

CM1988-1991

| CM1988 | | MNHVF | UseVF |
|---|---|---|---|
| **32¢** | Woody Guthrie, tagged | .50 | .20 |

| CM1989 | | MNHVF | UseVF |
|---|---|---|---|
| **32¢** | Sonny Terry, tagged | .50 | .20 |

| CM1990 | | MNHVF | UseVF |
|---|---|---|---|
| **32¢** | Huddle "Leadbelly" Ledbetter | .50 | .20 |

| CM1991 | | MNHVF | UseVF |
|---|---|---|---|
| **32¢** | Josh White | .50 | .20 |
| | FDC *(June 26, 1998)* any single | | 1.50 |
| | Plate block of 4 | 1.50 | |
| | y. Pane of 20 | 7.50 | |

**1998. SPANISH SETTLEMENT OF THE SOUTHWEST ISSUE** The 400th anniversary of the oldest European road in the southwestern U.S., "El Camino Real de Tierra Adentro" (the royal road to the interior land), and the founding of the settlement of San Gabriel is what is now New Mexico is honored. The mission replica is depicted, its situated in Espaäola, New Mexico. *Offset by Banknote Corporation of America, perforated 11 1/4.*

CM1992 *Mission de San Miguel de San Gabriel.*

| CM1992 | | MNHVF | UseVF |
|---|---|---|---|
| **32¢** | **multicolored** | .50 | .20 |
| | FDC *(July 11, 1998)* | | 1.50 |
| | Plate block of 4 | 1.50 | |
| | y. Pane of 20 | 7.50 | |

## Legends of American Music Series

**1998. GOSPEL SINGERS ISSUE** *Gravure. American Packaging Corp. for Sennett Security Products.*

CM1993-1996

| CM1993 | | MNHVF | UseVF |
|---|---|---|---|
| **32¢** | Mahala Jackson | .50 | 2.00 |

| CM1994 | | MNHVF | UseVF |
|---|---|---|---|
| **32¢** | Roberta Martin | .50 | .20 |

| CM1995 | | MNHVF | UseVF |
|---|---|---|---|
| **32¢** | Clara Ward | .50 | .20 |

| CM1996 | | MNHVF | UseVF |
|---|---|---|---|
| **32¢** | Sister Rosetta Tharpe | .50 | .20 |
| | FDC *(July 15, 1998)* any single | | 1.50 |
| | Plate block of 4 | 1.50 | |
| | y. Pane of 20 | 7.50 | |

## Literary Arts Series

**1998. STEPHEN VICENT BERÉT ISSUE** honors the poet on his birth centennial. Pulitzer Prize winning auther of John Browns Body. Berét's portrait is set against part of Augustus-St. Gauden's Shaw Memorial located on Boston Common. *Offset by Sterling Sommer for Ashton Potter, perforated 11.*

| CM1997 | | MNHVF | UseVF |
|---|---|---|---|
| **32¢** | **multicolored** | .50 | .20 |
| | FDC *(July 22, 1998)* | | 1.50 |
| | Plate block of 4 | 1.50 | |
| | Pane of 10 | 7.50 | |

**1998. TROPICAL BIRD ISSUE** features two birds of Puerto Rico, and one each from the the rain forest of Maui and the island of Samoa. *Offset, Banknote Corporation of America, perforated 11.*

CM1998-2001

| CM1998 | | MNHVF | UseVF |
|---|---|---|---|
| **32¢** | Antillean Euphonia | .50 | .20 |

| CM1999 | | MNHVF | UseVF |
|---|---|---|---|
| **32¢** | Green-throated Carib | .50 | .20 |

| CM2000 | | MNHVF | UseVF |
|---|---|---|---|
| **32¢** | Crested Honeycreeper | .50 | .20 |

| CM2001 | | MNHVF | UseVF |
|---|---|---|---|
| **32¢** | Cardinal Honeyeater | .50 | .20 |
| | FDC *(July 29, 1998)* any single | 7.50 | 1.50 |
| | Plate block of 4 | 1.50 | |
| | y. Pane of 20 | | |

**1998. ALFRED HITCHCOCK ISSUE** Legends of Hollywood Series. Printed by Sennett Security Products, perforated 11 1/4.

| CM2002 | | MNHVF | UseVF |
|---|---|---|---|
| **32¢** | **black and gray** | .75 | .20 |
| | FDC *(Aug. 3, 1998)* | | 1.00 |
| | Plate block of 4 | 2.00 | |
| | y. Pane of 20 | 8.50 | |

**1998. ORGAN & TISSUE DONATION ISSUE** Self-adhesive. Printed by Avery Dennison. Serpentine die cut.

| CM2003 | | MNHVF | UseVF |
|---|---|---|---|
| **32¢** | **multicolored** | .50 | .20 |
| | *(Aug. 5, 1998)* | | 1.00 |

**1998. BRIGHT EYES PET ISSUE** Self-adhesive die cut, printed by Bank Note Corporation of America.

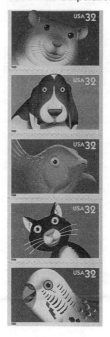

| CM2004 | | MNHVF | UseVF |
|---|---|---|---|
| 32¢ | Dog, tagged | .50 | .20 |

| CM2005 | | MNHVF | UseVF |
|---|---|---|---|
| 32¢ | Goldfish, tagged | .50 | .20 |

| CM2006 | | MNHVF | UseVF |
|---|---|---|---|
| 32¢ | Cat, tagged | .50 | .20 |

| CM2007 | | MNHVF | UseVF |
|---|---|---|---|
| 32¢ | Parakeet, tagged | .50 | .20 |

| CM2008 | | MNHVF | UseVF |
|---|---|---|---|
| 32¢ | Hamster, tagged | .50 | .20 |
| | FDC (Aug. 20, 1998), any single | | 1.00 |
| | y.  Pane of 20 | 7.50 | |

**1998. KLONDIKE GOLD RUSH ISSUE** Printed by Ashton-Potter, perforated 11.

| CM2009 | | MNHVF | UseVF |
|---|---|---|---|
| 32¢ | **multicolored**, tagged | .50 | .20 |
| | x.  Pane of 20 | 7.50 | |
| | FDC (Aug. 21, 1998) | | 1.00 |

**1998. AMERICAN ART ISSUE** featuring works of four centuries of American Artist Sennett Security Products, perforated 10 1/2 x 10.

| CM2010 | | MNHVF | UseVF |
|---|---|---|---|
| 32¢ | John Foster | .50 | .20 |

| CM2011 | | MNHVF | UseVF |
|---|---|---|---|
| 32¢ | The Freake Limner | .50 | .20 |

| CM2012 | | MNHVF | UseVF |
|---|---|---|---|
| 32¢ | Ammi Phillips | .50 | .20 |

| CM2013 | | MNHVF | UseVF |
|---|---|---|---|
| 32¢ | Rembrandt Peale | .50 | .20 |

| CM2014 | | MNHVF | UseVF |
|---|---|---|---|
| 32¢ | John J. Audubon | .50 | .20 |

| CM2015 | | MNHVF | UseVF |
|---|---|---|---|
| 32¢ | George Caleb Bingham | .50 | .20 |

| CM2016 | | MNHVF | UseVF |
|---|---|---|---|
| 32¢ | Asher B. Durand | .50 | .20 |

| CM2017 | | MNHVF | UseVF |
|---|---|---|---|
| 32¢ | Joshua Johnson | .50 | .20 |

| CM2018 | | MNHVF | UseVF |
|---|---|---|---|
| 32¢ | William M. Harnett | .50 | .20 |

| CM2019 | | MNHVF | UseVF |
|---|---|---|---|
| 32¢ | Winslow Homer | .50 | .20 |

| CM2020 | | MNHVF | UseVF |
|---|---|---|---|
| 32¢ | George Catlin | .50 | .20 |

| CM2021 | | MNHVF | UseVF |
|---|---|---|---|
| 32¢ | Thomas Moran | .50 | .20 |

| CM2022 | | MNHVF | UseVF |
|---|---|---|---|
| 32¢ | Albert Bierstadt | .50 | .20 |

| CM2023 | | MNHVF | UseVF |
|---|---|---|---|
| 32¢ | Frederic Edwin Church | .50 | .20 |

| CM2024 | | MNHVF | UseVF |
|---|---|---|---|
| 32¢ | Mary Cassalt | .50 | .20 |

| CM2025 | | MNHVF | UseVF |
|---|---|---|---|
| 32¢ | Edward Hopper | .50 | .20 |

| CM2026 | | MNHVF | UseVF |
|---|---|---|---|
| 32¢ | Grant Wood | .50 | .20 |

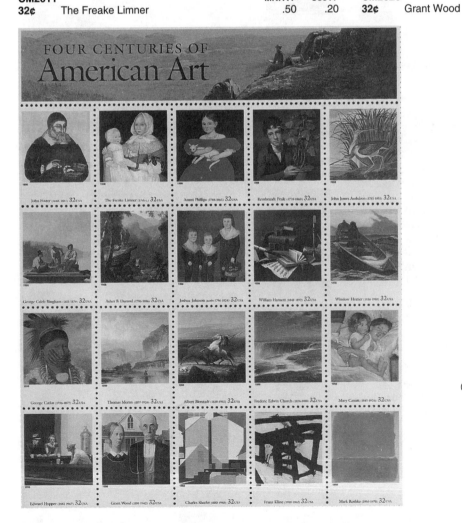

CM2010-2029

| CM2027 | | MNHVF | UseVF |
|---|---|---|---|
| 32¢ | Charles Sheeler | .50 | .20 |

| CM2028 | | MNHVF | UseVF |
|---|---|---|---|
| 32¢ | Franny Kline | .50 | .20 |

| CM2029 | | MNHVF | UseVF |
|---|---|---|---|
| 32¢ | Mark Rothko | .50 | .20 |
| | FDC *(Aug. 27, 1998)* any single | | 1.00 |
| | y. Pane of 20 | 8.50 | |

**1998. CELEBRATE THE CENTURY, 1930-39 ISSUE** Fourth in the seriehonoring each decade of the 20th Century printed by Ashton-Potter. Offset and intaglio, perforated 11 3/4.

| | | MNHVF | UseVF |
|---|---|---|---|
| CM2030 | | | |
| $4.80 | *Sheetlet of 15, tagged* | 10.00 | 7.50 |
| | a. Franklin D. Roosevelt | 10.00 | 7.50 |
| | b. Empire State Building | .75 | .50 |
| | c. Life Magazine | .75 | .50 |
| | d. Eleanor Roosevelt | .75 | .50 |
| | e. FDR's New Deal Programs | .75 | .50 |
| | f. Superman Arrives | .75 | .50 |
| | g. Household Conveniences | .75 | .50 |
| | h. Disney's Snow White | .75 | .50 |
| | i. Gone with the Wind | .75 | .50 |
| | j. Jesse Owens | .75 | .50 |
| | k. Streamline Design | .75 | .50 |
| | l. Golden Gate Bridge | .75 | .50 |
| | m. America Survives the Depression | .75 | .50 |
| | n. Bobby Jones | .75 | .50 |
| | o. Monopoly Game | .75 | .50 |

**1998. BALLET ISSUE** Ballerina performing the step "en pointe" in an "attitude derriere" pose honors the art form. Printed by Ashton Potter, perforated 11.

| CM2031 | | MNHVF | UseVF |
|---|---|---|---|
| 32¢ | **multicolored** | .50 | .20 |
| | FDC *(Sept. 16, 1998)* | | 1.00 |
| | y. Pane of 20 | 7.50 | |

**1998. SPACE DISCOVERY ISSUE** A panoramic scene by artist Attila Hejja depicts exotic spacecraft, a city on an alien planet and colonists. There are views of space ships as a hidden indicium visible only with the USPS optical decoder.

CM2032-2036

| CM2032 | MNHVF | UseVF |
|---|---|---|
| 32¢ | .50 | .30 |

| CM2033 | MNHVF | UseVF |
|---|---|---|
| 32¢ | .50 | .20 |

| CM2034 | MNHVF | UseVF |
|---|---|---|
| 32¢ | .50 | .20 |

| CM2035 | MNHVF | UseVF |
|---|---|---|
| 32¢ | .50 | .20 |

| CM2036 | MNHVF | UseVF |
|---|---|---|
| 32¢ | .50 | .20 |
| Plate Block of 10 (CM2032-2036) 2 each | 4.50 | |
| Se-tenant strip of 5 (CM2032- 2036) | 2.00 | |
| FDC *(Oct. 1 1998)* | | 1.50 |
| y. Pane of 20 | 7.50 | |

**1998. GIVING & SHARING ISSUE** Pays tribute to Philanthropy. The bee and flower is a metaphor for the symbolic relationship between the "giver" and the "receiver." Serpentine die cut.

 CM2037

| CM2037 | | MNHVF | UseVF |
|---|---|---|---|
| 32¢ | | .50 | .20 |
| | Plate block of 4 | 2.00 | |
| | FDC *(Oct. 7, 1998)* | | 1.50 |
| | y. Pane of 20 | 7.50 | |

# Air Mail

All airmail issues were printed by the Bureau of Engraving and Printing unless otherwise noted. Prices for FDC are unchacheted for A1-A20.

First Airmail Series got under way in 1918, when the U.S. Post Office Department announced that an airmail service from New York to Philadelphia to Washington D.C., would begin May 15.

Two days before the initial flight, the world's first stamp designed expressly for airmail was issued to pay the rate between any two of the three cities: 24¢ for the first ounce, including special delivery.

Later in the year, when the rate dropped to 16¢, another stamp was issued. Near the end of the year. a 6¢ stamp was issued which paid the airmail rate without special delivery.

All three stamps were of the same design, a army Curtiss biplane used by the Air Corp. since the carrying of airmail had been entrusted to army pilots flying army planes. The Curtiss biplanes were called "Jennys" from their official designation, which began with the initials "JN".

Intaglio (flat plate press), perforated 11.

**1918. CURTISS BIPLANE ISSUE** One sheet of 100 stamps of the 24¢ denomination (A3) the blue vignette of the airplane upside down was purchsed in a post office at Washington D.C., by William T. Robey, who sold it to Eugene Klein of Philadelphia, who in turn sold it ot Col. Edward H.R. Green. Green retained some of the errors, including the position pieces, 2nd through Klein disposed of the rest. One of the most famous post office finds in U.S. stamp history.

A1 *Curtiss Biplane*

| A1 | | UnFVF | UseFVF |
|---|---|---|---|
| 6¢ | **red orange** *(3,395,854)* | 75.00 | 30.00 |
| | pale orange | 75.00 | 30.00 |
| | Plate block of 6 w/arrow | 700. | |
| | Block of 4 w/arrow | 2.75 | 1.25 |
| | Center line block | 3.00 | 1.15 |
| | Double transfer | 30.00 | 40.00 |
| | On cover | | 150. |
| | First-flight cover *(Dec. 16, 1918)* | | 2700. |
| | FDC *(Dec. 10, 1918)* | | 26000. |

A2 *Curtis Biplane*

| A2 | | UnFVF | UseFVF |
|---|---|---|---|
| 16¢ | **green** *(3,793,887)* | 90.00 | 40.00 |
| | dark green | 90.00 | 40.00 |
| | Plate block of 6 w/arrow | 1200. | |
| | Block of 4 w/arrow | 425. | 150. |
| | Center line block | 450. | 175. |
| | On cover | 50.00 | |
| | First flight cover *(July 15, 1918)* | | 850. |
| | FDC *(July 11, 1918)* | | 26500. |

A3 *Curtiss Biplane*

| A3 | | UnFVF | UseFVF |
|---|---|---|---|
| 24¢ | **carmine red & blue** *(2,134,888)* | 90.00 | 45.00 |
| | dark carmine red & blue | 90.00 | 45.00 |
| | Plate block of 4, blue plate number & "TOP" | 450. | |
| | Plate block of 4, red plate number & "TOP" | 450. | |
| | Plate block of 4, red plate number only | 450. | |
| | Plate block of 12, 2 plate numbers, arrow, & 2 "TOP" inscriptions | 1400. | |
| | Plate block of 12, 2 plate numbers, arrow, & blue "TOP" only | 6000. | |
| | Block of 4, w/arrow at top or left | 425. | 125. |
| | Block of 4, w/arrow at bottom | 420. | 120. |
| | Block of 4, w/arrow at right | 450. | 175. |
| | Center line block | 450. | 150. |
| | On cover | | 850. |
| | First flight cover *(May 5, 1918)* | | 850. |
| | FDC *(May 13, 1918)* | | 26000. |
| | Center Inverted, single | 140000. | — |
| | Block of 4 center inverted | 600000. | |
| | Plate block of 4 center inverted | 1000000. | |

| C3a | | UnFVF | UseFVF |
|---|---|---|---|
| 24¢ | | | |
| | v. Inverted center | 125000. | |
| | Plate block of 4 | — | |
| | Center line block | — | |

*One sheet of 100 stamps with the blue vignette of the airplane uspside down ws purchased in a post office at Washington D.C., by William T. robey, who sold it to Eugene Klein of Philadelphia, who in turn sold it to Col. Edward H.R. Green. Green retained some of the errors, including the position pieces, and through Klein disposed of the rest. One of the most famous post office finds in U.S. stamp history.*

**1923. THE SECOND AIRMAIL SERIES ISSUE** was issued for use on airmail service between New York and San Francisco. Three airmail zones were established: New York to Chicago; Chicago to Cheyenne; and Cheyenne to San Francisco. The rate of postage was 8¢ an ounce for each zone. The stamps were available through the Philatelic Agency at Washington D.C. before they were issued to postmasters. *Intaglio, perforated 11.*

A4 *Propeller and plane radiator.*

| A4 | | UnFVF | UseFVF |
|---|---|---|---|
| 8¢ | **green** *(6,414,576)* | 25.00 | 15.00 |
| | dark green | 25.00 | 15.00 |
| | Plate block of 6 | 275. | |
| | Double transfer | 40.00 | 20.00 |
| | On cover | | 22.50 |
| | FDC *(Aug. 15, 1923)* | | 400. |

A5 *Air Mail service insignia*

| A5 | | UnFVF | UseFVF |
|---|---|---|---|
| 16¢ | **indigo** *(5,309,275)* | 85.00 | 30.00 |
| | Plate block of 6 | 1900. | |
| | Double transfer | 125. | 40.00 |
| | On cover | | 45.00 |
| | FDC *(Aug. 17, 1923)* | | 650. |

A6 *De Havilland Biplane*

**A6**

| 24¢ | | UnFVF | UseFVF |
|---|---|---|---|
| | **Carmine** *(5,285,775)* | 95.00 | 30.00 |
| | Plate block of 6 | 2100. | |
| | Double transfer | 175. | 40.00 |
| | On cover | | 40.00 |
| | FDC *(Aug. 21, 1923)* | | 800. |

**1926-27. MAP ISSUE** consists of three denominations: 10¢, 15¢, and 20¢, reflecting new rates: 10 cents per ounce up to 1,000 miles; 15 cents to 1,500 miles; and 20 cents for distances over 1,500 miles or Contract Air Mail routes. *Intaglio, perforated 11.*

A7-A9 *Relief map of United States and two mail planes.*

**A7**

| 10¢ | | UnFVF | UseFVF |
|---|---|---|---|
| | **blue** *(42,092,800)* | 3.00 | 45.00 |
| | light blue | 3.00 | .45 |
| | Plate block of 6 | 40.00 | |
| | Double transfer | 5.50 | 1.00 |
| | FDC *(Feb. 13, 1926)* | | 90.00 |

**A8**

| 15¢ | | UnFVF | UseFVF |
|---|---|---|---|
| | **olive brown** *(15,597,307)* | 3.75 | 2.50 |
| | light brown | 3.75 | 2.50 |
| | Plate block of 6 | 45.00 | |
| | FDC *(Sept 18, 1926)* | | 100. |

**A9**

| 20¢ | | UnFVF | UseFVF |
|---|---|---|---|
| | **yellow green** *(17,616,350)* | 9.00 | 2.00 |
| | green | 9.00 | 2.00 |
| | Plate block of 6 | 100. | |
| | FDC *(Jan. 25, 1927)* | | 125. |

**1927. LINDBERGH AIRMAIL ISSUE** honors Charles Augustus Lindbergh, the 25-year-old former air mail pilot who made the first nonstop solo flight from New York to Paris, May 20-21, 1927. Stamp collectors welcomed one of the few U.S. stamps ever to honor a living person. the stamp pictures Lindgergh's Ryan monoplane, *The Spirit of St. Louis,* which is now on display in the Smithsonian Institution at Washington, D.C. *Intaglio, perforated 11.*

A10 *Lindbergh's monoplane, Spirit of St. Louis.*

**A10**

| 10¢ | | UnFVF | UseFVF |
|---|---|---|---|
| | **indigo** *(20,379,179)* | 8.00 | 2.00 |
| | Plate block of 6 | 145. | |
| | Double transfer | 11.00 | 3.00 |
| | FDC *(June 18, 1927)* | | 150. |
| | n. Booklet pane of 3 | 90.00 | 50.00 |
| | Single, perforated 11 horizontally | 12.50 | |
| | FDC *(May 26, 1928)* | | 900. |

*First-day covers for No. A10 are from Washington D.C. Little Falls, Minn., St. Louis, Mo. and Detroit, Mich. FDCs for No. A10n are from Washington, D.C. and Cleveland, Ohio.*

**1928. AIR MAIL BEACON ISSUE** reflects the 5¢-per ounce rate that went into effect August 1, 1928.

A11 *Sherman Hill air mail beacon light.*

**A11**

| 5¢ | | UnFVF | UseFVF |
|---|---|---|---|
| | **carmine red and blue** *(106,887,675)* | 4.50 | .75 |
| | Plate block of 6, 2 plate numbers & red "TOP" | 45.00 | |
| | Plate block of 6, 2 plate numbers & blue "TOP" | 65.00 | |
| | Plate block of 6, 2 plate numbers & double "TOP" | 100. | |
| | Plate block of 8, 2 plate numbers only | 185. | |
| | Block of 4 w/arrow | 20.00 | 4.25 |
| | Double transfer | — | |
| | Recut frame line at left | 6.50 | 1.20 |
| | FDC *(July 25, 1928)* | | 225. |
| | v. Vertical pair, imperforate between | 6000. | |

**1930. WINGED GLOBE ISSUE** is sometimes confused with the 5¢ rotary-press version of 1931 (A16), but measures 46 3/4mm by 18 3/4mm. *Intaglio, (flat plate press), perforated 11.*

A12 *Winged Globe*

**A12**

| 5¢ | | UnFVF | UseFVF |
|---|---|---|---|
| | **purple** *(97,641,200)* | 10.00 | .50 |
| | Plate block of 6 | 140. | |
| | Double transfer | 18.00 | 1.25 |
| | FDC *(Feb. 10, 1930)* | | 15.00 |
| | v. Horizontal pair, imperforate between | 5000. | |

**1930. GRAF ZEPPELIN ISSUE** was issued for use on mail carried by the German dirigible, build and commanded by Dr. Hugo Eckener, during various stages of its flight from Germany to the United States and back during May and June. A former newspaper reporter and an early critic of Count Ferdinand von Zeppelin's experiments with dirigibles, Eckener became a pilot and in 1921 manager of the Zeppelin firm.

Although more than a million copies of each value were printed, sales were disappointing. After the stamps were withdrawn from circulation June 30, more than 90 percent of them were destroyed.

A13 *Graf Zeppelin in flight.*

**A13**

| 65¢ | | UnFVF | UseFVF |
|---|---|---|---|
| | **green** *(93,536)* | 325. | 240. |
| | Plate block of 6 | 2750. | |
| | On Flight cover | | 325. |
| | FDC *(April 19, 1930)* | | 1500. |

A14 *Zeppelin spanning the Atlantic.*

**A14**

| | | UnFVF | UseFVF |
|---|---|---|---|
| $1.30 | **yellow brown** (72,248) | 650. | 450. |
| | Plate block of 6 | 5750. | |
| | On Flight cover | | 550. |
| | FDC (April 19, 1930) | | 1100. |

A15 *Zeppelin circling globe.*

**A15**

| | | UnFVF | UseFVF |
|---|---|---|---|
| $2.60 | **blue** (61,296) | 975. | 700. |
| | Plate block of 6 | 8750. | |
| | On Flight cover | | 850. |
| | FDC (April 19, 1930) | | 1200. |

**1931-34. WINGED GLOBE ISSUE** has three values: 5¢, 6¢ and 8¢. the 5¢ stamp is sometimes confused with the 5¢ flat-plate issue of 1930 (A12), but measures 47 3/4mm by 19 1/4mm. *Intaglio (rotary press), perforated 10 1/2 x 11.*

A16-A18 *Winged Globe*

**A16**

| | | UnFVF | UseFVF |
|---|---|---|---|
| 5¢ | **reddish violet** (57,340,000) | 5.50 | .60 |
| | Plate block of 4 | 95.00 | |
| | FDC (Aug. 19, 1931) | | 190. |

**A17**

| | | UnFVF | UseFVF |
|---|---|---|---|
| 6¢ | **orange** (302,205,100) | 2.50 | .35 |
| | Plate block of 4 | 22.50 | |
| | Gutter pair | 400. | |
| | FDC (July 1, 1934) | | 200. |
| | FDC (June 30, 1934) Baltimore, Md. | | 225. |

**A18**

| | | UnFVF | UseFVF |
|---|---|---|---|
| 8¢ | **yellow olive** (76,648,803) | 2.50 | .35 |
| | Plate block of 4 | 40.00 | |
| | Gutter pair | 400. | |
| | FDC (Sept. 26, 1932) | | 17.50 |

**1933. CENTURY OF PROGRESS ZEPPELIN ISSUE** was released in connection with the flight of the *Graf Zeppelin* to the Chicago World's Fair, as a goodwill gesture to publicize the event. Although the stamp remained on sale at the Philatelic Agency at Washington until 1935, sales were disappointing, and more than 90 per cent of the issue was destroyed. *Intaglio, perforated 11.*

A19 *Airship* Graf Zeppelin

**A19**

| | | UnFVF | UseFVF |
|---|---|---|---|
| 50¢ | **green** (324,070) | 90.00 | 75.00 |
| | Plate block of 6 | 800. | |
| | On Flight cover | | 80.00 |
| | FDC (Oct. 2, 1933) | | 200. |

**1935-37. CHINA CLIPPER OVER PACIFIC ISSUE** released primarily to pay postage on mail carried over the transpacific airmail route. *Intaglio, perforated 11.*

A20 China Clipper *over Pacific*

**A20**

| | | UnFVF | UseFVF |
|---|---|---|---|
| 20¢ | **green** (12,794,600) | 10.00 | 1.50 |
| | dark green | 10.00 | 1.50 |
| | Plate block of 6 | 110. | |
| | FDC (Feb. 15, 1937) | | 60.00 |

**A21**

| | | UnFVF | UseFVF |
|---|---|---|---|
| 25¢ | **blue** (10,205,400) | 1.50 | 1.00 |
| | Plate block of 6 | 22.50 | |
| | FDC (Nov. 22, 1935) | | 50.00 |

**A22**

| | | UnFVF | UseFVF |
|---|---|---|---|
| 50¢ | **carmine** (9,285,300) | 10.00 | 4.50 |
| | Plate block of 6 | 110. | |
| | FDC (Feb. 15, 1937) | | 65.00 |

**1938. EAGLE AND SHIELD ISSUE** originally designed by Franklin D. Roosevelt, was issued to coincide with the U.S. Post Office Department's promotion of National Air Week. *Intaglio, perforated 11.*

A23 *Eagle and Shield*

**A23**

| | | UnFVF | UseFVF |
|---|---|---|---|
| 6¢ | **indigo and carmine** (349,946,500) | .50 | .20 |
| | ultramarine & carmine | .40 | .20 |
| | Block of 4, w/arrow | 7.50 | |
| | Center line block | 2.50 | .90 |
| | Plate block of 10, 2 plate numbers, arrow, 2 "TOP" & 2 registration markers | 15.00 | |
| | FDC (May 14, 1938) | | 17.50 |
| | v. Horizontal pair, imperforate vertically | 10000. | |
| | v1. Vertical pair, imperforate horizontally | 350. | |

**1939. TRANSATLANTIC ISSUE** a final Winged Globe design, celebrates the inauguration of transatlantic Airmail serive. *Intaglio, perforated 11.*

A24 *Winged Globe*

**A24**

| | | UnFVF | UseFVF |
|---|---|---|---|
| 30¢ | **slate blue** (19,768,150) | 9.00 | 1.50 |
| | Plate block of 6 | 150. | |
| | On Flight cover | | 5.00 |
| | FDC (May 16, 1939) | | 55.00 |

**1941-44. TWIN MOTORED TRANSPORT PLANE ISSUE** consist of seven denominations that were intended to cover all airmail postage requirements. Except for the color and denomination, all of the stamps are of the same design. *Intaglio, perforated 11 x 10 1/2.*

A25-a31 *Twin motored transport plane.*

**A25**

| | | MNHVF | UseVF |
|---|---|---|---|
| 6¢ | **rose red** (4,746,527,700) | .25 | .20 |
| | Plate block of 4 | 1.00 | |
| | Vertical gutter pair | 200. | |
| | Horizontal gutter pair | — | 6.00 |
| | FDC (June 25, 1941) | | 5.00 |
| | v. Horizontal pair, imperforate between | 1500. | |
| | n. Booklet pane of 3 | 2.95 | 3.00 |
| | FDC (March 18, 1943) | | 35.00 |

| A26 | | MNHVF | UseVF |
|---|---|---|---|
| 8¢ | **light olive green** (1,744,878,650) | .30 | .20 |
| | Plate block of 4 | 2.00 | |
| | Gutter pair | 300. | |
| | FDC (March 21, 1944) | | 6.00 |

| A27 | | MNHVF | UseVF |
|---|---|---|---|
| 10¢ | **violet** (67,117,400) | 1.40 | .20 |
| | Plate block of 4 | 11.00 | |
| | FDC (Aug. 15, 1941) | | 10.00 |

| A28 | | MNHVF | UseVF |
|---|---|---|---|
| 15¢ | **brown carmine** (78,434,800) | 2.75 | .40 |
| | Plate block of 4 | 12.50 | |
| | FDC (Aug. 19, 1941) | | 10.00 |

| A29 | | MNHVF | UseVF |
|---|---|---|---|
| 20¢ | **emerald** (42,359,850) | 2.75 | .40 |
| | Plate block of 4 | 12.50 | |
| | FDC (Aug. 27, 1941) | | 12.50 |

| A30 | | MNHVF | UseVF |
|---|---|---|---|
| 30¢ | **light blue** (59,880,850) | 2.75 | .50 |
| | Plate block of 4 | 14.00 | |
| | FDC (Sept. 25, 1941) | | 17.50 |

| A31 | | MNHVF | UseVF |
|---|---|---|---|
| 50¢ | **orange** (11,160,600) | 14.00 | 4.00 |
| | Plate block of 4 | 90.00 | |
| | FDC (Oct. 29, 1941) | | 32.50 |

**1946. SKYMASTER ISSUE** was released to prepay the new 5¢ airmail rate. *Intaglio, perforated 11 x 10 1/2.*

A32 *DC-4 Skymaster*

| A32 | | MNHVF | UseVF |
|---|---|---|---|
| 5¢ | **carmine** (864,753,100) | .25 | .20 |
| | Plate block of 4 | .75 | |
| | FDC (Sept. 25, 1946) | | 2.00 |

**1947. SMALL 5¢ SKYMASTER ISSUE** *Intaglio perforated 10 horizontally.*

A33 *DC-4 Skymaster*

| A33 | | MNHVF | UseVF |
|---|---|---|---|
| 5¢ | **carmine** (971,903,700) | .25 | .20 |
| | Plate block of 4 | .75 | |
| | FDC (March 26, 1947) | | 2.00 |

**1947. SMALL 5¢ SKYMASTER COIL ISSUE** replaced the large 5¢ stamp of 1946. *Intaglio, perforated 10 1/2 x 11.*

| A34 | | MNHVF | UseVF |
|---|---|---|---|
| 5¢ | **carmine** (33,244,500) | 1.00 | 1.00 |
| | Pair | 1.50 | |
| | Line pair | 9.00 | |
| | FDC (Jan. 15, 1948) | | 2.00 |

**1947. PICTORIAL AIRMAIL ISSUE** consist of three denominations intended to cover international air postage rates. *Intaglio, perforated 11 x 10 1/2.*

A35 *Pan-American Union Building, Washington.*

| A35 | | MNHVF | UseVF |
|---|---|---|---|
| 10¢ | **black** (207,976,550) | .40 | .20 |
| | Plate block of 4 | 1.40 | |
| | FDC (Aug. 30, 1947) | | 2.00 |
| | p. Dry printing | .75 | .25 |
| | Plate block of 4 | 2.75 | |

A36 15¢: Statue of Liberty and Skyline of New York.

| A36 | | MNHVF | UseVF |
|---|---|---|---|
| 15¢ | **blue green** (756,186,350) | .50 | .20 |
| | Plate block of 4 | 2.25 | |
| | Gutter pair | 625. | |
| | FDC (Aug. 20, 1947) | | 2.50 |
| | p. Dry printing | .75 | .25 |
| | Plate block of 4 | 3.25 | |
| | v. Horizontal pair, imperforate between | 2000. | |

A37 25¢: San Francisco- Oakland Bay Bridge

| A37 | | MNHVF | UseVF |
|---|---|---|---|
| 25¢ | **blue** (132,956,100) | 1.25 | .20 |
| | Plate block of 4 | 5.00 | |
| | FDC (July 31, 1947) | | 3.00 |
| | p. Dry printing | 1.50 | .40 |
| | Plate block of 4 | 7.00 | |

**1948. NEW YORK CITY ISSUE** commemorates the 50th anniversary of the consolidation of the five boroughs of New York City. *Intaglio, perforated 11 x 10 1/2.*

A38 *Map of the five boroughs encompassed by wedding ring.*

| A38 | | MNHVF | UseVF |
|---|---|---|---|
| 5¢ | **carmine red** (38,449,100) | .25 | .20 |
| | Plate block of 4 | 4.00 | |
| | FDC (July 31, 1948) | | 2.50 |

**1949. SMALL 6¢ SKYMASTER ISSUE** reflects the raise in rates to 6¢ for domestic airmail. *Intaglio, perforated 10 1/2 x 11.*

A39-A40 *DC-4 Skymaster*

| A39 | | MNHVF | UseVF |
|---|---|---|---|
| 6¢ | **carmine** (5,070,095,200) | .25 | .20 |
| | Plate block of 4 | .75 | |
| | FDC (Jan. 18, 1949) | | 2.00 |
| | n. Booklet pane of 6 (C39a) | 12.50 | 7.50 |
| | FDC (Nov. 18, 1949) | | 12.50 |
| | p. Dry printing | .75 | .30 |
| | Plate block of 4 | 3.50 | |
| | pn. Booklet pane of 6 | 25.00 | |

**1949. SMALL 6¢ SKYMASTER COIL ISSUE** *Intaglio, perforated 10 horizontally.*

| A40 | | MNHVF | UseVF |
|---|---|---|---|
| 6¢ | carmine | 3.50 | .20 |
| | Pair | 6.00 | |
| | Line pair | 14.00 | |
| | FDC (Aug. 25, 1949) | | 2.00 |

**1949. ALEXANDRIA BICENTENNIAL ISSUE** commemorates the 200th anniversary of the founding of Alexandria, Va. *Intaglio, perforated 11 x 10 1/2.*

A41 *Carlyle House, Alexandria seal and Gadsby's Tavern.*

| A41 | | MNHVF | UseVF |
|---|---|---|---|
| 6¢ | carmine (75,085,000) | .20 | .20 |
| | Plate block of 4 | .75 | |
| | FDC (May 11, 1949) | | 2.25 |

**1949. UNIVERSAL POSTAL UNION ISSUE** commemorates the 75th anniversary of the formation of the Universal Postal Union.

A42 *Post Office Department Building, Washington.*

| A42 | | MNHVF | UseVF |
|---|---|---|---|
| 10¢ | violet (21,061,300) | .40 | .30 |
| | Plate block of 4 | 1.50 | |
| | FDC (Nov. 18, 1949) | | 2.00 |

A43 *Globe surrounded by doves.*

| A43 | | MNHVF | UseVF |
|---|---|---|---|
| 15¢ | cobalt (36,613,100) | .50 | .40 |
| | Plate block of 4 | 2.00 | |
| | FDC (Oct. 7, 1949) | | 3.50 |

A44 *Plane and globe.*

| A44 | | MNHVF | UseVF |
|---|---|---|---|
| 25¢ | carmine (16,217,100) | .85 | .60 |
| | Plate block of 4 | 6.50 | |
| | FDC (Nov. 30, 1949) | | 4.50 |

**1949. WRIGHT BROTHERS ISSUE** commemorates the 46th anniversary of Wilbur and Orville Wright's first flight. On Dec. 17, 1903, at Kill Devil Hill, south of Kitty Hawk, N.C., Orville took the plane aloft for 12 seconds over a distance of 120 feet. Wilbur flew 59 seconds over a distance of 825 feet in the fourth flight that day. *Intaglio, perforated 11.*

A45 *Wright Brothers and their plane.*

| A45 | | MNHVF | UseVF |
|---|---|---|---|
| 6¢ | carmine purple (80,405,000) | .30 | .20 |
| | Plate block of 4 | 1.25 | |
| | FDC (Dec. 17, 1949) | | 2.25 |

**1952. HAWAII AIRMAIL ISSUE** provided a stamp to pay postage on one pound of air parcel post to the eight domestic zones (over 1,800 miles). *Intaglio, perforated 11 x 10 1/2.*

A46 *Diamond Head at Honolulu, Hawaii.*

| A46 | | MNHVF | UseVF |
|---|---|---|---|
| 80¢ | bright purple (18,876,800) | 6.00 | 1.50 |
| | Plate block of 4 | 32.50 | |
| | FDC (March 26, 1952) | | 17.50 |

**1953. POWERED FLIGHT ISSUE** marks the 50th anniversary of the Wright brothers first flight. *Intaglio, perforated 11 x 10 1/2.*

A47 *Old and new planes with slogan.*

| A47 | | MNHVF | UseVF |
|---|---|---|---|
| 6¢ | carmine (78,415,000) | .25 | .20 |
| | Plate block of 4 | .80 | |
| | FDC (May 29, 1953) | | 2.25 |

**1954. EAGLE ISSUE** was intended primarily for use on domestic airmail postcards. *Intaglio, perforated 11 x 10 1/2.*

A48,50 *Eagle in Flight*

| A48 | | MNHVF | UseVF |
|---|---|---|---|
| 4¢ | blue (40,483,600) | .25 | .20 |
| | Plate block of 4 | 2.00 | |
| | FDC (Sept. 3, 1954) | | 2.00 |

**1957. AIR FORCE ISSUE** marks the 50th anniversary of the U.S. Air Force. *Intaglio, perforated 11 x 10 1/2.*

A49 *U.S. military aircraft*

| A49 | | MNHVF | UseVF |
|---|---|---|---|
| 6¢ | bright Prussian blue (63,185,000) | .25 | .20 |
| | Plate block of 4 | 1.00 | |
| | FDC (Aug. 1, 1957) | | 2.25 |

**1958. EAGLE ISSUE** was made because of the increase in postage rates August 1. *Intaglio, perforated 11 x 10 1/2.*

| A50 | | MNHVF | UseVF |
|---|---|---|---|
| 5¢ | carmine red (72,480,000) | .25 | .20 |
| | Plate block of 4 | 1.75 | |
| | FDC (July 31, 1958) | | 2.00 |

**1958. JET SILHOUETTE ISSUE** was printed to meet the change in domestic airmail rates Aug. 1. *Intaglio, perforated 10 1/2 x 11.*

A51-A52, A60-A61 *Jet Airliner*

| A51 | | MNHVF | UseVF |
|---|---|---|---|
| 7¢ | blue *(1,326,960,000)* | .25 | .20 |
| | Plate block of 4 | 1.00 | |
| | FDC *(July 31, 1958)* | | 2.00 |
| | n. Booklet pane of 6 | 11.75 | 6.75 |
| | FDC, booklet pane | | 8.50 |

**1958. JET SILHOUETTE COIL ISSUE** *Coil stamp, perforated 10 horizontally.*

| A52 | | MNHVF | UseVF |
|---|---|---|---|
| 7¢ | blue *(157,035,000)* | 2.00 | .20 |
| | Pair | 3.50 | |
| | Line pair | 19.00 | |
| | FDC *(July 31, 1958)* | | 2.00 |
| | Small perfs | 10.00 | |
| | Imperforate pair | 150. | |

**1959. ALASKA STATEHOOD ISSUE** commemorates the addition to the union of the 49th state. *Intaglio, perforated 11 x 10 1/2.*

A53 *The "Big Dipper" and North Star superimposed on map of Alaska.*

| A53 | | MNHVF | UseVF |
|---|---|---|---|
| 7¢ | deep blue *(90,055,200)* | .30 | .20 |
| | Plate block of 4 | 1.00 | |
| | FDC *(Jan. 3, 1959)* | | 2.00 |

**1959. BALLOON JUPITER ISSUE** commemorates the 100th anniversary of the first U.S. transmission of airmail by balloon from Lafayette to Crawfordsville, Ind., a distance of 35 miles. *Intaglio, (Giori Press) perforated 11.*

A54 *Crowd watching John Wise ascending on first flight, Aug. 17, 1859.*

| A54 | | MNHVF | UseVF |
|---|---|---|---|
| 7¢ | deep blue and scarlet *(79,290,000)* | .30 | .20 |
| | Plate block of 4 | 1.00 | |
| | FDC *(Aug. 17, 1959)* | | 2.00 |

**1959. PAN AMERICAN GAMES ISSUE** marks the opening of the Pan American Games in Chicago, Ill. *Intaglio, (Giori Press) perforated 11.*

A55 *Runner holding torch.*

| A55 | | MNHVF | UseVF |
|---|---|---|---|
| 10¢ | deep blue and scarlet *(38,770,000)* | .35 | .30 |
| | Plate block of 4 | 1.50 | |
| | FDC *(Aug. 27, 1959)* | | 2.00 |

**1959. HAWAII STATEHOOD ISSUE** commemorates the admission of Hawaii to the Union as the 50th state. *Intaglio, perforated 11 x 10 1/2.*

A56 *Hawaiian warrior and map of islands.*

| A56 | | MNHVF | UseVF |
|---|---|---|---|
| 7¢ | dull scarlet *(84,815,000)* | .30 | .20 |
| | Plate block of 4 | 1.00 | |
| | FDC *(Aug. 27, 1959)* | | 2.00 |

## International Airmail Series

**1960. LIBERTY BELL ISSUE** was created to meet the demand for specific foreign airmail rates. The 10¢ value covered airmail to Central and South America and the West Indies exclusive of Mexico. The 15¢ denomination prepaid airmail postage to Europe and North Africa. The 25¢ stamp was for use to Asia, Africa and the Middle East. *Intaglio, (Giori Press) perforated 11.*

A57 *Liberty Bell*

| A57 | | MNHVF | UseVF |
|---|---|---|---|
| 10¢ | black and green *(39,960,000)* | 1.75 | .80 |
| | Plate block of 4 | 7.50 | |
| | FDC *(June 10, 1960)* | | 2.00 |

**1959. STATUE OF LIBERTY ISSUE** International Airmail Series

A58 *Statue of Liberty*

| A58 | | MNHVF | UseVF |
|---|---|---|---|
| 15¢ | black and orange *(98,160,000)* | .50 | .20 |
| | Plate block of 4 | 2.50 | |
| | FDC *(Nov. 20, 1959)* | | 2.00 |

**1966. ABRAHAM LINCOLN ISSUE** International Airmail Series

A59 *Abraham Lincoln*

| A59 | | MNHVF | UseVF |
|---|---|---|---|
| 25¢ | black and brown purple | .75 | .20 |
| | Plate block of 4 | 3.50 | |
| | FDC *(Apr. 22, 1960)* | | 2.00 |
| | z. Tagged | 1.00 | .40 |
| | Plate block of 4 | 4.50 | |
| | FDC, tagged *(Dec. 29, 1966)* | | 32.50 |

**1960. JET SILHOUETTE ISSUE** returned in a new color to facilitate handling of domestic airmail letters. *Intaglio, perforated 10 1/2 x 11.*

| A60 | | MNHVF | UseVF |
|---|---|---|---|
| 7¢ | **bright red** *(1,289,460,000)* | .25 | .20 |
| | Plate block of 4 | 1.25 | |
| | Gutter pair | 250. | |
| | FDC *(Aug. 12, 1960)* | | 2.00 |
| | n. Booklet pane of 6 | 13.00 | |
| | FDC *(Aug. 19, 1960)* | | 9.00 |

**1960. JET SILHOUETTE COIL ISSUE** International Airmail Series *Coil stamp, perforated 10 horizontally.*

| A61 | | MNHVF | UseVF |
|---|---|---|---|
| 7¢ | **bright red** *(87,140,000)* | 4.50 | .40 |
| | Pair | 7.50 | |
| | Line pair | 42.50 | |
| | FDC *(Oct. 22, 1960)* | | 2.00 |

**1961. STATUE OF LIBERTY ISSUE** International Airmail Series is a revision of the 1959 15¢ Statue of Liberty airmail stamp (A58), showing a revised frame line around the statue engraving. *Intaglio, (Giori Press) perforated 11.*

A62 Statue of Liberty, *redesigned frame line.*

| A62 | | MNHVF | UseVF |
|---|---|---|---|
| 15¢ | **black and orange** | .50 | .20 |
| | Plate block of 4 | 2.50 | |
| | FDC *(Jan. 13, 1961)* | | 2.00 |
| | z. Tagged | 1.50 | .75 |
| | Plate block of 4 | 16.50 | |
| | FDC *(Jan. 11, 1967)* | | 32.50 |
| | vz. Horizontal pair, imperforate vertically | 11500. | |

**1961. LIBERTY BELL ISSUE** International Airmail Series is a new denomination and color required because of new increased postal rates. *Intaglio (Giori Press, perforated 11.*

A63 *Liberty Bell*

| A63 | | MNHVF | UseVF |
|---|---|---|---|
| 13¢ | **black and scarlet** | .50 | .20 |
| | Plate block of 4 | 2.00 | |
| | FDC *(June 28, 1961)* | | 2.00 |
| | z. Tagged | .60 | .30 |
| | Plate block of 4 | 2.50 | |
| | FDC *(Feb. 15, 1967)* | | 32.50 |

**1962. AIRLINE OVER CAPITOL ISSUE** was made available to meet the increase in postage rates. *Rotary press printing, perforated 10 1/2 x 11.* Although this stamp was issued December 6, 1962, an experiment was started on August 1, 1963, in Dayton, Ohio, in which a luminescent ink was applied to these air mail stamps. The phosphor-tagged stamps, in conjunction with an ultraviolet sensing device, sped up air mail service.

A64 *Air mail carrier over Capitol dome.*

| A64 | | MNHVF | UseVF |
|---|---|---|---|
| 8¢ | **carmine** | .30 | .20 |
| | Plate block of 4 | 1.25 | |
| | FDC *(Dec. 5, 1962)* | | 2.00 |
| | n. Booklet pane of 5, plus Mailman label | 5.00 | |
| | n1. Booklet pane of 5, plus Zip label | | 14.50 |
| | n2. Booklet pane of 5, plus Zone # label | 70.00 | |
| | FDC *(Dec. 15, 1962)* | | 2.00 |
| | p1. Printed on Hi-brite paper | — | — |
| | Plate block of 4 | — | |
| | p1n. Booklet pane of 5, plus Mailman label | — | — |
| | z. Tagged, Type I | .35 | .20 |
| | Plate block of 4 | 1.75 | |
| | FDC *(Dayton, Ohio, Aug. 1, 1963)* | | 2.00 |
| | z1. Tagged, Type II or IIa | .35 | .20 |
| | Plate block of 4 | 1.75 | |
| | z1n. Booklet pane of 5, plus Zip label | 1.65 | 1.25 |

*Type I tagging: mat tagging, using four separate mats that did not cover entire sheet of 400 stamps (untagged areas identify the variety). Stamps from the four corners of a pane have two untagged margins.*

*Type II tagging: roll tagging, where continuous rolls replaced the tagging mats. Only the plate number selvage margin is partially tagged.*

**1962. AIRLINE OVER CAPITOL COIL ISSUE** *Type IIa tagging: wide roll tagging, where all margins are fully tagged.*
Coil stamp, perforated 10 horizontally.

| A65 | | MNHVF | UseVF |
|---|---|---|---|
| 8¢ | **carmine** | .60 | .20 |
| | Pair | .75 | |
| | Line pair | 6.50 | |
| | FDC *(Dec. 5, 1962)* | | 2.00 |
| | p1. On Hi-brite paper | — | — |
| | Pair | — | |
| | Line pair | — | |
| | z. Tagged, Type I | .40 | .20 |
| | Pair | 1.00 | |
| | Line pair | 2.75 | |
| | FDC, tagged *(Jan 14, 1965)* | | 32.50 |
| | z1. Tagged, Type II | .35 | .20 |
| | Pair | 1.00 | |
| | Line pair | 2.75 | |

**1963. MONTGOMERY BLAIR ISSUE** recalls Abraham Lincoln's post-master general and his role in the first universal postal conference in 1863. *Intaglio (Giori Press), perforated 11.*

A66 *Montgomery Blair and mail circling the globe.*

| A66 | | MNHVF | UseVF |
|---|---|---|---|
| 15¢ | **red, maroon and blue** *(42,245,000)* | .75 | .60 |
| | Plate block of 4 | 3.25 | |
| | FDC *(May 3, 1963)* | | 3.00 |

**1963. BALD EAGLE ISSUE** was prepared for use on domestic airmail postcards. *Intaglio, perforated 11 x 10.*

A67 *Bald Eagle*

| A67 | | MNHVF | UseVF |
|---|---|---|---|
| 6¢ | **carmine** | .25 | .20 |
| | Plate block of 4 | 2.00 | |
| | FDC *(July 12, 1963)* | | 2.00 |
| | z. Tagged | 4.50 | 3.50 |
| | Plate block of 4 | 95.00 | |
| | FDC *(Feb. 15, 1967)* | | 55.00 |

**1963. AMELIA EARHART ISSUE** marks the 65th birthday of America's most prominent female aviatrix, the first woman to fly across the Atlantic Ocean, and the first woman to fly across the United States non-stop. She was lost at sea while attempting to fly around the world. *Intaglio (Giori Press, perforated 11.*

A68 *Amelia Earhart*

| A68 | | MNHVF | UseVF |
|---|---|---|---|
| 8¢ | **carmine red and brown purple** | .35 | .20 |
| | (63,890,000) | | |
| | Plate block of 4 | 1.50 | |
| | FDC (July 24, 1963) | | 3.50 |

**1964. ROBERT H. GODDARD ISSUE** marks the 50th anniversary of the first patents granted to Goddard for his multi-stage booster rockets using liquid and solid fuels. *Intaglio (Giori Press), perforated 11.*

A69 *Dr. Goddard, rocket, and launching pad.*

| A69 | | MNHVF | UseVF |
|---|---|---|---|
| 8¢ | **multicolored** (65,170,000) | .45 | .20 |
| | Plate block of 4 | 2.25 | |
| | FDC (Oct. 5, 1964) | | 3.00 |
| | zo. Tagging omitted | — | |

**1967. ALASKA PURCHASE ISSUE** celebrates the 100th anniversary of the acquisition of Alaska from Russia. The date of issue, March 30, is a state holiday honoring Secretary of State William H. Seward, who arranged the sale for $7,200,000. *Intaglio (Giori Press), perforated 11.*

A70 *Totem Pole*

| A70 | | MNHVF | UseVF |
|---|---|---|---|
| 8¢ | **brown and light brown** (64,710,000) | .40 | .20 |
| | Plate block of 4 | 2.00 | |
| | FDC (March 20, 1967) | | 2.00 |

**1967. COLUMBIA JAYS ISSUE** prepared to meet the increase in air mail rates to Europe and Mediterranean Africa. The design is similar to the 1963 5¢ Audubon commemorative (CM526) and was used again because of its aesthetic and technical excellence. *Intaglio (Giori Press), perforated 11.*

A71 *John J. Audubon's Columbia Jays*

| A71 | | MNHVF | UseVF |
|---|---|---|---|
| 20¢ | **blue, brown and yellow,** tagged | 1.25 | .20 |
| | (165,430,000) | | |
| | Plate block of 4 | 4.50 | |
| | FDC (April 26, 1967) | | 3.00 |
| | zo. Tagging omitted | — | |

**1968. STAR RUNWAY ISSUE** met the increase in airmail rates that went into effect Jan. 7, 1968. *Intaglio, perforated 11 x 10 1/2.*

A72 *Poster type art showing 50 stars.*

| A72 | | MNHVF | UseVF |
|---|---|---|---|
| 10¢ | **red,** tagged | .40 | .20 |
| | Plate block of 4 | 1.35 | |
| | FDC (Jan. 5, 1968) | | 2.00 |
| | n. Booklet pane of 5 plus Mail Early label | 3.75 | 3.50 |
| | n1. Booklet pane of 5 plus Zip slogan label | 3.75 | 3.50 |
| | n2. Booklet pane of 8 | 2.50 | 2.25 |
| | n2z. Booklet pane of 8, tagging glows yellow rather than red orange | — | |
| | zo. Tagging omitted | — | |
| | zon1. Booklet pane of 8 | — | |
| | zon2. Booklet pane of 5 plus Mail Early label | — | |
| | zon3. Booklet pane of 5 plus Zip slogan label | — | |
| | Booklet pair, imperforate between vertically | 1750. | |

**1968. STAR RUNWAY COIL ISSUE** *Coil stamp, perforated 10 horizontally.*

| A73 | | MNHVF | UseVF |
|---|---|---|---|
| 10¢ | **red** | .40 | .20 |
| | Pair | .75 | |
| | Line pair | 2.00 | |
| | FDC (Jan. 5, 1968) | | 1.75 |
| | v. Imperforate pair | 625. | |

**1968. AIRMAIL SERVICE ISSUE** commemorates the 50th anniversary of the service, established May 15, 1918, when mail was carried by biplane on the Washington-New York flight. *Intaglio (Giori Press) and offset, perforated 11.*

A74 *Curtiss Jenny*

| A74 | | MNHVF | UseVF |
|---|---|---|---|
| 10¢ | **black, red and blue** (74,180,000) | .40 | .20 |
| | Plate block of 4 | 2.75 | |
| | FDC (May 15, 1968) | | 2.00 |
| | v. Red stripe on tail omitted | 3000. | |
| | zo. Tagging omitted | — | |

**1968. USA AND JET ISSUE** intended primarily for mail to Europe and points in North Africa. *Intaglio and offset, perforated 11.*

A75, A81 *"USA" and airplane*

| A75 | | MNHVF | UseVF |
|---|---|---|---|
| 20¢ | **multicolored** | .75 | .20 |
| | Plate block of 4 | 3.00 | |
| | FDC *(Nov. 22, 1968)* | | 2.00 |
| | zo. Tagging omitted | — | |

**1969. MOON LANDING ISSUE** paid tribute to the landing of a man on the Moon July 20, 1969, when Neil A. Armstrong and Col. Edwin E. Aldrin Jr., became the first humans to land on the lunar surface. The engraved master die from which the stamps were printed was carried to the Moon by the astronauts. *Intaglio and offset, perforated 11.*

A76 *First Man on the Moon*

| A76 | | MNHVF | UseVF |
|---|---|---|---|
| 10¢ | **multicolored,** *(152,364,800)* | .40 | .20 |
| | Plate block of 4 | 1.65 | |
| | FDC *(Sept. 9, 1969)* | | 5.50 |
| | v. Offset red omitted | 550. | |

*A76v. must have missing red from the entire design; including the dots on top of the yellow area as well as the astronaut's shoulder patch. Stamps with any red present are worth far less than the true red-omitted error.*

**1971. DELTA WING SILHOUETTE ISSUE** created to meet increases in domestic and international rates.
*Intaglio, perforated 10 1/2 x 11.*

A77 *Silhouette of delta wing plane.*

| A77 | | MNHVF | UseVF |
|---|---|---|---|
| 9¢ | **red** *(25,830,000)* | .30 | .20 |
| | Plate block of 4 | 1.30 | |
| | FDC *(May 15, 1971)* | | 2.00 |

**1971. JET SILOUETTE ISSUE** *Intaglio, perforated 11 x 10 1/2.*

A78-A79 *Silhouette of jet airliner.*

| A78 | | MNHVF | UseVF |
|---|---|---|---|
| 11¢ | **red,** *(317,810,000)* tagged | .40 | .20 |
| | Plate block of 4 | 1.50 | |
| | FDC *(May 7, 1971)* | | 2.00 |
| | n. Booklet pane of 4 plus 2 labels | 1.50 | |
| | zo. Tagging omitted | — | |
| | zx. Untagged (Bureau precancel) | .60 | |
| | FDC | | 80.00 |

**1971. JET SILHOUETTE COIL ISSUE** *Coil stamp, perforated 10 vertically.*

| A79 | | MNHVF | UseVF |
|---|---|---|---|
| 11¢ | **red** | .40 | .20 |
| | Pair | .75 | |
| | Line pair | .90 | |
| | FDC *(May 7, 1971)* | | 2.00 |
| | v. Imperforate pair | 275. | |

**1971. HEAD OF LIBERTY ISSUE** *Intaglio (Giori Press), perforated 11.*

A80 *Head of Liberty*

| A80 | | MNHVF | UseVF |
|---|---|---|---|
| 17¢ | **multicolored,** tagged | .60 | .20 |
| | Plate block of 4 | 2.25 | |
| | FDC *(July 13, 1971)* | | 2.00 |
| | zo. Tagging omitted | — | |

**1971. JET AND "USA" ISSUE** *Intaglio (Giori Press) and offset, perforated 11.*

| A81 | | MNHVF | UseVF |
|---|---|---|---|
| 21¢ | **multicolored,** *(49,815,000)* tagged | .75 | .20 |
| | Plate block of 4 | 3.00 | |
| | FDC *(May 21, 1971)* | | 2.00 |
| | zo. Tagging omitted | — | |
| | v. Black omitted | — | |

**1972. NATIONAL PARK ISSUE** is part of the National Parks Centennial series (see CM674-CM680). The City of Refuge depicted is an ancient sanctuary for taboo breakers or victims of wars on a lava ledge on the southwestern part of the island of Hawaii. *Intaglio (Giori Press) and offset, perforated 11.*

A82 *Wooden statue and palisaded temple.*

| A82 | | MNHVF | UseVF |
|---|---|---|---|
| 11¢ | **multicolored** *(78,210,000)* | .35 | .20 |
| | Plate block of 4 | 1.75 | |
| | FDC *(May 3, 1972)* | | 2.00 |
| | v. Blue and green omitted | 1000. | |
| | zo. Tagging omitted | — | |

**1972. OLYMPIC ISSUE** Released as part of the Olympic series (see CM686) for the Winter and Summer Games held in Japan and Germany. *Gravure, perforated 11 x 10 1/2.*

A83 *Skiing*

| A83 | | MNHVF | UseVF |
|---|---|---|---|
| 11¢ | **multicolored** *(92,710,000)* | .40 | .20 |
| | Plate block of 10 | 3.75 | |
| | FDC *(Aug. 17, 1972)* | | 2.00 |

**1973. PROGRESS IN ELECTRONICS ISSUE** was the fourth stamp and only airmail in a set commemorating advances in electronic communication. (see CM721-CM723). *Intaglio (Giori Press) and offset, perforated 11.*

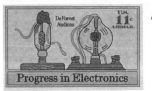
A84 *Lee DeForest's audion*

| A84 | | MNHVF | UseVF |
|---|---|---|---|
| 11¢ | **multicolored,** *(56,000,000)* tagged | .30 | .20 |
| | Plate block of 4 | 1.40 | |
| | FDC *(July 10, 1973)* | | 2.00 |
| | v. Vermilion and olive omitted | 1400. | |
| | zo. Tagging omitted | — | |

## 1973. WINGED ENVELOPE ISSUE was created to meet the basic domestic airmail letter rate increase. *Intaglio, perforated 11 x 10 1/2.*

A85, A86 *"Flying Envelope"*

| A85 | | MNHVF | UseVF |
|---|---|---|---|
| 13¢ | **red,** tagged | .40 | .20 |
| | Plate block of 4 | 1.60 | |
| | FDC *(Nov. 16, 1973)* | | 2.00 |
| | n. Booklet pane of 5 plus label *(Dec. 27, 1973)* | 1.75 | 1.50 |
| | zo. Tagging omitted (without precancel) | — | |
| | zx. Untagged (Bureau precancel) | .50 | .20 |

## 1973. WINGED ENVELOPE COIL ISSUE Coil stamp, perforated 10 vertically.

| A86 | | MNHVF | UseVF |
|---|---|---|---|
| 13¢ | **Red** | .50 | .20 |
| | Pair | .75 | |
| | Line pair | 1.25 | |
| | FDC *(Dec. 27, 1973)* | | 2.00 |
| | v. Imperforate pair | 75.00 | |

## 1974. STATUE OF LIBERTY ISSUE were released to meet increases in airmail rates to foreign destinations. *Intaglio (Giori Press) perforated 11.*

A87 *Statue of Liberty*

| A87 | | MNHVF | UseVF |
|---|---|---|---|
| 18¢ | **multicolored,** tagged | .60 | .50 |
| | Plate block of 4 | 2.50 | |
| | FDC *(Jan. 11, 1974)* | | 2.00 |
| | zo. Tagging omitted | — | |

## 1974. MOUNT RUSHMORE ISSUE

| A88 | | MNHVF | UseVF |
|---|---|---|---|
| 26¢ | **multicolored,** tagged | .75 | .20 |
| | Plate block of 4 | 3.50 | |
| | Gutter pair | 200. | |
| | FDC *(Jan. 2, 1974)* | | 2.00 |
| | zo. Tagging omitted | — | |

## 1976. PLANE AND GLOBES ISSUE was released to meet increases in airmail rates to foreign destinations. *Intaglio (Giori Press), perforated 11.*

A89 *Stylized Aircraft*

| A89 | | MNHVF | UseVF |
|---|---|---|---|
| 25¢ | **multicolored,** tagged | .75 | .20 |
| | Plate block of 4 | 3.25 | |
| | FDC *(Jan. 2, 1976)* | | 2.00 |
| | zo. Tagging omitted | — | |

## 1976. GLOBAL VIEWS ISSUE

A90 *Global views*

| A90 | | MNHVF | UseVF |
|---|---|---|---|
| 31¢ | **multicolored,** tagged | .90 | .20 |
| | Plate block of 4 | 4.00 | |
| | FDC *(Jan. 2, 1976)* | | 2.00 |
| | zo. Tagging omitted | — | |

## Pioneers of Aviation Series

**1978. ORVILLE AND WILBUR WRIGHT ISSUE** the first stamps in the Pioneers of Aviation series, marked the 75th anniversary of Orville and Wilbur Wright's historic first powered flight in 1903. *Intaglio (Giori Press) and offset, perforated 11.*

A91, A92 *Orville and Wilbur Wright, aviation pioneers.*

| A91 | | MNHVF | UseVF |
|---|---|---|---|
| 31¢ | **multicolored,** large portraits and bi-plane | 1.75 | 1.50 |
| A92 | | MNHVF | UseVF |
| 31¢ | **multicolored,** Small portraits bi-plane and hanger | 1.75 | 1.50 |
| | Plate block of 4 | 4.00 | |
| | y. Se-tenant pair A91-92 | 1.75 | |
| | FDC pair *(Sept. 23, 1978)* | | 3.00 |
| | vy. Pair with intaglio black omitted | — | |
| | v1y. Pair with intaglio, black & ultramarine omitted | 800. | |
| | v2y. Pair with offset black, yellow, magenta, blue & brown omitted | 2500. | |

**1978. OCTAVE CHANUTE ISSUE** Pioneers of Aviation Series honors the biplane hang glider designed by Chanute which became a standard for future glider design. Pioneers of Aviation series. *Intaglio (Giori Press) and offset, perforated 11.*

A93, A94 *Octave Chanute, aviaton pioneer.*

**A93**

| | | MNHVF | UseVF |
|---|---|---|---|
| 21¢ | large portrait | 1.75 | 1.50 |

**A94**

| | | MNHVF | UseVF |
|---|---|---|---|
| 21¢ | **multicolored,** small portrait | 1.75 | 1.50 |
| | Plate block of 4 | 4.75 | |
| | y. Se-tenant pair A93-94 | | |
| | FDC pair *(March 29, 1978)* | | 3.00 |
| | vy. Pair with intaglio, black omitted | — | |
| | v1y.Pair with Intaglio black & ultramarine omitted | 4750. | |

## The 1980 Olympic Games Series

**1979. HIGH JUMPER ISSUE** features a high jumper in action. (See also CM925-28, CM932-35.) *Gravure, perforated 11.*

A95 *High jumper*

**A95**

| | | MNHVF | UseVF |
|---|---|---|---|
| 31¢ | **multicolored,** tagged | 1.00 | .35 |
| | Plate block of 12 | 12.50 | |
| | FDC *(Nov. 1, 1979)* | | 2.00 |

**1979. WILEY POST ISSUE** Pioneers of Aviation Series honors the aviator famous for record-making flights, scientific research and aircraft designs. *Intaglio (Giori Press) and offset, perforated 11.*

A96, A97 *Wiley Post, aviation pioneer.*

**A96**

| | | MNHVF | UseVF |
|---|---|---|---|
| 25¢ | large portrait, tagged | 3.00 | 2.00 |

**A97**

| | | MNHVF | UseVF |
|---|---|---|---|
| 25¢ | small portrait, tagged | 3.00 | 2.00 |
| | Plate block of 4 | 9.00 | |
| | y. Se-tenant pair A96-97 | 3.75 | |
| | FDC pair *(Nov. 20, 1979)* | | 3.00 |

**1982. PHILIP MAZZEI ISSUE** honors the Italian-American patriot. He collaborated with the leaders of Virginia on political ideas and promoted independence through writings published in America and in Europe. *Gravure, perforated 11.*

A98 *Philip Mazzei*

**A98**

| | | MNHVF | UseVF |
|---|---|---|---|
| 40¢ | **multicolored,** tagged | 1.25 | .25 |
| | Plate block of 12 | 15.00 | |
| | FDC *(Oct. 13, 1980)* | | 2.00 |
| | v. Horizontal pair, imperforate vertically | — | |
| | v1. Imperforate pair | 3500. | |
| | v2. Perforated 10 1/2 x 11 (1982) | — | |
| | zo. Tagging omitted | — | |

**1980. BLANCHE STUART SCOTT ISSUE** Pioneers of Aviation Series commemorates the first American woman to make a solo flight in early September 1910. *Gravure, perforated 11.*

A99 *Blanche Stuart Scott*

**A99**

| | | MNHVF | UseVF |
|---|---|---|---|
| 28¢ | **multicolored,** tagged | .90 | .25 |
| | Plate block of 12 | 12.50 | |
| | FDC *(Dec. 30, 1980)* | | 2.00 |

**1980. GLENN CURTISS ISSUE** Pioneers of Aviation Series honors an early aviator and noted aircraft designer and manufacturer principally remembered for his invention and development of the aileron, and for his design and production of the first successful seaplanes and amphibious airplanes. *Gravure, perforated 11.*

A100 *Glenn Curtiss*

**A100**

| | | MNHVF | UseVF |
|---|---|---|---|
| 35¢ | **multicolored,** tagged | 1.00 | .25 |
| | Plate block of 12 | 12.50 | |
| | FDC *(Dec. 30, 1980)* | | 2.00 |

**1983. OLYMPIC ISSUES** three se-tenant blocks of four commemorates the 1984 Summer Olympic Games in Los Angeles, Calif. *Gravure, bullseye perforated 11 1/4.*

A101-104

**A101**

| | | MNHVF | UseVF |
|---|---|---|---|
| 40¢ | Men's shot put, tagged | 1.25 | .25 |
| | v. Line perforated 11 | — | |

**A102**

| | | MNHVF | UseVF |
|---|---|---|---|
| 40¢ | Mens gymnastics, tagged | 1.25 | .25 |
| | v. Line perforated 11 | | |

**A103**

| | | MNHVF | UseVF |
|---|---|---|---|
| 40¢ | Women's swimming, tagged | 1.25 | .25 |
| | v. Line perforated 11 | — | |

**A104**

| | | MNHVF | UseVF |
|---|---|---|---|
| 40¢ | Mens weight lifting, tagged | 1.25 | .25 |
| | Plate block of 4 | 6.50 | |
| | y. Se-tenant block of 4, A101-104 | 4.00 | |
| | FDC *(April 8, 1983)*, block | | 5.00 |
| | v. Line perforated 11 | 1.35 | |
| | Plate block of 4 line perforated 11 | 6.00 | |
| | vy. Se-tenant block of 4 line perforated 11 | 5.00 | |
| | v1y.Imperforate, block of 4 | 12.50 | |

## 1983. Olympics Second Issue *Gravure, perforated 11*

A105-A108

| A105 | | MNHVF | UseVF |
|---|---|---|---|
| 28¢ | Women's gymnastics, tagged | 1.25 | .25 |

| A106 | | MNHVF | UseVF |
|---|---|---|---|
| 28¢ | Mens hurdles, tagged | 1.25 | .25 |

| A107 | | MNHVF | UseVF |
|---|---|---|---|
| 28¢ | Women's basketball, tagged | 1.25 | .25 |

| A108 | | MNHVF | UseVF |
|---|---|---|---|
| 28¢ | Soccer, tagged | 1.25 | .25 |
| | Plate block of 4 | 6.50 | |
| | y. Se-tenant block of 4 A105-108 | 4.00 | |
| | FDC *(June 17, 1983)*, block | | 5.00 |
| | v. Block of 4, imperforate vertically | — | |

## 1983. Olympics Third Issue *Gravure, perforated 11*

A109-A111

| A109 | | MNHVF | UseVF |
|---|---|---|---|
| 35¢ | Fencing, tagged | 1.25 | .25 |

| A110 | | MNHVF | UseVF |
|---|---|---|---|
| 35¢ | Cycling, tagged | 1.25 | .25 |

| A111 | | MNHVF | UseVF |
|---|---|---|---|
| 35¢ | Women's volleyball, tagged | 1.25 | .25 |

| A112 | | MNHVF | UseVF |
|---|---|---|---|
| 35¢ | Pole vaulting, tagged | 1.25 | .25 |
| | Plate block of 4 | 12.50 | |
| | y. Se-tenant block of 4 A109-112 | 6.50 | |
| | FDC *(Nov. 4, 1983)*, block | | 5.00 |

## 1985. Alfred V. Verville Issue
Pioneers of Aviation Series honors the man who designed and produced aircraft with Lawrence Sperry and Glenn Curtiss. *Gravure press, perforated 11/*

A113 *Alfred V. Verville, aviation pioneer.*

| A113 | | MNHVF | UseVF |
|---|---|---|---|
| 33¢ | multicolored, tagged | 1.00 | .30 |
| | Plate block of 4 | 4.50 | |
| | FDC *(Feb. 13, 1985)* | | 1.75 |
| | v. Imperforate pair | 1100. | |

## 1985. Lawrence and Elmer Sperry Issue
Pioneers of Aviation Series commemorates the father/son duo of Elmer Sperry (father) who was awarded over 400 patents, such as the gyro-compass which revolutionized flying and Lawrence Sperry (son), who helped develop and test such aviation innovations as the automatic pilot and retractable landing gear. *Gravure press, perforated 11.*

A114 *Lawrence and Elmer Sperry, aviation pioneers.*

| A114 | | MNHVF | UseVF |
|---|---|---|---|
| 39¢ | multicolored, tagged | 1.25 | .40 |
| | Plate block of 4 | 5.50 | |
| | FDC *(Feb. 13, 1985)* | | 2.00 |
| | v. Imperforate pair | 1500. | |

## 1986. Transpacific Airmail Issue
marks the 50th anniversary of airmail service between the United States and the Far East. *Gravure, perforated 11.*

A115 *Martin M-150 China Clipper*

| A115 | | MNHVF | UseVF |
|---|---|---|---|
| 44¢ | multicolored, tagged | 1.25 | .40 |
| | Plate block of 4 | 6.00 | |
| | FDC *(Feb. 15, 1985)* | | 2.00 |
| | v. Imperforate pair | 1100. | |

## 1985. Junipero Serra Issue
honors the Franciscan friar (1713-84) who founded the California missions. *Gravure, perforated 11.*

A116 *Fr. Junipero Serra and San Gabriel Mission.*

| A116 | | MNHVF | UseVF |
|---|---|---|---|
| 44¢ | multicolored, tagged | 1.75 | .60 |
| | Plate block of 4 | 11.50 | |
| | FDC *(Aug. 22, 1985)* | | 2.50 |
| | v. Imperforate pair | 18.50 | |

## 1988. Settlement of New Sweden Issue
honors the 350th anniversary of colony established by Peter Minuit. Sweden and Finland released stamps the same day (Sweden 1460, Finland 1077) with a common design to that issued by the United States. *Intaglio and offset, perforated 11.*

A117 *Illustration from a 1602 book on the New Sweden Colony.*

**A117**

| | | MNHVF | UseVF |
|---|---|---|---|
| **44¢** | **multicolored, tagged** *(22,975,000)* | 1.40 | .50 |
| | Plate block of 4 | 9.00 | |
| | FDC *(March 29, 1988)* | 2.50 | |

**1988. SAMUEL P. LANGLEY ISSUE** Pioneers of Aviation Series honors the early pioneer flight engineer and the 70th anniversary of airmail service. Langley's early experiments in mechanical flight laid the groundwork for the Wright brothers, Glenn Curtiss and others. *Intaglio and offset, perforated 11.*

A118 *Samuel P. Langley, unmanned Aerodrome No. 5.*

**A118**

| | | MNHVF | UseVF |
|---|---|---|---|
| **45¢** | **multicolored,** tagged | 1.40 | .30 |
| | Plate block of 4 | 6.00 | |
| | FDC *(May 14, 1988)* | | 2.50 |
| | v. Overall tagged | 2.00 | .50 |
| | Plate block of 4 | 10.00 | |

**1988. IGOR SIKORSKY ISSUE** Pioneers of Aviation Series paid tribute to the man who designed and built many early helicopters. *Intaglio and offset, perforated 11.*

A119 *Igor Sikorsky and VS-300*

**A119**

| | | MNHVF | UseVF |
|---|---|---|---|
| **36¢** | **multicolored,** tagged | 1.25 | .40 |
| | Plate block of 4 | 6.00 | |
| | FDC *(June 23, 1988)* | | 2.50 |

*Traces of red have been detected in all copies of a so-called "red omitted" error of this stamp. Such stamps, on which even minute traces of red are present, are worth far less than a genuine color-omitted error would be.*

**1989. FRENCH REVOLUTION BICENTENNIAL ISSUE** part of a joint issue with France, was released both in Washington D.C., and in Paris. *Offset and intaglio, perforated 11 1/2 x 11.*

A120 *Liberte, Egalite and Fraternite.*

**A120**

| | | MNHVF | UseVF |
|---|---|---|---|
| **45¢** | **multicolored,** *(38,532,000)* tagged | 1.40 | .40 |
| | Plate block of 4 | 6.00 | |
| | FDC *(July 14, 1989)* | | 2.50 |

**1989. AMERICA ISSUE** depicts a rare wooden native sculpture of the Pre-Columbian era, was one of a pair of U.S. stamps (with CM1360) that were the first stamps issued by 24 postal administrations commemorating the 500th anniversary of Christopher Columbus's arrival in America. Part of a 1989-91 Columbian series by members of the Postal Union of the Americas and Spain (PUAS). *Gravure by American Book Note Co., perforated 11.*

A121 *Key Marco Cat, Calusa culture, pre-columbian period.*

**A121**

| | | MNHVF | UseVF |
|---|---|---|---|
| **45¢** | **multicolored,** *(39,325,000)* tagged | 1.50 | .30 |
| | Plate block of 4 | 7.50 | |
| | FDC *(Oct. 12, 1989)* | | 2.00 |

**1989. FUTURE MAIL TRANSPORTATION SOUVENIR SHEET** was part of a group of 11 postal items issued during World Stamp Expo '89 and the 20th Congress of the Universal Postal Union in Washington, D.C. *Offset and intaglio, perforated 11.*

A122a, A123 *Hypersonic airliner.*

A122b, A124 *Hovercraft*

A122c, A125 *Service rover*

A122d, A126 *Space Shuttle*

**A122**

| | | MNHVF | UseVF |
|---|---|---|---|
| **$1.80** | **multicolored,** souvenir sheet, *(1,944,000)* tagged | 7.00 | 5.00 |
| | FDC *(Nov. 24, 1989)* | | 8.00 |
| | a. 45¢ multicolored, tagged | | |
| | b. 45¢ multicolored, tagged | | |
| | c. 45¢ multicolored, tagged | | |
| | d. 45¢ multicolored, tagged | | |

**1989. FUTURE MAIL TRANSPORTATION ISSUE**

A123-126

**A123**

| | | MNHVF | UseVF |
|---|---|---|---|
| **45¢** | Hypersonic airliner, tagged | 1.25 | .25 |

**A124**

| | | MNHVF | UseVF |
|---|---|---|---|
| **45¢** | Hovercraft, tagged | 1.25 | .25 |

**A125**

| | | MNHVF | UseVF |
|---|---|---|---|
| **45¢** | Service rover, tagged | 1.25 | .25 |

**A126**

| | | MNHVF | UseVF |
|---|---|---|---|
| **45¢** | **multicolored,** tagged | 1.25 | .25 |
| | Plate block of 4 | 8.00 | |
| | y. Se-tenant block of 4, A123-26 | 7.00 | |
| | FDC *(Nov. 28, 1989)* | | 9.00 |
| | vy. Plate block of 4 w/light blue omitted | 1150. | |

**1990. AMERICA ISSUE** was the second in the PUAS Columbian series depicting scenes of the natural beauty of America prior to Columbus. *Gravure, perforated 11.*

A127 *Caribbean Coastland*

| A127 | | MNHVF | UseVF |
|---|---|---|---|
| 45¢ | **multicolored,** tagged | 1.50 | .50 |
| | Plate block of 4 | 7.50 | |
| | FDC *(Oct. 12, 1990)* | | 2.50 |

**1991. HARRIET QUIMBY ISSUE** Pioneers of Aviation Series honors the journalist, drama critic and first licensed American woman pilot. *Gravure by Stamp Venturers, perforated 11.*

A128 *Harriet Quimby, Bleriot airplane.*

| A128 | | MNHVF | UseVF |
|---|---|---|---|
| 50¢ | **multicolored,** tagged | 1.50 | .50 |
| | Plate block of 4 | 7.50 | |
| | FDC *(Apr. 27, 1991)* | | 2.50 |
| | v. Vertical pair, imperforate horizontally | 2100. | |

**1991. WILLIAM T. PIPER ISSUE** Pioneers of Aviation Series honors the "Henry Ford of Aviation," the developer of the Piper Cub aircraft. (See also A132). *Gravure by J. W. Fergusson & Sons for the American Bank Note Co., perforated 11.*

A129 *William T. Piper, Piper Club*

| A129 | | MNHVF | UseVF |
|---|---|---|---|
| 40¢ | **multicolored,** tagged | 1.40 | .50 |
| | Plate block of 4 | 6.00 | |
| | FDC *(May 17, 1991)* | | 2.50 |

**1991. ANTARCTIC TREATY ISSUE** honors the 30th anniversary of the 1961 treaty dedicating the region to peaceful purposes. *Gravure by Stamp Venturers, perforated 11.*

A130 *View of McMurdo Sound.*

| A130 | | MNHVF | UseVF |
|---|---|---|---|
| 50¢ | **multicolored,** tagged | 1.50 | .60 |
| | Plate block of 4 | 7.00 | |
| | FDC *(June 21, 1991)* | | 2.50 |

**1991. AMERICA ISSUE** had as its theme "Pre-Columbian Voyages of Discovery," and depicts a prehistoric Asian and the Bering land bridge by which the first native Americans are believed to have come to the Western Hemisphere thousands of years ago. *Gravure, perforated 11.*

A131 *Asian overlooking Bering land bridge.*

| A131 | | MNHVF | UseVF |
|---|---|---|---|
| 50¢ | **multicolored,** tagged | 1.50 | .50 |
| | Plate block of 4 | 7.00 | |
| | FDC *(Oct. 12, 1991)* | | 2.50 |

**1993. WILLIAM T. PIPER ISSUE** differs from the 1991 revision (A129) in that Piper's hair touches the top edge of the design of this stamp. There was no official first day of issue for the redesigned stamp. *Printed in gravure by Stamp Ventureres, perforated 11 1/4.*

A132

| A132 | | MNHVF | UseVF |
|---|---|---|---|
| 40¢ | **multicolored,** *(July 1993)* tagged | 1.50 | .50 |
| | Plate block of 4 | 7.00 | |
| | FDC | | 2.50 |

# Special Delivery

A special delivery stamp on any letter or article of mailable matter entitles the addressee to immediate delivery between the hours of 7 a.m. and midnight. This service began on October 1, 1885 and was limited to free delivery offices and post offices in towns of 4,000 population or more. At that time there were 555 such post offices. The Act of August 4, 1886, extended the service to all post offices.

**1885. MESSENGER, FIRST ISSUE** Inscribed "At a special delivery office." *Printed by the American Bank Note Company, flat press, unwatermarked, perforated 12.*

SD1 *Messenger on foot*

| SD1 | | UnFVF | UseFVF |
|---|---|---|---|
| 10¢ | **Prussian blue** | 115. | 22.50 |
| | dark blue | 115. | 22.50 |
| | Plate block of 8 | 6000. | |
| | Double transfer at top | 250. | |
| | FDC *(Oct. 1, 1885)* | | 10000. |

**1888. MESSENGER, SECOND ISSUE** Inscribed "At any post office." *Printed by the American Bank Note Company, flat press, unwatermarked, perforated 12.*

SD2, SD3 *Messenger on Foot*

| SD2 | | UnFVF | UseFVF |
|---|---|---|---|
| 10¢ | **Prussian blue** | 120. | 7.00 |
| | dark blue | 120. | 7.00 |
| | Plate block of 8 | 7500. | |
| | FDD *(Sept. 6, 1888)* | | |
| | EKU *(Dec. 18, 1888)* | | |

**1893. MESSENGER, THIRD ISSUE** Had a change of color and was released to avoid confusion with the 1- and 4-cent Columbian commemorative stamps. SD2 went on sale again in January 1894 and remained in use until it was replaced by SD4. *Printed by the American Bank Note Company, flat press, unwatermarked, perforated 12.*

| SD3 | | UnFVF | UseFVF |
|---|---|---|---|
| 10¢ | **orange yellow** | 75.00 | 10.00 |
| | dark orange | 75.00 | 10.00 |
| | Plate block of 8 | 5000. | |
| | FDD *(Jan. 24, 1893)* | | |
| | EKU *(Feb. 11, 1893)* | | |

**1894. MESSENGER ISSUE** Similar to SD2, with a line drawn under the words "Ten Cents." *Printed by intaglio by the Bureau of Engraving and Printing, perforated 12.*

SD4, SD5 *Messenger on foot*

| SD4 | | UnFVF | UseFVF |
|---|---|---|---|
| 10¢ | **deep blue** | 300. | 20.00 |
| | bright blue | 300. | 20.00 |
| | dark blue | 300. | 20.00 |
| | Plate block of 4, w/arrow | 2000. | |
| | Plate block of 6 | 8000. | |
| | Double transfer | 750. | |
| | v. Plate block of 6, imperforate & without gum | 5000. | |
| | FDD *(Oct. 10, 1894)* | | |
| | EKU *Oct. 24, 1894)* | | |

**1895. MESSENGER ISSUE** Same design as SD4. *Intaglio, perforated 12, watermarked double-line USPS (wmk187).*

| SD5 | | UnFVF | UseFVF |
|---|---|---|---|
| 10¢ | **blue** | 65.00 | 1.75 |
| | dark blue | 65.00 | 1.75 |
| | deep blue | 65.00 | 1.75 |
| | Plate block of 6 | 3000. | |
| | Block of 4, w/arrow | 300. | |
| | Colored line through "POSTAL DELIVERY" | 120. | |
| | Dots in frame (curved) above messenger | 150. | |
| | Double transfer | | 10.00 |
| | v. Printed on both sides | — | |
| | v1. Imperforate | — | |
| | FDD *(Aug. 16, 1895)* | | |
| | EKU *(Oct. 3, 1895)* | | |

**1902. SECOND BICYCLE MESSENGER ISSUE** *Intaglio, perforated 12, watermarked double-line UPSP (wmk187).*

SD6, *Messenger on bicycle*

| SD6 | | UnFVF | UseFVF |
|---|---|---|---|
| 10¢ | **ultramarine** | 75.00 | 3.00 |
| | blue | 75.00 | 3.00 |
| | dark blue | 75.00 | 3.00 |
| | Plate block of 6 | 2000. | |
| | Plate block of 6, from plates 5240, 5243, 5244 or 5245, with "09" added to number | 1800. | |
| | Plate block of 4, w/arrow | 300. | |
| | Double transfer | — | |
| | Transfer "damage" under "N" of "CENTS" | 100. | 2.50 |
| | FDD *(Dec. 9, 1902)* | | |
| | EKU *(Jan. 22, 1903)* | | |

**1908. HELMET OF MERCURY ISSUE** The "Merry Widow" is the nickname for this stamp due to the resemblance to a contemporary lady's hat, of the same name. *Intaglio, perforated 12, watermarked double-line USPS (wmk 187).*

SD7 *Helmet of Mercury*

| SD7 | | UnFVF | UseFVF |
|---|---|---|---|
| 10¢ | **green** | 50.00 | 30.00 |
| | dark green | 50.00 | 30.00 |
| | yellowish green | 50.00 | 30.00 |
| | Plate block of 6 | 850. | |
| | Double transfer | 250. | |
| | on cover | | 200. |
| | FDD *(Dec. 12, 1908)* | | — |
| | EKU *(Dec. 14, 1908)* | | |

**1911. MESSENGER ON BICYCLE ISSUE** *Intaglio, watermarked single-line USPS (wmk 273), perforated 12.*

SD8-SD11 *Messenger on bicylcle*

**SD8**

| 10¢ | | UnFVF | UseFVF |
|---|---|---|---|
| | ultramarine | 75.00 | 4.50 |
| | dark ultramarine | 75.00 | 4.50 |
| | pale untramarine | 75.00 | 4.50 |
| | violet blue | 75.00 | 4.50 |
| | Plate block of 6 | 1800. | |
| | Plate block of 6. w/imprint | 2000. | |
| | v. Top frame line missing | 90.00 | 5.00 |
| | FDD (Jan. 1911) | | |
| | EKU (Jan. 14, 1911) | | |

**1914. MESSENGER ON BICYCLE ISSUE** *Intaglio, watermarked single-line USPS (wmk 273), perforated 10.*

**SD9**

| 10¢ | | UnFVF | UseFVF |
|---|---|---|---|
| | ultramarine | 140. | 5.00 |
| | blue | 140. | 5.00 |
| | pale ultramarine | 140. | 5.00 |
| | Plate block of 6 | 2800. | |
| | Plate block of 6, w/imprint | 3250. | |
| | FDD (Sept. 1914) | | |
| | EKU (Oct. 26, 1914) | | |

**1916. MESSENGER ON BICYCLE ISSUE** *Intaglio, unwatermarked, perforated 10.*

**SD10**

| 10¢ | | UnFVF | UseFVF |
|---|---|---|---|
| | pale ultramarine | 225. | 22.50 |
| | blue | 225. | 22.50 |
| | ultramarine | 225. | 22.50 |
| | Plate block of 6 | 4250. | |
| | Plate block of 6, w/imprint | 4800. | |
| | FDD (Oct. 19, 1916) | | |
| | EKU (Nov. 4, 1916) | | |

**1917. MESSENGER ON BICYCLE ISSUE** *Intaglio, unwatermarked, perforated 11.*

**SD11**

| 10¢ | | UnFVF | UseFVF |
|---|---|---|---|
| | ultramarine | 14.50 | .50 |
| | blue | 14.50 | .50 |
| | dark unltramarine | 14.50 | .50 |
| | gray violet | 14.50 | .50 |
| | pale ultramarine | 14.50 | .50 |
| | Plate block of 6 | 200. | |
| | Plate block of 6, w/imprint | 500. | |
| | v. perforated 10 at left | — | |
| | FDD (May 2, 1917) | | |

**1922. MESSENGER AND MOTORCYCLE ISSUE** *Intaglio, unwatermarked, perforated 11.*

SD12, SD13, SD15-SD18 *Messenger and Motorcycle*

**SD12**

| 10¢ | | UnFVF | UseFVF |
|---|---|---|---|
| | gray blue | 22.50 | .25 |
| | deep ultramarine | 22.50 | .25 |
| | Plate block of 6 | 400. | |
| | Double transfer | 40.00 | 1.00 |
| | FDC (July 12, 1922) | | 375. |

**SD13**

| 15¢ | | UnFVF | UseFVF |
|---|---|---|---|
| | red orange | 19.00 | 1.00 |
| | Plate block of 6 | 250. | |
| | Double transfer | — | |
| | FDC (April 11, 1925) | | 275. |

**1925. POST OFFICE DELIVERY TRUCK ISSUE** *Intaglio, unwatermarked, perforated 11.*

SD14, SD19 *Post office delivery truck*

**SD14**

| 20¢ | | UnFVF | UseFVF |
|---|---|---|---|
| | black | 2.25 | 1.50 |
| | Plate block of 6 | 40.00 | |
| | FDC (April 25, 1925) | | 125. |

**1927. MESSENGER AND MOTORCYCLE ISSUE** *Rotary press printing, previous designs, perforated 11 x 10 1/2.*

**SD15**

| 10¢ | | UnFVF | UseFVF |
|---|---|---|---|
| | dark lilac | 1.00 | .20 |
| | gray lilac | 1.00 | |
| | red lilac | 1.00 | .20 |
| | violet | 1.00 | .20 |
| | Plate block of 4 | 7.00 | |
| | cracked plate | 75.00 | |
| | gouged plate | 100. | |
| | FDC (Nov. 29, 1927) | | 100. |
| | FDC, electric eye plate (Sept. 8, 1941) | | 25.00 |
| | v. Horizontal pair, imperforate between | 250. | |

**1944. MESSENGER AND MOTORCYCLE ISSUE**

**SD16**

| 13¢ | | MNHVF | UseVF |
|---|---|---|---|
| | blue | 1.00 | .20 |
| | Plate block of 4 | 5.00 | |
| | FDC (Oct. 30, 1944) | | 10.00 |

**1931. MESSENGER AND MOTORCYCLE ISSUE**

**SD17**

| 15¢ | | MNHVF | UseVF |
|---|---|---|---|
| | yellow orange | .75 | .20 |
| | Plate block of 4 | 4.00 | |
| | FDC, Washington D.C. (Aug. 13, 1931) | | 125. |
| | FDC, Easton, Penn. (Aug. 6, 1931) | | 1500. |

**1944. MESSENGER AND MOTORCYCLE ISSUE**

**SD18**

| 17¢ | | MNHVF | UseVF |
|---|---|---|---|
| | yellow | 3.50 | 3.00 |
| | Plate block of 4 | 27.50 | |
| | FDC (Oct. 30, 1944) | | 10.00 |

**1951. POST OFFICE DELIVERY TRUCK ISSUE**

**SD19**

| 20¢ | | MNHVF | UseVF |
|---|---|---|---|
| | black | 17.50 | .20 |
| | Plate block of 4 | 8.50 | |
| | FDC (Nov. 30, 1951) | | 4.50 |

**1954. LETTER AND HANDS ISSUE** *Rotary press printing, perforated 11 x 10 1/2.*

SD20, SD21 *Two hands and letter*

**SD20**

| 20¢ | | MNHVF | UseVF |
|---|---|---|---|
| | gray blue | .75 | .20 |
| | light blue | .75 | .20 |
| | Plate block of 4 | 3.00 | |
| | FDC (Oct. 13, 1954) | | 2.00 |

**1957. LETTER AND HANDS ISSUE**

**SD21**

| 30¢ | | MNHVF | UseVF |
|---|---|---|---|
| | maroon | .75 | .20 |
| | Plate block of 4 | 3.50 | |
| | FDC (Sept. 3, 1957) | | 2.00 |

**1969. DUAL ARROWS ISSUE** *Giori Press Printing issued for new rate. Perforated 11.*

SD22, SD23 *Arrows pointing in opposite directions.*

**SD22**

| 45¢ | | MNHVF | UseVF |
|---|---|---|---|
| | carmine and violet blue | 1.50 | .50 |
| | Plate block of 4 | 6.00 | |
| | FDC (Nov. 20, 1969) | | 2.50 |

**1971. DUAL ARROWS ISSUE** *New Rates, same design as SD22.*

**SD23**

| 60¢ | | MNHVF | UseVF |
|---|---|---|---|
| | violet blue and carmine | 1.50 | .25 |
| | Plate block of 4 | 7.50 | |
| | FDC (May 10, 1971) | | 2.50 |

# Air Mail/Special Delivery

**1934. BLUE AIR MAIL SPECIAL DELIVERY STAMP ISSUE** Prepaid, with one stamp, air postage and the special delivery fee. The stamp was designed by Pres. Franklin D. Roosevelt. The first day of issue was August 30 at the convention of the American Air Mail Society at Chicago. *Printed by intaglio, unwatermarked, perforated 11.*

 ASD1 *Great Seal*

| ASD1 | | UnFVF | UseFVF |
|---|---|---|---|
| 16¢ | **Prussian blue** *(9,215,750)* | .90 | .75 |
| | blue | .90 | .75 |
| | FDC *(Aug. 30, 1934)* | | 30.00 |
| | Plate block of 6 | 25.00 | |

**1936. RED AND BLUE AIRMAIL SPECIAL DELIVERY STAMP ISSUE** Is the same design as the 1934 stamp, but in two colors.

 ASD2

| ASD2 | | UnFVF | UseFVF |
|---|---|---|---|
| 16¢ | **carmine and blue** | .60 | .30 |
| | FDC *(Feb. 10, 1963)* | | 25.00 |
| | Center line block | — | |
| | Plate block of 4, Type 1, thin red and blue registration line above plate nos. | 12.50 | |
| | Plate block of 4, type II, thick red, thin blue registration line above plate nos. | 225. | |
| | Plate block of 4, type III, dotted blue, thin red registration line above plate nos. | 200. | |
| | Plate block of 4, type IV, thick red and blue registration line above plate nos. | 15.00 | |
| | Arrow block of 4, bottom or side arrow | — | |
| | v. Horizontal pair, imperforate between | — | |

# Post Offices in China

**1919. OFFICES IN CHINA ISSUE** Postage stamps of the 1917 United States series were overprinted and issued to our Postal Agency at Shanghai. The overprints are in black, except OC7 and OC16, which are in red. Sold in Shanghai at the local currency, which was one-half the value of ours at the time. These stamps were good for mail to addresses in the United States. After the closing of the China office in December 1922, the stamps were sold for a short time at the Philatelic Agency at Washington D.C. *Intaglio, unwatermarked, perforated 11.*

 OC1-OC16 *U.S. stamps 380-398 overprinted.*

| OC1 | | UnFVF | UseFVF |
|---|---|---|---|
| 2¢ on 1¢ **green** (380) | | 20.00 | 50.00 |
| | Plate block of 6 | 275. | |
| **OC2** | | UnFVF | UseFVF |
| 4¢ on 2¢ **rose red** (381) | | 20.00 | 50.00 |
| | Plate block of 6 | 275. | |
| **OC3** | | UnFVF | UseFVF |
| 6¢ on 3¢ **violet** (382) | | 40.00 | 55.00 |
| | Plate block of 6 | 475. | |
| **OC4** | | UnFVF | UseFVF |
| 8¢ on 4¢ **yellow brown** (383) | | 45.00 | 50.00 |
| | Plate block of 6 | 600. | |
| **OC5** | | UnFVF | UseFVF |
| 10¢ on 5¢ **blue** (384) | | 50.00 | 55.00 |
| | Plate block of 6 | 65.00 | |
| **OC6** | | UnFVF | UseFVF |
| 12¢ on 6¢ **red orange** (386) | | 65.00 | 80.00 |
| | Plate block of 6 | 750. | |
| **OC7** | | UnFVF | UseFVF |
| 14¢ on 7¢ **black** (387) | | 65.00 | 80.00 |
| | Plate block of 6 | 850. | |
| **OC8** | | UnFVF | UseFVF |
| 16¢ on 8¢ **yellow olive** (388) | | 50.00 | 55.00 |
| | a. oliver green | 40.00 | 45.00 |
| | Plate block of 6 | 600. | |
| **OC9** | | UnFVF | UseFVF |
| 18¢ on 9¢ **salmon** (389) | | 50.00 | 60.00 |
| | Plate block of 6 | 700. | |

| OC10 | | UnFVF | UseFVF |
|---|---|---|---|
| 20¢ on 10¢ **orange yellow** (390) | | 45.00 | 50.00 |
| | Plate block of 6 | 650. | |
| **OC11** | | UnFVF | UseFVF |
| 24¢ on 12¢ **brown purple** (392) | | 50.00 | 60.00 |
| | a. claret brown | 70.00 | 85.00 |
| | Plate block of 6 | 850. | |
| **OC12** | | UnFVF | UseFVF |
| 30¢ 15¢ **gray black** (394) | | 60.00 | 75.00 |
| | Plate block of 6 | 1000. | |
| **OC13** | | UnFVF | UseFVF |
| 40¢ on 20¢ **pale blue** (395) | | 90.00 | 120. |
| | Plate block of 6 | 1350. | |
| **OC14** | | UnFVF | UseFVF |
| 60¢ on 30¢ **orange red** (396) | | 85.00 | 100. |
| | Plate block of 6 | 1000. | |
| **OC15** | | UnFVF | UseFVF |
| $1 on 50¢ **reddish violet** (397) | | 325. | 425. |
| | Plate block of 6 | 9000. | |
| **OC16** | | UnFVF | UseFVF |
| $2 on $1 **black purple** (398) | | 300. | 350. |
| | Plate block of 6 | 6500. | |
| | Arrow block of 4 | 1400. | |

**1922. OFFICES IN CHINA ISSUE** Issues overprinted on No. 380. *Intaglio.*

 OC17, OC18

| OC17 | | UnFVF | UseFVF |
|---|---|---|---|
| 2¢ on 1¢ **green** (380) | | 90.00 | 90.00 |
| | Plate block of 6 | 725. | |

**1922. OFFICES IN CHINA ISSUE** Overprinted on No. 404, offset.

| OC18 | | UnFVF | UseFVF |
|---|---|---|---|
| 4¢ on 2¢ **rose red** (404) | | 75.00 | 75.00 |
| | Plate block of 6 | 725. | |
| | "CHINA" only | — | — |
| | "SHANGHAI" omitted | — | — |

# Parcel Post

**1912. PARCEL POST STAMPS** were provided to cover the rates of postage on fourth class mail, set up by the Act of Congress of August 24, 1912. Less than a year later, on July 1, 1913, the Postmaster General directed that ordinary postage stamps be valid for parcel post and that parcel post stamps be valid for postage purposes and be continued on sale until the supply was exhausted. The 75¢ value (PP11) outlasted all the others and in September 1921 the remainders, consisting of 3,510,345 copies, were destroyed. One of our more atractive set of stamps, the 20¢ value is the first stamp in the world to depict an airplane. *Printed by intaglio, watermarked single-line USPS (wmk 273) and perforated 12; marginal imprints (the denomination in words) were added to the plates on January 27, 1913.*

PP1 *Post Office Clerk*

**PP1**

| **1¢** | **carmine** *(209,691,094)* | **UnFVF** | **UseFVF** |
|---|---|---|---|
| | | 3.00 | 1.25 |
| | Double transfer | 90.00 | |
| | Plate block of 6, w/imprint | 75.00 | |
| | FDC *(Nov. 27, 1912)* | | 1250. |

PP2 *City Carrier*

**PP2**

| **2¢** | **carmine** *(206,417,253)* | **UnFVF** | **UseFVF** |
|---|---|---|---|
| | | 3.50 | 1.00 |
| | lake | 5.00 | |
| | Double transfer | 100. | |
| | Plate block of 6, w/imprint | 90.00 | |
| | FDC *(Nov. 27, 1912)* | | 1250. |

PP3 *Railway Postal Clerk*

**PP3**

| **3¢** | **carmine** *(29,027,433)* | **UnFVF** | **UseFVF** |
|---|---|---|---|
| | | 6.50 | 4.50 |
| | Double transfer | 17.50 | |
| | Lower right corner retouched | 17.50 | |
| | Plate block of 6, w/imprint | 150. | |
| | FDC *(April 5, 1913)* | | 3000. |

PP4 *Rural Carrier*

**PP4**

| **4¢** | **carmine** *(76,743,813)* | **UnFVF** | **UseFVF** |
|---|---|---|---|
| | | 17.50 | 2.50 |
| | Double transfer | 35.00 | |
| | Plate block of 6, w/imprint | 750. | |
| | FDC *(Dec. 12, 1912)* | | 3000. |

PP5 *Mail Train*

**PP5**

| **5¢** | **carmine** *(108,153,993)* | **UnFVF** | **UseFVF** |
|---|---|---|---|
| | | 17.50 | 1.75 |
| | Double transfer | 35.00 | |
| | Plate block of 6, w/imprint | 800. | |
| | FDC *(Nov. 27, 1912)* | | 3000. |

PP6 *Steamship and Mail Tender*

**PP6**

| **10¢** | **carmine** *(56,896,653)* | **UnFVF** | **UseFVF** |
|---|---|---|---|
| | | 30.00 | 2.50 |
| | Double transfer | 60.00 | |
| | Plate block of 6, w/imprint | 900. | |
| | FDC *(Dec. 9, 1912)* | | — |

PP7 *Automobile*

**PP7**

| **15¢** | **carmine** *(21,147,033)* | **UnFVF** | **UseFVF** |
|---|---|---|---|
| | | 45.00 | 8.00 |
| | Plate block of 6, w/imprint | 2000. | |
| | FDC *(Dec. 16, 1912)* | | — |

PP8 *Airplane Carrying Mail*

**PP8**

| **20¢** | **carmine** *(17,142,393)* | **UnFVF** | **UseFVF** |
|---|---|---|---|
| | | 85.00 | 16.00 |
| | Plate block of 6, w/imprint | 5000. | |
| | FDC *(Dec. 16, 1912)* | | — |

PP9 *Manufacturing*

**PP9**

| **25¢** | **carmine** *(21,940,653)* | **UnFVF** | **UseFVF** |
|---|---|---|---|
| | | 42.50 | 5.00 |
| | Plate block of 6, imprint | 3000. | |
| | FDC *(Nov. 27, 1912)* | | — |

PP10 *Dairying*

| PP10 | | UnFVF | UseFVF |
|------|------|-------|--------|
| 50¢ | carmine (2,117,793) | 190. | 32.50 |
| | Plate block of 6, imprint | 17500. | |
| | FDC (March 15, 1913) | | — |

PP11 *Harvesting*

| PP11 | | UnFVF | UseFVF |
|------|------|-------|--------|
| 75¢ | carmine (2,772,615) | 55.00 | 25.00 |
| | Plate block of 6, imprint | 3000. | |
| | FDC (Dec. 18, 1912) | | — |

PP12 *Fruit Growing*

| PP12 | | UnFVF | UseFVF |
|------|------|-------|--------|
| $1 | carmine (1,053,273) | 250. | 20.00 |
| | Plate block of 6, imprint | 17500. | |
| | FDC (Jan. 3, 1913) | | — |

## Parcel Post/Postage Due

**1912. PARCEL POST POSTAGE DUE STAMPS** These stamps were used to indicate the amount due by the addressee when parcel post was insufficiently prepaid by the sender. *Watermarked single-line UPSP (wmk 273), intaglio, perforated 12.*

PPD1-PPD5

| PPD1 | | UnFVF | UseFVF |
|------|------|-------|--------|
| 1¢ | green (7,322,400) | 6.00 | 3.50 |
| | FDC (Nov. 27, 1912) | | |

| PPD2 | | UnFVF | UseFVF |
|------|------|-------|--------|
| 2¢ | green (3,132,000) | 55.00 | 15.00 |
| | FDC (Dec. 9, 1912) | | |

| PPD3 | | UnFVF | UseFVF |
|------|------|-------|--------|
| 5¢ | green (5,840,100) | 9.00 | 3.50 |
| | FDC (Nov. 27, 1912) | | |

| PPD4 | | UnFVF | UseFVF |
|------|------|-------|--------|
| 10¢ | green (2,124,540) | 125. | 40.00 |
| | FDC (Dec. 12, 1912) | | |

| PPD5 | | UnFVF | UseFVF |
|------|------|-------|--------|
| 25¢ | green (2,117,700) | 65.00 | 3.75 |
| | FDC (Dec. 16, 1912) | | |

## Special Handling

**1925-29. ISSUE** The Postal Service Act of 1925 provided the same service for fourth class matter as normally according first class by payment of a 25¢ fee, for which a stamp was issued. The other denominations were issued to meet rate changes. *Printed by intaglio, unwatermarked, perforated 11.*

The 10¢, 15¢ and 20¢ denominations were dry-printed on pregummed paper (1955). They were issued in much smaller quantities than the usual wet-printed stamps. There is a minute size difference between the wet and dry printings: the latter are on a whiter, thicker and stiffer paper.

SH1-SH5

| SH1 | | UnFVF | UseFVF |
|------|------|-------|--------|
| 25¢ | green | 22.50 | 5.50 |
| | Plate block of 6 | 75.00 | |
| | FDC (April 11, 1925) | | 225. |
| SH2 | | UnFVF | UseFVF |
| 10¢ | yellow green | 2.25 | 1.00 |
| | FDC (June 25, 1928) | | 50.00 |
| | p. Dry printing (1955) | 1.25 | .90 |
| | Plate block of 6 | 5.50 | |
| SH3 | | UnFVF | UseFVF |
| 15¢ | yellow green | 2.25 | 1.00 |
| | FDC (June 25, 1928) | | 50.00 |
| | p. Dry printing (1955) | 2.00 | 1.50 |
| | Plate block of 6 | 25.00 | |
| SH4 | | UnFVF | UseFVF |
| 20¢ | yellow green | 3.00 | 1.75 |
| | FDC (June 25, 1928) | | 75.00 |
| | t. Dry printing (1955) | 2.00 | 1.50 |
| | Plate block of 6 | — | |
| SH5 | | UnFVF | UseFVF |
| 25¢ | yellow green, (1929) | 17.50 | 7.50 |
| | Plate block of 6 | 500. | |
| | "A" and "T" of "STATES" joined at top | 40.00 | 20.00 |
| | "A" and "T" of "STATES" and "T" and "A" of "POSTAGE" joined at top | 40.00 | 40.00 |

## Registation Stamp

**1911. REGISTRATION STAMP** Although we have had a registry since 1855, the Registry Stamp of 1911 was the only stamp issued for the specific purpose of paying registration fees. The stamp was valid for the fees only, not postage; regular postage stamps could be used to pay the fees. The Postmaster General abolished the issuance of these stamps in 1913, but allowed remaining stock to be used up. Printed by intaglio, single-line USPS watermark (wmk 273), perforated 12.

REG1

| REG1 | | UnFVF | UseFVF |
|------|------|-------|--------|
| 10¢ | bright blue | 65.00 | 5.00 |
| | Plate block of 6, w/imprint | 2000. | |
| | FDC (Dec. 1, 1911) | | 10000. |

## Certified Mail

**1955. CERTIFIED MAIL STAMP** This service provided mailer with a receipt of mailing and required signature of addresses or agent on delivery. *Printed by intaglio, perforated 10 1/2 x 11.*

CER1 *U.S. Mail Carrier*

| CER1 | | MNHVF | UseVF |
|------|------|-------|--------|
| 15¢ | red | .50 | .35 |
| | Plate block of 4 | 12.00 | |
| | FDC (June 6, 1955) | | 3.00 |

# Newspaper/Periodical Stamps

**1865. FIRST NEWSPAPER STAMP ISSUE** The first issue was *embossed and printed in letterpress, National Bank Note Company. Thin hard unwatermarked paper, without gum, and perforated 12. The design size is 51 x 95mm.*

N1, N4 *George Washington* N2 *Benjamin Franklin* Colored Border

| N1 | | UnFVF | UseFVF |
|---|---|---|---|
| 5¢ | **dark blue** | 250. | — |
| | a. light blue | 275. | — |
| N2 | | UnFVF | UseFVF |
| 10¢ | **green** | 100. | — |
| | a. blue green | 100. | — |
| | p. pelure paper | 125. | — |
| N3 | | UnFVF | UseFVF |
| 25¢ | **orange red** | 150. | — |
| | a. carmine red | 175. | — |
| | p. pelure paper | 150. | — |
| N4 | | UnFVF | UseFVF |
| 5¢ | **blue** | 75.00 | — |
| | a. dark blue | 75.00 | — |
| | p. pelure paper | 75.00 | — |

### SPECIAL PRINTING

First issued in September 1865 to prepay postage on bulk shipments of newspapers and periodicals, they were not attached to the items mailed, but rather to the statement of mailing, which was canceled and retained by the Post Office. the stamps were discontinued July 1, 1898.

**1875. FIRST REPRINT OF THE 1865 ISSUE** By the *Continental Bank Note Co. The 5¢ with white border, the 10¢ and 25¢ with colored border. Hard white paper, unwatermarked, issued without gum, perforated.*

| SPN1 | | UnFVF | UseFVF |
|---|---|---|---|
| 5¢ | **blue** | 75.00 | |
| SPN2 | | UnFVF | UseFVF |
| 10¢ | **bluish green** | 85.00 | |
| SPN3 | | UnFVF | UseFVF |
| 25¢ | **carmine** | 100. | |

**1881. SECOND REPRINT OF THE 1865 ISSUE** By the *American Bank Note Co. White border, soft porous paper, unwatermarked, perforated 12.*

| SPN4 | | UnFVF | UseFVF |
|---|---|---|---|
| 5¢ | **dark blue** | 175. | — |

**1875. ALLEGORY DESIGN ISSUE** *printed in intaglio, Continental Bank Note Company. Issued January 1, 1875, on thin hard paper. Design size 24 x 35mm.*

N5-N11 *"Freedom" after Crawford's statue on the dome of the Capitol.*

| N5 | | UnFVF | UseFVF |
|---|---|---|---|
| 2¢ | **black** | 25.00 | 12.50 |
| | gray black | 25.00 | 12.50 |
| | greenish black | 25.00 | 12.50 |
| N6 | | UnFVF | UseFVF |
| 3¢ | **black** | 27.50 | 15.00 |
| | gray black | 27.50 | 15.00 |
| N7 | | UnFVF | UseFVF |
| 4¢ | **black** | 27.50 | 15.00 |
| | gray black | 27.50 | 15.00 |
| | greenish black | 27.50 | 15.00 |
| N8 | | UnFVF | UseFVF |
| 6¢ | **black** | 30.00 | 20.00 |
| | gray black | 30.00 | 20.00 |
| | greenish black | 30.00 | 20.00 |
| N9 | | UnFVF | UseFVF |
| 8¢ | **black** | 45.00 | 24.00 |
| | gray black | 45.00 | 32.50 |
| | greenish black | 45.00 | |
| N10 | | UnFVF | UseFVF |
| 9¢ | **black** | 65.00 | 52.00 |
| | gray black | 85.00 | 60.00 |
| | greenish black | 65.00 | 52.00 |
| | Double transfer | 100. | 75.00 |
| N11 | | UnFVF | UseFVF |
| 10¢ | **black** | 45.00 | 32.50 |
| | gray black | 45.00 | 32.50 |
| | greenish black | 45.00 | 32.50 |
| N12 | | UnFVF | UseFVF |
| 12¢ | **rose** | 100. | 50.00 |
| | pale rose | 100. | 50.00 |
| N13 | | UnFVF | UseFVF |
| 24¢ | **rose** | 125. | 65.00 |
| | pale rose | 125. | 65.00 |
| N14 | | UnFVF | UseFVF |
| 36¢ | **rose** | 150. | 75.00 |
| | pale rose | 150. | 75.00 |
| N15 | | UnFVF | UseFVF |
| 48¢ | **rose** | 250. | 125. |
| | pale rose | 250. | 125. |
| N16 | | UnFVF | UseFVF |
| 60¢ | **rose** | 140. | 65.00 |
| | pale rose | 140. | 65.00 |
| N17 | | UnFVF | UseFVF |
| 72¢ | **rose** | 300. | 175. |
| | pale rose | 300. | 175. |
| N18 | | UnFVF | UseFVF |
| 84¢ | **rose** | 450. | 200. |
| | pale rose | 450. | 200. |
| N19 | | UnFVF | UseFVF |
| 96¢ | **rose** | 250. | 125. |
| | pale rose | 250. | 125. |
| N20 | | UnFVF | UseFVF |
| $1.92 | **brown** | 350. | 225. |
| | dark brown | 350. | 225. |
| N21 | | UnFVF | UseFVF |
| $3 | **vermilion** | 475. | 175. |

| N22 | | UnFVF | UseFVF |
|---|---|---|---|
| $6 | ultramarine | 750. | 150. |

| N23 | | UnFVF | UseFVF |
|---|---|---|---|
| $9 | yellow | 850. | 325. |

| N24 | | UnFVF | UseFVF |
|---|---|---|---|
| $12 | blue green | 1000. | 450. |

| N25 | | UnFVF | UseFVF |
|---|---|---|---|
| $24 | dark gray violet | 1000. | 450. |

| N26 | | UnFVF | UseFVF |
|---|---|---|---|
| $36 | brown rose | 1150. | 600. |

| N27 | | UnFVF | UseFVF |
|---|---|---|---|
| $48 | red brown | 1600. | 650. |

| N28 | | UnFVF | UseFVF |
|---|---|---|---|
| $60 | violet | 1600. | 650. |

## SPECIAL PRINTING

**1875. SPECIAL PRINTING OF THE 1875 ISSUE** By the Continental Bank Note Co. *Hard, white paper, unwatermarked, without gum, perforated 12.*

| SPN5 | | UnFVF | UseFVF |
|---|---|---|---|
| 2¢ | gray black *(19,514, quantity issued probable includes SPN 29)* | 125. | |

| SPN6 | | UnFVF | UseFVF |
|---|---|---|---|
| 3¢ | gray black *(6,952)* | 140. | |

| SPN7 | | UnFVF | UseFVF |
|---|---|---|---|
| 4¢ | gray black *(4,451)* | 150. | |

| SPN8 | | UnFVF | UseFVF |
|---|---|---|---|
| 6¢ | gray black *(2,348)* | 200. | |

| SPN9 | | UnFVF | UseFVF |
|---|---|---|---|
| 8¢ | gray black *(1,930)* | 250. | |

| SPN10 | | UnFVF | UseFVF |
|---|---|---|---|
| 9¢ | gray black *(1,795)* | 275. | |

| SPN11 | | UnFVF | UseFVF |
|---|---|---|---|
| 10¢ | gray black *(1,499)* | 350. | |

| SPN12 | | UnFVF | UseFVF |
|---|---|---|---|
| 12¢ | rose *(1,313)* | 425. | |

| SPN13 | | UnFVF | UseFVF |
|---|---|---|---|
| 24¢ | rose *(411)* | 600. | |

| SPN14 | | UnFVF | UseFVF |
|---|---|---|---|
| 36¢ | rose *(330)* | 700. | |

| SPN15 | | UnFVF | UseFVF |
|---|---|---|---|
| 48¢ | rose *(268)* | 800. | |

| SPN16 | | UnFVF | UseFVF |
|---|---|---|---|
| 60¢ | rose *(222)* | 850. | |

| SPN17 | | UnFVF | UseFVF |
|---|---|---|---|
| 72¢ | rose *(174)* | 1000. | |

| SPN18 | | UnFVF | UseFVF |
|---|---|---|---|
| 84¢ | rose *(164)* | 1250. | |

| SPN19 | | UnFVF | UseFVF |
|---|---|---|---|
| 96¢ | rose *(141)* | 1750. | |

| SPN20 | | UnFVF | UseFVF |
|---|---|---|---|
| $1.92 | dark brown *(41)* | 4500. | |

| SPN21 | | UnFVF | UseFVF |
|---|---|---|---|
| $3 | vermilion *(20)* | 8000. | |

| SPN22 | | UnFVF | UseFVF |
|---|---|---|---|
| $6 | ultrmarine *(14)* | 10000. | |

| SPN23 | | UnFVF | UseFVF |
|---|---|---|---|
| $9 | yellow *(4)* | 17500. | |

| SPN24 | | UnFVF | UseFVF |
|---|---|---|---|
| $12 | bluish green *(5)* | 16000. | |

| SPN25 | | UnFVF | UseFVF |
|---|---|---|---|
| $24 | gray violet *(2)* | — | |

| SPN26 | | UnFVF | UseFVF |
|---|---|---|---|
| $36 | brown rose *(2)* | — | |

| SPN27 | | UnFVF | UseFVF |
|---|---|---|---|
| $48 | red brown *(1)* | — | |

| SPN28 | | UnFVF | UseFVF |
|---|---|---|---|
| $60 | violet | — | |

| SPN29 | | UnFVF | UseFVF |
|---|---|---|---|
| 2¢ | black | 325. | |

**1879. ALLEGORY DESIGN ISSUE** American Bank Note Co., *soft porous paper, unwatermarked, perforated 12.*

| N29 | | UnFVF | UseFVF |
|---|---|---|---|
| 2¢ | black | 10.00 | 5.00 |
| | gray black | 10.00 | 5.00 |
| | greenish black | 19.00 | 5.00 |
| | Double transfer at top | 12.00 | 9.00 |
| | cracked plate | — | |
| | v. imperforate | — | |

**1879. ALLEGORY DESIGN ISSUE**

| N30 | | UnFVF | UseFVF |
|---|---|---|---|
| 3¢ | black | 12.50 | 5.50 |
| | gray black | | |
| | greenish black | 12.00 | 5.50 |
| | Double transfer at top | 14.00 | 10.00 |
| | v. imperforate | — | |

| N31 | | UnFVF | UseFVF |
|---|---|---|---|
| 4¢ | black | 12.50 | 5.50 |
| | gray black | 12.50 | 5.50 |
| | greenish black | 12.50 | 5.50 |
| | intense black | 12.50 | 5.50 |
| | Double transfer at top | 15.00 | 10.00 |
| | v. imperforate | — | |

| N32 | | UnFVF | UseFVF |
|---|---|---|---|
| 6¢ | black | 22.50 | 12.50 |
| | gray black | 22.50 | 12.50 |
| | greenish black | 22.50 | 12.50 |
| | intense black | 22.50 | 12.50 |
| | Double transfer at top | 27.50 | 22.50 |
| | v. imperforate | — | |

| N33 | | UnFVF | UseFVF |
|---|---|---|---|
| 8¢ | black | 22.50 | 12.50 |
| | gray black | 22.50 | 12.50 |
| | greenish black | 22.50 | 12.50 |
| | Double transfer at top | 27.50 | 22.50 |
| | v. imperforate | — | |

| N34 | | UnFVF | UseFVF |
|---|---|---|---|
| 10¢ | black | 25.00 | 12.50 |
| | gray black | 25.00 | 12.50 |
| | greenish black | 25.00 | 12.50 |
| | Double transfer at top | 27.50 | — |
| | v. imperforate | — | |

| N35 | | UnFVF | UseFVF |
|---|---|---|---|
| 12¢ | red | 90.00 | 35.00 |
| | v. imperforate | — | |

| N36 | | UnFVF | UseFVF |
|---|---|---|---|
| 24¢ | red | 90.00 | 35.00 |
| | v. imperforate | — | |

| N37 | | UnFVF | UseFVF |
|---|---|---|---|
| 36¢ | red | 250. | 125. |
| | v. imperforate | — | |

| N38 | | UnFVF | UseFVF |
|---|---|---|---|
| 48¢ | red | 225. | 75.00 |
| | v. imperforate | — | |

| N39 | | UnFVF | UseFVF |
|---|---|---|---|
| 60¢ | red | 175. | 75.00 |
| | v. imperforate | — | |

| N40 | | UnFVF | UseFVF |
|---|---|---|---|
| 72¢ | red | 350. | 150. |
| | v. imperforate | — | |

| N41 | | UnFVF | UseFVF |
|---|---|---|---|
| 84¢ | red | 250. | 125. |
| | imperforate | — | |

| N42 | | UnFVF | UseFVF |
|---|---|---|---|
| 96¢ | red | 175. | 75.00 |
| | pink carmine | 175. | 75.00 |
| | v. imperforate | — | |

| N43 | | UnFVF | UseFVF |
|---|---|---|---|
| $1.92 | pale brown | 125. | 100. |
| | brown | 125. | 100. |
| | cracked plate | 175. | |
| | v. imperforate | — | |

| N44 | | UnFVF | UseFVF |
|---|---|---|---|
| $3 | red vermilion | 125. | 75.00 |
| | v. imperforate | — | |

| N45 | | UnFVF | UseFVF |
|---|---|---|---|
| $6 | blue | 225. | 125. |
| | ultramarine | 225. | 125. |
| | v. imperforate | — | |

| N46 | | UnFVF | UseFVF |
|---|---|---|---|
| $9 | orange | 150. | 75.00 |
| | v. imperforate | — | |

| N47 | | UnFVF | UseFVF |
|---|---|---|---|
| $12 | yellow green | 225. | 100. |
| | v. imperforate | — | |

| N48 | | UnFVF | UseFVF |
|---|---|---|---|
| $24 | dark violet | 300. | 150. |
| | v. imperforate | — | |

| N49 | | UnFVF | UseFVF |
|---|---|---|---|
| $36 | Indian red | 350. | 150. |
| | v. imperforate | — | |

| N50 | | UnFVF | UseFVF |
|---|---|---|---|
| $48 | yellow brown | 450. | 225. |
| | v. imperforate | — | |

| N51 | | UnFVF | UseFVF |
|---|---|---|---|
| $60 | purple | 450. | 225. |
| | bright purple | 450. | 225. |
| | v. imperforate | — | |

**1885. ALLEGORY DESIGN ISSUE** Intaglio, American Bank Note Co., soft porous paper, perforated 12.

| N52 | | UnFVF | UseFVF |
|---|---|---|---|
| 1¢ | black | 12.50 | 5.50 |
| | gray black | 12.50 | 5.50 |
| | intense black | 12.50 | 5.50 |
| | Double transfer at top | 15.00 | 9.00 |

| N53 | | UnFVF | UseFVF |
|---|---|---|---|
| 12¢ | carmine | 40.00 | 15.00 |
| | deep carmine | 40.00 | 15.00 |
| | rose carmine | 40.00 | 15.00 |

| N54 | | UnFVF | UseFVF |
|---|---|---|---|
| 24¢ | carmine | 40.00 | 17.50 |
| | deep carmine | 40.00 | 17.50 |
| | rose carmine | 40.00 | 17.50 |

| N55 | | UnFVF | UseFVF |
|---|---|---|---|
| 36¢ | carmine | 60.00 | 25.00 |
| | deep carmine | 60.00 | 25.00 |
| | rose carmine | 60.00 | 25.00 |

| N56 | | UnFVF | UseFVF |
|---|---|---|---|
| 48¢ | carmine | 85.00 | 40.00 |
| | deep carmine | 85.00 | 40.00 |

| N57 | | UnFVF | UseFVF |
|---|---|---|---|
| 60¢ | carmine | 125. | 50.00 |
| | deep carmine | 125. | 50.00 |

| N58 | | UnFVF | UseFVF |
|---|---|---|---|
| 72¢ | carmine | 150. | 60.00 |
| | deep carmine | 150. | 60.00 |
| | rose carmine | 150. | 60.00 |

| N59 | | UnFVF | UseFVF |
|---|---|---|---|
| 84¢ | carmine | 300. | 140. |
| | rose carmine | 300. | 140. |

| N60 | | UnFVF | UseFVF |
|---|---|---|---|
| 96¢ | carmine | 225. | 100. |
| | rose carmine | 225. | 100. |

*Imperforates of N52-B60 exist, but they were not regularly issued.*

**1894. ALLEGORY DESIGN ISSUE** Intaglio, Bureau of Engraving, soft wove paper, perforated 12.

| N61 | | UnFVF | UseFVF |
|---|---|---|---|
| 1¢ | black | 100. | — |
| | Double transfer at top | 125. | |

| N62 | | UnFVF | UseFVF |
|---|---|---|---|
| 2¢ | black | 100. | — |
| | Double transfer at top | 125. | |

| N63 | | UnFVF | UseFVF |
|---|---|---|---|
| 4¢ | black | 125. | — |

| N64 | | UnFVF | UseFVF |
|---|---|---|---|
| 6¢ | black | 1500. | — |

| N65 | | UnFVF | UseFVF |
|---|---|---|---|
| 10¢ | black | 225. | — |

| N66 | | UnFVF | UseFVF |
|---|---|---|---|
| 12¢ | pink | 700. | — |

| N67 | | UnFVF | UseFVF |
|---|---|---|---|
| 24¢ | pink | 700. | — |

| N68 | | UnFVF | UseFVF |
|---|---|---|---|
| 36¢ | pink | 4500. | — |

| N69 | | UnFVF | UseFVF |
|---|---|---|---|
| 60¢ | pink | 4500. | — |

| N70 | | UnFVF | UseFVF |
|---|---|---|---|
| 96¢ | pink | 5500. | — |

| N71 | | UnFVF | UseFVF |
|---|---|---|---|
| $3 | scarlet | 6500. | — |

| N72 | | UnFVF | UseFVF |
|---|---|---|---|
| $6 | pale blue | 8500. | — |

**1895. NEW ALLEGORY DESIGNS ISSUE** Intaglio, Bureau of Engraving, soft wove paper, perforated 12.

N73-N76 "Freedom" N77-N78 *Astraea*

| N73 | | UnFVF | UseFVF |
|---|---|---|---|
| 1¢ | black | 40.00 | 10.00 |

| N74 | | UnFVF | UseFVF |
|---|---|---|---|
| 2¢ | black | 40.00 | 10.00 |
| | gray black | 30.00 | 10.00 |
| | Double transfer at top | 45.00 | |

| N75 | | UnFVF | UseFVF |
|---|---|---|---|
| 5¢ | black | 50.00 | 15.00 |
| | gray black | 50.00 | 15.00 |

| N76 | | UnFVF | UseFVF |
|---|---|---|---|
| 10¢ | black | 100. | 45.00 |

| N77 | | UnFVF | UseFVF |
|---|---|---|---|
| 25¢ | carmine | 150. | 50.00 |

| N78 | | UnFVF | UseFVF |
|---|---|---|---|
| 50¢ | carmine | 325. | 125. |

N79 *"Victory"* N80 *"Clio"*

| N79 | | UnFVF | UseFVF |
|---|---|---|---|
| $2 | scarlet | 400. | 100. |

| N80 | | UnFVF | UseFVF |
|---|---|---|---|
| $5 | ultramarine | 600. | 200. |

N81 *Vesta*

| N81 | | UnFVF | UseFVF |
|---|---|---|---|
| $10 | green | 550. | 225. |
| N82 | | UnFVF | UseFVF |
| $20 | slate | 825. | 400. |

N83 *"Commerce"* N84 *Indian Maiden*

| N83 | | UnFVF | UseFVF |
|---|---|---|---|
| $50 | dull rose | 850. | 400. |
| N84 | | UnFVF | UseFVF |
| $100. | purple | 1000. | 450. |
| N85 | | UnFVF | UseFVF |
| 1¢ | black | 4.00 | 3.25 |
| | gray black | 4.00 | 3.25 |
| N86 | | UnFVF | UseFVF |
| 2¢ | black | 4.50 | 3.75 |
| | gray black | 4.50 | 3.75 |
| N87 | | UnFVF | UseFVF |
| 5¢ | black | 7.00 | 5.50 |
| | gray black | 7.00 | 5.50 |
| N88 | | UnFVF | UseFVF |
| 10¢ | black | 4.50 | 3.75 |
| | gray black | 4.50 | 3.75 |
| N89 | | UnFVF | UseFVF |
| 25¢ | carmine | 8.50 | 8.50 |
| | lilac rose | 8.50 | 8.50 |

| N90 | | UnFVF | UseFVF |
|---|---|---|---|
| 50¢ | carmine | 12.50 | 14.00 |
| | rose carmine | 12.50 | 14.00 |
| | lilac rose | 12.50 | 14.00 |
| N91 | | UnFVF | UseFVF |
| $2 | scarlet | 15.00 | 17.50 |
| | scarlet vermilion | 15.00 | 17.50 |
| N92 | | UnFVF | UseFVF |
| $5 | dark blue | 25.00 | 30.00 |
| | light blue | 125. | 50.00 |
| N93 | | UnFVF | UseFVF |
| $10 | green | 25.00 | 30.00 |
| N94 | | UnFVF | UseFVF |
| $20 | slate | 25.00 | 35.00 |
| N95 | | UnFVF | UseFVF |
| $50 | dull rose | 30.00 | 40.00 |
| N96 | | UnFVF | UseFVF |
| $100. | purple | 35.00 | 42.50 |

**1899. REPRINTS OF THE 1895 ISSUE SPECIAL PRINTING** In 1899 the U.S. Government sold 26,898 sets of the Newspaper series of 1895-97 to collectors at $5 per set. Since the supply of high values was not great enough to make up the number of sets required, the values from the $5 through the $100 were reprinted. These special printings can be distinguished from the originals by the shade and whiteness of the paper and gum.

By Bureau of Engraving and Printing. Designs of 1895 Issue but on *double-line USPS watermark, with white instead of yellowish gum, perforated 12.*

| SPN30 | | UnFVF | UseFVF |
|---|---|---|---|
| $5 | blue | — | |
| SPN31 | | UnFVF | UseFVF |
| $10 | green | — | |
| SPN32 | | UnFVF | UseFVF |
| $20 | slate | — | |
| SPN33 | | UnFVF | UseFVF |
| $50 | rose | — | |
| SPN34 | | UnFVF | UseFVF |
| $100. | purple | — | |

# Official Carriers Stamp

**1875. REPRINT OFFICIAL CARRIER STAMP** Special Printing Reprint of the Official Carrier Stamps of 1851. The Franklin carrier was printed in a darker blue than the originals and appers on rose-colored paper as well as on a paler, thicker paper. The Eagle reprints are on hard white paper and also on a coarse paper. Printed by the Continental Bank Note Company. *Printed by intaglio, imperforate, without gum.*

REG1

| SPOCS1 | | UnFVF | UseFVF |
|---|---|---|---|
| 1¢ | blue on rose paper | 50.00 | |
| | v. Perforated 12 | 2500. | |

REG1

| SPOCS2 | | UnFVF | UseFVF |
|---|---|---|---|
| 1¢ | blue | 25.00 | |
| | v. Perforated 12 | 175. | |

# Official Stamps

The franking privilege for the various government departments was abolished July 1, 1873. On that date official stamps were issued to be used by the departments. In addition to the name of the department, inscribed at the top, the Post Office Department stamps have large numerals as the central design, while the stamps of the other departments feature busts of the following men: 1¢ Benjamin Franklin

    2¢ Andrew Jackson
    3¢ George Washington
    6¢ Abraham Lincoln
    7¢ Edwin Stanton
    10¢ Thomas Jefferson
    12¢ Henry Clay
    15¢ Daniel Webster
    24¢ Winfield Scott
    30¢ Alexander Hamilton
    90¢ Oliver Perry
    $2 to $20 William Seward

The first official stamps were printed in intaglio by the Continental Bank Note co. on thin, hard paper, but in 1879 the American Bank Note Co., using the same plates, made printings on soft, porous paper. this is the principal way that they can be identified, since all the paper is unwatermarked, and all the stamps are *perforated 12*. A marginal imprint reading "Continental" does not necessarily indicate the printer.

**1873. AGRICULTURE DEPT. ISSUE** Printed in intaglio on thin, hard paper, unwatermarked, perforated 12.

| OF1 | | UnFVF | UseFVF |
|---|---|---|---|
| 1¢ | yellow | 95.00 | 75.00 |
| | golden yellow | 110. | 80.00 |
| | olive yellow | 110. | 80.00 |
| | p. Ribbed paper | 125. | 80.00 |
| | On cover | — | |

| OF2 | | UnFVF | UseFVF |
|---|---|---|---|
| 2¢ | yellow | 85.00 | 32.50 |
| | golden yellow | 75.00 | 25.00 |
| | olive yellow | 75.00 | 27.50 |
| | p. Ribbed paper | 80.00 | 30.00 |
| | On cover | — | |

| OF3 | | UnFVF | UseFVF |
|---|---|---|---|
| 3¢ | yellow | 65.00 | 6.00 |
| | golden yellow | 70.00 | 6.50 |
| | olive yellow | 73.00 | 6.50 |
| | Double transfer | — | — |
| | p. Ribbed paper | 73.00 | 7.00 |
| | On cover | — | |

| OF4 | | UnFVF | UseFVF |
|---|---|---|---|
| 6¢ | yellow | 80.00 | 25.00 |
| | golden yellow | 80.00 | 27.50 |
| | olive yellow | 80.00 | 27.50 |
| | On cover | — | |

| OF5 | | UnFVF | UseFVF |
|---|---|---|---|
| 10¢ | yellow | 150. | 100. |
| | golden yellow | 165. | 110. |
| | olive yellow | 175. | 115. |
| | On cover | — | |

| OF6 | | UnFVF | UseFVF |
|---|---|---|---|
| 12¢ | yellow | 195. | 100. |
| | golden yellow | 210. | 110. |
| | olive yellow | 225. | 110. |
| | On cover | — | |

| OF7 | | UnFVF | UseFVF |
|---|---|---|---|
| 15¢ | yellow | 160. | 95.00 |
| | golden yellow | 170. | 100. |
| | olive yellow | 175. | 100. |
| | On cover | — | |

| OF8 | | UnFVF | UseFVF |
|---|---|---|---|
| 24¢ | yellow | 160. | 85.00 |
| | golden yellow | 175. | 85.00 |
| | On cover | — | |

| OF9 | | UnFVF | UseFVF |
|---|---|---|---|
| 30¢ | yellow | 225. | 115. |
| | olive yellow | 250. | 150. |
| | golden yellow | 235. | 140. |

**1879. AGRICULTURE DEPT. ISSUE** Printed by the American Bank Note Co. *Printed in intaglio on soft, porous paper unwatermarked, perforated 12.*

| OF10 | | UnFVF | UseFVF |
|---|---|---|---|
| 1¢ | yellow, | 2000. | |
| | issued without gum | 1500. | |
| | Plate pair | | |

*Some consider No. OF10 a special printing, circa 1883.*

| OF11 | | UnFVF | UseFVF |
|---|---|---|---|
| 3¢ | yellow | 225. | 40.00 |

**1873. EXECUTIVE DEPT. ISSUE** *Printed in intaglio on thin, hard paper, unwatermarked, perforated 12.*

| OF12 | | UnFVF | UseFVF |
|---|---|---|---|
| 1¢ | carmine | 335. | 200. |
| | dark carmine | 335. | 200. |

| OF13 | | UnFVF | UseFVF |
|---|---|---|---|
| 2¢ | carmine | 210. | 100. |
| | dark carmine | 210. | 100. |
| | Double transfer | — | — |

| OF14 | | UnFVF | UseFVF |
|---|---|---|---|
| 3¢ | carmine | 260. | 100. |
| | lilac red | 260. | 100. |

| OF15 | | UnFVF | UseFVF |
|---|---|---|---|
| 6¢ | carmine | 400. | 275. |
| | dark carmine | 400. | 275. |
| | dull carmine | 400. | 275. |

| OF16 | | UnFVF | UseFVF |
|---|---|---|---|
| 10¢ | carmine | 350. | 300. |
| | dark carmine | 350. | 300. |
| | dull carmine | 350. | 300. |

**1873. INTERIOR DEPT. ISSUE** *Printed in intaglio on thin, hard paper, unwatermarked, perforated 12.*

| OF17 | | UnFVF | UseFVF |
|---|---|---|---|
| 1¢ | orange red | 21.00 | 5.25 |
| | bright orange red | 21.00 | 5.25 |
| | dull orange red | 21.00 | 5.25 |
| | p. Ribbed paper | 25.00 | 6.00 |

| OF18 | | UnFVF | UseFVF |
|---|---|---|---|
| 2¢ | orange red | 16.50 | 3.25 |
| | bright orange red | 16.50 | 3.25 |
| | dull orange red | 16.50 | 3.25 |

| OF19 | | UnFVF | UseFVF |
|---|---|---|---|
| 3¢ | orange red | 28.00 | 3.00 |
| | bright orange red | 28.00 | 3.00 |
| | dull orange red | 28.00 | 3.00 |
| | p. Ribbed paper | 30.00 | 5.25 |

| OF20 | | UnFVF | UseFVF |
|---|---|---|---|
| 6¢ | orange red | 21.00 | 3.25 |
| | bright orange red | 21.00 | 3.25 |
| | dull orange red | 21.00 | 3.25 |

| OF21 | | UnFVF | UseFVF |
|---|---|---|---|
| 10¢ | orange red | 20.00 | 6.25 |
| | bright orange red | 20.00 | 6.25 |
| | dull orange red | 20.00 | 6.25 |

| OF22 | | UnFVF | UseFVF |
|---|---|---|---|
| 12¢ | orange red | 32.50 | 4.75 |
| | bright orange red | 32.50 | 4.75 |
| | dull orange red | 32.50 | 4.75 |

| OF23 | | UnFVF | UseFVF |
|---|---|---|---|
| 15¢ | orange red | 50.00 | 10.00 |
| | bright orange red | 50.00 | 10.00 |
| | dull orange red | 50.00 | 10.00 |
| | Double transfer | 90.00 | 25.00 |
| | p. Ribbed paper | — | — |

| OF24 | | UnFVF | UseFVF |
|---|---|---|---|
| 24¢ | **orange red** | 37.50 | 8.50 |
| | bright orange red | 37.50 | 8.50 |
| | dull orange red | 37.50 | 8.50 |

| OF25 | | UnFVF | UseFVF |
|---|---|---|---|
| 30¢ | **orange red** | 50.00 | 8.50 |
| | bright orange red | 50.00 | 8.50 |
| | dull orange red | 50.00 | 8.50 |

| OF26 | | UnFVF | UseFVF |
|---|---|---|---|
| 90¢ | **orange red** | 115. | 22.50 |
| | bright orange red | 115. | 22.50 |
| | dull orange red | 115. | 22.50 |
| | Double transfer | 160. | — |

**1879. INTERIOR DEPT. ISSUE** *Printed in intaglio on soft, porous paper unwatermarked, perforated 12.*

| OF27 | | UnFVF | UseFVF |
|---|---|---|---|
| 1¢ | **orange red** | 135. | 125. |
| | dull orange red | 135. | 125. |

| OF28 | | UnFVF | UseFVF |
|---|---|---|---|
| 2¢ | **orange red** | 2.50 | 1.25 |
| | dull orange red | 2.50 | 1.25 |

| OF29 | | UnFVF | UseFVF |
|---|---|---|---|
| 3¢ | **orange red** | 2.25 | .75 |
| | dull orange red | 2.25 | .75 |

| OF30 | | UnFVF | UseFVF |
|---|---|---|---|
| 6¢ | **orange red** | 3.50 | 3.75 |
| | dull orange red | 3.50 | 3.75 |

| OF31 | | UnFVF | UseFVF |
|---|---|---|---|
| 10¢ | **orange red** | 45.00 | 35.00 |
| | dull orange red | 45.00 | 35.00 |

| OF32 | | UnFVF | UseFVF |
|---|---|---|---|
| 12¢ | **orange red** | 90.00 | 60.00 |
| | dull orange red | 90.00 | 60.00 |

| OF33 | | UnFVF | UseFVF |
|---|---|---|---|
| 15¢ | **orange red** | 200. | 150. |
| | dull orange red | 200. | 150. |
| | Double transfer, left side | 275. | — |

| OF34 | | UnFVF | UseFVF |
|---|---|---|---|
| 24¢ | **orange red** | 2500. | — |
| | dull orange red | 2500. | — |

**1873. JUSTICE DEPT. ISSUE** *Printed in intaglio on thin, hard paper, unwatermarked, perforated 12.*

| OF35 | | UnFVF | UseFVF |
|---|---|---|---|
| 1¢ | **purple** | 65.00 | 47.50 |
| | dark purple | 65.00 | 47.50 |

| OF36 | | UnFVF | UseFVF |
|---|---|---|---|
| 2¢ | **purple** | 100. | 50.00 |
| | dark purple | 100. | 50.00 |

| OF37 | | UnFVF | UseFVF |
|---|---|---|---|
| 3¢ | **purple** | 100. | 10.00 |
| | dark purple | 100. | 10.00 |
| | Double transfer | — | — |

| OF38 | | UnFVF | UseFVF |
|---|---|---|---|
| 6¢ | **purple** | 95.00 | 16.00 |
| | bluish purple | 95.00 | 16.00 |
| | dull purple | 95.00 | 16.00 |

| OF39 | | UnFVF | UseFVF |
|---|---|---|---|
| 10¢ | **purple** | 110. | 35.00 |
| | bluish purple | 110. | 35.00 |
| | Double transfer | — | — |

| OF40 | | UnFVF | UseFVF |
|---|---|---|---|
| 12¢ | **purple** | 85.00 | 22.50 |
| | dark purple | 85.00 | 22.50 |

| OF41 | | UnFVF | UseFVF |
|---|---|---|---|
| 15¢ | **purple** | 160. | 75.00 |
| | Double transfer | — | — |

| OF42 | | UnFVF | UseFVF |
|---|---|---|---|
| 24¢ | **purple** | 425. | 165. |

| OF43 | | UnFVF | UseFVF |
|---|---|---|---|
| 30¢ | **purple** | 375. | 95.00 |
| | Double transfer | 400. | 95.00 |

| OF44 | | UnFVF | UseFVF |
|---|---|---|---|
| 90¢ | **purple** | 700. | 240. |
| | dark purple | 700. | 240. |

**1879. JUSTICE DEPT. ISSUE** *Printed in intaglio on soft, porous paper unwatermarked, perforated 12.*

| OF45 | | UnFVF | UseFVF |
|---|---|---|---|
| 3¢ | **bluish purple** | 65.00 | 40.00 |
| | dark bluish purple | 65.00 | 40.00 |

| OF46 | | UnFVF | UseFVF |
|---|---|---|---|
| 6¢ | **dark bluish purple** | 150. | 100. |
| | dark bluish purple | | |

**1873. NAVY DEPT. ISSUE** *Printed in intaglio on thin, hard paper, unwatermarked, perforated 12.*

| OF47 | | UnFVF | UseFVF |
|---|---|---|---|
| 1¢ | **ultramarine** | 45.00 | 22.50 |
| | dark ultramarine | 45.00 | 22.50 |
| | dull blue | 45.00 | 22.50 |

| OF48 | | UnFVF | UseFVF |
|---|---|---|---|
| 2¢ | **ultramarine** | 35.00 | 10.00 |
| | dark ultramarine | 35.00 | 10.00 |
| | dull blue | 45.00 | 12.50 |
| | gray blue | 45.00 | 12.50 |
| | Double transfer | — | — |

| OF49 | | UnFVF | UseFVF |
|---|---|---|---|
| 3¢ | **ultramarine** | 35.00 | 5.25 |
| | dark ultramarine | 35.00 | 5.25 |
| | dull blue | 35.00 | 5.25 |
| | pale ultramarine | 35.00 | 5.25 |
| | Double transfer | — | — |

| OF50 | | UnFVF | UseFVF |
|---|---|---|---|
| 6¢ | **ultramarine** | 37.50 | 8.50 |
| | bright ultrmarine | 37.50 | 8.50 |
| | dull blue | 45.00 | 8.50 |
| | Double transfer | — | — |
| | Vertical line through "N" of "NAVY" | 65.00 | 14.00 |

| OF51 | | UnFVF | UseFVF |
|---|---|---|---|
| 7¢ | **ultramarine** | 210. | 85.00 |
| | dark ultramarine | 210. | 85.00 |
| | dull blue | 210. | 85.00 |
| | Double transfer | — | — |

| OF52 | | UnFVF | UseFVF |
|---|---|---|---|
| 10¢ | **ultramarine** | 47.50 | 17.50 |
| | dark ultrmarine | 46.50 | 17.50 |
| | dull blue | 50.00 | 17.50 |
| | pale ultramarine | 47.50 | 17.50 |
| | Cracked plate | — | 125. |
| | p. Ribbed paper | 75.00 | 40.00 |

| OF53 | | UnFVF | UseFVF |
|---|---|---|---|
| 12¢ | **ultramarine** | 55.00 | 15.00 |
| | dark ultramarine | 55.00 | 15.00 |
| | pale ultramarine | 55.00 | 15.00 |
| | Double transfer, left side | 175. | 50.00 |

| OF54 | | UnFVF | UseFVF |
|---|---|---|---|
| 15¢ | **ultramarine** | 100. | 35.00 |
| | dark ultramarine | 100. | 35.00 |

| OF55 | | UnFVF | UseFVF |
|---|---|---|---|
| 24¢ | **ultramarine** | 100. | 35.00 |
| | dark ultramarine | 100. | 35.00 |
| | dull blue | 125. | — |

| OF56 | | UnFVF | UseFVF |
|---|---|---|---|
| 30¢ | **ultramarine** | 80.00 | 17.50 |
| | dark ultramarine | 80.00 | 17.50 |
| | Double transfer | 100. | 20.00 |

| OF57 | | UnFVF | UseFVF |
|---|---|---|---|
| 90¢ | **ultramarine** | 425. | 110. |
| | v. Double impression | — | 7500. |

**1873. POST OFFICE DEPT. ISSUE** *Printed by intaglio on thin, hard paper, unwatermarked, perforated 12.*

|  |  | UnFVF | UseFVF |
|---|---|---|---|
| **OF58** |  |  |  |
| 1¢ | **gray black** | 7.50 | 3.50 |
|  | black | 7.50 | 3.50 |
| **OF59** |  | UnFVF | UseFVF |
| 2¢ | **gray black** | 8.50 | 3.00 |
|  | black | 8.50 | 3.00 |
|  | v. Double Impression | 325. | — |
| **OF60** |  | UnFVF | UseFVF |
| 3¢ | **black** | 3.00 | 1.00 |
|  | gray black | 3.00 | 1.00 |
|  | Cracked plate | 10.00 | 7.00 |
|  | Double transfer | — | — |
|  | p. Ribbed paper | — | — |
|  | v. Printed on both sides | — | 3500. |
| **OF61** |  | UnFVF | UseFVF |
| 6¢ | **black** | 9.00 | 2.25 |
|  | gray black | 9.00 | 2.25 |
|  | p. Ribbed paper | — | 9.00 |
|  | y. Diagonal half used as 3¢ cover | — | 4500. |
| **OF62** |  | UnFVF | UseFVF |
| 10¢ | **black** | 40.00 | 20.00 |
|  | gray black | 40.00 | 20.00 |
| **OF63** |  | UnFVF | UseFVF |
| 12¢ | **black** | 20.00 | 5.50 |
|  | gray black | 20.00 | 5.50 |
| **OF64** |  | UnFVF | UseFVF |
| 15¢ | **black** | 27.50 | 9.00 |
|  | gray black | 27.50 | 9.00 |
|  | Double transfer | — | — |
|  | v. Imperforate, pair | — | 550. |
| **OF65** |  | UnFVF | UseFVF |
| 24¢ | **black** | 35.00 | 10.00 |
|  | gray black | 35.00 | 10.00 |
| **OF66** |  | UnFVF | UseFVF |
| 30¢ | **black** | 35.00 | 10.00 |
|  | gray black | 35.00 | 10.00 |
| **OF67** |  | UnFVF | UseFVF |
| 90¢ | **black** | 50.00 | 10.00 |
|  | gray black | 50.00 | 10.00 |
|  | Double transfer | — | — |

**1879. POST OFFICE DEPT. ISSUE** *Printed in intaglio on soft, porous paper, unwatermarked, perforated 12.*

|  |  | UnFVF | UseFVF |
|---|---|---|---|
| **OF68** |  |  |  |
| 3¢ | **black** | 9.00 | 3.25 |
|  | gray black | 9.00 | 3.25 |
|  | Block of 4 | 200. | — |

**1873. STATE DEPT. ISSUE** *Printed in intaglio on thin, hard paper, unwatermarked, perforated 12.*

|  |  | UnFVF | UseFVF |
|---|---|---|---|
| **OF69** |  |  |  |
| 1¢ | **green** | 65.00 | 25.00 |
|  | dark yellow green | 65.00 | 25.00 |
|  | pale green | 65.00 | 25.00 |
| **OF70** |  | UnFVF | UseFVF |
| 2¢ | **green** | 130. | 40.00 |
|  | dark yellow green | 130. | 40.00 |
|  | yellow green | 130. | 40.00 |
|  | Double transfer | — | — |
| **OF71** |  | UnFVF | UseFVF |
| 3¢ | **green** | 50.00 | 9.50 |
|  | bright green | 50.00 | 9.50 |
|  | yellow green | 50.00 | 9.50 |
| **OF72** |  | UnFVF | UseFVF |
| 6¢ | **green** | 50.00 | 11.50 |
|  | bright green | 50.00 | 11.50 |
|  | yellow green | 50.00 | 11.50 |
|  | Double transfer | — | — |

|  |  | UnFVF | UseFVF |
|---|---|---|---|
| **OF73** |  |  |  |
| 7¢ | **green** | 90.00 | 25.00 |
|  | dark yellow green | 90.00 | 25.00 |
|  | p. Ribbed paper | 125. | 27.50 |
| **OF74** |  | UnFVF | UseFVF |
| 10¢ | **green** | 70.00 | 16.00 |
|  | bright green | 70.00 | 16.00 |
|  | yellow green | 70.00 | 16.00 |
|  | Short transfer | 150. | 30.00 |
| **OF75** |  | UnFVF | UseFVF |
| 12¢ | **green** | 115. | 50.00 |
|  | Yellow green | 115. | 50.00 |
| **OF76** |  | UnFVF | UseFVF |
| 15¢ | **green** | 125. | 35.00 |
|  | dark yellow green | 125. | 35.00 |
| **OF77** |  | UnFVF | UseFVF |
| 24¢ | **green** | 256. | 90.00 |
|  | dark yellow green | 250. | 90.00 |
| **OF78** |  | UnFVF | UseFVF |
| 30¢ | **green** | 225. | 65.00 |
|  | dark yellow green | 225. | 65.00 |
| **OF79** |  | UnFVF | UseFVF |
| 90¢ | **green** | 450. | 140. |
|  | dark yellow green | 450. | 140. |
| **OF80** |  | UnFVF | UseFVF |
| $2 | **green & black** | 525. | 400. |
|  | yellow green & black | 525. | 400. |

OF81

|  |  | UnFVF | UseFVF |
|---|---|---|---|
| **OF81** |  |  |  |
| $5 | **green & black** | 4250. | 1800. |
|  | dark green & black | 4250. | 1800. |
|  | yellow green & black | 4250. | 1800. |
|  | Plate block of 6 | 42500. |  |
| **OF82** |  | UnFVF | UseFVF |
| $10 | **green & black** | 2800. | 1400. |
|  | dark green & black | 2800. | 1400. |
|  | yellow green & black | 2800. | 1400. |
| **OF83** |  | UnFVF | UseFVF |
| $20 | **green & black** | 1950. | 950. |
|  | dark green & black | 1950. | 950. |
|  | yellow green & black | 1950. | 950. |

**1873. TREASURY DEPT. ISSUE** *Printed in intaglio on thin, hard paper, unwatermarked, perforated 12.*

|  |  | UnFVF | UseFVF |
|---|---|---|---|
| **OF84** |  |  |  |
| 1¢ | **brown** | 25.00 | 3.00 |
|  | dark brown | 25.00 | 3.00 |
|  | yellow brown | 25.00 | 3.00 |
|  | Double transfer | 35.00 | 5.00 |
| **OF85** |  | UnFVF | UseFVF |
| 2¢ | **brown** | 27.50 | 3.00 |
|  | dark brown | 27.50 | 3.00 |
|  | yellow brown | 27.50 | 3.00 |
|  | Cracked plate | 40.00 | — |
|  | Double transfer | — | — |
| **OF86** |  | UnFVF | UseFVF |
| 3¢ | **brown** | 17.50 | 1.50 |
|  | dark brown | 17.50 | 1.50 |
|  | yellow brown | 17.50 | 1.50 |
|  | t. Shaded circle to right of right frame line | — | — |
|  | t1. Double impression | — | — |

| OF87 | | UnFVF | UseFVF |
|---|---|---|---|
| 6¢ | **brown** | 23.00 | 2.50 |
| | dark brown | 23.00 | 2.50 |
| | yellow brown | 23.00 | 2.50 |
| | Double transfer | — | — |
| | Worn plate | 23.00 | 3.00 |

| OF88 | | UnFVF | UseFVF |
|---|---|---|---|
| 7¢ | **brown** | 55.00 | 15.00 |
| | dark brown | 55.00 | 15.00 |
| | yellow brown | 55.00 | 15.00 |

| OF89 | | UnFVF | UseFVF |
|---|---|---|---|
| 10¢ | **brown** | 60.00 | 5.50 |
| | dark brown | 60.00 | 5.50 |
| | yellow brown | 60.00 | 5.50 |
| | Double transfer | — | — |

| OF90 | | UnFVF | UseFVF |
|---|---|---|---|
| 12¢ | **brown** | 60.00 | 4.00 |
| | dark brown | 60.00 | 4.00 |
| | yellow brown | 60.00 | 4.00 |

| OF91 | | UnFVF | UseFVF |
|---|---|---|---|
| 15¢ | **brown** | 55.00 | 5.50 |
| | dark brown | 55.00 | 5.50 |
| | yellow brown | 55.00 | 5.50 |

| OF92 | | UnFVF | UseFVF |
|---|---|---|---|
| 24¢ | **brown** | 250. | 45.00 |
| | dark brown | 250. | 45.00 |
| | yellow brown | 250. | 45.00 |
| | Double transfer | — | — |

| OF93 | | UnFVF | UseFVF |
|---|---|---|---|
| 30¢ | **brown** | 85.00 | 6.00 |
| | dark brown | 85.00 | 6.00 |
| | yellow brown | 85.00 | 6.00 |
| | Short transfer | — | — |

| OF94 | | UnFVF | UseFVF |
|---|---|---|---|
| 90¢ | **brown** | 85.00 | 6.00 |
| | dark brown | 85.00 | 6.00 |
| | yellow brown | 85.00 | 6.00 |

**1879. TREASURY DEPT. ISSUE** *Printed in intaglio on soft, porous paper, unwatermarked, perforated 12.*

| OF95 | | UnFVF | UseFVF |
|---|---|---|---|
| 3¢ | **brown** | | |
| | yellow brown | 30.00 | 4.50 |

| OF96 | | UnFVF | UseFVF |
|---|---|---|---|
| 6¢ | **brown** | 20.00 | |
| | yellow brown | 55.00 | 20.00 |

| OF97 | | UnFVF | UseFVF |
|---|---|---|---|
| 10¢ | **brown** | 85.00 | 25.00 |
| | dark brown | 85.00 | 25.00 |
| | yellow brown | 85.00 | 25.00 |

| OF98 | | UnFVF | UseFVF |
|---|---|---|---|
| 30¢ | **brown** | 800. | 175. |
| | yellow brown | 800. | 175. |

| OF99 | | UnFVF | UseFVF |
|---|---|---|---|
| 90¢ | **brown** | 1000. | 175. |
| | dark brown | 1000. | 175. |
| | yellow brown | 1000. | 175. |

**1873. WAR DEPT. ISSUE** *Printed in intaglio on thin, hard paper, unwatermarked, perforated 12.*

| OF100 | | UnFVF | UseFVF |
|---|---|---|---|
| 1¢ | **Venetian red** | 80.00 | 4.50 |
| | rose red | 80.00 | 4.50 |

| OF101 | | UnFVF | UseFVF |
|---|---|---|---|
| 2¢ | **Venetian red** | 70.00 | 6.50 |
| | rose red | 70.00 | 6.50 |
| | p. Ribbed paper | 65.00 | 9.00 |

| OF102 | | UnFVF | UseFVF |
|---|---|---|---|
| 3¢ | **Venetian red** | 70.00 | 1.75 |
| | rose red | 70.00 | 1.75 |

| OF103 | | UnFVF | UseFVF |
|---|---|---|---|
| 6¢ | **Venetian red** | 225. | 4.00 |
| | dull Venetian red | 225. | 4.00 |

| OF104 | | UnFVF | UseFVF |
|---|---|---|---|
| 7¢ | **Venetian red** | 70.00 | 40.00 |
| | dull Venetian red | 70.00 | 40.00 |
| | rose red | 70.00 | 40.00 |

| OF105 | | UnFVF | UseFVF |
|---|---|---|---|
| 10¢ | **Venetian red** | 25.00 | 7.50 |
| | rose red | 25.00 | 7.50 |

*The crack at lower left of* OF105 *was on the original die and is found on all copies.*

| OF106 | | UnFVF | UseFVF |
|---|---|---|---|
| 12¢ | **Venetian red** | 80.00 | 5.50 |
| | p. Ribbed paper | 110. | 7.50 |

| OF107 | | UnFVF | UseFVF |
|---|---|---|---|
| 15¢ | **Venetian red** | 19.00 | 6.75 |
| | dull Venetian red | 19.00 | 6.75 |
| | rose red | 22.50 | 7.50 |
| | p. Ribbed paper | 30.00 | 10.00 |

| OF108 | | UnFVF | UseFVF |
|---|---|---|---|
| 24¢ | **Venetian red** | 19.00 | 4.00 |
| | dull Venetian red | 19.00 | 4.00 |
| | rose red | 19.00 | 4.00 |

| OF109 | | UnFVF | UseFVF |
|---|---|---|---|
| 30¢ | **Venetian red** | 20.00 | 4.00 |
| | rose red | 20.00 | 4.00 |
| | p. Ribbed paper | 40.00 | 7.50 |

| OF110 | | UnFVF | UseFVF |
|---|---|---|---|
| 90¢ | **Venetian red** | 55.00 | 25.00 |
| | rose red | 55.00 | 25.00 |

**1879. WAR DEPT. ISSUE** Printed in intaglio on soft, porous paper, unwatermarked, perforated 12.

| OF111 | | UnFVF | UseFVF |
|---|---|---|---|
| 1¢ | **dull rose** | 3.00 | 2.00 |
| | Venetian red | 60.00 | 27.50 |
| | rose red | 60.00 | 27.50 |

| OF112 | | UnFVF | UseFVF |
|---|---|---|---|
| 2¢ | **dull rose** | 3.50 | 2.00 |
| | dark rose | 3.50 | 2.00 |
| | dull vermilion | 3.50 | 2.00 |

| OF113 | | UnFVF | UseFVF |
|---|---|---|---|
| 3¢ | **dull rose** | 3.50 | 1.25 |
| | rose red | 3.50 | 1.25 |
| | Double transfer | 6.00 | 4.00 |
| | v1. Double impression | 1000. | — |
| | v2. Imperforate pair | 1500. | — |

| OF114 | | UnFVF | UseFVF |
|---|---|---|---|
| 6¢ | **dull rose** | 4.00 | 1.25 |
| | dull vermilion | 4.00 | 1.25 |
| | rose red | 4.00 | 1.25 |

| OF115 | | UnFVF | UseFVF |
|---|---|---|---|
| 10¢ | **dull rose** | 25.00 | 20.00 |
| | rose red | 25.00 | 20.00 |

| OF116 | | UnFVF | UseFVF |
|---|---|---|---|
| 12¢ | **dull rose** | 20.00 | 7.50 |
| | rose red | 20.00 | 7.50 |

| OF117 | | UnFVF | UseFVF |
|---|---|---|---|
| 30¢ | **dull rose** | 65.00 | 42.50 |
| | rose red | 65.00 | 42.50 |

**1911. POSTAL SAVINGS ISSUE** When Postal Savings Depositories were set up in 1910 under the Post Office Department, special stamps were provided for that division. Their use was discontinued in 1914, and all remainders destroyed. *Printed in intaglio by the Bureau of Engraving and Printing, perforated 12.*

*OF118 and OF119 are Watermarked double-line USPS. OF120, OF121, OF122, and OF123 are Watermarked single-line USPS.*

 OF118, OF122

| OF118 | | **UnFVF** | **UseFVF** |
|---|---|---|---|
| **2¢** | **black** | 17.50 | 1.75 |
| | FDC *(Dec. 22, 1910)* | | |
| | Plate block of 6, w/imprint | 250. | |
| | Block of 4 (2mm apart) | 45.00 | 6.50 |
| | Block of 4 (3mm apart) | 42.00 | 5.50 |
| | Double transfer | 15.00 | 2.50 |

### 1911. POSTAL SAVINGS ISSUE

| OF119 | | **UnFVF** | **UseFVF** |
|---|---|---|---|
| **50¢** | **green** | 150. | 32.50 |
| | FDC *(Feb. 1, 1911)* | | |
| | Plate block of 6, w/imprint | 2400. | |
| | Block of 4 (2mm apart) | 550. | 170. |
| | Block of 4 (3mm apart) | 535. | 170. |
| | Margin block of 4, w/arrow | 560. | |

| OF120 | | **UnFVF** | **UseFVF** |
|---|---|---|---|
| **$1** | **bright blue** | 150. | 10.00 |
| | FDC *(Feb. 1, 1911)* | | |
| | Plate block of 6 w/imprint | 1900. | 375. |
| | Block of 4 (2mm apart) | 400. | 45.00 |
| | Block of 4 (3mm apart) | 390. | 45.00 |
| | Margin block of 4, w/arrow | 425. | |

| OF121 | | **UnFVF** | **UseFVF** |
|---|---|---|---|
| **1¢** | **dark red violet** | 8.50 | 1.25 |
| | FDC *(March 27, 1911)* | | |
| | Plate block of 6, w/imprint | 110. | |
| | Block of 4 (2mm apart) | 21.00 | 5.00 |
| | Block of 4 (3mm apart) | 20.00 | 4.75 |

| OF122 | | **UnFVF** | **UseFVF** |
|---|---|---|---|
| **2¢** | **black** | 45.00 | 4.25 |
| | FDC *(March 27, 1911)* | | |
| | Plate block of 6, w/imprint | 525. | |
| | Block of 4 (2mm apart) | 120. | 19.00 |
| | Block of 4 (3mm apart) | 118. | 19.00 |
| | Double transfer | 32.00 | 4.75 |

| OF123 | | **UnFVF** | **UseFVF** |
|---|---|---|---|
| **10¢** | **carmine** | 17.50 | 1.25 |
| | FDC *(Feb. 1, 1911)* | | |
| | Plate block of 6, w/imprint | 225. | |
| | Block of 4 (2mm apart) | 35.00 | 5.50 |
| | Block of 4 (3mm apart) | 33.00 | 5.00 |
| | Double transfer | 14.00 | 2.50 |

### 1983. OFFICIAL MAIL ISSUE Intaglio perforated 11.

 OF124-OF130

| OF124 | | **MNHVF** | **UseVF** |
|---|---|---|---|
| **1¢** | **blue, red & black** | .25 | .25 |
| | Plate block of 4 | .60 | |

| OF125 | | **MNHVF** | **UseVF** |
|---|---|---|---|
| **4¢** | **blue, red & black** | .25 | .25 |
| | Plate block of 4 | .75 | |

| OF126 | | **MNHVF** | **UseVF** |
|---|---|---|---|
| **13¢** | **blue, red & black** | .45 | .75 |
| | Plate block of 4 | 2.00 | |

| OF127 | | **MNHVF** | **UseVF** |
|---|---|---|---|
| **17¢** | **blue, red & black** | .50 | .40 |

| | | | |
|---|---|---|---|
| | Plate block of 4 | 2.50 | |

| OF128 | | **MNHVF** | **UseVF** |
|---|---|---|---|
| **$1** | **blue, red & black** | 3.00 | 1.25 |
| | Plate block of 4 | 14.00 | |

| OF129 | | **MNHVF** | **UseVF** |
|---|---|---|---|
| **$5** | **blue, red & black** | 10.00 | 5.00 |
| | Plate block of 4 | 45.00 | |

| OF130 | | **MNHVF** | **UseVF** |
|---|---|---|---|
| **20¢** | **blue, red & black** | 2.00 | 2.25 |
| | Pair | 4.50 | 4.50 |

### 1985. OFFICIAL MAIL NON-DENOMINATED ISSUE "D" rate, *intaglio.*

 OF131

| OF131 | | **MNHVF** | **UseVF** |
|---|---|---|---|
| **14¢** | **blue, red & black** | 4.50 | 5.50 |
| | Plate block of 4 | — | |
| | FDC *(Feb. 4, 1985)* | | 1.00 |

### 1985. OFFICIAL MAIL COILS ISSUE Coil, perforated 10 vertically.

 OF132

| OF132 | | **MNHVF** | **UseVF** |
|---|---|---|---|
| **22¢** | **blue, red & black** | 4.75 | 3.00 |
| | Pair | 7.50 | — |
| | FDC *(Feb. 4, 1985)* | | 1.00 |

 OF133, 134

| OF133 | | **MNHVF** | **UseVF** |
|---|---|---|---|
| **14¢** | **bue, red & black** | .40 | .65 |
| | FDC *(May 15, 1985)* | | |

| OF134 | | **MNHVF** | **UseVF** |
|---|---|---|---|
| **22¢** | **blue, red & black** | .75 | 2.25 |
| | Pair | 1.50 | 4.50 |
| | FDC *(May 15, 1985)* | | 1.00 |

 OF135

| OF135 | | **MNHVF** | **UseVF** |
|---|---|---|---|
| **25¢** | **blue, red & black** | 1.00 | 2.00 |
| | FDC *(May 15, 1985)* | | 1.00 |
| | Pair | | |

### 1988. OFFICIAL MAIL COILS ISSUE *Design similar to OF133. Coil, Offset, perforated 10 vertically.*

| OF136 | | **MNHVF** | **UseVF** |
|---|---|---|---|
| **20¢** | **blue, red & black** | .45 | .35 |
| | Pair | 1.00 | .75 |
| | FDC *(May 19, 1988)* | | 1.00 |

| OF137 | | **MNHVF** | **UseVF** |
|---|---|---|---|
| **15¢** | **blue, red & black** | .45 | .65 |
| | Pair | .75 | |
| | FDC *(June 11, 1988)* | | 1.00 |

| OF138 | | **MNHVF** | **UseVF** |
|---|---|---|---|
| **25¢** | **blue, red & black** | .75 | .50 |
| | FDC *(June 11, 1988)* | 1.00 | |
| | Pair | 1.00 | .75 |
| | v. Imperforate pair | — | |

**1989. OFFICIAL MAIL ISSUE** Similar to OF133. *Offset, perforated 11.*

| OF139 | | MNHVF | UseVF |
|---|---|---|---|
| 1¢ | **blue, red & black** | .25 | .25 |
| | FDC *(July 5, 1989)* | | 1.00 |

**1991. OFFICIAL MAIL COIL ISSUE** "F" rate non-denominated stamp. *Coil, Offset, perforated 10 vertically.*

 OF140

| OF140 | | MNHVF | UseVF |
|---|---|---|---|
| 29¢ | **blue, red & black** | .75 | .50 |
| | FDC *(Jan. 22, 1991)* | | 1.00 |
| | Pair | 1.00 | |

**1991. OFFICIAL MAIL ISSUE** Similar to OF133. *Offset, perforated 11.*

| OF141 | | MNHVF | UseVF |
|---|---|---|---|
| 4¢ | **blue, red & black** | .25 | .30 |
| | FDC *(April 6, 1991)* | | |

**1991. OFFICIAL MAIL ISSUE** Similar to OF133. *Offset, perforated 11.*

| OF142 | | MNHVF | UseVF |
|---|---|---|---|
| 19¢ | **blue, red & black** | .40 | .60 |
| | FDC *(May 24, 1991)* | | |

| OF143 | | MNHVF | UseVF |
|---|---|---|---|
| 23¢ | **blue, red & black** | .45 | .60 |
| | FDC *(May 24, 1991)* | | |

**1991. OFFICIAL MAIL COIL ISSUE** Similar to OF133. *Coil, printed by offset, perforated 10 vertically.*

| OF144 | | MNHVF | UseVF |
|---|---|---|---|
| 29¢ | **blue, red & black** | .75 | .50 |
| | Pair | 1.25 | 1.00 |
| | FDC *(May 24, 1991)* | | 1.00 |

**1993. OFFICIAL MAIL ISSUE** Similar to OF133. *Offset, perforated 11.*

 OF145

| OF145 | | MNHVF | UseVF |
|---|---|---|---|
| 10¢ | **blue, red & black** | .35 | .55 |
| | FDC *(Oct. 19, 1993)* | | |

 OF146

| OF146 | | MNHVF | UseVF |
|---|---|---|---|
| $1 | **blue, red & black** | 2.10 | 1.75 |
| | FDC *(Oct. 19, 1993)* | | |

**1994. OFFICIAL MAIL COIL ISSUE** G Rate non-denominated stamp. *Coil, Offset, perforated 9 3/4 vertically.*

| OF147 | | MNHVF | UseVF |
|---|---|---|---|
| 32¢ | **blue, red & black** | .75 | .50 |
| | FDC *(Dec. 13, 1994)* | | 1.00 |
| | Pair | 1.25 | 1.00 |

**1995. OFFICIAL MAIL ISSUE** Similar to OF133. *Offset, perforated 11.*

| OF148 | | MNHVF | UseVF |
|---|---|---|---|
| 1¢ | **blue, red & black** | .25 | .25 |
| | FDC *(May 9, 1995)* | | |

| OF149 | | MNHVF | UseVF |
|---|---|---|---|
| 20¢ | **blue, red & black** | .45 | .55 |

| OF150 | | MNHVF | UseVF |
|---|---|---|---|
| 23¢ | **blue, red & black** | .55 | .65 |

| OF151 | | MNHVF | UseVF |
|---|---|---|---|
| 32¢ | **blue, red & black** | .75 | .40 |

# Envelopes and Wrappers

Government stamped envelopes first were authorized by the United States under an Act of Congress of August 31, 1852. From the very first issue until the present they have been produced by private manufacturers under contract to the government. It is believed the first envelopes were issued some time in April 1853. The exact date is not known.

Unlike adhesive stamps, stamped envelopes are produced one at a time. Until 1965 the blanks were cut to shape by means of a cutting die (called a "knife" by collectors) much as one operates a cookie cutter. This die was placed on a pile of sheets of paper and was forced through by means of a press. Then a complex machine printed the stamp and whatever corner card might be requested; folded, gummed and sealed the flaps; applied gum to the top back flap; and counted the finished envelopes into multiples of 100 or any number desired.

Beginning in 1965 envelopes have been made from a continuous roll (web) of paper.

The embossed printing of the stamp is accomplished with a recessed printing die wich strikes against a resilient undersurface, or "tympan". The tympan forces the paper into the recesses, causing the embossed effect. Later issues are printed by more contemporary processes.

## Paper

While our envelopes have been made from paper of various colors, the most usual color is "white". During the first issue, the customer had his choice of "white" or "buff" paper envelopes, and at various times the choice of colors available was as many as six or seven. Since 1942, envelopes have been made of white paper only.

The paper colors used throughout the issues are:

White - and various shades thereof.

Buff - in early issues from a brownish color to a yellow.

Amber - shows a yellowish cast. Can be quite pronounced or very pale.

Cream - an intermediate shade between a yellow and a brown. It was discontinued in 1886 and "buff" (sometimes known as "oriental buff") substituted.

Blue - and various shades thereof.

Orange - in various shades thereof.

Fawn - a brownish shade.

Manila - made of manila fibers.

Amber-manila - manila paper died yellowish.

Canary - bright yellow (used for Post Office Department envelopes only).

It will be seen that all colors vary greatly in shades. Such variation is not intentional, but merely reflects the inability to match colors exactly in various batches of paper. The "white" of one issue may differ by a wide margin from the "white" of a later or earlier issue. The same holds true for any other color. Thus the colors of paper, while important to the collector, are not standardized and may only be considered within each individual issue of envelopes.

From 1853 to 1915, all envelopes were made of laid paper, and the laid lines will appear diagonal. This is the result of turning the cutting knife on the bias to the edge of the pile of paper in order to save as much waste as possible. On the other hand, wrappers, which are rectangular in shape, presented no great waste of paper, so they were cut parallel to the edge of the paper. The laid lines on wrappers will appear horizontal or vertical, depending on how they were inserted in the press. This is the principle method of distinguishing between a wrapper cut square and an envelope cut square.

From 1915 to the present, envelopes have been made of wove paper, and thus show no laid lines.

## Albinos and Misprints

Until the web-printing process was adopted in 1965, two envelope blanks will have occasionally been fed into the envelope-making machine at one time. The top sheet received an inked impression, and the bottom sheet an impression without ink. Such colorless impressions look like white "stamps" and are called "albinos". They are quite common for recent issues, including those even after web printing of envelopes began, but rather rare for early 19th century envelopes. Although they are interesting, they do not command near the premium as do envelopes with two impressions of the stamp in color (one over or partially over the other).

## Collecting Envelopes and wrappers

Envelopes and wrappers are collected as "entires" by size and watermarks and as cut squares. Cut squares are popular because, like postage stamps, they may be mounted easily into albums. Cut squares always should provide adequate margins which in most instances would be no less than 1/4 inch of paper margin beyond the design of the stamp on all four sides.

Prices in this catalog are for cut squares with such margins. Larger squares, "full corners", or extra large corners with all back flaps attached may bring premium prices. This is especially true for earlier issues.

Envelopes are manufactured in a variety of different sizes and shapes. Thus, a single basic stamp may appear on several different size envelopes and some of these sizes may be more valuable than others although the stamp remains the same. Certain envelopes exist in large sizes only. In the listing that follows, an asterisk (*) designates entires only available in large size.

Catalog values are for entires of the least value. It is required by law that all envelopes be manufactured with watermarked paper. From 1853 to 1870, a single style watermark was used for all issues (wmk1), but with a new manufacturer in 1870 a new watermark was introduced and beginning in 1874 it became the custom to change the watermark with the letting of each new contract (about every four years) through the late 1960's. It has been customary to allow remaining stocks of paper to be used up before the new watermarked paper is introduced. Most issues of envelopes, therefore, exist on at least two styles of watermarked paper and, when an issue extended over a very long period of years, there may be several watermarks involved. Indicated at the beginning of each issue are watermarks to be found on envelopes of that issue.

*Watermark No. 1*

*Watermark No. 2*

*Watermark No. 3*
*"CENTENNIAL"*

*Watermark No. 4*

Watermark No. 5 "STAR"

Watermark No.13

Watermark No. 14 (1903-1907)

Watermark No. 6

Watermark No. 15
(1907-1911)

Watermark No. 15a
(1907-1911)

Watermark
No. 16

U S S E
1911

Watermark No. 17
(1911-1915)

US-S E
1911

Watermark No.18
(1911-1915)

Watermark No. 7     Watermark No. 8

Watermark No. 9

### 1853-55. ISSUE

All envelopes issued from 1853 to 1870 were manufactured in New York City by the George F. Nesbitt Manufacturing Company and are known to collectors as the "Nesbitt Issues". The Nesbitt firm was established in 1795, and at the time it was awarded the contract to produce the first U.S. government stamped envelopes in 1852 it was said to be the largest firm of manufacturing stationers in the country. Following the death of Mr. Nesbitt in 1869, the firm lost the contract for manufacturing government envelopes, and although it entered bids on succeeding contracts for many years thereafter, it never again was successful.

Issued some time in April 1853, this issue featured the portrait of George Washington, after Houdon's bust. The complete design would appear to be adapted from the "Wyon" essay for the first stamped envelopes of Great Britain.

*Watermark No. 1, also No. 1A on EN1. Wmk 1 has the lines horizontal in the background with the letters "U.S. Postals" horizontal.*

Watermark No. 10

Watermark No. 11

EN1-EN2 *"THREE" within short label with curved ends. Die 1, 13mm wide, 12 varieties.*

| EN1 | | UnFVF | UseFVF |
|---|---|---|---|
| 3¢ | red on white | 190. | 16.00 |
| | entire | 1200. | 25.00 |
| | entire, wmk No. 1A | — | — |
| **EN2** | | **UnFVF** | **UseFVF** |
| 3¢ | red on buff | 70.00 | 10.00 |
| | entire | 750. | 20.00 |

EN3-EN4 *"THREE" within short label with straight ends. Die 2, 16mm wide, 3 varieties.*

| EN3 | | UnFVF | UseFVF |
|---|---|---|---|
| 3¢ | red on white | 680. | 35.00 |
| | entire | 3000. | 70.00 |

Watermark No. 12

**EN4**

| | | UnFVF | UseFVF |
|---|---|---|---|
| 3¢ | **red on buff** | 195. | 15.00 |
| | entire | 1500. | 32.00 |

EN5-EN6 *"THREE" within short, curved octagonal label, forming the letter 'K'. Dec. 3, 2 varieties.*

**EN5**

| | | UnFVF | UseFVF |
|---|---|---|---|
| 3¢ | **red on white** | 3500. | 360. |
| | entire | 12500. | 500. |

**EN6**

| | | UnFVF | UseFVF |
|---|---|---|---|
| 3¢ | **red on buff** | 190. | 40.00 |
| | entire | 1000. | 75.00 |

EN7-EN8 *"THREE" within wide label with straight ends. Die 4, 25mm wide.*

**EN7**

| | | UnFVF | UseFVF |
|---|---|---|---|
| 3¢ | **red on white** | 500. | 80.00 |
| | entire | 6200. | 130. |

**EN8**

| | | UnFVF | UseFVF |
|---|---|---|---|
| 3¢ | **red on buff** | 1100. | 90.00 |
| | entire | 4500. | 95.00 |

EN9-EN10 *"THREE" within medium wide label with curved ends. Die 5. 20mm wide, 20 varieties.*

**EN9**

| | | UnFVF | UseFVF |
|---|---|---|---|
| 3¢ | **red on white** | 18.00 | 2.50 |
| | entire | 75.00 | 9.00 |
| | reprint, cut square | 2.00 | |

**EN10**

| | | UnFVF | UseFVF |
|---|---|---|---|
| 3¢ | **red on buff** | 14.00 | 2.25 |
| | entire | 60.00 | 6.00 |
| | reprint, cut square | 2.00 | |

EN11-EN14 *"SIX" within short label with straight ends. Die 6, 4 varieties.*

**EN11**

| | | UnFVF | UseFVF |
|---|---|---|---|
| 6¢ | **green on white** | 175. | 100. |
| | entire | 300. | 150. |
| | reprint, cut square | — | |

**EN12**

| | | UnFVF | UseFVF |
|---|---|---|---|
| 6¢ | **green on buff** | 135. | 65.00 |
| | entire | 235. | 115. |
| | reprint, cut square | 200. | |

**EN13**

| | | UnFVF | UseFVF |
|---|---|---|---|
| 6¢ | **red on white** | 90.00 | 60.00 |
| | entire* | 210. | 105. |
| | reprint, cut square | 200. | |

**EN14**

| | | UnFVF | UseFVF |
|---|---|---|---|
| 6¢ | **red on buff** | 175. | 100. |
| | entire* | 300. | 150. |
| | reprint, cut square | 200. | |

EN15, EN16 *"TEN" within short label with straight ends. Die 7, 16mm wide.*

**EN15**

| | | UnFVF | UseFVF |
|---|---|---|---|
| 10¢ | **green on white** | 175. | 100. |
| | entire | 325. | 150. |

**EN16**

| | | UnFVF | UseFVF |
|---|---|---|---|
| 10¢ | **green on buff** | 65.00 | 50.00 |
| | entire | 200. | 80.00 |

EN17, EN18 *"TEN" within wide label. Die 8.*

**EN17**

| | | UnFVF | UseFVF |
|---|---|---|---|
| 10¢ | **green on white** | 200. | 100. |
| | entire | 350. | 150. |
| | reprint, cut square | 200. | |

**EN18**

| | | UnFVF | UseFVF |
|---|---|---|---|
| 10¢ | **green on buff** | 100. | 65.00 |
| | entire | 170. | 80.00 |
| | reprint, cut square | 200. | |

*Reprints EN9-14, 17, 18, are on white and buff wove or vertically laid paper. Known also only as cut squares.*

**1860. "STAR DIE" ISSUE The "Star Die" Series,** so-called because of the small stars at either side of the design, which do not appear on any other envelope stamp. The stars of the 1¢ denomination have five points; those of all other denominations have six points. With this series, 1¢ envelopes and newspaper wrappers were introduced for the first time. The series also introduced the 3¢-plus1¢ envelope. This was to provide for the carrier service, the fee for which was one cent, for transporting the letter from the lamp-post letter boxes to the post office. Use of the "compound envelopes" apparently was reserved for large cities and very possibly New York City only.

A very few are known used in Baltimore, Chicago and a few other cities where carrier service was operated. Usage in any city other than New York are rare and command premium values.

The series was introduced some time during the summer of 1860 (3¢ envelopes are known used in August) and remained in use for about one year. When the Civil War broke out, steps were taken to replace the issue with a new design. However, the 1¢ and 3¢-plus-1¢ envelopes continued in use and were not subjected to the general demonetization order.

Envelopes used by Southern states after their secession, as evidenced by cancellation, are scarce and command considerable premium values. Likewise, envelopes of this series overprinted (over the stamp) "CONFEDERATE STATES OF AMERICA" and other suitable indicia, used by the Confederate States Postal Department for official mail, are of considerable interest and value to collectors.

The buff paper for all envelopes of this series, and throughout the Nesbitt issues, exists in a multitude of shades which extend from a yellow through dark brown. None of these differences were intentional. They merely indicate various batches of paper, all of which were supposed to be "buff." Likewise, there are many shades of green of the 6¢ and 10¢ stamps, extending from "yellow green" to "dark green." The interested collector may be advised that the extreme dark shades are less numerous than the pale or yellow shades.

**Wrappers.** Newspaper wrappers were introduced with this series, and were continued with succeeding series up to 1934, when they were discontinued. Wrappers may be distinguished from envelopes in that they are on paper with either vertical or horizontal laid lines. Envelopes almost invariably are on paper with diagonally laid lines.

EN19-EN23 *Franklin. Period after "POSTAGE". Die 9.*

| EN19 | | | UnFVF | UseFVF |
|---|---|---|---|---|
| 1¢ | **blue on buff** | | 28.00 | 13.00 |
| | entire | | 55.00 | 25.00 |
| EN20 | | | UnFVF | UseFVF |
| 1¢ | **blue on orange,** | | — | — |
| | entire | | — | — |
| EN21 | | | UnFVF | UseFVF |
| 1¢ | **blue on buff,** wrapper | | 65.00 | 50.00 |
| | entire | | 100. | 65.00 |
| EN22 | | | UnFVF | UseFVF |
| 1¢ | **blue on manila,** wrapper | | 45.00 | 45.00 |
| | entire | | 85.00 | 85.00 |
| EN23 | | | UnFVF | UseFVF |
| 1¢ | **blue on orange,** wrapper | | 1800. | — |
| | entire | | 2800. | — |

EN24, EN25 *Franklin. Bust touches frame front and back. Die 10.*

| EN24 | | | UnFVF | UseFVF |
|---|---|---|---|---|
| 1¢ | **blue on orange** | | 410. | 360. |
| | entire | | 480. | 425. |
| EN25 | | | UnFVF | UseFVF |
| 1¢ | **blue on white** | | — | — |

EN26, EN27 *No period after "POSTAGE". Die 11, 2 varieties.*

| EN26 | | | UnFVF | UseFVF |
|---|---|---|---|---|
| 1¢ | **blue on amber** | | — | — |
| | entire | | — | — |
| EN27 | | | UnFVF | UseFVF |
| 1¢ | **blue on manila,** wrapper | | 2600. | 2000. |
| | entire | | 11000. | 3800. |

EN28, EN29 *Washington. Die 12.*

| EN28 | | | UnFVF | UseFVF |
|---|---|---|---|---|
| 3¢ | **red on white** | | 27.00 | 13.00 |
| | entire | | 37.00 | 23.00 |
| | reprint, cut square | | 150. | |
| EN29 | | | UnFVF | UseFVF |
| 3¢ | **red on buff** | | 25.00 | 23.00 |
| | entire | | 35.00 | 30.00 |
| | reprint, cut square | | 150. | |

EN30, EN31 *Franklin Bust does not toch frame.*

| EN30 | | | UnFVF | UseFVF |
|---|---|---|---|---|
| 3¢ + 1¢ | **red and blue on white** | | 335. | 235. |
| | entire | | 775. | 500. |
| EN31 | | | UnFVF | UseFVF |
| 3¢ + 1¢ | **red and blue on buff** | | 250. | 210. |
| | entire | | 825. | 500. |

EN32, EN33 *Franklin bust touches frame.*

| EN32 | | | UnFVF | UseFVF |
|---|---|---|---|---|
| 3¢ + 1¢ | **red and blue on white** | | — | — |
| | entire | | — | — |
| EN33 | | | UnFVF | UseFVF |
| 3¢ + 1¢ | **red and blue on buff** | | — | — |
| | entire | | — | — |
| | reprint, cut square | | 100. | |

EN34, EN35 *Die 12.*

| EN34 | | | UnFVF | UseFVF |
|---|---|---|---|---|
| 6¢ | **red on white** | | 2000. | 1300. |
| | entire* | | 3700. | |
| | reprint, cut square | | 100. | |
| EN35 | | | UnFVF | UseFVF |
| 6¢ | **red on buff** | | 1700. | 950. |
| | entire* | | 4300. | 4500. |
| | reprint, cut square | | 100. | |

EN36, EN37 *Die 12.*

| EN36 | | | UnFVF | UseFVF |
|---|---|---|---|---|
| 10¢ | **green on white** | | 1000. | 350. |
| | entire | | 10000. | 475. |
| | reprint, cut square | | 100. | |
| EN37 | | | UnFVF | UseFVF |
| 10¢ | **green on buff** | | 1000. | 275. |
| | entire | | 3800. | 475. |
| | reprint, cut square | | 100. | |

*Reprints are cut squares on vertical laid paper.*

**1861. ISSUE** This series was introduced in the summer of 1861. The previous "Star Die" series, was declared invalid for postage, due to the outbreak of The Civil War (except the 1¢ and 3¢-plus-1¢ envelopes). The series presents a novelty as the higher envelope stamps were printed in more than one color. These also are the first bi-colored postal emissions from the United States. Still another inovation was the introduction of the Letter Sheets which, it has been stated, were issued to provide the soldiers in the field with both stationery and stamps in a single package. The use of these did not prove popular, and they were withdrawn in April 1864.

EN38-EN41 *Die 13.*

| EN38 | | | UnFVF | UseFVF |
|---|---|---|---|---|
| 3¢ | **pink on white** | | 18.00 | 5.00 |
| | entire | | 45.00 | 15.00 |

**EN39**

| | | UnFVF | UseFVF |
|---|---|---|---|
| 3¢ | **pink on buff** | 16.00 | 6.00 |
| | entire | 18.00 | 12.00 |

**EN40**

| | | UnFVF | UseFVF |
|---|---|---|---|
| 3¢ | **pink on blue,** letter sheet | 70.00 | 55.00 |
| | entire | 200. | 90.00 |

**EN41**

| | | UnFVF | UseFVF |
|---|---|---|---|
| 3¢ | **pink on orange** | 2300. | — |
| | entire | 3900. | — |

EN42, EN43 *Die 14.*

**EN42**

| | | UnFVF | UseFVF |
|---|---|---|---|
| 6¢ | **pink on white** | 90.00 | 85.00 |
| | entire* | 145. | 145. |
| | reprint, cut square | — | — |

**EN43**

| | | UnFVF | UseFVF |
|---|---|---|---|
| 6¢ | **pink on buff** | 65.00 | 60.00 |
| | entire* | 100. | 145. |
| | reprint, cut square | — | — |

*Reprints, known in cut squares only, are on vertically laid paper.*

EN44-EN46 *Die 15.*

**EN44**

| | | UnFVF | UseFVF |
|---|---|---|---|
| 10¢ | **green on white** | 28.00 | 28.00 |
| | entire | 26.00 | 26.00 |

**EN45**

| | | UnFVF | UseFVF |
|---|---|---|---|
| 10¢ | **green on buff** | 27.00 | 19.00 |
| | entire | 60.00 | 35.00 |

**EN46**

| | | UnFVF | UseFVF |
|---|---|---|---|
| 10¢ | **green on amber** | — | — |
| | entire | — | — |

EN47 *Die 16.*

**EN47**

| | | UnFVF | UseFVF |
|---|---|---|---|
| 12¢ | **brown and red on amber** | 175. | 150. |
| | entire* | 460. | 650. |

EN48 *Die 16.*

**EN48**

| | | UnFVF | UseFVF |
|---|---|---|---|
| 20¢ | **blue and red on amber** | 175. | 150. |
| | entire* | 460. | 775. |

EN49, EN50 *Die 16.*

**EN49**

| | | UnFVF | UseFVF |
|---|---|---|---|
| 24¢ | **green and red on amber** | 185. | 145. |
| | entire* | 650. | 775. |

**EN50**

| | | UnFVF | UseFVF |
|---|---|---|---|
| 24¢ | **dark green and maroon on amber** | 190. | 180. |
| | entire* | 650. | 1000. |

EN51 *Die 16.*

**EN51**

| | | UnFVF | UseFVF |
|---|---|---|---|
| 40¢ | **red and black on amber** | 280. | 280. |
| | entire* | 850. | 1800. |

**1863-65. ISSUE** To provide for the, higher postal rates on drop letters and circular matter, it was necessary to provide 2¢ envelopes and wrappers (called "Black Jacks" because of the portrait of Andrew Jackson). At the same time, new designs were adopted for the 3¢, 6¢ and higher denominations.

EN52, EN53 *Andrew Jackson. Die A. "U.S. POSTAGE" at top. Down stroke of 2" and bottom stroke merge. Die 17*

**EN52**

| | | UnFVF | UseFVF |
|---|---|---|---|
| 2¢ | **black on buff** | 30.00 | 15.00 |
| | entire | 60.00 | 30.00 |

**EN53**

| | | UnFVF | UseFVF |
|---|---|---|---|
| 2¢ | **black on manila,** wrapper | 42.00 | 38.00 |
| | entire | 70.00 | 55.00 |

EN54, EN55 *Die B, down stroke of figure "2" joins but does not merge with bottom stroke. Die 18.*

**EN54**

| | | UnFVF | UseFVF |
|---|---|---|---|
| 2¢ | **black on buff** | 1700. | — |
| | entire | 3600. | — |

**EN55**

| | | UnFVF | UseFVF |
|---|---|---|---|
| 2¢ | **black on orange** | 1000. | — |
| | entire | 2500. | — |

EN56-EN59 *Andrew Jackson. Die C, "U.S. POST" at top. Width of design 24 to 25mm. Die 19, 25mm.*

**EN56**

| | | UnFVF | UseFVF |
|---|---|---|---|
| 2¢ | **black on buff** | 10.00 | 9.00 |
| | entire | 27.00 | 15.00 |

**EN57**

| | | UnFVF | UseFVF |
|---|---|---|---|
| 2¢ | **black on orange** | 12.00 | 8.00 |
| | entire | 22.00 | 10.00 |

**EN58**

| | | UnFVF | UseFVF |
|---|---|---|---|
| 2¢ | **black on buff,** wrapper | 160. | 160. |
| | entire | 260. | 260. |

**EN59**

| | | UnFVF | UseFVF |
|---|---|---|---|
| 2¢ | **black on dark manila,** wrapper | 35.00 | 22.00 |
| | entire | 120. | 60.00 |

EN60-EN64 *Die D. "U.S. POST" at top. Die 20, 25 1/2mm.*

**EN60**
2¢    **black on buff**                          UnFVF  UseFVF
                                                12.00  10.00
      entire                                    22.00  14.00

**EN61**
2¢    **black on amber**                         UnFVF  UseFVF
                                                   —      —
      entire                                       —      —

**EN62**
2¢    **black on orange**                        UnFVF  UseFVF
                                                12.00   8.00
      entire                                    17.00  11.00

**EN63**
2¢    **black on buff**, wrapper                 UnFVF  UseFVF
                                                80.00  50.00
      entire                                    125.    85.00

**EN64**
2¢    **black on light manila**, wrapper         UnFVF  UseFVF
                                                12.00  11.00
      entire                                    25.00  20.00

EN65-EN68 *Die 21.*

**EN65**
3¢    **pink on white**                          UnFVF  UseFVF
                                                 6.00   2.00
      entire                                    10.00   3.50

**EN66**
3¢    **pink on buff**                           UnFVF  UseFVF
                                                 5.00   1.50
      entire                                    10.00   2.50

**EN67**
3¢    **brown on white**                         UnFVF  UseFVF
                                                38.00  20.00
      entire*                                   75.00  75.00

**EN68**
3¢    **brown on buff**                          UnFVF  UseFVF
                                                40.00  22.00
      entire*                                   80.00  60.00

EN69-EN73 *Die 21.*

**EN69**
6¢    **pink on white**                          UnFVF  UseFVF
                                                50.00  30.00
      entire*                                   85.00  50.00

**EN70**
6¢    **pink on buff**                           UnFVF  UseFVF
                                                30.00  25.00
      entire*                                   85.00  50.00

**EN71**
6¢    **purple on white**                        UnFVF  UseFVF
                                                45.00  25.00
      entire                                    70.00  50.00

**EN72**
6¢    **purple on amber**                        UnFVF  UseFVF
                                                   —      —
      entire                                       —      —

**EN73**
6¢    **purple on buff**                         UnFVF  UseFVF
                                                42.00  18.00
      entire                                    60.00  50.00

EN74, EN75 *Die 22.*

**EN74**
9¢    **lemon on buff**                          UnFVF  UseFVF
                                                325.    200.
      entire*                                   500.    500.

**EN75**
9¢    **orange on buff**                         UnFVF  UseFVF
                                                95.00  75.00
      entire*                                   150.    200.

EN76, EN77 *Die 22.*

**EN76**
12¢   **brown on buff**                          UnFVF  UseFVF
                                                340.    200.
      entire*                                   500.    950.

**EN77**
12¢   **red brown on buff**                      UnFVF  UseFVF
                                                90.00  55.00
      entire*                                   130.    185.

EN78 *Die 22.*

**EN78**
18¢   **red on buff**                            UnFVF  UseFVF
                                                90.00  85.00
      entire*                                   180.    800.

EN79 *Die 22.*

**EN79**
24¢   **blue on buff**                           UnFVF  UseFVF
                                                95.00  80.00
      entire*                                   180.    800.

EN80 *Die 22.*

**EN80**
30¢   **green on buff**                          UnFVF  UseFVF
                                                60.00  50.00
      entire*                                   150.    800.

EN81 *Die 22.*

**EN81**
40¢   **pink on buff**                           UnFVF  UseFVF
                                                80.00  225.
      entire*                                   250.    9300.

**1870. ISSUE** By the end of 1869 there were various designs of stamps in use for our envelopes and wrappers, none of which even closely resembled the designs of the adhesive stamps then in use. To remedy this situation and bring order to confusion, as well as to meet the public clamor against awarding the envelope contract by negotiated bid, the government advertised for bids to supply the envelopes needed for the next four years. One provision of the proposal was that the new envelopes be in denominations of the adhesive stamps then in use and that the designs of the envelope stamps be as near as possible, in color and design, to the adhesive stamps in use. After considerable controversy, the contract was awarded to George H. Reay of Brooklyn, New York, a former associate of Nesbitt. Mr Reay proceeded to produce what has almost unanimously been considered the most beautiful designs and envelopes our post office ever has issued. The finely executed engravings, the beautiful inks, and careful printing on fine quality paper have earned for them the name "cameos" among collectors.

Although the contract provided that envelopes be manufactured in all denominations from 1¢ to 90¢, there was little use for envelopes in the denominations over 10¢. Hence, used examples of these high denominations are practically unknown.

Die A

EN82-EN85 *Franklin. Die A, front of the bust is narrow, back rounded. It points at letter "N" of "ONE". The neck forms a straight line between chest and chin. (Compare with EN120 and EN128.) Die 23.*

| EN82 | | UnFVF | UseFVF |
|---|---|---|---|
| 1¢ | **blue on white** | 28.00 | 23.00 |
| | entire | 50.00 | 28.00 |
| EN83 | | UnFVF | UseFVF |
| 1¢ | **blue on amber** | 28.00 | 23.00 |
| | entire | 50.00 | 28.00 |
| EN84 | | UnFVF | UseFVF |
| 1¢ | **blue on orange** | 18.00 | 10.00 |
| | entire | 26.00 | 17.00 |
| EN85 | | UnFVF | UseFVF |
| 1¢ | **blue on manila,** wrapper | 40.00 | 25.00 |
| | entire | 70.00 | 60.00 |

Die B

EN86-EN89 *Die B the choker around the neck is notched top and bottom.*

| EN86 | | UnFVF | UseFVF |
|---|---|---|---|
| 1¢ | **blue on white** | — | — |
| | entire | — | — |
| EN87 | | UnFVF | UseFVF |
| 1¢ | **blue on amber** | — | — |
| | entire | — | — |
| EN88 | | UnFVF | UseFVF |
| 1¢ | **blue on orange** | — | — |
| | entire | — | — |
| EN89 | | UnFVF | UseFVF |
| 1¢ | **blue on manila,** wrapper | — | — |
| | entire | — | — |

EN90-EN93 *Andrew Jackson, the figure "2" at right and left are within small circles. The top loop of "P" of "POSTAGE" is well formed. (Compare with EN142.) Die 24.*

| EN90 | | UnFVF | UseFVF |
|---|---|---|---|
| 2¢ | **brown on white** | 40.00 | 13.00 |
| | entire | 50.00 | 20.00 |
| EN91 | | UnFVF | UseFVF |
| 2¢ | **brown on amber** | 15.00 | 8.00 |
| | entire | 30.00 | 15.00 |
| EN92 | | UnFVF | UseFVF |
| 2¢ | **brown on orange** | 10.00 | 7.00 |
| | entire | 13.00 | 10.00 |
| EN93 | | UnFVF | UseFVF |
| 2¢ | **brown on manila,** wrapper | 20.00 | 15.00 |
| | entire | 40.00 | 30.00 |

EN94-EN96 *Small figure "3" within circles. The ponytail projects below the bust, (Compare with EN183 and EN187.) Die 25.*

| EN94 | | UnFVF | UseFVF |
|---|---|---|---|
| 3¢ | **green on white** | 7.00 | 1.00 |
| | entire | 12.00 | 2.50 |
| EN95 | | UnFVF | UseFVF |
| 3¢ | **green on amber** | 5.00 | 2.00 |
| | entire | 12.00 | 3.00 |
| EN96 | | UnFVF | UseFVF |
| 3¢ | **green on cream** | 8.00 | 3.00 |
| | entire | 16.00 | 5.00 |

EN97-EN99 *Abraham Lincoln. The neck is long at the back. (Compare with EN211) Die 26.*

| EN97 | | UnFVF | UseFVF |
|---|---|---|---|
| 6¢ | **red on white** | 17.00 | 13.00 |
| | entire | 18.00 | 16.00 |
| EN98 | | UnFVF | UseFVF |
| 6¢ | **red on amber** | 22.00 | 13.00 |
| | entire | 38.00 | 14.00 |
| EN99 | | UnFVF | UseFVF |
| 6¢ | **red on cream** | 27.00 | 13.00 |
| | entire | 15.00 | 19.00 |

*EN97-EN99 exist in a variety of shades from dark red to vermilion.*

**1870. Issue** By the end of 1869 there were various designs of stamps in use for our envelopes and wrappers, none of which even closely resembled the designs of the adhesive stamps then in use. To remedy this situation and bring order to confusion, as well as to meet the public clamor against awarding the envelope contract by negotiated bid, the government advertised for bids to supply the envelopes needed for the next four years. One provision of the proposal was that the new envelopes be in denominations of the adhesive stamps then in use and that the designs of the envelope stamps be as near as possible, in color and design, to the adhesive stamps in use. After considerable controversy, the contract was awarded to George H. Reay of Brooklyn, New York, a former associate of Nesbitt. Mr Reay proceeded to produce what has almost unanimously been considered the most beautiful designs and envelopes our post office ever has issued. The finely executed engravings, the beautiful inks, and careful printing on fine quality paper have earned for them the name "cameos" among collectors.

Although the contract provided that envelopes be manufactured in all denominations from 1¢ to 90¢, there was little use for envelopes in the denominations over 10¢. Hence, used examples of these high denominations are practically unknown.

EN100 *Edwin Stanton. The down strokes of the figure "7" do not curl up. (Compare with EN215). Die 27.*

| | | UnFVF | UseFVF |
|---|---|---|---|
| **EN100** | | | |
| 7¢ | **vermilion on amber** | 40.00 | 200. |
| | entire | 60.00 | 750. |

EN101-EN104 *Thomas Jefferson. The end of the ponytail does not project. (Compare with En219.) Die 28.*

| EN101 | | UnFVF | UseFVF |
|---|---|---|---|
| 10¢ | olive-black on white | 375. | 375. |
| | entire | 475. | 850. |

| EN102 | | UnFVF | UseFVF |
|---|---|---|---|
| 10¢ | olive-black on amber | 375. | 375. |
| | entire | 475. | 850. |

| EN103 | | UnFVF | UseFVF |
|---|---|---|---|
| 10¢ | brown on white | 50.00 | 70.00 |
| | entire | 70.00 | 75.00 |

| EN104 | | UnFVF | UseFVF |
|---|---|---|---|
| 10¢ | brown on amber | 70.00 | 50.00 |
| | entire | 85.00 | 70.00 |

EN105-EN107 *Henry Clay. The hair hides the ear. The nose is long and sharp. (Compare with EN227.) Die 29.*

| EN105 | | UnFVF | UseFVF |
|---|---|---|---|
| 12¢ | violet-black on white | 100. | 65.00 |
| | entire* | 200. | 375. |

| EN106 | | UnFVF | UseFVF |
|---|---|---|---|
| 12¢ | violet-black on amber | 110. | 85.00 |
| | entire* | 180. | 500. |

| EN107 | | UnFVF | UseFVF |
|---|---|---|---|
| 12¢ | violet-black on cream | 220. | 190. |
| | entire* | 335. | — |

EN108-EN110 *Daniel Webster. Hair not parted, cheeks with sideburns. (Compare with EN230.) Die 30.*

| EN108 | | UnFVF | UseFVF |
|---|---|---|---|
| 15¢ | red orange on white | 60.00 | 60.00 |
| | entire* | 140. | — |

| EN109 | | UnFVF | UseFVF |
|---|---|---|---|
| 15¢ | red orange on amber | 140. | 170. |
| | entire* | 360. | — |

| EN110 | | UnFVF | UseFVF |
|---|---|---|---|
| 15¢ | red orange on cream | 235. | 210. |
| | entire* | 325. | — |

EN111-EN113 *Winfield Scott. Ornamental lines around inner oval end in squares. (Compare with EN233). Die 31.*

| EN111 | | UnFVF | UseFVF |
|---|---|---|---|
| 24¢ | purple on white | 100. | 90.00 |
| | entire | 150. | — |

| EN112 | | UnFVF | UseFVF |
|---|---|---|---|
| 24¢ | purple on amber | 180. | 225. |
| | entire* | 335. | — |

| EN113 | | UnFVF | UseFVF |
|---|---|---|---|
| 24¢ | purple on cream | 180. | 250. |
| | entire* | 325. | — |

*EN108-EN113 exist in various shades.*

EN114-EN116 *Alexander Hamilton. The horizontal rectangles containing numerals are in alignment. Back of bust ends in narrow point. (Compare with EN236.) Die 32.*

| EN114 | | UnFVF | UseFVF |
|---|---|---|---|
| 30¢ | black on white | 70.00 | 85.00 |
| | entire* | 280. | — |

| EN115 | | UnFVF | UseFVF |
|---|---|---|---|
| 30¢ | black on amber | 180. | 210. |
| | entire* | 500. | — |

| EN116 | | UnFVF | UseFVF |
|---|---|---|---|
| 30¢ | black on cream | 200. | 325. |
| | entire* | 385. | — |

EN117-En119 *Oliver Perry. The shields containing the numerals of value do not project beyond the inner circle. (Compare with EN242.) Die 33.*

| EN117 | | UnFVF | UseFVF |
|---|---|---|---|
| 90¢ | carmine on white | 135. | 190. |
| | entire* | 190. | — |

| EN118 | | UnFVF | UseFVF |
|---|---|---|---|
| 90¢ | carmine on amber | 300. | 335. |
| | entire* | 800. | — |

| EN119 | | UnFVF | UseFVF |
|---|---|---|---|
| 90¢ | carmine on cream | 335. | 550. |
| | entire* | 875. | — |

**1874-76. ISSUE** In 1874, the Post Office advertised for bids to supply envelopes. After considerable legal difficulties with George H. Reay and other bidders, the contract was awarded to the Plimpton Manufacturing Co. Reay refused to surrender his printing dies and, to futher embarrass the new contractor, is said to have engaged the services of all known die engravers. The new contractors were thus forced to employ less skilled engravers to try to duplicate the Reay designs. The resulting delay embarrassed the Post Office officials, who were forced to purchase supplies of envelopes from Reay until the new contractors could produce acceptable dies. Several unsuitable designs were accepted to take care of the situaton until better dies could be made, which accounts for some of the designs of the lower denomination stamps.

Eventually the Plimpton Manufacturing Co. overcame its difficulties and, in combination with the Morgan Envelope Co., continued to be the successful bidders for the manufacture of envelopes until 1903.

The struggle George H. Reay put up to retain his contract is one of the classic stories of philately. In the end, to prevent his competitors from ever using his dies, it is stated that he finally agreed to turn them over to the authorities, only to instruct his wife to throw them overboard from a Brooklyn-Manhattan ferry. There seems to be much evidence to substantiate this story.

EN120-EN127 *Franklin. A copy of the Reay design (EN82). Die A, back of bust angles in sharp point. "O" of "POSTAGE" without network. (Compare with EN82.) Die 34. Watermarks 2, 5, 6, 7, 9.*

| EN120 | | UnFVF | UseFVF |
|---|---|---|---|
| 1¢ | dark blue on white | 85.00 | 40.00 |
| | entire | 100. | 80.00 |

| EN121 | | UnFVF | UseFVF |
|---|---|---|---|
| 1¢ | dark blue on amber | 100. | 67.50 |
| | entire | 140. | 100. |

| EN122 | | UnFVF | UseFVF |
|---|---|---|---|
| 1¢ | dark blue on cream | 775. | — |

| EN123 | | UnFVF | UseFVF |
|---|---|---|---|
| 1¢ | dark blue on orange | 17.50 | 15.00 |
| | entire | 27.50 | 20.00 |

| EN124 | | UnFVF | UseFVF |
|---|---|---|---|
| 1¢ | dark blue on manila, wrapper | 50.00 | 32.50 |
| | entire | 67.50 | 60.00 |

| EN125 | | UnFVF | UseFVF |
|---|---|---|---|
| 1¢ | light blue on white | 100. | 70.00 |
| | entire | 130. | 100. |

| EN126 | | UnFVF | UseFVF |
|---|---|---|---|
| 1¢ | light blue on orange | 20.00 | 12.50 |
| | entire | 25.00 | 20.00 |

| EN127 | | UnFVF | UseFVF |
|---|---|---|---|
| 1¢ | light blue on manila, wrapper | — | — |
| | entire | — | — |

EN128-EN141 *A copy of Reay design (EN82). Die B, back of bust is a straight line. Front of bust broad and blunt. "O" in "POSTAGE" with network. (Compare with EN82.) Die 35.*

| EN128 | | UnFVF | UseFVF |
|---|---|---|---|
| 1¢ | dark blue on white | 6.00 | 6.00 |
| | entire | 15.00 | 15.00 |

| EN129 | | UnFVF | UseFVF |
|---|---|---|---|
| 1¢ | dark blue on amber | 12.50 | 8.00 |
| | entire | 15.00 | 10.00 |

| EN130 | | UnFVF | UseFVF |
|---|---|---|---|
| 1¢ | dark blue on cream | 15.00 | 6.00 |
| | entire | 22.50 | 15.00 |

| EN131 | | UnFVF | UseFVF |
|---|---|---|---|
| 1¢ | dark blue on orange | 2.50 | 3.00 |
| | entire | 7.00 | 5.00 |

| EN132 | | UnFVF | UseFVF |
|---|---|---|---|
| 1¢ | dark blue on manila, wrapper | 6.00 | 7.50 |
| | entire | 10.00 | 12.50 |

| EN133 | | UnFVF | UseFVF |
|---|---|---|---|
| 1¢ | blue on white | 1.50 | 1.00 |
| | entire | 2.25 | 1.50 |

| EN134 | | UnFVF | UseFVF |
|---|---|---|---|
| 1¢ | blue on amber | 4.00 | 3.00 |
| | entire | 8.00 | 4.00 |

| EN135 | | UnFVF | UseFVF |
|---|---|---|---|
| 1¢ | blue on cream | 4.50 | 4.50 |
| | entire | 7.00 | 5.00 |

| EN136 | | UnFVF | UseFVF |
|---|---|---|---|
| 1¢ | blue on orange | .60 | .50 |
| | entire | .75 | .50 |

| EN137 | | UnFVF | UseFVF |
|---|---|---|---|
| 1¢ | blue on blue | 6.00 | 5.00 |
| | entire | 8.00 | 6.00 |

| EN138 | | UnFVF | UseFVF |
|---|---|---|---|
| 1¢ | blue on fawn | 6.00 | 5.00 |
| | entire | 7.00 | 6.00 |

| EN139 | | UnFVF | UseFVF |
|---|---|---|---|
| 1¢ | blue on manila | 6.00 | 4.00 |
| | entire | 7.00 | 6.00 |

| EN140 | | UnFVF | UseFVF |
|---|---|---|---|
| 1¢ | blue on amber-manila | 11.00 | 9.00 |
| | entire | 13.00 | 10.00 |

| EN141 | | UnFVF | UseFVF |
|---|---|---|---|
| 1¢ | blue on manila, wrapper | 1.50 | 1.50 |
| | entire | 3.00 | 2.00 |

*The "dark blue" of EN128-EN132 is very dark, almost indigo. The "blue" of EN133-EN141 is in various shades of "blue," "pale blue," etc.*

EN142-EN147 *Andrew Jackson. A copy of Reay design (EN90). Die A, thin narrow figure "2" within circles. Top loop of "P" in "POSTAGE" is very narrow. (Compare with EN90.) Die 36. Watermark 2.*

| EN142 | | UnFVF | UseFVF |
|---|---|---|---|
| 2¢ | brown on white | 80.00 | 37.00 |
| | entire | 95.00 | 75.00 |

| EN143 | | UnFVF | UseFVF |
|---|---|---|---|
| 2¢ | brown and amber | 50.00 | 40.00 |
| | entire | 80.00 | 65.00 |

| EN144 | | UnFVF | UseFVF |
|---|---|---|---|
| 2¢ | brown on cream | 675. | — |

| EN145 | | UnFVF | UseFVF |
|---|---|---|---|
| 2¢ | brown on orange | 7200. | — |
| | entire | 15000. | — |

| EN146 | | UnFVF | UseFVF |
|---|---|---|---|
| 2¢ | brown on manila, wrapper | 80.00 | 40.00 |
| | entire | 85.00 | 60.00 |

| EN147 | | UnFVF | UseFVF |
|---|---|---|---|
| 2¢ | vermilion on manila, wrapper | 1000. | 260. |
| | entire | 1500. | — |

EN148-EN151 *A copy of the Reay design (EN90). Die B, Figure "2" within tall ovals. "O" in "TWO" has plain center. (Compare with EN90, EN142 and following.) Die 37.*

| EN148 | | UnFVF | UseFVF |
|---|---|---|---|
| 2¢ | brown on white | 38.00 | 28.00 |
| | entire | 75.00 | 65.00 |

| EN149 | | UnFVF | UseFVF |
|---|---|---|---|
| 2¢ | brown on amber | 65.00 | 40.00 |
| | entire | 80.00 | 60.00 |

| EN150 | | UnFVF | UseFVF |
|---|---|---|---|
| 2¢ | brown on cream | 22000. | — |

| EN151 | | UnFVF | UseFVF |
|---|---|---|---|
| 2¢ | brown on manila, wrapper | 15.00 | 14.00 |
| | entire | 20.00 | 18.00 |

EN152, EN153 *Andrew Jackson. Die B2, similar to last except tail of left figure "2" touches the oval at right. Die 38.*

| EN152 | | UnFVF | UseFVF |
|---|---|---|---|
| 2¢ | brown on white | 55.00 | 25.00 |
| | entire | 75.00 | 65.00 |

| EN153 | | UnFVF | UseFVF |
|---|---|---|---|
| 2¢ | brown on amber | 160. | 55.00 |
| | entire | 175. | 85.00 |

EN154-EN161 *Die B3, same as EN148 but "O" in "TWO" with network in center. Die 39.*

| EN154 | | UnFVF | UseFVF |
|---|---|---|---|
| 2¢ | brown on white | 600. | 100. |
| | entire | 700. | 125. |

| EN155 | | UnFVF | UseFVF |
|---|---|---|---|
| 2¢ | brown on amber | 375. | 110. |
| | entire | 500. | 130. |

| EN156 | | UnFVF | UseFVF |
|---|---|---|---|
| 2¢ | brown on orange | 37.50 | 27.50 |
| | entire | 60.00 | 40.00 |

| EN157 | | UnFVF | UseFVF |
|---|---|---|---|
| 2¢ | brown on manila, wrapper | 50.00 | 32.50 |
| | entire | 65.00 | 35.00 |

**EN158**
2¢ **vermilion on white**    UnFVF UseFVF
17000.    —

**EN159**
2¢ **vermilion on amber**    UnFVF UseFVF
17000.    —

**EN160**
2¢ **vermilion on orange**    UnFVF UseFVF
17000.    —

**EN161**
2¢ **vermilion on manila**, wrapper    UnFVF UseFVF
6000.    —

EN162-EN172 *Andrew Jackson. Die C, short, thick figure "2" within small size ovals. (Compare with preceding and following; also with EN90.) Die 40.*

**EN162**
2¢ **brown on white**    UnFVF UseFVF
37.50    35.00
entire    50.00    40.00

**EN163**
2¢ **brown on amber**    UnFVF UseFVF
70.00    55.00
entire    85.00    60.00

**EN164**
2¢ **brown on manila**, wrapper    UnFVF UseFVF
35.00    25.00
entire    40.00    35.00

**EN165**
2¢ **brown red on orange**    UnFVF UseFVF
—    —
entire    —    —

**EN166**
2¢ **vermilion on orange**    UnFVF UseFVF
—    —
*Watermarks 2, 5 and 6.*

**EN167**
2¢ **red on white**    UnFVF UseFVF
5.50    2.50
entire    7.00    4.50

**EN168**
2¢ **red on amber**    UnFVF UseFVF
5.00    2.50
entire    6.00    4.00

**EN169**
2¢ **red on cream**    UnFVF UseFVF
11.00    5.50
entire    13.00    8.00

**EN170**
2¢ **red on blue**    UnFVF UseFVF
120.    28.00
entire    180.    135.

**EN171**
2¢ **red on fawn**    UnFVF UseFVF
6.50    4.50
entire    12.00    7.00

**EN172**
2¢ **red on manila**, wrapper    UnFVF UseFVF
4.00    4.00
entire    7.00    6.00

EN173-EN176 *Die C1, similar to last except ovals containing numerals are much heavier and there is a diagonal white line from about the letter "U" to the outer frame. (Compare with EN177.) Die 41.*

**EN173**
2¢ **red on white**    UnFVF UseFVF
50.00    30.00
entire    55.00    35.00

**EN174**
2¢ **red on amber**    UnFVF UseFVF
25.00    15.00
entire    28.00    17.00

**EN175**
2¢ **red on blue**    UnFVF UseFVF
10.00    8.00
entire    9.00    10.00

**EN176**
2¢ **red on fawn**    UnFVF UseFVF
10.00    4.00
entire    13.00    10.00

EN177-EN179 *Andrew Jackson. Die C2, similar to last except there is no diagonal line and the middle stroke of "N" in "CENTS" is as thin as the vertical strokes. (Compare with EN173.) Die 2.*

**EN177**
2¢ **red on white**    UnFVF UseFVF
50.00    25.00
entire    70.00    27.00

**EN178**
2¢ **red on amber**    UnFVF UseFVF
250.    75.00
entire    335.    100.

**EN179**
2¢ **red on manila**, wrapper    UnFVF UseFVF
16.00    9.00
entire    40.00    12.00

EN180-EN182 *Die D, the bottom of the bust forms a complete quarter circle. (Compare with EN162.) Die 43.*

**EN180**
2¢ **red on white**    UnFVF UseFVF
525.    100.
entire    625.    300.

**EN181**
2¢ **red on amber**    UnFVF UseFVF
16000.    16000.
entire    57000.    —

**EN182**
2¢ **red on manila**, wrapper    UnFVF UseFVF
80.00    55.00
entire    115.    95.00

EN183-EN186 *Washigton. Copy of Reay design (EN94). Die A, thin lettering. Long thin figures of value within tall ovals. (Compare with EN94 and EN187). Die 44.*

**EN183**
3¢ **green on white**    UnFVF UseFVF
18.00    5.50
entire    33.00    14.00

**EN184**
3¢ **green on amber**    UnFVF UseFVF
23.00    10.00
entire    38.00    14.00

**EN185**
3¢ **green on cream**    UnFVF UseFVF
33.00    10.00
entire    40.00    15.00

**EN186**
3¢ **green on blue**    UnFVF UseFVF
—    —

EN187-EN191 *Die B, thick lettering. Thick figures of value in short ovals. (Compare with EN183 and following.) Die 45.*

**EN187**
3¢ **green on white**    UnFVF UseFVF
1.25    .35
entire    2.25    1.00

**EN188**
3¢ **green on amber**    UnFVF UseFVF
1.50    .75
entire    2.50    1.25

**EN189**
3¢ **green on cream**    UnFVF UseFVF
8.00    7.00
entire    12.00    8.50

**EN190**
3¢ **green on blue**    UnFVF UseFVF
8.00    5.00
entire    13.00    8.50

| EN191 | | UnFVF | UseFVF |
|---|---|---|---|
| 3¢ | **green on fawn** | 5.00 | 3.00 |
| | entire | 8.00 | 4.00 |

EN192-EN195 *Washington. Similar to last. Die C, the top of the head is flat at back and there is a notch above and below the knot of the ponytail. (Compare with EN187.) Die 46.*

| EN192 | | UnFVF | UseFVF |
|---|---|---|---|
| 3¢ | **green on white** | 460. | 45.00 |
| | entire | 1800. | 75.00 |
| EN193 | | UnFVF | UseFVF |
| 3¢ | **green on amber** | 190. | 100. |
| | entire | 280. | 120. |
| EN194 | | UnFVF | UseFVF |
| 3¢ | **green on blue** | 8000. | 1800. |
| | entire | 17000. | 4300. |
| EN195 | | UnFVF | UseFVF |
| 3¢ | **green on fawn** | 25000. | 1700. |
| | entire | — | 15000. |

EN196-EN200 *Zachary Taylor. Die A, the numerals "5" with short thick top strokes. (Compare with EN201.) Die 47A.*

| EN196 | | UnFVF | UseFVF |
|---|---|---|---|
| 5¢ | **blue on white** | 10.00 | 8.00 |
| | entire | 12.00 | 12.00 |
| EN197 | | UnFVF | UseFVF |
| 5¢ | **blue on amber** | 10.00 | 8.00 |
| | entire | 12.00 | 15.00 |
| EN198 | | UnFVF | UseFVF |
| 5¢ | **blue on cream** | 82.00 | 38.00 |
| | entire* | 105. | 100. |
| EN199 | | UnFVF | UseFVF |
| 5¢ | **blue on blue** | 15.00 | 13.00 |
| | entire | 18.00 | 20.00 |

**1874-76. ISSUE** In 1874, the Post Office advertised for bids to supply envelopes. After considerable legal difficulties with George H. Reay and other bidders, the contract was awarded to the Plimpton Manufacturing Co. Reay refused to surrender his printing dies and, to futher embarrass the new contractor, is said to have engaged the services of all known die engravers. The new contractors were thus forced to employ less skilled engravers to try to duplicate the Reay designs. The resulting delay embarrassed the Post Office officials, who were forced to purchase supplies of envelopes from Reay until the new contractors could produce acceptable dies. Several unsuitable designs were accepted to take care of the situaton until better dies could be made, which accounts for some of the designs of the lower denomination stamps.

Eventually the Plimpton Manufacturing Co. overcame its difficulties and, in combination with the Morgan Envelope Co., continued to be the successful bidders for the manufacture of envelopes until 1903.

The struggle George H. Reay put up to retain his contract is one of the classic stories of philately. In the end, to prevent his competitors from ever using his dies, it is stated that he finally agreed to turn them over to the authorities, only to instruct his wife to throw them overboard from a Brooklyn-Manhattan ferry. There seems to be much evidence to substantiate this story.

| EN200 | | UnFVF | UseFVF |
|---|---|---|---|
| 5¢ | **blue on fawn** | 100. | 50.00 |
| | entire* | 175. | — |

EN201-EN205 *Zachary Taylor. Die B, the numerals "5" with long thin top strokes. (Compare with EN196.) Die 47B.*

| EN201 | | UnFVF | UseFVF |
|---|---|---|---|
| 5¢ | **blue on white** | 6.00 | 5.50 |
| | entire | 11.00 | 20.00 |
| EN202 | | UnFVF | UseFVF |
| 5¢ | **blue on amber** | 5.50 | 5.50 |
| | entire | 13.00 | 25.00 |
| EN203 | | UnFVF | UseFVF |
| 5¢ | **blue on cream** | 2500. | — |
| | entire* | 4200. | — |
| EN204 | | UnFVF | UseFVF |
| 5¢ | **blue on blue** | 13.00 | 8.00 |
| | entire | 16.00 | 20.00 |
| EN205 | | UnFVF | UseFVF |
| 5¢ | **blue on fawn** | 88.00 | 43.00 |
| | entire* | 110. | 100. |

EN206-EN210 *James Garfield. Die 59. Watermarks 5, 6.*

| EN206 | | UnFVF | UseFVF |
|---|---|---|---|
| 5¢ | **brown on white** | 3.00 | 2.00 |
| | entire | 5.50 | 15.00 |
| EN207 | | UnFVF | UseFVF |
| 5¢ | **brown on amber** | 4.00 | 2.25 |
| | entire | 7.50 | 18.00 |
| EN208 | | UnFVF | UseFVF |
| 5¢ | **brown on buff** | 90.00 | 60.00 |
| | entire | 120. | — |
| EN209 | | UnFVF | UseFVF |
| 5¢ | **brown on blue** | 50.00 | 30.00 |
| | entire | 65.00 | — |
| EN210 | | UnFVF | UseFVF |
| 5¢ | **brown on fawn** | 200. | — |
| | entire* | 250. | — |

EN211-EN214 *Abraham Lincoln. Copy of Reay design (EN97). The neck is short at the back. Lock of hair curves upward from forehead. (Compare with EN97.) Die 48. Watermarks 2, 3, 4, 5, 6.*

| EN211 | | UnFVF | UseFVF |
|---|---|---|---|
| 6¢ | **red on white** | 6.00 | 6.00 |
| | entire | 10.00 | 8.00 |
| EN212 | | UnFVF | UseFVF |
| 6¢ | **red on amber** | 10.00 | 6.00 |
| | entire | 16.00 | 11.00 |
| EN213 | | UnFVF | UseFVF |
| 6¢ | **red on cream** | 16.00 | 10.00 |
| | entire | 20.00 | 16.00 |
| EN214 | | UnFVF | UseFVF |
| 6¢ | **red on fawn** | 17.00 | 9.00 |
| | entire* | 25.00 | 14.00 |

EN215, EN216 *Edwin Stanton. Copy of Reay design (EN100). The down strokes of the figure "7" curve sharply upward. (Compare with EN100.) Die 49. Watermark 2.*

| EN215 | | UnFVF | UseFVF |
|---|---|---|---|
| 7¢ | **vermilion on white** | 1500. | — |

| EN216 | | UnFVF | UseFVF |
|---|---|---|---|
| 7¢ | **vermilion on amber** | 90.00 | 55.00 |
| | entire | 120. | — |

EN217, EN218 *Thomas Jefferson. Die A, very large head, called the "booby-head". (Compare with EN101 and following.) Die 50.*

| EN217 | | UnFVF | UseFVF |
|---|---|---|---|
| 10¢ | **brown on white** | 30.00 | 17.00 |
| | entire | 55.00 | — |

| EN218 | | UnFVF | UseFVF |
|---|---|---|---|
| 10¢ | **brown on amber** | 55.00 | 25.00 |
| | entire | 80.00 | — |

EN19-EN226 *Copy of Reay design (EN101). Die B, the end of the ponytail projects prominently and the head tilts downward. (Compare with EN101.) Die 51.*

| EN219 | | UnFVF | UseFVF |
|---|---|---|---|
| 10¢ | **brown on white** | 6.00 | 4.00 |
| | entire | 10.00 | 8.00 |

| EN220 | | UnFVF | UseFVF |
|---|---|---|---|
| 10¢ | **brown on amber** | 8.00 | 6.00 |
| | entire | 10.00 | 8.00 |

| EN221 | | UnFVF | UseFVF |
|---|---|---|---|
| 10¢ | **brown on buff** | 10.00 | 7.00 |
| | entire | 11.00 | 8.00 |

| EN222 | | UnFVF | UseFVF |
|---|---|---|---|
| 10¢ | **brown on blue** | 12.00 | 8.00 |
| | entire | 14.00 | 9.00 |

*EN219-EN222 exist in various shades.*

| EN223 | | UnFVF | UseFVF |
|---|---|---|---|
| 10¢ | **brown on manila** | 12.00 | 8.00 |
| | entire | 13.00 | 13.00 |
| | a. red brown on manila | 12.00 | 9.00 |
| | a. entire | 15.00 | 15.00 |

| EN224 | | UnFVF | UseFVF |
|---|---|---|---|
| 10¢ | **brown on amber-manila** | 12.00 | 7.00 |
| | entire* | 15.00 | 13.00 |
| | a. red brown on amber-manila | 16.00 | 7.00 |
| | a. entire | 22.00 | 17.00 |

| EN225 | | UnFVF | UseFVF |
|---|---|---|---|
| 10¢ | **ocher yellow on white** | 1050. | — |
| | entire* | 1500. | — |

| EN226 | | UnFVF | UseFVF |
|---|---|---|---|
| 10¢ | **ocher yellow on amber** | 1050. | — |
| | entire* | 1500. | — |

EN227-EN229 *Henry Clay. Copy of Reay design (EN105). The head is round and small. The ear is clearly defined. (Compare with EN105.) Die 52. Watermark 2.*

| EN227 | | UnFVF | UseFVF |
|---|---|---|---|
| 12¢ | **violet black on white** | 150. | 75.00 |
| | entire* | 160. | — |

| EN228 | | UnFVF | UseFVF |
|---|---|---|---|
| 12¢ | **violet black on amber** | 160. | 135. |
| | entire* | 235. | — |

| EN229 | | UnFVF | UseFVF |
|---|---|---|---|
| 12¢ | **violet black on cream** | 175. | 145. |
| | entire* | 720. | — |

EN230-EN232 *Daniel Webster. Copy of Reay design (EN108). Bust without sideburns. The hair parted. (Compare with EN108.) Die 53. Watermarks 2, 5.*

| EN230 | | UnFVF | UseFVF |
|---|---|---|---|
| 15¢ | **orange on white** | 40.00 | 30.00 |
| | entire* | 80.00 | 38.00 |

| EN231 | | UnFVF | UseFVF |
|---|---|---|---|
| 15¢ | **orange on amber** | 120. | 90.00 |
| | entire* | 175. | — |

| EN232 | | UnFVF | UseFVF |
|---|---|---|---|
| 15¢ | **orange on cream** | 335. | 335. |
| | entire* | 825. | — |

EN233-EN235 *Winfield Scott. Copy of Reay design (EN111). The ornaments around the inner oval end in points. (Compare with EN111.) Die 54. Watermark 2.*

| EN233 | | UnFVF | UseFVF |
|---|---|---|---|
| 24¢ | **purple on white** | 150. | 110. |
| | entire* | 220. | — |

| EN234 | | UnFVF | UseFVF |
|---|---|---|---|
| 24¢ | **purple on amber** | 150. | 110. |
| | entire* | 220. | — |

| EN235 | | UnFVF | UseFVF |
|---|---|---|---|
| 24¢ | **purple on cream** | 150. | 110. |
| | entire* | 700. | — |

EN236-EN241 *Alexander Hamilton. Copy of Reay design (EN114). The octagonal labels containing the figures of value are not in alignment; the one at the right tilts sharply downward. (Compare with EN114.) For brown stamps in this design, issued in 1887, see EN375-EN380. Die 55. Watermarks 2, 5, 6, 7, 9, 10.*

| EN236 | | UnFVF | UseFVF |
|---|---|---|---|
| 30¢ | **black on white** | 55.00 | 30.00 |
| | entire* | 65.00 | 65.00 |

| EN237 | | UnFVF | UseFVF |
|---|---|---|---|
| 30¢ | **black on amber** | 70.00 | 55.00 |
| | entire* | 125. | 275. |

| EN237A | | UnFVF | UseFVF |
|---|---|---|---|
| 30¢ | **black on cream** (see note) | 400. | 380. |
| | entire* | 725. | — |

*The only way to distinguish EN237A and EN243A - which both appear on cream paper - from the same designs on buff paper (EN238 and EN244) is to examine the watermark. Wmk 2 signifies cream paper.*

| EN238 | | UnFVF | UseFVF |
|---|---|---|---|
| 30¢ | **black on buff** | 95.00 | 75.00 |
| | entire | 135. | — |

| EN239 | | UnFVF | UseFVF |
|---|---|---|---|
| 30¢ | **black on blue** | 100. | 75.00 |
| | entire | 110. | — |

| EN240 | | UnFVF | UseFVF |
|---|---|---|---|
| 30¢ | **black on manila** | 90.00 | 75.00 |
| | entire | 135. | — |

| EN241 | | UnFVF | UseFVF |
|---|---|---|---|
| 30¢ | **black on amber-manila** | 110. | 75.00 |
| | entire | 140. | — |

EN242-EN247 *Oliver Perry. Copy of Reay design (EN117). The shields containing the numerals of value project considerably within the inner circle. (Compare with EN117.) For purple stamps of same design, issued in 1887, see EN381-EN386. Die 56.*

Watermarks 2, 6, 7, 9.

| EN242 | | UnFVF | UseFVF |
|---|---|---|---|
| 90¢ | carmine on white | 110. | 75.00 |
| | entire* | 120. | 85.00 |
| **EN243** | | **UnFVF** | **UseFVF** |
| 90¢ | carmine on amber | 150. | 195. |
| | entire* | 235. | — |
| **EN243A** | | **UnFVF** | **UseFVF** |
| 90¢ | carmine on cream (see note following EN237A) | 1100. | — |
| | entire* | 2000. | — |
| **EN244** | | **UnFVF** | **UseFVF** |
| 90¢ | carmine on buff | 200. | 230. |
| | entire | 235. | |
| **EN245** | | **UnFVF** | **UseFVF** |
| 90¢ | carmine on blue | 175. | 210. |
| | entire | 235. | — |
| **EN246** | | **UnFVF** | **UseFVF** |
| 90¢ | carmine on manila | 115. | 210. |
| | entire* | 195. | — |
| **EN247** | | **UnFVF** | **UseFVF** |
| 90¢ | carmine on amber-manila | 110. | 175. |
| | entire* | 195. | — |

**1876. CENTENNIAL ISSUE** Just before the great Centennial Exposition at Philadelphia in 1876, the Plimpton Morgan Envelope Co. had developed a machine that would gum the top back flap of the envelopes. Previously the machines in use would perform all operations of folding, printing and gluing together, but the gum on the top back flaps had to be applied by hand. To publicize this mechanical achievement, the Plimpton Co. requested permission to demonstrate its new machine at the exposition. The Post Office consented and provided that a specially designed stamp should be used to commemorate the exposition, thus authorizing the first commemorative postage stamp of the world. Two envelopes were authorized: The small would have the stamp printed in green, the slightly larger one would have the stamp in red. Also, paper bearing a special watermark was ordered for these envelopes. The advance demand proved so great that the envelopes were manufactured at Hartford, Connecticut, as well as on the demonstration machine at the exposition. In all, 8,000,000 envelopes were issued, approximately 4,000,000 of each size.

EN248, EN249 *Old and new methods of carring the post. There is a single line forming the bottom of the label containing the word "POSTAGE". (Compare with EN250.) Die 57.*

| | | UnFVF | UseFVF |
|---|---|---|---|
| **EN248** | | | |
| 3¢ | green on white | 50.00 | 13.00 |
| | entire | 60.00 | 35.00 |
| **EN249** | | **UnFVF** | **UseFVF** |
| 3¢ | red on white | 55.00 | 25.00 |
| | entire | 70.00 | 45.00 |

EN250, EN251 *The line at the bottom of the label containing the word "POSTAGE" is made up of two thin lines which sometimes merge. Die 58.*

| **EN250** | | **UnFVF** | **UseFVF** |
|---|---|---|---|
| 3¢ | green on white | 55.00 | 18.00 |
| | entire | 80.00 | 50.00 |
| **EN251** | | **UnFVF** | **UseFVF** |
| 3¢ | red on white | 19500. | — |
| | entire | 28000. | — |

**1883-86. ISSUE** With the change of the first class rate from 3¢ to 2¢, new envelopes of the 2¢ and 4¢ denomination were called for and new designs were adopted. The first design submitted was not considered entirely satisfactory, but so that envelopes would be available on time, it was approved. In the meantime, the new approved die was prepared and put into use in November, just one month after the new envelopes had been issued. Despite its short life, the first design (EN252-EN255) is not rare; apparently a very large supply was made. In May 1884, the color of the 2¢ envelope stamp was changed from carmine to brown to coincide with the color of the 2¢ adhesive stamp then in use. It is stated that the brown ink, because of its chemical construction, destroyed the printing dies and much recutting had to be done.

EN252-EN255 *Washington. Background of frame composed of scroll work ending in points around inner circle. Die 60. Watermarks 5, 6.*

| **EN252** | | **UnFVF** | **UseFVF** |
|---|---|---|---|
| 2¢ | red on white | 3.00 | 1.75 |
| | entire | 7.00 | 2.00 |
| | a. brown on white (error), entire | 2250. | — |
| **EN253** | | **UnFVF** | **UseFVF** |
| 2¢ | red on amber | 5.00 | 2.00 |
| | entire | 8.00 | 3.50 |
| **EN254** | | **UnFVF** | **UseFVF** |
| 2¢ | red on blue | 7.00 | 5.00 |
| | entire | 9.00 | 6.00 |
| **EN255** | | **UnFVF** | **UseFVF** |
| 2¢ | red on fawn | 7.00 | 3.50 |
| | entire | 13.00 | 4.00 |

EN256-EN265 *Four clear ornamental wavy lines within the circular frame of the design. (Compare with EN266 and EN302.) Die 61. EN256-EN260 Nov. 1883. EN261-EN265 May 1884. EN266 June 1984.*

| **EN256** | | **UnFVF** | **UseFVF** |
|---|---|---|---|
| 2¢ | red on white | 3.00 | 1.50 |
| | entire | 7.00 | 3.00 |
| **EN257** | | **UnFVF** | **UseFVF** |
| 2¢ | red on amber | 4.00 | 2.50 |
| | entire | 8.50 | 4.00 |
| **EN258** | | **UnFVF** | **UseFVF** |
| 2¢ | red on blue | 7.00 | 5.00 |
| | entire | 11.00 | 6.00 |
| **EN259** | | **UnFVF** | **UseFVF** |
| 2¢ | red on fawn | 5.00 | 3.00 |
| | entire | 7.00 | 4.00 |
| **EN260** | | **UnFVF** | **UseFVF** |
| 2¢ | red on manila, wrapper | 8.00 | 4.00 |
| | entire | 13.00 | 8.50 |
| **EN261** | | **UnFVF** | **UseFVF** |
| 2¢ | brown on white | 3.00 | 1.50 |
| | entire | 7.00 | 3.00 |
| **EN262** | | **UnFVF** | **UseFVF** |
| 2¢ | brown on amber | 4.00 | 3.00 |
| | entire | 8.00 | 4.00 |
| **EN263** | | **UnFVF** | **UseFVF** |
| 2¢ | brown on blue | 7.00 | 4.00 |
| | entire | 11.00 | 6.00 |

**EN264**
2¢    **brown on fawn**    | UnFVF | UseFVF |
|---|---|
| 5.00 | 3.00 |
entire    7.00    4.00

**EN265**
2¢    **brown on manila,** wrapper    | UnFVF | UseFVF |
|---|---|
| 8.00 | 4.00 |
entire    13.00    8.00

**EN266**
2¢    **red on white**    | UnFVF | UseFVF |
|---|---|
| 6.00 | 4.00 |
entire    9.00    6.00

*EN267-EN274 Washington. Retouched dies. Similar to EN256-EN266 but the pairs of wavy lines are no longer continuous, but merge at various points. Die 62.*

**EN267**
2¢    **red on amber**    | UnFVF | UseFVF |
|---|---|
| 10.00 | 7.00 |
entire    15.00    10.00

**EN268**
2¢    **red on blue**    | UnFVF | UseFVF |
|---|---|
| 13.00 | 8.00 |
entire    20.00    10.00

**EN269**
2¢    **red on fawn**    | UnFVF | UseFVF |
|---|---|
| 10.00 | 7.00 |
entire    13.00    8.00

**EN270**
2¢    **brown on white**    | UnFVF | UseFVF |
|---|---|
| 13.00 | 5.00 |
entire    18.00    10.00

**EN271**
2¢    **brown on amber**    | UnFVF | UseFVF |
|---|---|
| 60.00 | 35.00 |
entire    18.00    10.00

**EN272**
2¢    **brown on blue**    | UnFVF | UseFVF |
|---|---|
| 12.00 | 6.00 |
entire    13.00    8.00

**EN273**
2¢    **brown on fawn**    | UnFVF | UseFVF |
|---|---|
| 10.00 | 9.00 |
entire    14.00    13.00

**EN274**
2¢    **brown on manila,** wrapper    | UnFVF | UseFVF |
|---|---|
| 18.00 | 13.00 |
entire    24.00    13.00

*EN275-EN277 There are 3 1/2 links above the left figure "2". Die 63.*

**EN275**
2¢    **red on white**    | UnFVF | UseFVF |
|---|---|
| 50.00 | 35.00 |
entire    65.00    50.00

**EN276**
2¢    **red on amber**    | UnFVF | UseFVF |
|---|---|
| 600. | 300. |
entire    875.    525.

**EN277**
2¢    **red on fawn**    | UnFVF | UseFVF |
|---|---|
| — | 6500. |

*EN278-EN284 Washington. There are two links below the right figure "2". Center link below left figure "2" touches at left. Die 64.*

**EN278**
2¢    **red on white**    | UnFVF | UseFVF |
|---|---|
| 65.00 | 45.00 |
entire    85.00    70.00

**EN279**
2¢    **red on amber**    | UnFVF | UseFVF |
|---|---|
| 120. | 65.00 |

---

entire    135.    85.00

**EN280**
2¢    **red on blue**    | UnFVF | UseFVF |
|---|---|
| 270. | 110. |
entire    400.    135.

**EN281**
2¢    **red on fawn**    | UnFVF | UseFVF |
|---|---|
| 280. | 110. |
entire    350.    200.

**EN282**
2¢    **brown on white**    | UnFVF | UseFVF |
|---|---|
| 80.00 | 35.00 |
entire    180.    90.00

**EN283**
2¢    **brown on amber**    | UnFVF | UseFVF |
|---|---|
| 180. | 90.00 |
entire    260.    200.

**EN284**
2¢    **brown on fawn**    | UnFVF | UseFVF |
|---|---|
| 2100. | 925. |
entire    4000.    2100.

*EN285-EN291 A round "O" in "TWO," upright of letter "T" in "TWO" slants to right. Die 65.*

**EN285**
2¢    **red on white**    | UnFVF | UseFVF |
|---|---|
| 1200. | 300. |
entire    1600.    650.

**EN286**
2¢    **red on amber**    | UnFVF | UseFVF |
|---|---|
| 2100. | 775. |
entire    3000.    1000.

**EN287**
2¢    **red on fawn**    | UnFVF | UseFVF |
|---|---|
| 650. | 350. |
entire    950.    450.

**EN288**
2¢    **brown on white**    | UnFVF | UseFVF |
|---|---|
| 140. | 70.00 |
entire    160.    225.

**EN289**
2¢    **brown on amber**    | UnFVF | UseFVF |
|---|---|
| 160. | 70.00 |
entire    180.    90.00

**EN290**
2¢    **brown on blue**    | UnFVF | UseFVF |
|---|---|
| — | 5000. |

**EN291**
2¢    **brown on fawn**    | UnFVF | UseFVF |
|---|---|
| 775. | 625. |
entire    1100.    750.

*EN292-EN297 Andrew Jackson. Die A, the numeral "4" at left is narrow (2 3/4mm) and has a sharp point. (Compare with EN298.) Die 66A. Watermarks 6, 7. Oct. 1883.*

**EN292**
4¢    **green on white**    | UnFVF | UseFVF |
|---|---|
| 3.00 | 3.00 |
entire    5.00    5.00

**EN293**
4¢    **green on amber**    | UnFVF | UseFVF |
|---|---|
| 4.00 | 3.00 |
entire    6.00    5.00

**EN294**
4¢    **green on buff**    | UnFVF | UseFVF |
|---|---|
| 7.00 | 7.00 |
entire    11.00    10.00

**EN295**
4¢    **green on blue**    | UnFVF | UseFVF |
|---|---|
| 7.00 | 6.00 |
entire    10.00    7.00

**EN296**
4¢    **green on manila**    | UnFVF | UseFVF |
|---|---|
| 8.00 | 6.00 |
entire    11.00    11.00

**EN297**
4¢    **green on amber-manila**    | UnFVF | UseFVF |
|---|---|
| 16.00 | 9.00 |
entire    23.00    12.00

EN298-EN301 *Die B, the numeral "4" at left is wide (3mm) and has a blunt point. Die 66.*

| EN298 | | UnFVF | UseFVF |
|---|---|---|---|
| 4¢ | **green on white** | 5.00 | 4.00 |
| | entire | 11.00 | 6.00 |
| EN299 | | UnFVF | UseFVF |
| 4¢ | **green on amber** | 10.00 | 6.00 |
| | entire | 15.00 | 9.00 |

**1883-86. ISSUE** With the change of the first class rate from 3¢ to 2¢, new envelopes of the 2¢ and 4¢ denomination were called for and new designs were adopted. The first design submitted was not considered entirely satisfactory, but so that envelopes would be available on time, it was approved. In the meantime, the new approved die was prepared and put into use in November, just one month after the new envelopes had been issued. Despite its short life, the first design (EN252-EN255) is not rare; apparently a very large supply was made. In May 1884, the color of the 2¢ envelope stamp was changed from carmine to brown to coincide with the color of the 2¢ adhesive stamp then in use. It is stated that the brown ink, because of its chemical construction, destroyed the printing dies and much recutting had to be done.

| EN300 | | UnFVF | UseFVF |
|---|---|---|---|
| 4¢ | **green on manila** | 10.00 | 6.00 |
| | entire | 14.00 | 10.00 |
| EN301 | | UnFVF | UseFVF |
| 4¢ | **green on amber-manila** | 9.00 | 6.00 |
| | entire | 12.00 | 9.00 |

**1884. ISSUE July.** The previous printing dies having proved completely unsatisfactory, new designs were introduced in July 1884. The principal change consisted of simplifying the old design by removing one pair of the wavy lines from the inner and outer circle.

At first a few impressions were made in red ink and these are comparatively scarce. Later the stamps were printed in brown ink.

EN302-EN312 *Washington. Only two ornamental wavy lines in frame. (Compare with EN256) and the back of the bust forms an angle. (Compare with EN314.) Die 67. Watermark 6, 7, 9, 10.*

| EN302 | | UnFVF | UseFVF |
|---|---|---|---|
| 2¢ | **red on white** | 500. | — |
| | entire | 1200. | — |
| EN303 | | UnFVF | UseFVF |
| 2¢ | **red on blue** | 225. | — |
| | entire | 275. | — |
| EN304 | | UnFVF | UseFVF |
| 2¢ | **red on manila,** wrapper | 100. | — |
| | entire | 150. | — |
| EN305 | | UnFVF | UseFVF |
| 2¢ | **lake on white** | 25.00 | 20.00 |
| | entire | 30.00 | 24.00 |
| EN306 | | UnFVF | UseFVF |
| 2¢ | **brown on white** | .50 | .25 |
| | entire | .75 | .30 |
| EN307 | | UnFVF | UseFVF |
| 2¢ | **brown on amber** | .65 | .45 |
| | entire | 1.25 | .55 |
| EN308 | | UnFVF | UseFVF |
| 2¢ | **brown on buff** | 3.00 | 2.00 |
| | entire | 4.00 | 2.50 |
| EN309 | | UnFVF | UseFVF |
| 2¢ | **brown on blue** | 2.50 | .50 |
| | entire | 3.50 | 1.75 |

| EN310 | | UnFVF | UseFVF |
|---|---|---|---|
| 2¢ | **brown on fawn** | 3.00 | 2.00 |
| | entire | 3.50 | 2.25 |
| EN311 | | UnFVF | UseFVF |
| 2¢ | **brown on manila** | 9.00 | 3.50 |
| | entire | 13.00 | 5.00 |
| EN312 | | UnFVF | UseFVF |
| 2¢ | **brown on amber-manila** | 6.00 | 6.00 |
| | entire | 10.00 | 7.00 |
| EN313 | | UnFVF | UseFVF |
| 2¢ | **brown on manila,** wrapper | 5.25 | 5.00 |
| | entire | 7.00 | 6.00 |

EN314-EN318 *The back of the bust is rounded. (Compare with EN302.) Die 68.*

| EN314 | | UnFVF | UseFVF |
|---|---|---|---|
| 2¢ | **brown on white** | 150. | 40.00 |
| | entire | 375. | 70.00 |
| EN315 | | UnFVF | UseFVF |
| 2¢ | **brown on amber** | 14.00 | 12.00 |
| | entire | 18.00 | 14.00 |
| EN316 | | UnFVF | UseFVF |
| 2¢ | **brown on blue** | 700. | 125. |
| | entire | 775. | 225. |
| EN317 | | UnFVF | UseFVF |
| 2¢ | **brown on fawn** | 20.00 | 17.50 |
| | entire | 27.50 | 20.00 |
| EN318 | | UnFVF | UseFVF |
| 2¢ | **brown on manila,** wrapper | 20.00 | 15.00 |
| | entire | 22.50 | 18.00 |

**1886-87. ISSUE Letter sheet.** Despite the attempt in 1861 to popularize letter sheets, Congress authorized the Postmaster General, by an Act of March 3, 1879, to make letter sheets available to the public. It stipulated, however, that no royalty should be paid for any patents on such devices. This caused the Postmaster General much difficulty, since existing letter sheets had been patented. Eventually an arrangement was made with the American Bank Note Co. to produce letter sheets under a patent owned by the United States Postal Card Company. The sheets again proved unpopular and were discontinued in 1894.

EN319
*Ulysses S. Grant.*
*Unwatermarked or watermark "US".*

*Letter sheet watermark.*

| EN319 | | UnFVF | UseFVF |
|---|---|---|---|
| 2¢ | **green on white** | — | — |
| | entire | 22.00 | 11.00 |

*Letter sheets exist with three varieties of perforations at top: 83, 41 or 33, and with guide perforations for folding at either right or left. Watermarked sheets are inscribed "Series 1" through "Series 7" and always have 41 perforations at top.*

**1887-99. ISSUE** The new contract in 1886 again changed the designs and colors of the stamps on envelopes. The contractor, as before, was the Plimpton Morgan envelope Co. In 1894 the contractor lost the contract to James Purcell, whose factory was at Holyoke, Mass. Purcell had great difficulty completing the terms of his contract and soon was forced to enter into negotiations with the Plimpton Morgan Co. to complete the work. Purcell's work principally is noted by the 1¢ envelopes, which he printed in a very rare dark blue ink, the 4¢ envelopes which he printed in a scarlet and sometimes orange ink, and the 5¢ envelopes for which he prepared a new printing die on which the neckline of Gen. Grant had been eliminated (EN373-374).

EN320 Franklin. The bust leans forward and has a tremendously large lower portion. This is the so-called "Tiffany Die". which was rejected.

| EN320 | | UnFVF | UseFVF |
|---|---|---|---|
| 1¢ | blue on white | — | — |
| | entire | — | — |

*Watermarks 7, 8, 9, 10, 12.*

EN321-EN331 *The illustration at the right shows the "Spur Die", a sharp "spur" projecting downward from lower portion of the bust. Die 69 at left.*

| EN321 | | UnFVF | UseFVF |
|---|---|---|---|
| 1¢ | blue on white | .60 | .25 |
| | entire | 1.00 | .35 |
| | a. "Spur Die" | — | — |
| | entire | 2.00 | — |
| EN322 | | UnFVF | UseFVF |
| 1¢ | blue on amber | 3.00 | 1.50 |
| | entire | 6.00 | 4.00 |
| | a. "Sprur Die" | — | — |
| | entire | 10.00 | — |
| EN323 | | UnFVF | UseFVF |
| 1¢ | blue on buff | 2000. | — |
| | entire | 4100. | — |
| | a. "Specimen" | — | — |
| EN324 | | UnFVF | UseFVF |
| 1¢ | blue on blue | 3300. | — |
| | entire | 4400. | — |
| EN325 | | UnFVF | UseFVF |
| 1¢ | blue on manila | .65 | .35 |
| | entire | 1.00 | .50 |
| EN326 | | UnFVF | UseFVF |
| 1¢ | blue on amber-manila | 5.00 | 4.00 |
| | entire | 7.00 | 6.00 |
| EN327 | | UnFVF | UseFVF |
| 1¢ | blue on manila, wrapper | .45 | .30 |
| | entire | 1.00 | .50 |
| EN328 | | UnFVF | UseFVF |
| 1¢ | dark blue on white | 7.00 | 3.00 |
| | entire | 10.00 | 7.00 |
| EN329 | | UnFVF | UseFVF |
| 1¢ | dark blue on amber | 45.00 | 25.00 |
| | entire | 60.00 | 30.00 |
| EN330 | | UnFVF | UseFVF |
| 1¢ | dark blue on manila | 20.00 | 9.00 |
| | entire | 27.50 | 20.00 |
| EN331 | | UnFVF | UseFVF |
| 1¢ | dark blue on manila, wrapper | 12.00 | 10.00 |
| | entire | 20.00 | 13.00 |

EN338-EN343 *Washington. Die A, the bust points at the third colored tooth of the frame. "G" in "POSTAGE" has no cross bar. (Compare with EN344.) Die 70.*

| EN338 | | UnFVF | UseFVF |
|---|---|---|---|
| 2¢ | green on white | 9.00 | 8.00 |
| | entire | 18.00 | 11.00 |
| EN339 | | UnFVF | UseFVF |
| 2¢ | green on amber | 18.00 | 12.00 |
| | entire | 25.00 | 13.00 |
| EN340 | | UnFVF | UseFVF |
| 2¢ | green on buff | 65.00 | 30.00 |
| | entire | 85.00 | 35.00 |
| EN341 | | UnFVF | UseFVF |
| 2¢ | green on blue | 2700. | 700. |
| | entire | — | 4200. |
| EN342 | | UnFVF | UseFVF |
| 2¢ | green on manila | 1750. | 500. |
| | entire | 1500. | 500. |
| EN343 | | UnFVF | UseFVF |
| 2¢ | green on amber-manila | 1500. | 550. |
| | entire | 4750. | 1800. |

EN344-EN350 *Washington. Die B, bust points between first and second colored teeth of frame. "G" in "POSTAGE" has a cross bar. This is the common die of the series. (Compare with EN338.) The illustration at right shows the cap on "2" variety. Die 71, 71b.*

| EN344 | | UnFVF | UseFVF |
|---|---|---|---|
| 2¢ | green on white | .30 | .25 |
| | entire | .60 | .25 |
| | v. Cap on "2" | — | — |
| | entire | — | — |
| EN345 | | UnFVF | UseFVF |
| 2¢ | green on amber | .45 | .25 |
| | entire | .60 | .30 |
| | v. Cap on "2" | — | — |
| | entire | — | — |
| EN346 | | UnFVF | UseFVF |
| 2¢ | green on buff | .60 | .25 |
| | entire | 1.00 | .45 |
| | v. Cap on "2" | — | — |
| | entire | — | — |
| EN347 | | UnFVF | UseFVF |
| 2¢ | green on blue | .60 | .25 |
| | entire | 1.00 | .40 |
| | v. Cap on "2" | — | — |
| | entire | — | — |
| EN348 | | UnFVF | UseFVF |
| 2¢ | green on manila | 2.00 | .60 |
| | entire | 2.50 | 1.50 |
| | v. Cap on "2" | — | — |
| | entire | — | — |
| EN349 | | UnFVF | UseFVF |
| 2¢ | green on amber-manila | 2.50 | 2.00 |
| | entire | 5.00 | 2.50 |
| | v. Cap on "2" | — | — |
| | entire | — | — |
| EN350 | | UnFVF | UseFVF |
| 2¢ | green on manila, wrapper | 3.00 | 2.50 |
| | entire | 7.00 | 6.00 |

EN351-EN356 *Washington. Die C, similar to last, but head larger and well rounded. The ear is formed by two lines and there are two locks of hair in front of it. (Compare with EN355.) Die 72.*

| EN351 | | UnFVF | UseFVF |
|---|---|---|---|
| 2¢ | green on white | 100. | 13.00 |
| | entire | 125. | 40.00 |

| EN352 | | UnFVF | UseFVF |
|---|---|---|---|
| 2¢ | green on amber | 125. | 20.00 |
| | entire | 135. | 40.00 |

| EN353 | | UnFVF | UseFVF |
|---|---|---|---|
| 2¢ | green on buff | 150. | 40.00 |
| | entire | 160. | 60.00 |

| EN354 | | UnFVF | UseFVF |
|---|---|---|---|
| 2¢ | green on blue | 175. | 60.00 |
| | entire | 185. | 65.00 |

| EN355 | | UnFVF | UseFVF |
|---|---|---|---|
| 2¢ | green on manila | 125. | 65.00 |
| | entire | 160. | 90.00 |

| EN356 | | UnFVF | UseFVF |
|---|---|---|---|
| 2¢ | green on amber-manila | 325. | 80.00 |
| | entire | 375. | 120. |

EN357-EN362 *Die D, similar to EN344 but the bust has no ear.*

| EN357 | | UnFVF | UseFVF |
|---|---|---|---|
| 2¢ | green on white | — | — |
| | entire | — | — |

| EN358 | | UnFVF | UseFVF |
|---|---|---|---|
| 2¢ | green on amber | — | — |
| | entire | — | — |

| EN359 | | UnFVF | UseFVF |
|---|---|---|---|
| 2¢ | green on buff | — | — |
| | entire | — | — |

| EN360 | | UnFVF | UseFVF |
|---|---|---|---|
| 2¢ | green on blue | — | — |
| | entire | — | — |

| EN361 | | UnFVF | UseFVF |
|---|---|---|---|
| 2¢ | green on manila | — | — |
| | entire | — | — |

| EN362 | | UnFVF | UseFVF |
|---|---|---|---|
| 2¢ | green on amber-manila | — | — |
| | entire | — | — |

EN363-EN368 *Andrew Jackson. The scarlet and orange shades of the 4¢ stamps were manufactured by James Purcell, who obtained the contract in 1894 but due to lack of adequate machinery shortly thereafter was forced to sublet his contract to the previous manufacturer. Die 73.*

| EN363 | | UnFVF | UseFVF |
|---|---|---|---|
| 4¢ | carmine on white | 1.65 | 1.25 |
| | entire | 3.25 | 1.50 |
| | a. scarlet | 2.25 | 1.50 |
| | entire | 5.00 | 4.00 |
| | b. orange | — | — |
| | entire | — | — |

| EN364 | | UnFVF | UseFVF |
|---|---|---|---|
| 4¢ | carmine on amber | 3.00 | 2.00 |
| | entire | 5.00 | 3.50 |
| | a. scarlet | 3.00 | 3.25 |
| | entire | 6.00 | 4.00 |
| | b. orange | — | — |
| | entire | — | — |

| EN365 | | UnFVF | UseFVF |
|---|---|---|---|
| 4¢ | carmine on buff | 6.00 | 3.00 |
| | entire | 9.00 | 4.00 |

| EN366 | | UnFVF | UseFVF |
|---|---|---|---|
| 4¢ | carmine on blue | 5.00 | 4.50 |
| | entire | 7.00 | 6.00 |

| EN367 | | UnFVF | UseFVF |
|---|---|---|---|
| 4¢ | carmine on manila | 7.00 | 6.00 |
| | entire | 9.00 | 7.50 |

| EN368 | | UnFVF | UseFVF |
|---|---|---|---|
| 4¢ | carmine on amber-manila | 5.00 | 3.50 |
| | entire | 3.00 | 4.00 |

EN369-EN372 *Ulysses S. Grant. There is a space between the chin and the coat. (Compare with EN373.) Die 74.*

| EN369 | | UnFVF | UseFVF |
|---|---|---|---|
| 5¢ | blue on white | 4.00 | 3.50 |
| | entire | 6.00 | 15.00 |

| EN370 | | UnFVF | UseFVF |
|---|---|---|---|
| 5¢ | blue on amber | 4.50 | 2.50 |
| | entire | 8.00 | 18.00 |

| EN371 | | UnFVF | UseFVF |
|---|---|---|---|
| 5¢ | blue on buff | 5.00 | 4.00 |
| | entire | 10.00 | 20.00 |

| EN372 | | UnFVF | UseFVF |
|---|---|---|---|
| 5¢ | blue on blue | 6.00 | 5.00 |
| | entire | 10.00 | 16.00 |

EN373, EN374 *Ulysses S. Grant. There is no space between the chin and the coat. (Compare with EN369.) Die 75.*

| EN373 | | UnFVF | UseFVF |
|---|---|---|---|
| 5¢ | blue on white | 10.00 | 5.00 |
| | entire | 14.00 | 20.00 |

| EN374 | | UnFVF | UseFVF |
|---|---|---|---|
| 5¢ | blue on amber | 10.00 | 6.00 |
| | entire | 15.00 | 20.00 |

EN375-EN380 *Alexander Hamilton. Re-issue of old design. Die 55.*

| EN375 | | UnFVF | UseFVF |
|---|---|---|---|
| 30¢ | red brown on white | 40.00 | 43.00 |
| | entire | 50.00 | 225. |

| EN376 | | UnFVF | UseFVF |
|---|---|---|---|
| 30¢ | red brown on amber | 45.00 | 55.00 |
| | entire | 55.00 | 325. |

| EN377 | | UnFVF | UseFVF |
|---|---|---|---|
| 30¢ | red brown on buff | 40.00 | 45.00 |
| | entire | 50.00 | 360. |

| EN378 | | UnFVF | UseFVF |
|---|---|---|---|
| 30¢ | red brown on blue | 40.00 | 45.00 |
| | entire | 50.00 | 350. |

| EN379 | | UnFVF | UseFVF |
|---|---|---|---|
| 30¢ | red brown on manila | 45.00 | 45.00 |
| | entire | 50.00 | 275. |

| EN380 | | UnFVF | UseFVF |
|---|---|---|---|
| 30¢ | red brown on amber-manila | 50.00 | 30.00 |
| | entire | 55.00 | 275. |

EN381-EN386 *Oliver Perry. Re-issue of old design. Die 56.*

| EN381 | | UnFVF | UseFVF |
|---|---|---|---|
| 90¢ | purple on white | 65.00 | 70.00 |
| | entire | 80.00 | 450. |

| EN382 | | UnFVF | UseFVF |
|---|---|---|---|
| 90¢ | purple on amber | 75.00 | 75.00 |
| | entire | 100. | 450. |

| EN383 | | UnFVF | UseFVF |
|---|---|---|---|
| 90¢ | purple on buff | 75.00 | 80.00 |
| | entire | 100. | 450. |

| EN384 | | UnFVF | UseFVF |
|---|---|---|---|
| 90¢ | purple on blue | 75.00 | 85.00 |
| | entire | 120. | 450. |

| EN385 | | UnFVF | UseFVF |
|---|---|---|---|
| 90¢ | purple on manila | 80.00 | 85.00 |
| | entire | 120. | 450. |

| EN386 | | UnFVF | UseFVF |
|---|---|---|---|
| 90¢ | purple on amber-manila | 90.00 | 90.00 |
| | entire | 120. | 450. |

*EN375-EN380 are known in various shades of brown. EN381-EN386 exist in both dark and bright purple.*

**1893. COLUMBIAN EXPOSITION ISSUE** To commemorate the Columbian Exposition, the Post Office Department ordered a special series of stamped envelopes in the 1¢, 2¢, 4¢, 5¢ and 10¢ denominations. For reasons not known, the 4¢ envelope never was issued.

The designs of all denominations are identical, except in the face value of the stamp. Four varieties are widely recognized by collectors:
- A period after "CENT"; a meridian behind head of Columbus
- A period; no meridian
- No period; a meridian
- No period; no meridian

The first three will be found on the 1¢ stamps. All four are found on the 2¢ stamps; only the first two on the 5¢ stamps. The 10¢ stamp exists only without the period, but with the meridian.

*EN387-EN390 Christopher Columbus. "Liberty", American eagle. Designs identical except for face value. Die 76. Watermark II.*

| EN387 | | UnFVF | UseFVF |
|---|---|---|---|
| 1¢ | blue on white | 2.00 | 1.50 |
| | entire | 3.00 | 1.75 |

| EN388 | | UnFVF | UseFVF |
|---|---|---|---|
| 2¢ | violet on white | 1.50 | .75 |
| | entire | 2.50 | .75 |
| | a. slate (error) | 1900. | — |
| | entire | — | — |

| EN389 | | UnFVF | UseFVF |
|---|---|---|---|
| 5¢ | brown on white | 9.00 | 8.00 |
| | entire* | 15.00 | 12.00 |
| | a. slate (error) | 750. | 750. |
| | entire | 800. | 1200. |

| EN390 | | UnFVF | UseFVF |
|---|---|---|---|
| 10¢ | slate on white | 40.00 | 30.00 |
| | entire | 60.00 | 45.00 |

**1899. ISSUE** With this issue all denominations of stamps above 5¢ values were discontinued; envelopes in higher denominations had been found to be of little use or in little demand. This was the last issue manufactured by the Plimpton Morgan Envelope Co.

*EN391-EN396 Franklin. Die 77. Watermarks 12, 13.*

| EN391 | | UnFVF | UseFVF |
|---|---|---|---|
| 1¢ | green on white | .75 | .25 |
| | entire | 1.50 | .75 |

| EN392 | | UnFVF | UseFVF |
|---|---|---|---|
| 1¢ | green on amber | 4.75 | 1.50 |
| | entire | 7.75 | 3.00 |

| EN393 | | UnFVF | UseFVF |
|---|---|---|---|
| 1¢ | green on buff | 10.00 | 4.00 |
| | entire | 13.50 | 4.00 |

| EN394 | | UnFVF | UseFVF |
|---|---|---|---|
| 1¢ | green on blue | 10.00 | 7.00 |
| | entire | 13.00 | 20.00 |

| EN395 | | UnFVF | UseFVF |
|---|---|---|---|
| 1¢ | green on manila | 2.00 | 1.00 |
| | entire | 6.50 | 2.50 |

| EN396 | | UnFVF | UseFVF |
|---|---|---|---|
| 1¢ | green on manila, wrapper | 2.00 | 1.00 |
| | entire | 8.75 | 3.00 |

*EN397-EN400 Washington. Die A, point of bust broad and ends over the left corner of the shield containing numeral. (Compare with EN401.) Die 78.*

| EN397 | | UnFVF | UseFVF |
|---|---|---|---|
| 2¢ | carmine on white | 4.00 | 2.00 |
| | entire | 8.50 | 3.00 |

| EN398 | | UnFVF | UseFVF |
|---|---|---|---|
| 2¢ | carmine on amber | 17.50 | 10.00 |
| | entire | 27.50 | 12.00 |

| EN399 | | UnFVF | UseFVF |
|---|---|---|---|
| 2¢ | carmine on buff | 17.50 | 8.00 |
| | entire | 30.00 | 9.00 |

**1899. ISSUE** With this issue all denominations of stamps above 5¢ values were discontinued; envelopes in higher denominations had been found to be of little use or in little demand. This was the last issue manufactured by the Plimpton Morgan Envelope Co.

| EN400 | | UnFVF | UseFVF |
|---|---|---|---|
| 2¢ | carmine on blue | 60.00 | 30.00 |
| | entire | 75.00 | 35.00 |

*EN401-EN405 George Washington. Die B, point of bust elongated and points to the second tooth. Hair tied with ribbon at back. (Compare with EN397 and following.) Die 79.*

| EN401 | | UnFVF | UseFVF |
|---|---|---|---|
| 2¢ | carmine and white | .30 | .25 |
| | entire | .75 | .50 |

| EN402 | | UnFVF | UseFVF |
|---|---|---|---|
| 2¢ | carmine and amber | 1.25 | .25 |
| | entire | 3.25 | .75 |

| EN403 | | UnFVF | UseFVF |
|---|---|---|---|
| 2¢ | carmine on buff | 1.00 | .25 |
| | entire | 2.75 | .75 |

| EN404 | | UnFVF | UseFVF |
|---|---|---|---|
| 2¢ | carmine on blue | 1.25 | .50 |
| | entire | 3.50 | 1.75 |

| EN405 | | UnFVF | UseFVF |
|---|---|---|---|
| 2¢ | carmine on manila, wrapper | 6.00 | 3.00 |
| | entire | 12.50 | 6.00 |

*There are many shades for EN406-EN409.*

*EN406-EN409 Die C, re-cut die. Similar to last but the hair is without ribbon. Many varieties of the re-cutting exist, some of which show the hair in flowing curves; some with hair pulled straight down; and others with the ribbon obliterated with short lines (Compare with EN401). Die 80.*

**EN406**
| | | UnFVF | UseFVF |
|---|---|---|---|
| 2¢ | carmine on white | 5.00 | 2.50 |
| | entire | 9.50 | 7.00 |

*There are many shades for EN406-EN409.*

**EN407**
| | | UnFVF | UseFVF |
|---|---|---|---|
| 2¢ | carmine on amber | 12.00 | 8.00 |
| | entire | 22.50 | 15.00 |

**EN408**
| | | UnFVF | UseFVF |
|---|---|---|---|
| 2¢ | carmine on buff | 25.00 | 15.00 |
| | entire | 35.00 | 17.50 |

**EN409**
| | | UnFVF | UseFVF |
|---|---|---|---|
| 2¢ | carmine on blue | 10.00 | 7.00 |
| | entire | 22.50 | 15.00 |

*There are many shades for Nos. EN406-EN409.*

EN410, EN411 *Abraham Lincoln. Die A, bust pointed and undraped. Inner oval with teeth. (Compare with following.) Die 81.*

**EN410**
| | | UnFVF | UseFVF |
|---|---|---|---|
| 4¢ | brown on white | 17.00 | 12.00 |
| | entire | 30.00 | 15.00 |

**EN411**
| | | UnFVF | UseFVF |
|---|---|---|---|
| 4¢ | brown on amber | 17.00 | 12.00 |
| | entire | 30.00 | 25.00 |

EN412 *Die B, bust is draped and point broad. Inner oval with teeth. Die 82.*

**EN412**
| | | UnFVF | UseFVF |
|---|---|---|---|
| 4¢ | brown on white | 5000. | 325. |
| | entire | 5700. | — |

En413-EN415 *Abraham Lincoln. Die C, no teeth in innter oval. Bust broad and draped. Die 83. Watermarks 12, 13, 14.*

**EN413**
| | | UnFVF | UseFVF |
|---|---|---|---|
| 4¢ | brown on white | 10.00 | 7.00 |
| | entire | 25.00 | 11.00 |

**EN414**
| | | UnFVF | UseFVF |
|---|---|---|---|
| 4¢ | brown on amber | 37.50 | 15.00 |
| | entire | 50.00 | 20.00 |

**EN415**
| | | UnFVF | UseFVF |
|---|---|---|---|
| 4¢ | brown on manila, wrapper | 15.00 | 8.00 |
| | entire | 25.00 | 12.50 |

EN416, EN417 *Ulysses S. Grant. Die 84. Watermark 13.*

**EN416**
| | | UnFVF | UseFVF |
|---|---|---|---|
| 5¢ | blue on white | 10.00 | 9.50 |
| | entire | 14.00 | 13.00 |

**EN417**
| | | UnFVF | UseFVF |
|---|---|---|---|
| 5¢ | blue on amber | 13.00 | 10.00 |
| | entire | 22.50 | 15.00 |

**1903. ISSUE** This contract is the first for the Hartford Manufacturing Co. as producers of stamped envelopes.

EN418-EN423 *Franklin. Die 85. Watermarks 13, 14.*

**EN418**
| | | UnFVF | UseFVF |
|---|---|---|---|
| 1¢ | green on white | .50 | .25 |
| | entire | 1.25 | .50 |

**EN419**
| | | UnFVF | UseFVF |
|---|---|---|---|
| 1¢ | green on amber | 12.00 | 3.00 |
| | entire | 18.50 | 4.00 |

**EN420**
| | | UnFVF | UseFVF |
|---|---|---|---|
| 1¢ | green on buff | 13.00 | 3.00 |
| | entire | 17.00 | 4.00 |

**EN421**
| | | UnFVF | UseFVF |
|---|---|---|---|
| 1¢ | green on blue | 13.00 | 3.00 |
| | entire | 20.00 | 4.00 |

**EN422**
| | | UnFVF | UseFVF |
|---|---|---|---|
| 1¢ | green on manila | 3.00 | 1.50 |
| | entire | 4.50 | 2.00 |

**EN423**
| | | UnFVF | UseFVF |
|---|---|---|---|
| 1¢ | green on manila, wrapper | 1.50 | .75 |
| | entire | 2.00 | 1.00 |

EN424-EN428 *Washington. A short and two long lines of colorless shading are found in the right side of the ribbon containing the value. (Compare with EN434.)*

| | | UnFVF | UseFVF |
|---|---|---|---|
| **EN424** | | | |
| 2¢ | carmine on white | .50 | .25 |
| | entire | 1.00 | .50 |

**EN425**
| | | UnFVF | UseFVF |
|---|---|---|---|
| 2¢ | carmine on amber | 1.75 | .50 |
| | entire | 3.75 | 1.50 |

**EN426**
| | | UnFVF | UseFVF |
|---|---|---|---|
| 2¢ | carmine on buff | 2.00 | .50 |
| | entire | 2.50 | .75 |

**EN427**
| | | UnFVF | UseFVF |
|---|---|---|---|
| 2¢ | carmine on blue | 1.50 | .75 |
| | entire | 3.25 | .75 |

**EN428**
| | | UnFVF | UseFVF |
|---|---|---|---|
| 2¢ | carmine on manila, wrapper | 15.00 | 8.00 |
| | entire | 22.50 | 14.00 |

EN429-EN431 *Ulysses S. Grant*

**EN429**
| | | UnFVF | UseFVF |
|---|---|---|---|
| 4¢ | brown on white | 20.00 | 12.00 |
| | entire* | 27.50 | 15.00 |

**EN430**
| | | UnFVF | UseFVF |
|---|---|---|---|
| 4¢ | brown on amber | 20.00 | 12.00 |
| | entire* | 27.50 | 15.00 |

**EN431**

| | | UnFVF | UseFVF |
|---|---|---|---|
| 4¢ | **brown on manila,** wrapper | 18.00 | 11.00 |
| | entire* | 40.00 | 30.00 |

EN432, EN433 *Abraham Lincoln*

**EN432**

| | | UnFVF | UseFVF |
|---|---|---|---|
| 5¢ | **blue on white** | 17.00 | 10.00 |
| | entire | 25.00 | 17.50 |

**EN433**

| | | UnFVF | UseFVF |
|---|---|---|---|
| 5¢ | **blue on amber** | 18.00 | 13.00 |
| | entire | 25.00 | 20.00 |

EN434-EN438 *Washington. Re-cut die. The colorless shading lines at the right of the ribbon containing the value are all short. Lettering throughout is heavier. (Compare with EN424.)*

| | | UnFVF | UseFVF |
|---|---|---|---|
| **EN434** | | | |
| 2¢ | **carmine on white** | .50 | .25 |
| | entire | 1.00 | .50 |
| **EN435** | | UnFVF | UseFVF |
| 2¢ | **carmine on amber** | 7.00 | .75 |
| | entire | 12.00 | 2.00 |
| **EN436** | | UnFVF | UseFVF |
| 2¢ | **carmine on buff** | 6.00 | 2.00 |
| | entire | 7.50 | 2.00 |
| **EN437** | | UnFVF | UseFVF |
| 2¢ | **carmine on blue** | 4.00 | 2.00 |
| | entire | 6.00 | 2.50 |
| **EN438** | | UnFVF | UseFVF |
| 2¢ | **carmine on manila,** wrapper | 12.00 | 7.00 |
| | entire | 22.50 | 12.50 |

**1907-16. ISSUE** New contractors, The Mercantile Corp., brought a change from Hartford, Conn., where envelopes had been manufactured since 1874, to Dayton, Ohio. In 1915 the Middle West Supply Co. obtained the contract and in 1929 the International Envelope Co. was the successful bidder. These changes did not change the site of manufacture itself, and appear to be the merger of the corporations named. From 1929 until 1965, envelopes were manufactured by the International Envelope Co. at Dayton, Ohio.

*Beginning in 1915, laid paper was dropped for all envelopes in favor of wove paper and from then on all watermarks were of the same or similar design as illustrated. The watermark was changed every four years to mark each new contract. The various arrangement of the dates, at top, bottom, or diagonal, is identification of the paper manufacturer. From 1929 until 1958, the diagonally placed numerals identified "Extra quality" paper. Since 1958, all envelopes are of a single quality paper.*

Typical example of watermarks 1915 to 1960. (Reduced in size).

EN439-EN444 *Franklin. Die A, wide "D" in "UNITED". (Compare with EN445 and following.) Watermarks 12, 14, 15, 16, 17, 18.*

**EN439**

| | | UnFVF | UseFVF |
|---|---|---|---|
| 1¢ | **green on white** | .30 | .25 |
| | entire | .50 | .40 |
| | v. "NITED" instead of "UNITED", entire | — | — |

**EN440**

| | | UnFVF | UseFVF |
|---|---|---|---|
| 1¢ | **green on amber** | .75 | .50 |
| | entire | 1.25 | .75 |
| **EN441** | | UnFVF | UseFVF |
| 1¢ | **green on buff** | 4.00 | 2.00 |
| | entire | 6.00 | 2.50 |
| **EN442** | | UnFVF | UseFVF |
| 1¢ | **green on blue** | 5.00 | 2.00 |
| | entire | 6.00 | 3.00 |
| **EN443** | | UnFVF | UseFVF |
| 1¢ | **green on manila** | 3.00 | 2.00 |
| | entire | 4.50 | 2.50 |
| **EN444** | | UnFVF | UseFVF |
| 1¢ | **green on manila,** wrapper | .50 | .25 |
| | entire | .75 | .50 |

EN445-EN449 *Die B, narrow "D" in "UNITED". (Compare with EN439 and following.) Die 90.*

**EN445**

| | | UnFVF | UseFVF |
|---|---|---|---|
| 1¢ | **green on white** | 1.00 | .50 |
| | entire | 1.25 | .60 |
| **EN446** | | UnFVF | UseFVF |
| 1¢ | **green on amber** | 1.00 | .75 |
| | entire | 1.50 | 1.00 |
| **EN447** | | UnFVF | UseFVF |
| 1¢ | **green on buff** | 4.00 | 2.00 |
| | entire | 6.00 | 2.50 |
| **EN448** | | UnFVF | UseFVF |
| 1¢ | **green on blue** | 5.00 | 2.00 |
| | entire | 6.00 | 3.00 |
| **EN449** | | UnFVF | UseFVF |
| 1¢ | **green on manila,** wrapper | 37.50 | 20.00 |
| | entire | 42.50 | 27.50 |

EN450-EN455 *Franklin. Die C, both "S"'s in "STATES" are broad. (Compare with other 1¢ dies.) Die 90.*

**EN450**

| | | UnFVF | UseFVF |
|---|---|---|---|
| 1¢ | **green on white** | 1.00 | .50 |
| | entire | 1.25 | .75 |
| **EN451** | | UnFVF | UseFVF |
| 1¢ | **green on amber** | 1.00 | .80 |
| | entire | 2.00 | 1.00 |
| **EN452** | | UnFVF | UseFVF |
| 1¢ | **green on buff** | 6.00 | 2.00 |
| | entire | 7.00 | 3.00 |
| **EN453** | | UnFVF | UseFVF |
| 1¢ | **green on blue** | 5.00 | 4.00 |
| | entire | 5.50 | 4.50 |
| **EN454** | | UnFVF | UseFVF |
| 1¢ | **green on manila** | 4.00 | 3.00 |
| | entire | 6.00 | 5.00 |
| **EN455** | | UnFVF | UseFVF |
| 1¢ | **green on manila,** wrapper | 6.00 | 4.00 |
| | entire | 11.00 | 6.00 |

EN450-EN455 *So-called "Dayton Dies" of which there are 13 varieties. See note after illustration of EN492.*

EN456-EN460 *Die D, back of bust forms angle opposite "T" in "CENT". (Compare with other 1¢ dies.) Die 90.*

**EN456**
| 1¢ | green on white | UnFVF | UseFVF |
|---|---|---|---|
| | | .70 | .35 |
| | entire | .85 | .50 |

**EN457**
| 1¢ | green on amber | UnFVF | UseFVF |
|---|---|---|---|
| | | 1.00 | .75 |
| | entire | 1.25 | 1.00 |

**EN458**
| 1¢ | green on buff | UnFVF | UseFVF |
|---|---|---|---|
| | | 4.00 | 2.00 |
| | entire | 5.00 | 3.00 |

**EN459**
| 1¢ | green on blue | UnFVF | UseFVF |
|---|---|---|---|
| | | 4.00 | 2.00 |
| | entire | 6.00 | 4.00 |

**EN460**
| 1¢ | green on manila | UnFVF | UseFVF |
|---|---|---|---|
| | | 50.00 | |
| | entire | — | |

*Watermarks 15 to 23 (1907-1919).*

EN461-EN470 *Washington. Die A, both the "O" in "TWO" and the "C" in "CENTS" are ovals. (Compare with the following.) Die 91.*

**EN461**
| 2¢ | brown red on white | UnFVF | UseFVF |
|---|---|---|---|
| | | 1.00 | .50 |
| | entire | 1.75 | .75 |

**EN462**
| 2¢ | brown red on amber | UnFVF | UseFVF |
|---|---|---|---|
| | | 6.00 | 3.00 |
| | entire | 8.50 | 7.00 |

**EN463**
| 2¢ | brown red on buff | UnFVF | UseFVF |
|---|---|---|---|
| | | 7.00 | 2.00 |
| | entire | 11.00 | 4.50 |

**EN464**
| 2¢ | brown red on blue | UnFVF | UseFVF |
|---|---|---|---|
| | | 5.00 | 2.50 |
| | entire | 7.00 | 4.00 |

**EN465**
| 2¢ | brown red on manila, wrapper | UnFVF | UseFVF |
|---|---|---|---|
| | | 40.00 | 30.00 |
| | entire | 60.00 | 40.00 |

**EN466**
| 2¢ | carmine on white | UnFVF | UseFVF |
|---|---|---|---|
| | | .30 | .25 |
| | entire | .60 | .40 |

**EN467**
| 2¢ | carmine on amber | UnFVF | UseFVF |
|---|---|---|---|
| | | .30 | .25 |
| | entire | 1.00 | .25 |

**EN468**
| 2¢ | carmine on buff | UnFVF | UseFVF |
|---|---|---|---|
| | | .50 | .25 |
| | entire | .75 | .25 |

**EN469**
| 2¢ | carmine on blue | UnFVF | UseFVF |
|---|---|---|---|
| | | .50 | .25 |
| | entire | 1.00 | .25 |

**EN470**
| 2¢ | carmine on manila, wrapper | UnFVF | UseFVF |
|---|---|---|---|
| | | 5.00 | 3.00 |
| | entire | 9.50 | 5.00 |

EN471-EN479 *Die A2, similar to last except there is a prominent wedge-shaped lock of hair in the center of the head. (Compare with other 2¢ dies.) Die 91.*

**EN471**
| 2¢ | brown red on white | UnFVF | UseFVF |
|---|---|---|---|
| | | 30.00 | 8.00 |
| | entire | 40.00 | 25.00 |

**EN472**
| 2¢ | brown red on amber | UnFVF | UseFVF |
|---|---|---|---|
| | | 110. | 50.00 |
| | entire | 130. | 75.00 |

**EN473**
| 2¢ | brown red on buff | UnFVF | UseFVF |
|---|---|---|---|
| | | 135. | 60.00 |
| | entire | 150. | 100. |

**EN474**
| 2¢ | brown red on blue | UnFVF | UseFVF |
|---|---|---|---|
| | | 135. | 110. |
| | entire | 170. | 140. |

**EN475**
| 2¢ | carmine on white | UnFVF | UseFVF |
|---|---|---|---|
| | | .40 | .20 |
| | entire | .75 | .40 |

**EN476**
| 2¢ | carmine on amber | UnFVF | UseFVF |
|---|---|---|---|
| | | .40 | .25 |
| | entire | .80 | .60 |

**EN477**
| 2¢ | carmine on buff | UnFVF | UseFVF |
|---|---|---|---|
| | | .60 | .55 |
| | entire | .90 | .60 |

**EN478**
| 2¢ | carmine on blue | UnFVF | UseFVF |
|---|---|---|---|
| | | .45 | .40 |
| | entire | .80 | .50 |

**EN479**
| 2¢ | carmine on manila, wrapper | UnFVF | UseFVF |
|---|---|---|---|
| | | 5.00 | 3.00 |
| | entire | 7.00 | 5.00 |

EN480-EN487 *Washington. Die B, head is large, hair arranged in bumps. The "O" in "TWO" is circular. (Compare with EN488 and other 2¢ dies.) Die 91.*

**EN480**
| 2¢ | brown red on white | UnFVF | UseFVF |
|---|---|---|---|
| | | .60 | .40 |
| | entire | .90 | .50 |

**EN481**
| 2¢ | brown red on amber | UnFVF | UseFVF |
|---|---|---|---|
| | | 3.50 | 2.00 |
| | entire | 5.00 | 2.00 |

**EN482**
| 2¢ | brown red on buff | UnFVF | UseFVF |
|---|---|---|---|
| | | 7.00 | 3.25 |
| | entire | 10.00 | 6.00 |

**EN483**
| 2¢ | brown red on blue | UnFVF | UseFVF |
|---|---|---|---|
| | | 5.00 | 2.25 |
| | entire | 7.00 | 4.00 |

**EN484**
| 2¢ | carmine on white | UnFVF | UseFVF |
|---|---|---|---|
| | | .75 | .40 |
| | entire | 1.25 | .60 |

**EN485**
| 2¢ | carmine on amber | UnFVF | UseFVF |
|---|---|---|---|
| | | 1.35 | .50 |
| | entire | 1.75 | .80 |

**EN486**
| 2¢ | carmine on buff | UnFVF | UseFVF |
|---|---|---|---|
| | | 7.00 | 4.00 |
| | entire | 11.00 | 6.00 |

**EN487**
| 2¢ | carmine on blue | UnFVF | UseFVF |
|---|---|---|---|
| | | .90 | .70 |
| | entire | 1.50 | .75 |

EN488-EN491 *Die C, prominent slits in hair resembling the gills of a shark. Lettering clear and sharp. (Compare with EN480 and other 2¢ dies.) Die 91.*

**EN488**
| 2¢ | carmine on white | UnFVF | UseFVF |
|---|---|---|---|
| | | .50 | .25 |
| | entire | .75 | .50 |

**EN489**
| 2¢ | carmine on amber | UnFVF | UseFVF |
|---|---|---|---|
| | | .40 | .30 |
| | entire | .75 | .50 |

| EN490 | | UnFVF | UseFVF |
|---|---|---|---|
| 2¢ | carmine on buff | .45 | .35 |
| | entire | .70 | .50 |

| EN491 | | UnFVF | UseFVF |
|---|---|---|---|
| 2¢ | carmine on blue | .50 | .35 |
| | entire | .60 | .50 |

EN492-EN496 *Die D, the so-called "Dayton Dies" as they were made by a private die engraver on order from the factory at Dayton, Ohio. There are 13 varieties, some of which are quite valuable. Die 91.*

| EN492 | | UnFVF | UseFVF |
|---|---|---|---|
| 2¢ | carmine on white | .60 | .40 |
| | entire | 1.00 | .60 |

| EN493 | | UnFVF | UseFVF |
|---|---|---|---|
| 2¢ | carmine on amber | .60 | .40 |
| | entire | 1.00 | .60 |

| EN494 | | UnFVF | UseFVF |
|---|---|---|---|
| 2¢ | carmine on buff | 3.00 | 1.50 |
| | entire | 4.00 | 3.75 |

| EN495 | | UnFVF | UseFVF |
|---|---|---|---|
| 2¢ | carmine on blue | .75 | .50 |
| | entire | 1.50 | .75 |

| EN496 | | UnFVF | UseFVF |
|---|---|---|---|
| 2¢ | carmine on manila, wrapper | 5.00 | 3.00 |
| | entire | 8.00 | 3.00 |

EN497-EN500 *Washington. Die E, front of bust tapers and the end is rounded. (Compare with EN461 and others.) Die 91.*

| EN497 | | UnFVF | UseFVF |
|---|---|---|---|
| 2¢ | carmine on white | .40 | .25 |
| | entire | .85 | .40 |

| EN498 | | UnFVF | UseFVF |
|---|---|---|---|
| 2¢ | carmine on amber | .65 | .45 |
| | entire | 1.00 | .60 |

| EN499 | | UnFVF | UseFVF |
|---|---|---|---|
| 2¢ | carmine on buff | .75 | .50 |
| | entire | 1.25 | .70 |

**1907-16. ISSUE** New contractors, The Mercantile Corp., brought a change from Hartford, Conn., where envelopes had been manufactured since 1874, to Dayton, Ohio. In 1915 the Middle West Supply Co. obtained the contract and in 1929 the International Envelope Co. was the successful bidder. These changes did not change the site of manufacture itself, and appear to be the merger of the corporations named. From 1929 until 1965, envelopes were manufactured by the International Envelope Co. at Dayton, Ohio.

Beginning in 1915, laid paper was dropped for all envelopes in favor of wove paper and from then on all watermarks were of the same or similar design as illustrated. The watermark was changed every four years to mark each new contract. The various arrangement of the dates, at top, bottom, or diagonal, is identification of the paper manufacturer. From 1929 until 1958, the diagonally placed numerals identified "Extra quality" paper. Since 1958, all envelopes are of a single quality paper.

Typical example of watermarks 1915 to 1960. (Reduced in size).

| EN500 | | UnFVF | UseFVF |
|---|---|---|---|
| 2¢ | carmine on blue | .75 | .50 |
| | entire | 1.25 | .50 |

EN501-EN505 *Washington. Die F, unpright line of the "2"'s tapers. There is a very thin line where it meets the base of the numeral. The upper corner of the front end of the bust is usually, but not always, cut away in varying degress. Die 91.*

| EN501 | | UnFVF | UseFVF |
|---|---|---|---|
| 2¢ | carmine on white | 14.00 | 12.00 |
| | entire | 16.00 | 14.00 |
| | a. vermilion | — | — |
| | entire | — | — |

| EN502 | | UnFVF | UseFVF |
|---|---|---|---|
| 2¢ | carmine on amber | 12.00 | 9.00 |
| | entire | 14.00 | 12.00 |

| EN503 | | UnFVF | UseFVF |
|---|---|---|---|
| 2¢ | carmine on buff | 40.00 | 20.00 |
| | entire | 50.00 | 30.00 |

| EN504 | | UnFVF | UseFVF |
|---|---|---|---|
| 2¢ | carmine on blue | 15.00 | 9.00 |
| | entire | 20.00 | 16.00 |

| EN505 | | UnFVF | UseFVF |
|---|---|---|---|
| 2¢ | carmine on manila, wrapper | 45.00 | 40.00 |
| | entire | 55.00 | 45.00 |

EN506-EN508 *Die G, hair arranged as in EN471 (a wedge-shape lock in center). (Compare with EN501 and others.) Die 91.*

| EN506 | | UnFVF | UseFVF |
|---|---|---|---|
| 2¢ | carimine on white | 15.00 | 13.00 |
| | entire | 20.00 | 15.00 |

| EN507 | | UnFVF | UseFVF |
|---|---|---|---|
| 2¢ | carmine on buff | 13.00 | 10.00 |
| | entire | 20.00 | 13.00 |

| EN508 | | UnFVF | UseFVF |
|---|---|---|---|
| 2¢ | carmine on blue | 15.00 | 10.00 |
| | entire | 18.00 | 16.00 |

EN509, EN510 *Franklin. Die A, the "F" in "FOUR" is only 1mm from the "4". (Compare with EN511.) Die 90.*

| EN509 | | UnFVF | UseFVF |
|---|---|---|---|
| 4¢ | black on white | 4.00 | 3.00 |
| | entire* | 9.00 | 5.00 |

| EN510 | | UnFVF | UseFVF |
|---|---|---|---|
| 4¢ | black on amber | 6.00 | 3.00 |
| | entire* | 10.00 | 5.00 |

EN511, EN512 *Die B, the "F" in "FOUR" is 1 3/4mm from the figure "4". Die 90.*

| EN511 | | UnFVF | UseFVF |
|---|---|---|---|
| 4¢ | black on white | 5.00 | 4.00 |
| | entire* | 10.00 | 6.00 |

| EN512 | | UnFVF | UseFVF |
|---|---|---|---|
| 4¢ | black on amber | 6.00 | 3.00 |
| | entire* | 12.50 | 7.00 |

EN513-EN515 *Washington. Die A, large "F" in "FIVE" (2 3/4mm high). (Compare with EN516.) Die 91.*

**EN513**

| 5¢ | blue on white | UnFVF | UseFVF |
|---|---|---|---|
| | | 7.00 | 3.00 |
| | entire | 11.00 | 7.00 |

**EN514**

| 5¢ | blue on amber | UnFVF | UseFVF |
|---|---|---|---|
| | | 13.00 | 12.00 |
| | entire | 16.00 | 14.00 |

**EN515**

| 5¢ | blue on blue | UnFVF | UseFVF |
|---|---|---|---|
| | | 1200. | — |
| | entire | 1800. | — |

EN516-EN519 *Die B, Small "F" in "FIVE" (2 1/2mm tall). (Compare with EN513.) Die 91.*

**EN516**

| 5¢ | blue on white | UnFVF | UseFVF |
|---|---|---|---|
| | | 7.00 | 3.00 |
| | entire | 12.50 | 6.00 |

**EN517**

| 5¢ | blue on amber | UnFVF | UseFVF |
|---|---|---|---|
| | | 13.00 | 12.00 |
| | entire | 22.50 | 15.00 |

**EN518**

| 5¢ | blue on buff | UnFVF | UseFVF |
|---|---|---|---|
| | | 1000. | — |
| | entire | — | — |

**EN519**

| 5¢ | blue on blue | UnFVF | UseFVF |
|---|---|---|---|
| | | 1000. | — |
| | entire | — | — |

**1916-50. ISSUE** The circular design used on these envelopes was introduced in 1916 and continued without change until 1950. Many dies wore out through this long tenure and many new master dies were required, which accounts for the several different dies for each denomination. The 3¢ envelopes were issued in 1917, when the rate of postage was increased from 2¢ to 3¢. The stamps were printed in a violet ink. Twenty months later the firt class rate was returned to 2¢ and the 3¢ envelopes were discontinued.

After the reduction of first class postal rates from 3¢ (a war measure) to 2¢, the Post Office found itself with an enormous supply of 3¢ envelopes for which there was no practical use. The envelopes were revalued (1920) by running them through canceling machines with appropriate slugs to indicate the new value (2¢) inserted into them. It is estimated that some 63 million envelopes were revalued in the process.

When, in 1925, the rate for circular letters was advanced from 1¢ to 1 1/2¢, the government again found itself with an unusable supply of envelopes, this time the 1¢ denomination. Again revaluing was done by the use of canceling machines.

In July 1932, first class rates were advanced to 3¢, which called for production of 3¢ envelopes. This new issue was printed in a bright purple ink. Wrappers were discontinued in 1934.

EN520-EN528 *Franklin. Die A, "UNITED" small and nearer inner than outer circle. (Compare with following.) Die 92. Watermarks 19 to 42 (1915-1949).*

**EN520**

| 1¢ | green on white | UnFVF | UseFVF |
|---|---|---|---|
| | | .25 | .25 |
| | entire | .40 | .25 |

**EN521**

| 1¢ | green on amber | UnFVF | UseFVF |
|---|---|---|---|
| | | .40 | .35 |
| | entire | .75 | .50 |

**EN522**

| 1¢ | green on buff | UnFVF | UseFVF |
|---|---|---|---|
| | | 2.00 | 1.25 |
| | entire | 2.75 | 1.75 |

**EN523**

| 1¢ | green on blue | UnFVF | UseFVF |
|---|---|---|---|
| | | .50 | .40 |
| | entire | .75 | .50 |

**EN524**

| 1¢ | green on manila | UnFVF | UseFVF |
|---|---|---|---|
| | | 7.00 | 5.00 |
| | entire | 9.50 | 6.00 |

**EN525**

| 1¢ | green on manila, wrapper | UnFVF | UseFVF |
|---|---|---|---|
| | | .25 | .25 |
| | entire | .75 | .25 |

**EN526**

| 1¢ | green on brown (glazed) | UnFVF | UseFVF |
|---|---|---|---|
| | | 35.00 | 20.00 |
| | entire | 40.00 | 22.00 |

**EN527**

| 1¢ | green on brown, (glazed) wrapper | UnFVF | UseFVF |
|---|---|---|---|
| | | 65.00 | — |
| | entire | 75.00 | — |

**EN528**

| 1¢ | green on brown (unglazed) | UnFVF | UseFVF |
|---|---|---|---|
| | | 10.00 | 10.00 |
| | entire | 12.50 | 11.00 |

EN529, EN530 *Die B, the first "S" in "STATES" is larger than the last "S." "NT" in "CENT" are large. "U" in "UNITED" is close to circle. (Compare with EN531 and others.) Die 92.*

**EN529**

| 1¢ | green on white | UnFVF | UseFVF |
|---|---|---|---|
| | | 85.00 | 65.00 |
| | entire* | 100. | 75.00 |

**EN530**

| 1¢ | green on amber | UnFVF | UseFVF |
|---|---|---|---|
| | | 325. | 200. |
| | entire* | 500. | 250. |

EN531-EN533 *Franklin. Die C, hair projects strongly at back, forming a "bun". (Compare with EN529 and others.) Die 92.*

**EN531**

| 1¢ | green on white | UnFVF | UseFVF |
|---|---|---|---|
| | | .35 | .25 |
| | entire | .40 | .30 |

**EN532**

| 1¢ | green on amber | UnFVF | UseFVF |
|---|---|---|---|
| | | 1.35 | .75 |
| | entire | 1.75 | 1.00 |

**EN533**

| 1¢ | green on blue | UnFVF | UseFVF |
|---|---|---|---|
| | | 1.00 | .75 |
| | entire | 1.50 | .90 |

**EN533A**

| 1¢ | green on manila, wrapper | UnFVF | UseFVF |
|---|---|---|---|
| | | 150. | 135. |
| | entire | 175. | 150. |

EN534-EN537 *Die D, "UNITED" large and closer to outer than inner circle. (Compare with EN520 and others.) Die 92.*

**EN534**

| 1¢ | green on white | UnFVF | UseFVF |
|---|---|---|---|
| | | .40 | .30 |
| | entire | .50 | .35 |

**EN535**

| 1¢ | green on amber | UnFVF | UseFVF |
|---|---|---|---|
| | | 1.50 | 1.00 |
| | entire | 2.00 | 1.50 |

| EN536 | | UnFVF | UseFVF |
|---|---|---|---|
| 1¢ | **green on buff** | 4.00 | 1.50 |
| | entire | .50 | .35 |

| EN537 | | UnFVF | UseFVF |
|---|---|---|---|
| 1¢ | **green on blue** | 1.00 | .50 |
| | entire | 1.50 | .75 |

EN538-EN540 *"C" in "CENTS", "G" in "POSTAGE", AND "U" in "UNITED" are very narrow.(Compare with all others dies.) Die 92.*

| EN538 | | UnFVF | UseFVF |
|---|---|---|---|
| 1¢ | **green on white** | .40 | .30 |
| | entire | .55 | .50 |

| EN539 | | UnFVF | UseFVF |
|---|---|---|---|
| 1¢ | **green on amber** | 1.25 | .75 |
| | entire | 1.50 | 1.00 |

| EN540 | | UnFVF | UseFVF |
|---|---|---|---|
| 1¢ | **green on blue** | .75 | .40 |
| | entire | 1.10 | .75 |

EN541-EN545 *Washington. Die A, large head, well formed thick letters. Die 93.*

| EN541 | | UnFVF | UseFVF |
|---|---|---|---|
| 1-1/2¢ | **brown on white** | .25 | .25 |
| | entire | .60 | .25 |
| | a. purple (error) | 95.00 | — |
| | entire | 120. | — |

| EN542 | | UnFVF | UseFVF |
|---|---|---|---|
| 1-1/2¢ | **brown on amber** | 1.00 | .50 |
| | entire | 1.50 | .70 |

| EN543 | | UnFVF | UseFVF |
|---|---|---|---|
| 1-1/2¢ | **brown on blue** | 1.75 | 1.10 |
| | entire | 2.00 | 1.50 |

| EN544 | | UnFVF | UseFVF |
|---|---|---|---|
| 1-1/2¢ | **brown on manila** | 7.00 | 4.00 |
| | entire | 12.00 | 7.00 |

| EN545 | | UnFVF | UseFVF |
|---|---|---|---|
| 1-1/2¢ | **brown on manila**, wrapper | .90 | .25 |
| | entire | 1.50 | .60 |

EN546-EN548 *Die H2, slightly different head from EN541. Lettering thin and sharp; "T" with long top strokes. Die 93.*

| EN546 | | UnFVF | UseFVF |
|---|---|---|---|
| 1-1/2¢ | **brown on white** | .70 | .35 |
| | entire | .90 | .60 |

| EN547 | | UnFVF | UseFVF |
|---|---|---|---|
| 1-1/2¢ | **brown on amber** | 1.50 | .85 |
| | entire | 2.00 | .90 |

| EN548 | | UnFVF | UseFVF |
|---|---|---|---|
| 1-1/2¢ | **brown on blue** | 2.00 | 1.50 |
| | entire | 2.25 | 1.50 |

EN549-EN555 *Washington. Die A, head large. Base line of "2"'s horizontal. Lettering heavy and well formed. (Compare with following.) Die 93.*

| EN549 | | UnFVF | UseFVF |
|---|---|---|---|
| 2¢ | **carmine on white** | .25 | .25 |
| | entire | .50 | .25 |
| | a. green (error), entire | 7500. | — |
| | p. laid paper | — | — |
| | entire | — | — |
| | v. with added impression of 1¢ green (EN520) | 750. | — |
| | v1. with added impression of 1¢ green (EN439) | 750. | — |
| | v2. with added impression of 4¢ black (EN509) | 600. | — |

| EN550 | | UnFVF | UseFVF |
|---|---|---|---|
| 2¢ | **carmine on amber** | .30 | .25 |
| | entire | .50 | .25 |
| | p. laid paper | — | — |
| | entire | — | — |

| EN551 | | UnFVF | UseFVF |
|---|---|---|---|
| 2¢ | **carmine on buff** | 2.00 | .75 |
| | entire | 4.50 | 2.00 |

| EN552 | | UnFVF | UseFVF |
|---|---|---|---|
| 2¢ | **carmine on blue** | .25 | .25 |
| | entire | .75 | .25 |

| EN553 | | UnFVF | UseFVF |
|---|---|---|---|
| 2¢ | **carmine on manila**, wrapper | .25 | .25 |
| | entire | .50 | .25 |

| EN554 | | UnFVF | UseFVF |
|---|---|---|---|
| 2¢ | **carmine on brown** (glazed), wrapper | 80.00 | 55.00 |
| | entire | 100. | 70.00 |

| EN555 | | UnFVF | UseFVF |
|---|---|---|---|
| 2¢ | **carmine on brown** (unglazed, wrapper | 75.00 | 55.00 |
| | entire | 100. | 70.00 |

EN556-EN559 *Washington. Die B, head very large. Base line of both "2" slopes down to right. "U" in "UNITED" far from circle. (Compare with other 2¢ dies). Die 93.*

| EN556 | | UnFVF | UseFVF |
|---|---|---|---|
| 2¢ | **carmine on white** | 10.00 | 7.00 |
| | entire | 16.00 | 10.00 |

| EN557 | | UnFVF | UseFVF |
|---|---|---|---|
| 2¢ | **carmine on amber** | 10.00 | 8.00 |
| | entire | 16.00 | 11.00 |

| EN558 | | UnFVF | UseFVF |
|---|---|---|---|
| 2¢ | **carmine on buff** | 110. | 50.00 |
| | entire | 135. | 90.00 |

| EN559 | | UnFVF | UseFVF |
|---|---|---|---|
| 2¢ | **carmine on blue** | 20.00 | 15.00 |
| | entire | 25.00 | 22.50 |

EN560, EN561 *Die C, as EN556 except the large inner circle and circles around the figure "2"'s are very thin. (The rejected die.) Die 93.*

| EN560 | | UnFVF | UseFVF |
|---|---|---|---|
| 2¢ | **carmine on white** | 35.00 | 30.00 |
| | entire | 50.00 | 40.00 |

| EN561 | | UnFVF | UseFVF |
|---|---|---|---|
| 2¢ | **carmine on blue** | 80.00 | 75.00 |
| | entire | 150. | 125. |

EN562-EN565 *Washington. Die D, "C" in "CENTS" very close to circle. Base line of right "2" slopes downward to right. Head slightly smaller. (Compare with EN549 and others.) Die 93.*

| EN562 | | UnFVF | UseFVF |
|---|---|---|---|
| 2¢ | **carmine on white** | 10.00 | 8.00 |
| | entire | 13.00 | 11.00 |

**EN563**

| 2¢ | carmine on amber | UnFVF | UseFVF |
|---|---|---|---|
| | | 25.00 | 15.00 |
| | entire | 30.00 | 17.00 |

**EN564**

| 2¢ | carmine on buff | UnFVF | UseFVF |
|---|---|---|---|
| | | 35.00 | 35.00 |
| | entire | 45.00 | 45.00 |

**EN565**

| 2¢ | carmine on blue | UnFVF | UseFVF |
|---|---|---|---|
| | | 20.00 | 17.50 |
| | entire | 25.00 | 22.50 |

EN566-EN569 *Die E, smaller head than all other dies. "T" and "S" in "CENTS" close. Die 93.*

**EN566**

| 2¢ | carmine on white | UnFVF | UseFVF |
|---|---|---|---|
| | | .55 | .35 |
| | entire | .75 | .50 |

**EN567**

| 2¢ | carmine on amber | UnFVF | UseFVF |
|---|---|---|---|
| | | .60 | .40 |
| | entire | 1.60 | .70 |

**EN568**

| 2¢ | carmine on buff | UnFVF | UseFVF |
|---|---|---|---|
| | | 3.00 | 2.00 |
| | entire | 6.00 | 3.00 |

**EN569**

| 2¢ | carmine on blue | UnFVF | UseFVF |
|---|---|---|---|
| | | .75 | .25 |
| | entire | 1.75 | .60 |

EN570-EN573 *Washington. Die F, base line of left "2" slopes downward to right. Heavy strands of hair resemble bumps. "T" and "S" in "CENTS" widely spaced. (Compare with other 2¢ dies.) Die 93.*

**EN570**

| 2¢ | carmine on white | UnFVF | UseFVF |
|---|---|---|---|
| | | .70 | .40 |
| | entire | 1.10 | .70 |

**EN571**

| 2¢ | carmine on amber | UnFVF | UseFVF |
|---|---|---|---|
| | | 1.00 | .45 |
| | entire | 1.85 | .85 |

**EN572**

| 2¢ | carmine on buff | UnFVF | UseFVF |
|---|---|---|---|
| | | 4.50 | 3.00 |
| | entire | 7.00 | 3.50 |

**EN573**

| 2¢ | carmine on blue | UnFVF | UseFVF |
|---|---|---|---|
| | | .75 | .30 |
| | entire | 1.25 | .50 |

EN574-EN577 *Die H, base line of "2"s slope downward to right. Clear sharp impressions. Thin lettering. "T"s have short top strokes. Die 93.*

**EN574**

| 2¢ | carmine on white | UnFVF | UseFVF |
|---|---|---|---|
| | | .70 | .30 |
| | entire | 1.00 | .80 |

**EN575**

| 2¢ | carmine on amber | UnFVF | UseFVF |
|---|---|---|---|
| | | .80 | .40 |
| | entire | 1.60 | 1.00 |

**EN576**

| 2¢ | carmine on buff | UnFVF | UseFVF |
|---|---|---|---|
| | | 4.00 | 2.50 |
| | entire | 6.00 | 4.00 |

**EN577**

| 2¢ | carmine on blue | UnFVF | UseFVF |
|---|---|---|---|
| | | .80 | .40 |
| | entire | 1.50 | .70 |

**EN577A**

| 2¢ | carmine on manila | UnFVF | UseFVF |
|---|---|---|---|
| | | — | — |
| | entire | — | — |

EN578-EN580 *Washington. Die H2, similar to EN574 except all "T" have long top strokes. Die 93.*

**EN578**

| 2¢ | carmine on white | UnFVF | UseFVF |
|---|---|---|---|
| | | .50 | .25 |
| | entire | .75 | .55 |

**EN579**

| 2¢ | carmine on amber | UnFVF | UseFVF |
|---|---|---|---|
| | | .70 | .40 |
| | entire | 1.00 | .50 |

**EN580**

| 2¢ | carmine on blue | UnFVF | UseFVF |
|---|---|---|---|
| | | .50 | .25 |
| | entire | 1.00 | .50 |

EN581-EN585 *Die I, the letters "C", "U", and "G" are very narrow. (Compare with all other 2¢ dies.) Die 93.*

**EN581**

| 2¢ | carmine on white | UnFVF | UseFVF |
|---|---|---|---|
| | | .50 | .30 |
| | entire | .75 | .50 |

**EN582**

| 2¢ | carmine on amber | UnFVF | UseFVF |
|---|---|---|---|
| | | .60 | .30 |
| | entire | .70 | .40 |

**EN583**

| 2¢ | carmine on blue | UnFVF | UseFVF |
|---|---|---|---|
| | | .80 | .25 |
| | entire | 2.25 | .50 |

EN584-EN590 *Washington. Die A, similar to the 2¢ die (EN549). Dark violet stamps were issued from 1916-17, at which time the postage rate was reduced to 2¢. When rate again was raised to 3¢, in 1932, this denomination was reissued in a bright purple. Die 93.*

**EN584**

| 3¢ | dark violet on white | UnFVF | UseFVF |
|---|---|---|---|
| | | .60 | .25 |
| | entire | .75 | .25 |
| | a. carmine (error) | 35.00 | 30.00 |
| | entire | 40.00 | 35.00 |
| | v. with added impression of EN520, entire | 650. | — |
| | v1. with added impression of EN549, entire | 750. | — |

**EN585**

| 3¢ | dark violet on amber | UnFVF | UseFVF |
|---|---|---|---|
| | | 2.50 | 1.50 |
| | entire | 7.00 | 2.75 |
| | a. black (error) | 175. | — |
| | entire | 210. | — |

**EN586**

| 3¢ | dark violet on buff | UnFVF | UseFVF |
|---|---|---|---|
| | | 25.00 | 2.00 |
| | entire | 32.50 | 3.00 |

**EN587**

| 3¢ | dark violet on blue | UnFVF | UseFVF |
|---|---|---|---|
| | | 7.00 | 1.75 |
| | entire | 11.00 | 7.50 |

**EN588**

| 3¢ | purple on white | UnFVF | UseFVF |
|---|---|---|---|
| | | .25 | .20 |
| | entire | .50 | .25 |

**EN589**

| 3¢ | purple on amber | UnFVF | UseFVF |
|---|---|---|---|
| | | .50 | .25 |
| | entire | .75 | .40 |

**EN590**

| 3¢ | purple on blue | UnFVF | UseFVF |
|---|---|---|---|
| | | .30 | .25 |
| | entire | .75 | .30 |

EN591-EN594 *Die E, similar to 2¢ (EN566). Die 93.*

| EN591 | | UnFVF | UseFVF |
|---|---|---|---|
| 3¢ | **dark violet on white** | 1.75 | 1.00 |
| | entire | 3.25 | 1.00 |
| | a. carmine (error) | 35.00 | 30.00 |
| | entire | 40.00 | 35.00 |

| EN592 | | UnFVF | UseFVF |
|---|---|---|---|
| 3¢ | **dark violet on amber** | 5.00 | 3.00 |
| | entire | 9.00 | 4.00 |
| | a. carmine (error) | 375. | 265. |
| | entire | 425. | 350. |

| EN593 | | UnFVF | UseFVF |
|---|---|---|---|
| 3¢ | **dark violet on buff** | 30.00 | 1.75 |
| | entire | 27.50 | 1.25 |

| EN594 | | UnFVF | UseFVF |
|---|---|---|---|
| 3¢ | **dark violet on blue** | 7.00 | 4.50 |
| | entire | 9.00 | 5.00 |
| | a. carmine (error) | 300. | 300. |
| | entire | 425. | 775. |

EN595-EN598 *Die F, similar to 2¢ (EN570). Die 93.*

| EN595 | | UnFVF | UseFVF |
|---|---|---|---|
| 3¢ | **dark violet on white** | 2.50 | 1.75 |
| | entire | 4.00 | 2.00 |

| EN596 | | UnFVF | UseFVF |
|---|---|---|---|
| 3¢ | **dark violet on amber** | 6.50 | 3.00 |
| | entire | 8.00 | 3.50 |

| EN597 | | UnFVF | UseFVF |
|---|---|---|---|
| 3¢ | **dark violet on buff** | 33.00 | 2.00 |
| | entire | 35.00 | 3.00 |

| EN598 | | UnFVF | UseFVF |
|---|---|---|---|
| 3¢ | **dark violet on blue** | 7.00 | 5.00 |
| | entire | 10.00 | 5.00 |

EN599-EN602 *Die H, similar to 2¢, die H (EN574). Die 93.NI*

EN603-EN605 *Die I, similar to 2¢. (See EN581.)*

| EN599 | | UnFVF | UseFVF |
|---|---|---|---|
| 3¢ | **dark violet on on white** | 1.50 | 1.00 |
| | entire | 3.00 | 2.50 |

**1916-50. ISSUE** The circular design used on these envelopes was introduced in 1916 and continued without change until 1950. Many dies wore out through this long tenure and many new master dies were required, which accounts for the several different dies for each denomination. The 3¢ envelopes were issued in 1917, when the rate of postage was increased from 2¢ to 3¢. The stamps were printed in a violet ink. Twenty months later the firt class rate was returned to 2¢ and the 3¢ envelopes were discontinued.

After the reduction of first class postal rates from 3¢ (a war measure) to 2¢, the Post Office found itself with an enormous supply of 3¢ envelopes for which there was no practical use. The envelopes were revalued (1920) by running them through canceling machines with appropriate slugs to indicate the new value (2¢) inserted into them. It is

estimated that some 63 million envelopes were revalued in the process.

When, in 1925, the rate for circular letters was advanced from 1¢ to 1 1/2¢, the government again found itself with an unusable supply of envelopes, this time the 1¢ denomination. Again revaluing was done by the use of canceling machines.

In July 1932, first class rates were advanced to 3¢, which called for production of 3¢ envelopes. This new issue was printed in a bright purple ink. Wrappers were discontinued in 1934.

| EN600 | | UnFVF | UseFVF |
|---|---|---|---|
| 3¢ | **dark violet on amber** | 4.00 | 2.00 |
| | entire | 6.00 | 3.00 |

| EN601 | | UnFVF | UseFVF |
|---|---|---|---|
| 3¢ | **dark violet on buff** | 32.00 | 4.00 |
| | entire | 37.00 | 8.00 |

| EN602 | | UnFVF | UseFVF |
|---|---|---|---|
| 3¢ | **dark violet on blue** | 9.00 | 5.00 |
| | entire | 13.00 | 7.00 |

| EN603 | | UnFVF | UseFVF |
|---|---|---|---|
| 3¢ | **purple on white** | .50 | .25 |
| | entire | .50 | .35 |

| EN604 | | UnFVF | UseFVF |
|---|---|---|---|
| 3¢ | **purple on amber** | .60 | .25 |
| | entire | 1.10 | .40 |

| EN605 | | UnFVF | UseFVF |
|---|---|---|---|
| 3¢ | **purple on blue** | .60 | .25 |
| | entire | 1.10 | .55 |

| EN606 | | UnFVF | UseFVF |
|---|---|---|---|

| EN607 | | UnFVF | UseFVF |
|---|---|---|---|

| EN608 | | UnFVF | UseFVF |
|---|---|---|---|

EN609-EN611 *Franklin. Die 92.*

| EN609 | | UnFVF | UseFVF |
|---|---|---|---|
| 4¢ | **black on white** | 1.25 | .75 |
| | entire* | 3.25 | 2.55 |
| | v. with added impression of 2¢ (EN549) | — | — |
| | entire* | 275. | — |

| EN610 | | UnFVF | UseFVF |
|---|---|---|---|
| 4¢ | **black on amber** | 2.75 | 1.00 |
| | entire | 5.50 | 2.00 |

| EN611 | | UnFVF | UseFVF |
|---|---|---|---|
| 4¢ | **black on blue** | 3.00 | 1.00 |
| | entire | 5.50 | 2.00 |

EN612-EN614 *Washington. Die 93.*

| EN612 | | UnFVF | UseFVF |
|---|---|---|---|
| 5¢ | **blue on white** | 3.00 | 2.50 |
| | entire | 6.50 | 3.50 |

| EN613 | | UnFVF | UseFVF |
|---|---|---|---|
| 5¢ | **blue on amber** | 4.00 | 1.75 |
| | entire | 7.00 | 3.50 |

| EN614 | | UnFVF | UseFVF |
|---|---|---|---|
| 5¢ | **blue on blue** | 4.00 | 3.00 |
| | entire | 9.00 | 4.50 |

EN615-EN617 *Die 93.*

| EN615 | | UnFVF | UseFVF |
|---|---|---|---|
| 6¢ | **orange on white** | 6.00 | 3.50 |
| | entire* | 8.00 | 6.00 |

| EN616 | | UnFVF | UseFVF |
|---|---|---|---|
| 6¢ | **orange on amber** | 11.00 | 8.00 |
| | entire* | 15.00 | 10.00 |

| EN617 | | UnFVF | UseFVF |
|---|---|---|---|
| 6¢ | **orange on blue** | 11.00 | 8.00 |
| | entire* | 15.00 | 10.00 |

**1920. TYPE 1 SURCHARGE REVALUED ENVELOPES** When a double or triple overprint is listed it indicates that all of the overprints either are directly over the stamp or partly on the stamp. Envelopes which show overprints in various places other than on the stamp are freaks and command little or no premium value.
*On 3¢ envelopes of 1916-50 issue.*

Type 1 surcharge - black overprint.

| EN618 | | UnFVF | UseFVF |
|---|---|---|---|
| **2¢ on 3¢ on white,** Die A (EN584) | | 11.00 | 10.00 |
| entire | | 16.00 | 12.00 |

| EN619 | | UnFVF | UseFVF |
|---|---|---|---|
| **2¢ on 3¢ on white,** Die E (EN591) | | 11.00 | 10.00 |
| entire | | 14.00 | 12.00 |

**1920. TYPE 2 SURCHARGE REVALUED ENVELOPES**

Type 2 surcharge - rose overprint.

| EN620 | | UnFVF | UseFVF |
|---|---|---|---|
| **2¢ on 3¢ on white,** Die A, (EN584) | | 7.00 | 6.00 |
| entire | | 8.50 | 8.00 |

| EN621 | | UnFVF | UseFVF |
|---|---|---|---|
| **2¢ on 3¢ on white,** Die F (EN595) | | 7.00 | 6.00 |
| entire | | 9.50 | 9.00 |

| EN621A | | UnFVF | UseFVF |
|---|---|---|---|
| **2¢ on 3¢ on white,** Die A (EN549) | | 1600. | — |
| entire | | — | — |

| EN621B | | UnFVF | UseFVF |
|---|---|---|---|
| **2¢ on 3¢ on amber,** Die A (EN550) | | — | — |
| entire* | | — | — |

| EN622 | | UnFVF | UseFVF |
|---|---|---|---|
| **2¢ on 3¢ on white,** Die A (EN584) | | 2.50 | 2.00 |
| entire | | 3.00 | 2.50 |

| EN623 | | UnFVF | UseFVF |
|---|---|---|---|
| **2¢ on 3¢ on amber,** Die A (EN585) | | 6.00 | 6.00 |
| entire | | 7.00 | 7.00 |

| EN624 | | UnFVF | UseFVF |
|---|---|---|---|
| **2¢ on 3¢ on buff,** Die A (EN586) | | 15.00 | 13.00 |
| entire | | 18.00 | 17.00 |

| EN625 | | UnFVF | UseFVF |
|---|---|---|---|
| **2¢ on 3¢ on blue,** Die A (EN587) | | 12.00 | 11.00 |
| entire | | 13.00 | 11.00 |

| EN626 | | UnFVF | UseFVF |
|---|---|---|---|
| **2¢ on 3¢ on white,** Die E (EN591) | | — | — |
| entire | | — | — |

| EN627 | | UnFVF | UseFVF |
|---|---|---|---|
| **2¢ on 3¢ on amber,** Die E (EN592) | | — | — |
| entire | | — | — |

| EN628 | | UnFVF | UseFVF |
|---|---|---|---|
| **2¢ on 3¢ on buff,** Die E (EN593) | | — | — |
| entire | | — | — |

| EN629 | | UnFVF | UseFVF |
|---|---|---|---|
| **2¢ on 3¢ on blue,** Die E (EN594) | | — | — |
| entire | | — | — |

| EN630 | | UnFVF | UseFVF |
|---|---|---|---|
| **2¢ on 3¢ on white,** Die F (EN595) | | — | — |
| entire | | — | — |

| EN631 | | UnFVF | UseFVF |
|---|---|---|---|
| **2¢ on 3¢ on amber,** Die F (EN596) | | — | — |
| entire | | — | — |

| EN632 | | UnFVF | UseFVF |
|---|---|---|---|
| **2¢ on 3¢ on buff,** Die F (EN597) | | — | — |
| entire | | — | — |

| EN633 | | UnFVF | UseFVF |
|---|---|---|---|
| **2¢ on 3¢ on blue,** Die F (EN598) | | — | — |
| entire | | — | — |

| EN634 | | UnFVF | UseFVF |
|---|---|---|---|
| **2¢ on 3¢ on white,** Die H (EN599) | | — | — |
| entire | | — | — |

| EN635 | | UnFVF | UseFVF |
|---|---|---|---|
| **2¢ on 3¢ on amber,** Die H (EN600) | | — | — |
| entire | | — | — |

| EN636 | | UnFVF | UseFVF |
|---|---|---|---|
| **2¢ on 3¢ on buff,** Die H (EN601) | | — | — |
| entire | | — | — |

| EN637 | | UnFVF | UseFVF |
|---|---|---|---|
| **2¢ on 3¢ on blue,** Die H (EN602) | | — | — |
| entire | | — | — |

**1920. TYPE 3 SURCHARGE REVALUED ENVELOPES** *On 4¢ brown envelope of 1899 issue.*

Type 3 surcharge - black overprint.

| EN638A | | UnFVF | UseFVF |
|---|---|---|---|
| **2¢ on 4¢ on white,** (EN413) | | — | — |
| entire* | | — | — |

**1920. TYPE 3 SURCHARGE REVALUED ENVELOPES** *On 4¢ brown envelope of 1903 issue.*

| EN639 | | UnFVF | UseFVF |
|---|---|---|---|
| **2¢ on 4¢ on white,** (EN429) | | 350. | 175. |
| entire* | | 400. | 200. |

**1920. TYPE 3 SURCHARGE REVALUED ENVELOPES** *On 4¢ brown envelope of 1899 issue.*

| EN640 | | UnFVF | UseFVF |
|---|---|---|---|
| **2¢ on 4¢ on amber,** (EN430) | | 350. | 125. |
| entire* | | 400. | 175. |

**1920. TYPE 3 SURCHARGE REVALUED ENVELOPES** *On envelopes of 1907-16 issue.*

| EN641 | | UnFVF | UseFVF |
|---|---|---|---|
| **2¢ on 1¢ on white,** Die A (EN439) | | 1700. | — |
| entire | | — | — |

| EN642 | | UnFVF | UseFVF |
|---|---|---|---|
| **2¢ on 2¢ on white,** Die A (EN466) | | 900. | — |
| entire | | 1300. | — |

| EN643 | | UnFVF | UseFVF |
|---|---|---|---|
| **2¢ on 2¢ on buff,** Die A (EN468) | | 675. | — |
| entire | | 775. | — |

| | UnFVF | UseFVF |
|---|---|---|
| **EN644** | | |
| 2¢ on 2¢ on white, Die C (EN488) | 900. | — |
| entire | 1300. | — |
| **EN645** | **UnFVF** | **UseFVF** |
| 2¢ on 2¢ on buff, Die E (EN499) | 700. | 550. |
| entire | 800. | — |
| **EN646** | **UnFVF** | **UseFVF** |
| 2¢ on 2¢ on blue, Die E (EN500) | 700. | — |
| entire | 800. | — |
| **EN647** | **UnFVF** | **UseFVF** |
| 2¢ on 4¢ on white, Die B (EN511) | 750. | — |
| entire | 825. | — |

**1920. TYPE 3 SURCHARGE REVALUED ENVELOPES** *On 1¢ circular dies of 1916-50.*

| | UnFVF | UseFVF |
|---|---|---|
| **EN648** | | |
| 2¢ on 1¢ on white, Die A (EN520) | 900. | — |
| entire | 1100. | — |
| **EN649** | **UnFVF** | **UseFVF** |
| 2¢ on 1¢ on white, Die C (EN531) | — | — |
| entire | — | — |

**1920. TYPE 3 SURCHARGE REVALUED ENVELOPES** *On 2¢ circular dies of 1916-1950.*

| | UnFVF | UseFVF |
|---|---|---|
| **EN650** | | |
| 2¢ on 2¢ on white, Die A (EN549) | 75.00 | — |
| entire | 95.00 | — |
| **EN651** | **UnFVF** | **UseFVF** |
| 2¢ on 2¢ on amber, Die A (EN550) | 950. | — |
| entire | 1300. | — |
| **EN652** | **UnFVF** | **UseFVF** |
| 2¢ on 2¢ on buff, Die B (EN558) | 150. | — |
| entire | 185. | — |
| **EN653** | **UnFVF** | **UseFVF** |
| 2¢ on 2¢ on white, Die E (EN566) | — | — |
| entire | — | — |
| **EN654** | **UnFVF** | **UseFVF** |
| 2¢ on 2¢ on buff, Die E (EN568) | — | — |
| entire | — | — |
| **EN655** | **UnFVF** | **UseFVF** |
| 2¢ on 2¢ on blue, Die E (EN569) | — | — |
| entire | — | — |
| **EN656** | **UnFVF** | **UseFVF** |
| 2¢ on 2¢ on white, Die F (EN570) | — | — |
| entire | — | — |
| **EN657** | **UnFVF** | **UseFVF** |
| 2¢ on 2¢ on blue, Die F (EN573) | — | — |
| entire | — | — |
| **EN658** | **UnFVF** | **UseFVF** |
| 2¢ on 2¢ on white, Die H (EN574) | — | — |
| entire | — | — |
| **EN659** | **UnFVF** | **UseFVF** |
| 2¢ on 2¢ on buff, Die H (EN576) | — | — |
| entire | — | — |
| **EN660** | **UnFVF** | **UseFVF** |
| 2¢ on 2¢ on blue, Die H (EN577) | — | — |
| entire | — | — |

**1920. TYPE 3 SURCHARGE REVALUED ENVELOPES** *On 3¢ circular dies of 1916-50.*

| | UnFVF | UseFVF |
|---|---|---|
| **EN661** | | |
| 2¢ on 3¢ on white, Die A (EN584) | .50 | .40 |
| entire | .70 | .50 |
| v. Double overprint | 15.00 | 8.00 |
| entire | 40.00 | — |
| v1. Triple overprint | — | — |
| entire | — | — |

| | UnFVF | UseFVF |
|---|---|---|
| **EN662** | | |
| 2¢ on 3¢ on amber, Die A (EN585) | 3.00 | 1.50 |
| entire | 4.50 | 2.00 |
| v. Double overprint | 19.00 | — |
| entire | — | — |
| **EN663** | **UnFVF** | **UseFVF** |
| 2¢ on 3¢ on buff, Die A (EN586) | 3.00 | 1.50 |
| entire | 3.50 | 1.50 |
| v. Double overprint | 13.00 | — |
| entire | — | — |
| v1. Triple overprint | 30.00 | — |
| entire | — | — |
| **EN664** | **UnFVF** | **UseFVF** |
| 2¢ on 3¢ on blue, Die A (EN587) | 4.50 | 1.50 |
| entire | 6.00 | 2.00 |
| v. Double overprint | 16.00 | — |
| entire | — | — |
| **EN665** | **UnFVF** | **UseFVF** |
| 2¢ on 3¢ on white, Die E (EN591) | — | — |
| entire | — | — |
| v. Double overprint | — | — |
| entire | — | — |
| v1. Triple overprint | — | — |
| entire | — | — |
| **EN666** | **UnFVF** | **UseFVF** |
| 2¢ on 3¢ on amber, Die E (EN592) | 3.00 | 1.50 |
| entire | 4.50 | 2.00 |
| **EN667** | **UnFVF** | **UseFVF** |
| 2¢ on 3¢ on buff, Die E (EN593) | — | — |
| entire | — | — |
| v. Double overprint | — | — |
| entire | — | — |
| **EN668** | **UnFVF** | **UseFVF** |
| 2¢ on 3¢ on buff, Die E (EN594) | — | — |
| entire | — | — |
| v. Double overprint | — | — |
| entire | — | — |
| v1. Triple overprint | — | — |
| entire | — | — |
| **EN669** | **UnFVF** | **UseFVF** |
| 2¢ on 3¢ on white, Die F (EN595) | — | — |
| entire | — | — |
| v. Double overprint | — | — |
| entire | — | — |
| **EN670** | **UnFVF** | **UseFVF** |
| 2¢ on 3¢ on amber, Die F (EN596) | — | — |
| entire | — | — |
| v. Double overprint | — | — |
| entire | — | — |
| v1. Triple overprint | — | — |
| entire | — | — |
| **EN671** | **UnFVF** | **UseFVF** |
| 2¢ on 3¢ on buff, Die F (EN597) | — | — |
| entire | — | — |
| **EN672** | **UnFVF** | **UseFVF** |
| 2¢ on 3¢ on blue, Die F (EN598) | — | — |
| entire | — | — |
| **EN673** | **UnFVF** | **UseFVF** |
| 2¢ on 3¢ on white, Die H (EN599) | — | — |
| entire | — | — |
| x. Double overprint | — | — |
| entire | — | — |
| x1. Triple overprint | — | — |
| entire | — | — |
| **EN674** | **UnFVF** | **UseFVF** |
| 2¢ on 3¢ on amber, Die H (EN600) | — | — |
| entire | — | — |
| x. Double overprint | — | — |
| entire | — | — |
| x1. Triple overprint | — | — |
| entire | — | — |

**EN675**
2¢ on 3¢ on blue, Die H (EN602)    UnFVF  UseFVF
    entire                         —      —

**1920. TYPE 3 SURCHARGE REVALUED ENVELOPES** On 5¢ circular dies of 1916-50.

**EN676**                               UnFVF  UseFVF
2¢ on 5¢ on white, (EN612)           900.    —
    entire        1100.   —

**1920. TYPE 3 SURCHARGE REVALUED ENVELOPES** Type 3 over Type 7a - black overprint.
    On 3¢ circular dies of 1916-50.

**EN677**                               UnFVF  UseFVF
2¢ on 3¢ on white, Die F (EN595)      —      —
    entire         —      —

**1920. TYPE 4 SURCHARGE REVALUED ENVELOPES** On 3¢ circular dies of 1874-76.

Type 4 surcharge - Black overprint.

**EN678**                               UnFVF  UseFVF
2¢ on 3¢ on white, (EN187)           225.
    entire*       275.    —

**1920. TYPE 4 SURCHARGE REVALUED ENVELOPES** On 4¢ brown envelopes of 1903 issue.

**EN679**                               UnFVF  UseFVF
2¢ on 4¢ on white, (EN429)           12.00   9.00
    entire*       25.00   15.00
    v.  Double overprint   40.00   —
    entire*       —       —
**EN680**                               UnFVF  UseFVF
2¢ on 4¢ on amber, (EN430)           14.00   10.00
    entire        22.00   13.00

**1920. TYPE 4 SURCHARGE REVALUED ENVELOPES** On 2¢ carmine envelope of 1907-16 issue.

**EN681**                               UnFVF  UseFVF
2¢ on 2¢ on white, Die E (EN497)     3000.   —
    entire        3700.   —

**1920. TYPE 4 SURCHARGE REVALUED ENVELOPES** On 1¢ circular dies of 1916-21.

**EN682**                               UnFVF  UseFVF
2¢ on 1¢ on white, Die A (EN520)     750.    —
    entire        950.    —
**EN683**                               UnFVF  UseFVF
2¢ on 1¢ on white, Die C (EN531)      —      —
    entire        —       —

**1920. TYPE 4 SURCHARGE REVALUED ENVELOPES** On 3¢ circular dies of 1874-76.

**EN684**                               UnFVF  UseFVF
2¢ on 2¢ on white, Die A (EN549)     225.    —
    entire        275.    —

**1920. TYPE 4 SURCHARGE REVALUED ENVELOPES** On 2¢ circular dies of 1916-50.

**EN685**                               UnFVF  UseFVF
2¢ on 2¢ on amber, Die A (EN550)     1750.   —
    entire        2000.   —
**EN686**                               UnFVF  UseFVF
2¢ on 2¢ on white, Die E (EN566)     375.    —
    entire        —       —

**EN687**                               UnFVF  UseFVF
2¢ on 2¢ on white, Die H (EN574)      —      —
    entire        —       —

**1920. TYPE 4 SURCHARGE REVALUED ENVELOPES** On 3¢ circular dies of 1916-50.

**EN688**                               UnFVF  UseFVF
2¢ on 3¢ on white, Die A (EN584)     .70     .50
    entire        .90     .80
    x.  Double overprint   16.00
    entire        —       —
    x1. Triple overprint   25.00
    entire        —       —
**EN689**                               UnFVF  UseFVF
2¢ on 3¢ on amber, Die A (EN585)     3.25    2.00
    entire        5.00    3.00
    x.  Double overprint
    entire        —       —
**EN690**                               UnFVF  UseFVF
2¢ on 3¢ on buff, Die A (EN586)      5.00    3.00
    entire        7.00    5.00
    x.  Double overprint   20.00
    entire        —       —
**EN691**                               UnFVF  UseFVF
2¢ on 3¢ on blue, Die A (EN587)      3.50    1.50
    entire        10.00   4.00
    x.  Double overprint   20.00
    entire        —       —

**1920. TYPE 4 SURCHARGE REVALUED ENVELOPES** On Die E.

**EN692**                               UnFVF  UseFVF
2¢ on 3¢ on white (EN591)             —      —
    entire        —       —
    x.  double overprint   —   —
    entire        —       —
**EN693**                               UnFVF  UseFVF
2¢ on 3¢ on amber (EN592)             —      —
    entire        —       —
**EN694**                               UnFVF  UseFVF
2¢ on 3¢ on buff (EN593)              —      —
    entire        —       —
**EN695**                               UnFVF  UseFVF
2¢ on 3¢ on blue (EN594)              —      —
    entire        —       —
    x.  Double overprint   —   —
    entire        —       —

**1920. TYPE 4 SURCHARGE REVALUED ENVELOPES** On Die F.

**EN696**                               UnFVF  UseFVF
2¢ on 3¢ on white (EN595)             —      —
    entire        —       —
    x.  Double overprint   —   —
    entire        —       —
**EN697**                               UnFVF  UseFVF
2¢ on 3¢ on amber (EN596)             —      —
    entire        —       —
    x.  Double overprint   —   —
    entire        —       —
**EN698**                               UnFVF  UseFVF
2¢ on 3¢ on buff (EN597)              —      —
    entire        —       —
**EN699**                               UnFVF  UseFVF
2¢ on 3¢ on blue (EN598)              —      —
    entire        —       —

**1920. TYPE 4 SURCHARGE REVALUED ENVELOPE.** On Die H.

**EN700**                               UnFVF  UseFVF
2¢ on 3¢ on white (EN599)             —      —
    entire        —       —
    x.  Double overprint   —   —
    entire        —       —

| | UnFVF | UseFVF |
|---|---|---|
| **EN701** | | |
| 2¢ on 3¢ on amber (EN600) | — | — |
| entire | — | — |
| **EN702** | UnFVF | UseFVF |
| 2¢ on 3¢ on buff (EN601) | — | — |
| entire | — | — |
| **EN703** | UnFVF | UseFVF |
| 2¢ on 3¢ on blue (EN602) | — | — |
| entire | — | — |

**1920. TYPE 4 OVER TYPE 7A SURCHARGE REVALUED ENVE-LOPES** Black overprints.
*On 3¢ circular dies of 1916-50.*

| | UnFVF | UseFVF |
|---|---|---|
| **EN704** | | |
| 2¢ on 3¢ on white, Die A (EN584) | — | — |
| entire | — | — |
| **EN705** | UnFVF | UseFVF |
| 2¢ on 3¢ on amber, Die A (EN585) | — | — |
| entire | — | — |
| **EN706** | UnFVF | UseFVF |
| 2¢ on 3¢ on white, Die E (EN591) | — | — |
| entire | — | — |
| **EN707** | UnFVF | UseFVF |
| 2¢ on 3¢ on white, Die H (EN599) | — | — |
| entire | — | — |

**1920. TYPE 4 OVER TYPE 2 SURCHARGE REVALUED ENVELOPES**
Black overprints.
*On 3¢ circular dies of 1916-50.*
*On Die A.*

| | UnFVF | UseFVF |
|---|---|---|
| **EN708** | | |
| 2¢ on 3¢ on white (EN584) | — | — |
| entire | — | — |
| **EN709** | UnFVF | UseFVF |
| 2¢ on 3¢ on amber (EN585) | — | — |
| entire | — | — |
| **EN710** | UnFVF | UseFVF |
| 2¢ on 3¢ on buff (EN586) | — | — |
| entire | — | — |
| **EN711** | UnFVF | UseFVF |
| 2¢ on 3¢ on blue (EN587) | — | — |
| entire | — | — |

**1920. TYPE 4 OVER TYPE 2 SURCHARGE REVALUED ENVELOPES**
*On Die E.*

| | UnFVF | UseFVF |
|---|---|---|
| **EN712** | | |
| 2¢ on 3¢ on amber (EN592) | — | — |
| entire | — | — |
| **EN713** | UnFVF | UseFVF |
| 2¢ on 3¢ on buff (EN593) | — | — |
| entire | — | — |
| **EN714** | UnFVF | UseFVF |
| 2¢ on 3¢ on blue (EN594) | — | — |
| entire | — | — |

**1920. TYPE 4 OVER TYPE E SURCHARGE REVALUED ENVELOPES**
*On Die F.*

| | UnFVF | UseFVF |
|---|---|---|
| **EN715** | | |
| 2¢ on 3¢ on buff (EN597) | — | — |
| entire | — | — |
| **EN716** | UnFVF | UseFVF |
| 2¢ on 3¢ on blue (EN598) | — | — |
| entire | — | — |
| **EN717** | UnFVF | UseFVF |
| 2¢ on 3¢ on white, Die H (EN599) | — | — |
| entire | — | — |

**1920. TYPE 4 OVER TYPE 3 SURCHARGE REVALUED ENVELOPES**
Black overprints.
*On 3¢ circular dies of 1916-50.*
*On Die A.*

| | UnFVF | UseFVF |
|---|---|---|
| **EN718** | | |
| 2¢ on 3¢ on white (EN584) | — | — |
| entire | — | — |
| **EN719** | UnFVF | UseFVF |
| 2¢ on 3¢ on amber (EN585) | — | — |
| entire | — | — |
| **EN720** | UnFVF | UseFVF |
| 2¢ on 3¢ on buff (EN586) | — | — |
| entire | — | — |
| **EN721** | UnFVF | UseFVF |
| 2¢ on 3¢ on blue (EN587) | — | — |
| entire | — | — |

**1920. TYPE 4 OVER TYPE 3 SURCHARGE REVALUED ENVELOPES**
*On Die E.*

| | UnFVF | UseFVF |
|---|---|---|
| **EN722** | | |
| 2¢ on 3¢ on amber (EN592) | — | — |
| entire | — | — |
| **EN723** | UnFVF | UseFVF |
| 2¢ on 3¢ on buff (EN593) | — | — |
| entire | — | — |
| **EN724** | UnFVF | UseFVF |
| 2¢ on 3¢ on blue (EN594) | — | — |
| entire | — | — |
| **EN725** | UnFVF | UseFVF |
| 2¢ on 3¢ on blue, Die F (EN598) | — | — |
| entire | — | — |
| **EN726** | UnFVF | UseFVF |
| 2¢ on 3¢ on white, Die H (EN599) | — | — |
| entire | — | — |

**1920. TYPE 5 SURCHARGE REVALUED ENVELOPES** *On 3¢ circular dies of 1916-50.*

**2**

Type 5 surcharge - black overprint.

| | UnFVF | UseFVF |
|---|---|---|
| **EN727** | | |
| 2¢ on 3¢ on amber, Die A (EN585) | 100. | — |
| entire | 130. | — |
| **EN728** | UnFVF | UseFVF |
| 2¢ on 3¢ on amber, Die F (EN596) | — | — |
| entire | — | — |

**1920. TYPE 6 SURCHARGE REVALUED ENVELOPES** *On 3¢ circular dies of 1916-50.*
*On Die A.*

**2**  Type 6 surcharge - black overprint.

| | UnFVF | UseFVF |
|---|---|---|
| **EN729** | | |
| 2¢ on 3¢ on white (EN584) | 100. | — |
| entire | 130. | — |
| x.  Double overprint | — | — |
| entire | — | — |
| **EN730** | UnFVF | UseFVF |
| 2¢ on 3¢ on amber (EN585) | 200. | — |
| entire | 220. | — |
| **EN731** | UnFVF | UseFVF |
| 2¢ on 3¢ on white, Die E (EN591) | — | — |
| entire | — | — |
| **EN732** | UnFVF | UseFVF |
| 2¢ on 3¢ on white, Die F (EN595) | — | — |
| entire | — | — |
| **EN733** | UnFVF | UseFVF |
| 2¢ on 3¢ on white, Die H (EN599) | — | — |
| entire | — | — |

**1920. Type 7 Surcharge Revalued Envelopes** *On 3¢ circular dies of 1916-50.*

Type 7 surcharge - black overprint.

**EN734**
2¢ on 3¢ on white, Die A (EN584)

| | UnFVF | UseFVF |
|---|---|---|
| | 275. | — |
| entire | 325. | — |

**EN735**
2¢ on 3¢ on white, Die E (EN591)

| | UnFVF | UseFVF |
|---|---|---|
| | — | — |
| entire | — | — |

**EN736**
2¢ on 3¢ on white, Die H (EN599)

| | UnFVF | UseFVF |
|---|---|---|
| | — | — |
| entire | — | — |

**1920. Type 7A Surcharge Revalued Envelopes** **Type 7** - violet overprint.

Type 7A surcharge - violet overprint.

**EN737**
2¢ on 3¢ on white, Die H (EN599)

| | UnFVF | UseFVF |
|---|---|---|
| | 200. | — |
| entire | 225. | — |

**1920. Type 7A Surcharge Revalued Envelopes** *On 2¢ circular dies of 1916-50.*

**EN738**
1¢ on 2¢ on white, Die A (EN549)

| | UnFVF | UseFVF |
|---|---|---|
| | — | — |
| entire | — | — |

**EN739**
1¢ on 2¢ on white, Die H (EN574)

| | UnFVF | UseFVF |
|---|---|---|
| | — | — |
| entire | — | — |

**1920. Type 7A Surcharge Revalued Envelopes** *On 3¢ circular dies of 1916-50.*

**EN740**
1¢ on 3¢ on white, Die E (EN591)

| | UnFVF | UseFVF |
|---|---|---|
| | 200. | — |
| entire | 225. | — |

**1925. Type 8 Surcharge Revalued Envelopes** *On 2¢ green envelopes of 1887 issue.*

Type 8 Surcharge - black overprint.

**EN741**
1-1/2¢ on 2¢ on white (EN344)

| | UnFVF | UseFVF |
|---|---|---|
| | 600. | — |
| entire | 650. | — |

**EN742**
1-1/2¢ on 2¢ on amber (EN345)

| | UnFVF | UseFVF |
|---|---|---|
| | 700. | — |
| entire | 800. | — |

**1925. Type 8 Surcharge Revalued Envelopes** *On 1¢ green envelopes of 1899 issue.*

**EN743**
1-1/2¢ on 1¢ on white (EN391)

| | UnFVF | UseFVF |
|---|---|---|
| | 350. | — |
| entire | 650. | — |

**EN744**
1-1/2¢ on 1¢ on amber (EN392)

| | UnFVF | UseFVF |
|---|---|---|
| | 75.00 | 65.00 |
| entire | 120. | 100. |

**1925. Type 8 Surcharge Revalued Envelopes** *On 1¢ green envelopes of 1907-16. On Die A.*

**EN745**
1-1/2¢ on 1¢ on white (EN439)

| | UnFVF | UseFVF |
|---|---|---|
| | 5.00 | 4.00 |
| entire | 6.00 | 6.00 |

**EN746**
1-1/2¢ on 1¢ on amber (EN440)

| | UnFVF | UseFVF |
|---|---|---|
| | 8.00 | 3.00 |
| entire | 12.00 | 7.00 |

**EN747**
1-1/2¢ on 1¢ on manila (EN443)

| | UnFVF | UseFVF |
|---|---|---|
| | 200. | 75.00 |
| entire | 250. | 100. |

**1925. Type 8 Surcharge Revalued Envelopes** *On Die B.*

**EN748**
1-1/2¢ on 1¢ on white (EN445)

| | UnFVF | UseFVF |
|---|---|---|
| | 13.00 | 10.00 |
| entire | 15.00 | 13.00 |

**EN749**
1-1/2¢ on 1¢ on amber (EN446)

| | UnFVF | UseFVF |
|---|---|---|
| | 80.00 | 70.00 |
| entire | 200. | 90.00 |

**EN750**
1-1/2¢ on 1¢ on buff (EN447)

| | UnFVF | UseFVF |
|---|---|---|
| | 200. | 100. |
| entire | 225. | 110. |

**EN751**
1-1/2¢ on 1¢ on blue (EN448)

| | UnFVF | UseFVF |
|---|---|---|
| | 75.00 | 55.00 |
| entire | 100. | 65.00 |

**1925. Type 8 Surcharge Revalued Envelopes** *On Die C.*

**EN751A**
1-1/2¢ on 1¢ on white (EN450)

| | UnFVF | UseFVF |
|---|---|---|
| | 7.00 | 3.00 |
| entire | 9.00 | 5.00 |

**EN751B**
1-1/2¢ on 1¢ on amber (EN450)

| | UnFVF | UseFVF |
|---|---|---|
| | 4.50 | 2.50 |
| entire* | 8.00 | 5.00 |

**EN751C**
1-1/2¢ on 1¢ on manila (EN454)

| | UnFVF | UseFVF |
|---|---|---|
| | — | — |
| entire | — | — |

**1925. Type 8 Surcharge Revalued Envelopes** *On Die D.*

**EN752**
1-1/2¢ on 1¢ on white (EN456)

| | UnFVF | UseFVF |
|---|---|---|
| | — | — |
| entire | — | — |

**EN753**
1-1/2¢ on 1¢ on amber (EN457)

| | UnFVF | UseFVF |
|---|---|---|
| | 4.50 | 2.50 |
| entire | 8.00 | 5.00 |

**EN754**
1-1/2¢ on 1¢ on buff (EN458)

| | UnFVF | UseFVF |
|---|---|---|
| | 75.00 | 55.00 |
| entire | 100. | 65.00 |

**EN755**
1-1/2¢ on 1¢ on blue (EN459)

| | UnFVF | UseFVF |
|---|---|---|
| | — | — |
| entire | — | — |

**1925. Type 8 Surcharge Revalued Envelopes** *On 1¢ circular dies of 1916-50.*
Die A.

**EN756**
1-1/2¢ on 1¢ on white (EN520)

| | UnFVF | UseFVF |
|---|---|---|
| | .35 | .30 |
| entire | .60 | .50 |
| v. Double overprint | 5.00 | 2.50 |
| entire | — | — |

**EN757**
1-1/2¢ on 1¢ on amber (EN521)

| | UnFVF | UseFVF |
|---|---|---|
| | 14.00 | 13.00 |
| entire | 21.00 | 16.00 |

**EN758**
1-1/2¢ on 1¢ on buff (EN522)

| | UnFVF | UseFVF |
|---|---|---|
| | 4.00 | 2.50 |
| entire | 6.00 | 2.75 |

**EN759**
1-1/2¢ on 1¢ on blue (EN523)

| | UnFVF | UseFVF |
|---|---|---|
| | 1.25 | 1.00 |
| entire | 2.50 | 1.50 |

**EN760**
1-1/2¢ on 1¢ on manila (EN524)

| | UnFVF | UseFVF |
|---|---|---|
| | 11.00 | 7.00 |
| entire | 16.00 | 8.00 |

**EN761**
1-1/2¢ on 1¢ on brown (glazed) (EN526)

| | UnFVF | UseFVF |
|---|---|---|
| | 60.00 | 30.00 |
| entire | 70.00 | 40.00 |

**EN762**

| | UnFVF | UseFVF |
|---|---|---|
| 1-1/2¢ on 1¢on brown (unglazed) (EN528) | 60.00 | 35.00 |
| entire | 70.00 | 40.00 |

**1925. TYPE 8 SURCHARGE REVALUED ENVELOPES** *On Die B.*

**EN762A**

| | UnFVF | UseFVF |
|---|---|---|
| 1-1/2¢ on 1¢on white (EN529) | 2.00 | .75 |
| entire | — | — |

**1925. TYPE 8 SURCHARGE REVALUED ENVELOPES** *On Die C.*

**EN763**

| | UnFVF | UseFVF |
|---|---|---|
| 1-1/2¢ on 1¢on white (EN531) | 2.00 | 1.00 |
| entire | — | — |
| x. Double overprint | — | — |
| entire | — | — |

**EN764**

| | UnFVF | UseFVF |
|---|---|---|
| 1-1/2¢ on 1¢on blue (EN533) | — | — |
| entire | — | — |

**1925. TYPE 8 SURCHARGE REVALUED ENVELOPES** *On Die D.*

**EN765**

| | UnFVF | UseFVF |
|---|---|---|
| 1-1/2¢ on 1¢on white (EN534) | — | — |
| entire | — | — |
| x. Double overprint | — | — |
| entire | — | — |

**EN766**

| | UnFVF | UseFVF |
|---|---|---|
| 1-1/2¢ on 1¢on amber (EN535) | — | — |
| entire | — | — |

**EN767**

| | UnFVF | UseFVF |
|---|---|---|
| 1-1/2¢ on 1¢on blue (EN537) | — | — |
| entire | — | — |
| x. Double overprint | — | — |
| entire | — | — |

**1925. TYPE 8 SURCHARGE REVALUED ENVELOPES** *On 1 1/2¢ circular dies of 1916-50.*

**EN768**

| | UnFVF | UseFVF |
|---|---|---|
| 1-1/2¢ on 1 1/2¢on white, Die A (EN541) | 400. | — |
| entire | 475. | — |

**EN769**

| | UnFVF | UseFVF |
|---|---|---|
| 1-1/2¢ on 1 1/2¢on blue, Die H2 (EN548) | 350. | — |
| entire | 400. | — |

**1925. TYPE 8 SURCHARGE REVALUED ENVELOPES** *On 2¢ circular dies of 1916-50.*

**EN770**

| | UnFVF | UseFVF |
|---|---|---|
| 1-1/2¢ on 2¢on white, Die A (EN549) | 250. | — |
| entire* | 300. | — |

**EN771**

| | UnFVF | UseFVF |
|---|---|---|
| 1-1/2¢ on 2¢on buff, Die E (EN568) | 275. | — |
| entire | 300. | — |

**EN772**

| | UnFVF | UseFVF |
|---|---|---|
| 1-1/2¢ on 2¢on blue, Die F (EN573) | 250. | — |
| entire | 300. | — |

**1925. TYPE 9 SURCHARGE REVALUED ENVELOPES** *On 1¢ blue envelope of 1887 issue.*

![Type 9 surcharge - black overprint]

Type 9 surcharge - black overprint.

**EN773**

| | UnFVF | UseFVF |
|---|---|---|
| 1-1/2¢ on 1¢on white (EN321) | 1000. | — |
| entire | 1200. | — |

**1925. TYPE 9 SURCHARGE REVALUED ENVELOPES** *On 1¢ green envelope of 1899.*

**EN774**

| | UnFVF | UseFVF |
|---|---|---|
| 1-1/2¢ on 1¢on amber (EN392) | 60.00 | — |
| entire | 70.00 | — |

**1925. TYPE 9 SURCHARGE REVALUED ENVELOPES** *On 1¢ green envelopes of 1903 issue.*

**EN775**

| | UnFVF | UseFVF |
|---|---|---|
| 1-1/2¢ on 1¢on white (EN418) | 1500. | — |
| entire | 2400. | — |

**EN776**

| | UnFVF | UseFVF |
|---|---|---|
| 1-1/2¢ on 1¢on amber (EN419) | 14.00 | 12.00 |
| entire | 25.00 | 17.00 |
| x. Double overprint | 27.00 | — |
| entire | 33.00 | — |

**EN777**

| | UnFVF | UseFVF |
|---|---|---|
| 1-1/2¢ on 1¢on buff (EN420) | 60.00 | 50.00 |
| entire | 70.00 | 60.00 |

**1925. TYPE 9 SURCHARGE REVALUED ENVELOPES** *On 1¢ oval dies of 1907-16.*
    *On Die A.*

**EN778**

| | UnFVF | UseFVF |
|---|---|---|
| 1-1/2¢ on 1¢on white (EN439) | 2.00 | 1.50 |
| entire | 3.50 | 2.00 |
| x. Double overprint | 8.00 | — |
| entire | — | — |

**EN779**

| | UnFVF | UseFVF |
|---|---|---|
| 1-1/2¢ on 1¢on amber (EN440) | 175. | 80.00 |
| entire | 200. | 100. |

**EN780**

| | UnFVF | UseFVF |
|---|---|---|
| 1-1/2¢ on 1¢on buff (EN441) | 7.00 | 5.00 |
| entire | 12.00 | 7.00 |
| x. Double overprint | — | — |
| entire | — | — |

**EN781**

| | UnFVF | UseFVF |
|---|---|---|
| 1-1/2¢ on 1¢on blue (EN442) | 6.00 | 3.00 |
| entire | 8.00 | 5.00 |

**EN782**

| | UnFVF | UseFVF |
|---|---|---|
| 1-1/2¢ on 1¢on manila (EN443) | 25.00 | 11.00 |
| entire | 35.00 | 25.00 |

**EN783**

| | UnFVF | UseFVF |
|---|---|---|
| 1-1/2¢ on 1¢on white, Die B (EN445) | 7.00 | 5.00 |

**1925. TYPE 9 SURCHARGE REVALUED ENVELOPES** *On Die C.*

**EN784**

| | UnFVF | UseFVF |
|---|---|---|
| 1-1/2¢ on 1¢on white (EN450) | 17.00 | 9.00 |
| entire | 25.00 | 13.00 |

**EN785**

| | UnFVF | UseFVF |
|---|---|---|
| 1-1/2¢ on 1¢on manila (EN454) | 55.00 | 40.00 |
| entire | 60.00 | 50.00 |

**1925. TYPE 9 SURCHARGE REVALUED ENVELOPES** *On Die D.*

**EN786**

| | UnFVF | UseFVF |
|---|---|---|
| 1-1/2¢ on 1¢on white (EN456) | 4.00 | 1.50 |
| entire | 7.00 | 3.00 |

**EN787**

| | UnFVF | UseFVF |
|---|---|---|
| 1-1/2¢ on 1¢on buff (EN458) | 18.00 | 15.00 |
| entire | 25.00 | 19.00 |

**EN788**

| | UnFVF | UseFVF |
|---|---|---|
| 1-1/2¢ on 1¢on blue (EN459) | 6.00 | 5.00 |
| entire | 8.00 | 6.00 |

**1925. TYPE 9 SURCHARGE REVALUED ENVELOPES** *On 1¢ circular dies of 1916-50.*
On Die A.

| EN789 | UnFVF | UseFVF |
|---|---|---|
| 1-1/2¢ on 1¢ on white (EN520) | .40 | .30 |
| entire | .70 | .40 |
| x. Double overprint | 7.00 | — |
| entire | — | — |
| x1. Triple overprint | 13.00 | — |
| entire | — | — |
| x2. Inverted overprint | 11.00 | — |
| entire | — | — |

| EN790 | UnFVF | UseFVF |
|---|---|---|
| 1-1/2¢ on 1¢ on amber (EN521) | 50.00 | 35.00 |
| entire | 60.00 | 45.00 |

| EN791 | UnFVF | UseFVF |
|---|---|---|
| 1-1/2¢ on 1¢ on buff (EN522) | 5.00 | 2.00 |
| entire | 6.00 | 2.00 |

| EN792 | UnFVF | UseFVF |
|---|---|---|
| 1-1/2¢ on 1¢ on blue (EN523) | 5.00 | 2.00 |
| entire | 6.00 | 2.00 |
| x. Double overprint | 11.00 | — |
| entire | — | — |

| EN793 | UnFVF | UseFVF |
|---|---|---|
| 1-1/2¢ on 1¢ on manila (EN524) | 20.00 | 12.00 |
| entire | 28.00 | 15.00 |

| EN794 | UnFVF | UseFVF |
|---|---|---|
| 1-1/2¢ on 1¢ on white, Die B (EN529) | — | — |
| entire | — | — |

**1925. TYPE 9 SURCHARGE REVALUED ENVELOPES** *On Die C.*

| EN795 | UnFVF | UseFVF |
|---|---|---|
| 1-1/2¢ on 1¢ on white (EN531) | — | — |
| entire | — | — |
| x. Double overprint | — | — |
| entire | — | — |

| EN796 | UnFVF | UseFVF |
|---|---|---|
| 1-1/2¢ on 1¢ on blue (EN533) | — | — |
| entire | — | — |

**1925. TYPE 9 SURCHARGE REVALUED ENVELOPES** *On Die D.*

| EN797 | UnFVF | UseFVF |
|---|---|---|
| 1-1/2¢ on 1¢ on white (EN534) | — | — |
| entire | — | — |
| x. inverted overprint | — | — |
| entire | — | — |

| EN798 | UnFVF | UseFVF |
|---|---|---|
| 1-1/2¢ on 1¢ on amber (EN535) | — | — |
| entire | — | — |

| EN799 | UnFVF | UseFVF |
|---|---|---|
| 1-1/2¢ on 1¢ on buff (EN536) | — | — |
| entire | — | — |

**1925. TYPE 9 SURCHARGE REVALUED ENVELOPES** *On Die D.*

| EN800 | UnFVF | UseFVF |
|---|---|---|
| 1-1/2¢ on 1¢ on blue (EN537) | — | — |
| entire | — | — |

**1925. TYPE 9 SURCHARGE REVALUED ENVELOPES** *On 2¢ carmine envelopes of 1916-50 issue.*

| EN801 | UnFVF | UseFVF |
|---|---|---|
| 1-1/2¢ on 2¢ on white, Die A (EN549) | 175. | |
| entire | 225. | — |

| EN801A | UnFVF | UseFVF |
|---|---|---|
| 1-1/2¢ on 2¢ on white, Die E (EN566) | — | — |
| entire | — | — |

| EN801B | UnFVF | UseFVF |
|---|---|---|
| 1-1/2¢ on 2¢ on amber, Die E (EN567) | — | — |
| entire | — | — |

| EN802 | UnFVF | UseFVF |
|---|---|---|
| 1-1/2¢ on 2¢ on white, Die F (EN570) | — | — |
| entire | — | — |

| EN803 | UnFVF | UseFVF |
|---|---|---|
| 1-1/2¢ on 2¢ on white, Die H (EN574) | — | — |
| entire | — | — |

**1925. TYPE 9 SURCHARGE REVALUED ENVELOPES** **Type 9** - magneta overprint *On 1¢ green envelope of 1916-50 issue.*

| EN804 | UnFVF | UseFVF |
|---|---|---|
| 1-1/2¢ on 1¢ on white (EN531) | 5.00 | 4.00 |
| entire | 5.00 | 6.00 |
| x. Double overprint | 30.00 | — |
| entire | — | — |

**1925. TYPE 9 SURCHARGE REVALUED ENVELOPES** *On 1¢ circular dies of 1916-50.*

| EN805 | UnFVF | UseFVF |
|---|---|---|
| 1 + 1/2¢ on white (EN520) | — | — |
| entire | — | — |

## 1926. SESQUICENTENNIAL EXPOSITION ENVELOPE

EN806 *Liberty Bell, Center bar of "E" of "POSTAGE" shorter than top bar. Watermark 27 (1925).*

| EN806 | | UnFVF | UseFVF |
|---|---|---|---|
| 2¢ | carmine on white | 2.00 | 1.00 |
| | entire | 2.75 | 1.75 |
| | FDC *(July 27, 1926)* | | |

EN807 *The center bar of "E" in "POSTAGE" is the same length as top bar.*

| EN807 | | UnFVF | UseFVF |
|---|---|---|---|
| 2¢ | carmine on white | 10.00 | 7.00 |
| | entire | 12.50 | 10.00 |

## 1932. WASHINGTON BICENTENNIAL ISSUE

EN808-EN813 *Mount Vernon. All of the same design; only the denomination changes. Watermark 29 (1929).*

| EN808 | | UnFVF | UseFVF |
|---|---|---|---|
| 1¢ | green on white *(Jan. 1, 1932)* | 2.00 | 1.50 |
| | entire | 2.50 | 1.75 |

*Watermark 29 (1929).*

| EN809 | | UnFVF | UseFVF |
|---|---|---|---|
| 1-1/2¢ | brown on white *(Jan. 1, 1932)* | 3.50 | 2.00 |
| | entire | 3.75 | 2.75 |

| EN810 | | UnFVF | UseFVF |
|---|---|---|---|
| 2¢ | carmine on white *(Jan. 1, 1932)* | .50 | .25 |
| | entire | .75 | .30 |
| | a. carmine on blue (error), entire | 27000. | — |
| | v. "S" of "POSTAGE" high | — | — |
| | entire | 90.00 | 50.00 |

| EN811 | | UnFVF | UseFVF |
|---|---|---|---|
| 3¢ | purple on white *(June 16, 1932)* | 2.50 | .30 |
| | entire | 4.00 | .50 |

| EN812 | | UnFVF | UseFVF |
|---|---|---|---|
| 4¢ | black on white *(Jan. 1, 1932)* | 25.00 | 20.00 |
| | entire* | 30.00 | 25.00 |

| EN813 | | UnFVF | UseFVF |
|---|---|---|---|
| 5¢ | blue on white *(Jan. 1, 1932)* | 6.00 | 4.00 |
| | entire | 6.50 | 5.50 |

**1950. ISSUE New Oval Design.** As far back as 1941, the Post Office had submitted new designs for its envelope stamps and had ordered the necessary new printing dies to be made. The outbreak of World War II interfered with plans for the new design, and the new printing dies were not put into use. After the war, collectors brought ever-increasing pressure to bear on the Post Office Department to change the circular design which was well into a third decade of use.

In 1950 the Post Office determined to put some of the printing dies that had been prepared in 1941 into production and ordered 1¢, 2¢ and 3¢ envelopes printed on a demonstration machine at the annual stamp exhibition sponsored by the American Stamp Dealers Association in New York. Only a very few of the old dies were found to be usable in the more modern machines then in use. However, at least one printing die in each denomination was put into use, and the envelopes were then printed and sold at the ASDA stamp show.

New printing dies immediately were developed so that the new design could replace completely the old design. These first-printed envelopes are in very short supply. *These envelopes were issued on white paper only.*

EN814 *Franklin. Die A, thick, short, "1" within heavy circle.*

| EN814 | | MNHVF | UseVF |
|---|---|---|---|
| 1¢ | green, Die A (Nov. 16, 1950) | 6.00 | 2.00 |
| | entire | 8.00 | 3.00 |

EN815 *Die B, thin, long "1" within thin circle, "E" in "ONE" has long bars and is close. 1mm to circle.*

| EN815 | | MNHVF | UseVF |
|---|---|---|---|
| 1¢ | green, Die B | 7.00 | 4.00 |
| | entire | 9.00 | 4.50 |

EN816 *Die C, thin long "1". "E" in "ONE" with short bars and far (1 1/2mm) from circle.*

| EN816 | | MNHVF | UseVF |
|---|---|---|---|
| 1¢ | green, Die C | 7.00 | 4.00 |
| | entire | 9.00 | 4.50 |
| | v. precanceled, entire | 1.00 | 1.00 |

EN817 *Washington*

| EN817 | | MNHVF | UseVF |
|---|---|---|---|
| 1-1/2¢ | brown | 5.00 | 4.00 |
| | entire | 6.00 | 5.00 |
| | v. precanceled, entire | 1.25 | 1.25 |

EN818 *Washington. Die A, figure "2" set low in heavy circle.*

| EN818 | | MNHVF | UseVF |
|---|---|---|---|
| 2¢ | carmine, Die A *(Nov. 17, 1950)* | .80 | .35 |
| | entire | 1.50 | .50 |

EN818A *Die B, thin "2" with long hook. Center cross bar of "E" in "STATES" shorter than top or bottom bars.*

| EN818A | | MNHVF | UseVF |
|---|---|---|---|
| 2¢ | carmine, Die B | 1.50 | 1.00 |
| | entire | 2.00 | 1.10 |

EN819 *Die C, thin "2" set high in thin circle.*

| EN819 | | MNHVF | UseVF |
|---|---|---|---|
| 2¢ | carmine, Die C | .80 | .30 |
| | entire | | 1.25.50 |

EN819A *Washington. Die D, thick cross bar in "A" of "STATES."*

| EN819A | | MNHVF | UseVF |
|---|---|---|---|
| 2¢ | carmine, Die D | 1.50 | .70 |
| | entire | 1.60 | .70 |

EN820 *Die A, tall, thick "3" within thick circle. Narrow "E"s in "THREE."*

| EN820 | | MNHVF | UseVF |
|---|---|---|---|
| 3¢ | purple, Die A *(Nov. 18, 1950)* | 2.25 | .85 |
| | entire | .30 | 1.50 |

EN821 *Die B, tall, thin, "3" in thin circle. Narrow "E"s in "THREE."*

| EN821 | | MNHVF | UseVF |
|---|---|---|---|
| 3¢ | **purple,** Die B *(Nov. 19, 1950)* | .85 | .60 |
| | entire | 1.60 | .65 |

EN822 *Die C, short "3" in thin circle. Wide "E"s in "THREE." Line from left stand of "N" in "UNITED" to stand in "E" in "POSTAGE" well below chin.*

| EN822 | | MNHVF | UseVF |
|---|---|---|---|
| 3¢ | **purple,** Die C | .60 | .35 |
| | entire | 1.00 | .50 |

EN823 *Die D, short "3" in thin circle. Wide "E"s in "THREE". Line from left stand of "N" in "UNITED" to stand of "E" in "POSTAGE" almost touches chin. "N" in "UNITED" short; thin cross bar in "A" in "STATES".*

| EN823 | | MNHVF | UseVF |
|---|---|---|---|
| 3¢ | **purple,** Die D | .50 | .25 |
| | entire | .65 | .30 |

EN824 *Die E, similar to EN823 except "N" in "UNITED" tall, and thick cross bar in "A" in "STATES."*

| EN824 | | MNHVF | UseVF |
|---|---|---|---|
| 3¢ | **purple,** Die E | .90 | .50 |
| | entire | 1.35 | .75 |

**1958. ISSUE** On August 1, 1958, first class postage rates were raised to four cents. This necessitated new 4¢ stamped envelopes. In addition, to use up surplus stocks of 2¢ and 3¢ envelopes, the Post Office Department again revalued existing stocks.

EN825 *Franklin. Die A, head high in oval. Circle around "4" low (1mm from outer edge of color). Watermarks 46, 47, 48.*

| EN825 | | MNHVF | UseVF |
|---|---|---|---|
| 4¢ | **lilac,** Die A *(Aug. 1, 1958)* | .90 | .25 |
| | entire | 1.00 | .30 |

EN826 *Die B, head low in oval. Circle around "4" high (1 1/2mm from outer edge of color). To verify: right leg of "A" in "POSTAGE" shorter than left leg. Short leg on "P".*

| EN826 | | MNHVF | UseVF |
|---|---|---|---|
| 4¢ | **lilac,** Die B | 1.10 | .25 |
| | entire | 1.40 | .35 |

EN827 *Die C, head centered in oval. Circle around "4" high as on Die B. To verify: legs of "A" in "POSTAGE" are about equal in length. Long leg on "P".*

| EN827 | | MNHVF | UseVF |
|---|---|---|---|
| 4¢ | **lilac,** Die C | 1.25 | .25 |
| | entire | 1.40 | .35 |

**1958. TYPE 11 SURCHARGE REVALUED ENVELOPES**

*type 11 surcharge - Overprint in green to left of stamp. On 3¢ purple of 1916-50 issue.*

| EN828 | | MNHVF | UseVF |
|---|---|---|---|
| 1¢ on 3¢ **purple,** Die A (EN588) | | 15.00 | 11.00 |
| | entire | 16.00 | — |

| EN829 | | MNHVF | UseVF |
|---|---|---|---|
| 1¢ on 3¢ **purple,** Die H (EN603) | | 12.00 | 10.00 |
| | entire | 15.00 | — |

| EN830 | | MNHVF | UseVF |
|---|---|---|---|
| 1¢ on 3¢ **purple,** Die I (EN606) | | 35.00 | 20.00 |
| | entire | 40.00 | — |

**1958. TYPE 11 SURCHARGE REVALUED ENVELOPES** *On 3¢ purple of 1950.*

| EN831 | | MNHVF | UseVF |
|---|---|---|---|
| 1¢ on 3¢ **purple,** Die B (EN821) | | — | — |
| | entire | 1100. | — |

| EN832 | | MNHVF | UseVF |
|---|---|---|---|
| 1¢ on 3¢ **purple,** Die C (EN822) | | .60 | .25 |
| | entire | .70 | .35 |

| EN833 | | MNHVF | UseVF |
|---|---|---|---|
| 1¢ on 3¢ **purple,** Die D (EN823) | | .85 | .25 |
| | entire | 1.00 | .25 |

| EN834 | | MNHVF | UseVF |
|---|---|---|---|
| 1¢ on 3¢ **purple,** Die E (EN824) | | .85 | .25 |
| | entire | 1.10 | .25 |

**1958. TYPE 12 SURCHARGE REVALUED ENVELOPES** *On 2¢ circular dies of 1916-1950.*

*Type 12 surcharge - overprint in red to left of stamp.*

| EN835 | | MNHVF | UseVF |
|---|---|---|---|
| 2¢ on 2¢ **carmine,** Die A (EN549) | | 4.00 | 2.00 |
| | entire | 4.50 | — |

| EN836 | | MNHVF | UseVF |
|---|---|---|---|
| 2¢ on 2¢ **carmine,** Die H (EN574) | | 11.00 | 8.00 |
| | entire | 13.00 | — |

| EN837 | | MNHVF | UseVF |
|---|---|---|---|
| 2¢ on 2¢ **carmine,** Die I (EN581) | | 6.00 | 6.00 |
| | entire | 7.50 | — |

**1958. TYPE 12 SURCHARGE REVALUED ENVELOPES** *On 2¢ oval die of 1950.*

| EN838 | | MNHVF | UseVF |
|---|---|---|---|
| 2¢ on 2¢ **carmine,** Die A (EN818) | | .90 | .40 |
| | entire | 1.10 | .50 |

| EN839 | | MNHVF | UseVF |
|---|---|---|---|
| 2¢ on 2¢ **carmine,** Die B (EN818A) | | 1.10 | — |
| | entire | 1.50 | — |

| EN840 | | MNHVF | UseVF |
|---|---|---|---|
| 2¢ on 2¢ carmine, Die C (EN819) | | .90 | .35 |
| entire | | 1.10 | — |

| EN841 | | MNHVF | UseVF |
|---|---|---|---|
| 2¢ on 2¢ carmine, Die D (EN819A) | | .90 | — |
| entire | | 1.25 | — |

**1960. ISSUE** Effective July 1, 1960, the third class postage rate for bulk mailing was raised to 2 1/2 cents for commerical users and 1 1/4 cents for non-profit organizations. These envelopes are available only precanceled and were sold only to holders of proper permits. The small size of each (No. 6 3/4), however, were made available to collectors at COMPEX in Chicago (commercial rate) and DIXIPEX in Birmingham, Ala. (non-profit rate), and were on sale at the Philatelic Agency until December 31, 1960. These unprecanceled envelopes have gum on the top back flap and the precanceled envelopes are without such gum.

EN842 *Washington*

| EN842 | | MNHVF | UseVF |
|---|---|---|---|
| 2-1/2¢ | **blue on white** *(May 28, 1960)* | .90 | .60 |
| | entire | 1.00 | .70 |
| | v. precanceled | .25 | .25 |
| | entire | .30 | .30 |

EN843 *Die A, small "1 1/4". 2 1/4mm across bar of "4". Leaf cluster 2mm under "U".*

| EN843 | | MNHVF | UseVF |
|---|---|---|---|
| 1-1/4¢ | **turquoise on white,** Die A *(June 25, 1960)* | .85 | .60 |
| | entire | 1.00 | .65 |
| | v. precanceled | .25 | .25 |
| | entire | .25 | .25 |

EN843A *Die B, large "1 1/4". 2 3/4mm across bar of "4". Leaf cluster 1mm under "U".*

| EN843A | | MNHVF | UseVF |
|---|---|---|---|
| 1-1/4¢ | **turquoise on white,** | | |
| | precanceled | 3.00 | 3.00 |
| | entire | 3.50 | 3.50 |

EN844 *Pony Express Rider. Watermark 46.*

| EN844 | | MNHVF | UseVF |
|---|---|---|---|
| 4¢ | **brown on white,** blue inside *(July 19, 1960)* | .65 | .35 |
| | entire | .85 | .50 |

**1963. ISSUE** Effective January 7, 1963, first class postage rates were raised to 5¢. A new stamped envelope was prepared showing a bust of Lincoln. However, a sufficient number of working dies were unable to be delivered to service all of the machines at the factory. Hence the factory was authorized to continue printing 4¢ stamped en-velopes and revalue them to 5¢. This was accomplished by using the Type II surcharge printed in green to the left of the stamp. The revaluing was done on unfolded envelope blanks on the regular printing machines at the factory. These blanks were then passed to another machine, which printed the 4¢ stamps and folded the envelopes. At least two different dies were used to print the added 1¢ value.

While the effective date for the new postage rates was not until January 7, 1963, the Post Office made the new envelopes available as rapidly as they could be supplied. The authorized first day of issue for the 5¢ Lincoln envelope was November 19, 1962. No announcement was made regarding the 4¢ revalued envelopes, but they began making their appearance at post offices in December 1963.

All of these new envelopes are known with *watermarks 47 and 48*.

NOTE: EN846t and EN847t are the result of using the O'Connell machines to fold blanks on which the stamps already had been printed by the Huckins (Die B) and Harris (Die C) machines, which were incapable of folding. To accomplish the folding operation, the ink fountains were removed from some of the O'Connell machines still idle for lack of working dies of the 5¢ stamp. By error, the old 4¢ die was not removed on at least one of the O'Connell machines and this caused an albino impression of the 4¢ stamp to be printed over the 5¢ stamp. The error was not discovered until the O'Connell machine(s) had been performing the folding operation for some time.

EN845 *Abraham Lincoln. Die A, figure "5" centered in circle. Middle bar of "E" in "FIVE" equal length as top. Center bar in "E" in "POSTAGE" off center to top. Verification: small head, sharp pointed nose. Watermarks 47, 48.*

*Watermark 47.* Beginning in May 1961, a new watermark was introduced to mark the letting of the new contract. Two types were adopted: a star preceding the letters "USA" for paper manufactured by the International Paper Company (wmk47); star following the letters "USA" (wmk 48) for paper manufactured by the Howard Paper Co.

| EN845 | | MNHVF | UseVF |
|---|---|---|---|
| 5¢ | **dark blue,** Die A | 1.00 | .35 |
| | entire | 1.00 | .35 |

EN846 *Die B, "5" centered in circle. "FI" in "FIVE" close together. "C" in "CENTS" higher than "E". Verification: large wide head with blunt nose.*

| EN846 | | MNHVF | UseVF |
|---|---|---|---|
| 5¢ | **dark blue,** Die B | .75 | .25 |
| | entire | 1.00 | .30 |
| | v. with albino impression of 4¢, entire | 75.00 | — |

EN847 *Die C, "5" to right in circle. Short leg on "P" in "POSTAGE."*

| EN847 | | MNHVF | UseVF |
|---|---|---|---|
| 5¢ | **dark blue,** Die C *(Nov. 19, 1962)* | 1.00 | .40 |
| | entire | 1.25 | .50 |
| | v. with albino impression of 4¢, entire | 75.00 | — |

**1963. Type II Surcharge Revalued Envelopes** Two types of the surcharge are known:

*Type I:* large word "CENT", dot after "U" and "S" far from letters, long angle serif on center bar of "E".

*Type II:* small word "CENT", dot after "U" and "S".

 *Type II Surcharge - Printed in green to left of stamp on 4¢ envelope EN825.*

| **EN848** | | **MNHVF** | **UseVF** |
|---|---|---|---|
| 4¢ + 1¢ | **lilac, green** Type I (EN825) | 1.50 | .50 |
| | entire | 1.75 | .75 |
| | v. Type II | 1.50 | .50 |
| | entire | 1.75 | .75 |

**1964. New York World's Fair Issue**

 EN849 *Globe and orbit rings.*

| **EN849** | | **MNHVF** | **UseVF** |
|---|---|---|---|
| 5¢ | **red on white** *(April 22, 1964)* | .70 | .50 |
| | entire | .80 | .50 |

**1965. New Issue** Beginning January 1, 1965, the United States Envelope Co. was awarded the contract for making envelopes. This firm established a new facility at Williamsburg, Penn., and equipped it with new machinery that would produce envelopes from a continuous web (roll) of paper. The process is very rapid, with each individual machine being capable of producing one million envelopes every 24 hours. Envelopes produced by this method are of the old low-back design.

Watermark 49

New watermarks were introduced, as illustrated. Watermarks 47 and 48 also are known on these envelopes. Watermark 49 has the star below the letter "S" of "USA" and signifies the product of the Oxford Paper Co. Watermark 50 has the star above the "S" and distinguishes the product of Crown Zellerbach.

Also, a new watermark closely resembling Watermark 47 (star before "USA") but with a star somewhat larger distinguishes the product of the Champion Paper Co.

The small size (No. 6 3/4) and large size (No. 10) of the 5¢ envelopes (EN852), both regular and window, also exist tagged, consisting of a vertical luminescent rectangle to the left of the stamp. This method of tagging also was used for the 8¢ air mail envelopes in both sizes (AEN38).

 EN850 *Liberty Bell. The wavy lines at the sides indicate the stamp is precanceled.*

| **EN850** | | **MNHVF** | **UseVF** |
|---|---|---|---|
| 1-1/4¢ | **brown on white** *(Jan. 6, 1965)* | .25 | .25 |
| | entire | 1.00 | .25 |

 EN851 *USS Mattics Constitution under sail.*

| **EN851** | | **MNHVF** | **UseVF** |
|---|---|---|---|
| 4¢ | **bright blue on white** *(Jan. 6, 1965)* | .85 | .25 |
| | entire | 1.00 | .25 |

 EN852 *Eagle*

| **EN852** | | **MNHVF** | **UseVF** |
|---|---|---|---|
| 5¢ | **purple on white** *(Jan. 5, 1965)* | .80 | .25 |
| | entire | .90 | .30 |
| | z. Tagged *(Aug. 15, 1967)* | 1.10 | .25 |
| | entire | 1.35 | .35 |

**1968. Type 12 Surcharge Envelopes** *Printed in red to left of stamp on 4¢ envelope (EN851).*

| **EN853** | | **MNHVF** | **UseVF** |
|---|---|---|---|
| 4¢ + 2¢ | **bright blue, red on white** *(Feb. 1968)* | 3.50 | 2.00 |
| | entire | 4.50 | 2.50 |

**1968. Type 11 Surcharge Envelopes** *Printed in green to left of stamp on 5¢ envelope (EN852).*

| **EN854** | | **MNHVF** | **UseVF** |
|---|---|---|---|
| 5¢ + 1¢ | **purple, green on white** *(Feb. 1968)* | 3.50 | 2.00 |
| | entire | 4.25 | 2.50 |
| | z. Tagged *(Feb. 5, 1968)* | 3.50 | 2.00 |
| | entire | 4.25 | 2.50 |

**1968. Type 11 Surcharge Envelopes**

 EN855 *Statue of Liberty.*

| **EN855** | | **MNHVF** | **UseVF** |
|---|---|---|---|
| 6¢ | **turquoise green on white,** tagged *(Jan. 4, 1968)* | .75 | .25 |
| | entire | 1.00 | .35 |

*EN855 is tagged with luminescent materials mixed with the printing ink.*

**1968. Type 11 Surcharge Envelopes**

 EN856 *Liberty Bell. The wavy lines at sides indicate the envelope is precanceled.*

| **EN856** | | **MNHVF** | **UseVF** |
|---|---|---|---|
| 1.4¢ | **brown on white** *(March 26, 1968)* | .25 | .25 |
| | entire | 1.25 | .35 |

**1968. Type 11 Surcharge Envelopes**

| **EN857** | | **MNHVF** | **UseVF** |
|---|---|---|---|
| 1.6¢ | **orange on white** *(June 16, 1969)* | .25 | .25 |
| | entire | 1.00 | .25 |

## 1971. TYPE II SURCHARGE ENVELOPES

| EN858 | | MNHVF | UseVF |
|---|---|---|---|
| 1.7¢ | **purple on white** (May 10, 1971) | .25 | .25 |
| | entire | .50 | .25 |

## 1970. HERMAN MELVILLE ISSUE honored the writer and the whaling industry.

EN859 *Herman Melville's "Moby Dick".*

| EN859 | | MNHVF | UseVF |
|---|---|---|---|
| 6¢ | **light blue on white,** tagged (March 7, 1970) | .50 | .25 |
| | entire | .70 | .35 |

## 1971. WHITE HOUSE CONFERENCE ON YOUTH

EN860 *White House Conference on Youth emblem.*

| EN860 | | MNHVF | UseVF |
|---|---|---|---|
| 6¢ | **light blue on white,** tagged (Feb. 24, 1971) | .75 | .25 |
| | entire | 1.00 | .50 |

## 1971. ISSUE Issued to meet new first class postage rate.

EN861 *Eagle*

| EN861 | | MNHVF | UseVF |
|---|---|---|---|
| 8¢ | **ultramarine on white,** tagged (May 6, 1971) | .50 | .25 |
| | entire | .75 | .30 |

## 1971. TYPE 13 SURCHARGE ENVELOPES

*Type 13 surcharge - in green to left of stamp.*

| EN862 | | MNHVF | UseVF |
|---|---|---|---|
| 6¢ + 2¢ | **turquoise green (EN855), + 2¢ green on white,** tagged (May 16, 1971) | 1.00 | .50 |
| | entire | 1.25 | .50 |

| EN863 | | MNHVF | UseVF |
|---|---|---|---|
| 6¢ + 2¢ | **blue** (EN860) **+ 2¢ green on white,** tagged (May 16, 1971) | 2.00 | 1.00 |
| | entire | 2.75 | 1.50 |

*Sale of EN863, of which one million were produced, was limited to Washington D.C.*

## 1971. BOWLING ISSUE Honoring the seventh World Tournament of the International Bowling Federation.

EN865 *Bowling ball and pin.*

| EN864 | | MNHVF | UseVF |
|---|---|---|---|
| 8¢ | **red on white,** tagged (Aug. 21, 1971) | .50 | .25 |
| | entire | .75 | .25 |

*Available in both #6 small and #10 large size. EN864 is the first commemorative envelope since the Washington Bicentennial of 1932 to be available in two sizes.*

## 1971. THE WHITE HOUSE CONFERENCE ON AGING ISSUE

EN865 *Snowflake*

| EN865 | | MNHVF | UseVF |
|---|---|---|---|
| 8¢ | **blue on white,** tagged (Nov. 15, 1977) | .50 | .25 |
| | entire | .75 | .25 |

## 1972. FIRST U.S. INTERNATIONAL TRANSPORTAION EXPOSITION ISSUE

EN866 *Transpo '72 emblem.*

| EN866 | | MNHVF | UseVF |
|---|---|---|---|
| 8¢ | **red and blue on white,** tagged (May 2, 1972) | .75 | .25 |
| | entire | 1.00 | .25 |

## 1973. ISSUE Issued to meet new first class postage rate.

EN867 *Liberty Bell*

| EN867 | | MNHVF | UseVF |
|---|---|---|---|
| 10¢ | **turquoise green on white,** tagged (Dec. 5, 1973) | .50 | .25 |
| | entire | .50 | .25 |

## 1973. TYPE 12 SURCHARGE ENVELOPES ISSUE

*Type 12 surcharge - in ultramarine to left of stamp.*

| EN868 | | MNHVF | UseVF |
|---|---|---|---|
| 8¢ + 2¢ | **ultramarine, ultramarine on white,** tagged Dec. 1, 1973) | .50 | .25 |
| | entire | .50 | .20 |

## 1974. TENNIS CENTENNIAL

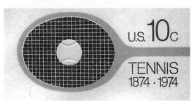

EN869 *Tennis Centennial.*

| EN869 | | MNHVF | UseVF |
|---|---|---|---|
| 10¢ | **yellow, green and blue on white,** tagged, entire (Aug. 31, 1974) | .85 | .50 |

## 1974. NON-PROFIT BULK MAILING

EN870 *Volunteerism*

| EN870 | | MNHVF | UseVF |
|---|---|---|---|
| 1.8¢ | **blue green on white,** tagged, entire *(Aug. 23, 1974)* | .35 | .25 |

## Bicentennial Era Series

### 1975. SEAFARING TRADITION ISSUE

EN871 *Compass Rose*

| EN871 | | MNHVF | UseVF |
|---|---|---|---|
| 10¢ | **brown and blue on light brown,** tagged, entire *(Oct. 13, 1975)* | .50 | .25 |
| | a. Brown omitted, entire | — | |

### 1975. ISSUE Issued to meet new first class postage rate.

EN872 *Liberty Tree*

| EN872 | | MNHVF | UseVF |
|---|---|---|---|
| 13¢ | **brown on white,** tagged, entire *(Nov. 8, 1975)* | .50 | .25 |

### 1976. THE AMERICAN HOME MAKER ISSUE

EN873 *Quilt Pattern*

| EN873 | | MNHVF | UseVF |
|---|---|---|---|
| 13¢ | **brown and bluish green on light brown,** tagged, entire *(Feb. 2, 1976)* | .50 | .25 |
| | a. Brown omitted, entire | — | |

### 1976. AMERICAN FARMER ISSUE Bicentennial Era Series

EN874 *Sheaf of Wheat*

| EN874 | | MNHVF | UseVF |
|---|---|---|---|
| 13¢ | **brown and green on light brown,** tagged, entire *(March 15, 1976)* | .50 | .25 |
| | a. Brown omitted, entire | — | |

### 1976. AMERICAN DOCTOR ISSUE Bicentennial Era Series

EN875 *Mortar and Pestle*

| EN875 | | MNHVF | UseVF |
|---|---|---|---|
| 13¢ | **orange and brown on light brown,** tagged, entire *(June 30, 1976)* | .50 | .25 |
| | a. brown omitted, entire | — | |

### 1976. AMERICAN CRAFTSMAN ISSUE Bicentennial Era Series

EN876 *Craftman's Tools.*

| EN876 | | MNHVF | UseVF |
|---|---|---|---|
| 13¢ | **red and brown on light brown,** tagged, entire *(Aug. 6, 1976)* | .50 | .25 |
| | a. Brown omitted, entire | — | |

### 1976. NON-PROFIT MAILING ISSUE

EN877 *Star in pinwheel.*

| EN877 | | MNHVF | UseVF |
|---|---|---|---|
| 2¢ | **red on white,** entire *(Sept. 10, 1976)* | .35 | .25 |

### 1976. ISSUE Bicentennial Era Series

EN878 *Centennial envelope design.*

| EN878 | | MNHVF | UseVF |
|---|---|---|---|
| 13¢ | **green on white,** tagged, entire *(Oct. 15, 1976)* | .50 | .25 |

### 1977. GOLF ISSUE *Printed by gravure, in addition to embossing.*

EN879 *Golf club in motion and ball.*

| EN879 | | MNHVF | UseVF |
|---|---|---|---|
| 13¢ | **blue, black and yellow green on white,** tagged, entire *(April 7, 1977)* | 1.00 | .50 |
| | a. Black omitted, entire | — | |
| | b. Black and blue omitted, entire | — | |

## 1977. Non-Profit Mailing Issue

EN880 *"2.1¢" in octagon.*

| EN880 | | MNHVF | UseVF |
|---|---|---|---|
| 2.1¢ | **yellow green on white,** entire *(June 3, 1977)* | .50 | .25 |

## 1977. Energy Issue

EN881 *Energy Conservation.*

| EN881 | | MNHVF | UseVF |
|---|---|---|---|
| 13¢ | **black, red and yellow on white,** tagged, entire *(Oct. 20, 1977)* | .50 | .25 |
| | a.  Black omitted, entire | — | |
| | b.  Black and red omitted, entire | — | |
| | c.  Red and yellow omitted, entire | — | |
| | d.  Yellow omitted, entire FDC *(Oct. 20, 1977)* | — | |

EN882 *Energy Development.*

| EN882 | | MNHVF | UseVF |
|---|---|---|---|
| 13¢ | **black, red and yellow on white,** entire | .60 | .30 |

## 1978. "A" Non-denominated Issue "A" Non-denominated Is-sue to accommodate new first class postage rate. The envelope was printed in 1975 and 1976 and stored for contingency use.

EN883 *Stylized Eagle and "A".*

| EN883 | | MNHVF | UseVF |
|---|---|---|---|
| 15¢ | **orange on white,** tagged, entire *(May 22, 1978)* | .60 | .25 |

## 1978. Uncle Sam Issue

EN884 *Stylized Uncle Sam Hat and Shield.*

| EN884 | | MNHVF | UseVF |
|---|---|---|---|
| 15¢ | **red on white,** tagged *(June 3, 1978)* | .50 | .25 |
| | entire | .60 | .25 |

## 1978. Non-Profit Mailing Issue

EN885 *"2.7¢" over "USA".*

| EN885 | | MNHVF | UseVF |
|---|---|---|---|
| 2.7¢ | **green on white** *(July 5, 1978)* | .25 | .25 |
| | entire | .40 | .25 |

## 1978. Type 14 Surcharge Revalued Issue *Downward Re-Valuing.*

EN886 *Type 14 surcharge - in black to left of stamp.*

| EN886 | | MNHVF | UseVF |
|---|---|---|---|
| 15¢ revalued from 16¢**blue on white,** tagged *(July 28, 1978)* | | .45 | .25 |
| | entire | .60 | .25 |
| | t.   Surcharge omitted, entire | — | — |

## 1978. Auto Racing Issue

EN887 *Indianapolis 500 racer.*

| EN887 | | MNHVF | UseVF |
|---|---|---|---|
| 15¢ | **black, blue and red on white,** tagged *(Sept. 2, 1975)* | .45 | .25 |
| | entire | .50 | .25 |
| | a.  Black omitted, entire | 175. | — |
| | b.  Black and blue omitted, entire | — | — |
| | c.  Red omitted, entire | — | — |
| | d.  Red and blue omitted, entire | — | — |
| | z.  Tagging omitted | — | — |

## 1978. Type 14 Surcharge Revalued Issue *Liberty Tree Re-valued.*

EN888 *Type 14 surcharge-in black to left of stamp.*

| EN888 | | MNHVF | UseVF |
|---|---|---|---|
| 15¢ revalued from 13¢**brown on white EN872,** tagged *(Nov. 28, 1978)* | | .40 | .25 |
| | entire | .55 | .25 |

## 1979. Non-Profit Mailing Issue

EN889 *Authorized nonprofit organization.*

| EN889 | | MNHVF | UseVF |
|---|---|---|---|
| 3.1¢ | blue on white *(May 18, 1979)* | .25 | .25 |
| | entire | .30 | .25 |

### 1979. VETERINARY MEDICINE ISSUE

EN890 *"V" on Aesculapius.*

| EN890 | | MNHVF | UseVF |
|---|---|---|---|
| 15¢ | gray and brown on white, tagged *(July 24, 1979)* | .40 | .25 |
| | entire | .55 | .25 |
| | a. Gray omitted, entire | — | — |

### 1979. OLYMPIC GAMES ISSUE *Soccer*

EN891 *1980 Moscow Olympics, Soccer players.*

| EN891 | | MNHVF | UseVF |
|---|---|---|---|
| 15¢ | red, green and black on white, tagged *(Dec. 10, 1979)* | .75 | .25 |
| | entire | 1.00 | .25 |
| | a. Black omitted, entire | 175. | — |
| | b. Black and green omitted, entire | 175. | — |
| | c. Red omitted, entire | 175. | — |
| | d. Red and green omitted, entire | — | — |

### 1980. BICYCLING ISSUE

EN892 *High-Wheel Bicycle.*

| EN892 | | MNHVF | UseVF |
|---|---|---|---|
| 15¢ | blue and maroon on white, tagged *(May 16, 1980)* | .50 | .25 |
| | entire | .65 | .25 |
| | a. Blue omitted, entire | 150. | — |

### 1980. NON-PROFIT MAILING ISSUE

EN893 *Weaver Violins*

| EN893 | | MNHVF | UseVF |
|---|---|---|---|
| 3.5¢ | purple on white *(June 23, 1980)* | .25 | .25 |
| | entire | .35 | .25 |

### 1980. AMERICA'S CUP YACHT RACES ISSUE.

EN894 *Yacht*

| EN894 | | MNHVF | UseVF |
|---|---|---|---|
| 15¢ | red & blue on white, tagged *(Sept. 15, 1980)* | .50 | .25 |
| | entire | .65 | .25 |

### 1980. HONEYBEE ISSUE *Printed by gravure, in addition to embossing.*

EN895 *Orange Blossom and Honeybee.*

| EN895 | | MNHVF | UseVF |
|---|---|---|---|
| 15¢ | green and yellow on white, tagged *(Oct. 10, 1980)* | .50 | .25 |
| | entire | .55 | .25 |
| | a. Brown omitted, entire | 200. | — |

### 1981. "B" NON-DENOMINATED ISSUE to accommodate new first class postage rate.

EN896 *Stylized Eagle and "B".*

| EN896 | | MNHVF | UseVF |
|---|---|---|---|
| 18¢ | purple on white, tagged *(March 15, 1981)* | .50 | .25 |
| | entire | .55 | .25 |

### 1981. STAR ISSUE Denominated to meet new first class postage rate.

EN897 *Star*

| EN897 | | MNHVF | UseVF |
|---|---|---|---|
| 18¢ | blue on white, tagged *(April 2, 1981)* | .50 | .25 |
| | entire | .55 | .25 |

### 1981. BLINDED VETERANS ASSOCIATION ISSUE

EN898 *Hand and braille.*

| EN898 | | MNHVF | UseVF |
|---|---|---|---|
| 18¢ | blue on white, tagged *(Aug. 13, 1981)* | .40 | .25 |
| | entire | .60 | .25 |
| | a. Red omitted, entire | — | — |

*The hand and braille message are embossed without color.*

### 1981. "C" NON-DENOMINATED ISSUE To meet new first class postage rate.

EN899 *Stylized eagle and "C".*

**EN899**

| | | MNHVF | UseVF |
|---|---|---|---|
| 20¢ | brown on white, tagged (Oct. 11, 1981) | .50 | .25 |
| | entire | .55 | .25 |

### 1981. CAPITOL DOME ISSUE

EN900 *Dome of U.S. Capitol.*

**EN900**

| | | MNHVF | UseVF |
|---|---|---|---|
| 20¢ | dark red on white, tagged (Nov. 13, 1981) | .50 | .25 |
| | entire | 5.15 | .25 |
| | z. Bar tagged | 2.00 | 2.00 |

### 1982. NON-PROFIT BULK MAILING ISSUE

 EN901

**EN901**

| | | MNHVF | UseVF |
|---|---|---|---|
| 5.9¢ | brown on white (Feb. 17, 1982) | .25 | .25 |
| | entire | .35 | .25 |

### 1982. GREAT SEAL ISSUE  The Great Seal of the United States bi-centennial.

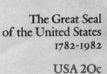

EN902 *Great Seal*

**EN902**

| | | MNHVF | UseVF |
|---|---|---|---|
| 20¢ | blue, black and red on white, tagged (June 15, 1982) | .50 | .25 |
| | entire | .55 | .25 |
| | a. Blue omitted, entire | — | — |

### 1982. PURPLE HEART ISSUE  The Purple Heart bicentennial.

EN903 *Purple Heart Medal.*

**EN903**

| | | MNHVF | UseVF |
|---|---|---|---|
| 20¢ | purple and black on white, tagged (Aug. 6, 1982) | .50 | .25 |
| | entire | .55 | .25 |

### 1983. NON-PROFIT MAILING ISSUE

EN904

**EN904**

| | | MNHVF | UseVF |
|---|---|---|---|
| 5.2¢ | orange on white (March 21, 1983) | .25 | .25 |
| | entire | .25 | .25 |

### 1983. PARALYZED VETERANS ISSUE

EN905 *Wheelchair*

**EN905**

| | | MNHVF | UseVF |
|---|---|---|---|
| 20¢ | red, blue and black on white, tagged (Aug. 3, 1983) | .50 | .25 |
| | entire | .55 | .25 |
| | a. Blue omitted, entire | — | — |
| | b. Blue and black omitted, entire | — | — |
| | c. Red omitted, entire | — | — |
| | d. Red and black omitted, entire | — | — |

### 1984. SMALL BUSINESS ISSUE

EN906 *Business Signs.*

**EN906**

| | | MNHVF | UseVF |
|---|---|---|---|
| 20¢ | multicolored on white, tagged (May 7, 1984) | .60 | .25 |
| | entire | .65 | .25 |

### 1985. "D" NON-DENOMINATED ISSUE  To meet new first class postage rate.

EN907 *Stylized eagle and "D".*

**EN907**

| | | MNHVF | UseVF |
|---|---|---|---|
| 22¢ | green on white, tagged (Feb. 1, 1985) | .50 | .25 |
| | entire | .65 | .25 |

### 1985. AMERICAN BISON ISSUE

EN908 *Bison*

**EN908**

| | | MNHVF | UseVF |
|---|---|---|---|
| 22¢ | brown on white, tagged (Feb. 25, 1985) | .50 | .25 |
| | entire | .60 | .25 |
| | z. Double tagged, phosphorescent ink and separate bar tagging | — | — |
| | z1. Untagged (precanceled) | | |

### 1985. NON-PROFIT MAILING ISSUE

EN909 *U.S.S. Constitution*

**EN909**
6¢     **aqua on white** *(May 3, 1985)*

| | MNHVF | UseVF |
|---|---|---|
| | .25 | .25 |
| entire | .30 | .25 |

**1986. THE MAYFLOWER ISSUE**

EN910

**EN910**
8.5¢     **black and gray on white,** precanceled *(Dec. 4, 1986)*

| | MNHVF | UseVF |
|---|---|---|
| | .25 | .25 |
| entire | .35 | .25 |

**1988. STARS ISSUE** *Printed by letter press in addition to embossing.*

EN911

**EN911**
25¢     **red and blue on white,** tagged *(March 26, 1988)*

| | MNHVF | UseVF |
|---|---|---|
| | .60 | .25 |
| entire | .75 | .35 |
| a. Red omitted, entire | 100. | — |

**1988. NON-PROFIT MAILING ISSUE USS Constellation.**

EN912 *U.S.S. Constellation.*

**EN912**
8.4¢     **black and blue on white,** precanceled *(April 12, 1988)*

| | MNHVF | UseVF |
|---|---|---|
| | .30 | .25 |
| entire | .50 | .25 |
| a. Black omitted, entire | — | — |
| o. Tagging omitted | | |

**1988. HOLIDAY GREETING SNOWFLAKE ISSUE** *Printed by letter press.*

EN913 *Snowflake*

**EN913**
25¢     **red and green on white,** tagged *(Sept. 8, 1988)*

| | MNHVF | UseVF |
|---|---|---|
| | .60 | .30 |
| entire | .75 | .35 |

**1989. PHILATELIC ISSUE** *Printed by letterpress.*

EN914

**EN914**
25¢     **red and blue on white,** tagged *(March 10, 1989)*

| | MNHVF | UseVF |
|---|---|---|
| | .50 | .25 |
| entire* | .65 | .30 |

**1989. SECURITY MAIL ISSUE** *Printed by letterpress.*

EN915

**EN915**
25¢     **red and blue on white,** tagged *(July 10, 1989)*

| | MNHVF | UseVF |
|---|---|---|
| | .50 | .25 |
| entire | .60 | .30 |

*Envelope is blue on inside to provide security for enclosures.*

**1989. LOVE ISSUE** *Printed by offset and letterpress.*

EN916 *Love*

**EN916**
25¢     **red and blue on white,** tagged *(Sept. 22, 1989)*

| | MNHVF | UseVF |
|---|---|---|
| | .50 | .25 |
| entire | .60 | .30 |
| a. Blue omitted, entire | — | — |

**1989. WORLD STAMP EXPO '89 ISSUE** *Printed by letterpress, with hologram.*

EN917 *Space Station and Shuttle.*

**EN917**
25¢     **ultramarine,** tagged *(Dec. 3, 1989)*

| | MNHVF | UseVF |
|---|---|---|
| | .50 | .30 |
| entire | 1.00 | .75 |
| a. Ultramarine omitted, entire | — | — |

*A hologram is affixed at upper right inside, visible through a die cut window.*

**1990. FOOTBALL ISSUE** *Printed by letterpress, with hologram.*

EN918 *Football Players and Lombardi Trophy.*

**EN918**
25¢     **vermilion,** tagged *(Sept. 9, 1990)*

| | MNHVF | UseVF |
|---|---|---|
| | .50 | .30 |
| entire | 1.00 | .75 |

*A hologram is affixed at upper right inside, visible through a die cut window.*

**1991. STAR ISSUE** To meet the new first class postage rate. *Printed by letterpress, with embossing.*

EN919 *Star*

| EN919 | | MNHVF | UseVF |
|---|---|---|---|
| 29¢ | **ultramarine and rose on white**, tagged *(Jan. 24, 1991)* | .70 | .35 |
| | entire | .85 | .45 |

**1991. NON-PROFIT MAILING ISSUE** *Printed by letterpress.*

EN920 *Sparrows on Wires.*

| EN920 | | MNHVF | UseVF |
|---|---|---|---|
| 11.1¢ | **red and blue on white**, tagged, precanceled *(May 3, 1991)* | .25 | .25 |
| | entire | .40 | .30 |

**1991. LOVE ISSUE** *Printed by offset.*

EN921 *Love*

| EN921 | | MNHVF | UseVF |
|---|---|---|---|
| 29¢ | **blue, maroon and rose on white**, tagged *(May 9, 1991)* | .65 | .35 |
| | entire | .75 | .40 |

**1991. SECURITY ISSUE** *Printed by letterpress.*

EN922 *Star*

| EN922 | | MNHVF | UseVF |
|---|---|---|---|
| 29¢ | **ultramarine and rose on white**, tagged *(July 20, 1991)* | .65 | .35 |
| | entire* | .75 | .40 |

*The inside of the envelope has a blue design as a security precaution for enclosures.*

**1991. MAGAZINE INDUSTRY ISSUE** *Printed by offset and letterpress, with gravure-printed vignette affixed through a die-cut window.*

EN923 *Stylized Globe 250th Anniversary, Magazine Industry.*

| EN923 | | MNHVF | UseVF |
|---|---|---|---|
| 29¢ | **multicolored on white**, tagged *(Oct. 7, 1991)* | .65 | .35 |
| | entire* | .75 | .40 |

**1991. COUNTRY GEESE ISSUE** *Printed by offset and letterpress.*

EN924 *Geese*

| EN924 | | MNHVF | UseVF |
|---|---|---|---|
| 29¢ | **bluish gray and yellow**, tagged *(Nov. 8, 1990)* | .65 | .35 |
| | entire | .75 | .40 |

**1992. SPACE STATION HOLOGRAM ISSUE** *Printed by letterpress, with hologram.*

EN925 *Space Station and Shuttle.*

| EN925 | | MNHVF | UseVF |
|---|---|---|---|
| 29¢ | **yellow green on white**, tagged *(Jan. 21, 1992)* | .65 | .35 |
| | entire* | .75 | .40 |

*A hologram is affixed at upper right inside, visible through a die cut window.*

**1992. WESTERN AMERICANA ISSUE** *Printed by offset and letterpress.*

EN926 *Western saddle.*

| EN926 | | MNHVF | UseVF |
|---|---|---|---|
| 29¢ | **multicolored on white**, tagged *(April 10, 1992)* | .60 | .35 |
| | entire* | .75 | .40 |

*A vignette, printed by offset, is affixed through a die cut window at upper right.*

**1992. PROTECT THE ENVIRONMENT ISSUE** *Printed by offset and letterpress.*

EN927 *Hillebrandia*

| EN927 | | MNHVF | UseVF |
|---|---|---|---|
| 29¢ | **multicolored on white,** tagged *(April 22, 1992)* | .60 | .35 |
| | entire* | .75 | .40 |

*A vignette, printed by offset, is affixed through a die cut window at upper right.*

**1992. Re-Issues on Recycled Paper Issue** All of the envelopes in this series have the "Recycle" tri-arrow logo on the reverse. Unwatermarked envelopes and/or those available only in large (No. 10) size are marked. This series is listed only as entires, to enable inclusion both of the "Recycle" logo and to verify watermarking. *Issued May 1, 1992.*

| EN928 | | MNHVF | UseVF |
|---|---|---|---|
| 29¢ | **ultramarine on white,** unwatermarked, tagged, entire (EN919) | .80 | .40 |

| EN929 | | MNHVF | UseVF |
|---|---|---|---|
| 11.1¢ | **red and blue on white,** unwatermarked, tagged, entire (EN920) | .40 | .30 |

| EN930 | | MNHVF | UseVF |
|---|---|---|---|
| 29¢ | **blue, maroon and rose on white,** tagged, entire (EN921) | .80 | .40 |

| EN931 | | MNHVF | UseVF |
|---|---|---|---|
| 29¢ | **red and blue on white,** tagged, entire* (EN922) | .80 | .40 |

| EN932 | | MNHVF | UseVF |
|---|---|---|---|
| 29¢ | **bluish gray and yellow,** unwatermarked, tagged, entire (EN924) | .80 | .40 |

| EN933 | | MNHVF | UseVF |
|---|---|---|---|
| 29¢ | **yellow green,** with hologram, tagged, entire* (EN925) | .80 | .40 |

**1992. Bulk Mailing Issue** *Printed by offset and letterpress.*

EN934 *Star*

| EN934 | | MNHVF | UseVF |
|---|---|---|---|
| 19.8¢ | **red and blue on white,** tagged, entire *(May 19, 1992)* | .55 | .40 |

**1992. Disabled American Issue** *Printed by letterpress.*

EN935 *Woman in wheelchair.*

| EN935 | | MNHVF | UseVF |
|---|---|---|---|
| 29¢ | **red and blue on white,** tagged, entire *(July 22, 1992)* | .75 | .40 |

**1993. Kitten Issue** *Printed by offset and letterpress.*

EN936 *Siamese kitten.*

| EN936 | | MNHVF | UseVF |
|---|---|---|---|
| 29¢ | **cyan, black and purple on white,** tagged, entire *(Oct. 2, 1993)* | .75 | .40 |

**1994. Football Issue** *Printed by offset and letterpress.*

EN937 *Football*

| EN937 | | MNHVF | UseVF |
|---|---|---|---|
| 29¢ | **brown and black on white,** tagged, entire *(Sept. 17, 1994)* | .75 | .40 |

**1994. Old Glory Issue** *Number 6 3/4 and 10 envelopes.*

EN938, EN939 *Flag*

| EN938 | | MNHVF | UseVF |
|---|---|---|---|
| 32¢ | **red and blue on white,** tagged, entire *(Jan. 3, 1995)* | .75 | .40 |

| EN939 | | MNHVF | UseVF |
|---|---|---|---|
| 32¢ | **red on blue on white,** tagged, entire | .75 | .40 |

**1995. Liberty Bell Issue**

EN940 *Liberty Bell*

| EN940 | | MNHVF | UseVF |
|---|---|---|---|
| 32¢ | **greenish blue and blue on white,** tagged, entire *(Jan. 3, 1995)* | .75 | .40 |

**1995. Non-Profit Issue**

EN941 *Sheep*

| EN941 | | MNHVF | UseVF |
|---|---|---|---|
| 5¢ | **green and red brown on white,** entire *(March 10, 1995)* | .75 | .40 |

**1995. Bulk Rate Issue**

| EN942 | | MNHVF | UseVF |
|---|---|---|---|
| 10¢ | **darkred and blue on white,** entire *(March 10, 1995)* | .75 | .40 |

**1995. Heart Spiral Issue**

EN943 *Heart*

**EN943**
32¢    **red on light blue,** entire *(March 12, 1995)*    MNHVF .75    UseVF .40

**1995. LIBERTY BELL ISSUE** *Number 9 size envelope.*

EN944 *Liberty Bell*

USA 32

**EN944**
32¢    **greenish blue and blue on security paper,** entire *(May 16, 1995)*    MNHVF .75    UseVF .40

**1995. SPACE HOLOGRAM ISSUE**

EN945 *Space station*

USA 32

**EN945**
32¢    **red on white,** entire *(Sept. 22, 1995)*    MNHVF .75    UseVF .40

**1996. SAVE OUR ENVIRONMENT ISSUE**

EN946

USA**32**
SAVE OUR ENVIRONMENT

**EN946**
32¢    **multicolored on white,** entire *(April 20, 1996)*    MNHVF .75    UseVF .40

**1996. PARALYMPIC GAMES ISSUE**

1996 ATLANTA
PARALYMPIC GAMES    USA 32

EN947

**EN947**
32¢    **multicolored on white,** entire *(May 2, 1996)*    MNHVF .75    UseVF .40

# Air Mail Envelopes

The order authorizing air mail envelopes expressly provided they be printed on white paper and have red, white and blue borders.

Some experimenting was needed to produce these borders. On the first issues, five different types of borders are known to collectors.

*Red Lozenge at Upper Right*

Border 1: The lozenges along the top edge and parallel to the edge measure 9 to 10mm, and with the top flap open measure along the oblique side 11 to 13mm. Small envelopes only.

Border 2: Like Border 1 except that the lozenges measure only 7 to 8mm along the oblique side (with the top flap open). Small size envelopes only.

Border 3: Like Border 1 except the lozenges measure 11 to 12mm parallel to the edge of the envelope. Large size envelopes only.

*Blue Lozenge at Upper Right* - Large size envelopes only.

Border 4: Like Border 2 except with a blue lozenge at upper right corner.

Border 5: Like Border 4 except the lozenges at top point to the right (all others point to the left).

The borders are of importance to collectors and cut squares should be preserved to include them.

After the experimentation on the first issue (AEN1-AEN2), the borders were standardized as Border 2 (red lozenge at upper right) for small size envelopes and Border 4 (blue lozenge at upper right) for large size envelopes.

**1929. PUERTO RICO AIR MAIL RATE ISSUE** The U.S. domestic air mail rate form 1929 to 1932 was five cents, as evidenced by the 5¢ stamps (AEN1-AEN2). The air mail rate to or from Puerto Rico, however, was 10 cents. Persons desiring to send air mail to, or from, either place simply used a 5¢ air mail envelope to which they affixed a 5¢ adhesive stamp.

In 1932 the domestic air mail rate for the United States was advanced to eight cents and new 8¢ air mail envelopes were issued (AEN3). In 1934 the rate was reduced to six cents with a resulting change in the stamps on the air mail envelopes (AEN4-AEN7).

AEN1 *Vertical rudder islopes off to the left.*

| AEN1 | | UnFVF | UseFVF |
|---|---|---|---|
| 5¢ | **blue,** Border 1 | 4.00 | 2.50 |
| | entire | 5.50 | 3.00 |
| | v. Border 2 | 4.00 | 2.50 |
| | entire | 5.50 | 3.00 |
| | v1. Border 3 | 4.00 | 2.50 |
| | entire | 7.50 | 6.00 |
| | v2. Border 4 | 4.00 | 2.50 |
| | entire | 9.00 | 6.00 |
| | v2a.entire, 1933 watermark | 750. | — |
| | v2b.entire, 1937 watermark | — | — |
| | v3. Border 5 | 4.00 | 2.50 |
| | entire | 9.00 | 6.00 |
| | v4. border omitted | 700. | — |
| | FDC *(Jan. 12, 1929)* | | |

AEN2 *Vertical rudder is semi-circular.*

| AEN2 | | UnFVF | UseFVF |
|---|---|---|---|
| 5¢ | **blue,** Border 2 | 12.50 | 6.00 |
| | entire | 17.50 | 7.00 |
| | entire, 1933 watermark | 700. | — |
| | v. Border 4 | 12.00 | 6.00 |
| | entire | 20.00 | 13.00 |
| | va. entire, 1933 watermark | 350. | — |
| | v1. Border 5 | — | — |
| | entire | — | — |

**1932. ISSUE**

AEN3

| AEN3 | | UnFVF | UseFVF |
|---|---|---|---|
| 8¢ | **olive,** Border 4 | 15.00 | 5.00 |
| | entire | 20.00 | 7.00 |
| | v. Border 2 | — | — |
| | entire | — | — |
| | FDC *(Sept. 26, 1932)* | | |

**1934-44. ISSUE 1934-44.** With the change of the air mail rate to six cents, the 6¢ orange design copied the old 5¢ design. The old master die of the 5¢ was used to produce blank printing dies, into each of which the figure "6" then was cut by hand. Eleven of these dies were so made; each, of course, differs materially from the other. To simplify the collecting of these, collectors divided the 11 varieties into three general classifications, as follows:

1 (AEN4): the figure "6" measures 6 1/2mm wide
2 (AEN5): the figure "6" measures 6mm wide
3 (AEN6): the figure "6" measures 5 1/2mm wide

Finally, in 1942, a new master 6¢ air mail die was made (AEN7), from which were struck as many printing dies as were necessary. All such printing dies struck from this past die were identical and may not be individually identified.

With the outbreak of World War II, there was an enormous demand by the armed forces overseas for air mail envelopes. To expedite manufacturing, the borders were ordered dropped. All borderless air mail envelopes were shipped overseas and were not available to the civilian population in this country until after the war.

AEN4-AEN6 *Vertical rudder is semi-circular.*

| AEN4 | | UnFVF | UseFVF |
|---|---|---|---|
| 6¢ | **orange,** Border 2 | 1.75 | .50 |
| | entire | 2.00 | .70 |
| | v. Border 4 | — | — |
| | entire | — | — |
| | v1. w/out border, entire | 3.00 | 1.75 |
| | FDC *(July 1, 1934)* | | |

**1934-44. ISSUE 1934-44.** With the change of the air mail rate to six cents, the 6¢ orange design copied the old 5¢ design. The old master die of the 5¢ was used to produce blank printing dies, into each of which the figure "6" then was cut by hand. Eleven of these dies were so made; each, of course, differs materially from the other. To simplify the collecting of these, collectors divided the 11 varieties into three general classifications, as follows:

1 (AEN4): the figure "6" measures 6 1/2mm wide
2 (AEN5): the figure "6" measures 6mm wide
3 (AEN6): the figure "6" measures 5 1/2mm wide

Finally, in 1942, a new master 6¢ air mail die was made (AEN7), from which were struck as many printing dies as were necessary. All such printing dies struck from this past die were identical and may not be individually identified.

With the outbreak of World War II, there was an enormous demand by the armed forces overseas for air mail envelopes. To expedite manufacturing, the borders were ordered dropped. All borderless air mail envelopes were shipped overseas and were not available to the civilian population in this country until after the war.

| AEN5 | | MNHVF | UseVF |
|---|---|---|---|
| 6¢ | **orange,** Border 2 (1942) | 3.00 | 2.25 |
| | entire | 60.00 | 25.00 |
| | v. Border 4 | — | — |
| | entire | — | — |
| | v1. w/out border, entire | 5.00 | 2.50 |

| AEN6 | | MNHVF | UseVF |
|---|---|---|---|
| 6¢ | **orange,** no border (1944) | 1.00 | .35 |
| | entire | 1.25 | .50 |

AEN7 *Vertical rudder slopes forward.*

| AEN7 | | MNHVF | UseVF |
|---|---|---|---|
| 6¢ | **orange,** Border 2 (1942) | 1.75 | .75 |
| | entire | 2.50 | 1.00 |
| | v.  Border 4 | — | — |
| | entire | — | — |
| | v1. w/out border, entire | 3.00 | 1.25 |
| | v2. on blue paper (error) no border, entire | 4000. | 2700. |
| | v3. Red lozenges of border omitted, entire | 1200. | — |

**1945. Issue** In March to alleviate the enormous demand for air mail envelopes which the printer had not been able to supply, the Post Office approved the overprinting of 60 million ordinary 2¢ envelopes (AEN8-AEN14). The overprinting was done in New York and great care was taken to keep any envelopes other than those authorized from being re-valued. All were shipped to the armed forces.

By the following September, the air mail rates had been reduced from 6¢ to 5¢, and re-valuing of the 6¢ air mail borderless envelopes was performed.

Following the war, remainders of these revalued envelopes were called in and destroyed, because they were confusing to the postal clerks. Adequate supplies, however, reached philatelic hands.

AEN8-AEN12

| AEN8 | | MNHVF | UseVF |
|---|---|---|---|
| 6¢ on 2¢ **carmine** (EN549), Die A | | 1.50 | .75 |
| | entire | 2.00 | 1.25 |
| **AEN9** | | MNHVF | UseVF |
| 6¢ on 2¢ **carmine** (EN574), Die H | | — | — |
| | entire | — | — |
| **AEN10** | | MNHVF | UseVF |
| 6¢ on 2¢ **carmine** (EN578), Die H2 | | — | — |
| | entire | — | — |
| **AEN11** | | MNHVF | UseVF |
| 6¢ on 2¢ **carmine** (EN581), Die I | | — | — |
| | entire | — | — |
| **AEN12** | | MNHVF | UseVF |
| 6¢ on 2¢ **carmine** (EN810) | | 80.00 | 45.00 |
| | entire | 125. | 75.00 |
| **AEN13** | | MNHVF | UseVF |
| 6¢ on 1¢ **green** (EN520), Die A | | 1900. | — |
| | entire | 2700. | — |

*On 1¢ green envelope of 1916-50 issue (error).*

**REVALUED**
**5¢**
**P.O. DEPT.**

AEN13-AEN18

| AEN14 | | MNHVF | UseVF |
|---|---|---|---|
| 6¢ on 3¢ **purple** (EN588), Die I | | 1900. | — |
| | entire | 2700. | — |

*On 3¢ purple envelope of 1916-50 issue (error).*

| AEN15 | | MNHVF | UseVF |
|---|---|---|---|
| 5¢ on 6¢ **orange** (AEN4v1) | | 3.50 | 2.00 |
| | entire | 4.00 | 3.00 |
| | v.  Double overprint, entire | 75.00 | |
| **AEN16** | | MNHVF | UseVF |
| 5¢ on 6¢ **orange** (AENv1) | | 10.00 | 6.00 |
| | entire | 12.50 | 8.00 |
| | v.  Double overprint, entire | — | — |
| **AEN17** | | MNHVF | UseVF |
| 5¢ on 6¢ **orange** (AEN6) | | .75 | .55 |
| | entire | 1.50 | .75 |
| | v.  Double overprint, entire | 65.00 | — |
| **AEN18** | | MNHVF | UseVF |
| 5¢ on 6¢ **orange** (AEN7v1) | | 1.00 | .75 |
| | entire | 125. | .75 |
| | v.  Double overprint, entire | 65.00 | — |

*Black overprint on 6¢ orange air mail envelopes, without borders, of 1934-44 issue.*

**1946. Issue  DC 4 Skymaster.**

AEN19 *DC-4 Skymaster. The small projection directly below the rudder is rounded.*

| AEN19 | | MNHVF | UseVF |
|---|---|---|---|
| 5¢ | **carmine,** Border 2 | .85 | .25 |
| | entire | 1.25 | .50 |
| | FDC *(Sept. 25, 1946)* | | |

AEN20 *The small projection directly below the rudder is a sharp point.*

| AEN20 | | MNHVF | UseVF |
|---|---|---|---|
| 5¢ | **carmine,** Border 2 | 1.00 | .35 |
| | entire | 1.25 | .50 |
| | v.  w/Border 4 | — | — |
| | entire | — | — |

**1947. Issue  U.S. Postage Stamp Centenary.** Issued to compliment the Centenary International Philatelic Exhibition in New York City. The envelopes were printed on a demonstration machine at the exhibition. The envelopes also were produced at the factory in Dayton, Ohio, from both a flat and a rotary die, for distribution throughout the country. Approximately eight million envelopes were issued, of which the rotary die printings are more common. *Flat Die measures 21 3/4mm high; rotary die measures 22 1/2mm high.*

AEN21

| AEN21 | | MNHVF | UseVF |
|---|---|---|---|
| 5¢ | **carmine,** Border 2, rotary die | .50 | .35 |
| | entire | .75 | .45 |
| | v.  Flat die | .60 | .40 |
| | entire | .75 | .50 |
| | FDC *(May 21, 1947)* | | |

## 1950. ISSUE

AEN22 *Type 1: figure "6"'s lean to the right.*

*Type 2; figure "6"'s are upright.*

| AEN22 | | MNHVF | UseVF |
|---|---|---|---|
| 6¢ | **carmine,** Border 2, Type 1 | .50 | .25 |
| | entire | .75 | .40 |
| | v. Type 2 | .90 | .35 |
| | entire | 1.15 | .40 |
| | v1. Border 4, Type 1 | — | — |
| | entire | — | — |
| | v2. Border 4, Type 2 | — | — |
| | entire | — | — |
| | FDC *(Sept. 22, 1950)* | | |

**1951-52. ISSUE** The return to a 6¢ air mail rate in 1950 caused the Post Office to revalue existing supplies of 5¢ air mail envelopes in some larger post offices. The re-valuing was done on a "ticometer", a new machine developed by Pitney-Bowes Co. This process first was done in 1951, and again in 1952. Different styles of slugs were used to make the overprint on each occasion.

AEN23, AEN24

| AEN23 | MNHVF | UseVF |
|---|---|---|
| 6¢ on 5¢ carmine, Border 2 (AEN19) | 1.00 | .65 |
| entire | 1.50 | 1.00 |
| FDC *(Sept. 29, 1951)* | | |

| AEN24 | MNHVF | UseVF |
|---|---|---|
| 6¢ on 5¢ carmine, Border 2 (AEN20) | .95 | .65 |
| entire | 1.40 | 1.10 |
| v. w/Border 4 (AEN20v) | — | — |
| entire | — | — |

*Overprint in red to left of stamp on 5¢ air mail envelopes of 1946 issue.*

AEN25, AEN27

| AEN25 | MNHVF | UseVF |
|---|---|---|
| 6¢ on 5¢ (AEN19) | 30.00 | 20.00 |
| entire | 35.00 | 25.00 |

AEN26

*Type 1: (Left) short cloud*

*Type 2: (Right) long cloud*

| AEN26 | | MNHVF | UseVF |
|---|---|---|---|
| 6¢ on 5¢ | (AEN20) | 4.00 | 3.00 |
| | entire | 6.00 | 5.00 |
| | v. w/Border 4 (AEN20t) | — | — |
| | entire | — | — |
| | FDC *(Aug. 29, 1952)* | | |

| AEN27 | MNHVF | UseVF |
|---|---|---|
| 6¢ on 5¢ carmine (AEN21) | — | — |
| entire | 1400. | — |

*Overprint in red to left of stamp on 5¢ air mail envelopes of 1946 and 1947 issues.*

**1956. ISSUE FIPEX Envelope.** Issued in celebration of the Fifth International Philatelic Exhibition. The embossed stamp shows an eagle in flight.

| AEN28 | | MNHVF | UseVF |
|---|---|---|---|
| 6¢ | **carmine red,** Type 1 | .90 | .65 |
| | entire | 1.25 | 1.00 |
| | v. Type 2 | — | — |
| | entire | — | — |
| | FDC *(May 2, 1956)* | | |

## 1958. ISSUE

AEN29

| AEN29 | | MNHVF | UseVF |
|---|---|---|---|
| 7¢ | **blue,** Border 2 | .80 | .70 |
| | entire | 1.25 | .75 |
| | v. Border 4 | — | — |
| | entire | — | — |
| | FDC *(July 31, 1958)* | | |

## 1958. ISSUE

AEN30

| AEN30 | | MNHVF | UseVF |
|---|---|---|---|
| 7¢ | **blue,** Border 2 | .70 | .35 |
| | entire | .80 | .40 |
| | v. w/Border 4 | — | — |
| | entire | — | — |
| | FDC *(Nov. 21, 1958)* | | |

**1958. ISSUE** On August 1, 1958, air mail rates were advanced to 7¢, necessitating new envelopes and the re-valuing of surplus stocks of the 6¢ air mail envelopes. The same surcharging device was used as for re-valuing the 3¢ regular postage stamps.

**Type 11 Surcharge**

**Type 12 Surcharge**

| AEN31 | | MNHVF | UseVF |
|---|---|---|---|
| 6¢ | **orange,** Die 1 (AEN4v1) | 250. | 250. |
| | entire | 300. | 400. |

| AEN32 | | MNHVF | UseVF |
|---|---|---|---|
| 6¢ | **orange,** Die 2 (AEN5v1) | 70.00 | 80.00 |
| | entire | 100. | 150. |

| AEN33 | | MNHVF | UseVF |
|---|---|---|---|
| 6¢ | **orange,** Die 3 (AEN6) | 40.00 | 55.00 |
| | entire | 50.00 | 100. |

Overprinted in green to left of stamp on 6¢ orange of 1934-44 (circular die) issue, no borders.

| AEN34 | | MNHVF | UseVF |
|---|---|---|---|
| 6¢ | **carmine,** Border 2, Type 1 (AEN22) | 1.25 | .65 |
| | entire | 1.35 | .80 |
| | v. Type 2 (AEN22v) | 1.25 | .65 |
| | entire | 1.35 | .80 |
| | v1. Border 4, Type 1 (AEN22v2) | — | — |
| | entire | — | — |
| | v2. Border 4, Type 2 (AEN22v3) | — | — |
| | entire | — | — |

On 6¢ carmine of 1950 (Skymaster design) issue.

| AEN35 | | MNHVF | UseVF |
|---|---|---|---|
| 6¢ | **carmine,** Type 1 (AEN28) | 1.25 | .75 |
| | entire | 1.75 | 1.00 |
| | v. Type 2 | — | — |
| | entire | — | — |

On 6¢ carmine of 1956 (FIPEX) issue.

**1960. ISSUE** Type AEN30 in new color.

| AEN36 | | MNHVF | UseVF |
|---|---|---|---|
| 7¢ | **red,** Border 2 | .75 | .40 |
| | entire | 1.00 | .45 |
| | v. Border 4 | — | — |
| | entire | — | — |
| | FDC *(Aug. 15, 1960)* | | |

**1963. ISSUE**

 AEN37

| AEN37 | | MNHVF | UseVF |
|---|---|---|---|
| 8¢ | **red,** Border 2 | .75 | .25 |
| | entire | 1.00 | .40 |
| | v. Border 4 | — | — |
| | entire | — | — |
| | FDC *(Nov. 17, 1962)* | | |

**1965. ISSUE**

 AEN38

| AEN38 | | MNHVF | UseVF |
|---|---|---|---|
| 8¢ | **red,** Border 6 | .50 | .25 |
| | entire | .60 | .40 |
| | v. Border 7 (error) | — | — |
| | entire | 25.00 | — |
| | z. Tagged (Aug. 15, 1967) | 1.50 | .50 |
| | entire | 2.00 | 1.00 |
| | FDC *(Jan. 7, 1965)* | | |

*Border 6 has a blue lozenge above and to left of stamp. Border 7 has a red lozenge above and to left of stamp.*

**1968. ISSUE**

 AEN39 *Type 12 surcharge printed in red to left of stamp on 8¢ air mail envelopes AEN38.*

| AEN39 | | MNHVF | UseVF |
|---|---|---|---|
| 8¢ | **red plus 2¢ red,** Border 6 | .80 | .25 |
| | entire | | 1.25 .50 |
| | FDC *(Feb. 5, 1968)* | | |

| AEN40 | | MNHVF | UseVF |
|---|---|---|---|
| 10¢ | **red,** Border 6, tagged | .60 | .25 |
| | entire | 1.00 | .25 |
| | FDC *(Jan. 8, 1968)* | | |

**1971. ISSUE**

 AEN41

| AEN41 | | MNHVF | UseVF |
|---|---|---|---|
| 11¢ | **red and blue** | .60 | .25 |
| | entire | .75 | .25 |
| | FDC *(May 6, 1971)* | | |

**1971. ISSUE** *Revalued at left of stamp, printed on AEN40.*

| AEN42 | | MNHVF | UseVF |
|---|---|---|---|
| 10¢ | **red plus 1¢ red** | 1.75 | .30 |
| | entire | 2.25 | .65 |
| | FDC *(June 28, 1971)* | | |

**1973. ISSUE**

 AEN43

| AEN43 | | MNHVF | UseVF |
|---|---|---|---|
| 13¢ | **red,** luminescent ink | .40 | .25 |
| | entire | .50 | .25 |
| | FDC *(Dec. 1, 1973)* | | |

# Air Letter Sheets, Aerogrammes

Listings are for entires, only.

**1947. ISSUE** *Printed by letterpress.* There are four types of inscription:

Type A: "AIR LETTER" on face; two-line inscription on back (when folded).

Type B: "AIR MAIL" on face; four-line inscription on back (when folded).

Type C: "AIR LETTER - AEROGRAMME" on face; four-line inscription on back (when folded).

Type D: "AIR LETTER - AEROGRAMME" on face; three-line inscription on back (when folded).

 ALS1

| ALS1 | | MNHVF | UseVF |
|---|---|---|---|
| 10¢ | **carmine on bluish,** Type A | 9.00 | 7.00 |
| | v. Blue overlay on inner side omitted | — | — |
| | v1. Reverse die cutting | 125. | — |
| | v2. Type B (UC168) (Sept. 1951) | 18.50 | 16.00 |
| | v2a. chocolate (error of color) | 450. | — |
| | v2a. Reverse die cutting | 300. | — |
| | v3. Type C (UC160) (Nov. 1953) | 55.00 | 15.00 |
| | v3a. Reverse die cutting | — | — |
| | v4. Type D (UC160) (1955) | 9.00 | 9.00 |
| | v4a. Reverse die cutting | 70.00 | — |
| | FDC *(Apr. 29, 1947)* | | |

**1958. ISSUE** Paper tinted blue without overlay. *Printed by letterpress*
New inscriptions:

Type E: two-line inscription on back (when folded).

Type F: three-line inscription on back (when folded).

 ALS2

| ALS2 | | MNHVF | UseVF |
|---|---|---|---|
| 10¢ | **blue and red,** Type E | 7.50 | 6.00 |
| | v. Red omitted | — | — |
| | v1. Blue omitted | — | — |
| | v2. Reverse die cutting | 80.00 | — |
| | v3. Type F | 12.50 | 7.50 |
| | FDC *(Sept. 12, 1958)* | | |

**1961. ISSUE** *Printed by typography.*

 ALS3

| ALS3 | | MNHVF | UseVF |
|---|---|---|---|
| 11¢ | **red and blue on bluish** | 3.50 | 2.50 |
| | v. Red omitted | 900. | — |
| | v1. Blue omitted | 900. | — |
| | v2. Reverse die cutting | 40.00 | — |
| | FDC *(June 16, 1961)* | | |

**1965. ISSUE Type G:** "AEROGRAMME PAR AVION" on face at bottom, two-line inscription on back.

 ALS4 *John F. Kennedy*

| ALS4 | | MNHVF | UseVF |
|---|---|---|---|
| 11¢ | **red and blue on bluish,** Type G | 4.00 | 3.00 |
| | v. reverse die cutting | 45.00 | — |
| | FDC *(May 29, 1965)* | | |

**1967. ISSUE** Same design as ALS4.

| ALS5 | | MNHVF | UseVF |
|---|---|---|---|
| 13¢ | **red and blue on bluish,** Type G | 3.50 | 3.00 |
| | v1. Blue omitted | 600. | — |
| | v2. Red omitted | 600. | — |
| | v3. Reverse die cutting | — | — |
| | FDC *(May 29, 1967)* | | |

**1968. HUMAN RIGHTS ISSUE** Commemorated the 20th Anniversary of Universal Declaration of Human Rights.

 ALS6

| ALS6 | | MNHVF | UseVF |
|---|---|---|---|
| 13¢ | **multicolored on bluish,** | 10.00 | 5.50 |
| | v. Black omitted | — | — |
| | v1. Brown omitted | — | — |
| | v2 Orange omitted | — | — |
| | z. Untagged (error) | — | — |
| | zo. Tagging omitted (error) | — | — |
| | FDC *(Dec. 3, 1968)* | | |

**1971. BIRDS ISSUE**

| ALS7 | | MNHVF | UseVF |
|---|---|---|---|
| 15¢ | **multicolored on bluish** | 2.00 | 1.50 |
| | FDC *(May 28, 1971)* | | |

**1971. ISSUE**

 ALS8

| ALS8 | | MNHVF | UseVF |
|---|---|---|---|
| 15¢ | **multicolored on bluish** | 2.00 | 1.50 |
| | FDC *(Dec. 13, 1971)* | | |

**1973. HOT AIR BALLOONING ISSUE**

 ALS9

| ALS9 | | MNHVF | UseVF |
|---|---|---|---|
| 15¢ | **multicolored on bluish,** Type G | 1.00 | 1.50 |
| | FDC *(Feb. 10, 1973)* | | |

**1974. GLOBE AND JET ISSUE**

 ALS10

| **ALS10** | | **MNHVF** | **UseVF** |
|---|---|---|---|
| 18¢ | **red and blue on bluish,** | 1.25 | 1.50 |
| | v.  Red omitted | — | — |
| | v1. Reverse die cutting | | |
| | FDC *(Jan. 4, 1974)* | | |

**1974. NATO Issue** Commemorated 25th Anniversary of NATO (North Atlantic Treaty Organization).

 ALS11

| **ALS11** | | **MNHVF** | **UseVF** |
|---|---|---|---|
| 18¢ | **red and blue on bluish,** | 1.25 | 2.00 |
| | FDC *(Apr. 4, 1974)* | | |

**1976. Issue**

 ALS12

| **ALS12** | | **MNHVF** | **UseVF** |
|---|---|---|---|
| 22¢ | **red and blue on bluish,** tagged | 1.25 | .50 |
| | v.  Reverse die cutting | — | — |
| | FDC *(Jan. 16, 1976)* | | |

**1978. Issue**

 ALS13

| **ALS13** | | **MNHVF** | **UseVF** |
|---|---|---|---|
| 22¢ | **blue on bluish,** tagged | 1.25 | .40 |
| | v.  Reverse die cutting | 30.00 | — |
| | FDC *(Nov. 3, 1978)* | | |

**1979. Olympic Issue**

 ALS14

| **ALS14** | | **MNHVF** | **UseVF** |
|---|---|---|---|
| 22¢ | **red, green and black on bluish,** tagged | 1.75 | 1.00 |
| | FDC *(Dec. 5, 1979)* | | |

**1980. Tourism and Travel Issue**

ALS15

| **ALS15** | | **MNHVF** | **UseVF** |
|---|---|---|---|
| 30¢ | **multicolored on bluish,** tagged | 1.00 | .40 |
| | v.  Red omitted | 100. | — |
| | v1. Reverse die cutting | — | — |
| | FDC *(Dec. 29, 1980)* | | |

**1981. Tourism and Travel Issue**

| **ALS16** | | **MNHVF** | **UseVF** |
|---|---|---|---|
| 30¢ | **yellow, red, blue and black on blue,** tagged | 1.00 | .40 |
| | v.  Reverse die cutting | 25.00 | — |
| | FDC *(Sept. 21, 1981)* | | |

**1982. World Trade Issue**

 ALS17 *Made in U.S.A.*

| **ALS17** | | **MNHVF** | **UseVF** |
|---|---|---|---|
| 30¢ | **multicolored on blue,** tagged | 1.25 | .40 |
| | FDC *(Sept. 16, 1982)* | | |

**1983. World Communications Issue**

 ALS18

| **ALS18** | | **MNHVF** | **UseVF** |
|---|---|---|---|
| 30¢ | **multicolored on blue,** tagged | 1.25 | .40 |
| | v.  Reverse die cutting | 35.00 | — |
| | FDC *(Jan. 7, 1983)* | | |

**1983. Olypics Issue**

ALS19

| **ALS19** | | **MNHVF** | **UseVF** |
|---|---|---|---|
| 30¢ | **multicolored,** tagged | 1.25 | 1.00 |
| | FDC *(Oct. 14, 1983)* | | |

**1985. Landsat Issue**

 ALS20

| **ALS20** | | **MNHVF** | **UseVF** |
|---|---|---|---|
| 36¢ | **multicolored on blue,** tagged | 1.25 | 1.00 |
| | v.  Reverse die cutting | 35.00 | — |
| | FDC *(Feb. 14, 1985)* | | |

**1985. TRAVEL ISSUE**

ALS21

| | | MNHVF | UseVF |
|---|---|---|---|
| **ALS21** | | | |
| 36¢ | **multicolored on blue,** tagged | 1.25 | 1.00 |
| | v. Black omitted | — | — |
| | v1. Reverse die cutting | 30.00 | — |
| | FDC *(May 21, 1985)* | | |

**1985. MARK TWAIN/HALLEY'S COMET ISSUE**

ALS22

| | | MNHVF | UseVF |
|---|---|---|---|
| **ALS22** | | | |
| 36¢ | **multicolored,** tagged | 3.00 | 2.00 |
| | v. Reverse die cutting | 30.00 | — |
| | FDC *(Dec. 4, 1985)* | | |

**1988. ISSUE**

ALS23

| | | MNHVF | UseVF |
|---|---|---|---|
| **ALS23** | | | |
| 39¢ | **multicolored,** tagged | 1.25 | 1.00 |
| | FDC *(May 9, 1988)* | | |

**1988. UPU ISSUE** Abraham Lincoln and Montgomery Blair are depicted.

ALS24

| | | MNHVF | UseVF |
|---|---|---|---|
| **ALS24** | | | |
| 39¢ | **multicolored,** tagged | 1.25 | 1.00 |
| | FDC *(Nov. 20, 1988)* | | |

**1991. ISSUE**

ALS25, ALS26 *Eagle*

| | | MNHVF | UseVF |
|---|---|---|---|
| **ALS25** | | | |
| 45¢ | **blue, gray and red,** tagged | 1.50 | .65 |
| | FDC *(May 17, 1991)* | | |
| **ALS26** | | **MNHVF** | **UseVF** |
| 45¢ | **blue, gray and red on blue,** tagged | 1.50 | .65 |

**1991. ISSUE.**

| | | MNHVF | UseVF |
|---|---|---|---|
| **ALS27** | | | |
| 50¢ | **multicolored on blue,** tagged | 1.50 | .65 |
| | FDC *(Sept. 23, 1995)* | | |

# Official Envelopes

**1873. POST OFFICE DEPARTMENT I** Official envelopes came into being when the franking privilege for government officials and departments was abolished in 1873. Adhesive stamps were issued for all departments of the government, but envelopes were issued for the Post Office and War Departments only. They were discontinued after 1879, although the War Department continued to use them for some years thereafter.

Manufactured by George H. Reay.
Envelope Watermark 2.

PDEN1 *Small, finely executed numeral "2".*

| PDEN1 | | UnFVF | UseFVF |
|---|---|---|---|
| 2¢ | black on canary | 11.00 | 7.00 |
| | entire | 15.00 | 11.00 |

PDEN2-PDEN3 *Small, finely executed numeral "3".*

| PDEN2 | | UnFVF | UseFVF |
|---|---|---|---|
| 3¢ | black on canary | 6.00 | 5.00 |
| | entire | 10.00 | 8.00 |
| **PDEN3** | | **UnFVF** | **UseFVF** |
| 3¢ | black on white | 7000. | — |
| | entire | 16000. | — |

PDEN4 *Small, finely executed numeral "6".*

| PDEN4 | | UnFVF | UseFVF |
|---|---|---|---|
| 6¢ | black on canary | 13.00 | 11.00 |
| | entire | 19.00 | 16.00 |

**1874. POST OFFICE DEPARTMENT** Manufactured by Plimpton Manufacturing Co.
Watermark 2, 4, 5.

PDEN5, PDEN6 *Tall, heavy "2".*

| PDEN5 | | UnFVF | UseFVF |
|---|---|---|---|
| 2¢ | black on canary | 5.00 | 4.00 |
| | entire | 8.00 | 5.00 |
| **PDEN6** | | **UnFVF** | **UseFVF** |
| 2¢ | black on white | 50.00 | 30.00 |
| | entire | 55.00 | 35.00 |

PDEN7-PDEN11 *Tall "3"*

| PDEN7 | | UnFVF | UseFVF |
|---|---|---|---|
| 3¢ | black on canary | 3.00 | 1.00 |
| | entire | 4.00 | 1.50 |

| PDEN8 | | UnFVF | UseFVF |
|---|---|---|---|
| 3¢ | black on white | 900. | 900. |
| | entire | 1000. | — |
| **PDEN9** | | **UnFVF** | **UseFVF** |
| 3¢ | black on amber | 40.00 | 29.00 |
| | entire | 50.00 | 45.00 |
| **PDEN10** | | **UnFVF** | **UseFVF** |
| 3¢ | black on blue | 16000. | — |
| | entire | 19000. | — |
| **PDEN11** | | **UnFVF** | **UseFVF** |
| 3¢ | blue on blue | 15000. | — |
| | entire | 17000. | — |

PDEN12, PDEN13 *Tall "6"*

| PDEN12 | | UnFVF | UseFVF |
|---|---|---|---|
| 6¢ | black on canary | 4.50 | 4.25 |
| | entire | 9.00 | 4.50 |
| **PDEN13** | | **UnFVF** | **UseFVF** |
| 6¢ | black on white | 550. | — |
| | entire | 750. | — |

**1877. POSTAL SERVICE DEPARTMENT ISSUE** Unwatermarked and Watermark 2, 4, 5.

PDEN14-PDEN17

| PDEN14 | | UnFVF | UseFVF |
|---|---|---|---|
| | black on white | 4.00 | 3.50 |
| | entire | 6.00 | 5.00 |
| **PDEN15** | | **UnFVF** | **UseFVF** |
| | black on amber | 30.00 | 21.00 |
| | entire | 90.00 | 40.00 |
| **PDEN16** | | **UnFVF** | **UseFVF** |
| | blue on amber | 35.00 | 25.00 |
| | entire | 90.00 | 45.00 |
| **PDEN17** | | **UnFVF** | **UseFVF** |
| | blue on blue | 6.00 | 6.00 |
| | entire | 8.00 | 8.00 |

**1873. WAR DEPARTMENT ISSUE** Manufactured by George H. Reay.
Watermarks 2, 3, 4, 5, 6.

WDEN18-WDEN20 *Benjamin Franklin. Point of bust narrow and points at "N" of "ONE".*

| WDEN18 | | UnFVF | UseFVF |
|---|---|---|---|
| 1¢ | dark red on white | 500. | 300. |
| | entire | 750. | 350. |
| **WDEN19** | | **UnFVF** | **UseFVF** |
| 1¢ | vermilion on white | 200. | — |
| | entire | 275. | — |
| **WDEN20** | | **UnFVF** | **UseFVF** |
| 1¢ | vermilion on manila, wrapper | 11.00 | 8.00 |
| | entire | 20.00 | 15.00 |

WDEN21-WDEN23 *Andrew Jackson. Point of bust broad and square.*

**WDEN21**

| | | UnFVF | UseFVF |
|---|---|---|---|
| 2¢ | dark red on white | 650. | 350. |
| | entire | 750. | — |

**WDEN22**

| | | UnFVF | UseFVF |
|---|---|---|---|
| 2¢ | vermilion on white | 260. | — |
| | entire | 5000. | — |

**WDEN23**

| | | UnFVF | UseFVF |
|---|---|---|---|
| 2¢ | vermilion on manila, wrapper | 200. | — |
| | entire | 300. | — |

WDEN24-WDEN29 *George Washington. The ponytail projects below the bottom of the bust.*

**WDEN24**

| | | UnFVF | UseFVF |
|---|---|---|---|
| 3¢ | dark red on white | 50.00 | 40.00 |
| | entire | 150. | — |

**WDEN25**

| | | UnFVF | UseFVF |
|---|---|---|---|
| 3¢ | dark red on amber | 13000. | — |
| | entire | 17000. | — |

**WDEN26**

| | | UnFVF | UseFVF |
|---|---|---|---|
| 3¢ | dark red on cream | 450. | 200. |
| | entire | 550. | 225. |

**WDEN27**

| | | UnFVF | UseFVF |
|---|---|---|---|
| 3¢ | vermilion on white | 75.00 | 40.00 |
| | entire | 150. | — |

**WDEN28**

| | | UnFVF | UseFVF |
|---|---|---|---|
| 3¢ | vermilion on amber | 85.00 | — |
| | entire | 250. | — |

**WDEN29**

| | | UnFVF | UseFVF |
|---|---|---|---|
| 3¢ | vermilion on cream | 13.00 | 7.00 |
| | entire | 40.00 | 20.00 |

WDEN30-WDEN33 *Abraham Lincoln. Back of neck is long.*

**WDEN30**

| | | UnFVF | UseFVF |
|---|---|---|---|
| 6¢ | dark red on white | 170. | 70.00 |
| | entire | 200. | — |

**WDEN31**

| | | UnFVF | UseFVF |
|---|---|---|---|
| 6¢ | dark red on cream | 1400. | 350. |
| | entire* | 2400. | 1500. |

**WDEN32**

| | | UnFVF | UseFVF |
|---|---|---|---|
| 6¢ | vermilion on white | — | — |
| | entire | — | — |

**WDEN33**

| | | UnFVF | UseFVF |
|---|---|---|---|
| 6¢ | vermilion on cream | 350. | — |
| | entire* | 6500. | — |

WDEN34, WDEN35 *Thomas Jefferson. The ponytail does not project at back.*

**WDEN34**

| | | UnFVF | UseFVF |
|---|---|---|---|
| 10¢ | dark red on white | 2700. | 280. |
| | entire* | 5000. | 550. |

**WDEN35**

| | | UnFVF | UseFVF |
|---|---|---|---|
| 10¢ | vermilion on white | 200. | — |
| | entire* | 350. | — |

WDEN36, WDEN37 *Henry Clay, ear covered by hair.*

**WDEN36**

| | | UnFVF | UseFVF |
|---|---|---|---|
| 12¢ | dark red on white | 100. | 40.00 |
| | entire* | 140. | — |

**WDEN37**

| | | UnFVF | UseFVF |
|---|---|---|---|
| 12¢ | vermilion on white | 150. | — |
| | entire* | 200. | — |

WDEN38, WDEN39 *Daniel Webster. Face with sideburns.*

**WDEN38**

| | | UnFVF | UseFVF |
|---|---|---|---|
| 15¢ | dark red on white | 100. | 45.00 |
| | entire* | 125. | 400. |

**WDEN39**

| | | UnFVF | UseFVF |
|---|---|---|---|
| 15¢ | vermilion on white | 250. | — |
| | entire* | 2500. | — |

WDEN40, WDEN41 *Winfield Scott*

**WDEN40**

| | | UnFVF | UseFVF |
|---|---|---|---|
| 24¢ | dark red on white | 135. | 35.00 |
| | entire* | 100. | — |

**WDEN41**

| | | UnFVF | UseFVF |
|---|---|---|---|
| 24¢ | vermilion on white | 375. | — |
| | entire* | 400. | — |

WDEN42, WDEN43 *Alexander Hamilton. Bust at back ends in a narrow point.*

**WDEN42**

| | | UnFVF | UseFVF |
|---|---|---|---|
| 30¢ | dark red on white | 400. | 110. |
| | entire* | 450. | 180. |

**WDEN43**

| | | UnFVF | UseFVF |
|---|---|---|---|
| 30¢ | vermilion on white | 375. | — |
| | entire* | 475. | — |

**1875. BENJAMIN FRANKLIN ISSUE** produced by Plimpton Manufacturing Co.
*Watermarks 2, 3, 4, 5, 6*

WDEN44-WDEN46 *Benjamin Franklin. Point of bust is broad.*

**WDEN44**

| | | UnFVF | UseFVF |
|---|---|---|---|
| 1¢ | red on white | 125. | 100. |
| | entire | 135. | — |

**WDEN45**

| | | UnFVF | UseFVF |
|---|---|---|---|
| 1¢ | red on amber | 750. | — |

**WDEN45A**

| | | UnFVF | UseFVF |
|---|---|---|---|
| 1¢ | red on orange | 18000. | — |

**WDEN46**

| | | UnFVF | UseFVF |
|---|---|---|---|
| 1¢ | red on manila, wrapper | 3.00 | 1.75 |
| | entire | 6.00 | 4.00 |

**1873. WAR DEPARTMENT ISSUE** Manufactured by George H. Reay.
Watermarks 2, 3, 4, 5, 6.

WDEN47-WDEN50 *Andrew Jackson. Forward slope of bust is rounded.*

**WDEN47**

| | | UnFVF | UseFVF |
|---|---|---|---|
| 2¢ | red on white | 100. | — |
| | entire | 125. | — |

**WDEN48**

| | | UnFVF | UseFVF |
|---|---|---|---|
| 2¢ | red on amber | 25.00 | 15.00 |
| | entire | 35.00 | 25.00 |

**WDEN49**

| | | UnFVF | UseFVF |
|---|---|---|---|
| 2¢ | red on orange | 45.00 | 13.00 |
| | entire | 45.00 | 20.00 |

**WDEN50**

| | | UnFVF | UseFVF |
|---|---|---|---|
| 2¢ | red on manila, wrapper | 70.00 | 45.00 |
| | entire | 90.00 | — |

WDEN51-WDEN55 *George Washington. The ponytail does not project below bust but protrudes toward rear.*

**WDEN51**

| | | UnFVF | UseFVF |
|---|---|---|---|
| 3¢ | red on white | 11.00 | 9.00 |
| | entire | 12.00 | 10.00 |

**WDEN52**

| | | UnFVF | UseFVF |
|---|---|---|---|
| 3¢ | red on amber | 12.00 | 9.00 |
| | entire | 15.00 | 13.00 |

**WDEN53**

| | | UnFVF | UseFVF |
|---|---|---|---|
| 3¢ | red on cream | 6.00 | 3.00 |
| | entire | 8.00 | 5.00 |

**WDEN54**

| | | UnFVF | UseFVF |
|---|---|---|---|
| 3¢ | red on blue | 4.00 | 3.00 |
| | entire | 5.00 | 4.00 |

**WDEN55**

| | | UnFVF | UseFVF |
|---|---|---|---|
| 3¢ | red on fawn | 5.00 | 2.00 |
| | entire | 7.00 | 3.00 |

WDEN56-WDEN58 *Abraham Lincoln. Back of bust is short.*

**WDEN56**

| | | UnFVF | UseFVF |
|---|---|---|---|
| 6¢ | red on white | 35.00 | 22.00 |
| | entire | 70.00 | — |

**WDEN57**

| | | UnFVF | UseFVF |
|---|---|---|---|
| 6¢ | red on amber | 70.00 | 30.00 |
| | entire | 75.00 | — |

**WDEN58**

| | | UnFVF | UseFVF |
|---|---|---|---|
| 6¢ | red on cream | 170. | 70.00 |
| | entire | 200. | — |

WDEN59, WDEN60 *Thomas Jefferson. The ponytail projects at back.*

**WDEN59**

| | | UnFVF | UseFVF |
|---|---|---|---|
| 10¢ | red on white | 150. | 90.00 |
| | entire | 175. | — |

**WDEN60**

| | | UnFVF | UseFVF |
|---|---|---|---|
| 10¢ | red on amber | 1100. | — |
| | entire | 1400. | — |

WDEN61-WDEN63 *Henry Clay. Clearly defined ear.*

**WDEN61**

| | | UnFVF | UseFVF |
|---|---|---|---|
| 12¢ | red on white | 40.00 | 35.00 |
| | entire* | 100. | — |

**WDEN62**

| | | UnFVF | UseFVF |
|---|---|---|---|
| 12¢ | red on white | 650. | — |
| | entire* | 700. | — |

**WDEN63**

| | | UnFVF | UseFVF |
|---|---|---|---|
| 12¢ | red on cream | 600. | — |
| | entire* | 750. | — |

WDEN64-WDEN67 *Daniel Webster. Face without sideburns.*

**WDEN64**

| | | UnFVF | UseFVF |
|---|---|---|---|
| 15¢ | red on white | 175. | 135. |
| | entire* | 200. | — |

**WDEN65**

| | | UnFVF | UseFVF |
|---|---|---|---|
| 15¢ | red on amber | 700. | — |
| | entire* | 750. | — |

**WDEN66**

| | | UnFVF | UseFVF |
|---|---|---|---|
| 15¢ | red on cream | 650. | — |
| | entire* | 700. | — |

WDEN67-WDEN69 *Alexander Hamilton. Bust at back is broad.*

**WDEN67**

| | | UnFVF | UseFVF |
|---|---|---|---|
| 30¢ | red on white | 150. | 125. |
| | entire* | 180. | — |

**WDEN68**

| | | UnFVF | UseFVF |
|---|---|---|---|
| 30¢ | red on amber | 1000. | — |
| | entire* | 1100. | — |

**WDEN69**

| | | UnFVF | UseFVF |
|---|---|---|---|
| 30¢ | red on cream | 1000. | — |
| | entire* | 1100. | — |

**1910. UNITED STATES POSTAL SAVINGS ISSUE** Watermarks 15, 16, 17, 18.

PSEN70, PSEN71 (l) PSEN72, PSEN73 (r)
*Watermarks 15, 16, 17, 18.*

**PSEN70**

| | | UnFVF | UseFVF |
|---|---|---|---|
| 1¢ | green on white | 60.00 | 15.00 |
| | entire* | 75.00 | 45.00 |

**PSEN71**

| | | UnFVF | UseFVF |
|---|---|---|---|
| 1¢ | green on buff | 185. | 60.00 |
| | entire* | 220. | 75.00 |

**PSEN72**

| | | UnFVF | UseFVF |
|---|---|---|---|
| 2¢ | carmine on white | 8.00 | 3.00 |
| | entire* | 13.00 | 9.00 |

**PSEN73**

| | | UnFVF | UseFVF |
|---|---|---|---|
| 2¢ | carmine on manila | 1700. | — |
| | entire* | 2500. | — |

# Postal Cards

Postal cards vary greatly in size. Card sizes are not indicated except in those cases where the difference is important in making proper identification. So, too, the text on the face of the cards has been changed on numberous occasions. The exact wording is not indicated except when it is the determining factor of identification.

Postal cards normally are collected intact in one of the following three conditions: mint; unused (preprinted with address or messages, but no postal marking); or used (with postal marking).

**1873. PROFILE OF LIBERTY ISSUE** Watermarked with large (90mm x 60mm) "USPOD."

PC1, PC2, *Profile of Liberty.*

PC1 *Watermark*

| PC1 | | UnFVF | UseFVF |
|---|---|---|---|
| 1¢ | reddish brown on buff | 350. | 20.00 |
| | Preprinted | 60.00 | |
| | Date of Issue *(May 13, 1873)* | | |

*Watermark with small (55mm x 38mm) "USPOD".*

| PC2 | | UnFVF | UseFVF |
|---|---|---|---|
| 1¢ | reddish brown on buff | 75.00 | 3.00 |
| | Preprinted | 22.50 | |
| | v. Unwatermarked | — | — |
| | Date of Issue *(July 6, 1973)* | | |

**1875. LIBERTY ISSUE** Inscribed "WRITE THE ADDRESS ON THIS SIDE - THE MESSAGE ON THE OTHER". *Watermarked small (52mm x 36mm) "USPOD".*

PC3, PC4, PC6 *Liberty*

| PC3 | | UnFVF | UseFVF |
|---|---|---|---|
| 3¢ | black on buff | 2800. | 325. |
| | Preprinted | 650. | |
| | Date of Issue *(Sept. 28, 1875)* | | |

*Unwatermarked. All subsequent U.S. Postal cards also are without watermarks.*

| PC4 | | UnFVF | UseFVF |
|---|---|---|---|
| 1¢ | black on buff | 65.00 | 7.00 |
| | Preprinted | 6.50 | |
| | Date of Issue *(Sept. 30, 1875)* | | |

**1879. UNIVERSAL POSTAL UNION CARD ISSUE** Frame around card. Size 5 1/8 inches x 3 inches.

PC5, PC12, PC15, *Liberty*

| PC5 | | UnFVF | UseFVF |
|---|---|---|---|
| 2¢ | blue on buff | 30.00 | 20.00 |
| | Preprinted | 11.50 | |
| | a. dark blue on buff | 35.00 | 22.00 |
| | Preprinted | 12.50 | |
| | Date of Issue *(Dec. 1 1879)* | | |

**1881. UNIVERSAL POSTAL UNION CARD ISSUE** Inscribed: "NOTHING BUT THE ADDRESS CAN BE PLACED ON THIS SIDE". 21 teeth 23 teeth

PC21 Normal, 21 teeth,

PC6 23 teeth.

| PC6 | | UnFVF | UseFVF |
|---|---|---|---|
| 1¢ | black on buff, 21 teeth | 55.00 | 5.00 |
| | Preprinted | 5.00 | |
| | v. 23 teeth | 750. | 35.00 |
| | Preprinted | 185. | |
| | v1. Printed on both sides | 600. | 425. |
| | Date of Issue *(Oct. 17, 1881)* | | |

**1885. THOMAS JEFFERSON ISSUE**

PC7 *Thomas Jefferson*

| PC7 | | UnFVF | UseFVF |
|---|---|---|---|
| 1¢ | brown on buff | 50.00 | 2.50 |
| | Preprinted | 10.00 | |
| | a. chocolate | 75.00 | 10.00 |
| | Preprinted | 12.50 | |
| | b. orange brown | 50.00 | 2.50 |
| | Preprinted | 10.00 | |
| | c. red brown | 50.00 | 3.00 |
| | Preprinted | 10.00 | |
| | v. Double impression | — | |
| | v1. double impression, 1 inverted | — | |
| | v2. Printed on both sides | — | |
| | Date of Issue *(Aug. 24, 1885)* | | |

## 1886. THOMAS JEFFERSON ISSUE

PC8 *Thomas Jefferson*

| PC8 | | UnFVF | UseFVF |
|---|---|---|---|
| 1¢ | **black on buff** | 17.50 | .65 |
| | Preprinted | 1.50 | |
| | a. black on dark buff | 20.00 | 2.50 |
| | Preprinted | 5.50 | |
| | v. Double impression | — | |
| | v1. Double impression, 1 inverted | — | |
| | Date of Issue *(Dec. 1, 1886)* | | |

## 1891. ULYSSES S. GRANT ISSUE

PC9, PC10 *Ulysses S. Grant*

| PC9 | | UnFVF | UseFVF |
|---|---|---|---|
| 1¢ | **black on buff,** 155mm x 95mm | 35.00 | 2.50 |
| | Preprinted | 7.50 | |
| | v. Double impression | — | |
| | Date of Issue *(Dec. 16, 1891)* | | |

| PC10 | | UnFVF | UseFVF |
|---|---|---|---|
| 1¢ | **blue on grayish,** 117mm x 75mm | 15.00 | 4.00 |
| | Preprinted | 2.50 | |
| | v. Double impression, 1 inverted | — | |
| | Date of Issue *(Dec. 16, 1891)* | | |

## 1894. THOMAS JEFFERSON ISSUE

PC11 *Thomas Jefferson with small wreath.*

| PC11 | | UnFVF | UseFVF |
|---|---|---|---|
| 1¢ | **black on buff** | 40.00 | 1.50 |
| | Preprinted | 2.50 | |
| | v. Double impression | — | |
| | Date of Issue *(Jan. 2, 1894)* | | |

## 1897. UNIVERSAL POSTAL UNION Same design as PC5, but larger (5 1/2 inches x 3 1/2 inches).

| PC12 | | UnFVF | UseFVF |
|---|---|---|---|
| 2¢ | **blue on light blue** | 165. | 90.00 |
| | Preprinted | 80.00 | |
| | Date of Issue *(Jan. 25, 1897)* | | |

## 1897. UNIVERSAL POSTAL UNION THOMAS JEFFERSON

PC13 *Thomas Jefferson with large wreath.*

| PC13 | | UnFVF | UseFVF |
|---|---|---|---|
| 1¢ | **black on buff** | 30.00 | 2.00 |
| | Preprinted | 3.00 | |
| | v. Double impression, 1 inverted | — | |
| | v1. Printed on both sides | — | |
| | Date of Issue *(Dec. 1, 1897)* | | |

## 1898. JOHN ADAMS ISSUE

PC14 *John Adams*

| PC14 | | UnFVF | UseFVF |
|---|---|---|---|
| 1¢ | **black on buff** | 45.00 | 27.50 |
| | Preprinted | 12.00 | |
| | Date of Issue *(March 31, 1898)* | | |

## 1898. UNIVERSAL POSTAL UNION same design as PC5 and PC12, but without frame around card. (140mm x 82mm).

| PC15 | | UnFVF | UseFVF |
|---|---|---|---|
| 2¢ | **black on buff** | 12.50 | 10.00 |
| | Preprinted | 5.50 | |

## 1902. FULL-FACE MCKINLEY CARD

PC16 *William McKinley, full face (at left) at right)*

| PC16 | | UnFVF | UseFVF |
|---|---|---|---|
| 1¢ | **black on buff** | 5000. | 2500. |
| | Preprinted | 3250. | |

## 1902. PROFILE MCKINLEY CARD

PC17 *William McKinley, profile. (at left) (at right)*

| PC17 | | UnFVF | UseFVF |
|---|---|---|---|
| 1¢ | **black on buff** | 12.50 | 2.00 |
| | Preprinted | 2.00 | |
| | v. Double impression | — | |

## 1907. WILLIAM MCKINLEY

PC18, PC19 *William McKinley*

**PC18**

| | | UnFVF | UseFVF |
|---|---|---|---|
| 1¢ | black on buff | 40.00 | 1.50 |
| | Preprinted | 2.00 | |

Date of Issue *(June 1907)*

**1908. WILLIAM MCKINLEY** Same design as PC18. Message space at left side. Inscribed (vertically) at side: "THE SPACE BELOW MAY BE USED FOR CORRESPONDENCE."

**PC19**

| | | UnFVF | UseFVF |
|---|---|---|---|
| 1¢ | black on buff | 50.00 | 7.50 |
| | Preprinted | 8.00 | |

Date of Issue *(Jan. 2, 1908)*

**1910. WILLIAM MCKINLEY**

PC20 *William McKinley, area around head shaded.*

**PC20**

| | | UnFVF | UseFVF |
|---|---|---|---|
| 1¢ | blue on bluish | 100. | 7.50 |
| | Preprinted | 16.50 | |
| | a. bronze blue on bluish | 170. | 15.00 |
| | Preprinted | 27.50 | |
| | b. Points on 4 outer areas above & below "IS" in inscription to left of imprinted stamp. | 2000. | 550. |
| | Preprinted | 1000. | |
| | v1. Double impression | — | |
| | v2. Double impression, 1 inverted | — | |
| | v3. Triple impression | — | |

Date of Issue *(Feb. 18, 1910)*

PC21, PC23 *William McKinley, area around head without shading.*

**PC21**

| | | UnFVF | UseFVF |
|---|---|---|---|
| 1¢ | blue on bluish | 15.00 | .50 |
| | Preprinted | 1.75 | |
| | p. Printed on thin paper (0.008 inches thickness) | — | — |
| | v. Double impression, normal position | — | |

Date of Issue *(April 13, 1910)*

**1911. ABRAHAM LINCOLN ISSUE**

PC22, PC25 *Abraham Lincoln*

**PC22**

| | | UnFVF | UseFVF |
|---|---|---|---|
| 1¢ | red on cream, 127mm x 76mm | 10.00 | 7.50 |
| | Preprinted | 3.50 | |
| | v. Double impression | — | |

Date of Issue *(Jan 21, 1911)*

**1911. ABRAHAM LINCOLN ISSUE** same design as PC21.

**PC23**

| | | UnFVF | UseFVF |
|---|---|---|---|
| 1¢ | carmine on cream | 12.50 | 7.50 |
| | Preprinted | 1.75 | |
| | a. scarlet | — | |
| | v. Double impression | — | |

Date of Issue *(Aug. 10, 1911)*

**1911. UNIVERSAL POSTAL UNION**

PC24 *Ulysses S. Grant*

**PC24**

| | | UnFVF | UseFVF |
|---|---|---|---|
| 2¢ | carmine on cream | 1.75 | 9.00 |
| | Preprinted | 1.00 | |
| | v. Double impression | — | |

Date of Issue *(Oct. 27, 1911)*

**1913. ABRAHAM LINCOLN ISSUE** Same design as PC22; same size: 5 x 3 inches.

**PC25**

| | | UnFVF | UseFVF |
|---|---|---|---|
| 1¢ | green on cream | 12.50 | 7.50 |
| | Preprinted | | |

Date of Issue *(July 29, 1913)*

**1914. THOMAS JEFFERSON ISSUE**

PC26, PC27 *Thomas Jefferson*

**PC26**

| | | UnFVF | UseFVF |
|---|---|---|---|
| 1¢ | green on buff | .40 | .30 |
| | Preprinted | .25 | |
| | a. green on cream | 3.75 | .75 |
| | Preprinted | 1.25 | |
| | b. green on off-white | 3.75 | .75 |
| | Preprinted | 1.25 | |
| | v. Double impression | — | |

Date of Issue *(June 4, 1914)*

**1916. THOMAS JEFFERSON ISSUE** Same design as PC26. Due to wartime shortages, an inferior rough-textured bluish gray paper was used for a short period. PC27 and PC28 were printed on this substitute paper.

**PC27**

| | | UnFVF | UseFVF |
|---|---|---|---|
| 1¢ | dark green on bluish gray | 2700. | 175. |

**1916. THOMAS JEFFERSON ISSUE** Recut die consisting of heavy hair lines and distinct hair lines in queue.

PC28 *Recut die*

**PC28**

| | | UnFVF | UseFVF |
|---|---|---|---|
| 1¢ | dark green on bluish gray | 3000. | 140. |

Date of Issue *(Dec. 22, 1916)*

## 1917. ABRAHAM LINCOLN ISSUE  Small "library" size: 5 x 3 inches.

PC29 *Abraham Lincoln*

| PC29 | | UnFVF | UseFVF |
|---|---|---|---|
| 1¢ | **green on cream** | .75 | .50 |
| | Preprinted | .35 | |
| | a. green on dark buff | 1.75 | .75 |
| | Preprinted | .65 | |
| | b green on canary | — | — |
| | v. Double impression | — | |
| | Date of Issue *(March 14, 1917)* | | |

## 1917. THOMAS JEFFERSON ISSUE

*Points* PC30 *Die 1, coarse impression.*

| PC30 | | UnFVF | UseFVF |
|---|---|---|---|
| 2¢ | **carmine on cream** | 50.00 | 3.00 |
| | Preprinted | 7.50 | |
| | a. vermilion on cream | 300. | 70.00 |
| | Preprinted | 75.00 | |
| | b. lake on cream | 50.00 | 3.00 |
| | Preprinted | 7.50 | |
| | c. carmine on buff | 40.00 | 3.00 |
| | Preprinted | 6.00 | |
| | Date of Issue *(Oct. 22, 1917)* | | |

## 1918. THOMAS JEFFERSON ISSUE

PC31 *Balls Die 2, clear impression Balls*

| PC31 | | UnFVF | UseFVF |
|---|---|---|---|
| 2¢ | **carmine on cream** | 30.00 | 2.75 |
| | Preprinted | 4.50 | |
| | Date of Issue *(Jan. 23, 1918)* | | |

## 1920. JEFFERSON SURCHARGE ISSUE  Surcharged "1 CENT" in black on PC30 (die 1). PC32, PC33

*The overprints were applied by a canceling machine (below left) or a printing press (below right).*

PC32, PC33

| PC32 | | UnFVF | UseFVF |
|---|---|---|---|
| 1¢ | **red on cream,** *canceling machine* | 55.00 | 12.50 |
| | Preprinted | 16.00 | |
| | a. Press printing (UX34) | 550. | 50.00 |
| | Preprinted | 110. | |
| | v. Double surcharge | — | |
| | v1. Inverted surcharge | — | |
| | Date of Issue *(April 1920)* | | |

## 1920. JEFFERSON SURCHARGE (DIE 2) ISSUE

| PC33 | | UnFVF | UseFVF |
|---|---|---|---|
| 1¢ | **red on cream** | 15.00 | 12.50 |
| | Preprinted | 2.50 | |
| | a. Press printing (UX35) | 225. | 35.00 |
| | Preprinted | 60.00 | |
| | v. Double surcharge | 90.00 | |
| | v1. Double surcharge, 1 inverted | 300. | |
| | v2. Inverted surcharge | 60.00 | |
| | v3. Triple surcharge | 375. | |
| | Date of Issue *(April 1920)* | | |

## 1920. JEFFERSON ISSUE

PC34 *Overprinted in black on PC31 (Die 2).*

| PC34 | | UnFVF | UseFVF |
|---|---|---|---|
| 1¢on 2¢+1¢on 2¢ **red on cream** | | 4000. | 4500. |
| | Preprinted | 3000. | |
| | Date of Issue *(April 1920)* | | |

## 1926. UNIVERSAL POSTAL UNION

PC35 *William McKinley*

| PC35 | | UnFVF | UseFVF |
|---|---|---|---|
| 3¢ | **red orange on cream** | 5.00 | 10.00 |
| | Preprinted | 2.00 | |
| | a. red on canary | 5.50 | 12.50 |
| | b. deep carmine on canary | — | — |
| | c. orange red on dark buff | — | — |
| | FDC *(Feb. 1, 1926)* | | 225. |

## 1951. BENJAMIN FRANKLIN ISSUE

PC36 *Benjamin Franklin*

| PC36 | | MNHVF | UseVF |
|---|---|---|---|
| 2¢ | **carmine on buff** | .50 | .30 |
| | Preprinted | .30 | |
| | a. lake on buff | — | — |
| | v. Double impression | 225. | |
| | FDC *(Nov. 16, 1951)* | | 1.00 |

## 1952. 2¢ OVPT. ON THOMAS JEFFERSON ISSUE

PC37 *Overprinted in green on PC26.*

**PC37**

| | | MNHVF | UseVF |
|---|---|---|---|
| 2¢ on 1¢ | green on buff | .75 | .40 |
| | Preprinted | .35 | |
| | v. Double surcharge | 20.00 | 25.00 |
| | v1. Surcharge vertical at left | 7.50 | 9.00 |
| | v2. Surcharge vertical below stamp | — | |
| | FDC (March 22, 1952) | | 12.50 |

**PC37A**

| | | MNHVF | UseVF |
|---|---|---|---|
| 2¢ on 1¢ | green on buff | 5.50 | 2.50 |
| | Preprinted | 2.00 | |
| | v. Inverted surcharge, lower left | 80.00 | 130. |
| | Preprinted | 60.00 | |
| | v1. Double surcharge | — | |
| | v2. Split surcharge, top & bottom | — | |

*Press-printed surcharge.*

**1952. 2¢ OVPT. ON LINCOLN ISSUE** PC29. *Surcharged, printed by Pitney Bowes Tickometer.*

**PC38**

| | | MNHVF | UseVF |
|---|---|---|---|
| 2¢ on 1¢ | green on buff | .75 | .50 |
| | Preprinted | .40 | |
| | a. green on cream | .75 | .50 |
| | Preprinted | .40 | |
| | b. green on canary | .75 | .50 |
| | Preprinted | .40 | |
| | v. Double surcharge, normal position | — | |
| | v1. Inverted surcharge, lower left | — | |
| | v2. Double surcharge, 1 inverted | — | |
| | v3. Vertical surcharge, left of stamp, reading down | 7.00 | 5.50 |
| | FDC (March 22, 1952) | | 110. |

**PC38A**

| | | MNHVF | UseVF |
|---|---|---|---|
| 2¢ on 1¢ | green on buff | 6.00 | 2.50 |
| | Preprinted | 3.00 | |
| | v. Surcharge on back | 85.00 | |

*Press-printed surcharge.*

**1952. SMALL "LIBRARY" SIZE ISSUE** 5 x 3 inches.

PC39 *Abraham Lincoln*

**PC39**

| | | MNHVF | UseVF |
|---|---|---|---|
| 2¢ | carmine on buff | .30 | 1.50 |
| | Preprinted | .15 | |
| | a. lake on buff | — | |
| | FDC (July 31, 1952) | | 1.00 |

**1956. FIPEX ISSUE**

PC40 *Liberty*

**PC40**

| | | MNHVF | UseVF |
|---|---|---|---|
| 2¢ | red & dark violet blue on buff | .30 | 2.00 |
| | a. rose & dark violet blue | 1.75 | 1.25 |
| | v. Dark violet blue omitted | 475. | 250. |
| | v1. Double impression of dark violet blue | 18.00 | 11.00 |
| | FDC (May 4, 1956) | | 1.00 |

**1956. STATUE OF LIBERTY ISSUE**

PC41 *Liberty*

**PC41**

| | | MNHVF | UseVF |
|---|---|---|---|
| 4¢ | scarlet & ultramarine on buff | 1.75 | 75.00 |
| | FDC (Nov. 16, 1956) | | 1.00 |

**1958. STATUE OF LIBERTY ISSUE**

PC42 *Liberty*

**PC42**

| | | MNHVF | UseVF |
|---|---|---|---|
| 3¢ | violet on buff | .60 | .30 |
| | v. Double impression | — | |
| | v1. "I" of "IN" omitted | 13.00 | 26.00 |
| | x. printed precancel bars (Sept. 15, 1961) | 4.00 | 3.00 |
| | FDC (Aug. 1, 1958) | | 1.00 |

**1958. BENJAMIN FRANKLIN ISSUE** PC36 revalued in black.

PC43 *Overprinted in black at left of PC36.*

**PC43**

| | | MNHVF | UseVF |
|---|---|---|---|
| 1¢ on 2¢ | carmine on buff, preprinted | 175. | 500. |
| | v. Surcharge inverted lower left | — | |

*This surcharge was authorized for use by the General Electric Co. in Owensboro, Ky. which had prepared a large number of cards for an advertising campaign prior to the 1958 rate increase. In all, some 750,000 cards were surcharged.*

**1962. ABRAHAM LINCOLN ISSUE**

PC44 *Abraham Lincoln*

**PC44**

| | | MNHVF | UseVF |
|---|---|---|---|
| 4¢ | lilac on white, precanceled | .30 | .25 |
| | p. Non-fluorescent paper, non-phosphorescent ink | — | — |
| | p1. Fluorescent paper, non-phosphorescent ink | — | — |
| | p2. Non-fluorescent paper, phosphorescent ink | .75 | .25 |
| | v. Double impression, normal | — | |
| | FDC (Nov. 19, 1962) | | 1.00 |

*The phosphorescent ink was experimental tagging for expediting mail processing (cards placed on sale June 25, 1966).*

**1963. VACATIONLAND ISSUE** International Postal Card. Designed to promote tourism to the United States.

PC45 *Map of North America*

**PC45**

| | | MNHVF | UseVF |
|---|---|---|---|
| 7¢ | **red & blue on white** | 4.50 | 50.00 |
| | v. Blue omitted | — | |
| | v1. Red omitted | — | |
| | FDC (Aug. 30, 1963) | | 1.00 |

**1964. U.S. CUSTOMS SERVICE ISSUE** Honoring their 175th anniversary.

PC46 *Map of United States and flags.*

**PC46**

| | | MNHVF | UseVF |
|---|---|---|---|
| 4¢ | **red & blue on white** | .55 | 1.50 |
| | a. Blue omitted | 600. | |
| | v1. Red omitted | — | |
| | FDC (Feb. 22, 1964) | | 1.00 |

**1964. SOCIAL SECURITY ISSUE** In compliment to the International Social Security Association conference.

PC47

**PC47**

| | | MNHVF | UseVF |
|---|---|---|---|
| 4¢ | **red & blue on white** | .50 | 1.50 |
| | p. Fluorescent paper | — | — |
| | v. Red omitted | — | |
| | v1. Blue omitted | 750. | |
| | FDC (Sept. 29, 1964) | | 1.00 |

**1965. U.S. COAST GUARD ISSUE** Honoring their 175th anniversary.

PC48 *U.S. Coast Guard flag.*

**PC48**

| | | MNHVF | UseVF |
|---|---|---|---|
| 4¢ | **red & blue on white** | .50 | 1.50 |
| | v. Blue omitted | — | |
| | FDC (Aug. 4, 1965) | | 1.00 |

**1965. U.S. CENSUS BUREAU ISSUE** Honoring their 175th anniversary.

PC49 *Census Anniversary*

**PC49**

| | | MNHVF | UseVF |
|---|---|---|---|
| 4¢ | **blue, light blue, & black on white** | .40 | 1.50 |
| | FDC (Oct. 21, 1965) | | 1.00 |

**1967. VACATIONLAND ISSUE** International Postal Card, design of PC45.

**PC50**

| | | MNHVF | UseVF |
|---|---|---|---|
| 8¢ | **red & blue on white** | 4.25 | |
| | FDC (Dec. 4, 1967) | | 1.00 |

**1968. ABRAHAM LINCOLN ISSUE**

PC51 *Abraham Lincoln*

**PC51**

| | | MNHVF | UseVF |
|---|---|---|---|
| 5¢ | **green on white** | .35 | .50 |
| | v. Double impression | — | |
| | FDC (Jan. 4, 1968) | | 1.00 |

**1968. WOMEN MARINES ISSUE** Honoring their 25th anniversary.

PC52 *Women Marines.*

**PC52**

| | | MNHVF | UseVF |
|---|---|---|---|
| 5¢ | **olive green and rose red on white** | .40 | 1.50 |
| | FDC (July 26, 1968) | | 1.00 |

**1970. WEATHER SERVICES CENTENNIAL ISSUE**

PC53 *Weather recording equipment.*

**PC53**

| | | MNHVF | UseVF |
|---|---|---|---|
| 5¢ | **yellow, blue, red, and black on white, tagged** | .35 | 1.50 |
| | v. Black omitted | 600. | |
| | v1. Black & yellow omitted | 700. | |
| | v2. Blue omitted | 650. | |
| | FDC (Sept. 1, 1970) | | 1.00 |

## Patriot Series

**1971. PAUL REVERE ISSUE**

PC54 *Paul Revere*

**PC54**

| | | MNHVF | UseVF |
|---|---|---|---|
| 6¢ | **brown on white,** tagged | .35 | 2.00 |
| | v. Double impression | 325. | — |
| | FDC (May 15, 1971) | | 1.00 |

**1971. VACATIONLAND ISSUE** Design of PC45, vacationland.

**PC55**

| | | MNHVF | UseVF |
|---|---|---|---|
| 10¢ | **red and blue on white,** tagged | 4.75 | 50.00 |
| | FDC (June 10, 1971) | | 1.00 |

**1971. NEW YORK HOSPITAL BICENTENNIAL ISSUE**

PC56 *New York Hospital*

**PC56**

| | | MNHVF | UseVF |
|---|---|---|---|
| 6¢ | **multicolored on white,** tagged | .35 | 2.00 |
| | v. Blue & yellow omitted | 700. | |
| | v1. Red omitted | — | |
| | v2. Red & black omitted | — | |
| | v3. Yellow omitted | — | |
| | v4. Red & black impressions shifted 25mm left | — | |
| | za. Tagging omitted | — | |
| | FDC (Sept. 16, 1971) | | 1.00 |

**1972. TOURISM YEAR OF THE AMERICAS ISSUE** A luminescent panel of tagging is printed at the left of the stamp.

PC58 *Monument Valley*

| PC58 | | MNHVF | UseVF |
|---|---|---|---|
| 6¢ | **black on manila,** tagged | .50 | 4.50 |
| | zo. Tagging omitted | — | |
| | FDC | | 1.00 |

PC59 *USF Constellation*

| PC59 | | MNHVF | UseVF |
|---|---|---|---|
| 6¢ | **black on manila,** tagged | .50 | 4.50 |
| | v. Address side blank | 325. | |
| | zo. Tagging omitted | — | |
| | FDC | | 1.00 |

*First-day cancels were available from any post office which had the cards in stock that day.*

**1972. JOHN HANSON ISSUE** Patriot Series

PC60 *John Hanson*

| PC60 | | MNHVF | UseVF |
|---|---|---|---|
| 6¢ | **blue on white,** tagged, smooth paper | .30 | 1.00 |
| | FDC *(Sept. 1, 1972)* | | 1.00 |
| | p. Coarse paper | .30 | 1.00 |

**1973. U.S. POST CARD CENTENNIAL ISSUE**

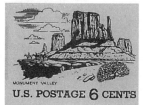

PC61 *Design similar to PC1.*

| PC61 | | MNHVF | UseVF |
|---|---|---|---|
| 6¢ | **magenta on manila** | .30 | 2.00 |
| | FDC *(Sept. 14, 1973)* | | 1.00 |
| | v. Double impression | — | |
| | zo. Tagging omitted | — | |
| | zv. Tagging inverted to lower left | — | |

**1973. SAMUEL ADAMS ISSUE** Patriot Series

PC62 *Samuel Adams*

| PC62 | | MNHVF | UseVF |
|---|---|---|---|
| 8¢ | **orange on white,** tagged, smooth paper | .50 | 1.00 |
| | FDC *(Dec. 16, 1973)* | | 1.00 |
| | p. Printed on coarse paper | .50 | 1.00 |

**1974. SHIP'S FIGUREHEAD ISSUE** International surface mail.

PC63 *Ship's Figurehead*

| PC63 | | MNHVF | UseVF |
|---|---|---|---|
| 12¢ | **multicolored on white,** tagged | .40 | 35.00 |
| | FDC *(Jan. 4, 1974)* | | 1.00 |
| | v. Yellow omitted | 1000. | |

**1975. CHARLES THOMSON ISSUE** Patriot Series

PC64 *Charles Thomson*

| PC64 | | MNHVF | UseVF |
|---|---|---|---|
| 7¢ | **emerald green on white,** tagged, smooth paper | .40 | 7.50 |
| | If used after Dec. 31, 1975 | | .35 |
| | FDC *(Sept. 14, 1975)* | | 1.00 |
| | p. Printed on coarse paper | — | |

**1975. JOHN WITHERSPOON ISSUE** Patriot Series

PC65 *JOhn Witherspoon*

| PC65 | | MNHVF | UseVF |
|---|---|---|---|
| 9¢ | **yellow brown on white,** tagged | .40 | 1.00 |
| | FDC *(Nov. 10,1975)* | | 1.00 |

**1976. CAESER RODNEY ISSUE** Patriot Series

PC66 *Caesar Rodney*

| PC66 | | MNHVF | UseVF |
|---|---|---|---|
| 9¢ | **blue on white,** tagged | .35 | 1.00 |
| | v. Double impression | — | |
| | FDC *(July 1, 1976)* | | 1.00 |

## Historic Preservation Series

**1977. FEDERAL COURT HOUSE, GALVESTON, TEXAS ISSUE**

PC67 *Federal Court House, Galveston, Texas.*

**PC67**

| | | MNHVF | UseVF |
|---|---|---|---|
| 9¢ | **multicolored on white,** tagged | .40 | 1.50 |
| | FDC *(July 20, 1977)* | | 1.00 |
| | v. Black omitted | — | |
| | zo. Tagging omitted | — | |

**1977. NATHAN HALE ISSUE** Patriot Series

PC68 *Nathan Hale*

**PC68**

| | | MNHVF | UseVF |
|---|---|---|---|
| 9¢ | **green on white,** tagged | .35 | 1.00 |
| | FDC *(Oct. 14, 1977)* | | 1.00 |
| | v. Double impression | — | |

**1978. THE MUSIC HALL, CINCINNATI, OHIO ISSUE** Historic Preservation Series

PC69 *Music Hall, Cincinnati, Ohio*

**PC69**

| | | MNHVF | UseVF |
|---|---|---|---|
| 10¢ | **multicolored on white,** tagged | .40 | 1.50 |
| | FDC *(May 12, 1978)* | | 1.00 |

**1978. JOHN HANCOCK (NON-DENOMINATED) ISSUE** Patriot Series

PC70 *Hancock (for domestic use only)*

**PC70**

| | | MNHVF | UseVF |
|---|---|---|---|
| 10¢ | **brown orange on white,** tagged | .40 | 1.50 |
| | FDC *(May 19, 1978)* | | 1.00 |

**1978. JOHN HANCOCK (DECORATED "10¢") ISSUE** Patriot Series

PC71 *John Hancock (denomination as numeral).*

**PC71**

| | | MNHVF | UseVF |
|---|---|---|---|
| 10¢ | **orange on white,** tagged | .35 | .20 |
| | FDC *(June 20, 1978)* | | 1.00 |

**1978. U.S.C.G. EAGLE ISSUE** International surface mail rate.

PC72 *U.S. Coast Guard Cutter Eagle*

**PC72**

| | | MNHVF | UseVF |
|---|---|---|---|
| 14¢ | **multicolored on white,** tagged | .45 | 2.00 |
| | FDC *(Aug. 4, 1978)* | | 1.00 |

## American Revolution Series

**1978. MOLLY PITCHER ISSUE**

PC73 *Molly Pitcher (Mary Ludwig Hays)*

**PC73**

| | | MNHVF | UseVF |
|---|---|---|---|
| 10¢ | **multicolored on white,** tagged | .35 | 2.00 |
| | FDC *(Sept. 8, 1978)* | | 1.00 |

**1979. GEORGE ROGERS CLARK ISSUE** American Revolution Series

PC74 *George Rogers Clark*

**PC74**

| | | MNHVF | UseVF |
|---|---|---|---|
| 10¢ | **multicolored on white,** tagged | .35 | 2.00 |
| | FDC *(Feb. 3, 1979)* | | 1.00 |
| | v. Yellow omitted | — | |

**1979. SUMMER OLYMPICS ISSUE**

PC75 *Sprinter*

**PC75**

| | | MNHVF | UseVF |
|---|---|---|---|
| 10¢ | **multicolored,** tagged | .75 | 2.00 |
| | FDC *(Sept. 17, 1979)* | | 1.00 |
| | zo. Tagging omitted | — | |

**1979. IOLANI PALACE, HONOLULU, HAWAII ISSUE** Historic Preservation Series

PC76 *Iolani Palace, Hawaii*

**PC76**

| | | MNHVF | UseVF |
|---|---|---|---|
| 10¢ | **multicolored on white,** tagged | .35 | 2.00 |
| | FDC *(Oct. 1, 1979)* | | 1.00 |
| | zo. Tagging omitted | — | |

**1979. CASIMIR PULASKI ISSUE** American Revolution Series

PC77 *Gen. Casimir Pulaski*

**PC77**

| | | MNHVF | UseVF |
|---|---|---|---|
| 10¢ | **multicolored on white,** tagged | .35 | 2.00 |
| | FDC *(Oct. 11, 1979)* | | 1.00 |

**1980. WINTER OLYMPICS ISSUE** Women's figure skater.

PC78 *Figure Skater*

| PC78 | | MNHVF | UseVF |
|---|---|---|---|
| 14¢ | **multicolored,** tagged | .75 | 12.50 |
| | FDC *(Jan. 15, 1980)* | | 1.00 |

**1980. SALT LAKE TEMPLE ISSUE** Historic Preservation Series

PC79 *Mormon Temple, Salt Lake City, Utah*

| PC79 | | MNHVF | UseVF |
|---|---|---|---|
| 10¢ | **multicolored on white,** tagged | .35 | 2.00 |
| | FDC *(April 5, 1980)* | | 1.00 |
| | zo. Tagging omitted | — | |

**1980. LANDING OF ROCHAMBEAU ISSUE** American Revolution Series

PC80 *Count Jean-Baptiste de Rochambeau*

| PC80 | | MNHVF | UseVF |
|---|---|---|---|
| 10¢ | **multicolored on white,** tagged | .35 | 2.00 |
| | FDC *(July 11, 1980)* | | 1.00 |
| | v. Black & yellow printed on reverse, front normal | — | |

**1980. BATTLE OF KINGS MOUNTAIN ISSUE** American Revolution Series

PC81 *Battle of Kings Mountain, 1780.*

| PC81 | | MNHVF | UseVF |
|---|---|---|---|
| 10¢ | **multicolored,** tagged | .35 | 2.00 |
| | FDC *(Oct. 7, 1980)* | | 1.00 |

**1980. DRAKE'S GOLDEN HINDE ISSUE** International surface rate. Celebrating the 300th anniversary of the circumnavigation of the globe by Drake.

PC82 The Golden Hinde, *ship of Sir Francis Drake*

| PC82 | | MNHVF | UseVF |
|---|---|---|---|
| 19¢ | **multicolored on white,** tagged | .75 | 15.00 |
| | FDC *(Nov. 21, 1980)* | | 1.00 |

**1981. BATTLE OF COWPENS ISSUE** American Revolution Series

PC83 *Battle of Cowpens, 1781*

| PC83 | | MNHVF | UseVF |
|---|---|---|---|
| 10¢ | **multicolored,** tagged | .35 | 4.00 |
| | FDC *(Jan. 17, 1981)* | | 1.00 |

**1981. NON-DENOMINATED EAGLE ISSUE**

PC84 *Stylized Eagle*

| PC84 | | MNHVF | UseVF |
|---|---|---|---|
| 12¢ | **purple on white** | .40 | 1.00 |
| | FDC *(March 15, 1981)* | | 1.00 |

**1981. ISAIAH THOMAS ISSUE** Patriot Series

PC85 *Isaiah Thomas*

| PC85 | | MNHVF | UseVF |
|---|---|---|---|
| 12¢ | **blue on white** | .35 | 1.00 |
| | FDC *(May 5, 1981)* | | 1.00 |

**1981. NATHANAEL GREENE, EUTAW SPRINGS ISSUE** American Revolution Series

PC86 *Nathanael Greene and The Battle at Eutaw Springs, 1781.*

| PC86 | | MNHVF | UseVF |
|---|---|---|---|
| 12¢ | **multicolored on white** | .35 | 2.00 |
| | FDC *(Sept. 8, 1981)* | | 1.00 |
| | v. Magenta & yellow omitted | — | |

**1981. LEWIS AND CLARK EXPEDITION ISSUE**

PC87 *Lewis and Clark Expedition, 1806.*

| PC87 | | MNHVF | UseVF |
|---|---|---|---|
| 12¢ | **multicolored** | .35 | 4.00 |
| | FDC *(Sept. 23, 1981)* | | 1.00 |

**1981. ROBERT MORRIS ISSUE** Patriot Series
U.S. Domestic Rate.

PC88 *Robert Morris US Domestic Rate only.*

| PC88 | | MNHVF | UseVF |
|---|---|---|---|
| 13¢ | **brown on white** | .35 | 1.00 |
| | FDC *(Oct. 11, 1981)* | | 1.00 |

**1981. ROBERT MORRIS ISSUE** Patriot Series
U.S. Postage 13.

PC89 *Robert Morris (denomination, as numeral).*

| PC89 | | MNHVF | UseVF |
|---|---|---|---|
| 13¢ | **brown on white** | .35 | 1.00 |
| | FDC *(Nov. 10, 1981)* | | 1.00 |

**1982. "SWAMP FOX" FRANCIS MARION ISSUE** American Revolution Series

PC90 *Gen. Francis Marion*

| PC90 | | MNHVF | UseVF |
|---|---|---|---|
| 13¢ | **multicolored on white** | .35 | 1.00 |
| | FDC *(April 3, 1982)* | | 1.00 |

**1982. LASALLE CLAIMS LOUISIANA ISSUE**

PC91 *LaSalle Expedition*

| PC91 | | MNHVF | UseVF |
|---|---|---|---|
| 13¢ | **multicolored on white** | .35 | 1.00 |
| | FDC *(April 7, 1982)* | | 1.00 |

**1982. PHILADELPHIA ACADEMY OF MUSIC ISSUE**

PC92 *Philadelphia Academy of Music*

| PC92 | | MNHVF | UseVF |
|---|---|---|---|
| 13¢ | **brown, dark beige, red on tan** | .35 | 1.00 |
| | FDC *(June 18, 1982)* | | 1.00 |
| | v.  Brown & dark beige omitted | — | |

**1982. OLD POST OFFICE, ST. LOUIS ISSUE** Historic Preservation Series

PC93 *Old St. Louis Post Office.*

Historic Preservation

| PC93 | | MNHVF | UseVF |
|---|---|---|---|
| 13¢ | **multicolored on white** | .35 | 1.00 |
| | FDC *(Oct. 14, 1982)* | | 1.00 |

**1983. LANDING OF GEN. OGLETHORPE, GEORGIA ISSUE**

PC94 *Landing of James Oglethorpe in Georgia.*

Landing of Oglethorpe, Georgia, 1733

| PC94 | | MNHVF | UseVF |
|---|---|---|---|
| 13¢ | **multicolored on white** | .35 | 1.00 |
| | FDC *(Feb. 12, 1983)* | | 1.00 |

**1983. OLD POST OFFICE, WASHINGTON, D.C. ISSUE** Historic Preservation Series

PC95 *Old Post Office, Washington, D.C.*

| PC95 | | MNHVF | UseVF |
|---|---|---|---|
| 13¢ | **multicolored on white** | .35 | 1.00 |
| | FDC *(April 19, 1983)* | | 1.00 |

**1983. SUMMER OLYMPICS ISSUE**

PC96 *Yachting*

| PC96 | | MNHVF | UseVF |
|---|---|---|---|
| 13¢ | **multicolored on white** | .35 | 1.00 |
| | FDC *(Aug. 5, 1983)* | | 1.00 |
| | v.  Black, magenta & yellow omitted | | |

**1984. ARK AND DOVE, MARYLAND, 1634 ISSUE**

PC97 *Ark and Dove*

Ark and Dove, Maryland, 1634

**PC97**

| | | MNHVF | UseVF |
|---|---|---|---|
| 13¢ | multicolored on white | .35 | 1.00 |
| | FDC (March 25, 1984) | | 1.00 |

### 1984. Summer Olympics Issue

PC98 Olympic Torch Carrier.

**PC98**

| | | MNHVF | UseVF |
|---|---|---|---|
| 13¢ | multicolored on white | .35 | 1.00 |
| | FDC (April 30, 1984) | | 1.00 |
| | v. Yellow & black inverted | — | |
| | zo. Tagging omitted | — | |

### 1984. Frederic Baraga Issue

PC99 Frederic Baraga

Frederic Baraga, Michigan, 1835

**PC99**

| | | MNHVF | UseVF |
|---|---|---|---|
| 13¢ | multicolored on white | .35 | 1.00 |
| | FDC (June 29, 1984) | | 1.00 |

## Historic Preservation Series

### 1984. Rancho San Pedro Issue

PC100 Rancho San Pedro

**PC100**

| | | MNHVF | UseVF |
|---|---|---|---|
| 13¢ | multicolored | .35 | 1.00 |
| | FDC (Sept. 16, 1984) | | 1.00 |
| | a. Black & blue omitted | — | |
| | z. Tagging omitted | — | |

## Patriot Series

### 1985. Charles Carroll Non-Denominated Issue U.S. domestic rate.

PC101 Charles Carroll (Domestic Rate).

**PC101**

| | | MNHVF | UseVF |
|---|---|---|---|
| 14¢ | green on white, non-denominated | .35 | .50 |
| | FDC (Feb. 1, 1985) | | 1.00 |

### 1985. Clipper Flying Cloud Issue

PC102 Clipper Flying Cloud, 1852

**PC102**

| | | MNHVF | UseVF |
|---|---|---|---|
| 25¢ | multicolored on white | .75 | 7.50 |
| | x. Cachet for CUP.PEX '87, Perth, Australia | — | 1.25 |
| | FDC (Feb. 27, 1985) | | 1.00 |

### 1985. Charles Carroll Denominated Issue Patriot Series USA 14.

PC103 Charles Carroll (denomination as numeral).

**PC103**

| | | MNHVF | UseVF |
|---|---|---|---|
| 14¢ | green on white | .35 | .25 |
| | FDC (March 6, 1985) | | 1.00 |

### 1985. George Wythe Issue Patriot Series

PC104 George Wythe

**PC104**

| | | MNHVF | UseVF |
|---|---|---|---|
| 14¢ | olive green on white | .35 | .50 |
| | FDC (June 20, 1985) | | 1.00 |

### 1986. Settling of Connecticut Issue

PC105 Settling of Connecticut

Settling of Connecticut, 1636

**PC105**

| | | MNHVF | UseVF |
|---|---|---|---|
| 14¢ | multicolored on white | .30 | 1.00 |
| | FDC (April 18, 1986) | | 1.00 |

### 1986. Stamp Collecting Issue

PC106

**PC106**

| | | MNHVF | UseVF |
|---|---|---|---|
| 14¢ | multicolored on white | .35 | 1.00 |
| | x. Cachet for NAJURBIA '86, Germany. | 7.50 | — |
| | FDC (May 23, 1986) | | 1.00 |

### 1986. Francis Vigo Issue

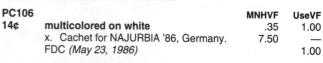

PC107 Francis Vigo, Battle of Vincennes.

Francis Vigo, Vincennes, 1779

| PC107 | | MNHVF | UseVF |
|---|---|---|---|
| 14¢ | multicolored on white | .35 | 1.00 |
| | FDC *(May 24, 1986)* | | 1.00 |

## 1986. SETTLING OF RHODE ISLAND ISSUE

PC108 *Roger Williams Landing at Providence.*

| PC108 | | MNHVF | UseVF |
|---|---|---|---|
| 14¢ | multicolored on white | .35 | 1.00 |
| | FDC *(June 26, 1986)* | | 1.00 |

## 1986. WISCONSIN TERRITORY SESQUICENTENNIAL ISSUE

PC109 *Wisconsin Territory 150th Anniversary.*

| PC109 | | MNHVF | UseVF |
|---|---|---|---|
| 14¢ | multicolored on white | .35 | 1.00 |
| | FDC *(July 3, 1986)* | | 1.00 |

## 1986. NATIONAL GUARD ISSUE

PC110 *National Guard, 350th Anniversary.*

| PC110 | | MNHVF | UseVF |
|---|---|---|---|
| 14¢ | multicolored on white | .35 | 1.00 |
| | FDC *(Dec. 12, 1986)* | | 1.00 |

## 1987. SELF-SCOURING PLOW ISSUE

PC111 *150th Anniversary, Steel Plow by John Deere.*

| PC111 | | MNHVF | UseVF |
|---|---|---|---|
| 14¢ | multicolored on white | .35 | 1.00 |
| | FDC *(May 22, 1987)* | | 1.00 |

## 1987. CONSTITUTIONAL CONVENTION ISSUE

PC112 *Constitutional Convention, 1787*

| PC112 | | MNHVF | UseVF |
|---|---|---|---|
| 14¢ | multicolored on white | .35 | 1.00 |
| | FDC *(May 25, 1987)* | | 1.00 |

## 1987. U.S. FLAG ISSUE

PC113 *Flag*

| PC113 | | MNHVF | UseVF |
|---|---|---|---|
| 14¢ | black, blue, and red on white | .35 | .50 |
| | FDC *(June 14, 1987)* | | 1.00 |
| | x. Cachet for Philatelia '87 (exhibition in Koln, Germany) | 1.00 | |
| | vz. Tagging double, 1 normal & 1 split top & bottom | — | |

## 1987. PRIDE IN AMERICA ISSUE

PC114 *Landscape*

| PC114 | | MNHVF | UseVF |
|---|---|---|---|
| 14¢ | multicolored on white | .35 | 1.00 |
| | FDC *(Sept. 22, 1987)* | | 1.00 |

## 1987. TIMBERLINE LODGE, MOUNT HOOD, OREGON ISSUE Historic Preservation Series

PC115 *Timberline Lodge, Mt. Hood, Ore.*

| PC115 | | MNHVF | UseVF |
|---|---|---|---|
| 14¢ | multicolored on white | .35 | 1.00 |
| | FDC *(Sept. 28, 1987)* | | 1.00 |

## America the Beautiful Series

## 1988. PRAIRIE SCENE ISSUE

PC116 *Bison on the Prairie.*

| PC116 | | MNHVF | UseVF |
|---|---|---|---|
| 15¢ | multicolored on white, | .35 | 1.00 |
| | FDC *(March 28, 1988)* | | 1.00 |
| | p. Fluorescent paper | — | |
| | v. Printed on both sides | 650. | |
| | v1. Black & blue on reverse, front normal | 650. | |
| | v2. Black omitted | — | |

## 1988. BLAIR HOUSE ISSUE

PC117 *Blair House, Washington, D.C.*

| PC117 | | MNHVF | UseVF |
|---|---|---|---|
| 15¢ | multicolored on white | .35 | 1.00 |
| | FDC *(May 4, 1988)* | | 1.00 |

## 1988. SQUARE-RIGGED PACKET SHIP *YORKSHIRE* ISSUE International surface rate.

PC118 *Yorkshire*

| PC118 | | MNHVF | UseVF |
|---|---|---|---|
| 28¢ | multicolored | .75 | 4.00 |
| | FDC *(June 29, 1988)* | | 1.00 |

## 1988. IOWA TERRITORY SESQUICENTENNIAL ISSUE

PC119 *Corn Harvesting*

| PC119 | | MNHVF | UseVF |
|---|---|---|---|
| 15¢ | multicolored on white | .35 | 1.00 |
| | FDC *(July 2, 1988)* | | 1.00 |

## 1988. SETTLING OF OHIO ISSUE The Bicentennial of the settling of Ohio, then in the Northwest Territory.

PC120 *Flatboat ferry transporting settlers.*

| PC120 | | MNHVF | UseVF |
|---|---|---|---|
| 15¢ | multicolored on white | .35 | 1.00 |
| | FDC *(July 15, 1988)* | | 1.00 |

## 1988. HEARST CASTLE ISSUE Hearst Castle is located at San Simeon, Calif.

PC121 *Hearst Castle, San Simeon, Calif.*

| PC121 | | MNHVF | UseVF |
|---|---|---|---|
| 15¢ | multicolored on white | .35 | 1.00 |
| | FDC *(Sept. 20, 1988)* | | 1.00 |

## 1988. FEDERALIST PAPERS ISSUE

PC122 *Colonial Pressman*

| PC122 | | MNHVF | UseVF |
|---|---|---|---|
| 15¢ | multicolored on white | .35 | 1.00 |
| | FDC *(Oct. 27, 1988)* | | 1.00 |

## 1989. SONORA DESERT ISSUE America the Beautiful Series

PC123 *Hawk and Sonora Desert Sunset*

| PC123 | | MNHVF | UseVF |
|---|---|---|---|
| 15¢ | multicolored on white | .35 | 1.00 |
| | FDC *(Jan. 13, 1989)*NI | | 1.00 |

## College Series

### 1989. GEORGETOWN UNIVERSITY ISSUE

PC124 *Healy Hall, Georgetown University.*

| PC124 | | MNHVF | UseVF |
|---|---|---|---|
| 15¢ | multicolored on white | .35 | 1.00 |
| | FDC *(Jan. 23, 1989)* | | 1.00 |

## 1989. BLUE HERON AND MARSH ISSUE America the Beautiful Series

PC125 *Great Blue Heron in Marsh Scene.*

| PC125 | | MNHVF | UseVF |
|---|---|---|---|
| 15¢ | multicolored on white | .35 | 1.00 |
| | FDC *(March 17, 1989)* | | 1.00 |

## 1989. SETTLING OF OKLAHOMA ISSUE

PC126 *Land rush scene.*

**PC126**
|  |  | MNHVF | UseVF |
|---|---|---|---|
| 15¢ | multicolored on white | .35 | .35 |
| | FDC *(April 22, 1989)* | | 1.00 |

**1989. MOUNTAIN SCENE, GEESE ISSUE** America the Beautiful Series

Card paid surface rate to Canada.

PC127 *Geese in flight.*

**PC127**
|  |  | MNHVF | UseVF |
|---|---|---|---|
| 21¢ | multicolored on white | .65 | 5.00 |
| | FDC *(May 5, 1989)* | | 1.00 |

**1989. SEA SHORE ISSUE** America the Beautiful Series

PC128 *Sea Shore*

**PC128**
|  |  | MNHVF | UseVF |
|---|---|---|---|
| 15¢ | multicolored on white | .35 | 1.00 |
| | FDC *(June 17, 1898)* | | 1.00 |

**1989. FOREST STREAM ISSUE** America the Beautiful Series

PC129 *Deer in forest.*

**PC129**
|  |  | MNHVF | UseVF |
|---|---|---|---|
| 15¢ | multicolored on white | .35 | 1.00 |
| | FDC *(Aug. 26, 1989)* | | 1.00 |

**1989. HULL HOUSE ISSUE**

PC130 *Jane Addam's Hull House Community Center, Chicago.*

**PC130**
|  |  | MNHVF | UseVF |
|---|---|---|---|
| 15¢ | multicolored on white | .35 | 1.00 |
| | FDC *(Sept. 16, 1989)* | | 1.00 |

**1989. INDEPENDENCE HALL ISSUE** America the Beautiful Series

PC131 *Independence Hall, Philadelphia*

**PC131**
|  |  | MNHVF | UseVF |
|---|---|---|---|
| 15¢ | multicolored on white | .35 | 1.00 |
| | FDC *(Sept. 25, 1989)* | | 1.00 |

**1989. BALTIMORE HARBOR ISSUE** America the Beautiful Series

PC132 *Inner Harbor; USS Constellation Baltimore, Maryland.*

**PC132**
|  |  | MNHVF | UseVF |
|---|---|---|---|
| 15¢ | multicolored on white | .35 | 1.00 |
| | FDC *(Oct. 7, 1989)* | | 1.00 |

**1989. MANHATTAN SKYLINE ISSUE** America the Beautiful Series

PC133 *Manhattan skyline, Queensboro bridge.*

**PC133**
|  |  | MNHVF | UseVF |
|---|---|---|---|
| 15¢ | multicolored on white | .35 | 1.00 |
| | FDC *(Nov. 8. 1989)* | | 1.00 |

**1989. U.S. CAPITOL BUILDING ISSUE** America the Beautiful Series

PC134 *U.S. Capitol Building.*

**PC134**
|  |  | MNHVF | UseVF |
|---|---|---|---|
| 15¢ | multicolored on white | .35 | 1.00 |
| | FDC *(Nov. 26, 1989)* | | 1.00 |

**1989. WHITE HOUSE PICTURE POST CARD ISSUE** Sold for 50 cents each with the illustration of the White House enlarged on the reverse.

PC135 *White House*

**PC135**
|  |  | MNHVF | UseVF |
|---|---|---|---|
| 15¢ | multicolored on white | 1.25 | 2.50 |
| | FDC *(Nov. 30, 1989)* | | 1.00 |

**1989. AMERICA THE BEAUTIFUL SE-TENANT SHEET ISSUE** Designs of PC131-PC134 were issued in a se-tenant sheet of four cards, with rouletting between them for separation, for World Stamp Expo '89. The sheet includes two labels showing the emblems of either World Stamp Expo '89 or the 20th UPU Congress. These cards do not include inscription and copyright symbols at lower left. Rouletted 9 1/2 on two or three sides.

**PC136**
|  |  | MNHVF | UseVF |
|---|---|---|---|
| 15¢ | multicolored on white, design of PC132 | 2.00 | 2.00 |
| | FDC *(Dec. 1, 1989)* | | 1.00 |

**PC136A**

| | | MNHVF | UseVF |
|---|---|---|---|
| 15¢ | multicolored on white, design of PC131 | 2.00 | 2.00 |
| | FDC | | 1.00 |

**PC136B**

| | | MNHVF | UseVF |
|---|---|---|---|
| 15¢ | multicolored on white, design of PC134 | 2.00 | 2.00 |
| | FDC | | 1.00 |

**PC136C**

| | | MNHVF | UseVF |
|---|---|---|---|
| 15¢ | multicolored on white, design of PC133 | 2.00 | 2.00 |
| | FDC | | 1.00 |
| | y.  Se-tenant block of 4 PC136-136C w/2 lables | 12.50 | |

**1989. JEFFERSON MEMORIAL PICTURE POST CARD ISSUE** Sold for 50 cents each, with the illustration of the Jefferson Memorial enlarged, covering the reverse.

PC137 *Jefferson Memorial*

**PC137**

| | | MNHVF | UseVF |
|---|---|---|---|
| 15¢ | multicolored on white | 1.25 | 2.50 |
| | FDC *(Dec. 2, 1989)* | | 1.00 |

**1990. RITTENHOUSE PAPER MILL ISSUE**

PC138 *Rittenhouse Paper Mill, Germantown, Penn.*

**PC138**

| | | MNHVF | UseVF |
|---|---|---|---|
| 15¢ | multicolored on white | .35 | 1.00 |
| | FDC *(March 13, 1990)* | | 1.00 |

**1990. WORLD LITERACY YEAR ISSUE**

PC139 *Book and globe, World Literacy Year.*

**PC139**

| | | MNHVF | UseVF |
|---|---|---|---|
| 15¢ | multicolored on white | .35 | .50 |
| | FDC *(March 22, 1990)* | | 1.00 |

**1990. GEORGE CALEB BINGHAM PICTURE POST CARD ISSUE** Sold for 50 cents, with the painting *Fur Traders Descending the Missouri* covering the reverse.

PC140 *Furtraders on the Missouri.*

**PC140**

| | | MNHVF | UseVF |
|---|---|---|---|
| 15¢ | multicolored on white | 1.25 | 2.50 |
| | FDC *(May 4, 1990)* | | 1.00 |

**1990. ISAAC ROYALL HOUSE ISSUE** Historic Preservation Series

PC141 *Isaac Royall House, Medford, Mass.*

**PC141**

| | | MNHVF | UseVF |
|---|---|---|---|
| 15¢ | multicolored on white | .45 | 1.00 |
| | FDC *(June 16, 1990)* | | 1.00 |

**1990. POSTAL BUDDY ISSUE** computer-generated and printed USPS Eagle card, available from a vending machine under a special license agreement. The cards cost 33 cents, plus state sales tax, from one of a group of test machines in Virginia. A variety of borders, messages and backs are known. The cards also were produced in sheets of four.

PC142 *Postal Buddy Card*

**PC142**

| | | MNHVF | UseVF |
|---|---|---|---|
| 15¢ | black on white | 8.50 | 15.00 |
| | FDC *(July 5, 1990)* | | 2.50 |

**1990. STANFORD UNIVERSITY ISSUE** College Series

PC143 *Quadrangle, Stanford University*

**PC143**

| | | MNHVF | UseVF |
|---|---|---|---|
| 15¢ | multicolored on white | .35 | 1.00 |
| | FDC *(Sept. 11, 1990)* | | 1.00 |

**1990. CONSTITUTION HALL PICTURE POST CARD ISSUE** Sold for 50 cents with an enlarged picture of Constitution Hall, Washington, D.C. covering the reverse.

PC144 *Constitution Hall, Washington, D.C.*

**PC144**

| | | MNHVF | UseVF |
|---|---|---|---|
| 15¢ | multicolored on white | 1.25 | 2.50 |
| | FDC *(Oct. 11, 1990)* | | 1.00 |

**1990. CHICAGO ORCHESTRA HALL ISSUE** Historic Preservation Series

PC145 *Chicago Orchestra Hall*

**PC145**

| | | MNHVF | UseVF |
|---|---|---|---|
| 15¢ | multicolored on white | .45 | 1.00 |
| | FDC *(Oct. 19, 1990)* | | 1.00 |

## 1991. FLAG ISSUE

PC146 *Flag*

| PC146 | | MNHVF | UseVF |
|---|---|---|---|
| 19¢ | **black, blue, and red on white** | .50 | .50 |
| | FDC *(April 1, 1991)* | | 1.00 |

## 1991. POSTAL BUDDY USPS EAGLE CARD ISSUE Available in sheets of four from vending machines. (See PC142.)

PC147 *Postal Buddy Card*

| PC147 | | MNHVF | UseVF |
|---|---|---|---|
| 19¢ | **black on white** | 4.00 | 15.00 |
| | FDC *(Feb. 3, 1991)* | | 2.50 |

## 1991. CARNEGIE HALL CENTENNIAL ISSUE

PC148 *Carnegie Hall, New York City*

| PC148 | | MNHVF | UseVF |
|---|---|---|---|
| 19¢ | **multicolored on white** | .50 | 1.00 |
| | FDC *(April 1, 1991)* | | 1.00 |

## 1991. U OF T MEDICAL BRANCH AT GALVESTON ISSUE College Series

PC149 *Old Red, University of Texas Medical Branch, Galveston.*

| PC149 | | MNHVF | UseVF |
|---|---|---|---|
| 19¢ | **multicolored on white** | .50 | 1.00 |
| | FDC *(June 14, 1991)* | | 1.00 |

## 1991. NIAGARA FALLS ISSUE America the Beautiful Series

PC150 *Niagara Falls*

| PC150 | | MNHVF | UseVF |
|---|---|---|---|
| 30¢ | **multicolored on white** | 1.00 | 2.00 |
| | FDC *(Aug. 21, 1991)* | | 1.00 |

## 1991. BILL OF RIGHTS ISSUE

PC151 *Ratification of the Bill of Rights*

| PC151 | | MNHVF | UseVF |
|---|---|---|---|
| 19¢ | **black, blue, and red on white** | .50 | .75 |
| | FDC *(Sept. 25, 1991)* | | 1.00 |

## 1991. UNIVERSITY OF NOTRE DAME ISSUE College Series

PC152 *Main Building, University of Notre Dame, South Bend, Ind.*

| PC152 | | MNHVF | UseVF |
|---|---|---|---|
| 19¢ | **multicolored on white** | .50 | 1.00 |
| | FDC *(Oct. 15, 1991)* | | 1.00 |

## 1991. UNIVERSITY OF VERMONT ISSUE College Series

PC153 *The Old Mill, University of Vermont.*

| PC153 | | MNHVF | UseVF |
|---|---|---|---|
| 19¢ | **multicolored on white** | .50 | 1.00 |
| | FDC *(Oct. 29, 1991)* | | 1.00 |

## 1992. WADSWORTH ATHENEUM SESQUICENTENNIAL ISSUE

PC154 *Wadsworth Atheneum, Hartford, Conn.*

| PC154 | | MNHVF | UseVF |
|---|---|---|---|
| 19¢ | **multicolored on white** | .50 | 1.00 |
| | FDC *(Jan. 16, 1992)* | | 1.00 |

## 1992. UNIVERSITY OF CHICAGO ISSUE College Series

PC155 *Cobb Hall, University of Chicago.*

| PC155 | | MNHVF | UseVF |
|---|---|---|---|
| 19¢ | **multicolored on white** | .50 | .75 |
| | FDC *(Jan. 23, 1992)* | | 1.00 |

## 1992. WILLAMETTE UNIVERSITY ISSUE College Series

PC156 *Waller Hall, Willamette University, Salem Ore.*

| PC156 | | MNHVF | UseVF |
|---|---|---|---|
| 19¢ | multicolored on white | .50 | .75 |
| | FDC *(Feb. 1, 1992)* | | 1.00 |

## 1992. AMERICA'S CUP PICTURE POST CARD ISSUE

PC157 *America's Cup. The Reliance, 1903.*

| PC157 | | MNHVF | UseVF |
|---|---|---|---|
| 19¢ | multicolored on white | 1.25 | 1.25 |
| | FDC *(May 6, 1992)* | | 1.00 |

## 1992. COLUMBIA RIVER GORGE ISSUE

PC158 *Columbia River Gorge*

| PC158 | | MNHVF | UseVF |
|---|---|---|---|
| 19¢ | multicolored on white | .50 | .75 |
| | FDC *(May 9, 1992)* | | 1.00 |

## 1992. ELLIS ISLAND CENTENNIAL ISSUE

PC159 *Ellis Island Immigration Museum*

| PC159 | | MNHVF | UseVF |
|---|---|---|---|
| 19¢ | multicolored on white | .50 | .75 |
| | FDC *(May 11, 1992)* | | 1.00 |

## 1992. POSTAL BUDDY ISSUE Available only in sheets of four from vending machines. Price raised to 39 cents per card, plus any state sales tax. (See PC142.)

PC160 *Postal Buddy Post Card*

| PC160 | | MNHVF | UseVF |
|---|---|---|---|
| 19¢ | multicolored on white, tagged | 15.00 | 35.00 |
| | FDC *(Nov. 13, 1992)* | | 1.00 |
| | p. Fluorescent paper | — | |

## 1993. WASHINGTON NATIONAL CATHEDRAL ISSUE

PC161 *Washington National Cathedral*

| PC161 | | MNHVF | UseVF |
|---|---|---|---|
| 19¢ | multicolored on white | .50 | .75 |
| | FDC *(Jan. 6, 1993)* | | 1.00 |

## 1993. COLLEGE OF WILLIAM & MARY ISSUE College Series

PC162 *Wren Building, College of William & Mary.*

| PC162 | | MNHVF | UseVF |
|---|---|---|---|
| 19¢ | multicolored on white | .50 | .75 |
| | FDC *(Feb. 8, 1993)* | | 1.00 |

## 1993. HOLOCAUST MEMORIAL PICTURE POST CARD ISSUE Sold for 50 cents with a view of the museum covering the reverse.

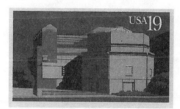

PC163 *Holocaust Memorial Museum*

| PC163 | | MNHVF | UseVF |
|---|---|---|---|
| 19¢ | multicolored on white | 1.25 | 2.00 |
| | FDC *(March 23, 1993)* | | 3.00 |

## 1993. FORT RECOVERY ISSUE

PC164 *Ft. Recovery, Ohio*

| PC164 | | MNHVF | UseVF |
|---|---|---|---|
| 19¢ | multicolored on white | .50 | .75 |
| | FDC *(June 13, 1993)* | | 1.00 |

## 1993. UNIVERSITY OF NORTH CAROLINA ISSUE College Series

PC165 *Playmaker's Theater at Chapel Hill, N.C.*

**PC165**

| | | MNHVF | UseVF |
|---|---|---|---|
| 19¢ | multicolored on white | .50 | .75 |
| | FDC *(Sept. 14, 1993)* | | 1.00 |

### 1993. COLLEGE OF THE HOLY CROSS ISSUE College Series

PC166 *O'Kane Hall, College of the Holy Cross, Worcester, Ma.*

**PC166**

| | | MNHVF | UseVF |
|---|---|---|---|
| 19¢ | multicolored on white | .50 | .45 |
| | FDC *(Sept. 17, 1993)* | | 1.00 |

### 1993. ILLINOIS COLLEGE ISSUE College Series

PC167 *Beecher Hall at Illinois College, Jacksonville, Il.*

**PC167**

| | | MNHVF | UseVF |
|---|---|---|---|
| 19¢ | multicolored | .50 | .45 |
| | FDC *(Oct. 9, 1993)* | | 1.00 |

### 1993. BOWDOIN COLLEGE ISSUE College Series

PC168 *Massachusetts Hall, Bowdoin College, Brunswick, Maine.*

**PC168**

| | | MNHVF | UseVF |
|---|---|---|---|
| 19¢ | multicolored | .50 | .75 |
| | FDC *(Oct. 14, 1993)* | | 1.00 |

### 1994. LINCOLN HOME ISSUE

PC169 *Lincoln's Home, Springfield, Illinois.*

**PC169**

| | | MNHVF | UseVF |
|---|---|---|---|
| 19¢ | multicolored | .50 | .60 |
| | FDC *(Feb. 12, 1994)* | | 1.00 |

### 1994. WITTENBERG UNIVERSITY ISSUE College Series

PC170 *Meyers Hall, Wittenbery University, Springfield, Ohio.*

**PC170**

| | | MNHVF | UseVF |
|---|---|---|---|
| 19¢ | multicolored | .50 | .75 |
| | FDC *(March 11, 1994)* | | 1.00 |

### 1994. CANYON DE CHELLY ISSUE

PC171 *Canyon de Chelly, Arizona.*

**PC171**

| | | MNHVF | UseVF |
|---|---|---|---|
| 19¢ | multicolored | .50 | .75 |
| | FDC *(Aug. 7, 1994)* | | 1.00 |

### 1994. ST. LOUIS UNION STATION ISSUE

PC172 *St. Louis Union Station, St. Louis, Mo.*

**PC172**

| | | MNHVF | UseVF |
|---|---|---|---|
| 19¢ | multicolored | .50 | .75 |
| | FDC *(Sept. 3, 1994)* | | 1.00 |

### 1994. LEGENDS OF THE WEST PICTURE POST CARD ISSUE

Issued in conjunction with the 20-stamp sheetlet depicting 16 individuals and four "themes" from the Old West. Each card depicts a design from the sheetlet with the 19¢ postal card rate, while the reverse of the card is an enlarged version of the stamp design. The cards were issued Oct. 18, 1994.

PC173          PC174          PC175

**PC173**

| | | MNHVF | UseVF |
|---|---|---|---|
| 19¢ | Home on the Range | .60 | 5.00 |

**PC174**

| | | MNHVF | UseVF |
|---|---|---|---|
| 19¢ | Buffalo Bill | .60 | 5.00 |

**PC175**

| | | MNHVF | UseVF |
|---|---|---|---|
| 19¢ | Jim Bridger | .60 | 5.00 |

PC176          PC177          PC178

**PC176**

| | | MNHVF | UseVF |
|---|---|---|---|
| 19¢ | Annie Oakley | .60 | 5.00 |

**PC177**

| | | MNHVF | UseVF |
|---|---|---|---|
| 19¢ | Native American Culture | .60 | 5.00 |

**PC178**

| | | MNHVF | UseVF |
|---|---|---|---|
| 19¢ | Chief Joseph | .60 | 5.00 |

PC179

PC180

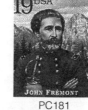
PC181

PC191

PC192

| **PC179** | | MNHVF | UseVF |
|---|---|---|---|
| 19¢ | Bill Pickett | .60 | 5.00 |
| **PC180** | | MNHVF | UseVF |
| 19¢ | Bat Masterson | .60 | 5.00 |
| **PC181** | | MNHVF | UseVF |
| 19¢ | John Fremont | .60 | 5.00 |

| **PC191** | | MNHVF | UseVF |
|---|---|---|---|
| 19¢ | Sacagawea | .60 | 5.00 |
| **PC192** | | MNHVF | UseVF |
| 19¢ | Overland Mail | .60 | 5.00 |

### 1994. OLD GLORY 'G' NON-DENOMINATED ISSUE

PC193 *Old Glory, 'G'.*

PC182

PC183

PC184

| **PC182** | | MNHVF | UseVF |
|---|---|---|---|
| 19¢ | Wyatt Earp | .60 | 5.00 |
| **PC183** | | MNHVF | UseVF |
| 19¢ | Nellie Cashman | .60 | 5.00 |
| **PC184** | | MNHVF | UseVF |
| 19¢ | Charles Goodnight | .60 | 5.00 |

| **PC193** | | MNHVF | UseVF |
|---|---|---|---|
| 20¢ | multicolored | .40 | .50 |
| | FDC *(Dec. 13, 1994)* | | 1.00 |

### 1994. RED BARN ISSUE

PC194 *Red Barn*

PC185

PC186

PC187

| **PC185** | | MNHVF | UseVF |
|---|---|---|---|
| 19¢ | Geronimo | .60 | 5.00 |
| **PC186** | | MNHVF | UseVF |
| 19¢ | Kit Carson | .60 | 5.00 |
| **PC187** | | MNHVF | UseVF |
| 19¢ | Wild Bill Hickock | .60 | 5.00 |

| **PC194** | | MNHVF | UseVF |
|---|---|---|---|
| 20¢ | multicolored | .40 | .50 |
| | FDC *(Jan. 3, 1995)* | | 1.00 |

**1995. CIVIL WAR PICTURE POST CARD ISSUE** Issued in conjunction with the 20 stamp sheetlet. Each card depicts a design from the sheetlet with the 20¢ post card rate, while the reverse of the card is an enlarged version of the stamp design. Available on June 29, 1995.

PC188

PC189

PC190

PC195

PC196

PC197

| **PC188** | | MNHVF | UseVF |
|---|---|---|---|
| 19¢ | Western Wildlife | .60 | 5.00 |
| **PC189** | | MNHVF | UseVF |
| 19¢ | Jim Beckwourth | .60 | 5.00 |
| **PC190** | | MNHVF | UseVF |
| 19¢ | Bill Tilghman | .60 | 5.00 |

| **PC195** | | MNHVF | UseVF |
|---|---|---|---|
| 20¢ | monitor and Virginia | .75 | 3.50 |
| **PC196** | | MNHVF | UseVF |
| 20¢ | Robert E. Lee | .75 | 3.50 |
| **PC197** | | MNHVF | UseVF |
| 20¢ | Clara Barton | .75 | 3.50 |

PC198

PC199

| PC198 | | MNHVF | UseVF |
|---|---|---|---|
| 20¢ | Ulysses Grant | .75 | 3.50 |
| PC199 | | MNHVF | UseVF |
| 20¢ | Battle of Shiloh | .75 | 3.50 |

**1995. CIVIL WAR PICTURE POST CARD ISSUE** Issued in conjunction with the 20 stamp sheetlet. Each card depicts a design from the sheetlet with the 20¢ post card rate, while the reverse of the card is an enlarged version of the stamp design. Available on June 29, 1995.

| PC200 | | MNHVF | UseVF |
|---|---|---|---|
| 20¢ | Jefferson Davis | .75 | 3.50 |

PC201

PC202

PC203

| PC201 | | MNHVF | UseVF |
|---|---|---|---|
| 20¢ | David Farragut | .75 | 3.50 |
| | | MNHVF | UseVF |
| PC202 | | | |
| 20¢ | Frederick Douglass | .75 | 3.50 |
| PC203 | | MNHVF | UseVF |
| 20¢ | Raphael Semmes | .75 | 3.50 |

PC204

PC205

PC206

| PC204 | | MNHVF | UseVF |
|---|---|---|---|
| 20¢ | Abraham Lincoln | .75 | 3.50 |
| PC205 | | MNHVF | UseVF |
| 20¢ | Harriet Tubman | .75 | 3.50 |
| PC206 | | MNHVF | UseVF |
| 20¢ | Stand Watie | .75 | 3.50 |

PC207

PC208

PC209

| PC207 | | MNHVF | UseVF |
|---|---|---|---|
| 20¢ | Joseph E. Johnston | .75 | 3.50 |
| PC208 | | MNHVF | UseVF |
| 20¢ | Winfield Hancock | .75 | 3.50 |
| PC209 | | MNHVF | UseVF |
| 20¢ | Mary Chestnut | .75 | 3.50 |

PC210

PC211

PC212

| PC210 | | MNHVF | UseVF |
|---|---|---|---|
| 20¢ | Battle of Chancellorville | .75 | 3.50 |
| PC211 | | MNHVF | UseVF |
| 20¢ | William T. Sherman | .75 | 3.50 |
| PC212 | | MNHVF | UseVF |
| 20¢ | Phoebe Pember | .75 | 3.50 |

PC213

PC214

| PC213 | | MNHVF | UseVF |
|---|---|---|---|
| 20¢ | Stonewall Jackson | .75 | 3.50 |
| PC214 | | MNHVF | UseVF |
| 20¢ | Battle of Gettysburg | .75 | 3.50 |

**1995. AMERICAN CLIPPER SHIPS ISSUE**

PC215 *American Clipper Ships*

| PC215 | | MNHVF | UseVF |
|---|---|---|---|
| 20¢ | multicolored | .40 | .50 |
| | FDC *(Sept. 3, 1995)* | | 1.00 |

**1995. COMIC STRIP PICTURE POST CARD ISSUE** Issued in conjunction with the sheetlet of 20 stamps having the centennial of "The Comic Strip." An enlarged version of the design appears on the reverse.

PC216

PC217

| PC216 | | MNHVF | UseVF |
|---|---|---|---|
| 20¢ | The Yellow Kid | .60 | 3.00 |

| PC217 | | MNHVF | UseVF |
|---|---|---|---|
| 20¢ | Katzenjammer Kids | .60 | 3.00 |

PC218                    PC219

| PC218 | | MNHVF | UseVF |
|---|---|---|---|
| 20¢ | Little Nemo in Slumberland | .60 | 3.00 |

| PC219 | | MNHVF | UseVF |
|---|---|---|---|
| 20¢ | Bringing up Father | .60 | 3.00 |

PC220                    PC221

| PC220 | | MNHVF | UseVF |
|---|---|---|---|
| 20¢ | Krazy Kat | .60 | 3.00 |

| PC221 | | MNHVF | UseVF |
|---|---|---|---|
| 20¢ | Rube Goldbery's Inventions | .60 | 3.00 |

PC222                    PC223

| PC222 | | MNHVF | UseVF |
|---|---|---|---|
| 20¢ | Toonerville Folks | .60 | 3.00 |

| PC223 | | MNHVF | UseVF |
|---|---|---|---|
| 20¢ | Gasoline Alley | .60 | 3.00 |

PC224                    PC225

| PC224 | | MNHVF | UseVF |
|---|---|---|---|
| 20¢ | Barney Google | .60 | 3.00 |

| PC225 | | MNHVF | UseVF |
|---|---|---|---|
| 20¢ | Little Orpan Annie | .60 | 3.00 |

PC226                    PC227

| PC226 | | MNHVF | UseVF |
|---|---|---|---|
| 20¢ | Popeye | .60 | 3.00 |

| PC227 | | MNHVF | UseVF |
|---|---|---|---|
| 20¢ | Blondie | .60 | 3.00 |

PC228                    PC229

| PC228 | | MNHVF | UseVF |
|---|---|---|---|
| 20¢ | Dick Tracey | .60 | 3.00 |

| PC229 | | MNHVF | UseVF |
|---|---|---|---|
| 20¢ | Alley OOP | .60 | 3.00 |

PC230                    PC231

| PC230 | | MNHVF | UseVF |
|---|---|---|---|
| 20¢ | Nancy | .60 | 3.00 |

| PC231 | | MNHVF | UseVF |
|---|---|---|---|
| 20¢ | Flash Gordon | .60 | 3.00 |

PC232                    PC233

| PC232 | | MNHVF | UseVF |
|---|---|---|---|
| 20¢ | Li'l Abner | .60 | 3.00 |

| PC233 | | MNHVF | UseVF |
|---|---|---|---|
| 20¢ | Terry and the Pirates | .60 | 3.00 |

PC234                    PC235

| PC234 | | MNHVF | UseVF |
|---|---|---|---|
| 20¢ | Prince Valiant | .60 | 3.00 |

| PC235 | | MNHVF | UseVF |
|---|---|---|---|
| 20¢ | Brenda Starr, Reporter | .60 | 3.00 |

**1996. WINTER FARM SCENE ISSUE**

PC236 *Winter farms scene*

| PC236 | | MNHVF | UseVF |
|---|---|---|---|
| 20¢ | multicolored | .40 | .50 |
| | FDC *(Feb. 23, 1996)* | | 1.00 |

**1996. ATLANTA OLYMPICS PICTURE POST CARD ISSUE** Issued in conjunction with the 20 stamp sheetlet. The reverse features are enlarged image.

PC237        PC238        PC239

**PC237**
**20¢** **Men's Cycling**
FDC *(May 2, 1996)*

|       | MNHVF | UseVF |
|-------|-------|-------|
|       | .60   | 5.00  |

**PC238**
**20¢** **Women's Diving**

|       | MNHVF | UseVF |
|-------|-------|-------|
|       | .60   | 5.00  |

**PC239**
**20¢** **Women's Running**

|       | MNHVF | UseVF |
|-------|-------|-------|
|       | .60   | 5.00  |

PC240        PC241        PC242

**PC240**
**20¢** **Men's Canoeing**

|       | MNHVF | UseVF |
|-------|-------|-------|
|       | .60   | 5.00  |

**PC241**
**20¢** **Decathalon (Javelin)**

|       | MNHVF | UseVF |
|-------|-------|-------|
|       | .60   | 5.00  |

**PC242**
**20¢** **Women's Soccer**

|       | MNHVF | UseVF |
|-------|-------|-------|
|       | .60   | 5.00  |

PC243        PC244        PC245

**PC243**
**20¢** **Men's Shot Put**

|       | MNHVF | UseVF |
|-------|-------|-------|
|       | .60   | 5.00  |

**PC244**
**20¢** **Women's Sailboarding**

|       | MNHVF | UseVF |
|-------|-------|-------|
|       | .60   | 5.00  |

**PC245**
**20¢** **Women's Gymnastics**

|       | MNHVF | UseVF |
|-------|-------|-------|
|       | .60   | 5.00  |

PC246        PC247        PC248

**PC246**
**20¢** **Freestyle Wrestling**

|       | MNHVF | UseVF |
|-------|-------|-------|
|       | .60   | 5.00  |

**PC247**
**20¢** **Women's Softball**

|       | MNHVF | UseVF |
|-------|-------|-------|
|       | .60   | 5.00  |

**PC248**
**20¢** **Women's Swimming**

|       | MNHVF | UseVF |
|-------|-------|-------|
|       | .60   | 5.00  |

PC249        PC250        PC251

**PC249**
**20¢** **Men's Sprints**

|       | MNHVF | UseVF |
|-------|-------|-------|
|       | .60   | 5.00  |

**PC250**
**20¢** **Men's Rowing**

|       | MNHVF | UseVF |
|-------|-------|-------|
|       | .60   | 5.00  |

**PC251**
**20¢** **Volleyball**

|       | MNHVF | UseVF |
|-------|-------|-------|
|       | .60   | 5.00  |

PC252        PC253        PC254

**PC252**
**20¢** **Men's Basketball**

|       | MNHVF | UseVF |
|-------|-------|-------|
|       | .60   | 5.00  |

**PC253**
**20¢** **Equestrian**

|       | MNHVF | UseVF |
|-------|-------|-------|
|       | .60   | 5.00  |

**PC254**
**20¢** **Men's Gymnastics**

|       | MNHVF | UseVF |
|-------|-------|-------|
|       | .60   | 5.00  |

PC255        PC256

**PC255**
**20¢** **Men's Swimming**

|       | MNHVF | UseVF |
|-------|-------|-------|
|       | .60   | 5.00  |

**PC256**
**20¢** **Men's Hurdles**

|       | MNHVF | UseVF |
|-------|-------|-------|
|       | .60   | 5.00  |

## College Series

**1996. ST. JOHN'S COLLEGE ISSUE**

PC257 McDowell Hall, St. John's College, Annapolis, Md.

St. John's College, Annapolis, Maryland

**PC257**
**20¢** **multicolored**
FDC *(June 1, 1996)*

|       | MNHVF | UseVF |
|-------|-------|-------|
|       | .50   | .50   |
|       |       | 1.00  |

## 1996. PRINCETON UNIVERSITY ISSUE College Series

PC258

PRINCETON UNIVERSITY • 250TH ANNIVERSARY

| PC258 | | MNHVF | UseVF |
|---|---|---|---|
| 20¢ | multicolored | .50 | .50 |
| | FDC *(Sept. 20, 1996)* | | 1.00 |

## 1996. ENDANGERED SPECIES PICTURE POST CARD ISSUE issued in conjunction with the 15 strip sheetlet. Each postcard features an enlargement of the stamp image.

PC259              PC260

| PC259 | | MNHVF | UseVF |
|---|---|---|---|
| 20¢ | Florida Panther | .75 | 5.00 |
| PC260 | | MNHVF | UseVF |
| 20¢ | Black Footed Ferret | .75 | 5.00 |

PC261              PC262

| PC261 | | MNHVF | UseVF |
|---|---|---|---|
| 20¢ | American Crocodile | .75 | 5.00 |
| PC262 | | MNHVF | UseVF |
| 20¢ | Piping Plover | .75 | 5.00 |

PC263              PC264

| PC263 | | MNHVF | UseVF |
|---|---|---|---|
| 20¢ | Gila Trout | .75 | 5.00 |
| PC264 | | MNHVF | UseVF |
| 20¢ | Florida Manatee | .75 | 5.00 |

PC265              PC266

| PC265 | | MNHVF | UseVF |
|---|---|---|---|
| 20¢ | Schaus Swallowtail Butterfly | .75 | 5.00 |
| PC266 | | MNHVF | UseVF |
| 20¢ | Woodland Caribou | .75 | 5.00 |

PC267              PC268

| PC267 | | MNHVF | UseVF |
|---|---|---|---|
| 20¢ | Thick-Billed Parrot | .75 | 5.00 |
| PC268 | | MNHVF | UseVF |
| 20¢ | San Fransisco Garter Snake | .75 | 5.00 |

PC269              PC270

| PC269 | | MNHVF | UseVF |
|---|---|---|---|
| 20¢ | Ocelot | .75 | 5.00 |
| PC270 | | MNHVF | UseVF |
| 20¢ | Wyoming Toad | .75 | 5.00 |

PC271              PC272

| PC271 | | MNHVF | UseVF |
|---|---|---|---|
| 20¢ | California Condor | .75 | 5.00 |
| PC272 | | MNHVF | UseVF |
| 20¢ | Hawaiian Monk Seal | .75 | 5.00 |

PC273

| PC273 | | MNHVF | UseVF |
|---|---|---|---|
| 20¢ | Brown Pelican | .75 | 5.00 |

## 1997. LOVE SWANS PICTURE POST CARD ISSUE Previous stamp designs enlarged on back.

Previous Love

| PC274 | | MNHVF | UseVF |
|---|---|---|---|
| | multicolored | | |
| | a. Bird in Rose Heart | .75 | 2.25 |
| | b. 2 Birds in Rose Basket | .75 | 2.25 |
| | c. Swans, Tall | .75 | 2.25 |
| | d. Swans, Long | .75 | 2.25 |
| | e. Puppy | .75 | 2.25 |
| | f. Paper-cut out Heart | .75 | 2.25 |
| | g. Penn-Dutch 2 birds & Heart | .75 | 2.25 |
| | h. Heart Sunrise | .75 | 2.25 |

## 1997. CITY COLLEGE OF NEW YORK ISSUE College Series

PC275 *City College of New York.*

The City College of New York ■ CUNY ■ 150TH ANNIVERSARY

| PC275 | | MNHVF | UseVF |
|---|---|---|---|
| 20¢ | multicolored | .60 | 1.50 |
| | FDC *(May 7, 1997)* | | 1.00 |

## 1997. GOLDEN GATE BRIDGE AND SAN FRANSICO HARBOR ISSUE Issued in conjunction with Pacific '97.

PC276 *Golden Gate Bridge, San Francisco Harbor.*

**PC276**
20¢     multicolored                          MNHVF  UseVF
                                                .60    1.00
        FDC *(June 2, 1997)*                          1.00

## 1997. GOLDEN GATE BRIDGE AND SUNSET ISSUE

PC277 *Golden Gate Bridge at Sunset.*

**PC277**
50¢     multicolored                          MNHVF  UseVF
                                                .60    1.00
        FDC *(June 2, 1997)*                          1.00

## Warner Brothers Cartoon Character Series

### 1997. BUGS BUNNY ISSUE
Issued in conjunction with the self adhesive stamp, an enlarged image appears on the back.

PC278 *Bugs Bunny*

**PC278**
20¢     multicolored, single                  MNHVF  UseVF
                                                .50    2.50
        FDC                                          1.00
        Booklet of 20                          7.50

### 1997. FT. MCHENRY ISSUE

PC279 *Ft. McHenry, Baltimore, Md.*

**PC279**
20¢     multicolored                          MNHVF  UseVF
                                                .50     .75
        FDC *(Sept. 9, 1997)*                        1.00

### 1997. MOVIE MONSTER ISSUE
Issued in conjuction with the 20 image sheetlet, packs of 20. Each postcard features an enlargment of the stamp image CM1956-60.

PC280            PC281            PC282

---

**PC280**                                     MNHVF  UseVF
20¢     Lon Chaney, Phantom of the Opera       .75    3.50
**PC281**                                     MNHVF  UseVF
20¢     Bela Lugosi, Dracula                   .75    3.50
**PC282**                                     MNHVF  UseVF
20¢     Boris Karloff, Frankenstein            .75    3.50

PC283            PC284

**PC283**                                     MNHVF  UseVF
20¢     Boris Karloff, The Mummy               .75    3.50
**PC284**                                     MNHVF  UseVF
20¢     Lon Chaney, Jr., The Wolfman           .75    3.50

### 1998. UNIVERSITY OF MISSISSIPPI ISSUE
College Series
The Lyceum is depicted.

**PC285**                                     MNHVF  UseVF
20¢     multicolored                           .50     .75
        FDC *(april 20, 1998)*                       1.00

### SYLVESTER & TWETTE POST CARD ISSUE
Warner Brothers Cartoon Character Series
An enlargment of the stamp image appears on the back.

**PC286**                                     MNHVF  UseVF
20¢     multicolored                           .75    3.50
        Booklet of 10                         5.00
        FDC *(April 27, 1998)*                       1.00

### 1998. GIARD COLLEGE ISSUE
College Series

**PC287**                                     MNHVF  UseVF
20¢     multicolored                           .50     .75
        FDC *(May 1, 1998)*                          1.00

# Message & Reply Cards

First issued in 1892, message and reply cards consist of two postal cards attached to each other. One card is used for sending the message and the other card, when separated, is used to send the reply. The term "used" when referring to the unsevered card signifies a used message card and an unused reply card. Listings are for unsevered and severed (individual) cards.

**1892. ISSUE** Frame around edge of card.

MRC1

| MRC1 | | UnFVF | UseFVF |
|---|---|---|---|
| 1¢ + 1¢ | **Black on buff,** unsevered | 37.50 | 8.00 |
| m. | Message card | 7.00 | 1.50 |
| r. | Reply card | 7.00 | 1.50 |
| t. | Message card printed on both sides, reply card blank | 275. | — |
| t1. | Message card blank, reply card printed on both sides | 325. | — |

**1893. UNIVERSAL POSTAL UNION CARD** Frame around edge of card.

MRC2

| MRC2 | | UnFVF | UseFVF |
|---|---|---|---|
| 2¢ + 2¢ | **blue on grayish white,** unsevered | 18.50 | 25.00 |
| a. | dark blue on grayish white | 20.00 | 25.00 |
| m. | Message reply card | 6.00 | 7.00 |
| r. | Reply card | 6.00 | 7.00 |
| t. | Message card printed on both sides, reply card blank | 325. | — |
| t1. | Message card blank, reply card printed on both sides | — | — |
| t2. | Message card normal, reply card blank | 325. | — |
| | FDC *(March 1, 1893)* | | |

**1898. ISSUE** Same design as MRC1, but without frame around edge of card.

| MRC3 | | UnFVF | UseFVF |
|---|---|---|---|
| 1¢ + 1¢ | **black on buff,** unsevered | 70.00 | 20.00 |
| m. | Message reply card | 15.00 | 3.00 |
| r. | Reply card | 15.00 | 3.00 |
| t. | Message card printed on both sides, reply card blank | 275. | — |
| t1. | Message card blank, reply card printed on both sides | 275. | — |
| t2. | Message card blank, reply card normal | — | 275. |
| t3. | Message card normal, reply card printed on both sides | — | — |
| t4. | Message card without "detach annexed card/for answer" | 275. | 160. |
| t5. | Message card printed on both sides, reply card normal | — | — |
| t6. | Message card printed on both halves | — | — |
| | FDC *(Sept. 1898)* | | |

**1904. ISSUE**

MRC4

| MRC4 | | UnFVF | UseFVF |
|---|---|---|---|
| 1¢ + 1¢ | **black on buff,** unsevered | 50.00 | 6.00 |
| m. | Message card | 10.00 | 2.00 |
| r. | Reply card | 10.00 | 2.00 |
| t. | Message card printed on both sides, reply card blank | 300. | — |
| t1. | Message card blank, reply card printed on both sides | — | 185. |
| t2. | Message card blank, reply card normal | — | 300. |
| t3. | Message card normal, reply card blank | 300. | — |
| | FDC *(March 1904)* | | |

**1910. ISSUE**

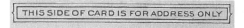

MRC5

| MRC5 | | UnFVF | UseFVF |
|---|---|---|---|
| 1¢ + 1¢ | **dark blue on bluish,** unsevered | 150. | 25.00 |
| m. | Message card | 11.00 | 4.00 |
| r. | Reply card | 11.00 | 4.00 |
| t. | Message card normal, reply card blank | 220. | — |
| | FDC *(Sept. 14, 1910)* | | |

**1911. ISSUE** Same design.

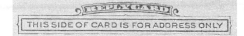

MRC6

**MRC6**

|  | UnFVF | UseFVF |
|---|---|---|
| 1¢ + 1¢  **green on cream,** unsevered | 150. | 25.00 |
| m. Message card | 25.00 | 6.00 |
| r.  Reply card | 40.00 | 45.00 |
| t.  Message card normal, reply card blank | — | — |
| FDC *(Oct. 27, 1911)* | | |

**1915. ISSUE** Same design. Single frame around inscription.

MRC7

**MRC7**

|  | UnFVF | UseFVF |
|---|---|---|
| 1¢ + 1¢  **green on cream,** unsevered | 1.50 | 55.00 |
| dark green on buff | 1.50 | 55.00 |
| m. Message reply card | .30 | .25 |
| r.  Reply card | .30 | .25 |
| t.  Message card normal, reply card blank | — | — |
| FDC *(Sept. 18, 1915)* | | |

**1918. ISSUE**

MRC8

**MRC8**

|  | UnFVF | UseFVF |
|---|---|---|
| 2¢ + 2¢  **red on cream,** unsevered | 80.00 | 45.00 |
| m. Message card | 22.50 | 7.50 |
| r.  Reply card | 22.50 | 7.50 |
| FDC *(Aug. 2, 1918)* | | |

**1920-21. ISSUE** Re-valued. *Surcharged in black by canceling machine.*

MRC9 *Overprinted on MRC8*

**MRC9**

|  | UnFVF | UseFVF |
|---|---|---|
| 1¢on 2¢+1¢on 2¢ **red on cream,** unsevered | 20.00 | 10.00 |
| m. Message card | 6.00 | 4.00 |
| r.  Reply card | 6.00 | 4.00 |
| x.  Message card double surcharge, reply card normal | 80.00 | — |

**MRC9**

|  | UnFVF | UseFVF |
|---|---|---|
| x1. Message card normal, reply card no surcharge | 90.00 | — |
| x2. Message card normal, reply card double surcharge | 80.00 | — |
| x3. Message card no surcharge, reply card normal | 80.00 | — |
| x4. Message card no surcharge, reply card double surcharge | 80.00 | — |
| x5. Message card double surcharge reply card no surcharge | — | — |
| x6. Message card no surcharge, reply card double surcharge, one inverted | — | — |

**MRC9A**

|  | UnFVF | UseFVF |
|---|---|---|
| 1¢on 2¢+1¢on 2¢ **red on cream,** unsevered | 325. | 200. |
| m. Message card | 95.00 | 45.00 |
| p.  red on buff | — | — |
| r.  Reply card | 95.00 | 45.00 |
| x.  Message card no surcharge, reply card normal | — | — |
| x1. Message card double surcharge, reply card no surcharge | — | — |
| x2. Message card no surcharge, reply card double surcharge | — | — |

*Same surcharge press printed.*

**1924. UNIVERSAL POSTAL UNION CARD** Universal Postal Union Card. Same design and size as MRC2.

MRC10

**MRC10**

|  | UnFVF | UseFVF |
|---|---|---|
| 2¢ + 2¢  **red on buff,** unsevered | 3.00 | 50.00 |
| m. Message card | .50 | 20.00 |
| r.  Reply card | .50 | 20.00 |
| FDC *(Mar. 18, 1924)* | | |

**1926. UNIVERSAL POSTAL UNION CARD** Universal Postal Union Card. Same size as PC11.

Same size as PC11. MRC11
*William McKinley*

**MRC11**

|  | UnFVF | UseFVF |
|---|---|---|
| 3¢ + 3¢  **red on cream,** unsevered | 15.00 | 35.00 |
| a.  carmine on cream | — | — |
| b.  pale red on cream | — | — |
| c.  scarlet on cream | — | — |
| m. Message card | 3.00 | 16.00 |
| p.  red on buff | — | — |
| p1. red on canary | 10.00 | 17.50 |
| p2. red on light buff | — | — |
| p3. red on yellow buff | — | — |
| r.  Reply card | 3.00 | 6.00 |
| FDC *(Jan. 29, 1926)* | | |

**1951. ISSUE** Size PC13.

MRC12 *George Washington, message card; Martha Washington, reply card.*

**MRC12**

| | | MNHVF | UseVF |
|---|---|---|---|
| 2¢ + 2¢ | **carmine on cream,** unsevered | 1.75 | 3.00 |
| m. | Message card | .50 | 1.00 |
| r. | Reply card | .50 | 1.00 |
| | FDC *(Dec. 29, 1951)* | | |

**1952. ISSUE** Re-valued, overprinted in green by Pitney-Bowes Tickometers.

MRC13 *Overprinted on MRC7*

**MRC13**

| | | MNHVF | UseVF |
|---|---|---|---|
| 2¢ on 1¢ + 2¢ on 1¢ | **light green on buff,** unsevered | 1.75 | 4.00 |
| m. | Message card | .50 | 2.00 |
| r. | Reply card | .50 | 2.00 |
| x. | Both cards double surcharge | 55.00 | 40.00 |
| x1. | Inverted surcharge horizontal, to left of stamps | 150. | 100. |
| x2. | Message card double surcharge, reply card normal | 45.00 | 30.00 |
| x3. | Message card no surcharge, reply card normal | 40.00 | 45.00 |
| x4. | Message card normal, reply card double surcharge | 45.00 | 30.00 |
| x5. | Message card normal, reply card no surcharge | 40.00 | 45.00 |
| x6. | Surcharge horizontal, to left of stamps | 15.00 | 15.00 |
| x7. | Surcharge vertical, to left of stamps | 7.00 | 7.00 |
| x8. | Surcharge vertical below stamp | — | — |
| x9. | Black surcharge vertical below stamp | — | — |
| x10. | Message card no surcharge, reply card double surcharge | — | — |
| x11. | Message card double surcharge, reply card no surcharge | — | — |
| | FDC *(Jan. 1952)* | | |

**1952. ISSUE** Same as MRC13, but dark green horizontal overprint applied by printing press.

**MRC14**

| | | MNHVF | UseVF |
|---|---|---|---|
| 2¢ on 1¢ + 2¢ on 1¢ | **green on cream,** unsevered | 135. | 55.00 |
| m. | Message card | 20.00 | 12.50 |
| r. | Reply card | 20.00 | 12.50 |
| x. | Message card normal plus one on back, reply card no surcharge | — | — |
| x1. | Reply card normal plus one on back, with Tickometer surcharge vertical below stamp on message card | — | — |

**1956. ISSUE** Design of OC42, Liberty.

MRC15

**MRC15**

| | | MNHVF | UseVF |
|---|---|---|---|
| 4¢ + 4¢ | **scarlet and ultramarine on cream,** unsevered | 1.50 | 60.00 |
| m. | Message card | .50 | 40.00 |
| r. | Reply card | .50 | 35.00 |
| t. | Message card printed on both halves | 140. | — |
| t1. | Reply message printed on both halves | 140. | — |
| | FDC *(Nov. 16, 1956)* | | |

**1958. ISSUE** Design of PC42, Liberty.

**MRC16**

| | | MNHVF | UseVF |
|---|---|---|---|
| 3¢ + 3¢ | **purple on buff,** unsevered | 4.00 | 5.00 |
| t. | One card blank | 140. | — |
| t1. | Printed by electrotype | — | — |
| t2. | Printed by steel plate | — | — |
| | FDC *(July 31, 1958)* | | |

**1962. ISSUE** Design of PC44, Abraham Lincoln, two cards are identical.

MRC17 *Abraham Lincoln*

**MRC17**

| | | MNHVF | UseVF |
|---|---|---|---|
| 4¢ + 4¢ | **red violet on white,** unsevered | 4.50 | 5.00 |
| a. | light violet | — | — |
| p. | Fluorescent paper, non-fluorescent ink | — | — |
| t. | Printed by electrotype | — | — |
| t1. | Printed by steel plate | — | — |
| z. | Non-fluorescent paper, fluorescent ink | 6.50 | 3.50 |
| | *(Mar. 7, 1967)* | | |
| | FDC *(Nov. 19, 1962)* | | |

**1963. ISSUE** Design of PC45, Vacationland.

MRC18

**MRC18**

| | | MNHVF | UseVF |
|---|---|---|---|
| 7¢ + 7¢ | **red and blue on white,** unsevered | 3.00 | 50.00 |
| t. | Message card blank, reply card normal | 140. | — |
| t1. | Message card normal, reply card blank | 140. | — |
| | FDC *(Aug. 30, 1963)* | | |

**1968. ISSUE** Design of MRC18 (PC45), Vacationland.

**MRC19**

| | | MNHVF | UseVF |
|---|---|---|---|
| 8¢ + 8¢ | **red and blue on white,** unsevered | 3.50 | 50.00 |
| | FDC *(Dec. 4, 1967)* | | |

**1968. ISSUE** Design of PC51, Abraham Lincoln, two cards are identical.

**MRC20**

| | | MNHVF | UseVF |
|---|---|---|---|
| 5¢ + 5¢ | **emerald green on white,** unsevered | 1.75 | 3.00 |
| t. | One half blank (printed one side only) | — | — |
| | FDC *(Jan. 4, 1968)* | | |

**1971. ISSUE** Design of PC54, Paul Revere, two cards are identical.

MRC21

**MRC21**

| | | MNHVF | UseVF |
|---|---|---|---|
| 6¢ + 6¢ | **brown on white,** unsevered, tagged | 1.25 | 2.50 |
| | FDC *(May 15, 1971)* | | |

**1972. ISSUE** Design of PC60, John Hanson, two cards are identical.

**MRC22**

| | | MNHVF | UseVF |
|---|---|---|---|
| 6¢ + 6¢ | **cobalt blue on white,** unsevered, tagged | 1.25 | 2.00 |
| | FDC *(Sept. 1, 1972)* | | |

**1973. ISSUE** Design of PC62, Samuel Adams, two cards are identical.

| MRC23 | | MNHVF | UseVF |
|---|---|---|---|
| 8¢ + 8¢ **orange on white,** unsevered, tagged | | 1.25 | 2.00 |
| p. Smooth paper | | — | — |
| p1. Coarse Paper | | 1.35 | 4.00 |
| t. One half blank (printed one side only) | | — | — |
| FDC *(Dec. 16, 1973)* | | | |

**1975. ISSUE** Design of PC64, Charles Thomson, two cards are identical.

| MRC24 | | MNHVF | UseVF |
|---|---|---|---|
| 7¢ + 7¢ **emerald green on white,** unsevered, tagged | | 1.25 | 5.00 |
| FDC *(Sept. 14, 1975)* | | | |

**1975. ISSUE** Design of PC65, John Witherspoon, two cards are identical.

| MRC25 | | MNHVF | UseVF |
|---|---|---|---|
| 9¢ + 9¢ **brown on white,** unsevered, tagged | | 1.25 | 5.00 |
| FDC *(Nov. 10, 1975)* | | | |

**1976. ISSUE** Design of PC66, Caesar Rodney, two cards are identical.

| MRC26 | | MNHVF | UseVF |
|---|---|---|---|
| 9¢ + 9¢ **blue on white,** unsevered, tagged | | 1.25 | 2.00 |
| FDC *(July 1, 1976)* | | | |

**1977. ISSUE** Design of PC68, Nathan Hale, two cards are identical.

| MRC27 | | MNHVF | UseVF |
|---|---|---|---|
| 9¢ + 9¢ **green on white,** unsevered, tagged | | 1.25 | 2.00 |
| FDC *(Oct. 14, 1977)* | | | |

**1978. ISSUE** Design of PC70, John Hancock (non-denominated), two cards are identical.

| MRC28 | | MNHVF | UseVF |
|---|---|---|---|
| 10¢ + 10¢ **brown orange on white,** unsevered, tagged | | 11.00 | 9.00 |
| t. Printed with MRC28 one side, MRC29 on back side | | — | — |
| FDC *(May 19, 1978)* | | | |

**1978. ISSUE** Design of PC71, John Hancock (with denomination), two cards are identical.

| MRC29 | | MNHVF | UseVF |
|---|---|---|---|
| 10¢ + 10¢ **brown orange on white,** unsevered, tagged | | 1.25 | 3.00 |
| t. One half blank (printed one side only) | | — | — |
| FDC *(June 20, 1978)* | | | |

**1981. ISSUE** Design of PC84, stylized eagle, two cards are identical.

| MRC30 | | MNHVF | UseVF |
|---|---|---|---|
| 12¢ + 12¢ **purple on white,** unsevered, tagged | | 1.25 | 3.00 |
| FDC *(Mar. 15, 1981)* | | | |

**1981. ISSUE** Design of PC85, Isaiah Thomas, two cards are identical.

| MRC31 | | MNHVF | UseVF |
|---|---|---|---|
| 12¢ + 12¢ **blue on white,** unsevered, tagged | | 1.50 | 4.00 |
| t. Large stamp die on both sides | | — | — |
| t1. Large stamp die on one side, small stamp die on back | | 3.00 | 2.25 |
| FDC *(May 5, 1981)* | | | |

**1981. ISSUE** Design of PC88, Robert Morris (non-denominated), two cards are identical.

| MRC32 | | MNHVF | UseVF |
|---|---|---|---|
| 13¢ + 13¢ **brown on white,** unsevered, tagged | | 2.25 | 4.00 |
| FDC *(Oct. 11, 1981)* | | | |

**1981. ISSUE** Design of PC89, Robert Morris (with denomination), two cards are identical.

| MRC33 | | MNHVF | UseVF |
|---|---|---|---|
| 13¢ + 13¢ **brown on white,** unsevered, tagged | | 1.25 | 3.00 |
| t. One half blank (printed one side only) | | — | — |
| t1. Additional copyright notice, inverted on back of message card | | — | — |
| FDC *(Nov. 10, 1981)* | | | |

**1985. ISSUE** Design of PC101, Charles Carroll (non-denomimated), two cards are identical.

| MRC34 | | MNHVF | UseVF |
|---|---|---|---|
| 14¢ + 14¢ **green on white,** unsevered, tagged | | 3.50 | 5.00 |
| FDC *(Feb. 1, 1985)* | | | |

**1985. ISSUE** Design of PC103, Charles Carroll (with denomination), two cards are identical.

| MRC35 | | MNHVF | UseVF |
|---|---|---|---|
| 14¢ + 14¢ **green on white,** unsevered, tagged | | 1.25 | 3.00 |
| t. One half blank (printed one side only) | | — | — |
| FDC *(Mar. 6, 1985)* | | | |

**1985. ISSUE** Design of PC104, George Wythe, two cards are identical.

| MRC36 | | MNHVF | UseVF |
|---|---|---|---|
| 14¢ + 14¢ **olive green on white,** unsevered, tagged | | 1.20 | 3.00 |
| t. One half blank (printed one side only) | | — | — |
| FDC *(June 20, 1985)* | | | |

**1987. ISSUE** Design of PC113, U.S. Flag, two cards are identical.

| MRC37 | | MNHVF | UseVF |
|---|---|---|---|
| 14¢ + 14¢ **black, blue and red on white,** unsevered, tagged | | 1.25 | 3.00 |
| FDC *(Sept. 1, 1987)* | | | |

**1988. ISSUE** Design of PC116, America the Beautiful, two cards are identical.

| MRC38 | | MNHVF | UseVF |
|---|---|---|---|
| 15¢ + 15¢ **multicolored on white,** unsevered, tagged | | 1.25 | 3.00 |
| p. Fluorescent paper | | — | — |
| FDC *(July 11, 1988)* | | | |

**1991. ISSUE** Design of PC146, U.S. Flag, two cards are identical.

| MRC39 | | MNHVF | UseVF |
|---|---|---|---|
| 19¢ + 19¢ **black, blue and red on white,** unsevered, tagged | | 1.25 | 3.00 |
| FDC *(Mar. 27, 1991)* | | | |

**1995. ISSUE** Design of PC, Red Barn

| MRC40 | | MNHVF | UseVF |
|---|---|---|---|
| 20¢ + 20¢ **multicolored,** unsevered | | 1.25 | 3.00 |
| t. One half blank (printed one side only) | | — | — |
| FDC *(Feb. 1, 1995)* | | | |

# Savings Stamps

United States Savings Stamps fall into five classifications: Postal Savings and Defense Postal Savings, both issued by the Post Office Department; and War Savings, Savings, and Treasury Savings, issued by the Treasury Department.

For many years the Treasury Department objected to the listings of Savings Stamps as collectors' items, but in a letter dated July 13, 1942, these objections were withdrawn and since that date the collecting of these stamps has been encouraged.

## Postal Savings Stamp Series

Issued by the Post Office Department

In 1910 the U.S. Post Office Department started a Postal Savings Department where accounts could be opened in even dollar amounts. To enable small depositors to accumulate dollar deposits, stamps were provided with a face value of 10¢ each so that when nine were secured they could be mounted on a card with one integral stamp. The Postal Savings Department, as a banking activity, was closed April 27, 1966.

**1911. FIRST ISSUE** Inscribed "U.S. Postal SAVINGS 10 CENTS." *Intaglio, watermark double-line "USPS" (wmk. 187), perforated 12.*

 PS1, PS3

| PS1 | | UnFVF | UseFVF |
|---|---|---|---|
| 10¢ | orange | 7.00 | 1.25 |
| | Plate block of 6, w/imprint and open star | 450. | — |
| | Plate strip of 3, w/imprint and open star | 45.00 | — |
| | Block of 4, 2mm spacing between stamps | 30.00 | — |
| | Block of 4, 3mm spacing between stamps | 35.00 | — |
| | FDC *(Jan. 3, 1911)* | | |

**1911. IMPRINTED CARD ISSUE** Postal Savings Stamp Series

Same design as No. PS1. Imprinted on deposit card with spaces for nine additional stamps. *Intaglio, unwatermarked, imperforate.*

 PS2

After being redeemed, these cards were canceled with a large killer device and interesting combinations of stamps are available.

Proofs in red and blue on thin paper and a deposit card in blue, with an entirely different design showing the head of George Washington in circle and space for nine stamps are known. It is believed that they were not issued.

| PS2 | | UnFVF | UseFVF |
|---|---|---|---|
| 10¢ | orange | 150. | 40.00 |
| | Canceled with nine additional stamps | — | — |
| | FDC *(Jan. 3, 1911)* | | |

**1911. SECOND ISSUE** Postal Savings Stamp Series

**Aug. 14.** Same design as No. PS1. *Intaglio, watermark single-line "USPS" (wmk 237), perforated 12.*

| PS3 | | UnFVF | UseFVF |
|---|---|---|---|
| 10¢ | blue | 4.25 | 1.00 |
| | Plate block of 6, w/imprint and open star | 150. | — |
| | Plate strip of 3, w/imprint and open star | 27.50 | — |
| | Block of 4, 2mm spacing between stamps | 22.50 | — |
| | Block of 4, 3mm spacing between stamps | 25.00 | — |

**1911. THIRD ISSUE** Postal Savings Stamp Series

Design type of No. PS2, with change in color. IM printed on deposit card. *Intaglio, unwatermarked, imperforate.*

| PS4 | | UnFVF | UseFVF |
|---|---|---|---|
| 10¢ | blue | 100. | 22.50 |
| | Canceled with 9 additional stamps | — | — |
| | FDC *(Aug. 14, 1911)* | | |

*In September 1920, the Post Office Department issued a new type of deposit card (form PS333) without imprint of the first stamp. These are not listed as regular postal issues, but can be found canceled with 10 stamps of either No. PS1 or No. PS3.*

**1936. ISSUE** Postal Savings Stamp Series

Type of No. PS1. *Intaglio, unwatermarked, perforated 11.*

| PS5 | | UnFVF | UseFVF |
|---|---|---|---|
| 10¢ | blue | 4.75 | 1.25 |
| | violet blue | 4.75 | 1.25 |
| | Plate block of 6, w/imprint and closed star | 125. | — |

## Postal Savings Stamp Series

Issued by the Post Office Department

In 1910 the U.S. Post Office Department started a Postal Savings Department where accounts could be opened in even dollar amounts. To enable small depositors to accumulate dollar deposits, stamps were provided with a face value of 10¢ each so that when nine were secured they could be mounted on a card with one integral stamp. The Postal Savings Department, as a banking activity, was closed April 27, 1966.

**1940. ISSUE** Inscribed "UNITED STATES" at top, "POSTAL SAVINGS" at bottom, and either "CENTS" or "DOLLAR" diagonally in center, with denomination above and below. *Intaglio, unwatermarked, perforated 11.*

PS6-PS9

| PS6 | | MNHVF | UseVF |
|---|---|---|---|
| 10¢ | blue | 12.50 | 6.00 |
| | Plate block of 6 | 225. | — |
| | FDC *(April 3, 1940)* | | |

| PS7 | | MNHVF | UseVF |
|---|---|---|---|
| 25¢ | red | 17.50 | 9.00 |
| | Plate block of 6 | 325. | — |
| | FDC *(April 1, 1940)* | | |

| PS8 | | MNHVF | UseVF |
|---|---|---|---|
| 50¢ | green | 50.00 | 16.00 |
| | Plate block of 6 | 1400. | — |
| | FDC *(April 1, 1940)* | | |

| PS9 | | MNHVF | UseVF |
|---|---|---|---|
| $1 | black | 150. | 15.00 |
| | Plate block of 6 | 1900. | — |
| | FDC *(April 1, 1940)* | | |

*Both a yellow and a manila card for 25 10¢ stamps, a salmon card for 25 25¢ stamps, a green card for 25 50¢ stamps, and a manila card for 18 $1 stamps and 3 25¢ stamps were produced. Any total of $18.75 was redeemable for a $25 U.S. Savings bond.*

## Defense Postal Savings Stamp Series

Issued by the Post Office Department

On May 1, 1941, the Post Office Department issued Defense Postal Savings Stamps, redeemable in U.S. Treasury Defense or War Bonds. Daniel Chester French, who created the Minute Man used in the design, was one of the artists honored on the Famous Americans Series of commemorative stamps (CM229).

**1941. ISSUE May 1.** Inscribed "AMERICA ON GUARD--U.S. POST-AL SAVINGS--1941." *Intaglio, unwatermarked.*

PS10-PS14 *Minute Man*

| PS10 | | MNHVF | UseVF |
|---|---|---|---|
| 10¢ | **red** | .60 | — |
| | Plate block of 4 | 7.25 | |
| | Booklet pane of 10, w/horizontal edges trimmed | | |
| | (July 30, 1941) | 55.00 | |
| | n. Booklet pane of 10, w/trimmed edges, electric eye marks at left | 60.00 | |
| | Booklet pane of 10, perforated at horizontal edges | 120. | |
| | Booklet pane of 10, perforated at edges, electric eye marks at left | 135. | |

| PS11 | | MNHVF | UseVF |
|---|---|---|---|
| 25¢ | **green** | 1.85 | — |
| | Plate block of 4 | 16.00 | |
| | Booklet pane of 10 (July 30, 1941) | | |
| | (July 30, 1941) | 65.00 | |
| | n. Booklet pane of 10, electric eye marks at left | 70.00 | |

| PS12 | | MNHVF | UseVF |
|---|---|---|---|
| 50¢ | **ultramarine** | 4.50 | — |
| | Plate block of 4 | 40.00 | |

| PS13 | | MNHVF | UseVF |
|---|---|---|---|
| $1 | **black** | 10.00 | — |
| | Plate block of 4 | 77.00 | |

| PS14 | | MNHVF | UseVF |
|---|---|---|---|
| $5 | **sepia, perforated 11** | 37.00 | — |
| | Plate block of 6 | 535. | |

## War Savings Stamp Series

Issued by the Treasury Department

In 1917, the Treasury Department brought out the first of a series of War Savings Stamps which were redeemable in Treasury War Certificates, War Bonds, or Defense Bonds. A 25¢ Thrift Stamp was issued to enable small purchasers to accumulate them on a Deposit Card exchangeable for a $5 stamp when full.

**1917. ISSUE Dec. 1.** *Intaglio, unwatermarked, perforated 11.*

WS1

| WS1 | | UnFVF | UseFVF |
|---|---|---|---|
| 25¢ | **green** | 7.00 | 2.25 |
| | Plate block of 6 | 750. | |
| | Plate strip of 3 | 50.00 | |

**1918. ISSUE** War Savings Stamp Series

In 1918, 1919, 1920 and 1921, $5 stamps were issued. They sold at $4.12 when first issued and increased in value each month until they became worth par in five years and could be cashed or applied on bonds at the face value of $5.

**Nov. 17.** *Intaglio, unwatermarked, perforated 11.*

WS2 *George Washington*

| WS2 | | UnFVF | UseFVF |
|---|---|---|---|
| $5 | **green** | 70.00 | 22.00 |
| | Single with plate number | 80.00 | |
| | v. Vertical pair, imperforate horizontally | — | |

| WS2A | | UnFVF | UseFVF |
|---|---|---|---|
| $5 | **green** | 1100. | — |
| | Single w/plate number | 1350. | |

*Rouletted 7*

**1919. ISSUE** War Savings Stamp Series
**July 3.** *Intaglio, unwatermarked, perforated 11.*

WS3 *Benjamin Franklin*

| WS3 | | UnFVF | UseFVF |
|---|---|---|---|
| $5 | **blue** | 275. | — |
| | Single w/plate number | 300. | |
| | Single w/inverted plate number | 325. | |

**1920. ISSUE** War Savings Stamp Series
**Dec. 11.** *Intaglio, unwatermarked, perforated 11.*

WS5 *George Washington*

| WS4 | | UnFVF | UseFVF |
|---|---|---|---|
| $5 | **carmine** | 675. | 160. |
| | Single w/plate number | 700. | |

**1921. ISSUE** War Savings Stamp Series
**Dec. 21.** *Intaglio, unwatermarked, perforated 11.*

WS5 *Abraham Lincoln*

| WS5 | | UnFVF | UseFVF |
|---|---|---|---|
| $5 | orange on green paper | 2600. | — |
| | Single w/plate number | 2750. | |

## War Savings Stamp Series

Issued by the Treasury Department

In 1917, the Treasury Department brought out the first of a series of War Savings Stamps which were redeemable in Treasury War Certificates, War Bonds, or Defense Bonds. A 25¢ Thrift Stamp was issued to enable small purchasers to accumulate them on a Deposit Card exchangeable for a $5 stamp when full.

**1942. ISSUE** Early in 1942 the Treasury Department issued a new series of War Savings Stamps to replace the Defense Postal Savings Stamps of 1941 issued by the Post Office Department. *Intaglio, unwatermarked.*

WS6-WS10 *Minute Man*

| WS6 | | MNHVF | UseVF |
|---|---|---|---|
| 10¢ | red | 55.00 | — |
| | Plate block of 4 | 5.25 | |
| | Booklet pane of 10 | | |
| | (Oct. 27, 1942) | 40.00 | |
| | Booklet pane of 10 w/electric eye mark at left | 45.00 | |
| | a. carmine rose | 55.00 | — |
| | FDC (Oct. 29, 1942) | | |

| WS7 | | MNHVF | UseVF |
|---|---|---|---|
| 25¢ | green | 1.25 | — |
| | Plate block of 4 | 8.50 | |
| | Booklet pane of 10 | | |
| | (Oct. 15, 1942) | 50.00 | |
| | Booklet pane of 10 w/electric eye mark at left | 55.00 | |
| | FDC (Oct. 15, 1942) | | |

| WS8 | | MNHVF | UseVF |
|---|---|---|---|
| 50¢ | ultramarine | 2.75 | — |
| | Plate block of 4 | 27.50 | |
| | FDC (Nov. 12, 1942) | | |

| WS9 | | MNHVF | UseVF |
|---|---|---|---|
| $1 | black | 9.00 | — |
| | Plate block of 4 | 60.00 | |
| | FDC (Nov. 17, 1942) | | |

*Perforated 11 x 10 1/2.*

| WS10 | | MNHVF | UseVF |
|---|---|---|---|
| $5 | violet brown | 45.00 | — |
| | Plate block of 6 | 475. | |
| | FDC (1945) | | |

*Perforated 11.*

**1943. COIL ISSUE** War Savings Stamp Series

*Coil stamps.* Although plates for coil stamps were prepared for the 1941 issue, they were not used. Thus, this is the first Saving Stamp issued in coil form: 500 stamps to a roll.

**Aug. 5.** Type of No. WS6. *Intaglio, unwatermarked, perforated 10 vertically.*

| WS11 | | MNHVF | UseVF |
|---|---|---|---|
| 10¢ | red | 2.75 | — |
| | Pair | 6.00 | — |
| | Line pair | 11.00 | — |

| WS12 | | MNHVF | UseVF |
|---|---|---|---|
| 25¢ | green | 4.50 | — |
| | Pair | 9.50 | — |
| | Line pair | 21.00 | — |

## Treasury Savings Stamps Series

Issue by the Treasury Department

While the $5 orange-on-greenpaper (No. WS5) was still current, the Treasury Department brought out a $1 stamp redeemable in War Savings Stamps or Treasury Savings Certificates. It is the scarcest of the Savings Stamps.

**1921. ISSUE** Dec. 21. *Intaglio, unwatermarked, perforated 11.*

TS1 *Alexander Hamilton*

| TS1 | | UnFVF | UseFVF |
|---|---|---|---|
| $1 | red on green paper | 3250. | — |
| | Single with plate number | 3000. | |

## Savings Stamp Series

Issued by the Treasury Department

**1954. ISSUE** Figure of Minute Man, same as 1942 War Savings Stamps. Inscribed "UNITED STATES SAVINGS STAMP." *Intaglio, unwatermarked.*

| S1 | | MNHVF | UseVF |
|---|---|---|---|
| 10¢ | red | .60 | — |
| | Plate block of 4 | 3.75 | |
| | Booklet pane of 10 | | |
| | (April 22, 1955) | 145. | |
| | v. Booklet w/electric eye mark at left | 155. | |
| | FDC (Nov. 30, 1954) | | |

**1954. ISSUE.** Savings Stamp Series

| S2 | | MNHVF | UseVF |
|---|---|---|---|
| 25¢ | green | 5.75 | — |
| | Plate block of 4 | 30.00 | |
| | Booklet pane of 10 | | |
| | (Aug. 15, 1955) | 775. | |
| | v. Booklet pane w/electric eye mark at left | 800. | |
| | FDC (Dec. 30, 1954) | | |

**1956. ISSUE.** Savings Stamp Series

| S3 | | MNHVF | UseVF |
|---|---|---|---|
| 50¢ | ultramarine | 8.00 | — |
| | Plate block of 4 | 45.00 | |
| | FDC (Dec. 31, 1956) | | |

**1957. ISSUE.** Savings Stamp Series

| S4 | | MNHVF | UseVF |
|---|---|---|---|
| $1 | black | 22.50 | — |
| | Plate block of 4 | 110. | |
| | FDC (March 13, 1957) | | |

**1956. ISSUE.** Savings Stamp Series
Perforated 11.

| S5 | | MNHVF | UseVF |
|---|---|---|---|
| $5 | violet brown | 70.00 | — |
| | Plate block of 6 | 725. | |
| | FDC (Nov. 30, 1956) | | |

## 1959. ISSUE Savings Stamp Series

**Nov. 18.** Figure of Minute Man and 48-star U.S. flag. *Intaglio on the Giori Press, unwatermarked, perforated 11.*

S6 *Minute Man, flag*

| S6 | | MNHVF | UseVF |
|---|---|---|---|
| 25¢ | **dark blue and carmine** | 1.75 | — |
| | Plate block of 4 | 8.50 | |
| | Booklet pane of 10 | 65.00 | |
| | FDC *(Nov. 18, 1959)* | | |

## 1961. ISSUE Savings Stamp Series

Figure of Minute Man and 50-star U.S. flag. *Intaglio on the Giori Press, unwatermarked, perforated 11.*

| S7 | | MNHVF | UseVF |
|---|---|---|---|
| 25¢ | **dark blue and carmine** | 1.25 | — |
| | Plate block of 4 | 8.00 | |
| | Booklet pane of 10 | 275. | |

## 1960. FEDERAL BOATING STAMP

To quote from the regulation: "Effective April 1, 1960, boats of more then ten horsepower operated on waters of the United States must be numbered under the Federal Boating Act of 1958. Boating stamps available from April 1 on are available in two denominations. The $3 denomination will cover the filing of an application and will be valid for a period of three years. A $1 stamp will cover charges for the reissuance of a lost or destroyed certificate of number."

*Offset, with serial number printed by letter press; unwatermarked, rouletted.*

FB1 *Motor boat in action*

| FB1 | | MNHVF | UseVF |
|---|---|---|---|
| $1 | **carmine red, number in black** | 35.00 | — |
| | Plate block of 4 | 150. | |

| FB2 | | MNHVF | UseVF |
|---|---|---|---|
| $3 | **blue, number in red** | 50.00 | 30.00 |
| | Plate block of 4 | 210. | |

## 1945. POSTAL NOTE ISSUE

Postal Notes were issued to supplement the money order service. The stamps were affixed and canceled to make up fractions of a dollar. *Intaglio, perforated 11 x 10 1/2.*

PO1-PO18

| PO1 | | MNHVF | UseVF |
|---|---|---|---|
| 1¢ | **black** | .25 | .20 |
| | Plate block of 4 | 3.00 | |
| | FDC *(Feb. 1, 1945)* | | 1.00 |

| PO2 | | MNHVF | UseVF |
|---|---|---|---|
| 2¢ | **black** | .25 | .20 |
| | Plate block of 4 | 3.00 | |
| | FDC *(Feb. 1, 1945)* | | 1.00 |

| PO3 | | MNHVF | UseVF |
|---|---|---|---|
| 3¢ | **black** | .25 | .20 |
| | Plate block of 4 | 3.75 | |
| | FDC *(Feb. 1, 1945)* | | 1.00 |

| PO4 | | MNHVF | UseVF |
|---|---|---|---|
| 4¢ | **black** | .30 | .20 |
| | Plate block of 4 | 4.50 | |
| | FDC *(Feb. 1, 1945)* | | 1.00 |

| PO5 | | MNHVF | UseVF |
|---|---|---|---|
| 5¢ | **black** | .40 | .20 |
| | Plate block of 4 | 6.00 | |
| | FDC *(Feb. 1, 1945)* | | 1.00 |

| PO6 | | MNHVF | UseVF |
|---|---|---|---|
| 6¢ | **black** | .45 | .20 |
| | Plate block of 4 | 6.75 | |
| | FDC *(Feb. 1, 1945)* | | 1.00 |

| PO7 | | MNHVF | UseVF |
|---|---|---|---|
| 7¢ | **black** | .55 | .20 |
| | Plate block of 4 | 8.25 | |
| | FDC *(Feb. 1, 1945)* | | 1.00 |

| PO8 | | MNHVF | UseVF |
|---|---|---|---|
| 8¢ | **black** | .70 | .20 |
| | Plate block of 4 | 10.00 | |
| | FDC *(Feb. 1, 1945)* | | 1.00 |

| PO9 | | MNHVF | UseVF |
|---|---|---|---|
| 9¢ | **black** | .75 | .20 |
| | Plate block of 4 | 11.00 | |
| | FDC *(Feb. 1, 1945)* | | 1.00 |

| PO10 | | MNHVF | UseVF |
|---|---|---|---|
| 10¢ | **black** | 1.00 | .20 |
| | Plate block of 4 | 14.00 | |
| | FDC *(Feb. 1, 1945)* | | 1.00 |

| PO11 | | MNHVF | UseVF |
|---|---|---|---|
| 20¢ | **black** | 1.75 | .20 |
| | Plate block of 4 | 27.50 | |
| | FDC *(Feb. 1, 1945)* | | 1.00 |

| PO12 | | MNHVF | UseVF |
|---|---|---|---|
| 30¢ | **black** | 2.50 | .20 |
| | Plate block of 4 | 37.50 | |
| | FDC *(Feb. 1, 1945)* | | 1.00 |

| PO13 | | MNHVF | UseVF |
|---|---|---|---|
| 40¢ | **black** | 3.00 | .20 |
| | Plate block of 4 | 45.00 | |
| | FDC *(Feb. 1, 1945)* | | 1.00 |

| PO14 | | MNHVF | UseVF |
|---|---|---|---|
| 50¢ | **black** | 3.50 | .20 |
| | Plate block of 4 | 52.50 | |
| | FDC *(Feb. 1, 1945)* | | 1.00 |

| PO15 | | MNHVF | UseVF |
|---|---|---|---|
| 60¢ | **black** | 4.75 | .20 |
| | Plate block of 4 | 70.00 | |
| | FDC *(Feb. 1, 1945)* | | 1.00 |

| PO16 | | MNHVF | UseVF |
|---|---|---|---|
| 70¢ | **black** | 5.25 | .20 |
| | Plate block of 4 | 80.00 | |
| | FDC *(Feb. 1, 1945)* | | 1.00 |

| PO17 | | MNHVF | UseVF |
|---|---|---|---|
| 80¢ | **black** | 6.50 | .20 |
| | Plate block of 4 | 95.00 | |
| | FDC *(Feb. 1, 1945)* | | 1.00 |

| PO18 | | MNHVF | UseVF |
|---|---|---|---|
| 90¢ | **black** | 7.00 | .20 |
| | Plate block of 4 | 110. | |
| | FDC *(Feb. 1, 1945)* | | 1.00 |

# Revenue Stamps

For both sides, the costs of the War Between the States were appallingly high. In human terms, the casualty rates rose to possibly 40 per cent, and almost half a million men died fighting for the Union or for the Confederacy. In financial terms, a week before the war ended the government of the United States had already spent $3,250,000,000: a figure larger than the total previously spent since the founding of the republic. (The final cost to both sides was more than $10,000,000,000.) During the war the Union borrowed $2,600,000,000, issued paper money to an extent that brought the value of the dollar down to 39 cents, and introduced a variety of new taxes.

In collecting some of the taxes, the government issued receipts in the form of tax stamps, which we call Revenue Stamps.

**1862-64. THE FIRST REVENUE ISSUE.** In August 1862 the Commissioner of Internal Revenue advertised for bids for the printing of revenue stamps. The contract was awarded to Butler & Carpenter, and most of the first issue of revenues appeared near the end of 1862 and early in 1863. At first the stamps paid specific taxes, according to the designation on the stamp, but after December 25, 1862, they were used indiscriminately. Different kinds of paper were used from time to time, and wide differences in shades and colors exist due to chemical reactions or fading. They are noticeable in the violets and lilacs, which often look gray, and in the reds, which are often on the brown side. Usually these stamps were canceled with pen and ink, and they are priced accordingly in this catalog. Printed cancellations are worth more; cancellations that cut into the paper are worth less.

All of the stamps came unwatermarked and perforated 12, but most of them also exist imperforate. Some stamps are perforated only horizontally and imperforate vertically, or vice versa. These are called "parts perfs".

The collector should be careful of these, and make sure that they have good margins on the imperforate sides; people have been known to trim a perforated stamp in an attempt to make it look like a "part perf" or an imperforate stamp.

**1871. THE SECOND REVENUE ISSUE.** Unscrupulous people soon found that the First Issue could be cleaned and used over again, thus avoiding the payment of taxes and cheating the government of a just return. Experiments were made and a special patented paper, violet in shade, and with tiny silk threads woven into it, was placed in use. The ink too, was special, so that any attempt to clean the stamps was disastrous. All the stamps, except for the last two values, were bi-colored, with the frames printed in blue and Washington's head in black. Each value had its individual frame. The first nine values were all small in size and the head of Washington was enclosed in an octagon. From the 25¢ value on they were quite tall and narrow and the Washington head was enclosed in a circle. In bi-colored printings there is always a chance that a sheet after having been printed in one color, may be reversed before being put through the machine for the second color. That happened with some of these stamps, for eight of the values are known with "inverted centers", and are quite valuable. Excellent imitations of inverted centers exist; and the collector interested in buying one should inspect it carefully, and do business only with a firm he can trust. **Prices given are for the normal "herringbone" cancellation: a row of arrowheads, one within the other, impressed or cut into the paper.** These stamps were printed by Joseph R. Carpenter of Philadelphia, on unwatermarked paper and perforated 12.

**1871-72. THE THIRD REVENUE ISSUE.** The second issue was a great success in preventing the cleaning and re-use of stamps. There were, however, complaints that the stamps were difficult to distinguish because the colors were uniform in nearly all values. A third issue was therefore prepared, again by Joseph R. Carpenter of Philadelphia, using the same plates but this time with varying colors, so that identification might be much easier. They are on violet paper with silk threads, unwatermarked and perforated 12.

### 1862-64. U.S. INTERNAL REVENUE ISSUE

| | | Perf | Part Perf | Imperf |
|---|---|---|---|---|
| **R1** | | | | |
| 2¢ | orange yellow | .20 | — | |
| **R2** | | Perf | Part Perf | Imperf |
| $50 | green | 75.00 | | 75.00 |

| | | Perf | Part Perf | Imperf |
|---|---|---|---|---|
| **R3** | | | | |
| $200. | red & green | 500. | | 1200. |

### 1862-64. AGREEMENT ISSUE

| | | Perf | Part Perf | Imperf |
|---|---|---|---|---|
| **R4** | | | | |
| 5¢ | rose red | .20 | | |

### 1862-64. BANK CHECK ISSUE

| | | Perf | Part Perf | Imperf |
|---|---|---|---|---|
| **R5** | | | | |
| 2¢ | light blue | .20 | 1.50 | 1.50 |
| **R6** | | Perf | Part Perf | Imperf |
| 2¢ | orange | .20 | .85 | |

### 1862-64. BILL OF LADING ISSUE

| | | Perf | Part Perf | Imperf |
|---|---|---|---|---|
| **R7** | | | | |
| 10¢ | blue | .75 | 150. | 50.00 |

### 1862-64. BOND ISSUE

| | | Perf | Part Perf | Imperf |
|---|---|---|---|---|
| **R8** | | | | |
| 25¢ | brown red | 2.00 | 6.00 | 125. |

### 1862-64. CERTIFICATE ISSUE

| | | Perf | Part Perf | Imperf |
|---|---|---|---|---|
| **R9** | | | | |
| 2¢ | light blue | 25.00 | | 10.00 |
| **R10** | | Perf | Part Perf | Imperf |
| 2¢ | orange yellow | 25.00 | | |
| **R11** | | Perf | Part Perf | Imperf |
| 5¢ | rose red | .20 | 10.00 | 2.50 |
| **R12** | | Perf | Part Perf | Imperf |
| 10¢ | blue | .25 | 165. | 190. |
| **R13** | | Perf | Part Perf | Imperf |
| 25¢ | brown red | .20 | 5.00 | 7.50 |

### 1862-64. CHARTER PARTY ISSUE

| | | Perf | Part Perf | Imperf |
|---|---|---|---|---|
| **R14** | | | | |
| $3 | green | 4.50 | | 900. |
| **R15** | | Perf | Part Perf | Imperf |
| $5 | orange red | 6.00 | | 225. |
| **R16** | | Perf | Part Perf | Imperf |
| $10 | blue green | 20.00 | | 450. |

### 1862-64. CONTRACT ISSUE

| | | Perf | Part Perf | Imperf |
|---|---|---|---|---|
| **R17** | | | | |
| 10¢ | blue | .35 | 140. | |
| | a. ultramarine | .40 | 160. | |

### 1862-64. CONVEYANCE ISSUE

| | | Perf | Part Perf | Imperf |
|---|---|---|---|---|
| **R18** | | | | |
| 50¢ | dark blue | .20 | 1.25 | 12.50 |
| | a. ultramarine | 25.00 | | |
| **R19** | | Perf | Part Perf | Imperf |
| $1 | brown red | 3.50 | 375. | 10.00 |
| **R20** | | Perf | Part Perf | Imperf |
| $2 | rose red | 2.50 | 1250. | 90.00 |
| **R21** | | Perf | Part Perf | Imperf |
| $5 | orange red | 6.00 | | 35.00 |
| **R22** | | Perf | Part Perf | Imperf |
| $10 | blue green | 55.00 | | 80.00 |
| **R23** | | Perf | Part Perf | Imperf |
| $20 | orange | 45.00 | | 100. |

### 1862-64. ENTRY OF GOODS ISSUE

| | | Perf | Part Perf | Imperf |
|---|---|---|---|---|
| **R24** | | | | |
| 25¢ | brown red | .60 | 50.00 | 15.00 |
| **R25** | | Perf | Part Perf | Imperf |
| 50¢ | dark blue | .25 | 11.50 | |
| **R26** | | Perf | Part Perf | Imperf |
| $1 | brown red | 1.50 | | 27.50 |

### 1862-64. EXPRESS ISSUE

| | | Perf | Part Perf | Imperf |
|---|---|---|---|---|
| **R27** | | | | |
| 1¢ | rose red | 1.00 | 40.00 | 50.00 |

*One-cent and Two-cent Stamps*

*R89, R120*

*R90, R121, R137*

*R109, R131*

*Three-cent to Twenty-cent Stamps*

*R91*

*R92, R122*

*R114, R135*

*R93, R123*

*R94, R124*

*2c to 40c Stamps*    *50c to 90c Stamps*

*R95*

*R96, R125*

*R116*

*$2 to $3.50 Stamps*    *Five-dollar to Ten-dollar Stamps*

*R99, R126*

*R97*

*R102, R128*

*R104, R130*

*R119*

*Two-hundred-dollar Stamp*

| R28 | | Perf | Part Perf | Imperf |
|---|---|---|---|---|
| 2¢ | light blue | .25 | 16.00 | 10.00 |

| R29 | | Perf | Part Perf | Imperf |
|---|---|---|---|---|
| 2¢ | orange yellow | 6.00 | | |

| R30 | | Perf | Part Perf | Imperf |
|---|---|---|---|---|
| 5¢ | rose red | .30 | 450. | 4.00 |

## 1862-64. FOREIGN EXCHANGE ISSUE

| R31 | | Perf | Part Perf | Imperf |
|---|---|---|---|---|
| 3¢ | dark yellow green | 3.00 | 225. | |

| R32 | | Perf | Part Perf | Imperf |
|---|---|---|---|---|
| 5¢ | rose red | .35 | | |

| R33 | | Perf | Part Perf | Imperf |
|---|---|---|---|---|
| 10¢ | blue | 6.50 | | |
| | a. ultramarine (R35e) | 8.00 | | |

| R34 | | Perf | Part Perf | Imperf |
|---|---|---|---|---|
| 15¢ | dark brown | 12.50 | | |

| R35 | | Perf | Part Perf | Imperf |
|---|---|---|---|---|
| 20¢ | rose red | 27.50 | | 40.00 |

| R36 | | Perf | Part Perf | Imperf |
|---|---|---|---|---|
| 30¢ | lilac gray | 35.00 | 825. | 65.00 |

| R37 | | Perf | Part Perf | Imperf |
|---|---|---|---|---|
| 50¢ | dark blue | 5.00 | 32.50 | 35.00 |

| R38 | | Perf | Part Perf | Imperf |
|---|---|---|---|---|
| 70¢ | blue green | 6.50 | 75.00 | 275. |

| R39 | | Perf | Part Perf | Imperf |
|---|---|---|---|---|
| $1 | brown red | .75 | | 60.00 |

| R40 | | Perf | Part Perf | Imperf |
|---|---|---|---|---|
| $1.30 | orange yellow | 50.00 | | |

| R41 | | Perf | Part Perf | Imperf |
|---|---|---|---|---|
| $1.60 | green | 85.00 | | 800. |

| R42 | | Perf | Part Perf | Imperf |
|---|---|---|---|---|
| $1.90 | brown violet | 65.00 | | 2000. |

## 1862-64. INLAND EXCHANGE ISSUE

| R43 | | Perf | Part Perf | Imperf |
|---|---|---|---|---|
| 4¢ | gray brown | 1.75 | | |

| R44 | | Perf | Part Perf | Imperf |
|---|---|---|---|---|
| 5¢ | rose red | .20 | 3.50 | 4.25 |

| R45 | | Perf | Part Perf | Imperf |
|---|---|---|---|---|
| 6¢ | yellow orange | 15.00 | | |

| R46 | | Perf | Part Perf | Imperf |
|---|---|---|---|---|
| 10¢ | blue | .25 | 3.50 | 165. |

| R47 | | Perf | Part Perf | Imperf |
|---|---|---|---|---|
| 15¢ | dark brown | 1.20 | 10.00 | 25.00 |

| R48 | | Perf | Part Perf | Imperf |
|---|---|---|---|---|
| 20¢ | rose red | .50 | 15.00 | 14.50 |

| R49 | | Perf | Part Perf | Imperf |
|---|---|---|---|---|
| 30¢ | lilac gray | 3.00 | 55.00 | 45.00 |

| R50 | | Perf | Part Perf | Imperf |
|---|---|---|---|---|
| 40¢ | brown gray | 3.00 | 6.00 | 475. |

| R51 | | Perf | Part Perf | Imperf |
|---|---|---|---|---|
| 60¢ | red orange | 6.00 | 45.00 | 75.00 |

| R52 | | Perf | Part Perf | Imperf |
|---|---|---|---|---|
| $1 | brown red | .50 | 275. | 12.50 |

| R53 | | Perf | Part Perf | Imperf |
|---|---|---|---|---|
| $1.50 | gray blue | 3.00 | | 20.00 |

| R54 | | Perf | Part Perf | Imperf |
|---|---|---|---|---|
| $2.50 | red violet | 3.50 | | 1850. |

| R55 | | Perf | Part Perf | Imperf |
|---|---|---|---|---|
| $3.50 | blue | 45.00 | | 1500. |

## 1862-64. INSURANCE ISSUE

| R56 | | Perf | Part Perf | Imperf |
|---|---|---|---|---|
| 25¢ | brown red | .25 | 10.00 | 9.00 |

## 1862-64. LEASE ISSUE

| R57 | | Perf | Part Perf | Imperf |
|---|---|---|---|---|
| 50¢ | dark blue | 6.50 | 55.00 | 22.50 |

| R58 | | Perf | Part Perf | Imperf |
|---|---|---|---|---|
| $1 | brown red | 1.75 | | 30.00 |

## 1862-64. LIFE INSURANCE ISSUE

| R59 | | Perf | Part Perf | Imperf |
|---|---|---|---|---|
| 25¢ | brown red | 6.00 | 175. | 30.00 |

| R60 | | Perf | Part Perf | Imperf |
|---|---|---|---|---|
| 50¢ | dark blue | .75 | 50.00 | 30.00 |

| R61 | | Perf | Part Perf | Imperf |
|---|---|---|---|---|
| $1 | brown red | 5.00 | | 125. |

## 1862-64. MANIFEST ISSUE

| R62 | | Perf | Part Perf | Imperf |
|---|---|---|---|---|
| $1 | brown red | 22.50 | | 45.00 |

| R63 | | Perf | Part Perf | Imperf |
|---|---|---|---|---|
| $3 | yellow green | 20.00 | | 100. |

| R64 | | Perf | Part Perf | Imperf |
|---|---|---|---|---|
| $5 | orange red | 75.00 | | 100. |

## 1862-64. MORTGAGE ISSUE

| R65 | | Perf | Part Perf | Imperf |
|---|---|---|---|---|
| 50¢ | dark blue | .35 | 2.25 | 10.00 |

| R66 | | Perf | Part Perf | Imperf |
|---|---|---|---|---|
| $1 | brown red | 140. | | 17.50 |

| R67 | | Perf | Part Perf | Imperf |
|---|---|---|---|---|
| $2 | rose red | 2.25 | | 85.00 |

| R68 | | Perf | Part Perf | Imperf |
|---|---|---|---|---|
| $5 | orange red | 17.50 | | 90.00 |

| R69 | | Perf | Part Perf | Imperf |
|---|---|---|---|---|
| $10 | blue green | 20.00 | | 325. |

| R70 | | Perf | Part Perf | Imperf |
|---|---|---|---|---|
| $15 | blue | 100. | | 850. |
| | a. ultramarine (R97e) | 125. | | |

| R71 | | Perf | Part Perf | Imperf |
|---|---|---|---|---|
| $25 | rose red | 90.00 | | 800. |

## 1862-64. ORIGINAL PROCESS ISSUE

| R72 | | Perf | Part Perf | Imperf |
|---|---|---|---|---|
| 50¢ | dark blue | .40 | 475. | 3.00 |

## 1862-64. PASSAGE TICKET ISSUE

| R73 | | Perf | Part Perf | Imperf |
|---|---|---|---|---|
| 50¢ | dark blue | .70 | 125. | 65.00 |

| R74 | | Perf | Part Perf | Imperf |
|---|---|---|---|---|
| $1 | brown red | 150. | | 225. |

## 1862-64. POWER OF ATTORNEY ISSUE

| R75 | | Perf | Part Perf | Imperf |
|---|---|---|---|---|
| 10¢ | blue | .45 | 20.00 | 425. |

| R76 | | Perf | Part Perf | Imperf |
|---|---|---|---|---|
| 25¢ | brown red | .25 | 25.00 | 5.00 |

| R77 | | Perf | Part Perf | Imperf |
|---|---|---|---|---|
| $1 | brown red | 1.75 | | 60.00 |

## 1862.64. PROBATE OF WILL ISSUE

| R78 | | Perf | Part Perf | Imperf |
|---|---|---|---|---|
| 50¢ | dark blue | 17.50 | 50.00 | 30.00 |

| R79 | | Perf | Part Perf | Imperf |
|---|---|---|---|---|
| $1 | brown red | 32.50 | | 60.00 |

| R80 | | Perf | Part Perf | Imperf |
|---|---|---|---|---|
| $2 | rose red | 47.50 | | 1750. |

| R81 | | Perf | Part Perf | Imperf |
|---|---|---|---|---|
| $5 | orange red | 17.50 | | 400. |

| R82 | | Perf | Part Perf | Imperf |
|---|---|---|---|---|
| $10 | blue green | 20.00 | | 1000. |

| R83 | | Perf | Part Perf | Imperf |
|---|---|---|---|---|
| $20 | orange | 900. | | 1000. |

## 1862-64. PROTEST ISSUE

| R84 | | Perf | Part Perf | Imperf |
|---|---|---|---|---|
| 25¢ | brown red | 7.00 | 225. | 22.50 |

## 1862-64. SURETY BOND ISSUE

| R85 | | Perf | Part Perf | Imperf |
|---|---|---|---|---|
| 50¢ | dark blue | .25 | 2.50 | 140. |
| | a. ultramarine | 1.50 | | |

## 1862-64. TELEGRAPH ISSUE

| R86 | | Perf | Part Perf | Imperf |
|---|---|---|---|---|
| $1 | rose red | 10.00 | | 400. |

| R87 | | Perf | Part Perf | Imperf |
|---|---|---|---|---|
| $3 | dark yellow green | 2.50 | 17.50 | 50.00 |

## 1862-64. WAREHOUSE RECEIPT ISSUE

| R88 | | Perf | Part Perf | Imperf |
|---|---|---|---|---|
| 25¢ | brown red | 20.00 | 200. | 40.00 |

For stamps inscribed: **Playing Cards** see numbers RPC1-6 in the Playing Cards Revenues Section.

For stamps inscribed: **Proprietary** see numbers RP1-8 in the Proprietary Revenues Section.

## 1871. U.S. INTERNAL REVENUE ISSUE

| R89 | | Perf | PerfCnl |
|---|---|---|---|
| 1¢ | blue and gray black | 30.00 | |
| | a. Inverted center | 900. | |

| R90 | | Perf | PerfCnl |
|---|---|---|---|
| 2¢ | blue and gray black | 1.00 | |
| | a. Inverted center | 3250. | |

| R91 | | Perf | PerfCnl |
|---|---|---|---|
| 3¢ | blue and gray black | 12.50 | |

| R92 | | Perf | PerfCnl |
|---|---|---|---|
| 4¢ | blue and gray black | 55.00 | |

| R93 | | Perf | PerfCnl |
|---|---|---|---|
| 5¢ | blue and gray black | 1.40 | |
| | a. Inverted center | 1400. | |

| R94 | | Perf | PerfCnl |
|---|---|---|---|
| 6¢ | blue and gray black | 85.00 | |

| R95 | | Perf | PerfCnl |
|---|---|---|---|
| 10¢ | blue and gray black | .85 | |
| | a. Inverted center | 1400. | |

| R96 | | Perf | PerfCnl |
|---|---|---|---|
| 15¢ | blue and gray black | 22.50 | |

| R97 | | Perf | PerfCnl |
|---|---|---|---|
| 20¢ | blue and gray black | 5.00 | |
| | a. Inverted center | 7000. | |

| R98 | | Perf | PerfCnl |
|---|---|---|---|
| 25¢ | blue and gray black | .60 | |
| | a. Inverted center | 7500. | |

| R99 | | Perf | PerfCnl |
|---|---|---|---|
| 30¢ | blue and gray black | 60.00 | |

| R100 | | Perf | PerfCnl |
|---|---|---|---|
| 40¢ | blue and gray black | 40.00 | |

| R101 | | Perf | PerfCnl |
|---|---|---|---|
| 50¢ | blue and gray black | .60 | |
| | a. Inverted center (R115b) | 750. | |
| | b. Inverted center, punch cancellation | 200. | |
| | c. Sewing machine, perf. (R115a) | 70.00 | |

| R102 | | Perf | PerfCnl |
|---|---|---|---|
| 60¢ | blue and gray black | 85.00 | |

| R103 | | Perf | PerfCnl |
|---|---|---|---|
| 70¢ | blue and gray black | 30.00 | |
| | a. Inverted center (R117a | 2500. | |

| R104 | | Perf | PerfCnl |
|---|---|---|---|
| $1 | blue and gray black | 3.00 | |
| | a. Inverted center (R118a) | 4000. | |
| | b. Inverted center, punch cancellation | 700. | |

| R105 | | Perf | PerfCnl |
|---|---|---|---|
| $1.30 | blue and gray black | 250. | |

| R106 | | Perf | PerfCnl |
|---|---|---|---|
| $1.50 | blue and gray black | 12.50 | |

| R107 | | Perf | PerfCnl |
|---|---|---|---|
| $1.60 | blue and gray black | 325. | |

| R108 | | Perf | PerfCnl |
|---|---|---|---|
| $1.90 | blue and gray black | 160. | |

| R109 | | Perf | PerfCnl |
|---|---|---|---|
| $2 | blue and gray black | 12.50 | |

| R110 | | Perf | PerfCnl |
|---|---|---|---|
| $2.50 | blue and gray black | 25.00 | |

| R111 | | Perf | PerfCnl |
|---|---|---|---|
| $3 | blue and gray black | 30.00 | |

| R112 | | Perf | PerfCnl |
|---|---|---|---|
| $3.50 | blue and gray black | 150. | |

| R113 | | Perf | PerfCnl |
|---|---|---|---|
| $5 | blue and gray black | 17.50 | |
| | a. Inverted center (R127a) | 2000. | |
| | b. Inverted center, punch cancellation | 600. | |

| R114 | | Perf | PerfCnl |
|---|---|---|---|
| $10 | blue and gray black | 90.00 | |

| R115 | | Perf | PerfCnl |
|---|---|---|---|
| $20 | blue and gray black | 300. | |

| R116 | | Perf | PerfCnl |
|---|---|---|---|
| $25 | blue and gray black | 300. | |

| R117 | | Perf | PerfCnl |
|---|---|---|---|
| $50 | blue and gray black | 325. | |

| R118 | | Perf | PerfCnl |
|---|---|---|---|
| $200. | blue, gray black and red | 4500. | |

| R119 | | Perf | PerfCnl |
|---|---|---|---|
| $500. | gray black, green and red | 10000. | |

## 1871-72. U.S. INTERNAL REVENUE ISSUE

| R120 | | Perf | PerfCnl |
|---|---|---|---|
| 1¢ | claret and gray black | 25.00 | |

| R121 | | Perf | PerfCnl |
|---|---|---|---|
| 2¢ | yellow orange and gray black | .20 | |
| | a. Inverted center (R135b) | 275. | |
| | b. claret and gray black (error of color) (R135a) | 500. | |

| R122 | | Perf | PerfCnl |
|---|---|---|---|
| 4¢ | gray brown and gray black | 30.00 | |

| R123 | | Perf | PerfCnl |
|---|---|---|---|
| 5¢ | orange and gray black | .20 | |
| | a. Inverted center (R137a) | 3000. | |

| R124 | | Perf | PerfCnl |
|---|---|---|---|
| 6¢ | orange and gray black | 30.00 | |

| R125 | | Perf | PerfCnl |
|---|---|---|---|
| 15¢ | gray brown and gray black | 7.50 | |
| | a. Inverted center (R139a) | 7500. | |

| R126 | | Perf | PerfCnl |
|---|---|---|---|
| 30¢ | orange and gray black | 12.50 | |
| | a. Inverted center (R140a) | 2000. | |

| R127 | | Perf | PerfCnl |
|---|---|---|---|
| 40¢ | gray brown and gray black | 30.00 | |

| R128 | | Perf | PerfCnl |
|---|---|---|---|
| 60¢ | yellow orange and gray black | 55.00 | |

| R129 | | Perf | PerfCnl |
|---|---|---|---|
| 70¢ | yellow green and gray black | 35.00 | |

| R130 | | Perf | PerfCnl |
|---|---|---|---|
| $1 | yellow green and gray black | 1.25 | |
| | a. Inverted center (144a) | 5000. | |

| R131 | | Perf | PerfCnl |
|---|---|---|---|
| $2 | vermilion and gray black | 17.50 | |

| R132 | | Perf | PerfCnl |
|---|---|---|---|
| $2.50 | claret and gray black | 30.00 | |
| | a. Inverted Center (R146a) | 12500. | |

| R133 | | Perf | PerfCnl |
|---|---|---|---|
| $3 | yellow green and gray black | 30.00 | |

| R134 | | Perf | PerfCnl |
|---|---|---|---|
| $5 | vermilion and gray black | 17.50 | |

| R135 | | Perf | PerfCnl |
|---|---|---|---|
| $10 | yellow green and gray black | 70.00 | |

**R136**

| | | Perf | PerfCnl |
|---|---|---|---|
| $20 | **orange and gray black** | 450. | |
| | a. vermilion and black *(R150a)* | 550. | |

**1874. U.S. INTERNAL REVENUE ISSUE** The Two Cent Stamp No. R121 was issued on green paper, perforated 12.

**R137**

| | | Perf | PerfCnl |
|---|---|---|---|
| 2¢ | **orange and gray black on green paper** | .20 | |
| | a. Inverted center *(R151a)* | 325. | |

**1875-78. U.S. INTERNAL REVENUE ISSUE** The Profile of Liberty was used as the central design of the new two-cent stamps printed on blue silk or watermarked paper. The stamps were perforated 12, imperforate or rouletted 6.

R138-R141 *Silk paper, unwatermarked, perforated 12.*

**R138**

| | | UnCnl | UseFVF |
|---|---|---|---|
| 2¢ | **blue, on blue paper** | 1.50 | .20 |
| | Pair | 3.50 | .50 |
| | Block of 4 | 8.00 | 1.25 |

**1875-78. U.S. INTERNAL REVENUE ISSUE** Watermarked paper, perforated 12.

**R139**

| | | UnCnl | UseFVF |
|---|---|---|---|
| 2¢ | **blue, on blue paper** | 1.50 | .20 |
| | Pair | 3.50 | .50 |
| | Block of 4 | 8.00 | 1.25 |

**1875-78. U.S. INTERNAL REVENUE** Double Line USIR watermark, imperforate.

**R140**

| | | UnCnl | UseFVF |
|---|---|---|---|
| 2¢ | **blue, on blue paper** | | 75.00 |
| | Pair | | 225. |

**1875-78. U.S. INTERNAL REVENUE** Double Line USIR watermark, rouletted 6.

**R141**

| | | UnCnl | UseFVF |
|---|---|---|---|
| 2¢ | **blue, on blue paper** | — | 30.00 |
| | Pair | — | 75.00 |

**1898. U.S. INTERNAL REVENUE ISSUE** Regular Issue Nos. 189, 191, overprinted.

R142 *Overprint A.*

**R142**

| | | UnCnl | UseFVF |
|---|---|---|---|
| 1¢ | **deep green,** red overprint A | 3.00 | 3.00 |

R143, R144 *Overprint B.*

**R143**

| | | UnCnl | UseFVF |
|---|---|---|---|
| 1¢ | **deep green,** red overprint B | .25 | .20 |
| | a. Inverted overprint *(R154a)* | 20.00 | 17.50 |

**R144**

| | | UnCnl | UseFVF |
|---|---|---|---|
| 2¢ | **carmine,** blue overprint B | .30 | .20 |
| | a. Inverted overprint *(R155a)* | .60 | .50 |

*The 8¢ purple brown, 10¢ dark green and 15¢ indigo of the 1895 regular postage issue exist with overprint B in magenta but they were not officially issued. They are valued at approximately $300.00 each.*

**1898. NEWSPAPER STAMP ISSUE** Newspaper Stamp No. N92, overprinted.

**R145**

| | | UnCnl | UseFVF |
|---|---|---|---|
| $5 | **dark blue,** red overprint A | 225. | 150. |

**R146**

| | | UnCnl | UseFVF |
|---|---|---|---|
| $5 | **dark blue,** red overprint B | 100. | 75.00 |

**1898. DOCUMENTARY ISSUE** "The Battleship Issue" featured a new design, officially designated as a "Battleship, second class." The blowing-up of the battleship Maine in the harbor of Havana on February 15, 1898, had touched off the Spanish-American War and the slogan "Remember the Maine;" and many people thought that the new design represented the unfortunate Maine. This, however, was officially denied. The stamps were printed on paper with double-line watermark USIR, and rouletted 5 1/2 or hyphen-hole perforated 7. Stamps identical with these, except that the word "Proprietary" is printed on the base instead of "Documentary" are found listed with the Proprietary stamps later on.

R147-R158 *Rouletted 5 1/2.*

| **R147** | | UnCnl | UseFVF | CutCnl |
|---|---|---|---|---|
| 1/2¢ | **orange,** | 2.25 | 6.00 | |
| **R148** | | UnCnl | UseFVF | CutCnl |
| 1/2¢ | **dark gray,** | .30 | .20 | |
| **R148a** | | UnCnl | UseFVF | CutCnl |
| 1/2¢ | **dark gray,** | .30 | .20 | |
| **R149** | | UnCnl | UseFVF | CutCnl |
| 1¢ | **pale blue,** | .35 | .20 | |
| **R149a** | | UnCnl | UseFVF | CutCnl |
| 1¢ | **pale blue,** | .35 | .20 | |
| **R150** | | UnCnl | UseFVF | CutCnl |
| 2¢ | **rose,** | .25 | .20 | |
| **R150a** | | UnCnl | UseFVF | CutCnl |
| 2¢ | **rose,** | .25 | .20 | |
| **R151** | | UnCnl | UseFVF | CutCnl |
| 3¢ | **indigo,** | 1.25 | .20 | |
| **R151a** | | UnCnl | UseFVF | CutCnl |
| 3¢ | **indigo,** | 1.25 | .20 | |
| **R152** | | UnCnl | UseFVF | CutCnl |
| 4¢ | **pale rose,** | .75 | .20 | |
| **R152a** | | UnCnl | UseFVF | CutCnl |
| 4¢ | **pale rose,** | .75 | .20 | |
| **R153** | | UnCnl | UseFVF | CutCnl |
| 5¢ | **lilac,** | .25 | .20 | |
| **R153a** | | UnCnl | UseFVF | CutCnl |
| 5¢ | **lilac,** | .25 | .20 | |
| **R154** | | UnCnl | UseFVF | CutCnl |
| 10¢ | **gray brown,** | 1.25 | .20 | |
| **R154a** | | UnCnl | UseFVF | CutCnl |
| 10¢ | **gray brown,** | 1.25 | .20 | |
| **R155** | | UnCnl | UseFVF | CutCnl |
| 25¢ | **lilac brown,** | 1.25 | .20 | |
| **R155a** | | UnCnl | UseFVF | CutCnl |
| 25¢ | **lilac brown,** | 1.25 | .20 | |
| **R156** | | UnCnl | UseFVF | CutCnl |
| 40¢ | **blue lilac,** | 100. | 2.00 | .25 |
| **R156a** | | UnCnl | UseFVF | CutCnl |
| 40¢ | **blue lilac,** | 100. | 2.00 | .25 |

| R157 | | UnCnl | UseFVF | CutCnl |
|---|---|---|---|---|
| 50¢ | violet gray, | 10.00 | .20 | |

| R157a | | UnCnl | UseFVF | CutCnl |
|---|---|---|---|---|
| 50¢ | violet gray, | 10.00 | .20 | |

| R158 | | UnCnl | UseFVF | CutCnl |
|---|---|---|---|---|
| 80¢ | bistre, | 55.00 | .40 | .20 |

| R158a | | UnCnl | UseFVF | CutCnl |
|---|---|---|---|---|
| 80¢ | bistre, | 55.00 | .40 | .20 |

**1898-1900. DOCUMENTARY ISSUE** Allegorical Figure of Commerce design on the $1 through $50 values. These stamps are rouletted 5 1/2 or perforated 7, all on the Double Line USIR watermark paper. The cancelled stamps usually are without gum.

| R159 | | UnCnl | UseFVF | CutCnl |
|---|---|---|---|---|
| $1 | blue green *(1898),* | 7.00 | .20 | |

| R159a | | UnCnl | UseFVF | CutCnl |
|---|---|---|---|---|
| $1 | blue green, | 7.00 | .20 | |

| R160 | | UnCnl | UseFVF | CutCnl |
|---|---|---|---|---|
| $1 | carmine rose *(1900),* | 14.00 | .50 | |

| R161 | | UnCnl | UseFVF | CutCnl |
|---|---|---|---|---|
| $3 | purple brown *(1898),* | 14.00 | .75 | .20 |

| R161a | | UnCnl | UseFVF | CutCnl |
|---|---|---|---|---|
| $3 | purple brown, | 14.00 | .75 | .20 |

| R162 | | UnCnl | UseFVF | CutCnl |
|---|---|---|---|---|
| $3 | lake *(1900),* | 45.00 | 100. | 8.00 |

| R163 | | UnCnl | UseFVF | CutCnl |
|---|---|---|---|---|
| $5 | red orange *(1898),* | 17.50 | 1.50 | .25 |

| R164 | | UnCnl | UseFVF | CutCnl |
|---|---|---|---|---|
| $10 | black, | 55.00 | 2.50 | .75 |

| R165 | | UnCnl | UseFVF | CutCnl |
|---|---|---|---|---|
| $30 | red, | 175. | 85.00 | 40.00 |

| R166 | | UnCnl | UseFVF | CutCnl |
|---|---|---|---|---|
| $50 | gray brown, | 80.00 | 6.00 | 2.00 |

**1899. DOCUMENTARY ISSUE** Portrait in Frame, each stamp inscribed: "Series of 1898". Double Line watermark, imperforate.

| R167 | | UnCnl | UseFVF | CutCnl |
|---|---|---|---|---|
| $100. | pale brown and black | 90.00 | 30.00 | 17.50 |
| | (Marshall) | | | |

| R168 | | UnCnl | UseFVF | CutCnl |
|---|---|---|---|---|
| $500. | carmine lake and black | 600. | 425. | 225. |
| | (Hamilton) | | | |

| R169 | | UnCnl | UseFVF | CutCnl |
|---|---|---|---|---|
| $1000. | dark green and black | 600. | 350. | 100. |
| | (Madison) | | | |

**1900. DOCUMENTARY ISSUE** Allegorical Figure of Commerce, same designs as 1898-1900 but of different colors and overprinted with large outline numerals of value. Hyphen-hole perforation 7, Double Line USIR watermark.

| R170 | | UnCnl | UseFVF | CutCnl |
|---|---|---|---|---|
| $1 | olive gray | 8.00 | .25 | .20 |

| R171 | | UnCnl | UseFVF | CutCnl |
|---|---|---|---|---|
| $2 | olive gray | 8.00 | .25 | .20 |

| R172 | | UnCnl | UseFVF | CutCnl |
|---|---|---|---|---|
| $3 | olive gray | 45.00 | 12.50 | 2.25 |

| R173 | | UnCnl | UseFVF | CutCnl |
|---|---|---|---|---|
| $5 | olive gray | 35.00 | 8.50 | 1.25 |

| R174 | | UnCnl | UseFVF | CutCnl |
|---|---|---|---|---|
| $10 | olive gray | 60.00 | 17.50 | 3.50 |

| R175 | | UnCnl | UseFVF | CutCnl |
|---|---|---|---|---|
| $50 | olive gray | 600. | 350. | 75.00 |

**1902. DOCUMENTARY ISSUE** Allegorical Figure of Commerce, overprinted in black with large filigree numerals of value. A small square of water-soluble varnish was printed on the face of each stamp before it was overprinted; that part of the overprint that is on this small square of varnish will disappear when the stamp is soaked in water. Double Line USIR watermark, hyphen-hole roulette perforated 7.

R176 *Filigree Numeral Overprint*

| R176 | | UnCnl | UseFVF | CutCnl |
|---|---|---|---|---|
| $1 | blue green | 17.50 | 3.50 | .25 |

| R177 | | UnCnl | UseFVF | CutCnl |
|---|---|---|---|---|
| $2 | blue green | 15.00 | 1.50 | .25 |

| R178 | | UnCnl | UseFVF | CutCnl |
|---|---|---|---|---|
| $5 | blue green | 125. | 30.00 | 4.50 |
| | Overprint omitted | 55.00 | | |

| R179 | | UnCnl | UseFVF | CutCnl |
|---|---|---|---|---|
| $10 | blue green | 300. | 140. | 50.00 |

| R180 | | UnCnl | UseFVF | CutCnl |
|---|---|---|---|---|
| $50 | blue green | 900. | 750. | 225. |

**1914. DOCUMENTARY ISSUE** A White Numeral in Circle was the new design of the small size stamps, printed in one color. They are inscribed "Series of 1914", printed on Single Line USPS watermark paper, and are perforated 10. The unused stamps valued as with gum.

| R181 | | UnFVF | UseFVF |
|---|---|---|---|
| 1/2¢ | pale rose | 6.50 | 3.50 |

| R182 | | UnFVF | UseFVF |
|---|---|---|---|
| 1¢ | pale rose | 1.50 | .20 |

| R183 | | UnFVF | UseFVF |
|---|---|---|---|
| 2¢ | pale rose | 1.75 | .20 |

| R184 | | UnFVF | UseFVF |
|---|---|---|---|
| 3¢ | pale rose | 45.00 | 27.50 |

| R185 | | UnFVF | UseFVF |
|---|---|---|---|
| 4¢ | pale rose | 11.00 | 2.00 |

| R186 | | UnFVF | UseFVF |
|---|---|---|---|
| 5¢ | pale rose | 4.00 | .20 |

| R187 | | UnFVF | UseFVF |
|---|---|---|---|
| 10¢ | pale rose | 3.25 | .20 |

| R188 | | UnFVF | UseFVF |
|---|---|---|---|
| 25¢ | pale rose | 27.50 | .75 |

| R189 | | UnFVF | UseFVF |
|---|---|---|---|
| 40¢ | pale rose | 17.50 | 1.00 |

| R190 | | UnFVF | UseFVF |
|---|---|---|---|
| 50¢ | pale rose | 5.50 | .20 |

| R191 | | UnFVF | UseFVF |
|---|---|---|---|
| 80¢ | pale rose | 80.00 | 10.00 |

**1914. SECOND DOCUMENTARY ISSUE** Same as the preceding stamps Nos. R181-R191, but on Double Line USIR watermark paper, perforated 10.

| R192 | | UnCnl | UseFVF | CutCnl |
|---|---|---|---|---|
| 1/2¢ | rose red | | .60 | |

| R193 | | UnCnl | UseFVF | CutCnl |
|---|---|---|---|---|
| 1¢ | rose red | | .20 | |

| R194 | | UnCnl | UseFVF | CutCnl |
|---|---|---|---|---|
| 2¢ | rose red | | .20 | |

| R195 | | UnCnl | UseFVF | CutCnl |
|---|---|---|---|---|
| 3¢ | rose red | | .20 | |

| R196 | | UnCnl | UseFVF | CutCnl |
|---|---|---|---|---|
| 4¢ | rose red | | .40 | |

| R197 | | UnCnl | UseFVF | CutCnl |
|---|---|---|---|---|
| 5¢ | rose red | | .30 | |

| R198 | | UnCnl | UseFVF | CutCnl |
|---|---|---|---|---|
| 10¢ | rose red | | .20 | |

| R199 | | UnCnl | UseFVF | CutCnl |
|---|---|---|---|---|
| 25¢ | rose red | | 1.25 | |

| R200 | | UnCnl | UseFVF | CutCnl |
|---|---|---|---|---|
| 40¢ | rose red | | 12.50 | .75 |

| R201 | | UnCnl | UseFVF | CutCnl |
|---|---|---|---|---|
| 50¢ | rose red | | .35 | |

| R202 | | UnCnl | UseFVF | CutCnl |
|---|---|---|---|---|
| 80¢ | rose red | | 17.50 | 1.00 |

**1914. THIRD DOCUMENTARY ISSUE** Head of Liberty design, inscribed "Series 1914", Flat Press printing. Double Line USIR watermark, perforated 10.

| R203 | | UnCnl | UseFVF | CutCnl |
|---|---|---|---|---|
| $1 | yellow green | | .30 | .20 |

| R204 | | UnCnl | UseFVF | CutCnl |
|---|---|---|---|---|
| $2 | carmine | | .50 | .20 |

| R205 | | UnCnl | UseFVF | CutCnl |
|---|---|---|---|---|
| $3 | purple | | 2.50 | .20 |

| R206 | | UnCnl | UseFVF | CutCnl |
|---|---|---|---|---|
| $5 | dark blue | | 3.00 | .75 |

| R207 | | UnCnl | UseFVF | CutCnl |
|---|---|---|---|---|
| $10 | yellow | | 5.00 | 1.00 |

| R208 | | UnCnl | UseFVF | CutCnl |
|---|---|---|---|---|
| $30 | vermilion orange | | 12.50 | 2.50 |

| R209 | | UnCnl | UseFVF | CutCnl |
|---|---|---|---|---|
| $50 | violet | | 750. | 300. |

**1914-15. DOCUMENTARY ISSUE** Portraits, are featured on high values printed on Double Line USIR watermark paper, perforated 12. These stamps always come with one or two straight edges, since they were printed in strips of four that were imperforate at the top, bottom and right side.

| R210 | | UnCnl | UseFVF | CutCnl |
|---|---|---|---|---|
| $60 | brown (Lincoln) | | 115. | 45.00 |

| R211 | | UnCnl | UseFVF | CutCnl |
|---|---|---|---|---|
| $100. | green (Washington) | | 40.00 | 17.50 |

| R212 | | UnCnl | UseFVF | CutCnl |
|---|---|---|---|---|
| $500. | blue (Hamilton) | | 475. | 200. |

| R213 | | UnCnl | UseFVF | CutCnl |
|---|---|---|---|---|
| $1000. | yellow (Madison) | | 475. | 200. |

**1917. DOCUMENTARY ISSUE** White Numerals in Ovals were used on horizontal stamps 21mm wide and 18mm high. Double Line USIR watermark, perforated 11. See Nos. R237-249, for stamps of the same designs but with different perforations.

| R214 | | UnCnl | UseFVF |
|---|---|---|---|
| 1¢ | rose | .30 | .20 |

| R215 | | UnCnl | UseFVF |
|---|---|---|---|
| 2¢ | rose | .30 | .20 |

| R216 | | UnCnl | UseFVF |
|---|---|---|---|
| 3¢ | rose | 1.50 | .40 |

| R217 | | UnCnl | UseFVF |
|---|---|---|---|
| 4¢ | rose | .50 | .20 |

| R218 | | UnCnl | UseFVF |
|---|---|---|---|
| 5¢ | rose | .30 | .20 |

| R219 | | UnCnl | UseFVF |
|---|---|---|---|
| 8¢ | rose | 1.75 | .30 |

| R220 | | UnCnl | UseFVF |
|---|---|---|---|
| 10¢ | rose | .50 | .20 |

| R221 | | UnCnl | UseFVF |
|---|---|---|---|
| 20¢ | rose | 1.25 | .20 |

| R222 | | UnCnl | UseFVF |
|---|---|---|---|
| 25¢ | rose | 1.25 | .20 |

| R223 | | UnCnl | UseFVF |
|---|---|---|---|
| 40¢ | rose | 1.50 | .40 |

| R224 | | UnCnl | UseFVF |
|---|---|---|---|
| 50¢ | rose | 2.00 | .20 |

| R225 | | UnCnl | UseFVF |
|---|---|---|---|
| 80¢ | rose | 4.50 | .20 |

**1917-33. DOCUMENTARY ISSUE UNDATED** Head of Liberty design (No. R203) but without dates. Double Line USIR watermark, perforated 11.

R226-R231 *Frame*

| R226 | | UnCnl | UseFVF | CutCnl |
|---|---|---|---|---|
| $1 | green | 6.00 | .20 | |

| R227 | | UnCnl | UseFVF | CutCnl |
|---|---|---|---|---|
| $2 | rose | 10.00 | .20 | |

| R228 | | UnCnl | UseFVF | CutCnl |
|---|---|---|---|---|
| $3 | violet | 30.00 | .75 | .20 |

| R229 | | UnCnl | UseFVF | CutCnl |
|---|---|---|---|---|
| $4 | ochre | 22.50 | 1.75 | .20 |

| R230 | | UnCnl | UseFVF | CutCnl |
|---|---|---|---|---|
| $5 | blue | 15.00 | .30 | .20 |

| R231 | | UnCnl | UseFVF | CutCnl |
|---|---|---|---|---|
| $10 | yellow | 27.50 | 1.00 | .20 |

**1917. DOCUMENTARY ISSUE** Portraits in Frame Without Dates, Double Line USIR watermark, perforated 12.

| R232 | | UnCnl | UseFVF | CutCnl |
|---|---|---|---|---|
| $30 | orange, green numerals (Grant) | 45.00 | 10.00 | 1.50 |
| | blue numerals | 50.00 | 12.50 | 1.50 |

| R233 | | UnCnl | UseFVF | CutCnl |
|---|---|---|---|---|
| $60 | brown (Lincoln) | 50.00 | 7.50 | 1.00 |

R234

| R234 | | UnCnl | UseFVF | CutCnl |
|---|---|---|---|---|
| $100. | pale green (Washington) | 27.50 | 1.50 | .50 |

| R235 | | UnCnl | UseFVF | CutCnl |
|---|---|---|---|---|
| $500. | blue (Hamilton), red numerals | 200. | .50 | 10.00 |

| R236 | | UnCnl | UseFVF | CutCnl |
|---|---|---|---|---|
| $1000. | orange yellow (Madison) | 125. | 15.00 | 5.00 |

**1928-29. DOCUMENTARY ISSUE** Similar to the 1917 issue but perforated 10.

| R237 | | UnCnl | UseFVF | CutCnl |
|---|---|---|---|---|
| 1¢ | pale red | 2.00 | 1.50 | |

| R238 | | UnCnl | UseFVF | CutCnl |
|---|---|---|---|---|
| 2¢ | pale red | .60 | .25 | |

| R239 | | UnCnl | UseFVF | CutCnl |
|---|---|---|---|---|
| 4¢ | pale red | 6.00 | 4.00 | |

| R240 | | UnCnl | UseFVF | CutCnl |
|---|---|---|---|---|
| 5¢ | pale red | 1.25 | .60 | |

| R241 | | UnCnl | UseFVF | CutCnl |
|---|---|---|---|---|
| 10¢ | pale red | 1.75 | 1.25 | |

| R242 | | UnCnl | UseFVF | CutCnl |
|---|---|---|---|---|
| 20¢ | pale red | 6.00 | 5.25 | |

| R243 | | UnCnl | UseFVF | CutCnl |
|---|---|---|---|---|
| $1 | green | 80.00 | 27.50 | 5.00 |

| R244 | | UnCnl | UseFVF | CutCnl |
|---|---|---|---|---|
| $2 | rose | 30.00 | 2.50 | |

| R245 | | UnCnl | UseFVF | CutCnl |
|---|---|---|---|---|
| $10 | yellow | 100. | 40.00 | 22.50 |

**1929-30. DOCUMENTARY ISSUE** Similar to the 1917 issue but perforated 11 x 10.

| R246 | | UnCnl | UseFVF | CutCnl |
|---|---|---|---|---|
| 2¢ | carmine rose | 1.00 | .80 | |

| R247 | | UnCnl | UseFVF | CutCnl |
|---|---|---|---|---|
| 5¢ | carmine rose | .45 | .40 | |

| R248 | | UnCnl | UseFVF | CutCnl |
|---|---|---|---|---|
| 10¢ | carmine rose | 3.50 | 3.50 | |

| R249 | | UnCnl | UseFVF | CutCnl |
|---|---|---|---|---|
| 20¢ | carmine rose | 5.50 | 5.25 | |

**1940. DOCUMENTARY ISSUE** Stamps of 1917-33 overprinted in black SERIES 1940 and perforated 11.

| R250 | | UnCnl | UseVF | PunchCnl |
|---|---|---|---|---|
| 1¢ | pink | 2.50 | 2.00 | .30 |

| R251 | | UnCnl | UseVF | PunchCnl |
|---|---|---|---|---|
| 2¢ | pink | 2.50 | 1.75 | .40 |

| R252 | | UnCnl | UseVF | PunchCnl |
|---|---|---|---|---|
| 3¢ | pink | 8.00 | 4.00 | .60 |

| R253 | | UnCnl | UseVF | PunchCnl |
|---|---|---|---|---|
| 4¢ | pink | 3.25 | .50 | .20 |

R254

| R254 | | UnCnl | UseVF | PunchCnl |
|---|---|---|---|---|
| 5¢ | pink | 3.50 | .75 | .25 |

| R255 | | UnCnl | UseVF | PunchCnl |
|---|---|---|---|---|
| 8¢ | pink | 14.00 | 12.50 | 3.00 |

| R256 | | UnCnl | UseVF | PunchCnl |
|---|---|---|---|---|
| 10¢ | pink | 1.75 | .40 | .20 |

| R257 | | UnCnl | UseVF | PunchCnl |
|---|---|---|---|---|
| 20¢ | pink | 2.25 | .50 | .20 |

| R258 | | UnCnl | UseVF | PunchCnl |
|---|---|---|---|---|
| 25¢ | pink | 5.50 | 1.00 | .20 |

| R259 | | UnCnl | UseVF | PunchCnl |
|---|---|---|---|---|
| 40¢ | pink | 5.50 | .65 | .20 |

| R260 | | UnCnl | UseVF | PunchCnl |
|---|---|---|---|---|
| 50¢ | pink | 6.00 | .50 | .20 |

| R261 | | UnCnl | UseVF | PunchCnl |
|---|---|---|---|---|
| 80¢ | pink | 10.00 | .85 | .20 |

| R262 | | UnCnl | UseVF | PunchCnl |
|---|---|---|---|---|
| $1 | yellow green | 30.00 | .50 | .20 |

| R263 | | UnCnl | UseVF | PunchCnl |
|---|---|---|---|---|
| $2 | rose | 30.00 | 1.00 | .20 |

| R264 | | UnCnl | UseVF | PunchCnl |
|---|---|---|---|---|
| $3 | dark violet | 45.00 | 25.00 | 3.25 |

| R265 | | UnCnl | UseVF | PunchCnl |
|---|---|---|---|---|
| $4 | ochre | 75.00 | 30.00 | 5.00 |

| R266 | | UnCnl | UseVF | PunchCnl |
|---|---|---|---|---|
| $5 | blue | 45.00 | 10.00 | 1.00 |

| R267 | | UnCnl | UseVF | PunchCnl |
|---|---|---|---|---|
| $10 | orange yellow | 100. | 27.50 | 2.00 |

**1940. DOCUMENTARY ISSUE** Stamps of 1917 handstamped in green SERIES 1940.

| R268 | | UnCnl | UseVF | PunchCnl |
|---|---|---|---|---|
| $30 | vermilion | | 425. | |

| R269 | | UnCnl | UseVF | PunchCnl |
|---|---|---|---|---|
| $60 | brown | | 625. | |

| R270 | | UnCnl | UseVF | PunchCnl |
|---|---|---|---|---|
| $100. | green | | 900. | |

| R271 | | UnCnl | UseVF | PunchCnl |
|---|---|---|---|---|
| $500. | blue | | 1250. | |

| R272 | | UnCnl | UseVF | PunchCnl |
|---|---|---|---|---|
| $1000. | orange | | 600. | |

**1940. DOCUMENTARY ISSUE** Stamp of 1917 handstamped in green SERIES 1940.

| R273 | | UnCnl | UseVF | PunchCnl |
|---|---|---|---|---|
| $500. | blue | | 1750. | |

**1940. DOCUMENTARY ISSUE** Secretaries of the Treasury from Alexander Hamilton the first secretary, to Salmon P. Chase, who served under Lincoln, were featured on a new series of stamps. Included were portraits of Walter Forward, the first Comptroller of the Treasury, in 1841, and Roger B. Taney, who served until his appointment was rejected by Congress. The stamps were printed in three different sizes and overprinted for use in different years. Stamps Nos. R274-R298 were overprinted in black SERIES 1940. Stamps with a face value of $30.00 and above were issued without gum and are usually handstamped documents. They were issued with straight edges on 1 or 2 sides. Nos. R274-R285 size: 19 x 22mm, perforated 11.

| R274 | | MnHVF | UseVF | Perfin |
|---|---|---|---|---|
| 1¢ | carmine | 3.00 | 2.50 | .75 |

R275 *Oliver Wolcott Jr.*

| R275 | | MnHVF | UseVF | Perfin |
|---|---|---|---|---|
| 2¢ | carmine | 4.00 | 2.50 | 1.00 |

| R276 | | MnHVF | UseVF | Perfin |
|---|---|---|---|---|
| 3¢ | carmine | 15.00 | 7.50 | 3.00 |

| R277 | | MnHVF | UseVF | Perfin |
|---|---|---|---|---|
| 4¢ | carmine | 35.00 | 17.50 | 4.00 |

R278 *G. W. Campbell*

| R278 | | MnHVF | UseVF | Perfin |
|---|---|---|---|---|
| 5¢ | carmine | 2.75 | .50 | .20 |
| R279 | | MnHVF | UseVF | Perfin |
| 8¢ | carmine | 55.00 | 40.00 | 15.00 |

R280 *Wm. H. Crawford*

| R280 | | MnHVF | UseVF | Perfin |
|---|---|---|---|---|
| 10¢ | carmine | 2.00 | .35 | .20 |

R281 *Richard Rush*

| R281 | | MnHVF | UseVF | Perfin |
|---|---|---|---|---|
| 20¢ | carmine | 3.50 | 2.00 | 1.25 |

R282 *S. D. Ingham*

| R282 | | MnHVF | UseVF | Perfin |
|---|---|---|---|---|
| 25¢ | carmine | 2.50 | .50 | .20 |

R283 *Louis McLane*

| R283 | | MnHVF | UseVF | Perfin |
|---|---|---|---|---|
| 40¢ | carmine | 35.00 | 15.00 | 3.00 |

R284 *Wm. J. Duane*

| R284 | | MnHVF | UseVF | Perfin |
|---|---|---|---|---|
| 50¢ | carmine | 4.00 | .35 | .20 |

R285 *Roger B. Taney*

| R285 | | MnHVF | UseVF | Perfin |
|---|---|---|---|---|
| 80¢ | carmine | 75.00 | 50.00 | 20.00 |

**1940. DOCUMENTARY ISSUE** Nos. R286-R292 Size: 21 1/2 x 36 1/4 mm, perforated 11.

| R286 | | MnHVF | UseVF | Perfin |
|---|---|---|---|---|
| $1 | carmine | 30.00 | .50 | .20 |
| R287 | | MnHVF | UseVF | Perfin |
| $2 | carmine | 35.00 | .70 | .20 |
| R288 | | MnHVF | UseVF | Perfin |
| $3 | carmine | 100. | 70.00 | 8.50 |
| R289 | | MnHVF | UseVF | Perfin |
| $4 | carmine | 60.00 | 30.00 | 5.00 |
| R290 | | MnHVF | UseVF | Perfin |
| $5 | carmine | 35.00 | 1.25 | .25 |
| R291 | | MnHVF | UseVF | Perfin |
| $10 | carmine | 70.00 | 4.50 | .60 |
| R292 | | MnHVF | UseVF | Perfin |
| $20 | carmine | 1250. | 500. | 300. |

**1940. DOCUMENTARY ISSUE** Nos. R293-R298 Size: 28 1/2 x 42mm, perforated 12.

| R293 | | MnHVF | UseVF | Perfin |
|---|---|---|---|---|
| $30 | carmine | 100. | 35.00 | 10.00 |
| R294 | | | UseVF | Perfin |
| $50 | carmine | | 1000. | 900. |
| R295 | | MnHVF | UseVF | Perfin |
| $60 | carmine | 200. | 40.00 | 25.00 |
| R296 | | MnHVF | UseVF | Perfin |
| $100. | carmine | 150. | 50.00 | 20.00 |

R297 *J. A. Dix*

| R297 | | MnHVF | UseVF | Perfin |
|---|---|---|---|---|
| $500. | carmine | | 800. | 450. |

R298 *S. P. Chase*

| R298 | | MnHVF | UseVF | Perfin |
|---|---|---|---|---|
| $1000. | carmine | | 400. | 165. |

**1941. DOCUMENTARY ISSUE** Secretaries of the Treasury, stamps Nos. R274-298, overprint reads SERIES 1941.

R299

| R299 | | MnHVF | UseVF | Perfin |
|---|---|---|---|---|
| 1¢ | carmine | 2.50 | 1.65 | .60 |
| R300 | | MnHVF | UseVF | Perfin |
| 2¢ | carmine | 2.50 | .75 | .30 |

R301

| R301 | | MnHVF | UseVF | Perfin |
|---|---|---|---|---|
| 3¢ | carmine | 6.00 | 3.00 | 1.00 |

R302

| R302 | | MnHVF | UseVF | Perfin |
|---|---|---|---|---|
| 4¢ | carmine | 4.50 | 1.00 | .25 |
| R303 | | MnHVF | UseVF | Perfin |
| 5¢ | carmine | | .20 | .20 |

R304

| R304 | | MnHVF | UseVF | Perfin |
|---|---|---|---|---|
| 8¢ | carmine | 12.50 | 6.50 | 2.75 |
| R305 | | MnHVF | UseVF | Perfin |
| 10¢ | carmine | 1.25 | .20 | .20 |
| R306 | | MnHVF | UseVF | Perfin |
| 20¢ | carmine | 2.75 | .40 | .20 |
| R307 | | MnHVF | UseVF | Perfin |
| 25¢ | carmine | 1.50 | .20 | .20 |
| R308 | | MnHVF | UseVF | Perfin |
| 40¢ | carmine | 8.50 | 2.25 | .80 |
| R309 | | MnHVF | UseVF | Perfin |
| 50¢ | carmine | 2.25 | .20 | .20 |
| R310 | | MnHVF | UseVF | Perfin |
| 80¢ | carmine | 40.00 | 8.50 | 2.50 |
| R311 | | MnHVF | UseVF | Perfin |
| $1 | carmine | 8.00 | .20 | .20 |

| R312 | | MnHVF | UseVF | Perfin |
|---|---|---|---|---|
| $2 | carmine | 9.00 | .30 | .20 |
| R313 | | MnHVF | UseVF | Perfin |
| $3 | carmine | 15.00 | 2.00 | .25 |
| R314 | | MnHVF | UseVF | Perfin |
| $4 | carmine | 25.00 | 12.50 | .65 |

| R315 | | MnHVF | UseVF | Perfin |
|---|---|---|---|---|
| $5 | carmine | 30.00 | .50 | .20 |

| R316 | | MnHVF | UseVF | Perfin |
|---|---|---|---|---|
| $10 | carmine | 45.00 | 3.50 | .25 |
| R317 | | MnHVF | UseVF | Perfin |
| $20 | carmine | 475. | 165. | 65.00 |
| R318 | | MnHVF | UseVF | Perfin |
| $30 | carmine | 45.00 | 20.00 | 8.00 |
| R319 | | MnHVF | UseVF | Perfin |
| $50 | carmine | 165. | 140. | 70.00 |
| R320 | | MnHVF | UseVF | Perfin |
| $60 | carmine | | 40.00 | 12.50 |
| R321 | | MnHVF | UseVF | Perfin |
| $100. | carmine | 40.00 | 15.00 | 5.00 |
| R322 | | MnHVF | UseVF | Perfin |
| $500. | carmine | | 175. | 85.00 |
| R323 | | MnHVF | UseVF | Perfin |
| $1000. | carmine | | 95.00 | 25.00 |

**1942. DOCUMENTARY ISSUE** Secretaries of the Treasury, stamps Nos. R274-298, overprint reads SERIES 1942.

| R324 | | MnHVF | UseVF | Perfin |
|---|---|---|---|---|
| 1¢ | carmine | .40 | .30 | .20 |
| R325 | | MnHVF | UseVF | Perfin |
| 2¢ | carmine | .40 | .30 | .20 |
| R326 | | MnHVF | UseVF | Perfin |
| 3¢ | carmine | .60 | .50 | .20 |
| R327 | | MnHVF | UseVF | Perfin |
| 4¢ | carmine | 1.25 | 1.00 | .30 |
| R328 | | MnHVF | UseVF | Perfin |
| 5¢ | carmine | .40 | .20 | .20 |
| R329 | | MnHVF | UseVF | Perfin |
| 8¢ | carmine | 5.00 | 4.00 | 1.00 |
| R330 | | MnHVF | UseVF | Perfin |
| 10¢ | carmine | 1.00 | .20 | .20 |
| R331 | | MnHVF | UseVF | Perfin |
| 20¢ | carmine | 1.00 | .40 | .20 |
| R332 | | MnHVF | UseVF | Perfin |
| 25¢ | carmine | 2.00 | .40 | .20 |
| R333 | | MnHVF | UseVF | Perfin |
| 40¢ | carmine | 4.50 | 1.00 | .50 |
| R334 | | MnHVF | UseVF | Perfin |
| 50¢ | carmine | 2.50 | .20 | .20 |
| R335 | | MnHVF | UseVF | Perfin |
| 80¢ | carmine | 15.00 | 8.00 | 2.50 |

| R336 | | MnHVF | UseVF | Perfin |
|---|---|---|---|---|
| $1 | carmine | 7.50 | .20 | .20 |

| R337 | | MnHVF | UseVF | Perfin |
|---|---|---|---|---|
| $2 | carmine | 8.50 | .20 | .20 |

| R338 | | MnHVF | UseVF | Perfin |
|---|---|---|---|---|
| $3 | carmine | 12.50 | 2.00 | .25 |

| R339 | | MnHVF | UseVF | Perfin |
|---|---|---|---|---|
| $4 | carmine | 20.00 | 3.50 | .25 |

| R340 | | MnHVF | UseVF | Perfin |
|---|---|---|---|---|
| $5 | carmine | 22.50 | .75 | .20 |

| R341 | | MnHVF | UseVF | Perfin |
|---|---|---|---|---|
| $10 | carmine | 50.00 | 2.00 | .20 |

| R342 | | MnHVF | UseVF | Perfin |
|---|---|---|---|---|
| $20 | carmine | 100. | 25.00 | 12.50 |

| R343 | | MnHVF | UseVF | Perfin |
|---|---|---|---|---|
| $30 | carmine | 35.00 | 17.50 | 7.00 |

| R344 | | MnHVF | UseVF | Perfin |
|---|---|---|---|---|
| $50 | carmine | 300. | 225. | 100. |

| R345 | | MnHVF | UseVF | Perfin |
|---|---|---|---|---|
| $60 | carmine | 650. | 550. | 150. |

| R346 | | MnHVF | UseVF | Perfin |
|---|---|---|---|---|
| $100. | carmine | 125. | 85.00 | 35.00 |

| R347 | | MnHVF | UseVF | Perfin |
|---|---|---|---|---|
| $500. | carmine | | 175. | 100. |

| R348 | | MnHVF | UseVF | Perfin |
|---|---|---|---|---|
| $1000. | carmine | | 90.00 | 40.00 |

**1943. DOCUMENTARY ISSUE** Secretaries of the Treasury, stamps Nos. R274-298, overprint reads SERIES 1943.

| R349 | | MnHVF | UseVF | Perfin |
|---|---|---|---|---|
| 1¢ | carmine | .50 | .40 | .20 |

| R350 | | MnHVF | UseVF | Perfin |
|---|---|---|---|---|
| 2¢ | carmine | .40 | .30 | .20 |

| R351 | | MnHVF | UseVF | Perfin |
|---|---|---|---|---|
| 3¢ | carmine | 2.25 | 2.00 | .40 |

| R352 | | MnHVF | UseVF | Perfin |
|---|---|---|---|---|
| 4¢ | carmine | .80 | .80 | .25 |

| R353 | | MnHVF | UseVF | Perfin |
|---|---|---|---|---|
| 5¢ | carmine | .40 | .25 | .20 |

| R354 | | MnHVF | UseVF | Perfin |
|---|---|---|---|---|
| 8¢ | carmine | 3.50 | 2.75 | 1.25 |

| R355 | | MnHVF | UseVF | Perfin |
|---|---|---|---|---|
| 10¢ | carmine | .50 | .25 | .20 |

| R356 | | MnHVF | UseVF | Perfin |
|---|---|---|---|---|
| 20¢ | carmine | 1.50 | .50 | .20 |

| R357 | | MnHVF | UseVF | Perfin |
|---|---|---|---|---|
| 25¢ | carmine | 1.40 | .20 | .20 |

| R358 | | MnHVF | UseVF | Perfin |
|---|---|---|---|---|
| 40¢ | carmine | 4.50 | 1.75 | 1.00 |

| R359 | | MnHVF | UseVF | Perfin |
|---|---|---|---|---|
| 50¢ | carmine | 1.00 | .20 | .20 |

| R360 | | MnHVF | UseVF | Perfin |
|---|---|---|---|---|
| 80¢ | carmine | 10.00 | 5.00 | 1.00 |

| R361 | | MnHVF | UseVF | Perfin |
|---|---|---|---|---|
| $1 | carmine | 4.50 | .30 | .20 |

| R362 | | MnHVF | UseVF | Perfin |
|---|---|---|---|---|
| $2 | carmine | 8.50 | .25 | .20 |

| R363 | | MnHVF | UseVF | Perfin |
|---|---|---|---|---|
| $3 | carmine | 15.00 | 1.50 | .25 |

| R364 | | MnHVF | UseVF | Perfin |
|---|---|---|---|---|
| $4 | carmine | 20.00 | 2.50 | .35 |

| R365 | | MnHVF | UseVF | Perfin |
|---|---|---|---|---|
| $5 | carmine | 25.00 | .40 | .20 |

| R366 | | MnHVF | UseVF | Perfin |
|---|---|---|---|---|
| $10 | carmine | 40.00 | 2.50 | .40 |

| R367 | | MnHVF | UseVF | Perfin |
|---|---|---|---|---|
| $20 | carmine | 90.00 | 17.50 | 4.50 |

| R368 | | MnHVF | UseVF | Perfin |
|---|---|---|---|---|
| $30 | carmine | 30.00 | 17.50 | 3.50 |

| R369 | | MnHVF | UseVF | Perfin |
|---|---|---|---|---|
| $50 | carmine | 60.00 | 20.00 | 7.50 |

| R370 | | MnHVF | UseVF | Perfin |
|---|---|---|---|---|
| $60 | carmine | | 65.00 | 12.50 |

| R371 | | MnHVF | UseVF | Perfin |
|---|---|---|---|---|
| $100. | carmine | | 8.50 | 5.00 |

| R372 | | MnHVF | UseVF | Perfin |
|---|---|---|---|---|
| $500. | carmine | | 160. | 80.00 |

| R373 | | MnHVF | UseVF | Perfin |
|---|---|---|---|---|
| $1000. | carmine | | 140. | 40.00 |

**1944. DOCUMENTARY ISSUE** Secretaries of the Treasury, stamps Nos. R274-298, overprint reads SERIES 1944.

| R374 | | MnHVF | UseVF | Perfin |
|---|---|---|---|---|
| 1¢ | carmine | .40 | .30 | .20 |

| R375 | | MnHVF | UseVF | Perfin |
|---|---|---|---|---|
| 2¢ | carmine | .40 | .30 | .20 |

| R376 | | MnHVF | UseVF | Perfin |
|---|---|---|---|---|
| 3¢ | carmine | .40 | .30 | .20 |

| R377 | | MnHVF | UseVF | Perfin |
|---|---|---|---|---|
| 4¢ | carmine | .50 | .40 | .20 |

| R378 | | MnHVF | UseVF | Perfin |
|---|---|---|---|---|
| 5¢ | carmine | .40 | .20 | .20 |

| R379 | | MnHVF | UseVF | Perfin |
|---|---|---|---|---|
| 8¢ | carmine | 1.50 | 1.00 | .40 |

| R380 | | MnHVF | UseVF | Perfin |
|---|---|---|---|---|
| 10¢ | carmine | .40 | .20 | .20 |

| | | MnHVF | UseVF | Perfin |
|---|---|---|---|---|
| R381 20¢ | carmine | .70 | .20 | .20 |
| R382 25¢ | carmine | 1.25 | .20 | .20 |
| R383 40¢ | carmine | 2.50 | .50 | .20 |
| R384 50¢ | carmine | 2.50 | .20 | .20 |
| R385 80¢ | carmine | 10.00 | 3.50 | 1.00 |
| R386 $1 | carmine | 5.00 | .20 | .20 |
| R387 $2 | carmine | 7.50 | .20 | .20 |
| R388 $3 | carmine | 10.00 | 1.25 | .30 |
| R389 $4 | carmine | 15.00 | 9.00 | .80 |
| R390 $5 | carmine | 17.50 | .25 | .20 |
| R391 $10 | carmine | 35.00 | 1.00 | .20 |
| R392 $20 | carmine | 75.00 | 12.50 | 2.75 |

| | | MnHVF | UseVF | Perfin |
|---|---|---|---|---|
| R393 $30 | carmine | 40.00 | 17.50 | 4.50 |
| R394 $50 | carmine | 17.50 | 10.00 | 4.00 |
| R395 $60 | carmine | 85.00 | 40.00 | 7.50 |
| R396 $100. | carmine | | 8.00 | 4.00 |
| R397 $500. | carmine | | 1000. | 800. |
| R398 $1000. | carmine | | 155. | 50.00 |

**1945. DOCUMENTARY ISSUE** Secretaries of the Treasury, stamps Nos. R274-298, overprint reads SERIES 1945.

| | | MnHVF | UseVF | Perfin |
|---|---|---|---|---|
| R399 1¢ | carmine | .20 | .20 | .20 |
| R400 2¢ | carmine | .20 | .20 | .20 |
| R401 3¢ | carmine | .50 | .45 | .20 |
| R402 4¢ | carmine | .25 | .25 | .20 |
| R403 5¢ | carmine | .25 | .20 | .20 |
| R404 8¢ | carmine | 4.00 | 1.75 | .50 |
| R405 10¢ | carmine | .75 | .20 | .20 |

| | | MnHVF | UseVF | Perfin |
|---|---|---|---|---|
| R406 20¢ | carmine | 4.00 | .75 | .20 |
| R407 25¢ | carmine | 1.00 | .25 | .20 |
| R408 40¢ | carmine | 4.50 | .80 | .30 |
| R409 50¢ | carmine | 2.50 | .20 | .20 |
| R410 80¢ | carmine | 15.00 | 7.50 | 3.00 |
| R411 $1 | carmine | 6.50 | .20 | .20 |
| R412 $2 | carmine | 6.50 | .20 | .20 |
| R413 $3 | carmine | 12.50 | 2.00 | .80 |
| R414 $4 | carmine | 17.50 | 3.00 | .50 |
| R415 $5 | carmine | 17.50 | .30 | .20 |
| R416 $10 | carmine | 35.00 | 1.25 | .20 |
| R417 $20 | carmine | 75.00 | 10.00 | 3.00 |
| R418 $30 | carmine | 55.00 | 18.00 | 5.00 |
| R419 $50 | carmine | 60.00 | 20.00 | 12.50 |
| R420 $60 | carmine | 100. | 35.00 | 12.50 |
| R421 $100. | carmine | | 10.00 | 8.00 |
| R422 $500. | carmine | 185. | 150. | 65.00 |
| R423 $1000. | carmine | 100. | 80.00 | 20.00 |

**1946. DOCUMENTARY ISSUE** Secretaries of the Treasury, stamps Nos. R274-298, overprint reads SERIES 1946.

| | | MnHVF | UseVF | Perfin |
|---|---|---|---|---|
| R424 1¢ | carmine | .25 | .20 | .20 |
| R425 2¢ | carmine | .30 | .30 | .20 |
| R426 3¢ | carmine | .35 | .25 | .20 |
| R427 4¢ | carmine | .50 | .40 | .20 |
| R428 5¢ | carmine | .25 | .20 | .20 |
| R429 8¢ | carmine | 1.00 | .80 | .20 |
| R430 10¢ | carmine | .70 | .20 | .20 |
| R431 20¢ | carmine | 1.20 | .35 | .20 |
| R432 25¢ | carmine | 3.80 | .20 | .15 |
| R433 40¢ | carmine | 2.25 | .75 | .20 |
| R434 50¢ | carmine | 2.25 | .20 | .20 |
| R435 80¢ | carmine | 8.50 | 3.50 | .50 |
| R436 $1 | carmine | 7.00 | .20 | .20 |
| R437 $2 | carmine | 8.00 | .20 | .20 |

| No. | Denom. | Color | MnHVF | UseVF | Perfin |
|---|---|---|---|---|---|
| R438 | $3 | carmine | 12.50 | 4.50 | .90 |
| R439 | $4 | carmine | 17.50 | 7.50 | 1.50 |
| R440 | $5 | carmine | 17.50 | .40 | .20 |
| R441 | $10 | carmine | 35.00 | 1.35 | .20 |
| R442 | $20 | carmine | 75.00 | 7.50 | 2.00 |
| R443 | $30 | carmine | 40.00 | 12.50 | 3.00 |
| R444 | $50 | carmine | 17.50 | 8.00 | 3.00 |
| R445 | $60 | carmine | 35.00 | 15.00 | 10.00 |
| R446 | $100. | carmine | 40.00 | 10.00 | 3.00 |
| R447 | $500. | carmine | | 90.00 | 30.00 |
| R448 | $1000. | carmine | | 90.00 | 25.00 |

**1947. DOCUMENTARY ISSUE** Secretaries of the Treasury, stamps Nos. R274-298, overprint reads SERIES 1947.

| No. | Denom. | Color | MnHVF | UseVF | Perfin |
|---|---|---|---|---|---|
| R449 | 1¢ | carmine | .65 | .45 | .20 |
| R450 | 2¢ | carmine | .50 | .40 | .20 |
| R451 | 3¢ | carmine | .50 | .45 | .20 |
| R452 | 4¢ | carmine | .65 | .55 | .20 |
| R453 | 5¢ | carmine | .30 | .25 | .20 |
| R454 | 8¢ | carmine | 1.15 | .65 | .20 |
| R455 | 10¢ | carmine | 1.10 | .25 | .20 |
| R456 | 20¢ | carmine | 1.75 | .50 | .20 |
| R457 | 25¢ | carmine | 2.25 | .50 | .20 |
| R458 | 40¢ | carmine | 3.50 | .75 | .20 |
| R459 | 50¢ | carmine | 3.00 | .20 | .20 |
| R460 | 80¢ | carmine | 7.50 | 6.00 | .50 |
| R461 | $1 | carmine | 5.75 | .20 | .20 |
| R462 | $2 | carmine | 8.50 | .40 | .20 |
| R463 | $3 | carmine | 8.50 | 6.50 | 1.00 |
| R464 | $4 | carmine | 10.00 | 4.00 | .35 |
| R465 | $5 | carmine | 15.00 | .40 | .20 |
| R466 | $10 | carmine | 35.00 | 2.00 | .50 |
| R467 | $20 | carmine | 50.00 | 8.50 | 1.00 |
| R468 | $30 | carmine | 55.00 | 15.00 | 3.50 |
| R469 | $50 | carmine | 25.00 | 11.00 | 3.50 |
| R470 | $60 | carmine | 65.00 | 30.00 | 13.50 |
| R471 | $100. | carmine | 25.00 | 8.50 | 3.50 |

| No. | Denom. | Color | MnHVF | UseVF | Perfin |
|---|---|---|---|---|---|
| R472 | $500. | carmine | | 140. | 40.00 |
| R473 | $1000. | carmine | | 75.00 | 30.00 |

**1948. DOCUMENTARY ISSUE** Secretaries of the Treasury, stamps Nos. R274-298, overprint reads SERIES 1948.

| No. | Denom. | Color | MnHVF | UseVF | Perfin |
|---|---|---|---|---|---|
| R474 | 1¢ | carmine | .20 | .20 | .20 |
| R475 | 2¢ | carmine | .30 | .25 | .20 |
| R476 | 3¢ | carmine | .40 | .35 | .20 |
| R477 | 4¢ | carmine | .40 | .25 | .20 |
| R478 | 5¢ | carmine | .30 | .20 | .20 |
| R479 | 8¢ | carmine | .75 | .30 | .20 |
| R480 | 10¢ | carmine | .50 | .20 | .20 |
| R481 | 20¢ | carmine | 1.50 | .30 | .20 |
| R482 | 25¢ | carmine | 1.35 | .20 | .20 |
| R483 | 40¢ | carmine | 4.00 | 1.40 | .25 |
| R484 | 50¢ | carmine | 2.25 | .20 | .20 |
| R485 | 80¢ | carmine | 6.50 | 4.00 | 1.00 |
| R486 | $1 | carmine | 6.50 | .20 | .20 |
| R487 | $2 | carmine | 9.00 | .20 | .20 |
| R488 | $3 | carmine | 12.50 | 2.00 | .35 |
| R489 | $4 | carmine | 17.50 | 2.00 | .50 |
| R490 | $5 | carmine | 15.00 | .40 | .20 |
| R491 | $10 | carmine | 35.00 | 1.00 | .20 |
| R492 | $20 | carmine | 75.00 | 8.50 | 3.00 |
| R493 | $30 | carmine | 40.00 | 17.50 | 4.00 |
| R494 | $50 | carmine | 40.00 | 15.00 | 4.00 |
| R495 | $60 | carmine | 55.00 | 20.00 | 8.00 |
| R496 | $100. | carmine | 45.00 | 8.00 | 3.25 |
| R497 | $500. | carmine | 110. | 100. | 40.00 |
| R498 | $1000. | carmine | 75.00 | 60.00 | 25.00 |

**1949. DOCUMENTARY ISSUE** Secretaries of the Treasury, stamps Nos. R274-298, overprint reads SERIES 1949.

| R499 | | MnHVF | UseVF | Perfin |
|---|---|---|---|---|
| 1¢ | carmine | .25 | .20 | .20 |

| R500 | | MnHVF | UseVF | Perfin |
|---|---|---|---|---|
| 2¢ | carmine | .50 | .30 | .20 |

| R501 | | MnHVF | UseVF | Perfin |
|---|---|---|---|---|
| 3¢ | carmine | .35 | .30 | .20 |

| R502 | | MnHVF | UseVF | Perfin |
|---|---|---|---|---|
| 4¢ | carmine | .50 | .40 | .20 |

| R503 | | MnHVF | UseVF | Perfin |
|---|---|---|---|---|
| 5¢ | carmine | .30 | .20 | .20 |

| R504 | | MnHVF | UseVF | Perfin |
|---|---|---|---|---|
| 8¢ | carmine | .65 | .50 | .20 |

| R505 | | MnHVF | UseVF | Perfin |
|---|---|---|---|---|
| 10¢ | carmine | .35 | .25 | .20 |

| R506 | | MnHVF | UseVF | Perfin |
|---|---|---|---|---|
| 20¢ | carmine | 1.25 | .60 | .20 |

| R507 | | MnHVF | UseVF | Perfin |
|---|---|---|---|---|
| 25¢ | carmine | 1.75 | .65 | .20 |

| R508 | | MnHVF | UseVF | Perfin |
|---|---|---|---|---|
| 40¢ | carmine | 4.00 | 2.00 | .40 |

| R509 | | MnHVF | UseVF | Perfin |
|---|---|---|---|---|
| 50¢ | carmine | 3.50 | .30 | .20 |

| R510 | | MnHVF | UseVF | Perfin |
|---|---|---|---|---|
| 80¢ | carmine | 8.00 | 4.50 | 1.25 |

| R511 | | MnHVF | UseVF | Perfin |
|---|---|---|---|---|
| $1 | carmine | 6.50 | .40 | .20 |

| R512 | | MnHVF | UseVF | Perfin |
|---|---|---|---|---|
| $2 | carmine | 8.50 | 2.00 | .35 |

| R513 | | MnHVF | UseVF | Perfin |
|---|---|---|---|---|
| $3 | carmine | 13.50 | 5.75 | 1.50 |

| R514 | | MnHVF | UseVF | Perfin |
|---|---|---|---|---|
| $4 | carmine | 17.00 | 6.00 | 2.50 |

| R515 | | MnHVF | UseVF | Perfin |
|---|---|---|---|---|
| $5 | carmine | 17.00 | 2.50 | .50 |

| R516 | | MnHVF | UseVF | Perfin |
|---|---|---|---|---|
| $10 | carmine | 35.00 | 2.50 | 1.00 |

| R517 | | MnHVF | UseVF | Perfin |
|---|---|---|---|---|
| $20 | carmine | 75.00 | 8.00 | 2.00 |

| R518 | | MnHVF | UseVF | Perfin |
|---|---|---|---|---|
| $30 | carmine | 45.00 | 20.50 | 5.00 |

| R519 | | MnHVF | UseVF | Perfin |
|---|---|---|---|---|
| $50 | carmine | 55.00 | 35.00 | 9.00 |

| R520 | | MnHVF | UseVF | Perfin |
|---|---|---|---|---|
| $60 | carmine | | 40.00 | 20.00 |

| R521 | | MnHVF | UseVF | Perfin |
|---|---|---|---|---|
| $100. | carmine | 40.00 | 12.50 | 3.00 |

| R522 | | MnHVF | UseVF | Perfin |
|---|---|---|---|---|
| $500. | carmine | | 175. | 100. |

| R523 | | MnHVF | UseVF | Perfin |
|---|---|---|---|---|
| $1000. | carmine | | 100. | 30.00 |

**1950. DOCUMENTARY ISSUE** Secretaries of the Treasury, stamps Nos. R274-298, overprint reads SERIES 1950.

| R524 | | MnHVF | UseVF | Perfin |
|---|---|---|---|---|
| 1¢ | carmine | .20 | .20 | .20 |

| R525 | | MnHVF | UseVF | Perfin |
|---|---|---|---|---|
| 2¢ | carmine | .30 | .20 | .20 |

| R526 | | MnHVF | UseVF | Perfin |
|---|---|---|---|---|
| 3¢ | carmine | .35 | .30 | .20 |

| R527 | | MnHVF | UseVF | Perfin |
|---|---|---|---|---|
| 4¢ | carmine | .45 | .35 | .20 |

| R528 | | MnHVF | UseVF | Perfin |
|---|---|---|---|---|
| 5¢ | carmine | .30 | .20 | .20 |

| R529 | | MnHVF | UseVF | Perfin |
|---|---|---|---|---|
| 8¢ | carmine | 1.20 | .65 | .20 |

| R530 | | MnHVF | UseVF | Perfin |
|---|---|---|---|---|
| 10¢ | carmine | .60 | .20 | .20 |

| R531 | | MnHVF | UseVF | Perfin |
|---|---|---|---|---|
| 20¢ | carmine | 1.00 | .30 | .20 |

| R532 | | MnHVF | UseVF | Perfin |
|---|---|---|---|---|
| 25¢ | carmine | 1.25 | .35 | .25 |

| R533 | | MnHVF | UseVF | Perfin |
|---|---|---|---|---|
| 40¢ | carmine | 3.00 | 1.50 | .40 |

| R534 | | MnHVF | UseVF | Perfin |
|---|---|---|---|---|
| 50¢ | carmine | 3.50 | .20 | .20 |

| R535 | | MnHVF | UseVF | Perfin |
|---|---|---|---|---|
| 80¢ | carmine | 6.50 | 3.50 | .75 |

| R536 | | MnHVF | UseVF | Perfin |
|---|---|---|---|---|
| $1 | carmine | 6.50 | .20 | .20 |

| R537 | | MnHVF | UseVF | Perfin |
|---|---|---|---|---|
| $2 | carmine | 8.50 | 1.50 | .20 |

| R538 | | MnHVF | UseVF | Perfin |
|---|---|---|---|---|
| $3 | carmine | 8.50 | 3.50 | 1.25 |

| R539 | | MnHVF | UseVF | Perfin |
|---|---|---|---|---|
| $4 | carmine | 12.50 | 4.50 | 2.00 |

| R540 | | MnHVF | UseVF | Perfin |
|---|---|---|---|---|
| $5 | carmine | 17.50 | .75 | .20 |

| R541 | | MnHVF | UseVF | Perfin |
|---|---|---|---|---|
| $10 | carmine | 35.00 | 7.50 | .75 |

| R542 | | MnHVF | UseVF | Perfin |
|---|---|---|---|---|
| $20 | carmine | 75.00 | 8.00 | 2.00 |

| R543 | | MnHVF | UseVF | Perfin |
|---|---|---|---|---|
| $30 | carmine | 60.00 | 40.00 | 8.00 |

| R544 | | MnHVF | UseVF | Perfin |
|---|---|---|---|---|
| $50 | carmine | 35.00 | 12.50 | 6.50 |

| R545 | | MnHVF | UseVF | Perfin |
|---|---|---|---|---|
| $60 | carmine | | 50.00 | 15.00 |

| R546 | | MnHVF | UseVF | Perfin |
|---|---|---|---|---|
| $100. | carmine | 40.00 | 17.50 | 5.00 |

| R547 | | MnHVF | UseVF | Perfin |
|---|---|---|---|---|
| $500. | carmine | | 100. | 45.00 |

| R548 | | MnHVF | UseVF | Perfin |
|---|---|---|---|---|
| $1000. | carmine | | 70.00 | 20.00 |

**1951. DOCUMENTARY ISSUE** Secretaries of the Treasury, stamps Nos. R274-298, overprint reads SERIES 1951.

| R549 | | MnHVF | UseVF | Perfin |
|---|---|---|---|---|
| 1¢ | carmine | .20 | .20 | .20 |

| R550 | | MnHVF | UseVF | Perfin |
|---|---|---|---|---|
| 2¢ | carmine | .25 | .20 | .20 |

| R551 | | MnHVF | UseVF | Perfin |
|---|---|---|---|---|
| 3¢ | carmine | .25 | .20 | .20 |

| R552 | | MnHVF | UseVF | Perfin |
|---|---|---|---|---|
| 4¢ | carmine | .30 | .20 | .20 |

| R553 | | MnHVF | UseVF | Perfin |
|---|---|---|---|---|
| 5¢ | carmine | .30 | .20 | .20 |

| R554 | | MnHVF | UseVF | Perfin |
|---|---|---|---|---|
| 8¢ | carmine | .85 | .30 | .20 |

| R555 | | MnHVF | UseVF | Perfin |
|---|---|---|---|---|
| 10¢ | carmine | .50 | .20 | .20 |

| R556 | | MnHVF | UseVF | Perfin |
|---|---|---|---|---|
| 20¢ | carmine | 1.25 | .40 | .20 |

| R557 | | MnHVF | UseVF | Perfin |
|---|---|---|---|---|
| 25¢ | carmine | 1.25 | .40 | .20 |

| R558 | | MnHVF | UseVF | Perfin |
|---|---|---|---|---|
| 40¢ | carmine | 3.00 | 1.25 | .30 |

| R559 | | MnHVF | UseVF | Perfin |
|---|---|---|---|---|
| 50¢ | carmine | 2.50 | .35 | .20 |

| R560 | | MnHVF | UseVF | Perfin |
|---|---|---|---|---|
| 80¢ | carmine | 5.00 | 2.00 | 1.50 |

| R561 | | MnHVF | UseVF | Perfin |
|---|---|---|---|---|
| $1 | carmine | 6.50 | .20 | .20 |

| R562 | | MnHVF | UseVF | Perfin |
|---|---|---|---|---|
| $2 | carmine | 8.50 | .40 | .20 |

| R563 | | MnHVF | UseVF | Perfin |
|---|---|---|---|---|
| $3 | carmine | 12.50 | 3.00 | 1.75 |

| R564 | | MnHVF | UseVF | Perfin |
|---|---|---|---|---|
| $4 | carmine | 15.00 | 5.00 | 2.00 |

| R565 | | MnHVF | UseVF | Perfin |
|---|---|---|---|---|
| $5 | carmine | 12.50 | .50 | .20 |

| R566 | | MnHVF | UseVF | Perfin |
|---|---|---|---|---|
| $10 | carmine | 30.00 | 2.50 | 1.00 |

| R567 | | MnHVF | UseVF | Perfin |
|---|---|---|---|---|
| $20 | carmine | 70.00 | 8.00 | 3.00 |

| R568 | | MnHVF | UseVF | Perfin |
|---|---|---|---|---|
| $30 | carmine | 60.00 | 10.00 | 5.00 |

| R569 | | MnHVF | UseVF | Perfin |
|---|---|---|---|---|
| $50 | carmine | 45.00 | 12.50 | 5.00 |

| R570 | | MnHVF | UseVF | Perfin |
|---|---|---|---|---|
| $60 | carmine | | 40.00 | 20.00 |

| R571 | | MnHVF | UseVF | Perfin |
|---|---|---|---|---|
| $100. | carmine | 40.00 | 12.50 | 6.50 |

| R572 | | MnHVF | UseVF | Perfin |
|---|---|---|---|---|
| $500. | carmine | 120. | 80.00 | 40.00 |

| R573 | | MnHVF | UseVF | Perfin |
|---|---|---|---|---|
| $1000. | carmine | | 80.00 | 30.00 |

**1952. DOCUMENTARY ISSUE** Secretaries of the Treasury, stamps Nos. R274-298, and new values showing L. J. Gage, William Windom, C. J. Folger and W. Q. Gresham, all former Secretaries of the Treasury. Overprint: SERIES 1952.

| R574 | | MnHVF | UseVF | Perfin |
|---|---|---|---|---|
| 1¢ | carmine | .20 | .20 | .20 |

| R575 | | MnHVF | UseVF | Perfin |
|---|---|---|---|---|
| 2¢ | carmine | .30 | .20 | .20 |

| R576 | | MnHVF | UseVF | Perfin |
|---|---|---|---|---|
| 3¢ | carmine | .25 | .20 | .20 |

| R577 | | MnHVF | UseVF | Perfin |
|---|---|---|---|---|
| 4¢ | carmine | .25 | .20 | .20 |

| R578 | | MnHVF | UseVF | Perfin |
|---|---|---|---|---|
| 5¢ | carmine | .20 | .20 | .20 |

| R579 | | MnHVF | UseVF | Perfin |
|---|---|---|---|---|
| 8¢ | carmine | .60 | .40 | .20 |

| R580 | | MnHVF | UseVF | Perfin |
|---|---|---|---|---|
| 10¢ | carmine | .40 | .20 | .20 |

| R581 | | MnHVF | UseVF | Perfin |
|---|---|---|---|---|
| 20¢ | carmine | .90 | .30 | .20 |

| R582 | | MnHVF | UseVF | Perfin |
|---|---|---|---|---|
| 25¢ | carmine | 1.25 | .35 | .20 |

| R583 | | MnHVF | UseVF | Perfin |
|---|---|---|---|---|
| 40¢ | carmine | .20 | .80 | .40 |

| R584 | | MnHVF | UseVF | Perfin |
|---|---|---|---|---|
| 50¢ | carmine | 2.50 | .20 | .20 |

| R585 | | MnHVF | UseVF | Perfin |
|---|---|---|---|---|
| 55¢ | carmine | 17.50 | 10.00 | 1.25 |

| R586 | | MnHVF | UseVF | Perfin |
|---|---|---|---|---|
| 80¢ | carmine | 8.50 | 2.75 | .75 |

| R587 | | MnHVF | UseVF | Perfin |
|---|---|---|---|---|
| $1 | carmine | 4.50 | 1.50 | .30 |

| R588 | | MnHVF | UseVF | Perfin |
|---|---|---|---|---|
| $1.10 | carmine | 30.00 | 20.00 | 10.00 |

| R589 | | MnHVF | UseVF | Perfin |
|---|---|---|---|---|
| $1.65 | carmine | 120. | 40.00 | 25.00 |

| R590 | | MnHVF | UseVF | Perfin |
|---|---|---|---|---|
| $2 | carmine | 8.00 | .30 | .20 |

| R591 | | MnHVF | UseVF | Perfin |
|---|---|---|---|---|
| $2.20 | carmine | 75.00 | 50.00 | 30.00 |

| R592 | | MnHVF | UseVF | Perfin |
|---|---|---|---|---|
| $2.75 | carmine | 100. | 55.00 | 25.00 |

| R593 | | MnHVF | UseVF | Perfin |
|---|---|---|---|---|
| $3 | carmine | 20.00 | 3.50 | 1.00 |

| R594 | | MnHVF | UseVF | Perfin |
|---|---|---|---|---|
| $3.30 | carmine | 80.00 | 60.00 | 30.00 |

| R595 | | MnHVF | UseVF | Perfin |
|---|---|---|---|---|
| $4 | carmine | 17.50 | 3.50 | 2.00 |

| R596 | | MnHVF | UseVF | Perfin |
|---|---|---|---|---|
| $5 | carmine | 17.50 | 1.00 | .30 |

| R597 | | MnHVF | UseVF | Perfin |
|---|---|---|---|---|
| $10 | carmine | 30.00 | 1.25 | .20 |

| R598 | | MnHVF | UseVF | Perfin |
|---|---|---|---|---|
| $20 | carmine | 50.00 | 9.00 | 2.50 |

| R599 | | MnHVF | UseVF | Perfin |
|---|---|---|---|---|
| $30 | carmine | 40.00 | 17.50 | 5.00 |

| R600 | | MnHVF | UseVF | Perfin |
|---|---|---|---|---|
| $50 | carmine | 40.00 | 10.00 | 5.00 |

| R601 | | MnHVF | UseVF | Perfin |
|---|---|---|---|---|
| $60 | carmine | | 50.00 | 12.50 |

| R602 | | MnHVF | UseVF | Perfin |
|---|---|---|---|---|
| $100. | carmine | 30.00 | 7.50 | 2.50 |

| R603 | | MnHVF | UseVF | Perfin |
|---|---|---|---|---|
| $500. | carmine | | 90.00 | 55.00 |

| R604 | | MnHVF | UseVF | Perfin |
|---|---|---|---|---|
| $1000. | carmine | | 30.00 | 15.00 |

| R605 | | MnHVF | UseVF | Perfin |
|---|---|---|---|---|
| $2500. | carmine | | 150. | 110. |

| R606 | | MnHVF | UseVF | Perfin |
|---|---|---|---|---|
| $5000. | carmine | | 1000. | 800. |

| R607 | | MnHVF | UseVF | Perfin |
|---|---|---|---|---|
| $10000. | carmine | | 650. | 400. |

**1953. DOCUMENTARY ISSUE** Secretaries of the Treasury, stamps Nos. R274-298, R585, R588, R589, R591, R592, R594 and R605-607, overprint reads SERIES 1953.

| R608 | | MnHVF | UseVF | Perfin |
|---|---|---|---|---|
| 1¢ | carmine | .20 | .20 | .20 |

| R609 | | MnHVF | UseVF | Perfin |
|---|---|---|---|---|
| 2¢ | carmine | .20 | .20 | .20 |

| R610 | | MnHVF | UseVF | Perfin |
|---|---|---|---|---|
| 3¢ | carmine | .25 | .20 | .20 |

| R611 | | MnHVF | UseVF | Perfin |
|---|---|---|---|---|
| 4¢ | carmine | .30 | .25 | .20 |

| R612 | | MnHVF | UseVF | Perfin |
|---|---|---|---|---|
| 5¢ | carmine | .20 | .20 | .20 |

| R613 | | MnHVF | UseVF | Perfin |
|---|---|---|---|---|
| 8¢ | carmine | .70 | .70 | .20 |

| R614 | | MnHVF | UseVF | Perfin |
|---|---|---|---|---|
| 10¢ | carmine | .35 | .25 | .20 |

| R615 | | MnHVF | UseVF | Perfin |
|---|---|---|---|---|
| 20¢ | carmine | .70 | .35 | .20 |

| R616 | | MnHVF | UseVF | Perfin |
|---|---|---|---|---|
| 25¢ | carmine | .80 | .40 | .20 |

| R617 | | MnHVF | UseVF | Perfin |
|---|---|---|---|---|
| 40¢ | carmine | 1.50 | 1.00 | .35 |

| R618 | | MnHVF | UseVF | Perfin |
|---|---|---|---|---|
| 50¢ | carmine | 2.25 | .20 | .20 |

| R619 | | MnHVF | UseVF | Perfin |
|---|---|---|---|---|
| 55¢ | carmine | 3.25 | 1.75 | .75 |

| R620 | | MnHVF | UseVF | Perfin |
|---|---|---|---|---|
| 80¢ | carmine | 5.50 | 1.75 | 1.25 |

| R621 | | MnHVF | UseVF | Perfin |
|---|---|---|---|---|
| $1 | carmine | 3.50 | .20 | .20 |

| R622 | | MnHVF | UseVF | Perfin |
|---|---|---|---|---|
| $1.10 | carmine | 6.50 | 2.25 | 2.00 |

| R623 | | MnHVF | UseVF | Perfin |
|---|---|---|---|---|
| $1.65 | carmine | 7.50 | 3.50 | 2.75 |

| R624 | | MnHVF | UseVF | Perfin |
|---|---|---|---|---|
| $2 | carmine | 6.00 | .55 | .25 |

| R625 | | MnHVF | UseVF | Perfin |
|---|---|---|---|---|
| $2.20 | carmine | 9.00 | 6.00 | 2.25 |

| R626 | | MnHVF | UseVF | Perfin |
|---|---|---|---|---|
| $2.75 | carmine | 12.50 | 6.50 | 3.00 |

| R627 | | MnHVF | UseVF | Perfin |
|---|---|---|---|---|
| $3 | carmine | 7.50 | 3.00 | 1.50 |

| R628 | | MnHVF | UseVF | Perfin |
|---|---|---|---|---|
| $3.30 | carmine | 22.50 | 7.50 | 4.50 |

| R629 | | MnHVF | UseVF | Perfin |
|---|---|---|---|---|
| $4 | carmine | 15.00 | 7.00 | 2.00 |

| R630 | | MnHVF | UseVF | Perfin |
|---|---|---|---|---|
| $5 | carmine | 15.00 | .90 | .35 |

| R631 | | MnHVF | UseVF | Perfin |
|---|---|---|---|---|
| $10 | carmine | 30.00 | 2.00 | 1.00 |

| R632 | | MnHVF | UseVF | Perfin |
|---|---|---|---|---|
| $20 | carmine | 65.00 | 17.50 | 3.00 |

| R633 | | MnHVF | UseVF | Perfin |
|---|---|---|---|---|
| $30 | carmine | 40.00 | 12.00 | 5.00 |

| R634 | | MnHVF | UseVF | Perfin |
|---|---|---|---|---|
| $50 | carmine | 70.00 | 20.00 | 6.50 |

| R635 | | MnHVF | UseVF | Perfin |
|---|---|---|---|---|
| $60 | carmine | 275. | 125. | 80.00 |

| R636 | | MnHVF | UseVF | Perfin |
|---|---|---|---|---|
| $100. | carmine | 30.00 | 12.50 | 5.00 |

| R637 | | MnHVF | UseVF | Perfin |
|---|---|---|---|---|
| $500. | carmine | 225. | 100. | 30.00 |

| R638 | | MnHVF | UseVF | Perfin |
|---|---|---|---|---|
| $1000. | carmine | 125. | 55.00 | 20.00 |

| R639 | | MnHVF | UseVF | Perfin |
|---|---|---|---|---|
| $2500. | carmine | 450. | 450. | 250. |

| R640 | | MnHVF | UseVF | Perfin |
|---|---|---|---|---|
| $5000. | carmine | | 1100. | 850. |

| R641 | | MnHVF | UseVF | Perfin |
|---|---|---|---|---|
| $10000. | carmine | | 900. | 600. |

**1954. DOCUMENTARY ISSUE** Secretaries of the Treasury, stamps Nos. R274-298, R585, R588, R589, R591, R592, R594 and R605-607. Nos. R642-666 are without overprint. On stamps Nos. 667-675 overprint reads: SERIES 1954.

| R642 | | MnHVF | UseVF | Perfin |
|---|---|---|---|---|
| 1¢ | carmine | .20 | .20 | .20 |

| R643 | | MnHVF | UseVF | Perfin |
|---|---|---|---|---|
| 2¢ | carmine | .20 | .20 | .20 |

| R644 | | MnHVF | UseVF | Perfin |
|---|---|---|---|---|
| 3¢ | carmine | .20 | .20 | .20 |

| R645 | | MnHVF | UseVF | Perfin |
|---|---|---|---|---|
| 4¢ | carmine | .20 | .20 | .20 |

| R646 | | MnHVF | UseVF | Perfin |
|---|---|---|---|---|
| 5¢ | carmine | .20 | .20 | .20 |

| R647 | | MnHVF | UseVF | Perfin |
|---|---|---|---|---|
| 8¢ | carmine | .25 | .20 | .20 |

| R648 | | MnHVF | UseVF | Perfin |
|---|---|---|---|---|
| 10¢ | carmine | .25 | .20 | .20 |

| R649 | | MnHVF | UseVF | Perfin |
|---|---|---|---|---|
| 20¢ | carmine | .40 | .30 | .20 |

| R650 | | MnHVF | UseVF | Perfin |
|---|---|---|---|---|
| 25¢ | carmine | .60 | .30 | .20 |

| R651 | | MnHVF | UseVF | Perfin |
|---|---|---|---|---|
| 40¢ | carmine | 1.25 | .60 | .20 |

| R652 | | MnHVF | UseVF | Perfin |
|---|---|---|---|---|
| 50¢ | carmine | 1.60 | .20 | .20 |

| R653 | | MnHVF | UseVF | Perfin |
|---|---|---|---|---|
| 55¢ | carmine | 1.50 | 1.25 | .50 |

| R654 | | MnHVF | UseVF | Perfin |
|---|---|---|---|---|
| 80¢ | carmine | 2.25 | 1.75 | 1.00 |

| R655 | | MnHVF | UseVF | Perfin |
|---|---|---|---|---|
| $1 | carmine | 1.50 | .30 | .20 |

| R656 | | MnHVF | UseVF | Perfin |
|---|---|---|---|---|
| $1.10 | carmine | 3.25 | 2.50 | 1.50 |

| R657 | | MnHVF | UseVF | Perfin |
|---|---|---|---|---|
| $1.65 | carmine | 80.00 | 50.00 | 40.00 |

| R658 | | MnHVF | UseVF | Perfin |
|---|---|---|---|---|
| $2 | carmine | 1.75 | .25 | .25 |

| R659 | | MnHVF | UseVF | Perfin |
|---|---|---|---|---|
| $2.20 | carmine | 4.50 | 3.50 | 2.50 |

| R660 | | MnHVF | UseVF | Perfin |
|---|---|---|---|---|
| $2.75 | carmine | 90.00 | 50.00 | 35.00 |

| R661 | | MnHVF | UseVF | Perfin |
|---|---|---|---|---|
| $3 | carmine | 3.00 | 2.00 | 1.00 |

| R662 | | MnHVF | UseVF | Perfin |
|---|---|---|---|---|
| $3.30 | carmine | 6.50 | 5.00 | 3.00 |

| R663 | | MnHVF | UseVF | Perfin |
|---|---|---|---|---|
| $4 | carmine | 4.00 | 3.50 | 2.00 |

| R664 | | MnHVF | UseVF | Perfin |
|---|---|---|---|---|
| $5 | carmine | 6.00 | .45 | .30 |

| R665 | | MnHVF | UseVF | Perfin |
|---|---|---|---|---|
| $10 | carmine | 12.50 | 1.25 | .75 |

| R666 | | MnHVF | UseVF | Perfin |
|---|---|---|---|---|
| $20 | carmine | 20.00 | 5.25 | 3.00 |

| R667 | | MnHVF | UseVF | Perfin |
|---|---|---|---|---|
| $30 | carmine | 30.00 | 12.00 | 4.00 |

| R668 | | MnHVF | UseVF | Perfin |
|---|---|---|---|---|
| $50 | carmine | 40.00 | 15.00 | 9.00 |

| R669 | | MnHVF | UseVF | Perfin |
|---|---|---|---|---|
| $60 | carmine | 65.00 | 20.00 | 12.50 |

| R670 | | MnHVF | UseVF | Perfin |
|---|---|---|---|---|
| $100. | carmine | 30.00 | 7.00 | 4.50 |

| R671 | | MnHVF | UseVF | Perfin |
|---|---|---|---|---|
| $500. | carmine | | 75.00 | 22.50 |

| R672 | | MnHVF | UseVF | Perfin |
|---|---|---|---|---|
| $1000. | carmine | 150. | 50.00 | 17.50 |

| R673 | | MnHVF | UseVF | Perfin |
|---|---|---|---|---|
| $2500. | carmine | | 175. | 80.00 |

| R674 | | MnHVF | UseVF | Perfin |
|---|---|---|---|---|
| $5000. | carmine | | 700. | 500. |

| R675 | | MnHVF | UseVF | Perfin |
|---|---|---|---|---|
| $10000. | carmine | | 450. | 175. |

**1955. DOCUMENTARY ISSUE** Secretaries of the Treasury, stamps Nos. R293-298 and R604-607, overprint reads SERIES 1955.

| R676 | | MnHVF | UseVF | Perfin |
|---|---|---|---|---|
| $30 | carmine #R293 | 35.00 | 10.00 | 5.00 |

| R677 | | MnHVF | UseVF | Perfin |
|---|---|---|---|---|
| $50 | carmine #R294 | 35.00 | 12.50 | 8.00 |

| R678 | | MnHVF | UseVF | Perfin |
|---|---|---|---|---|
| $60 | carmine #R295 | 65.00 | 20.00 | 10.00 |

| R679 | | MnHVF | UseVF | Perfin |
|---|---|---|---|---|
| $100. | carmine #R296 | 30.00 | 6.00 | 4.00 |

| R680 | | MnHVF | UseVF | Perfin |
|---|---|---|---|---|
| $500. | carmine #R297 | | 120. | 25.00 |

| R681 | | MnHVF | UseVF | Perfin |
|---|---|---|---|---|
| $1000. | carmine #R298 | | 30.00 | 17.50 |

| R682 | | MnHVF | UseVF | Perfin |
|---|---|---|---|---|
| $2500. | carmine #R605 | | 125. | 75.00 |

| R683 | | MnHVF | UseVF | Perfin |
|---|---|---|---|---|
| $5000. | carmine #R606 | | 650. | 400. |

| R684 | | MnHVF | UseVF | Perfin |
|---|---|---|---|---|
| $10000. | carmine #R607 | | 450. | 175. |

**1956. DOCUMENTARY ISSUE** Secretaries of the Treasury, stamps Nos. R293-298 and R605-607, overprint reads SERIES 1956.

| R685 | | MnHVF | UseVF | Perfin |
|---|---|---|---|---|
| $30 | carmine #R293 | 50.00 | 12.50 | 8.00 |

| R686 | | MnHVF | UseVF | Perfin |
|---|---|---|---|---|
| $50 | carmine #R294 | 50.00 | 17.50 | 8.00 |

| R687 | | MnHVF | UseVF | Perfin |
|---|---|---|---|---|
| $60 | carmine #R295 | | 30.00 | 10.00 |

| R688 | | MnHVF | UseVF | Perfin |
|---|---|---|---|---|
| $100. | carmine #R296 | 50.00 | 12.50 | 5.00 |

| R689 | | MnHVF | UseVF | Perfin |
|---|---|---|---|---|
| $500. | carmine #R297 | | 70.00 | 25.00 |

| R690 | | MnHVF | UseVF | Perfin |
|---|---|---|---|---|
| $1000. | carmine #R298 | | 50.00 | 10.00 |

| R691 | | MnHVF | UseVF | Perfin |
|---|---|---|---|---|
| $2500. | carmine #R605 | | 250. | 100. |

| R692 | | MnHVF | UseVF | Perfin |
|---|---|---|---|---|
| $5000. | carmine #R606 | | 1100. | 900. |

| R693 | | MnHVF | UseVF | Perfin |
|---|---|---|---|---|
| $10000. | carmine #R607 | | 400. | 125. |

**1957. DOCUMENTARY ISSUE** Secretaries of the Treasury, stamps Nos. R293-298 and R605-607, overprint reads SERIES 1957.

| R694 | | MnHVF | UseVF | Perfin |
|---|---|---|---|---|
| $30 | carmine #R293 | 65.00 | 25.00 | 10.00 |

| R695 | | MnHVF | UseVF | Perfin |
|---|---|---|---|---|
| $50 | carmine #R294 | 40.00 | 22.50 | 8.00 |

| R696 | | MnHVF | UseVF | Perfin |
|---|---|---|---|---|
| $60 | carmine #R295 | | 140. | 80.00 |

| R697 | | MnHVF | UseVF | Perfin |
|---|---|---|---|---|
| $100. | carmine #R296 | 40.00 | 10.00 | 8.00 |

| R698 | | MnHVF | UseVF | Perfin |
|---|---|---|---|---|
| $500. | carmine #R297 | 175. | 80.00 | 40.00 |

| R699 | | MnHVF | UseVF | Perfin |
|---|---|---|---|---|
| $1000. | carmine #R298 | | 75.00 | 25.00 |

| R700 | | MnHVF | UseVF | Perfin |
|---|---|---|---|---|
| $2500. | carmine #R605 | | 500. | 350. |

| R701 | | MnHVF | UseVF | Perfin |
|---|---|---|---|---|
| $5000. | carmine #R606 | | 550. | 350. |

| R702 | | MnHVF | UseVF | Perfin |
|---|---|---|---|---|
| $10000. | carmine #R607 | | 425. | 150. |

**1958. DOCUMENTARY ISSUE** Secretaries of the Treasury, stamps Nos. R293-298 and R605-607, overprint reads SERIES 1958.

| R703 | | MnHVF | UseVF | Perfin |
|---|---|---|---|---|
| $30 | carmine #R293 | 70.00 | 20.00 | 15.00 |

| R704 | | MnHVF | UseVF | Perfin |
|---|---|---|---|---|
| $50 | carmine #R294 | 60.00 | 20.00 | 12.50 |

| R705 | | MnHVF | UseVF | Perfin |
|---|---|---|---|---|
| $60 | carmine #R295 | | 25.00 | 15.00 |

| R706 | | MnHVF | UseVF | Perfin |
|---|---|---|---|---|
| $100. | carmine #R296 | 50.00 | 10.00 | 5.00 |

| R707 | | MnHVF | UseVF | Perfin |
|---|---|---|---|---|
| $500. | carmine #R297 | 125. | 50.00 | 30.00 |

| R708 | | MnHVF | UseVF | Perfin |
|---|---|---|---|---|
| $1000. | carmine #R298 | | 65.00 | 30.00 |

| R709 | | MnHVF | UseVF | Perfin |
|---|---|---|---|---|
| $2500. | carmine #R605 | | 500. | 375. |

| R710 | | MnHVF | UseVF | Perfin |
|---|---|---|---|---|
| $5000. | carmine #R606 | | 1200. | 900. |

| R711 | | MnHVF | UseVF | Perfin |
|---|---|---|---|---|
| $10000. | carmine #R607 | | 600. | 500. |

**1962. DOCUMENTARY ISSUE** For the 100th anniversary of Internal Revenue, the Federal Government's first commemorative documentary stamp was issued. It features the Internal Revenue Building. This stamp was replaced at a later date with similar design but dateline removed. Ciori Press printing.

| R712 | | MnHVF | UseVF | Perfin |
|---|---|---|---|---|
| 10¢ | **blue and green** | 1.00 | .25 | .20 |
| | Plate block of 4 | 12.00 | | |

**1963. DOCUMENTARY ISSUE** Date line remove.

| R713 | | MnHVF | UseVF | Perfin |
|---|---|---|---|---|
| 10¢ | **blue and green** | 3.00 | .30 | .20 |
| | Plate block of 4 | 25.00 | | |

*Documentary stamps were no longer required after Dec. 31, 1967.*

# Proprietary Stamps

**1871-73. PROPRIETARY ISSUE** Portrait of Washington in black in an oval. The stamps are of different sizes and the frames vary in design according to the denominations. Printed by Joseph R. Carpenter of Philadelphia on unwatermarked violet paper, perforated 12.

| | | UnCnl | Cnl |
|---|---|---|---|
| **RP9** | | | |
| 1¢ | **green and black** | | 4.00 |
| | a. imperforate *(RB1c)* | | |
| | b. inverted center *(RB1d)* | 2850. | |
| **RP10** | | UnCnl | Cnl |
| 2¢ | **green and black** | | 4.50 |
| **RP11** | | UnCnl | Cnl |
| 3¢ | **green and black** | | 11.00 |
| | a. inverted center *RB3a)* | 15000. | |
| **RP12** | | UnCnl | Cnl |
| 4¢ | **green and black** | | 8.00 |
| | a. inverted center *(RB4c)* | 20000. | |
| **RP13** | | UnCnl | Cnl |
| 5¢ | **green and black** | | 125. |
| | a. inverted center *(RB5c)* | 75000. | |
| **RP14** | | UnCnl | Cnl |
| 6¢ | **green and black** | | 25.00 |
| **RP15** | | UnCnl | Cnl |
| 10¢ | **green and black** | | 275. |
| **RP16** | | UnCnl | Cnl |
| 50¢ | **green and black** | | 550. |
| **RP17** | | UnCnl | Cnl |
| $1 | **green and black** | | 1000. |
| **RP18** | | UnCnl | Cnl |
| $5 | **green and black** | | 3000. |

**1874. PROPRIETARY ISSUE.** Green paper.

| | | UnCnl | Cnl |
|---|---|---|---|
| **RP19** | | UnCnl | Cnl |
| 1¢ | **green and black** | | 6.75 |
| **RP20** | | UnCnl | Cnl |
| 2¢ | **green and black** | | 14.00 |
| | a. inverted center | 7500. | |
| **RP21** | | UnCnl | Cnl |
| 3¢ | **green and black** | | 45.00 |
| **RP22** | | UnCnl | Cnl |
| 4¢ | **green and black** | | 15.00 |
| **RP23** | | UnCnl | Cnl |
| 5¢ | **green and black** | | 125. |
| **RP24** | | UnCnl | Cnl |
| 6¢ | **green and black** | | 75.00 |
| **RP25** | | UnCnl | Cnl |
| 10¢ | **green and black** | | 50.00 |
| **RP26** | | UnCnl | Cnl |
| 50¢ | **green and black** | | 850. |
| **RP27** | | UnCnl | Cnl |
| $1 | **green and black** | | 3500. |
| **RP28** | | UnCnl | Cnl |
| $5 | green and black | | 25000. |

**1875. PROPRIETARY ISSUE** Portrait of Washington in various frames engraved and printed by the National Bank Note Co. At first the stamps were printed on green silk paper and perforated 12. Later the stamps were printed on green paper with doubleline USIR watermark and perforated 12. All prices are for used examples.

| | | Perf | Roul |
|---|---|---|---|
| **RP29** | | | |
| 1¢ | **green** | 1.75 | |

| | | Perf | Roul |
|---|---|---|---|
| **RP30** | | Perf | Roul |
| 2¢ | **brown** | 2.50 | |
| **RP31** | | Perf | Roul |
| 3¢ | **orange** | 11.50 | |
| **RP32** | | Perf | Roul |
| 4¢ | **red brown** | 5.50 | |
| **RP33** | | Perf | Roul |
| 5¢ | **black** | 90.00 | |

| | | Perf | Roul |
|---|---|---|---|
| **RP34** | | | |
| 6¢ | **violet blue** | 22.50 | |

**1880-81. PROPRIETARY ISSUE** Green paper, watermarked USIR, perforated 12 or rouletted 6.

| | | Perf | Roul |
|---|---|---|---|
| **RP35** | | Perf | Roul |
| 1¢ | **green** | .50 | 55.00 |
| **RP36** | | Perf | Roul |
| 2¢ | **brown** | 1.50 | 75.00 |
| **RP37** | | Perf | Roul |
| 3¢ | **orange** | 4.50 | 75.00 |
| **RP38** | | Perf | Roul |
| 4¢ | **red brown** | 5.50 | |
| **RP39** | | Perf | Roul |
| 4¢ | **red** | 4.50 | 110. |

| RP40 | | Perf | Roul |
|---|---|---|---|
| 5¢ | black | 75.00 | 1000. |
| **RP41** | | **Perf** | **Roul** |
| 6¢ | violet blue | 17.50 | 200. |
| **RP42** | | **Perf** | **Roul** |
| 6¢ | violet | 25.00 | |
| **RP43** | | **Perf** | **Roul** |
| 10¢ | blue | 275. | |

# Future Delivery Stamps

Issued to pay the tax on sales, agreements of sale or agreements to sell any products at an exchange or equivalent establishment for future delivery.

**1918-34. FUTURE DELIVERY ISSUE** Documentary stamps of 1917 overprinted in black or red as illustrated. Double-line watermark USIR (R139), perforated 11. #RFD1, 5, 12 Type 2: Words 2mm apart. #RFD 2-4, 6-11 Type 1: Words about 8 1/2mm apart.

| RFD1 | | UnFVF | UseFVF |
|---|---|---|---|
| 1¢ | **rose** (2mm) Type 2 | 1.20 | .20 |

| | | UnFVF | UseFVF |
|---|---|---|---|
| **RFD2** | | | |
| 2¢ | **rose** Type 1 | 3.00 | .20 |
| | Cut cancellation | 12.50 | |
| **RFD3** | | **UnFVF** | **UseFVF** |
| 3¢ | **rose** Type 1 | | 25.00 |

| | | UnFVF | UseFVF |
|---|---|---|---|
| **RFD4** | | | |
| 4¢ | **rose** Type 1 | 6.00 | .20 |
| **RFD5** | | **UnFVF** | **UseFVF** |
| 5¢ | **rose** (2mm) Type 2 | 60.00 | 7.00 |

| | | UnFVF | UseFVF |
|---|---|---|---|
| **RFD6** | | | |
| 10¢ | **rose** Type 1 | 10.00 | .20 |
| | Cut cancellation | .20 | |

| | | UnFVF | UseFVF |
|---|---|---|---|
| **RFD7** | | | |
| 20¢ | **rose** Type 1 | 12.50 | .20 |
| | Cut cancellation | .20 | |

| RFD8 | | UnFVF | UseFVF |
|---|---|---|---|
| 25¢ | **rose** Type 1 | 32.50 | .75 |
| **RFD9** | | **UnFVF** | **UseFVF** |
| 40¢ | **rose** Type 1 | 35.00 | 1.00 |
| | Cut cancellation | .75 | |
| **RFD10** | | **UnFVF** | **UseFVF** |
| 50¢ | **rose** Type 1 | 7.50 | .40 |
| **RFD11** | | **UnFVF** | **UseFVF** |
| 80¢ | **rose** Type 1 | 65.00 | 8.00 |
| | Cut cancellation | | |
| **RFD12** | | **UnFVF** | **UseFVF** |
| 80¢ | **rose** (2mm) Type 2 | 50.00 | 3.00 |
| | Cut cancellation | .30 | |

**1918-34. FUTURE DELIVERY ISSUE** Words about 2mm apart.

| RFD13 | | UnFVF | UseFVF |
|---|---|---|---|
| $1 | **yellow green,** red overprint | 25.00 | .25 |
| | a. green, black overprint | .20 | |
| | Cut cancellation | | 175. |

| | | UnFVF | UseFVF |
|---|---|---|---|
| **RFD14** | | | |
| $2 | **rose,** black overprint | 30.00 | .25 |
| | Cut cancellation | | .20 |
| **RFD15** | | **UnFVF** | **UseFVF** |
| $3 | **violet,** red overprint | 75.00 | 2.25 |
| | Cut cancellation | | .50 |
| **RFD16** | | **UnFVF** | **UseFVF** |
| $5 | **blue,** red overprint | 45.00 | .50 |
| | Cut cancellation | 1.50 | |
| **RFD17** | | **UnFVF** | **UseFVF** |
| $10 | **yellow** | 75.00 | 1.00 |
| | Cut cancellation | .75 | |
| **RFD18** | | **UnFVF** | **UseFVF** |
| $20 | **olive** | 125. | 5.00 |
| | Cut cancellation | .75 | .70 |

**1918-34. FUTURE DELIVERY ISSUE** Words 11 1/2mm apart, perforated 12.

| RFD19 | | UnFVF | UseFVF |
|---|---|---|---|
| $30 | **orange,** blue numerals | 65.00 | 3.50 |
| | Cut cancellation | 1.50 | 1.25 |
| **RFD20** | | **UnFVF** | **UseFVF** |
| $50 | **olive green** | 50.00 | 1.00 |
| | Cut cancellation | .60 | .35 |

| | | UnFVF | UseFVF |
|---|---|---|---|
| **RFD21** | | | |
| $60 | **brown** | 65.00 | 2.00 |
| | Cut cancellation | .75 | .60 |

# Stock Transfer Stamps

These stamps are used to pay the tax due on the transfer of legal title of shares or stock certificates.

**1918-29. STOCK TRANSFER ISSUE** Documentary Stamps of 1917 overprinted in black or red. *Double-line watermark USIR, perforated 11.*

| RST1 | | UnFVF | UseFVF |
|---|---|---|---|
| 1¢ | rose | .90 | .20 |

| RST2 | | UnFVF | UseFVF |
|---|---|---|---|
| 2¢ | rose | .30 | .20 |

| RST3 | | UnFVF | UseFVF |
|---|---|---|---|
| 4¢ | rose | .30 | .20 |

| RST4 | | UnFVF | UseFVF |
|---|---|---|---|
| 5¢ | rose | .30 | .20 |

| RST5 | | UnFVF | UseFVF |
|---|---|---|---|
| 10¢ | rose | .30 | .20 |

| RST6 | | UnFVF | UseFVF |
|---|---|---|---|
| 20¢ | rose | .60 | .20 |

| RST7 | | UnFVF | UseFVF |
|---|---|---|---|
| 25¢ | rose | 1.25 | .25 |

| RST8 | | UnFVF | UseFVF |
|---|---|---|---|
| 40¢ | rose | 1.25 | .25 |

| RST9 | | UnFVF | UseFVF |
|---|---|---|---|
| 50¢ | rose | .60 | .20 |

| RST10 | | UnFVF | UseFVF |
|---|---|---|---|
| 80¢ | rose | 2.50 | .30 |

| RST11 | | UnFVF | UseFVF |
|---|---|---|---|
| $1 | yellow green, red overprint | 60.00 | 17.50 |
| | Cut cancellation | | 4.50 |
| | a. Overprint reading down | 10.00 | 8.00 |
| | Cut cancellation | | 2.00 |

| RST12 | | UnFVF | UseFVF |
|---|---|---|---|
| 3¢ | yellow green, black overprint | 2.25 | .25 |
| | a. Overprint reading down | | 7.00 |

| RST13 | | UnFVF | UseFVF |
|---|---|---|---|
| $2 | rose | 2.25 | .20 |
| | a. Overprint reading down | | 12.75 |
| | Cut cancellation | | 2.25 |

| RST14 | | UnFVF | UseFVF |
|---|---|---|---|
| $3 | violet, red overprint | 17.50 | 4.00 |
| | Cut cancellation | | .20 |

| RST15 | | UnFVF | UseFVF |
|---|---|---|---|
| $4 | ochre | 7.50 | .20 |
| | Cut cancelation | | .20 |

| RST16 | | UnFVF | UseFVF |
|---|---|---|---|
| $5 | blue, red overprint | 5.50 | .20 |
| | a. Overprint reading down | | .50 |
| | Cut cancellation | | .20 |

| RST17 | | UnFVF | UseFVF |
|---|---|---|---|
| $10 | yellow | 14.00 | .35 |
| | Cut cancellation | | .08 |

| RST18 | | UnFVF | UseFVF |
|---|---|---|---|
| $20 | olive | 70.00 | 20.00 |
| | Cut cancellation | | 1.10 |
| | a. olive bistre | | 11.00 |
| | Cut cancellation | | 1.10 |

**1918-29. STOCK TRANSFER ISSUE** *Perforated 12.*

| RST19 | | UnFVF | UseFVF |
|---|---|---|---|
| $30 | orange, green numerals | 17.50 | 5.00 |
| | Cut cancellation | | 2.25 |

| RST20 | | UnFVF | UseFVF |
|---|---|---|---|
| $50 | olive green (Cleveland) | 100. | 55.00 |
| | Cut cancellation | | 20.00 |

| RST21 | | UnFVF | UseFVF |
|---|---|---|---|
| $60 | brown | 100. | 22.50 |
| | Cut cancellation | | 8.50 |

| RST22 | | UnFVF | UseFVF |
|---|---|---|---|
| $100. | pale green | 22.50 | 5.50 |
| | Cut cancellation | | 2.25 |

| RST23 | | UnFVF | UseFVF |
|---|---|---|---|
| $500. | blue, red overprint | 300. | 120. |
| | Cut cancellation | | 65.00 |

| RST24 | | UnFVF | UseFVF |
|---|---|---|---|
| $1000. | orange yellow | 160. | 75.00 |
| | Cut cancellation | | 30.00 |

**1928-32. STOCK TRANSFER ISSUE** Same as 1918-29 issue, *perforated 10.*

| RST25 | | UnFVF | UseFVF |
|---|---|---|---|
| 2¢ | rose | 2.25 | .30 |

| RST26 | | UnFVF | UseFVF |
|---|---|---|---|
| 4¢ | rose | 2.25 | .30 |

| RST27 | | UnFVF | UseFVF |
|---|---|---|---|
| 10¢ | rose | 2.00 | .30 |

| RST28 | | UnFVF | UseFVF |
|---|---|---|---|
| 20¢ | rose | 2.75 | .30 |

| RST29 | | UnFVF | UseFVF |
|---|---|---|---|
| 50¢ | rose | 3.50 | .20 |

| RST30 | | UnFVF | UseFVF |
|---|---|---|---|
| $1 | yellow green | 27.50 | .20 |

| RST31 | | UnFVF | UseFVF |
|---|---|---|---|
| $2 | rose | 27.50 | .20 |

| RST32 | | UnFVF | UseFVF |
|---|---|---|---|
| $10 | yellow | 30.00 | .30 |

**1920. STOCK TRANSFER ISSUE** Same as 1918-29 issue, but letters of overprint with serifs. *Perforated 11.*

| RST33 | | UnFVF | UseFVF |
|---|---|---|---|
| 2¢ | rose | 6.50 | .75 |

| RST34 | | UnFVF | UseFVF |
|---|---|---|---|
| 10¢ | rose | 1.25 | .25 |

| RST35 | | UnFVF | UseFVF |
|---|---|---|---|
| 20¢ | rose | 1.25 | .25 |

| RST36 | | UnFVF | UseFVF |
|---|---|---|---|
| 50¢ | rose | 2.75 | .25 |

| RST37 | | UnFVF | UseFVF |
|---|---|---|---|
| $1 | yellow green | 37.50 | 9.00 |
| | Cut cancellation | | .25 |

| RST38 | | UnFVF | UseFVF |
|---|---|---|---|
| $2 | rose | 35.00 | 9.00 |
| | Cut cancellation | | .25 |

**1929. STOCK TRANSFER ISSUE** Same as 1918 issue but letters letters of overprint with serifs. *Perforated 10.*

| RST39 | | UnFVF | UseFVF |
|---|---|---|---|
| 2¢ | rose | 5.00 | .50 |

| RST40 | | UnFVF | UseFVF |
|---|---|---|---|
| 10¢ | rose | 1.25 | .50 |

| RST41 | | UnFVF | UseFVF |
|---|---|---|---|
| 20¢ | rose | 2.00 | .25 |

**1940. FIRST STOCK TRANSFER ISSUE** Documentary Stamps of 1917-33 overprinted as illustrated, in black. *Double-line USIR watermark, perforated 11.*

| RST42 | | MnHVF | UseVF | CutCnl |
|---|---|---|---|---|
| 1¢ | pink | 2.75 | .40 | .20 |

| RST43 | | MnHVF | UseVF | CutCnl |
|---|---|---|---|---|
| 2¢ | pink | 2.75 | .40 | .20 |

| RST44 | | MnHVF | UseVF | CutCnl |
|---|---|---|---|---|
| 4¢ | pink | 2.75 | .20 | .20 |

| RST45 | | MnHVF | UseVF | CutCnl |
|---|---|---|---|---|
| 5¢ | pink | 3.00 | .20 | .20 |

| RST46 | | MnHVF | UseVF | CutCnl |
|---|---|---|---|---|
| 10¢ | pink | 3.00 | .20 | .20 |

| RST47 | | MnHVF | UseVF | CutCnl |
|---|---|---|---|---|
| 20¢ | pink | 7.00 | .20 | .20 |

| RST48 | | MnHVF | UseVF | CutCnl |
|---|---|---|---|---|
| 25¢ | pink | 7.00 | .50 | .20 |

| RST49 | | MnHVF | UseVF | CutCnl |
|---|---|---|---|---|
| 40¢ | pink | 4.50 | .50 | .20 |

| RST50 | | MnHVF | UseVF | CutCnl |
|---|---|---|---|---|
| 50¢ | pink | 5.50 | .20 | .20 |

| RST51 | | MnHVF | UseVF | CutCnl |
|---|---|---|---|---|
| 80¢ | pink | 80.00 | 40.00 | 25.00 |

| RST52 | | MnHVF | UseVF | CutCnl |
|---|---|---|---|---|
| $1 | green | 17.50 | .30 | .20 |

| RST53 | | MnHVF | UseVF | CutCnl |
|---|---|---|---|---|
| $2 | rose | 17.50 | .50 | .20 |

| RST54 | | MnHVF | UseVF | CutCnl |
|---|---|---|---|---|
| $3 | violet | 110. | 8.00 | .20 |

| RST55 | | MnHVF | UseVF | CutCnl |
|---|---|---|---|---|
| $4 | yellow brown | 35.00 | .75 | .20 |

| RST56 | | MnHVF | UseVF | CutCnl |
|---|---|---|---|---|
| $5 | blue | 35.00 | .75 | .20 |

| RST57 | | MnHVF | UseVF | CutCnl |
|---|---|---|---|---|
| $10 | yellow | 85.00 | 5.00 | .40 |

| RST58 | | MnHVF | UseVF | CutCnl |
|---|---|---|---|---|
| $20 | olive bistre | 200. | 70.00 | 15.00 |

**1940. SECOND STOCK TRANSFER ISSUE** Stock Transfer Stamps of 1918-29 handstamped "Series 1940" in blue. *Perforated 12.*

| RST59 | | MnHVF | UseVF | CutCnl |
|---|---|---|---|---|
| $30 | vermilion | 700. | 400. | 250. |

| RST60 | | MnHVF | UseVF | CutCnl |
|---|---|---|---|---|
| $50 | olive green | 700. | 650. | 175. |

| RST61 | | MnHVF | UseVF | CutCnl |
|---|---|---|---|---|
| $60 | brown | | 900. | 200. |

| RST62 | | MnHVF | UseVF | CutCnl |
|---|---|---|---|---|
| $100. | green | | 500. | 125. |

| RST63 | | MnHVF | UseVF | CutCnl |
|---|---|---|---|---|
| $500. | blue | | 1750. | 1100. |

| RST64 | | MnHVF | UseVF | CutCnl |
|---|---|---|---|---|
| $1000. | orange | | 2100. | 1750. |

**1940. STOCK TRANSFER ISSUE** New designs, overprinted "Series 1940" in black. No. RST65-74 perforated 11, size 19 x 22mm. No. RST75-81 size 21 1/2 x 36 1/4mm. No. RST82-87 similar designs, 28 1/2 x 42mm, perforated 12.

| RST65 | | MnHVF | UseVF | CutCnl |
|---|---|---|---|---|
| 1¢ | green | 7.50 | 2.50 | .40 |

| RST66 | | MnHVF | UseVF | CutCnl |
|---|---|---|---|---|
| 2¢ | green | 5.00 | 1.25 | .20 |

| RST67 | | MnHVF | UseVF | CutCnl |
|---|---|---|---|---|
| 4¢ | green | 8.00 | 3.50 | .50 |

| RST68 | | MnHVF | UseVF | CutCnl |
|---|---|---|---|---|
| 5¢ | green | 6.00 | 1.25 | .20 |

| RST69 | | MnHVF | UseVF | CutCnl |
|---|---|---|---|---|
| 10¢ | green | 7.50 | 1.50 | .20 |

| RST70 | | MnHVF | UseVF | CutCnl |
|---|---|---|---|---|
| 20¢ | green | 25.00 | 7.50 | .50 |

| RST71 | | MnHVF | UseVF | CutCnl |
|---|---|---|---|---|
| 25¢ | green | 50.00 | 27.50 | 2.00 |

| RST72 | | MnHVF | UseVF | CutCnl |
|---|---|---|---|---|
| 40¢ | green | 8.00 | 1.50 | .25 |

| RST73 | | MnHVF | UseVF | CutCnl |
|---|---|---|---|---|
| 50¢ | green | 65.00 | 45.00 | 20.00 |

| RST74 | | MnHVF | UseVF | CutCnl |
|---|---|---|---|---|
| 80¢ | green | 27.50 | 3.50 | .30 |

| RST75 | | MnHVF | UseVF | CutCnl |
|---|---|---|---|---|
| $1 | green | 30.00 | 8.00 | .50 |

| RST76 | | MnHVF | UseVF | CutCnl |
|---|---|---|---|---|
| $2 | green | 50.00 | 10.00 | .50 |

| RST77 | | MnHVF | UseVF | CutCnl |
|---|---|---|---|---|
| $3 | green | 50.00 | 10.00 | .50 |

| RST78 | | MnHVF | UseVF | CutCnl |
|---|---|---|---|---|
| $4 | green | 225. | 175. | 60.00 |

| RST79 | | MnHVF | UseVF | CutCnl |
|---|---|---|---|---|
| $5 | green | 50.00 | 10.00 | .30 |

| RST80 | | MnHVF | UseVF | CutCnl |
|---|---|---|---|---|
| $10 | green | 110. | 30.00 | 4.00 |

| RST81 | | MnHVF | UseVF | CutCnl |
|---|---|---|---|---|
| $20 | green | 400. | 70.00 | 8.00 |

| RST82 | | MnHVF | UseVF | CutCnl |
|---|---|---|---|---|
| $30 | green | | 110. | 50.00 |

| RST83 | | MnHVF | UseVF | CutCnl |
|---|---|---|---|---|
| $50 | green | 275. | 175. | 75.00 |

| RST84 | | MnHVF | UseVF | CutCnl |
|---|---|---|---|---|
| $60 | green | | 275. | 50.00 |

| RST85 | | MnHVF | UseVF | CutCnl |
|---|---|---|---|---|
| $100. | green | | 160. | 60.00 |

| RST86 | | MnHVF | UseVF | CutCnl |
|---|---|---|---|---|
| $500. | green | | 800. | 600. |

| RST87 | | MnHVF | UseVF | CutCnl |
|---|---|---|---|---|
| $1000. | green | | 700. | 500. |

**1941. STOCK TRANSFER ISSUE** Types of 1940 overprinted "Series 1941" in black. No. RST88-104 perforated 11. No. RST105-110 perforated 12.

| RST88 | | MnHVF | UseVF | CutCnl |
|---|---|---|---|---|
| 1¢ | green | .60 | .50 | .20 |

| RST89 | | MnHVF | UseVF | CutCnl |
|---|---|---|---|---|
| 2¢ | green | .40 | .20 | .20 |

| RST90 | | MnHVF | UseVF | CutCnl |
|---|---|---|---|---|
| 4¢ | green | .35 | .20 | .20 |

| RST91 | | MnHVF | UseVF | CutCnl |
|---|---|---|---|---|
| 5¢ | green | .30 | .20 | .20 |

| RST92 | | MnHVF | UseVF | CutCnl |
|---|---|---|---|---|
| 10¢ | green | .65 | .20 | .20 |

| RST93 | | MnHVF | UseVF | CutCnl |
|---|---|---|---|---|
| 20¢ | green | 1.60 | .20 | .20 |

| RST94 | | MnHVF | UseVF | CutCnl |
|---|---|---|---|---|
| 25¢ | green | 1.60 | .20 | .20 |

| RST95 | | MnHVF | UseVF | CutCnl |
|---|---|---|---|---|
| 40¢ | green | 2.00 | .60 | .20 |

| RST96 | | MnHVF | UseVF | CutCnl |
|---|---|---|---|---|
| 50¢ | green | 3.50 | .30 | .20 |

| RST97 | | MnHVF | UseVF | CutCnl |
|---|---|---|---|---|
| 80¢ | green | 17.50 | 7.00 | .50 |

| RST98 | | MnHVF | UseVF | CutCnl |
|---|---|---|---|---|
| $1 | green | 10.00 | .20 | .20 |

| RST99 | | MnHVF | UseVF | CutCnl |
|---|---|---|---|---|
| $2 | green | 11.00 | .20 | .20 |

| RST100 | | MnHVF | UseVF | CutCnl |
|---|---|---|---|---|
| $3 | green | 17.50 | 1.25 | .20 |

| RST101 | MnHVF | UseVF | CutCnl |
|---|---|---|---|
| $4    green | 30.00 | 7.00 | .30 |

| RST102 | MnHVF | UseVF | CutCnl |
|---|---|---|---|
| $5    green | 30.00 | .50 | .20 |

| RST103 | MnHVF | UseVF | CutCnl |
|---|---|---|---|
| $10    green | 70.00 | 3.50 | .50 |

| RST104 | MnHVF | UseVF | CutCnl |
|---|---|---|---|
| $20    green | 130. | 50.00 | 8.00 |

| RST105 | MnHVF | UseVF | CutCnl |
|---|---|---|---|
| $30    green | 135. | 120. | 25.00 |

| RST106 | MnHVF | UseVF | CutCnl |
|---|---|---|---|
| $50    green | 220. | 135. | 20.00 |

| RST107 | MnHVF | UseVF | CutCnl |
|---|---|---|---|
| $60    green | 400. | 160. | 140. |

| RST108 | MnHVF | UseVF | CutCnl |
|---|---|---|---|
| $100.    green | | 65.00 | 20.00 |

| RST109 | MnHVF | UseVF | CutCnl |
|---|---|---|---|
| $500.    green | 850. | 700. | 550. |

| RST110 | MnHVF | UseVF | CutCnl |
|---|---|---|---|
| $1000.    green | | 800. | 550. |

**1942. STOCK TRANSFER ISSUE** Types of 1940 overprinted "Series 1942" in black. No. RST111-127 perforated 11. No. RST128-133 perforated 12.

| RST111 | MnHVF | UseVF | CutCnl |
|---|---|---|---|
| 1¢    green | .40 | .25 | .20 |

| RST112 | MnHVF | UseVF | CutCnl |
|---|---|---|---|
| 2¢    green | .40 | .25 | .20 |

| RST113 | MnHVF | UseVF | CutCnl |
|---|---|---|---|
| 4¢    green | 2.75 | .80 | .45 |

| RST114 | MnHVF | UseVF | CutCnl |
|---|---|---|---|
| 5¢    green | .35 | .20 | .20 |

| RST115 | MnHVF | UseVF | CutCnl |
|---|---|---|---|
| 10¢    green | 1.50 | .20 | .20 |

| RST116 | MnHVF | UseVF | CutCnl |
|---|---|---|---|
| 20¢    green | 1.75 | .25 | .20 |

| RST117 | MnHVF | UseVF | CutCnl |
|---|---|---|---|
| 25¢    green | 1.75 | .25 | .20 |

| RST118 | MnHVF | UseVF | CutCnl |
|---|---|---|---|
| 40¢    green | 3.50 | .25 | .20 |

| RST119 | MnHVF | UseVF | CutCnl |
|---|---|---|---|
| 50¢    green | 4.50 | .20 | .20 |

| RST120 | MnHVF | UseVF | CutCnl |
|---|---|---|---|
| 80¢    green | 17.50 | 5.00 | 1.00 |

| RST121 | MnHVF | UseVF | CutCnl |
|---|---|---|---|
| $1    green | 11.00 | .30 | .20 |

| RST122 | MnHVF | UseVF | CutCnl |
|---|---|---|---|
| $2    green | 15.00 | .30 | .20 |

| RST123 | MnHVF | UseVF | CutCnl |
|---|---|---|---|
| $3    green | 22.50 | 1.00 | .25 |

| RST124 | MnHVF | UseVF | CutCnl |
|---|---|---|---|
| $4    green | 30.00 | 20.00 | .30 |

| RST125 | MnHVF | UseVF | CutCnl |
|---|---|---|---|
| $5    green | 27.50 | .30 | .20 |

| RST126 | MnHVF | UseVF | CutCnl |
|---|---|---|---|
| $10    green | 55.00 | 7.00 | 1.00 |

| RST127 | MnHVF | UseVF | CutCnl |
|---|---|---|---|
| $20    green | 130. | 30.00 | 4.00 |

| RST128 | MnHVF | UseVF | CutCnl |
|---|---|---|---|
| $30    green | 80.00 | 40.00 | 15.00 |

| RST129 | MnHVF | UseVF | CutCnl |
|---|---|---|---|
| $50    green | 125. | 80.00 | 15.00 |

| RST130 | MnHVF | UseVF | CutCnl |
|---|---|---|---|
| $60    green | | 100. | 40.00 |

| RST131 | MnHVF | UseVF | CutCnl |
|---|---|---|---|
| $100.    green | | 75.00 | 20.00 |

| RST132 | MnHVF | UseVF | CutCnl |
|---|---|---|---|
| $500.    green | | 7000. | 4000. |

| RST133 | MnHVF | UseVF | CutCnl |
|---|---|---|---|
| $1000.    green | | 350. | 175. |

**1943. STOCK TRANSFER ISSUE** Types of 1940 overprinted "Series 1943" in black. No. RST134-150 perforated 11. No. RST151-156 perforated 12.

| RST134 | MnHVF | UseVF | CutCnl |
|---|---|---|---|
| 1¢    green | .40 | .25 | .20 |

| RST135 | MnHVF | UseVF | CutCnl |
|---|---|---|---|
| 2¢    green | .50 | .35 | .20 |

| RST136 | MnHVF | UseVF | CutCnl |
|---|---|---|---|
| 4¢    green | 1.50 | .20 | .20 |

| RST137 | MnHVF | UseVF | CutCnl |
|---|---|---|---|
| 5¢    green | .40 | .20 | .20 |

| RST138 | MnHVF | UseVF | CutCnl |
|---|---|---|---|
| 10¢    green | .85 | .20 | .20 |

| RST139 | MnHVF | UseVF | CutCnl |
|---|---|---|---|
| 20¢    green | 1.50 | .20 | .20 |

| RST140 | MnHVF | UseVF | CutCnl |
|---|---|---|---|
| 25¢    green | 3.25 | .20 | .20 |

| RST141 | MnHVF | UseVF | CutCnl |
|---|---|---|---|
| 40¢    green | 3.25 | .20 | .20 |

| RST142 | MnHVF | UseVF | CutCnl |
|---|---|---|---|
| 50¢    green | 3.25 | .20 | .20 |

| RST143 | MnHVF | UseVF | CutCnl |
|---|---|---|---|
| 80¢    green | 10.00 | 4.00 | 1.25 |

| RST144 | MnHVF | UseVF | CutCnl |
|---|---|---|---|
| $1    green | 10.00 | .20 | .20 |

| RST145 | MnHVF | UseVF | CutCnl |
|---|---|---|---|
| $2    green | 12.50 | .20 | .20 |

| RST146 | MnHVF | UseVF | CutCnl |
|---|---|---|---|
| $3    green | 15.00 | .80 | .20 |

| RST147 | MnHVF | UseVF | CutCnl |
|---|---|---|---|
| $4    green | 30.00 | 12.50 | .75 |

| RST148 | MnHVF | UseVF | CutCnl |
|---|---|---|---|
| $5    green | 45.00 | .25 | .20 |

| RST149 | MnHVF | UseVF | CutCnl |
|---|---|---|---|
| $10    green | 60.00 | 4.00 | .75 |

| RST150 | MnHVF | UseVF | CutCnl |
|---|---|---|---|
| $20    green | 120. | 30.00 | 12.50 |

| RST151 | MnHVF | UseVF | CutCnl |
|---|---|---|---|
| $30    green | 175. | 80.00 | 50.00 |

| RST152 | MnHVF | UseVF | CutCnl |
|---|---|---|---|
| $50    green | 250. | 120. | 22.50 |

| RST153 | MnHVF | UseVF | CutCnl |
|---|---|---|---|
| $60    green | | 275. | 130. |

| RST154 | MnHVF | UseVF | CutCnl |
|---|---|---|---|
| $100.    green | | 50.00 | 17.50 |

| RST155 | MnHVF | UseVF | CutCnl |
|---|---|---|---|
| $500.    green | | 375. | 175. |

| RST156 | MnHVF | UseVF | CutCnl |
|---|---|---|---|
| $1000.    green | | 250. | 150. |

**1944. STOCK TRANSFER ISSUE** Type of 1940 overprinted "Series 1944" in black. No. RST157-173 perforated 11. No. RST174-182 perforated 12.

| RST157 | MnHVF | UseVF | CutCnl |
|---|---|---|---|
| 1¢    green | .60 | .60 | .20 |

| RST158 | MnHVF | UseVF | CutCnl |
|---|---|---|---|
| 2¢    green | .40 | .20 | .20 |

| RST159 | MnHVF | UseVF | CutCnl |
|---|---|---|---|
| 4¢    green | .60 | .20 | .20 |

| RST160 | MnHVF | UseVF | CutCnl |
|---|---|---|---|
| 5¢    green | .50 | .20 | .20 |

| RST161 | MnHVF | UseVF | CutCnl |
|---|---|---|---|
| 10¢    green | .65 | .20 | .20 |

| RST162 | | MnHVF | UseVF | CutCnl |
|---|---|---|---|---|
| 20¢ | green | 1.20 | .20 | .20 |

| RST163 | | MnHVF | UseVF | CutCnl |
|---|---|---|---|---|
| 25¢ | green | 1.75 | .30 | .20 |

| RST165 | | MnHVF | UseVF | CutCnl |
|---|---|---|---|---|
| 50¢ | green | 4.25 | .20 | .20 |

| RST166 | | MnHVF | UseVF | CutCnl |
|---|---|---|---|---|
| 80¢ | green | 7.25 | 4.00 | 1.75 |

| RST167 | | MnHVF | UseVF | CutCnl |
|---|---|---|---|---|
| $1 | green | 7.25 | .30 | .20 |

| RST168 | | MnHVF | UseVF | CutCnl |
|---|---|---|---|---|
| $2 | green | 27.50 | .50 | .20 |

| RST169 | | MnHVF | UseVF | CutCnl |
|---|---|---|---|---|
| $3 | green | 22.50 | 1.20 | .20 |

| RST170 | | MnHVF | UseVF | CutCnl |
|---|---|---|---|---|
| $4 | green | 27.50 | 4.50 | .20 |

| RST171 | | MnHVF | UseVF | CutCnl |
|---|---|---|---|---|
| $5 | green | 25.00 | .80 | .20 |

| RST172 | | MnHVF | UseVF | CutCnl |
|---|---|---|---|---|
| $10 | green | 55.00 | 4.00 | .40 |

| RST173 | | MnHVF | UseVF | CutCnl |
|---|---|---|---|---|
| $20 | green | 90.00 | 7.50 | 3.50 |

| RST174 | | MnHVF | UseVF | CutCnl |
|---|---|---|---|---|
| $30 | green | 110. | 55.00 | 12.50 |

| RST175 | | MnHVF | UseVF | CutCnl |
|---|---|---|---|---|
| $50 | green | 80.00 | 45.00 | 12.50 |

| RST176 | | MnHVF | UseVF | CutCnl |
|---|---|---|---|---|
| $60 | green | 135. | 90.00 | 60.00 |

| RST177 | | MnHVF | UseVF | CutCnl |
|---|---|---|---|---|
| $100. | green | 100. | 45.00 | 20.00 |

| RST178 | | MnHVF | UseVF | CutCnl |
|---|---|---|---|---|
| $500. | green | | 375. | 250. |

| RST179 | | MnHVF | UseVF | CutCnl |
|---|---|---|---|---|
| $1000. | green | | — | 200. |

| RST180 | | MnHVF | UseVF | CutCnl |
|---|---|---|---|---|
| $2500. | green (William Windom) | | — | — |

| RST181 | | MnHVF | UseVF | CutCnl |
|---|---|---|---|---|
| $5000. | green (C. J. Folger) | | — | — |

| RST182 | | MnHVF | UseVF | CutCnl |
|---|---|---|---|---|
| $10000. | green (W. Q. Gresham) | | — | 1100. |

**1945. STOCK TRANSFER ISSUE** Types of 1940 overprinted "Series 1945" in black. No. RST183-199 perforated 11. No. RST200-208 perforated 12.

| RST183 | | MnHVF | UseVF | CutCnl |
|---|---|---|---|---|
| 1¢ | green | .20 | .20 | .20 |

| RST184 | | MnHVF | UseVF | CutCnl |
|---|---|---|---|---|
| 2¢ | green | .25 | .20 | .20 |

| RST185 | | MnHVF | UseVF | CutCnl |
|---|---|---|---|---|
| 4¢ | green | .25 | .20 | .20 |

| RST186 | | MnHVF | UseVF | CutCnl |
|---|---|---|---|---|
| 5¢ | green | .25 | .20 | .20 |

| RST187 | | MnHVF | UseVF | CutCnl |
|---|---|---|---|---|
| 10¢ | green | .70 | .30 | .20 |

| RST188 | | MnHVF | UseVF | CutCnl |
|---|---|---|---|---|
| 20¢ | green | 1.20 | .30 | .20 |

| RST189 | | MnHVF | UseVF | CutCnl |
|---|---|---|---|---|
| 25¢ | green | 1.75 | .30 | .20 |

| RST190 | | MnHVF | UseVF | CutCnl |
|---|---|---|---|---|
| 40¢ | green | 2.75 | .20 | .20 |

| RST191 | | MnHVF | UseVF | CutCnl |
|---|---|---|---|---|
| 50¢ | green | 3.25 | .20 | .20 |

| RST192 | | MnHVF | UseVF | CutCnl |
|---|---|---|---|---|
| 80¢ | green | 6.75 | 2.25 | .60 |

| RST193 | | MnHVF | UseVF | CutCnl |
|---|---|---|---|---|
| $1 | green | 11.50 | .20 | .20 |

| RST194 | | MnHVF | UseVF | CutCnl |
|---|---|---|---|---|
| $2 | green | 15.00 | .40 | .20 |

| RST195 | | MnHVF | UseVF | CutCnl |
|---|---|---|---|---|
| $3 | green | 27.50 | .50 | .20 |

| RST196 | | MnHVF | UseVF | CutCnl |
|---|---|---|---|---|
| $4 | green | 27.50 | 2.25 | .60 |

| RST197 | | MnHVF | UseVF | CutCnl |
|---|---|---|---|---|
| $5 | green | 17.50 | .40 | .20 |

| RST198 | | MnHVF | UseVF | CutCnl |
|---|---|---|---|---|
| $10 | green | 40.00 | 6.00 | .70 |

| RST199 | | MnHVF | UseVF | CutCnl |
|---|---|---|---|---|
| $20 | green | 70.00 | 8.00 | 1.25 |

**1945. STOCK TRANSFER ISSUE** Types of 1940 overprinted "Series 1945" in black. No. RST183-199 perforated 11. No. RST200-208 perforated 12.

| RST200 | | MnHVF | UseVF | CutCnl |
|---|---|---|---|---|
| $30 | green | 80.00 | 40.00 | .70 |

| RST201 | | MnHVF | UseVF | CutCnl |
|---|---|---|---|---|
| $50 | green | 50.00 | 15.00 | 4.00 |

| RST202 | | MnHVF | UseVF | CutCnl |
|---|---|---|---|---|
| $60 | green | 130. | 100. | 40.00 |

| RST203 | | MnHVF | UseVF | CutCnl |
|---|---|---|---|---|
| $100. | green | | 20.50 | 12.50 |

| RST204 | | MnHVF | UseVF | CutCnl |
|---|---|---|---|---|
| $500. | green | | 375. | 200. |

| RST205 | | MnHVF | UseVF | CutCnl |
|---|---|---|---|---|
| $1000. | green | | 450. | 250. |

| RST206 | | MnHVF | UseVF | CutCnl |
|---|---|---|---|---|
| $2500. | green | | — | — |

| RST207 | | MnHVF | UseVF | CutCnl |
|---|---|---|---|---|
| $5000. | green | | — | — |

| RST208 | | MnHVF | UseVF | CutCnl |
|---|---|---|---|---|
| $10000. | green | | — | 1200. |

**1946. STOCK TRANSFER ISSUE** Types of 1940 overprinted "Series 1946" in black. No. RST209-225 perforated 11. No. RST226-234 perforated 12.

| RST209 | | MnHVF | UseVF | CutCnl |
|---|---|---|---|---|
| 1¢ | green | .20 | .20 | .20 |

| RST210 | | MnHVF | UseVF | CutCnl |
|---|---|---|---|---|
| 2¢ | green | .30 | .20 | .20 |

| RST211 | | MnHVF | UseVF | CutCnl |
|---|---|---|---|---|
| 4¢ | green | .30 | .20 | .20 |

| RST212 | | MnHVF | UseVF | CutCnl |
|---|---|---|---|---|
| 5¢ | green | .30 | .20 | .20 |

| RST213 | | MnHVF | UseVF | CutCnl |
|---|---|---|---|---|
| 10¢ | green | .75 | .20 | .20 |

| RST214 | | MnHVF | UseVF | CutCnl |
|---|---|---|---|---|
| 20¢ | green | 1.30 | .20 | .20 |

| RST215 | | MnHVF | UseVF | CutCnl |
|---|---|---|---|---|
| 25¢ | green | 1.30 | .20 | .20 |

| RST216 | | MnHVF | UseVF | CutCnl |
|---|---|---|---|---|
| 40¢ | green | 3.00 | .50 | .20 |

| RST217 | | MnHVF | UseVF | CutCnl |
|---|---|---|---|---|
| 50¢ | green | 4.00 | .20 | .20 |

| RST218 | | MnHVF | UseVF | CutCnl |
|---|---|---|---|---|
| 80¢ | green | 8.50 | 5.50 | 1.75 |

| RST219 | | MnHVF | UseVF | CutCnl |
|---|---|---|---|---|
| $1 | green | 7.50 | .50 | .20 |

| RST220 | | MnHVF | UseVF | CutCnl |
|---|---|---|---|---|
| $2 | green | 7.50 | .40 | .20 |

| RST221 | | MnHVF | UseVF | CutCnl |
|---|---|---|---|---|
| $3 | green | 15.00 | 1.20 | .20 |

| RST222 | | MnHVF | UseVF | CutCnl |
|---|---|---|---|---|
| $4 | green | 15.00 | 5.00 | 1.75 |

| RST223 | | MnHVF | UseVF | CutCnl |
|---|---|---|---|---|
| $5 | green | 22.50 | 1.00 | .20 |

| | | MnHVF | UseVF | CutCnl |
|---|---|---|---|---|
| RST224 | | | | |
| $10 | green | 45.00 | 2.25 | .50 |
| RST225 | | | | |
| $20 | green | 75.00 | 30.00 | 8.50 |
| RST226 | | | | |
| $30 | green | 65.00 | 25.00 | 16.50 |
| RST227 | | | | |
| $50 | green | 50.00 | 30.00 | 10.00 |
| RST228 | | | | |
| $60 | green | 120. | 80.00 | 30.00 |
| RST229 | | | | |
| $100. | green | 75.00 | 30.00 | 15.00 |
| RST230 | | | | |
| $500. | green | | 150. | 90.00 |
| RST231 | | | | |
| $1000. | green | | 135. | 90.00 |
| RST232 | | | | |
| $2500. | green | | | 4500. |
| RST233 | | | | |
| $5000. | green | | | 5000. |
| RST234 | | | | |
| $10000. | green | | | 1800. |

**1947. STOCK TRANSFER ISSUE** Types of 1940 overprinted "Series 1947" in black. No. RST235-251 perforated 11. No. RST252-260 perforated 12.

| | | MnHVF | UseVF | CutCnl |
|---|---|---|---|---|
| RST235 | | | | |
| 1¢ | green | .60 | .50 | .20 |
| RST236 | | | | |
| 2¢ | green | .50 | .40 | .20 |
| RST237 | | | | |
| 4¢ | green | .40 | .30 | .20 |
| RST238 | | | | |
| 5¢ | green | .40 | .30 | .20 |
| RST239 | | | | |
| 10¢ | green | .50 | .40 | .20 |
| RST240 | | | | |
| 20¢ | green | 1.00 | .40 | .20 |
| RST241 | | | | |
| 25¢ | green | 1.60 | .40 | .20 |
| RST242 | | | | |
| 40¢ | green | 2.75 | .60 | .20 |
| RST243 | | | | |
| 50¢ | green | 3.50 | .25 | .20 |
| RST244 | | | | |
| 80¢ | green | 12.50 | 11.00 | 3.50 |
| RST245 | | | | |
| $1 | green | 7.25 | .40 | .20 |
| RST246 | | | | |
| $2 | green | 11.50 | .60 | .20 |
| RST247 | | | | |
| $3 | green | 17.50 | 1.25 | .30 |
| RST248 | | | | |
| $4 | green | 30.00 | 5.00 | 1.00 |
| RST249 | | | | |
| $5 | green | 25.00 | 1.25 | .25 |
| RST250 | | | | |
| $10 | green | 40.00 | 4.50 | 1.50 |
| RST251 | | | | |
| $20 | green | 80.00 | 25.00 | 5.00 |
| RST252 | | | | |
| $30 | green | 55.00 | 30.00 | 7.50 |
| RST253 | | | | |
| $50 | green | 120. | 80.00 | 22.50 |
| RST254 | | | | |
| $60 | green | 140. | 120. | 40.00 |

| | | MnHVF | UseVF | CutCnl |
|---|---|---|---|---|
| RST255 | | | | |
| $100. | green | | 25.00 | 12.50 |
| RST256 | | | | |
| $500. | green | | 225. | 100. |
| RST257 | | | | |
| $1000. | green | | 80.00 | 40.00 |
| RST258 | | | | |
| $2500. | green | | | 250. |
| RST259 | | | | |
| $5000. | green | | | 300. |
| RST260 | | | | |
| $10000. | green | | | 50.00 |

**1948. STOCK TRANSFER ISSUE** Types of 1940 overprinted "Series 1948" in black. Nos. RST261-277 perforated 11. Nos. RST278-286 perforated 12.

| | | MnHVF | UseVF | CutCnl |
|---|---|---|---|---|
| RST261 | | | | |
| 1¢ | green | .25 | .20 | .20 |
| RST262 | | | | |
| 2¢ | green | .25 | .20 | .20 |
| RST263 | | | | |
| 4¢ | green | .30 | .25 | .20 |
| RST264 | | | | |
| 5¢ | green | .20 | .20 | .20 |
| RST265 | | | | |
| 10¢ | green | .30 | .20 | .20 |
| RST266 | | | | |
| 20¢ | green | 1.20 | .30 | .20 |
| RST267 | | | | |
| 25¢ | green | 1.20 | .30 | .20 |
| RST268 | | | | |
| 40¢ | green | 1.65 | .60 | .20 |
| RST269 | | | | |
| 50¢ | green | 4.00 | .35 | .20 |
| RST270 | | | | |
| 80¢ | green | 10.00 | 5.00 | 2.25 |
| RST271 | | | | |
| $1 | green | 7.50 | .40 | .20 |
| RST272 | | | | |
| $2 | green | 10.00 | .50 | .20 |
| RST273 | | | | |
| $3 | green | 12.50 | 3.50 | 1.50 |
| RST274 | | | | |
| $4 | green | 15.00 | 8.00 | 2.25 |
| RST275 | | | | |
| $5 | green | 22.50 | 2.25 | .20 |
| RST276 | | | | |
| $10 | green | 40.00 | 4.00 | .65 |
| RST277 | | | | |
| $20 | green | 70.00 | 17.50 | 6.00 |
| RST278 | | | | |
| $30 | green | 80.00 | 35.00 | 20.00 |
| RST279 | | | | |
| $50 | green | 50.00 | 35.00 | 10.00 |
| RST280 | | | | |
| $60 | green | 135. | 90.00 | 25.00 |
| RST281 | | | | |
| $100. | green | | 17.50 | 6.00 |
| RST282 | | | | |
| $500. | green | | 200. | 100. |
| RST283 | | | | |
| $1000. | green | | 100. | .35 |
| RST284 | | | | |
| $2500. | green | 275. | 250. | 140. |
| RST285 | | | | |
| $5000. | green | | 225. | 150. |
| RST286 | | | | |
| $10000. | green | | | 50.00 |

**1949. Stock Transfer Issue** Types of 1940 overprinted "Series 1949" in black. Nos. RST287-303 perforated 11. Nos. RST304-312 perforated 12.

| Cat. No. | Denom. | Color | MnHVF | UseVF | CutCnl |
|---|---|---|---|---|---|
| RST287 | 1¢ | green | .40 | .35 | .20 |
| RST288 | 2¢ | green | .40 | .35 | .20 |
| RST289 | 4¢ | green | .50 | .40 | .20 |
| RST290 | 5¢ | green | .50 | .40 | .20 |
| RST291 | 10¢ | green | 1.25 | .50 | .20 |
| RST292 | 20¢ | green | 2.00 | .50 | .20 |
| RST293 | 25¢ | green | 2.50 | .75 | .20 |
| RST294 | 40¢ | green | 5.00 | 1.25 | .20 |
| RST295 | 50¢ | green | 5.00 | .20 | .20 |
| RST296 | 80¢ | green | 40.00 | 6.00 | 2.50 |
| RST297 | $1 | green | 9.00 | .60 | .20 |
| RST298 | $2 | green | 12.50 | .75 | .20 |
| RST299 | $3 | green | 30.00 | 4.00 | 1.00 |
| RST300 | $4 | green | 27.50 | 7.00 | 2.00 |
| RST301 | $5 | green | 35.00 | 2.00 | .25 |
| RST302 | $10 | green | 40.00 | 4.00 | 1.25 |
| RST303 | $20 | green | 100. | 12.50 | 5.00 |
| RST304 | $30 | green | | 35.00 | 12.50 |
| RST305 | $50 | green | 130. | 50.00 | 15.50 |
| RST306 | $60 | green | 150. | 130. | 40.00 |
| RST307 | $100. | green | | 50.00 | 22.50 |
| RST308 | $500. | green | | 180. | 60.00 |
| RST309 | $1000. | green | | 75.00 | 35.00 |
| RST310 | $2500. | green | | | 300. |
| RST311 | $5000. | green | | | 300. |
| RST312 | $10000. | green | | 250. | 25.00 |

**1950. Stock Transfer Issue** Types of 1940 overprinted "Series 1950" in black. Nos. RST313-329 perforated 11. Nos. RST330-338 perforated 12.

| Cat. No. | Denom. | Color | MnHVF | UseVF | CutCnl |
|---|---|---|---|---|---|
| RST313 | 1¢ | green | .35 | .30 | .20 |
| RST314 | 2¢ | green | .35 | .25 | .20 |
| RST315 | 4¢ | green | .35 | .30 | .20 |
| RST316 | 5¢ | green | .35 | .20 | .20 |
| RST317 | 10¢ | green | 1.75 | .25 | .20 |
| RST318 | 20¢ | green | 2.50 | .40 | .20 |
| RST319 | 25¢ | green | 3.50 | .50 | .20 |
| RST320 | 40¢ | green | 4.50 | .80 | .20 |
| RST321 | 50¢ | green | 7.00 | .30 | .20 |
| RST322 | 80¢ | green | 9.00 | 5.00 | 2.00 |
| RST323 | $1 | green | 9.00 | .35 | .20 |
| RST324 | $2 | green | 15.00 | .60 | .20 |
| RST325 | $3 | green | 25.00 | 4.00 | .50 |
| RST326 | $4 | green | 30.00 | 6.50 | 2.50 |
| RST327 | $5 | green | 30.00 | 1.50 | .20 |
| RST328 | $10 | green | 75.00 | 4.50 | 1.00 |
| RST329 | $20 | green | 100. | 22.50 | 4.00 |
| RST330 | $30 | green | 75.00 | 40.00 | 20.00 |
| RST331 | $50 | green | 70.00 | 65.00 | 35.00 |
| RST332 | $60 | green | | 100. | 40.00 |
| RST333 | $100. | green | | 32.50 | 20.00 |
| RST334 | $500. | green | | 150. | 100. |
| RST335 | $1000. | green | | 65.00 | 25.00 |
| RST336 | $2500. | green | | 900. | 600. |
| RST337 | $5000. | green | | 500. | 300. |
| RST338 | $10000. | green | | | 50.00 |

**1951. Stock Transfer Issue** Types of 1940 overprinted "Series 1951" in black. Nos. RST339-355 perforated 11. Nos. RST356-364 perforated 12.

| Cat. No. | Denom. | Color | MnHVF | UseVF | CutCnl |
|---|---|---|---|---|---|
| RST339 | 1¢ | green | 1.00 | .30 | 2.00 |
| RST340 | 2¢ | green | 1.00 | .30 | .20 |
| RST341 | 4¢ | green | 1.25 | .40 | .30 |
| RST342 | 5¢ | green | 1.00 | .30 | .20 |
| RST343 | 10¢ | green | 1.25 | .30 | .20 |
| RST344 | 20¢ | green | 3.50 | .75 | .20 |
| RST345 | 25¢ | green | 4.50 | .80 | .20 |
| RST346 | 40¢ | green | 11.00 | 7.50 | 1.50 |
| RST347 | 50¢ | green | 8.00 | .75 | .20 |

| RST348 | | MnHVF | UseVF | CutCnl |
|---|---|---|---|---|
| 80¢ | green | 12.50 | 8.50 | 3.50 |

| RST349 | | MnHVF | UseVF | CutCnl |
|---|---|---|---|---|
| $1 | green | 15.00 | .75 | .20 |

| RST350 | | MnHVF | UseVF | CutCnl |
|---|---|---|---|---|
| $2 | green | 22.50 | 1.00 | .20 |

| RST351 | | MnHVF | UseVF | CutCnl |
|---|---|---|---|---|
| $3 | green | 30.00 | 8.50 | 3.00 |

| RST352 | | MnHVF | UseVF | CutCnl |
|---|---|---|---|---|
| $4 | green | 35.00 | 10.00 | 4.00 |

| RST353 | | MnHVF | UseVF | CutCnl |
|---|---|---|---|---|
| $5 | green | 40.00 | 2.00 | .20 |

| RST354 | | MnHVF | UseVF | CutCnl |
|---|---|---|---|---|
| $10 | green | 75.00 | 8.00 | .20 |

| RST355 | | MnHVF | UseVF | CutCnl |
|---|---|---|---|---|
| $20 | green | 110. | 15.00 | 5.00 |

| RST356 | | MnHVF | UseVF | CutCnl |
|---|---|---|---|---|
| $30 | green | | 40.00 | 20.00 |

| RST357 | | MnHVF | UseVF | CutCnl |
|---|---|---|---|---|
| $50 | green | | 45.00 | 20.00 |

| RST358 | | MnHVF | UseVF | CutCnl |
|---|---|---|---|---|
| $60 | green | | 400. | 200. |

| RST359 | | MnHVF | UseVF | CutCnl |
|---|---|---|---|---|
| $100. | green | | 50.00 | 17.50 |

| RST360 | | MnHVF | UseVF | CutCnl |
|---|---|---|---|---|
| $500. | green | | 125. | 75.00 |

| RST361 | | MnHVF | UseVF | CutCnl |
|---|---|---|---|---|
| $1000. | green | | 70.00 | 60.00 |

| RST362 | | MnHVF | UseVF | CutCnl |
|---|---|---|---|---|
| $2500. | green | | 900. | 400. |

| RST363 | | MnHVF | UseVF | CutCnl |
|---|---|---|---|---|
| $5000. | green | | 900. | 400. |

| RST364 | | MnHVF | UseVF | CutCnl |
|---|---|---|---|---|
| $10000. | green | | 100. | 50.00 |

**1952. STOCK TRANSFER ISSUE** Types of 1940 overprinted "Series 1952" on black. *Perforated 11.*

| RST365 | | MnHVF | UseVF | CutCnl |
|---|---|---|---|---|
| 1¢ | green | 30.00 | 15.00 | 3.00 |

| RST366 | | MnHVF | UseVF | CutCnl |
|---|---|---|---|---|
| 10¢ | green | 30.00 | 15.00 | 3.00 |

| RST367 | | MnHVF | UseVF | CutCnl |
|---|---|---|---|---|
| 20¢ | green | 275. | | |

| RST368 | | MnHVF | UseVF | CutCnl |
|---|---|---|---|---|
| 25¢ | green | 375. | | |

| RST369 | | MnHVF | UseVF | CutCnl |
|---|---|---|---|---|
| 40¢ | green | 70.00 | 20.00 | 8.00 |

| RST370 | | MnHVF | UseVF | CutCnl |
|---|---|---|---|---|
| $4 | green | 650. | 400. | |

| RST371 | | MnHVF | UseVF | CutCnl |
|---|---|---|---|---|
| $10 | green | 1500. | | |

| RST372 | | MnHVF | UseVF | CutCnl |
|---|---|---|---|---|
| $20 | green | 2250. | | |

*Stock transfer stamps were discontinued in 1952.*

| RFD22 | | UnFVF | UseFVF |
|---|---|---|---|
| $100. | pale green | 75.00 | 25.00 |
| | Cut cancellation | 6.00 | .70 |

| RFD23 | | UnFVF | UseFVF |
|---|---|---|---|
| $500. | blue, red numerals | 65.00 | 12.50 |
| | Cut cancellation | 5.00 | 4.00 |

| RFD24 | | UnFVF | UseFVF |
|---|---|---|---|
| $1000. | orange yellow | 65.00 | 5.25 |
| | Cut cancellation | 2.00 | 2.25 |

**1918-34. FUTURE DELIVERY ISSUE** Perforated 11.

| RFD25 | | UnFVF | UseFVF |
|---|---|---|---|
| $1 | green, red overprint ('25) | 25.00 | 1.00 |
| | Cut cancellation | | |

| RFD26 | | UnFVF | UseFVF |
|---|---|---|---|
| $10 | yellow, black overprint | 80.00 | 15.00 |
| | Cut cancellation | | 9.00 |

**1928-29. FUTURE DELIVERY ISSUE** Previous Future Delivery stamps, overprinted as illustrated and perforated 10. The prices given are tentative but are based on actual sales to date. It is possible that other denominations in perforation 10 will be found with this overprint.

| RFD27 | | UnFVF | UseFVF |
|---|---|---|---|
| 10¢ | rose | 1000. | 1000. |

| RFD28 | | UnFVF | UseFVF |
|---|---|---|---|
| 20¢ | rose | 1000. | 1000. |

# Silver Purchase Stamps

The Silver Purchase Act of 1934 placed a 50% tax on net profits realized from the sale of silver bullion.

**1934. SILVER PURCHASE ISSUE** Documentary Stamps of 1917 overprinted. *Under $30.00 perforated 11; over $30.00 perforated 12 and w/o gum.*

| RSP1 | | UnFVF | UseFVF | CutCnl |
|---|---|---|---|---|
| 1¢ | rose | 1.25 | 1.00 | |

| RSP2 | | UnFVF | UseFVF | CutCnl |
|---|---|---|---|---|
| 2¢ | rose | 1.75 | .35 | |

| RSP3 | | UnFVF | UseFVF | CutCnl |
|---|---|---|---|---|
| 3¢ | rose | 1.75 | 1.00 | |

| RSP4 | | UnFVF | UseFVF | CutCnl |
|---|---|---|---|---|
| 4¢ | rose | 2.25 | 1.75 | |

| RSP5 | | UnFVF | UseFVF | CutCnl |
|---|---|---|---|---|
| 5¢ | rose | 3.50 | 1.75 | |

| RSP6 | | UnFVF | UseFVF | CutCnl |
|---|---|---|---|---|
| 8¢ | rose | 4.50 | 3.75 | |

| RSP7 | | UnFVF | UseFVF | CutCnl |
|---|---|---|---|---|
| 10¢ | rose | 5.00 | 2.00 | |

| RSP8 | | UnFVF | UseFVF | CutCnl |
|---|---|---|---|---|
| 20¢ | rose | 7.00 | 3.50 | |

| RSP9 | | UnFVF | UseFVF | CutCnl |
|---|---|---|---|---|
| 25¢ | rose | 7.50 | 4.00 | |

| RSP10 | | UnFVF | UseFVF | CutCnl |
|---|---|---|---|---|
| 40¢ | rose | 7.75 | 5.50 | |

| RSP11 | | UnFVF | UseFVF | CutCnl |
|---|---|---|---|---|
| 50¢ | rose | 7.00 | 6.50 | |

| RSP12 | | UnFVF | UseFVF | CutCnl |
|---|---|---|---|---|
| 80¢ | rose | 14.00 | 9.50 | |

| RSP13 | | UnFVF | UseFVF | CutCnl |
|---|---|---|---|---|
| $1 | yellow green | 22.50 | 11.00 | |

| RSP14 | | UnFVF | UseFVF | CutCnl |
|---|---|---|---|---|
| $2 | rose | 22.50 | 15.00 | |

| RSP15 | | UnFVF | UseFVF | CutCnl |
|---|---|---|---|---|
| $3 | violet | 55.00 | 25.00 | |

| RSP16 | | UnFVF | UseFVF | CutCnl |
|---|---|---|---|---|
| $4 | ochre | 45.00 | 18.00 | |

| RSP17 | | UnFVF | UseFVF | CutCnl |
|---|---|---|---|---|
| $5 | blue | 45.00 | 18.00 | |

| RSP18 | | UnFVF | UseFVF | CutCnl |
|---|---|---|---|---|
| $10 | yellow | 65.00 | 18.00 | |

| RSP19 | | UnFVF | UseFVF | CutCnl |
|---|---|---|---|---|
| $30 | orange | 120. | 50.00 | 20.00 |

| RSP20 | | UnFVF | UseFVF | CutCnl |
|---|---|---|---|---|
| $60 | brown | 125. | 70.00 | 30.00 |

| RSP21 | | UnFVF | UseFVF | CutCnl |
|---|---|---|---|---|
| $100. | pale green | 120. | 30.00 | |

| RSP22 | | UnFVF | UseFVF | CutCnl |
|---|---|---|---|---|
| $500. | blue | 375. | 225. | 100. |

| RSP23 | | UnFVF | UseFVF | CutCnl |
|---|---|---|---|---|
| $1000. | orange yellow | | 110. | 60.00 |
| | cut cancellation | | 32.50 | |

## 1940. DOCUMENTARY STAMPS OF 1940 OVERPRINTED *Double-line USIR watermark (R139), perforated 11.*

RSP24- RSP41 *Series 1940, Silver tax.*

| RSP24 | | MnHVF | UseVF | CutCnl |
|---|---|---|---|---|
| 1¢ | pink | 15.00 | | |

| RSP25 | | MnHVF | UseVF | CutCnl |
|---|---|---|---|---|
| 2¢ | pink | 15.00 | | |

| RSP26 | | MnHVF | UseVF | CutCnl |
|---|---|---|---|---|
| 3¢ | pink | 15.00 | | |

| RSP27 | | MnHVF | UseVF | CutCnl |
|---|---|---|---|---|
| 4¢ | pink | 17.50 | | |

| RSP28 | | MnHVF | UseVF | CutCnl |
|---|---|---|---|---|
| 5¢ | pink | 9.00 | | |

| RSP29 | | MnHVF | UseVF | CutCnl |
|---|---|---|---|---|
| 8¢ | pink | 17.50 | | |

| RSP30 | | MnHVF | UseVF | CutCnl |
|---|---|---|---|---|
| 10¢ | pink | 15.00 | | |

| RSP31 | | MnHVF | UseVF | CutCnl |
|---|---|---|---|---|
| 18¢ | pink | 17.50 | | |

| RSP32 | | MnHVF | UseVF | CutCnl |
|---|---|---|---|---|
| 25¢ | pink | 17.50 | | |

| RSP33 | | MnHVF | UseVF | CutCnl |
|---|---|---|---|---|
| 40¢ | pink | 25.00 | | |

| RSP34 | | MnHVF | UseVF | CutCnl |
|---|---|---|---|---|
| 50¢ | pink | 25.00 | | |

| RSP35 | | MnHVF | UseVF | CutCnl |
|---|---|---|---|---|
| 80¢ | pink | 25.00 | | |

| RSP36 | | MnHVF | UseVF | CutCnl |
|---|---|---|---|---|
| $1 | yellow green | 100. | | |

| RSP37 | | MnHVF | UseVF | CutCnl |
|---|---|---|---|---|
| $2 | rose | 165. | | |

| RSP38 | | MnHVF | UseVF | CutCnl |
|---|---|---|---|---|
| $3 | violet | 220. | | |

| RSP39 | | MnHVF | UseVF | CutCnl |
|---|---|---|---|---|
| $4 | ochre | 400. | | |

| RSP40 | | MnHVF | UseVF | CutCnl |
|---|---|---|---|---|
| $5 | dark blue | 525. | | |

| RSP41 | | MnHVF | UseVF | CutCnl |
|---|---|---|---|---|
| $10 | orange yellow | 575. | | |

## 1940. DOCUMENTARY STAMPS OF 1940 OVERPRINTED Same overprint, hand-stamped. *Perforated 12.*

| RSP41a | | MnHVF | UseVF | CutCnl |
|---|---|---|---|---|
| 80¢ | rose | | | |

| RSP42 | | MnHVF | UseVF | CutCnl |
|---|---|---|---|---|
| $30 | orange | | | |

| RSP43 | | MnHVF | UseVF | CutCnl |
|---|---|---|---|---|
| $60 | brown | | | |

| RSP44 | | MnHVF | UseVF | CutCnl |
|---|---|---|---|---|
| $100. | pale green | | | |

| RSP45 | | MnHVF | UseVF | CutCnl |
|---|---|---|---|---|
| $500. | blue | 175. | 100. | |

| RSP46 | | MnHVF | UseVF | CutCnl |
|---|---|---|---|---|
| $1000. | orange yellow | | 500. | |

## 1941. SILVER TAX ISSUE New designs similar to Stock Transfer Stamps of 1940 but inscribed "Silver Tax". Overprinted "Series 1941" as illustrated. Double-line USIR watermark (R139). *Perforated 11.*

RSP47-RSP58 *Size: 19 x 22mm.*

| RSP47 | | MnHVF | UseVF | CutCnl |
|---|---|---|---|---|
| 1¢ | gray (Alexander Hamilton) | 3.50 | | |

| RSP48 | | MnHVF | UseVF | CutCnl |
|---|---|---|---|---|
| 2¢ | gray (Oliver Wolcott, Jr.) | 3.50 | | |

| RSP49 | | MnHVF | UseVF | CutCnl |
|---|---|---|---|---|
| 3¢ | gray (Samuel Dexter) | 3.50 | | |

| RSP50 | | MnHVF | UseVF | CutCnl |
|---|---|---|---|---|
| 4¢ | gray (Albert Gallatin) | 5.25 | | |

| RSP51 | | MnHVF | UseVF | CutCnl |
|---|---|---|---|---|
| 5¢ | gray (G. W. Campbell) | 6.00 | | |

| RSP52 | | MnHVF | UseVF | CutCnl |
|---|---|---|---|---|
| 8¢ | gray (A. J. Dallas) | 7.00 | | |

| RSP53 | | MnHVF | UseVF | CutCnl |
|---|---|---|---|---|
| 10¢ | gray (Wm. H. Crawford) | 8.00 | | |

| RSP54 | | MnHVF | UseVF | CutCnl |
|---|---|---|---|---|
| 20¢ | gray (Richard Rush) | 12.50 | | |

| RSP55 | | MnHVF | UseVF | CutCnl |
|---|---|---|---|---|
| 25¢ | gray (S. D. Ingham) | 15.00 | | |

| RSP56 | | MnHVF | UseVF | CutCnl |
|---|---|---|---|---|
| 40¢ | gray (Louis McLane) | 25.00 | | |

| RSP57 | | MnHVF | UseVF | CutCnl |
|---|---|---|---|---|
| 50¢ | gray (Wm. J. Duane) | 30.00 | | |

| RSP58 | | MnHVF | UseVF | CutCnl |
|---|---|---|---|---|
| 80¢ | gray (Roger B. Taney) | 55.00 | | |

RSP59-RSP65 *Size: 2 1/2 x 36 1/2mm.*

| RSP59 | | | MnHVF | UseVF | CutCnl |
|---|---|---|---|---|---|
| $1 | gray (Levi Woodbury) | | 65.00 | 30.00 | |

| RSP60 | | | MnHVF | UseVF | CutCnl |
|---|---|---|---|---|---|
| $2 | gray (Thomas Ewing) | | 165. | 55.00 | |

| RSP61 | | | MnHVF | UseVF | CutCnl |
|---|---|---|---|---|---|
| $3 | gray (Walter Forward) | | 135. | 65.00 | |

| RSP62 | | | MnHVF | UseVF | CutCnl |
|---|---|---|---|---|---|
| $4 | gray (J. C. Spencer) | | 190. | 75.00 | |

| RSP63 | | | MnHVF | UseVF | CutCnl |
|---|---|---|---|---|---|
| $5 | gray (G. M. Bibb) | | 165. | 75.00 | |

| RSP64 | | | MnHVF | UseVF | CutCnl |
|---|---|---|---|---|---|
| $10 | gray (R. J. Walker) | | 260. | 95.00 | |

| RSP65 | | | MnHVF | UseVF | CutCnl |
|---|---|---|---|---|---|
| $20 | gray (Wm. M. Meredith) | | 450. | 300. | |

**1941. SILVER TAX ISSUE** *Size 28 1/2 x 42mm, perforated 12 (without gum).*

| RSP66 | | | MnHVF | UseVF | CutCnl |
|---|---|---|---|---|---|
| $30 | gray (Thomas Corwin) | | 250. | 140. | 75.00 |

| RSP67 | | | MnHVF | UseVF | CutCnl |
|---|---|---|---|---|---|
| $50 | gray (James Guthrie) | | | | |

| RSP68 | | | MnHVF | UseVF | CutCnl |
|---|---|---|---|---|---|
| $60 | gray (Howell Cobb) | | | 200. | 100. |

| RSP69 | | | MnHVF | UseVF | CutCnl |
|---|---|---|---|---|---|
| $100. | gray (P. F. Thomas) | | | 300. | 110. |

| RSP70 | | | MnHVF | UseVF | CutCnl |
|---|---|---|---|---|---|
| $500. | gray (J. A. Dix) | | | | |

| RSP71 | | | MnHVF | UseVF | CutCnl |
|---|---|---|---|---|---|
| $1000. | gray (S. P. Chase) | | | | |

**1942. ISSUE** Types of 1941 overprinted "Series 1942" in black. *Perforated 11.*

| RSP72 | | MnHVF | UseVF | CutCnl |
|---|---|---|---|---|
| 1¢ | gray | 2.50 | | |

| RSP73 | | MnHVF | UseVF | CutCnl |
|---|---|---|---|---|
| 2¢ | gray | 2.50 | | |

| RSP74 | | MnHVF | UseVF | CutCnl |
|---|---|---|---|---|
| 3¢ | gray | 2.50 | | |

| RSP75 | | MnHVF | UseVF | CutCnl |
|---|---|---|---|---|
| 4¢ | gray | 2.50 | | |

| RSP76 | | MnHVF | UseVF | CutCnl |
|---|---|---|---|---|
| 5¢ | gray | 2.50 | | |

| RSP77 | | MnHVF | UseVF | CutCnl |
|---|---|---|---|---|
| 8¢ | gray | 5.00 | | |

| RSP78 | | MnHVF | UseVF | CutCnl |
|---|---|---|---|---|
| 10¢ | gray | 5.00 | | |

| RSP79 | | MnHVF | UseVF | CutCnl |
|---|---|---|---|---|
| 20¢ | gray | 8.00 | | |

| RSP80 | | MnHVF | UseVF | CutCnl |
|---|---|---|---|---|
| 25¢ | gray | 17.50 | | |

| RSP81 | | MnHVF | UseVF | CutCnl |
|---|---|---|---|---|
| 40¢ | gray | 20.00 | | |

| RSP82 | | MnHVF | UseVF | CutCnl |
|---|---|---|---|---|
| 50¢ | gray | 20.00 | | |

| RSP83 | | MnHVF | UseVF | CutCnl |
|---|---|---|---|---|
| 80¢ | gray | 55.00 | | |

| RSP84 | | MnHVF | UseVF | CutCnl |
|---|---|---|---|---|
| $1 | gray | 70.00 | | |
| | a. Overprint "Series 5942" | 175. | | |

| RSP85 | | MnHVF | UseVF | CutCnl |
|---|---|---|---|---|
| $2 | gray | 70.00 | | |
| | a. Overprint "Series 5942" | 175. | | |

| RSP86 | | MnHVF | UseVF | CutCnl |
|---|---|---|---|---|
| $3 | gray | 125. | | |
| | a. Overprint "Series 5942" | 175. | | |

| RSP87 | | MnHVF | UseVF | CutCnl |
|---|---|---|---|---|
| $4 | gray | 125. | | |
| | a. Overprint "Series 5942" | 175. | | |

| RSP88 | | | MnHVF | UseVF | CutCnl |
|---|---|---|---|---|---|
| $5 | gray | | 140. | | |
| | a. Overprint "Series 5942" | | 175. | | |

| RSP89 | | | MnHVF | UseVF | CutCnl |
|---|---|---|---|---|---|
| $10 | gray | | 350. | | |

| RSP90 | | | MnHVF | UseVF | CutCnl |
|---|---|---|---|---|---|
| $20 | gray | | 450. | | |
| | a. Overprint "Series 5942" | | 175. | | |

**1944. ISSUE** *Perforated 12 (no gum).*

| RSP91 | | MnHVF | UseVF | CutCnl |
|---|---|---|---|---|
| $30 | gray | | | |

| RSP92 | | MnHVF | UseVF | CutCnl |
|---|---|---|---|---|
| $50 | gray | | | |

| RSP93 | | MnHVF | UseVF | CutCnl |
|---|---|---|---|---|
| $60 | gray | | 150. | |
| | Cut cancellation | 100. | | |

| RSP94 | | MnHVF | UseVF | CutCnl |
|---|---|---|---|---|
| $100. | gray | | | |
| | Cut cancellation | 75.00 | | |

| RSP95 | | MnHVF | UseVF | CutCnl |
|---|---|---|---|---|
| $500. | gray | | | |

| RSP96 | | MnHVF | UseVF | CutCnl |
|---|---|---|---|---|
| $1000. | gray | | | |

**1944. ISSUE** Types of 1941 w/out overprint. *Perforated 11.*

| RSP97 | | MnHVF | UseVF | CutCnl |
|---|---|---|---|---|
| 1¢ | gray | 1.25 | | |

| RSP98 | | MnHVF | UseVF | CutCnl |
|---|---|---|---|---|
| 2¢ | gray | 1.25 | | |

| RSP99 | | MnHVF | UseVF | CutCnl |
|---|---|---|---|---|
| 3¢ | gray | 1.25 | | |

| RSP100 | | MnHVF | UseVF | CutCnl |
|---|---|---|---|---|
| 4¢ | gray | 1.25 | | |

**RSP101**
5¢     gray

| MnHVF | UseVF | CutCnl |
|---|---|---|
| 2.25 | | |

**RSP102**
8¢     gray

| MnHVF | UseVF | CutCnl |
|---|---|---|
| 3.50 | | |

**RSP103**
10¢     gray

| MnHVF | UseVF | CutCnl |
|---|---|---|
| 3.50 | | |

**RSP104**
20¢     gray

| MnHVF | UseVF | CutCnl |
|---|---|---|
| 7.00 | | |

**RSP105**
25¢     gray

| MnHVF | UseVF | CutCnl |
|---|---|---|
| 9.00 | | |

**RSP106**
40¢     gray

| MnHVF | UseVF | CutCnl |
|---|---|---|
| 14.00 | | |

**RSP107**
50¢     gray

| MnHVF | UseVF | CutCnl |
|---|---|---|
| 14.00 | | |

**RSP108**
80¢     gray

| MnHVF | UseVF | CutCnl |
|---|---|---|
| 20.00 | | |

**RSP109**
$1     gray

| MnHVF | UseVF | CutCnl |
|---|---|---|
| 40.00 | 15.00 | |

**RSP110**
$2     gray

| MnHVF | UseVF | CutCnl |
|---|---|---|
| 60.00 | 35.00 | |

**RSP111**
$3     gray

| MnHVF | UseVF | CutCnl |
|---|---|---|
| 65.00 | 25.00 | |

**RSP112**
$4     gray

| MnHVF | UseVF | CutCnl |
|---|---|---|
| 80.00 | 60.00 | |

**RSP113**
$5     gray

| MnHVF | UseVF | CutCnl |
|---|---|---|
| 90.00 | 30.00 | |

**RSP114**
$10     gray

| MnHVF | UseVF | CutCnl |
|---|---|---|
| 125. | 50.00 | 15.00 |

**RSP115**
$20     gray

| MnHVF | UseVF | CutCnl |
|---|---|---|
| 475. | 375. | |

**1944. ISSUE** *Perforated 12 (no gum).*

**RSP116**
$30     gray

| MnHVF | UseVF | CutCnl |
|---|---|---|
| 250. | 125. | 60.00 |

**RSP117**
$50     gray

| MnHVF | UseVF | CutCnl |
|---|---|---|
| 550. | 525. | 300. |

**RSP118**
$60     gray

| MnHVF | UseVF | CutCnl |
|---|---|---|
| | 375. | 175. |

**RSP119**
$100.     gray

| MnHVF | UseVF | CutCnl |
|---|---|---|
| | 35.00 | 15.00 |

**RSP120**
$500.     gray

| MnHVF | UseVF | CutCnl |
|---|---|---|
| | 425. | 250. |

**RSP121**
$1000.     gray

| MnHVF | UseVF | CutCnl |
|---|---|---|
| | 150. | 75.00 |

*Silver Tax Stamps were discontinued on June 4, 1963.*

# Cigarette Tubes Stamps

**1919. ISSUE** Documentary Stamp of 1917 overprinted as "CIGTTE TUBES". *Double-line USIR watermark (R139), perforated 10.*

**RCT1**
1¢     rose

| UnFVF | UseFVF |
|---|---|
| .75 | .25 |

**1919. ISSUE** Same, *perforated 11.*

**RCT2**
1¢     rose

| UnFVF | UseFVF |
|---|---|
| 30.00 | 10.00 |

**1933. ISSUE** Large numerals in center and inscribed "Cigarette Tubes, Series of 1933." Size: 40 x 20 1/2mm. *Double-line USIR watermark (R139), perforated 11.*

**RCT3**
1¢     pale pink

| UnFVF | UseFVF |
|---|---|
| 2.50 | 1.00 |

**RCT4**
2¢     pale pink

| UnFVF | UseFVF |
|---|---|
| 7.50 | 2.00 |

# Potato Stamps

**1935. ISSUE** Portrait of a girl. *Unwatermarked, perforated 11.* Potato Stamps were discontinued January 6, 1936 when the Agricultural Adjustment Act was discontinued.

**RPS1**
3/4¢     rose pink

| UnFVF | UseFVF |
|---|---|
| .30 | |

**RPS2**
1-1/2¢     black brown

| UnFVF | UseFVF |
|---|---|
| .75 | |

**RPS3**
2-1/4¢     yellow green

| UnFVF | UseFVF |
|---|---|
| .75 | |

**RPS4**
3¢     pale violet

| UnFVF | UseFVF |
|---|---|
| .75 | |

**RPS5**
3-3/4¢     olive

| UnFVF | UseFVF |
|---|---|
| .75 | |

**RPS6**
7-1/2¢     orange brown

| UnFVF | UseFVF |
|---|---|
| 1.50 | |

**RPS7**
11-1/4¢     deep orange

| UnFVF | UseFVF |
|---|---|
| 2.00 | |

**RPS8**
18-3/4¢     violet brown

| UnFVF | UseFVF |
|---|---|
| 4.50 | |

**RPS9**
37-1/2¢     orange

| UnFVF | UseFVF |
|---|---|
| 4.50 | |

**RPS10**
75¢     blue

| UnFVF | UseFVF |
|---|---|
| 4.50 | |

**RPS11**
93-3/4¢     lake

| UnFVF | UseFVF |
|---|---|
| 7.50 | |

**RPS12**
$1.12-1/2¢ green

| UnFVF | UseFVF |
|---|---|
| 12.50 | |

**RPS13**
$1.50     brown

| UnFVF | UseFVF |
|---|---|
| 12.50 | |

# Tobacco Sale Tax Stamps

**1934-35. ISSUE** Documentary Stamps of 1917 overprinted "TOBACCO SALE TAX" in two horizontal lines except on $20 value where it is vertical, reading up. Doulbe-line USIR watermark (R139), perforated 11.

**RTS1**
1¢     rose

| UnFVF | UseFVF |
|---|---|
| .40 | .20 |

**RTS2**
2¢     rose

| UnFVF | UseFVF |
|---|---|
| .40 | .20 |

**RTS3**
5¢     rose

| UnFVF | UseFVF |
|---|---|
| 1.00 | .30 |

**RTS4**
10¢     rose

| UnFVF | UseFVF |
|---|---|
| 1.35 | .30 |

| RTS5 | | UnFVF | UseFVF |
|---|---|---|---|
| 25¢ | rose | 4.00 | 1.50 |

| RTS6 | | UnFVF | UseFVF |
|---|---|---|---|
| 50¢ | rose | 4.00 | 1.50 |

| RTS7 | | UnFVF | UseFVF |
|---|---|---|---|
| $1 | green | 8.00 | 1.75 |

| RTS8 | | UnFVF | UseFVF |
|---|---|---|---|
| $2 | rose | 15.00 | 2.00 |

| RTS9 | | UnFVF | UseFVF |
|---|---|---|---|
| $5 | blue | 22.50 | 4.00 |

| RTS10 | | UnFVF | UseFVF |
|---|---|---|---|
| $10 | yellow | 35.00 | 10.00 |

| RTS11 | | UnFVF | UseFVF |
|---|---|---|---|
| $20 | olive | 85.00 | 15.00 |

# Playing Card Stamps

These Revenue Stamps are placed on packaged decks of playing cards. First applied during the War Between the States, this tax is still collected.

**1862-63. PLAY CARD ISSUE** Designs of the first revenue issue, inscribed "PLAYING CARDS." *Unwatermarked, perforated 12.*

RPC2

| RPC1 | | Perf | Part Perf | Imperf |
|---|---|---|---|---|
| 1¢ | rose red | 100. | 600. | 800. |

| RPC2 | | Perf | Part Perf | Imperf |
|---|---|---|---|---|
| 2¢ | light blue | 3.50 | 140. | |

| RPC3 | | Perf | Part Perf | Imperf |
|---|---|---|---|---|
| 2¢ | orange yellow | 30.00 | | |

| RPC4 | | Perf | Part Perf | Imperf |
|---|---|---|---|---|
| 3¢ | dark yellow green | 100. | | |

| RPC5 | | Perf | Part Perf | Imperf |
|---|---|---|---|---|
| 4¢ | gray brown | 375. | | |

| RPC6 | | Perf | Part Perf | Imperf |
|---|---|---|---|---|
| 5¢ | rose red | 15.00 | | |

**1894-96. PLAYING CARD ISSUE** Inscribed "ON HAND," unwatermarked rouletted 5 1/2.

RPC7

| RPC7 | | UnFVF | UseFVF |
|---|---|---|---|
| 2¢ | lake | .60 | .30 |

**1894-96. PLAYING CARD ISSUE** Inscribed "ACT OF" instead of "ON HAND," unwatermarked, rouletted 5 1/2.

| RPC8 | | UnFVF | UseFVF |
|---|---|---|---|
| 2¢ | ultramarine | 12.50 | 2.00 |
| | a. blue | | 3.00 |

**1896-99. PLAYING CARD ISSUE** Same design as No. RPC8, Double-line USIR watermark, rouletted 5 1/2 or 7.

| RPC9 | | UnFVF | UseFVF |
|---|---|---|---|
| 2¢ | pale blue | 4.50 | .40 |
| | a. ultra marine *(RF32)* | 5.00 | 1.20 |

**1902. PLAYING CARD ISSUE** Same design as No. RPC8, perforated 12.

| RPC10 | | UnFVF | UseFVF |
|---|---|---|---|
| 2¢ | dark blue | | 35.00 |

*This stamp was first used in 1902 although it will sometimes be found cancelled 1899 from an old cancelling place.*

**1917. PLAYING CARD ISSUE** Stamp No. RPC9, handstamped in rose. Rouletted 7.

The overprint on No. RPC11 was applied at an Internal Revenue office, those on Nos. RPC12-RPC19 and on No. RPC21 were applied by the manufacturers and, together with the manufacturer's initials, dates, etc., formed a combination of overprint and cancellation.

| RPC11 | | UnFVF | UseFVF |
|---|---|---|---|
| 7¢ on 2¢ ultramarine | | 600. | 400. |

**1917-18. PLAYING CARD ISSUE** Stamp No. RPC9 with various overprints. Rouletted 7.

| RPC12 | | UnFVF | UseFVF |
|---|---|---|---|
| 7¢ on 2¢ blue | | | 35.00 |
| | a. Inverted overprint | | 35.00 |

| RPC13 | | UnFVF | UseFVF |
|---|---|---|---|
| 7¢ on 2¢ blue | | | 500. |
| | a. Inverted overprint | 375. | 375. |

| RPC14 | | UnFVF | UseFVF |
|---|---|---|---|
| 7¢ on 2¢ blue | | | 800. |

| RPC15 | | UnFVF | UseFVF |
|---|---|---|---|
| 7¢ on 2¢ blue | | | 7.50 |
| | a. Overprint reading down | | 9.00 |

*There are many varieties of No. RPC15 such as "double surcharge," "7 omitted" etc. All command premiums.*

| RPC16 | | UnFVF | UseFVF |
|---|---|---|---|
| 7¢ on 2¢ blue | | | 50.00 |
| | a. Inverted overprint | | 30.00 |

**1918-19. PLAYING CARD ISSUE** New Design, inscribed "playing Cards-Class A." Double-line USIR watermark, imperforate. Size 21 x 40mm.

| RPC17 | | UnFVF | UseFVF |
|---|---|---|---|
| 7¢ | pale blue | 40.00 | 27.50 |

**1918-19. PLAYING CARD ISSUE** Same as No. RPC17 but private roulette 14.

| RPC18 | | UnFVF | UseFVF |
|---|---|---|---|
| 7¢ | pale blue | | 200. |

*Both RPC17 and RPC18 served as 7¢ stamps when used before April 1, 1919 and as 8¢ stamps after that date.*

| RPC19 | | UnFVF | UseFVF |
|---|---|---|---|
| 7¢ | pale blue | | 35.00 |
| | a. Inverted overprint | | 30.00 |

**1919. PLAYING CARD ISSUE** Stamp No. RPC9 overprinted with various overprints. Rouletted 7.

| RPC20 | | UnFVF | UseFVF |
|---|---|---|---|
| 8¢ on 2¢ dark blue | | | 75.00 |

| RPC21 | | UnFVF | UseFVF |
|---|---|---|---|
| 8¢ on 2¢ blue (inverted) | | | 500. |

| RPC22 | | UnFVF | UseFVF |
|---|---|---|---|
| 8¢ on 2¢ blue | | 100. | .60 |

**1922. PLAYING CARD ISSUE** Inscribed "Class A". Doubleline USIR watermark, rouletted 7. Size: 19 x 22mm. No denomination but valued at 8¢ .

RPC23

**RPC23**

| | | UnFVF | UseFVF |
|---|---|---|---|
| 8¢ | pale blue | 15.00 | 1.00 |

**1922. PLAYING CARD ISSUE** Stamp No. RPC23 overprinted in carmine, blue or black.

**RPC24**

| | | UnFVF | UseFVF |
|---|---|---|---|
| 8¢ | pale blue | | 30.00 |
| | a. Inverted overprint | | 30.00 |

**1924. PLAYING CARD ISSUE** Flat Plate printing, rouletted 7.

RPC25-RPC28 *Numeral in center of design. Double-line USIR watermark (R139).*

**RPC25**

| | | UnFVF | UseFVF |
|---|---|---|---|
| 10¢ | blue | 10.00 | .30 |

**1926. PLAYING CARD ISSUE** Rotary Press Coil Stamp, perforated 10 vertically.

**RPC26**

| | | UnFVF | UseFVF |
|---|---|---|---|
| 10¢ | blue | | .20 |

**1927. PLAYING CARD ISSUE** Flat Plate printing, perforated 11.

**RPC27**

| | | UnFVF | UseFVF |
|---|---|---|---|
| 10¢ | blue | 20.00 | 4.50 |

**1929. PLAYING CARD ISSUE** Flat Plate printing, perforated 10.

**RPC28**

| | | UnFVF | UseFVF |
|---|---|---|---|
| 10¢ | blue | 10.00 | 3.50 |

**1929. PLAYING CARD ISSUE** Rotary Press Coil stamp, perforated 10 horizontally.

RPC29-RPC31 *Size 37 1/2 x 20mm.*

**RPC29**

| | | UnFVF | UseFVF |
|---|---|---|---|
| 10¢ | light blue | | .20 |

**1929. PLAYING CARD ISSUE** Flat Plate printing, perforated 10.

**RPC30**

| | | UnFVF | UseFVF |
|---|---|---|---|
| 10¢ | blue | 10.00 | 1.00 |

**1929. PLAYING CARD ISSUE** Flat Plate printing, perforated 11.

**RPC31**

| | | UnFVF | UseFVF |
|---|---|---|---|
| 10¢ | blue | 10.00 | 1.00 |

**1940. PLAYING CARD ISSUE** Inscribed "PLAYING CARDS PACK," size 20 x 22 1/2mm, rotary press coil stamp, perforated 10 vertically.

**RPC32**

| | | MNHVF | UseVF |
|---|---|---|---|
| 1 Pack | blue | | .35 |

**1940. PLAYING CARD ISSUE** Rotary Press Coil stamp, perforated 10 horizontally.

**RPC33**

| | | MNHVF | UseVF |
|---|---|---|---|
| 1 Pack | blue | 2.50 | .20 |

**1940. PLAYING CARD ISSUE** Flat Plate printing, perforated 11.

**RPC34**

| | | MNHVF | UseVF |
|---|---|---|---|
| 1 Pack | light blue | 4.50 | .60 |

**1940. PLAYING CARD ISSUE** Rotary Press printing, perforated 10 x 11.

**RPC35**

| | | MNHVF | UseVF |
|---|---|---|---|
| 1 Pack | light blue | 160. | 75.00 |

*The tax on playing cards was repealed effective June 22, 1965.*

# Wine Stamps

**1914. WINE STAMP ISSUE** These stamps were issued to pay the tax on Cordials, Wines and similar liquors. A large white numeral is in the center of the design. Single-line USPS watermark (273), perforated 10. Size of design, 19 1/2 x 22 1/4mm.

RW1-RW14

**RW1**

| | | UnFVF | UseFVF |
|---|---|---|---|
| 1/4¢ | gray green | .50 | .40 |

**RW2**

| | | UnFVF | UseFVF |
|---|---|---|---|
| 1/2¢ | gray green | .30 | .20 |

**RW3**

| | | UnFVF | UseFVF |
|---|---|---|---|
| 1¢ | gray green | .40 | .25 |

**RW4**

| | | UnFVF | UseFVF |
|---|---|---|---|
| 1-1/2¢ | gray green | 2.00 | 1.25 |

**RW5**

| | | UnFVF | UseFVF |
|---|---|---|---|
| 2¢ | gray green | 2.50 | 2.50 |

**RW6**

| | | UnFVF | UseFVF |
|---|---|---|---|
| 3¢ | gray green | 2.50 | 1.00 |

**RW7**

| | | UnFVF | UseFVF |
|---|---|---|---|
| 4¢ | gray green | 2.25 | 1.25 |

**RW8**

| | | UnFVF | UseFVF |
|---|---|---|---|
| 5¢ | gray green | .80 | .40 |

**RW9**

| | | UnFVF | UseFVF |
|---|---|---|---|
| 6¢ | gray green | 6.00 | 3.00 |

**RW10**

| | | UnFVF | UseFVF |
|---|---|---|---|
| 8¢ | gray green | 3.25 | 1.25 |

**RW11**

| | | UnFVF | UseFVF |
|---|---|---|---|
| 10¢ | gray green | 3.25 | 2.50 |

**RW12**

| | | UnFVF | UseFVF |
|---|---|---|---|
| 20¢ | gray green | 4.00 | 1.50 |

**RW13**

| | | UnFVF | UseFVF |
|---|---|---|---|
| 24¢ | gray green | 12.50 | 7.00 |

**RW14**

| | | UnFVF | UseFVF |
|---|---|---|---|
| 40¢ | gray green | 2.50 | .50 |

**1914. WINE STAMP ISSUE** Imperforate, size: 47 x 40mm.

**RW15**

| | | UnFVF | UseFVF |
|---|---|---|---|
| $2 | pale green | 7.00 | .20 |

**1914-18. WINE STAMP ISSUE** Same designs as 1914, double-line USIR watermark (R139), perforated 10.

**RW16**

| | | UnFVF | UseFVF |
|---|---|---|---|
| 1/4¢ | pale green | 5.25 | 4.25 |

**RW17**

| | | UnFVF | UseFVF |
|---|---|---|---|
| 1/2¢ | pale green | 3.50 | 2.50 |

**1941-52. WINE STAMP ISSUE** New design, inscribed "Series of 1941". The values are printed in black. Double-line USIR watermark (R139), size 28 x 25mm, offset printing, rouletted 7. Issued w/o gum.

**RW18**

| | | UnFVF | UseFVF |
|---|---|---|---|
| | pale green | | |

**1914-18. WINE STAMP ISSUE** Same designs as 1914, double-line USIR watermark (R139), perforated 10.

| RW19 | | UnFVF | UseFVF |
|---|---|---|---|
| 1-1/2¢ | pale green | 42.50 | 30.00 |

| RW20 | | UnFVF | UseFVF |
|---|---|---|---|
| 2¢ | pale green | .25 | .20 |

| RW21 | | UnFVF | UseFVF |
|---|---|---|---|
| 3¢ | pale green | 2.25 | 1.50 |

| RW22 | | UnFVF | UseFVF |
|---|---|---|---|
| 4¢ | pale green | .75 | .90 |

| RW23 | | UnFVF | UseFVF |
|---|---|---|---|
| 5¢ | pale green | 10.00 | 9.00 |

| RW24 | | UnFVF | UseFVF |
|---|---|---|---|
| 6¢ | pale green | .40 | .25 |

| RW25 | | UnFVF | UseFVF |
|---|---|---|---|
| 8¢ | pale green | 1.75 | .40 |

| RW26 | | UnFVF | UseFVF |
|---|---|---|---|
| 10¢ | pale green | .40 | .20 |

| RW27 | | UnFVF | UseFVF |
|---|---|---|---|
| 20¢ | pale green | .60 | .30 |

| RW28 | | UnFVF | UseFVF |
|---|---|---|---|
| 24¢ | pale green | 12.50 | .65 |

| RW29 | | UnFVF | UseFVF |
|---|---|---|---|
| 40¢ | pale green | 27.50 | 10.00 |

**1914-18 WINE STAMP ISSUE** Imperforate

| RW30 | | UnFVF | UseFVF |
|---|---|---|---|
| $2 | pale green | 27.50 | 2.75 |

**1914-18. WINE STAMP ISSUE** Perforated 11.

| RW31 | | UnFVF | UseFVF |
|---|---|---|---|
| 2¢ | pale green | 70.00 | 80.00 |

**1916-18. WINE STAMP ISSUE** New design, inscribed "Series of 1916", double-line USIR watermark (R139).

RW32-RW52 *Size 40 x 47mm, offset printing, rouletted 3-1/2.*

| RW32 | | UnFVF | UseFVF |
|---|---|---|---|
| 1¢ | green | .30 | .30 |

| RW33 | | UnFVF | UseFVF |
|---|---|---|---|
| 3¢ | green | 4.25 | 3.75 |

| RW34 | | UnFVF | UseFVF |
|---|---|---|---|
| 4¢ | green | .25 | .25 |

| RW35 | | UnFVF | UseFVF |
|---|---|---|---|
| 6¢ | green | 1.25 | .65 |

| RW36 | | UnFVF | UseFVF |
|---|---|---|---|
| 7-1/2¢ | green | 7.25 | 3.50 |

| RW37 | | UnFVF | UseFVF |
|---|---|---|---|
| 10¢ | green | 1.00 | .35 |

| RW38 | | UnFVF | UseFVF |
|---|---|---|---|
| 12¢ | green | 2.75 | 3.50 |

| RW39 | | UnFVF | UseFVF |
|---|---|---|---|
| 15¢ | green | 1.50 | 1.50 |

| RW40 | | UnFVF | UseFVF |
|---|---|---|---|
| 18¢ | green | 22.50 | 20.00 |

| RW41 | | UnFVF | UseFVF |
|---|---|---|---|
| 20¢ | green | .25 | .25 |

| RW42 | | UnFVF | UseFVF |
|---|---|---|---|
| 24¢ | green | 3.75 | 2.75 |

| RW43 | | UnFVF | UseFVF |
|---|---|---|---|
| 30¢ | green | 3.00 | 2.25 |

| RW44 | | UnFVF | UseFVF |
|---|---|---|---|
| 36¢ | green | 17.50 | 12.50 |

| RW45 | | UnFVF | UseFVF |
|---|---|---|---|
| 50¢ | green | .50 | .40 |

| RW46 | | UnFVF | UseFVF |
|---|---|---|---|
| 60¢ | green | 3.75 | 1.75 |

| RW47 | | UnFVF | UseFVF |
|---|---|---|---|
| 72¢ | green | 30.00 | 25.00 |

| RW48 | | UnFVF | UseFVF |
|---|---|---|---|
| 80¢ | green | .60 | .50 |

| RW49 | | UnFVF | UseFVF |
|---|---|---|---|
| $1.20 | green | 6.50 | 5.50 |

| RW50 | | UnFVF | UseFVF |
|---|---|---|---|
| $1.44 | green | 8.50 | 2.75 |

| RW51 | | UnFVF | UseFVF |
|---|---|---|---|
| $1.60 | green | 22.50 | 15.00 |

| RW52 | | UnFVF | UseFVF |
|---|---|---|---|
| $2 | green | 1.60 | 1.40 |

*RW53-RW55 Flat Plate printing.*

| RW53 | | UnFVF | UseFVF |
|---|---|---|---|
| $4 | green | .80 | .20 |

| RW54 | | UnFVF | UseFVF |
|---|---|---|---|
| $4.80 | green | 3.00 | 2.75 |

| RW55 | | UnFVF | UseFVF |
|---|---|---|---|
| $9.60 | green | 1.10 | .25 |

*RW56-RW59 Size 51 x 81mm, perforated 11 1/2 at left.*

| RW56 | | UnFVF | UseFVF |
|---|---|---|---|
| $20 | green | 80.00 | 35.00 |

| RW57 | | UnFVF | UseFVF |
|---|---|---|---|
| $40 | green | 165. | 45.00 |

| RW58 | | UnFVF | UseFVF |
|---|---|---|---|
| $50 | green | 55.00 | 40.00 |

| RW59 | | UnFVF | UseFVF |
|---|---|---|---|
| $100. | green | 225. | 130. |

**1933-34. WINE STAMP ISSUE** Designs of 1916-18, slightly smaller in size. Offset, double-line USIR watermark (R139), rouletted 7.

| RW60 | | UnFVF | UseFVF |
|---|---|---|---|
| 1¢ | pale green | 2.75 | .25 |

| RW61 | | UnFVF | UseFVF |
|---|---|---|---|
| 3¢ | pale green | 7.00 | 2.25 |

| RW62 | | UnFVF | UseFVF |
|---|---|---|---|
| 4¢ | pale green | 1.25 | .25 |

| RW63 | | UnFVF | UseFVF |
|---|---|---|---|
| 6¢ | pale green | 10.00 | 4.50 |

| RW64 | | UnFVF | UseFVF |
|---|---|---|---|
| 7-1/2¢ | pale green | 2.75 | .40 |

| RW65 | | | UnFVF | UseFVF |
|---|---|---|---|---|
| 10¢ | pale green | | 1.75 | .20 |

| RW66 | | | UnFVF | UseFVF |
|---|---|---|---|---|
| 12¢ | pale green | | 8.00 | 4.00 |

| RW67 | | | UnFVF | UseFVF |
|---|---|---|---|---|
| 15¢ | pale green | | 3.75 | .25 |

| RW68 | | | UnFVF | UseFVF |
|---|---|---|---|---|
| 20¢ | pale green | | 4.50 | .20 |

| RW69 | | | UnFVF | UseFVF |
|---|---|---|---|---|
| 24¢ | pale green | | 4.50 | .20 |

| RW70 | | | UnFVF | UseFVF |
|---|---|---|---|---|
| 30¢ | pale green | | 4.50 | .20 |

| RW71 | | | UnFVF | UseFVF |
|---|---|---|---|---|
| 36¢ | pale green | | 10.00 | .50 |

| RW72 | | | UnFVF | UseFVF |
|---|---|---|---|---|
| 50¢ | pale green | | 4.00 | .20 |

| RW73 | | | UnFVF | UseFVF |
|---|---|---|---|---|
| 60¢ | | | 7.00 | .20 |

| RW74 | | | UnFVF | UseFVF |
|---|---|---|---|---|
| 72¢ | | | 12.00 | .25 |

| RW75 | | | UnFVF | UseFVF |
|---|---|---|---|---|
| 80¢ | pale green | | 12.00 | .20 |

| RW76 | | | UnFVF | UseFVF |
|---|---|---|---|---|
| $1.20 | pale green | | 9.00 | 1.25 |

| RW77 | | | UnFVF | UseFVF |
|---|---|---|---|---|
| $1.44 | pale green | | 12.00 | 3.50 |

| RW78 | | | UnFVF | UseFVF |
|---|---|---|---|---|
| $1.60 | pale green | | 300. | 150. |

| RW79 | | | UnFVF | UseFVF |
|---|---|---|---|---|
| $2 | pale green | | 32.50 | 3.50 |

**1933-34. WINE STAMP ISSUE** *Flat Plate printing.*

| RW80 | | | UnFVF | UseFVF |
|---|---|---|---|---|
| $4 | pale green | | 27.50 | 6.50 |

| RW81 | | | UnFVF | UseFVF |
|---|---|---|---|---|
| $4.80 | pale green | | 27.50 | 12.50 |

| RW82 | | | UnFVF | UseFVF |
|---|---|---|---|---|
| $9.60 | pale green | | 125. | 75.00 |

**1934-40. WINE STAMP ISSUE** New designs inscribed "Series of 1934", double-line USIR watermark (R139). Size 28 x 25mm, offset, rouletted 7. gum.

RW83-RW102

| RW83 | | | UnFVF | UseFVF |
|---|---|---|---|---|
| 1/5¢ | pale green | | .70 | .20 |

| RW84 | | | UnFVF | UseFVF |
|---|---|---|---|---|
| 1/2¢ | pale green | | .50 | .35 |

| RW85 | | | UnFVF | UseFVF |
|---|---|---|---|---|
| 1¢ | pale green | | .60 | .20 |

| RW86 | | | UnFVF | UseFVF |
|---|---|---|---|---|
| 1-1/4¢ | pale green | | .80 | .70 |

| RW87 | | | UnFVF | UseFVF |
|---|---|---|---|---|
| 1-1/2¢ | pale green | | 5.50 | 5.00 |

| RW88 | | | UnFVF | UseFVF |
|---|---|---|---|---|
| 2¢ | pale green | | 1.50 | .60 |

| RW89 | | | UnFVF | UseFVF |
|---|---|---|---|---|
| 2-1/2¢ | pale green | | 1.50 | .40 |

| RW90 | | | UnFVF | UseFVF |
|---|---|---|---|---|
| 3¢ | pale green | | 4.50 | 3.75 |

| RW91 | | | UnFVF | UseFVF |
|---|---|---|---|---|
| 4¢ | pale green | | 2.25 | .20 |

| RW92 | | | UnFVF | UseFVF |
|---|---|---|---|---|
| 5¢ | pale green | | .55 | .20 |

| RW93 | | | UnFVF | UseFVF |
|---|---|---|---|---|
| 6¢ | pale green | | 1.65 | .45 |

| RW94 | | | UnFVF | UseFVF |
|---|---|---|---|---|
| 7-1/2¢ | pale green | | 2.00 | .20 |

| RW95 | | | UnFVF | UseFVF |
|---|---|---|---|---|
| 10¢ | pale green | | .40 | .20 |

| RW96 | | | UnFVF | UseFVF |
|---|---|---|---|---|
| 12¢ | pale green | | 1.30 | .20 |

| RW97 | | | UnFVF | UseFVF |
|---|---|---|---|---|
| 14-2/5¢ | pale green | | 125. | 2.75 |

| RW98 | | | UnFVF | UseFVF |
|---|---|---|---|---|
| 15¢ | pale green | | .60 | .20 |

| RW99 | | | UnFVF | UseFVF |
|---|---|---|---|---|
| 18¢ | pale green | | 1.25 | .20 |

| RW100 | | | UnFVF | UseFVF |
|---|---|---|---|---|
| 20¢ | pale green | | 1.00 | .20 |

| RW101 | | | UnFVF | UseFVF |
|---|---|---|---|---|
| 24¢ | pale green | | 1.75 | .20 |

| RW102 | | | UnFVF | UseFVF |
|---|---|---|---|---|
| 30¢ | pale green | | 1.25 | .20 |

*RW103-RW109 Inscribed "Series of 1934." Size about 39 x 46mm, rouletted 7 issued without gum.*

| RW103 | | | UnFVF | UseFVF |
|---|---|---|---|---|
| 40¢ | pale green | | 3.00 | .20 |

| RW104 | | | UnFVF | UseFVF |
|---|---|---|---|---|
| 43-1/5¢ | pale green | | 12.50 | 1.75 |

| RW105 | | | UnFVF | UseFVF |
|---|---|---|---|---|
| 48¢ | pale green | | 12.50 | 1.00 |

| RW106 | | | UnFVF | UseFVF |
|---|---|---|---|---|
| $1 | pale green | | 15.00 | 10.00 |

| RW107 | | | UnFVF | UseFVF |
|---|---|---|---|---|
| $1.50 | pale green | | 27.50 | 12.50 |

**1934-40. WINE STAMP ISSUE** *Intaglio, flat Plate printing, size: 30 x 46mm. Perforated initial cancelled are worth half used price.*

| RW108 | | | UnFVF | UseFVF |
|---|---|---|---|---|
| $2.50 | pale green | | 30.00 | 15.00 |

| RW109 | | | UnFVF | UseFVF |
|---|---|---|---|---|
| $5 | pale green | | 25.00 | 7.00 |

**1934-40. WINE STAMP ISSUE** *Size 51 x 81mm, Flat Plate printing, perforated 11 1/2 at left.*

| RW110 | | | UnFVF | UseFVF |
|---|---|---|---|---|
| $20 | yellow green | | — | 1500. |

| RW111 | | | UnFVF | UseFVF |
|---|---|---|---|---|
| $40 | yellow green | | — | 3000. |

| RW112 | | | UnFVF | UseFVF |
|---|---|---|---|---|
| $50 | yellow green | | — | 1500. |

| RW113 | | | UnFVF | UseFVF |
|---|---|---|---|---|
| $100. | yellow green | | 950. | 350. |

**1941-52. WINE STAMP ISSUE** New design, inscribed "Series of 1941". The values are printed in black. Double-line USIR watermark (R139), size 28 x 25mm, offset printing, rouletted 7. Issued w/o gum.

RW114-RW165 *Size 28 x 25mm, offset printing.*

| RW114 | | MNHVF | UseVF |
|---|---|---|---|
| 1/5¢ | blue green | .50 | .40 |

| RW115 | | MNHVF | UseVF |
|---|---|---|---|
| 1/4¢ | blue green | 1.75 | 1.50 |

| RW116 | | MNHVF | UseVF |
|---|---|---|---|
| 1/2¢ | blue green | 2.25 | 1.75 |

| RW117 | | MNHVF | UseVF |
|---|---|---|---|
| 1¢ | blue green | 1.00 | .65 |

| RW117A | | MNHVF | UseVF |
|---|---|---|---|
| 1-7/10¢ | blue green | | |

| RW119 | | MNHVF | UseVF |
|---|---|---|---|
| 2¢ | blue green | 4.50 | 4.50 |

| RW120 | | MNHVF | UseVF |
|---|---|---|---|
| 3¢ | blue green | 4.50 | 4.50 |

| RW121 | | MNHVF | UseVF |
|---|---|---|---|
| 3-2/5¢ | blue green | 50.00 | 45.00 |

| RW121A | | MNHVF | UseVF |
|---|---|---|---|
| 3-1/2¢ | blue green | — | 5750. |

| RW122 | | MNHVF | UseVF |
|---|---|---|---|
| 3-3/4¢ | blue green | 7.50 | 5.50 |

| RW123 | | MNHVF | UseVF |
|---|---|---|---|
| 4¢ | blue green | 3.25 | 2.75 |

| RW124 | | MNHVF | UseVF |
|---|---|---|---|
| 5¢ | blue green | 2.25 | 2.00 |

| RW125 | | MNHVF | UseVF |
|---|---|---|---|
| 6¢ | blue green | 2.75 | 2.25 |

| RW127 | | MNHVF | UseVF |
|---|---|---|---|
| 7¢ | blue green | 5.25 | 4.25 |

| RW128 | | MNHVF | UseVF |
|---|---|---|---|
| 7-1/2¢ | blue green | 7.50 | 4.50 |

| RW129 | | MNHVF | UseVF |
|---|---|---|---|
| 8¢ | blue green | 4.50 | 3.50 |

| RW130 | | MNHVF | UseVF |
|---|---|---|---|
| 8-1/2¢ | blue green | 27.50 | 17.50 |

| RW131 | | MNHVF | UseVF |
|---|---|---|---|
| 9¢ | blue green | 8.00 | 7.50 |

| RW132 | | MNHVF | UseVF |
|---|---|---|---|
| 10¢ | blue green | 4.25 | .75 |

| RW134 | | MNHVF | UseVF |
|---|---|---|---|
| 11-1/4¢ | blue green | 4.50 | 4.50 |

| RW135 | | MNHVF | UseVF |
|---|---|---|---|
| 12¢ | blue green | 6.50 | 5.50 |

| RW136 | | MNHVF | UseVF |
|---|---|---|---|
| 13-2/5¢ | blue green | 90.00 | 75.00 |

| RW137 | | MNHVF | UseVF |
|---|---|---|---|
| 14¢ | blue green | 22.50 | 20.00 |

| RW138 | | MNHVF | UseVF |
|---|---|---|---|
| 15¢ | blue green | 4.50 | 3.50 |

| RW139 | | MNHVF | UseVF |
|---|---|---|---|
| 16¢ | blue green | 8.50 | 6.50 |

| RW140 | | MNHVF | UseVF |
|---|---|---|---|
| 17¢ | blue green | 15.00 | 12.50 |

| RW141 | | MNHVF | UseVF |
|---|---|---|---|
| 19-1/5¢ | blue green | 125. | 6.50 |

| RW142 | | MNHVF | UseVF |
|---|---|---|---|
| 20¢ | blue green | 5.50 | 1.50 |

| RW143 | | MNHVF | UseVF |
|---|---|---|---|
| 20-2/5¢ | blue green | 100. | 50.00 |

| RW144 | | MNHVF | UseVF |
|---|---|---|---|
| 24¢ | blue green | 3.75 | .20 |

| RW145 | | MNHVF | UseVF |
|---|---|---|---|
| 28¢ | blue green | 1500. | 950. |

| RW146 | | MNHVF | UseVF |
|---|---|---|---|
| 30¢ | blue green | 1.00 | .20 |

| RW147 | | MNHVF | UseVF |
|---|---|---|---|
| 32¢ | blue green | 125. | 7.00 |

| RW148 | | MNHVF | UseVF |
|---|---|---|---|
| 33-1/2¢ | blue green | 80.00 | 65.00 |

| RW149 | | MNHVF | UseVF |
|---|---|---|---|
| 36¢ | blue green | 2.75 | .20 |

| RW150 | | MNHVF | UseVF |
|---|---|---|---|
| 38-1/4¢ | blue green | 110. | 80.00 |

| RW151 | | MNHVF | UseVF |
|---|---|---|---|
| 40¢ | blue green | 2.25 | .20 |

| RW152 | | MNHVF | UseVF |
|---|---|---|---|
| 40-4/5¢ | blue green | 3.25 | .50 |

| RW153 | | MNHVF | UseVF |
|---|---|---|---|
| 45¢ | blue green | 5.00 | .20 |

| RW154 | | MNHVF | UseVF |
|---|---|---|---|
| 48¢ | blue green | 12.50 | 5.00 |

| RW155 | | MNHVF | UseVF |
|---|---|---|---|
| 50¢ | blue green | 8.00 | 6.50 |

| RW156 | | MNHVF | UseVF |
|---|---|---|---|
| 51¢ | blue green | 3.75 | 1.00 |

| RW157 | | MNHVF | UseVF |
|---|---|---|---|
| 60¢ | blue green | 3.00 | .20 |

| RW158 | | MNHVF | UseVF |
|---|---|---|---|
| 67¢ | blue green | 10.00 | 3.50 |

| RW159 | | MNHVF | UseVF |
|---|---|---|---|
| 68¢ | blue green | 3.00 | .50 |

| RW160 | | MNHVF | UseVF |
|---|---|---|---|
| 72¢ | blue green | 9.00 | .80 |

| RW161 | | MNHVF | UseVF |
|---|---|---|---|
| 80¢ | blue green | 250. | 9.00 |

| RW162 | | MNHVF | UseVF |
|---|---|---|---|
| 80-2/5¢ | blue green | 110. | 85.00 |

| RW163 | | MNHVF | UseVF |
|---|---|---|---|
| 84¢ | blue green | — | 55.00 |

| RW164 | | MNHVF | UseVF |
|---|---|---|---|
| 90¢ | blue green | 15.00 | .20 |

| RW165 | | MNHVF | UseVF |
|---|---|---|---|
| 96¢ | blue green | 10.00 | .20 |

*RW166-RW209 Size 39 x 45 1/2mm. Engraved rouletted 7.*

| RW167 | | MNHVF | UseVF |
|---|---|---|---|
| $1.20 | blue green | 2.75 | .15 |

| RW168 | | MNHVF | UseVF |
|---|---|---|---|
| $1.44 | blue green | 1.00 | .15 |

| RW169 | | MNHVF | UseVF |
|---|---|---|---|
| $1.50 | blue green | 60.00 | 30.00 |

| RW170 | | MNHVF | UseVF |
|---|---|---|---|
| $1.50-3/4 | blue green | 45.00 | 35.00 |

| RW171 | | MNHVF | UseVF |
|---|---|---|---|
| $1.60 | blue green | 5.00 | .65 |

| RW172 | | MNHVF | UseVF |
|---|---|---|---|
| $1.60-4/5 | blue green | 4.00 | .50 |
| | Numeral 2 1/2mm inch, 4 less slanted. | 4.00 | 1.75 |
| | v. Error "Dolllar" | 35.00 | 18.00 |
| | Numeral perforated, initials | | 10.00 |

| RW173 | | MNHVF | UseVF |
|---|---|---|---|
| $1.60-4/5 | blue green | 27.50 | 5.50 |

**1941-51. WINE STAMP ISSUE** Denomination 28 1/2mm long.

| RW174 | | MNHVF | UseVF |
|---|---|---|---|
| $1.68 | blue green | 85.00 | 45.00 |
| | Perforated initials | | 32.50 |

| | | MNHVF | UseVF |
|---|---|---|---|
| **RW175** | | | |
| $1.80 | **blue green** | 2.75 | .20 |
| **RW176** | | MNHVF | UseVF |
| **$1.88-3/10blue green** | | 200. | 65.00 |
| | Perforated initials | | 30.00 |
| **RW177** | | MNHVF | UseVF |
| $1.92 | **blue green** | 45.00 | 35.00 |
| **RW179** | | MNHVF | UseVF |
| $2.01 | **blue green** | 3.25 | .60 |
| **RW180** | | MNHVF | UseVF |
| $2.40 | **blue green** | 8.00 | .75 |
| **RW181** | | MNHVF | UseVF |
| $2.68 | **blue green** | 3.25 | 1.10 |
| **RW182** | | MNHVF | UseVF |
| $3 | **blue green** | 65.00 | 35.00 |
| **RW183** | | MNHVF | UseVF |
| $3.36 | **blue green** | 70.00 | 25.00 |
| **RW184** | | MNHVF | UseVF |
| $3.60 | **blue green** | 125. | 5.50 |
| **RW185** | | MNHVF | UseVF |
| $4 | **blue green** | 27.50 | 4.50 |
| **RW186** | | MNHVF | UseVF |
| $4.08 | **blue green** | 60.00 | 30.00 |
| **RW187** | | MNHVF | UseVF |
| $4.80 | **blue green** | 115. | 2.50 |
| **RW188** | | MNHVF | UseVF |
| $5 | **blue green** | 12.50 | 8.50 |
| **RW189** | | MNHVF | UseVF |
| $5.76 | **blue green** | 210. | 100. |
| **RW193** | | MNHVF | UseVF |
| $7.20 | **blue green** | 18.00 | .40 |
| **RW195** | | MNHVF | UseVF |
| $8.16 | **blue green** | 15.00 | 6.00 |
| **RW195A** | | MNHVF | UseVF |
| $9.60 | **blue green** | — | 2250. |
| **RW196** | | MNHVF | UseVF |
| $10 | **blue green** | 175. | 135. |
| **RW197** | | MNHVF | UseVF |
| $20 | **blue green** | 100. | 65.00 |
| **RW198** | | MNHVF | UseVF |
| $50 | **blue green** | 100. | 65.00 |
| | Perforated initials | | 17.50 |
| **RW199** | | MNHVF | UseVF |
| $100. | **blue green** | 275. | 27.50 |
| | Perforated initials | | 11.50 |
| **RW200** | | MNHVF | UseVF |
| $200. | **blue green** | 135. | 17.50 |
| | Perforated initials | | 7.50 |
| **RW200A** | | MNHVF | UseVF |
| $300. | **blue green** | | — |
| **RW200B** | | MNHVF | UseVF |
| $400. | **blue green** | | 4250. |
| **RW201** | | MNHVF | UseVF |
| $500. | **blue green** | | 135. |
| | Perforated initials | | 30.00 |

| | | MNHVF | UseVF |
|---|---|---|---|
| **RW202** | | | |
| $600. | **blue green** | | 110. |
| | Perforated | | |
| **RW202A** | | MNHVF | UseVF |
| $700. | **blue green** | | — |
| **RW202B** | | MNHVF | UseVF |
| $800. | **blue green** | | — |
| **RW203** | | MNHVF | UseVF |
| $900. | **blue green** | | 2700. |
| | Perforated initials | | 1250. |
| **RW204** | | MNHVF | UseVF |
| $1000. | **blue green** | | 150. |
| **RW205** | | MNHVF | UseVF |
| $2000. | **blue green** | | 900. |
| **RW206** | | MNHVF | UseVF |
| $3000. | **blue green** | | 180. |
| **RW207** | | MNHVF | UseVF |
| $4000. | **blue green** | | 700. |

**1941-51. WINE STAMP ISSUE** *Denominations spelled out in one line.*

| | | MNHVF | UseVF |
|---|---|---|---|
| **RW208** | | | |
| $1 | **blue green** | 3.50 | 1.25 |
| **RW209** | | MNHVF | UseVF |
| $2 | **blue green** | 6.00 | 1.75 |
| **RW210** | | MNHVF | UseVF |
| $4 | **blue green** | 800. | 350. |
| | Perforated initials | | 150. |
| **RW211** | | MNHVF | UseVF |
| $5 | **blue green** | | 75.00 |
| **RW212** | | MNHVF | UseVF |
| $6 | **blue green** | | 350. |
| **RW213** | | MNHVF | UseVF |
| $7 | **blue green** | 40.00 | 60.00 |
| **RW214** | | MNHVF | UseVF |
| $8 | **blue green** | 300. | 800. |
| **RW215** | | MNHVF | UseVF |
| $10 | **blue green** | 8.50 | 4.00 |
| | Perforated initials | | 1.75 |
| **RW215A** | | MNHVF | UseVF |
| $12 | **blue green** | — | — |
| **RW216** | | MNHVF | UseVF |
| $20 | **blue green** | 17.50 | 3.50 |
| | Perforated initials | | 1.50 |
| **RW217** | | MNHVF | UseVF |
| $30 | **blue green** | 900. | 700. |
| **RW218** | | MNHVF | UseVF |
| $40 | **blue green** | — | — |
| **RW219** | | MNHVF | UseVF |
| $60 | **blue green** | — | — |
| **RW220** | | MNHVF | UseVF |
| $70 | **blue green** | — | — |

*Wine stamps were discontinued Jan. 1, 1955.*

# Migratory Bird Hunting Permit

An act of Congress in March 1934 authorized the issue of receipts in the form of attractive stamps to license hunters, with the proceeds going to maintain waterfowl life in the United States. When J.N. Darling, a well known cartoonist and artist, also Pulitzer Prize winner, designed the first "duck" stamp, the beauty and novelty of it immediately appealed to stamp collectors, and the desire to own one became widespread.

The government was adamant, the stamp was for hunters only and it had to be attached to a license. The hunter had to keep it intact for a whole year; it was not for collectors, but the pressure became too great to refuse, so that 15 days before the first duck stamp issue expired, the stamps were placed on sale for stamp collectors, and ever since philatelists have happily contributed "to the maintenance of waterfowl in the United States."

Designed by some of the finest artists, stamps of great beauty have resulted, and no page in a stamp album can be more beautiful than the Duck Stamp Page. All the stamps are inscribed "Migratory Bird Hunting Stamp," the first five read "Department of Agriculture," and after that "Department of the Interior." From 1946 on, all the stamps are inscribed on the back "It is unlawful to hunt waterfowl unless you sign your name in ink on the face of the stamp."

Since a stamp is issued on July 1 of every year, and expires on June 30 of the following year, we list a two-year date for each. The first date is the year of issuance, and the second the year of expiration. Each stamp reads "Void after June 30th 19-," with the dashes being the year of expiration. Stamps are *unwatermarked*.

Note: Plate blocks must have selvage on two sides.
Issued in pane of 28.

## 1934. MALLARD ISSUE designed by J. N. Darling. *Intaglio, unwatermarked, perforated 11.*

RH1

| RH1 | | UnFVF | UseFVF |
|---|---|---|---|
| $1 | blue | 575. | 115. |
| | Plate block of 6 | 10000. | |
| | v. Vertical pair, imperforate | 20000. | |
| | vl. Vertical pair, imperforate horizontally | 20000. | |

## 1935. CANVASBACK DUCK ISSUE by Frank W. Benson. *Intaglio, unwatermarked, perforated 11.*

RH2

| RH2 | | UnFVF | UseFVF |
|---|---|---|---|
| $1 | crimson | 525. | 135. |
| | Plate block of 6 | 9000. | |

## 1936. CANADA GEESE ISSUE by Richard E. Bishop. *Intaglio, unwatermrked, perforated 11.*

RH3

| RH3 | | UnFVF | UseFVF |
|---|---|---|---|
| $1 | brown black | 300. | 65.00 |
| | Plate block of 6 | 2500. | |

## 1937. SCAUP DUCKS ISSUE by J. D. Knap. *Intaglio, unwatermarked, perforated 11.*

RH4

| RH4 | | UnFVF | UseFVF |
|---|---|---|---|
| $1 | dull green | 250. | 45.00 |
| | Plate block of 6 | 2250. | |

## 1938. PINTAIL DUCK ISSUE by Roland Clark. *Intaglio, unwatermarked, perforated 11.*

RH5

| RH5 | | UnFVF | UseFVF |
|---|---|---|---|
| $1 | violet | 250. | 45.00 |
| | Plate block of 6 | 2750. | |

## 1939. GREEN-WINGED TEAL ISSUE by Lynn B. Hunt. *Intaglio, unwatermarked, perforated 11.*

RH6

| RH6 | | UnFVF | UseFVF |
|---|---|---|---|
| $1 | sepia | 140. | 40.00 |
| | Plate block of 6 | 1500. | |

## 1940. BLACK MALLARD ISSUE by Francis L. Jacques. *Intaglio, unwatermarked, perforated 11.*

RH7

**RH7**
**$1**     **black brown**
Plate block of 6

| | MNHVF | UseVF |
|---|---|---|
| | 140. | 40.00 |
| | 1200. | |

### 1941. Ruddy Ducks Issue by E. R. Kalmbach. *Intaglio, unwatermarked, perforated 11.*

RH8

**RH8**
**$1**     **red brown**
Plate block of 6

| | MNHVF | UseVF |
|---|---|---|
| | 140. | 35.00 |
| | 1200. | |

### 1942. Baldpates Issue by A. Lassell Ripley. *Intaglio, unwatermarked, perforated 11.*

RH9

**RH9**
**$1**     **sepia**
Plate block of 6

| | MNHVF | UseVF |
|---|---|---|
| | 140. | 35.00 |
| | 1200. | |

### 1943. Wood Duck Issue by Walter E. Bohl. *Intaglio, unwatermarked, perforated 11.*

RH10

**RH10**
**$1**     **carmine red**
Plate block of 6

| | MNHVF | UseVF |
|---|---|---|
| | 60.00 | 35.00 |
| | 450. | |

### 1944. White-Fronted Geese Issue by Walter A. Weber. *Intaglio, unwatermarked, perforated 11.*

RH11

**RH11**
**$1**     **red orange**
Plate block of 6

| | MNHVF | UseVF |
|---|---|---|
| | 60.00 | 25.00 |
| | 450. | |

### 1945. Shoveller Ducks Issue by Owen J. Gromme. *Intaglio, unwatermarked, perforated 11.*

RH12

**RH12**
**$1**     **black**
Plate block of 6

| | MNHVF | UseVF |
|---|---|---|
| | 45.00 | 18.00 |
| | 350. | |

### 1946. Redhead Ducks Issue by Robert W. Hines. *Intaglio, unwatermarked, perforated 11.*

RH13

**RH13**
**$1**     **chestnut brown**
Plate block of 6
a.  rose red

| | MNHVF | UseVF |
|---|---|---|
| | 35.00 | 13.50 |
| | 300. | |
| | | — |

### 1947. Snow Geese Issue by Jack Murray. *Intaglio, unwatermarked, perforated 11.*

RH14

**RH14**
**$1**     **black**
Plate block of 6

| | MNHVF | UseVF |
|---|---|---|
| | 35.00 | 13.50 |
| | 300. | |

### 1948. Bufflehead Ducks Issue by Maynard Reece. *Intaglio, unwatermarked, perforated 11.*

RH15

**RH15**
**$1**     **light blue**
Plate block of 6

| | MNHVF | UseVF |
|---|---|---|
| | 45.00 | 13.50 |
| | 300. | |

### 1949. Goldeneye Ducks Issue by "Roge" E. Preuss. *Intaglio, unwatermarked, perforated 11.*

RH16

**RH16**　　　　　　　　　　　　　　　　　　MNHVF　UseVF
$2　　　**emerald**　　　　　　　　　　　　50.00　13.50
　　　　Plate block of 6　　　　　　　　350.

**1950. TRUMPETER SWANS ISSUE** by Walter A. Weber. *Intaglio, unwatermarked, perforated 11.*

RH17

**RH17**　　　　　　　　　　　　　　　　　　MNHVF　UseVF
$2　　　**violet**　　　　　　　　　　　　　60.00　10.00
　　　　Plate block of 6　　　　　　　　400.

**1951. GADWALL DUCKS ISSUE** Maynard Reece. *Intaglio, unwatermarked, perforated 11.*

RH18

**RH18**　　　　　　　　　　　　　　　　　　MNHVF　UseVF
$2　　　**gray black**　　　　　　　　　　60.00　10.00
　　　　Plate block of 6　　　　　　　　400.

**1952. HARLEQUIN DUCKS ISSUE** by John H. Dick. *Intaglio, unwatermarked, perforated 11.*

RH19

**RH19**　　　　　　　　　　　　　　　　　　MNHVF　UseVF
$2　　　**deep ultramarine**　　　　　　60.00　10.00
　　　　Plate block of 6　　　　　　　　400.

**1953. BLUE-WINGED TEAL ISSUE** by Clayton Seagears. *Intaglio, unwatermarked, perforated 11.*

RH20

**RH20**　　　　　　　　　　　　　　　　　　MNHVF　UseVF
$2　　　**lavender brown**　　　　　　　60.00　12.00
　　　　Plate block of 6　　　　　　　　400.

**1954. RING-NECKED DUCKS ISSUE** by Harvey Sandstrom. *Intaglio, unwatermarked, perforated 11.*

RH21

**RH21**　　　　　　　　　　　　　　　　　　MNHVF　UseVF
$2　　　**black**　　　　　　　　　　　　　60.00　8.00
　　　　Plate block of 6　　　　　　　　400.

**1955. BLUE GEESE ISSUE** by Stanley Stearns. *Intaglio, unwatermarked, perforated 11.*

RH22

**RH22**　　　　　　　　　　　　　　　　　　MNHVF　UseVF
$2　　　**deep blue**　　　　　　　　　　60.00　8.00
　　　　Plate block of 6　　　　　　　　400.

**1956. AMERICAN MERGANSER ISSUE** by Edward J. Bierly. *Intaglio, unwatermarked, perforated 11.*

RH23

**RH23**　　　　　　　　　　　　　　　　　　MNHVF　UseVF
$2　　　**black**　　　　　　　　　　　　　60.00　8.00
　　　　Plate block of 6　　　　　　　　400.

**1957. AMERICAN EIDER ISSUE** by Jackson M. Abbott. *Intaglio, unwatermarked, perforated 11.*

RH24

**RH24**　　　　　　　　　　　　　　　　　　MNHVF　UseVF
$2　　　**yellow emerald**　　　　　　　60.00　8.00
　　　　Plate block of 6　　　　　　　　400.
　　　　v.　Writing inverted on reverse　3500.　—

**1958. CANADA GEESE ISSUE** by Leslie C. Kouba. *Intaglio Giori Press, unwatermarked, perforated 11.*

RH25

**RH25**　　　　　　　　　　　　　　　　　　MNHVF　UseVF
$2　　　**black**　　　　　　　　　　　　　60.00　8.00
　　　　Plate block of 6　　　　　　　　400.

**1959. RETRIEVER CARRYING MALLARD ISSUE** by Maynard Reece. Inscription added to the back of the stamp: "DUCK STAMP DOLLARS BUY WETLANDS TO PERPETUATE WATERFOWL." RW26, from 1959 to present stamps are printed in panes of 30. *Intaglio, unwatermarked, perforated 11.*

RH26

| RH26 | | MNHVF | UseVF |
|---|---|---|---|
| $3 | **blue, orange brown and black** | 85.00 | 8.00 |
| | Plate block of 4 | 375. | |
| | v. Writing inverted on reverse | — | — |

**1960. REDHEAD DUCKS ISSUE** by John A. Ruthven. *Intaglio, unwatermarked, perforated 11.*

RH27

| RH27 | | MNHVF | UseVF |
|---|---|---|---|
| $3 | **multicolored** | 65.00 | 8.00 |
| | Plate block of 4 | 350. | |

**1961. MALLARDS ISSUE** by Edward A. Morris. *Intaglio, unwatermarked, perforated 11.*

RH28

| RH28 | | MNHVF | UseVF |
|---|---|---|---|
| $3 | **blue, brown and yellow brown** | 70.00 | 8.00 |
| | Plate block of 4 | 375. | |

**1962. PINTAILS ISSUE** by Edward A. Morris. *Intaglio, unwatermarked, perforated 11.*

RH29

| RH29 | | MNHVF | UseVF |
|---|---|---|---|
| $3 | **multicolored** | 70.00 | 8.00 |
| | Plate block of 4 | 400. | |

**1963. PACIFIC BRANT ISSUE** by Edward J. Bierly. *Intaglio, unwatermarked, perforated 11.*

RH30

| RH30 | | MNHVF | UseVF |
|---|---|---|---|
| $3 | **multicolored** | 70.00 | 8.00 |
| | Plate block of 4 | 400. | |

**1964. NENE GEESE ISSUE** by Stanley Searns. *Intaglio, unwatermarked, perforated 11.*

RH31

| RH31 | | MNHVF | UseVF |
|---|---|---|---|
| $3 | **multicolored** | 70.00 | 8.00 |
| | Plate block of 6 | 2000. | |

**1965. CANVASBACKS ISSUE** by Ron Jenkins. *Intaglio, unwatermarked, perforated 11.*

RH32

| RH32 | | MNHVF | UseVF |
|---|---|---|---|
| $3 | **multicolored** | 70.00 | 8.00 |
| | Plate block of 4 | 400. | |

**1966. WHISTLING SWANS ISSUE** by Stanley Searns. *Intaglio, unwatermarked, perforated 11.*

RH33

**RH33**
$3  **deep green, black and blue**   MNHVF UseVF
             70.00 8.00
   Plate block of 4       400.

**1967. OLD SQUAW DUCKS ISSUE** by Leslie C. Kouba. *Intaglio, unwatermarked, perforated 11.*

RH34

**RH34**          MNHVF UseVF
$3  **multicolored**      70.00 8.00
   Plate block of 4      400.

**1968. HOODED MERGANSERS ISSUE** by C. G. Pritchard. Inscription on back of the stamp changed to "BUY DUCK STAMPS SAVE WETLANDS. SEND IN ALL BIRD BANDS. SIGN YOUR DUCK STAMP." *Intaglio, unwatermarked, perforated 11.*

RH35

**RH35**          MNHVF UseVF
$3  **multicolored**      55.00 8.00
   Plate block of 4      280.

**1969. WHITE-WINGED SCOTERS ISSUE** by Maynard Reece. *Intaglio, unwatermarked, perforated 11.*

RH36

**RH36**          MNHVF UseVF
$3  **multicolored**      40.00 7.00
   Plate block of 4      250.

**1970. ROSS'S GEESE ISSUE** by Edward J. Bierly. Combination of intaglio and offset, unwatermarked, perforated 11.

RH37

**RH37**          MNHVF UseVF
$3  **multicolored**      40.00 7.00
   Plate block of 4      250.

**1971. CINNAMON TEAL ISSUE** by Maynard Reece. *Combination of intaglio and offset, unwatermarked, perforated 11.*

RH38

**RH38**          MNHVF UseVF
$3  **multicolored**      35.00 7.00
   Plate block of 4      175.

**1972. EMPEROR GEESE ISSUE** by Arthur M. Cook. *Combination of intaglio and offset, unwatermarked, perforated 11.*

RH39

**RH39**          MNHVF UseVF
$5  **multicolored**      22.50 7.00
   Plate block of 4      125.

**1973. STELLER'S EIDER ISSUE** by Lee LeBlanc. *Combination of intaglio and offset, unwatermarked, perforated 11.*

RH40

**RH40**          MNHVF UseVF
$5  **multicolored**      20.00 7.00
   Plate block of 4      100.

**1974. WOOD DUCKS ISSUE** by David A. Maass. *Combination of intaglio and offset, unwatermarked, perforated 11.*

RH41

**RH41**          MNHVF UseVF
$5  **multicolored**      18.00 7.00
   Plate block of 4      90.00

**1975. CANVASBACKS ISSUE** by James L. Fisher. *Combination of intaglio and offset, unwatermarked, perforated 11.*

RH42

**RH42**
| | | MNHVF | UseVF |
|---|---|---|---|
| $5 | multicolored | 14.00 | 7.00 |
| | Plate block of 4 | 62.50 | |

**1976. CANADA GEESE ISSUE** by Alderson Magee. *Intaglio, unwatermarked, perforated 11.*

RH43

**RH43**
| | | MNHVF | UseVF |
|---|---|---|---|
| $5 | green and black | 14.00 | 7.00 |
| | Plate block of 4 | 62.50 | |

**1977. ROSS' GEESE ISSUE** by Martin R. Murk. *Combination of intaglio and offset, unwatermarked, perforated 11.*

RH44

**RH44**
| | | MNHVF | UseVF |
|---|---|---|---|
| $5 | multicolored | 14.00 | 7.00 |
| | Plate block of 4 | 62.50 | |

**1978. HOODED MERGANSER ISSUE** by Albert Earl Gilbert. *Combination of intaglio and offset, unwatermarked, perforated 11.*

RH45

**RH45**
| | | MNHVF | UseVF |
|---|---|---|---|
| $5 | multicolored | 14.00 | 7.00 |
| | Plate block of 4 | 62.50 | |

**1979-80. GREEN-WINGED TEAL ISSUE** by Kenneth L. Michaelsen. *Combination of intaglio and offset, unwatermarked, perforated 11.*

RH46

**RH46**
| | | MNHVF | UseVF |
|---|---|---|---|
| $7.50 | multicolored | 17.50 | 7.00 |
| | Plate block of 4 | 55.00 | |

**1980. MALLARDS ISSUE** by Richard W. Plasschaert. *Combination of intaglio and offset, unwatermarked, perforated 11.*

RH47

**RH47**
| | | MNHVF | UseVF |
|---|---|---|---|
| $7.50 | multicolored | 17.50 | 7.00 |
| | Plate block of 4 | 55.00 | |

**1981. RUDDY DUCKS ISSUE** by John S. Wilson. *Combination of intaglio and offset, unwatermarked, perforated 11.*

RH48

**RH48**
| | | MNHVF | UseVF |
|---|---|---|---|
| $7.50 | multicolored | 17.50 | 7.00 |
| | Plate block of 4 | 75.00 | |

**1982. CANVASBACKS ISSUE** by David A. Maass. *Combination of intaglio and offset, unwatermarked, perforated 11.*

RH49

**RH49**
| | | MNHVF | UseVF |
|---|---|---|---|
| $7.50 | multicolored | 17.50 | 7.00 |
| | Plate block of 4 | 75.00 | |

**1983. PINTAILS ISSUE** by Phil Scholer. *Combination of intaglio and offset, unwatermarked, perforated 11.*

RH50

**RH50**
| | | MNHVF | UseVF |
|---|---|---|---|
| $7.50 | multicolored | 17.50 | 7.00 |
| | Plate block of 4 | 75.00 | |

**1984. WIDGEONS ISSUE** by William C. Morris. *Combination of intaglio and offset, unwatermarked, perforated 11.*

RH51

| RH51 | | MNHVF | UseVF |
|---|---|---|---|
| $7.50 | multicolored | 17.50 | 7.00 |
| | Plate block of 4 | 75.00 | |

**1984. SPECIAL COMMEMORATIVE ISSUE**

| RH51a | | MNHVF | UseVF |
|---|---|---|---|
| $7.50 | Special Commemorative Issue (All examples must have P.F. certificates) | | |
| | single | 325. | |
| | Plate block of 6 | 3500. | |
| | Center gutter block | 6000. | |
| | Horizontal pair w/gutter | 750. | |
| | Vertical pair, w/gutter between | 850. | |

**1985. CINNAMON TEAL ISSUE** by Gerald Mobley. *Combination of intaglio and offset, unwatermarked, perforated 11.*

RH52

| RH52 | | MNHVF | UseVF |
|---|---|---|---|
| $7.50 | multicolored | 17.50 | 7.00 |
| | Plate block of 4 | 75.00 | |

**1986. FULVOUS WHISTLING DUCK ISSUE** by Burton E. Moore Jr. *Combination of intaglio and offset, unwatermarked, perforated 11.*

RH53

| RH53 | | MNHVF | UseVF |
|---|---|---|---|
| $7.50 | multicolored | 17.50 | 7.00 |
| | Plate block of 4 | 75.00 | |
| | t. Black engraved omitted | 4000. | — |

**1987. REDHEAD ISSUE** by Arthur G. Anderson. *Combination of intaglio and offset, unwatermarked, perforated 11 1/2 x 11.*

RH54

| RH54 | | MNHVF | UseVF |
|---|---|---|---|
| $10 | multicolored | 20.00 | 10.00 |
| | Plate block of 4 | 90.00 | |

**1988. SNOW GOOSE ISSUE** by Daniel Smith. *Combination of intaglio and offset, unwatermarked, perforated 11 1/2 x 11.*

RH55

| RH55 | | MNHVF | UseVF |
|---|---|---|---|
| $10 | multicolored | 20.00 | 7.00 |
| | Plate block of 4 | 100. | |

**1989. LESSER SCOUP ISSUE** by Neal R. Anderson. *Combination of intaglio and offset, unwatermarked, perforated 11 1/2 x 11.*

RH56

| RH56 | | MNHVF | UseVF |
|---|---|---|---|
| $12.50 | multicolored | 22.50 | 7.00 |
| | Plate block of 4 | 100. | |

**1990. BLACK-BELLIED WHISTLING DUCK ISSUE** by Jim Hautman. *Combination of intaglio and offset, unwatermarked, perforated 11 1/2 x 11.*

RH57

| RH57 | | MNHVF | UseVF |
|---|---|---|---|
| $12.50 | multicolored | 22.50 | 7.00 |
| | Plate block of 4 | 100. | |
| | v. Back printing omitted | 375. | |

*NOTE: printing on back of stamp normally is on top of gum. No. RW57v can only exist unused. Beware of copies with gum removed.*

**1991. KING EIDERS ISSUE** by Nancy Howe. *Combination of intaglio and offset, unwatermarked, perforated 11 1/2 x 11.*

RH58

| RH58 | | MNHVF | UseVF |
|---|---|---|---|
| $15 | multicolored | 27.50 | 12.50 |
| | Plate block of 4 | 135. | |
| | t. Black engraved omitted | — | |

**1992. SPECTACLED EIDER ISSUE** by Joe Hautman. *Combination of intaglio and offset, unwatermarked, perforated 11 1/2 x 11.*

RH59

| RH59 | | MNHVF | UseVF |
|---|---|---|---|
| $15 | multicolored | 27.50 | 12.50 |
| | Plate block of 4 | 83.00 | |

**1993. CANVASBACK ISSUE** by Bruce Miller. *Combination of intaglio and offset, unwatermarked, perforated 11 1/2 x 11.*

 RH60

| RH60 | | MNHVF | UseVF |
|---|---|---|---|
| $15 | multicolored | 27.50 | 12.50 |
| | Plate block of 4 | 135. | |
| | a. Black engraved omitted | 3000. | |

**1994. RED-BREASTED MERGANSERS ISSUE** by Neal Anderson. *Combination of intaglio and offset, unwatermarked, perforated 11 1/2 x 11.*

 RH61

| RH61 | | MNHVF | UseVF |
|---|---|---|---|
| $15 | multicolored | 25.00 | 10.00 |
| | Plate block of 4 | 135. | |

**1995. MALLARD ISSUE** by Jim Hautman. *Combination of intaglio and offset, unwatermarked, perforated 11 1/2 x 11.*

 RH62

| RH62 | | MNHVF | UseVF |
|---|---|---|---|
| $15 | multicolored | 25.00 | 10.00 |
| | Plate block of 4 | 135. | |

**1996. SURF SCOTER ISSUE** by Wilhelm J. Goebel. *Combination of intaglio and offset, unwatermarked, perforated 11 1/2 x 11.*

RH63

| RH63 | | MNHVF | UseVF |
|---|---|---|---|
| $15 | multicolored | 25.00 | 10.00 |
| | Plate block of 4 | 135. | |

**1997. CANADA GOOSE ISSUE** by Robert Hautman. *Combination of intaglio and offset, unwatemarked, perforated 11 1/2 x 11.*

RH64

| RH64 | | MNHVF | UseVF |
|---|---|---|---|
| **$15** | **multicolored** | 25.00 | 10.00 |
| | Plate block of 4 | 135. | |

**1998. BARROW'S GOLDENEYE ISSUE** By Robert Steiner. Combination of intaglio and offset, unwatemarked, perforated 11 1/2 x 11.

RH65

| RH65 | | MNHVF | UseVF |
|---|---|---|---|
| **$15** | **multicolored** | 25.00 | 10.00 |
| | Plate block of 4 | 135. | |

**1998. BARROW'S GOLDENEYE SELF-ADHESIVE ISSUE** First in a three year test of self-adhesive hunting permit stamps. Serpentine die cut.

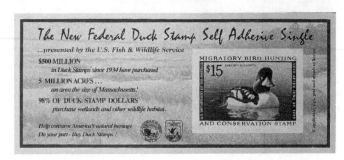
RH66

| RH66 | | MNHVF | UseVF |
|---|---|---|---|
| **$15** | **multicolored** | 30.00 | 15.00 |
| | Plate block of 4 | 150. | |

# Confederate States

The First Government stamps were put into use early in July 1847. They superseded Postmaster's Provisionals and other stamps which were thereafter not tolerated by the Postmaster General. The 5¢ stamp paid for carrying an ordinary letter up to 300 miles, and the 10¢ value was used for letters requiring higher postage.

Rawdon, Wright, Hatch & Edson of New York engraved the stamps and printed them in sheets of 200 that were cut into panes of 100 before distribution to the post offices. *The stamps were printed on thin, bluish wove paper. They were unwatermarked and imperforate, Intaglio.*

**1861. THE FIRST ISSUE.** consisted of 5¢ and 10¢ stamps, lithographed *(offset)* from various stones on soft porous paper. Earliest known dates of use are given.

Hoyer and Ludwig of Richmond, Va., printed the 5¢ green stamps from 4 different stones. Stones A and B are nearly identical. They are sharp and clear and almost always in the olive green shade. The 1st printing from Stone C was in olive green, and others followed in various shades of green. The impressions are clear, but not as sharp as those from Stones A and B. Stone D impressions come in all shades of green known except olive. They are noticably poor and some were unofficially rouletted (Baton Rouge, La.).

CS1 *Jefferson Davis*

| CS1 | | UnFVF | UseFVF |
|---|---|---|---|
| 5¢ | **olive green,** Stone A | | |
| | On cover (single) | | 250. |
| | a. olive green, Stone B *(Oct. 16, 1861)* | 200. | 150. |
| | On cover (single) | | 250. |
| | b1. green, Stone C *(Oct. 18, 1861)* | 180. | 125. |
| | On cover (single) | | 200. |
| | b2. bright green | 175. | 115. |
| | b3. dark green | 180. | 125. |
| | b4. dull green | 175. | 115. |
| | b5. olive green | | 150. |
| | c. green, Stone D *(Dec. 2, 1861)* | 200. | 175. |
| | c1. bright green | 225. | 150. |
| | c2. dark green | 200. | |
| | c3. pale green | 200. | 150. |
| | *Earliest documented cover:* (Oct. 16, 1861) | | |

*The 10¢ stamp was lithographed (offset) by Hoyer & Ludwig from Stone 1 and J.T. Patterson & Co. from Stone 2 and probably Stone 3. The impressions from Stone 1 are clear and distinct and always in a uniform shade of dark blue. The stamps from Stone 2 come in a wide range of shades and the impressions are not as clear as those of Stone 1. They show a small colored dash below the lowest point of the upper left triangle. Stamps from Stone 3 always are in a light milky or greenish blue and the impressions are worn and blurred. They show a large flaw back of the head and have the small colored dash below the upper left triangle.*

CS2 *Thomas Jefferson*

| CS2 | | UnFVF | UseFVF |
|---|---|---|---|
| 10¢ | **dark blue,** Stone 2 | 375. | 175. |
| | Horizontal pair, w/gutter between | — | |
| | v. Printed on both sides | — | |
| | *Earliest documented cover:* (Nov. 8, 1861) | | |

| CS2A | | UnFVF | UseFVF |
|---|---|---|---|
| 10¢ | **blue,** Stone 2 | 250. | 175. |
| | dark blue | 275. | 200. |
| | indigo | 2200. | 1750. |
| | pale blue | 275. | 200. |
| | a. light milky blue, Stone 3 | | |
| | a1. greenish blue | — | |
| | *Earliest documented cover:* (July 25, 1861) | | |

CS3 *Andrew Jackson*

| CS3 | | UnFVF | UseFVF |
|---|---|---|---|
| 2¢ | **green** | 450. | 550. |
| | emerald green | 475. | 600. |
| | olive yellow green | 500. | 650. |
| | pale green | 475. | 600. |
| | dark green | 500. | 650. |
| | On cover (single) | | 1750. |
| | On cover (strip of 5) | | 9550. |
| | *Earliest documented cover:* (March 21, 1862) | | |

| CS4 | | UnFVF | UseFVF |
|---|---|---|---|
| 5¢ | **blue,** Stone 2 | 150. | 125. |
| | dark blue *(4a)* | 175. | 150. |
| | dull blue *(4b)* | 225. | 175. |
| | On cover (single) | | 225. |
| | a. blue, Stone 3 *(April 10, 1862)* | 200. | 125. |
| | a1. dark blue *(4a)* | 225. | 175. |
| | a2. dull blue *(4b)* | 275. | 200. |
| | On cover (single) | | 275. |
| | *Earliest documented cover:* (Feb. 28, 1862) | | |

| CS5 | | UnFVF | UseFVF |
|---|---|---|---|
| 10¢ | **rose** | 700. | 400. |
| | deep carmine *(4a)* | 725. | 425. |
| | dull rose | 700. | 400. |
| | dark rose | 700. | 400. |
| | brown rose | 950. | 700. |
| | On cover (single) | | 600. |
| | *Earliest documented cover:* (March 10, 1862) | | |

*The deep carmine used on cover is a major Confederate variety. Its earliest known use is May 1, 1862.*

**1862. SECOND ISSUE** of *letter-press* stamps. Printed locally by Archer & Daly of Richmond Va. from plates made by Thomas de la Rue & Co., London.

CS6 *Jefferson Davis*

| CS6 | | UnFVF | UseFVF |
|---|---|---|---|
| 1¢ | **orange** (not issued) | 75.00 | |
| | deep orange *(14a)* | 85.00 | |

CS7 *Jefferson Davis*

| CS7 | | UnFVF | UseFVF |
|---|---|---|---|
| 5¢ | **light blue** | 13.50 | 20.00 |
| | On cover (single) | | |
| | *Earliest documented cover:* (April 16, 1862) | | |

CS8 *Jefferson Davis*

**CS8**

| | | UnFVF | UseFVF |
|---|---|---|---|
| 5¢ | **blue,** normal paper | 9.00 | 22.50 |
| | dark blue | 9.00 | 22.50 |
| | Horizontal pair, w/gutter between | 180. | |
| | On cover (single) | | 110. |
| | On cover (pair) | | 80.00 |
| | p. blue, printed on thin glazed paper | 25.00 | 35.00 |
| | p1. dark blue, printed on thin glazed paper | 25.00 | 35.00 |
| | p2. blue, printed on thick paper | 30.00 | 35.00 |
| | p3. dark blue, printed on thin glazed paper | 30.00 | 35.00 |
| | v. pair, printed on both sides | 2000. | 800. |
| | v1. "White tie" | — | |

*Earliest documented cover:* (Aug. 15, 1862)

*Private printings, erroneously called "Reprints," in both blue and black on modern paper were made for philatelic purposes.*

*After the change in postage rates on July 1, 1862, the Confederate Post Office Department instructed the firm of Thomas de la Rue & Co. in London to alter the denominations of the 2 typographed (letterpress) stamps for which they had previously made plates. Thus the value line of "ONE CENT" and that of "FIVE CENTS" to "TEN CENTS." While these 2 new plates were duly shipped to the Confederacy and arrived safely, no official printing was ever made from them. The complete plate of 400 subjects of the 2¢ denomination was discoverd many years ago, but only broken sections of the 20¢ plate were ever found. Various private printings have since been made from the 2¢ plate, and from the sections, and panes reconstructed from the 10¢ - the 2¢ usually in green and the 10¢ in various colors. None are officially printed government stamps and as private emissions they have little value.*

**1863-64. THIRD ISSUE** engraved and printed by Archer & Dally in Richmond, Va., unless otherwise stated. *Imperforate.*

**CS9**

| | | UnFVF | UseFVF |
|---|---|---|---|
| 2¢ | **brown red** | 30.00 | 165. |
| | pale red *(8a)* | 50.00 | 200. |
| | Double transfer | 100. | 300. |
| | Horizontal pair, w/gutter between | 250. | |
| | On cover (single) | | 900. |
| | On cover (pair) | | 2750. |
| | On cover (strip of 5) | | 4000. |

*Earlist documented cover:* (April 21, 1863)

 CS10 *Jefferson Davis*

**CS10**

| | | UnFVF | UseFVF |
|---|---|---|---|
| 10¢ | **blue** | 400. | 275. |
| | milky blue *(9a)* | 550. | 500. |
| | gray blue *(9b)* | 800. | 350. |
| | On cover (single) | | 1250. |
| | Double transfer | 750. | 750. |
| | Damaged plate | 800. | 800. |

*Earliest documented cover:* (April 23, 1863)

 CS11 *Jefferson Davis*

**CS11**

| | | UnFVF | UseFVF |
|---|---|---|---|
| 10¢ | **blue** | 1750. | 750. |
| | milky blue *(10a)* | 1750. | 750. |
| | greenish blue *(10b)* | — | |
| | dark blue *(10c)* | 2000. | |
| | Double transfer | 3500. | 1250. |
| | On cover (single) | | 2000. |

*Earliest documented cover:* (April 19, 1863)

*First printing from Archer & Daly in 1863 (No. CS12) shows uniformly clear impressions with an even distribution of a good quality of gum. In 1864 another firm, Keatinge & Ball of Columbia, S.C., printed stamps (Nos. CS12-CS13) from the same plates. They are of poorer quality, usually with filled-in impressions, the gum is brown and unevenly applied. Intaglio on paper that varies from thin to thick.*

 CS12 *Jefferson Davis*

**CS12**

| | | UnFVF | UseFVF |
|---|---|---|---|
| 10¢ | **blue** | 7.50 | 10.00 |
| | milky blue *(11a)* | 15.00 | 22.50 |
| | greenish blue *(11c)* | 13.50 | 13.50 |
| | green *(11d)* | 60.00 | 65.00 |
| | Double transfer | 60.00 | 75.00 |
| | Horizontal pair, w/gutter between | 90.00 | |
| | On cover | | 50.00 |
| | v. Perforated 12 1/2 *(11e)* | 250. | 225. |
| | On cover (single) | | 350. |

*Earliest documented cover:* (April 21, 1863)

**CS12A**

| | | UnFVF | UseFVF |
|---|---|---|---|
| 10¢ | **deep blue** | 8.00 | 25.00 |

*Earliest documented cover:* (Oct. 4, 1864)

*Printed by Ball Keatinge.*

 CS13 *Jefferson Davis*

**CS13**

| | | UnFVF | UseFVF |
|---|---|---|---|
| 10¢ | **blue** | | |
| | milky blue *(12a)* | 9.00 | 12.50 |
| | dark blue *(12d)* | 17.50 | 30.00 |
| | greenish blue *(12c)* | 20.00 | 12.50 |
| | green *(12e)* | 75.00 | 100. |
| | On cover (single) | | 75.00 |
| | v. Perforated 12 1/2 *(12f)* | 250. | 250. |
| | On cover (single) | | 375. |

*Earliest documented cover:* (May 1, 1863)

**CS13A**

| | | UnFVF | UseFVF |
|---|---|---|---|
| 10¢ | **deep blue** | 12.00 | 15.00 |
| | FDC *(Sept. 4, 1864)* | | |

 CS14 *George Washington*

**CS14**

| | | UnFVF | UseFVF |
|---|---|---|---|
| 20¢ | **green** | 30.00 | 325. |
| | dark green *(13b)* | 60.00 | 500. |
| | yellow green *(13a)* | 55.00 | 400. |
| | On cover (single) | | 800. |
| | v. Diagonal bisect, used as 10¢ on cover *(13c)* | | 2000. |
| | v1. Horizontal bisect, used as 10¢ on cover *(13d)* | | 2000. |

*Earliest documented cover:* (June 1, 1863)

# Canal Zone

Former U.S. Government reservation, administered by a governor appointed by the President. Area: 648.01 sq. mi. Headquarters: Balboa Heights.

100 Centavos= 1 Peso; 100 Centesimos = 1 Balboa; 100 Cents = 1 Dollar.

The Canal Zone was a strip of territory across the Isthmus of Panama, extending five miles on each side of the Panama Canal but excluding the cities of Panama and Colón. It was leased from the Republic of Panama under a treaty of 1903 which granted the U.S. full control over the territory.

The idea of a canal across Panama dates back almost to Balboa's discovery in 1513, that Panama was an insthmus. The Spanish conducted several surveys between 1534 and 1779, but afraid of the treat to their monopoly of communication with Latin America, generally discouraged even the isthmus.

U.S.Canal interest began with the California gold rush, when westbound settlers had to trek across the continent, sail around Cape Horn or make two sea voyages separated by a journey across Panama. A U.S. postal service using the latter route was instituted in 1848 through the Pacific Mail Steamship Company.

In 1878 the French obtained a Panamanian canal concession from the government of New Granada (Columbia) and formed a canal company headed by Ferdinand de Lesseps, who had constructed the Suez Canal. The French plan, to dig a sea level canal following essentially the line of the Panama Railroad (completed in 1855), was later changed to include locks. Because of climate, fever-breeding mosquitoes and financial mismanagement, the French company went bankrupt in 1889 after having cut 12 miles of canal and spent $260,000,000. A receiver company was equaly unsuccessful.

A U.S. commission had recommended Nicaragua as the most feasible site for an American canal project, but changed its mind when the French company offered to sell its concession and works for $40,000,000. Congress authorized President Theodore Roosevelt to make the purchase, and a treaty was signed which the Colombian Senate refused (August 1903) to ratify. In November the Department of Panama declared itself independent of Colombia and leased the Canal Zone to the U.S. The Canal was officially opened August 16, 1914.

In 1979 Panama declared itself independent of U.S.

All stamps engraved and recess printed unless otherwise stated.

The Canal Zone postal service was established on June 24, 1904. Its first stamps were secured from the Republic of Panama for temporary use pending the arrival of overprinted United States stamps. They were current 2, 5 and 10 centavos provisional stamps of the Republic overprinted efore deivery with the words *CANAL ZONE*. The nominal values were expressed in Colombian silver, 100 centavos of which equaled 50 cents of United States gold currency. Temporary first class postage rates for the first issue only, in Colombian silver, were: domestic post cards, 2¢; domestic lettes, 5¢ per ounce or fraction; foreign letters, 10¢ per half ounce or fraction.

## Regular Postal Issues

### 1904. MAP DESIGN OVERPRINT ISSUE

1 *Map design PANAMA, 13 1/2 mm long.*

| 1 | | UnFVF | UseFVF |
|---|---|---|---|
| 2¢ | **rose carmine** *(June 24, 1904)* | 520. | 500. |
| | v.  *PANAMA* 15mm long | 600. | 500. |
| | v1. *PANAMA* reading up & down | 650. | 500. |
| | v2. *P NAMA* | 600. | 500. |
| | v3. *CANAL ZONE* double overprint | 2000. | 1500. |
| | v4. *CANAL ZONE* inverted overprint | 850. | 600. |
| | v5. *CANAL ZONE* double inverted | 5000. | |

2, 3 *Map design PANAMA, 15 mm long.*

| 2 | | UnFVF | UseFVF |
|---|---|---|---|
| 5¢ | **deep blue** | 250. | 180. |
| | v.  2 1/4mm between bar & *A* of *PANAMA* | 500. | 500. |
| | v1. colon between bar & *P* of *PANAMA* | 500. | 500. |
| | v2. *CANAL ZONE* diagonally down to right | 400. | 350. |
| | v3. *CANAL ZONE* double overprint | 2250. | 1500. |
| | v4. *CANAL ZONE* inverted overprint | 600. | 625. |
| | v5. pair, 1 w/o overprint | 5000. | 5000. |

| 3 | | UnFVF | UseFVF |
|---|---|---|---|
| 10¢ | **yellow orange** | 425. | 275. |
| | v.  2 1/4mm between bar & *A* of *PANAMA* | 625. | 625. |
| | v1. colon between bar & *P* of *PANAMA* | 600. | 600. |
| | v2. *CANAL ZONE* double overprint | | 12500. |
| | v3. *CANAL ZONE* inverted overprint | 625. | 625. |
| | v4. pair, 1 w/o overprint | 6000. | 5000. |

Counterfeit *CANAL ZONE* handstamps and cancellations are numerous.

*Nos. 1-3 were withdrawn on July 17 and overprinted U.S. stamps were placed on sale the following day. Beginning with this issue, rates and denominations were expressed in U.S. currency or its equivalent.*

### 1904. CANAL ZONE OVERPRINT ISSUE

4

| 4 | | UnFVF | UseFVF |
|---|---|---|---|
| 4¢ | **deep blue green, #211** | 30.00 | 20.00 |
| 5 | | UnFVF | UseFVF |
| 2¢ | **camine, #231** | 25.00 | 21.00 |
| | a.  scarlet *(5a)* | 27.50 | 25.00 |
| 6 | | UnFVF | UseFVF |
| 5¢ | **deep blue, #215** | 105. | 60.00 |
| 7 | | UnFVF | UseFVF |
| 8¢ | **violet black, #217** | 160. | 85.00 |
| 8 | | UnFVF | UseFVF |
| 10¢ | **pale red brown, #218** | 160. | 97.50 |

*Dissatisfaction and concern in Panama over early United States administration led to conferences between the Panamanian authorities and William Howard Taft, U.S. Secretary of War, and a series of executive orders collectively known as the Taft Agreement.*

*One of the provisions required the use of Panama stamps overprinted CANAL ZONE. This automatically invalidated the current United States overprints. The new arrangements which were to cover the construction period of the Canal, required that a stable currency be established in Panama equivalent to that of the United States. Panama stamps used in the Canal Zone were to be purchased from Panama at 40 percent of their face value. Accordingly, in succeeding issues, the Canal Zone authorities were limited to whatever Panama could supply.*

### 1904-1906. CANAL ZONE OVERPRINT ISSUE

9, 10

| 9 | | UnFVF | UseFVF |
|---|---|---|---|
| 1¢ | **green** | 2.80 | 2.00 |
| | v. *CANAL* Type II | 100. | 100. |
| | v1. *CANA L* | 125. | 125. |
| | v2. *ZONE* Type II | 70.00 | 70.00 |
| | v3. *ZONE* | 275. | 275. |
| | v4. inverted overprint | | 2250. |
| | v5. double overprint | 1250. | 1000. |

| 10 | | UnFVF | UseFVF |
|---|---|---|---|
| 2¢ | **carmine red** | 4.50 | 2.00 |
| | v. *CANA L* | 85.00 | 85.00 |
| | v1. *L* sideways | 2500. | 2000. |
| | v2. *ZONE* | 275. | 275. |
| | v3. inverted overprint | 250. | 275. |

## 1904-06. CANAL ZONE OVERPRINT ISSUE

  11, 12, 13

| 11 | | UnFVF | UseFVF |
|---|---|---|---|
| 2¢ | **rose carmine**, (Dec. 9, 1905) | 7.00 | 4.00 |
| | v. *ZONE* Type II | 175. | 175. |
| | v1. *PANAMA* 16mm long | 45.00 | 45.00 |
| | v2. *PANAWA* | 45.00 | 45.00 |
| | v3. *PANAMA* inverted overprint | 400. | 400. |

| 12 | | UnFVF | UseFVF |
|---|---|---|---|
| 5¢ | **deep blue** | 7.50 | 3.00 |
| | v. *CANAL* Type II | 75.00 | 75.00 |
| | v1. *CANA L* | 90.00 | 90.00 |
| | v2. *ZONE* Type II | 75.00 | 75.00 |
| | v3. *CANAL ZONE* double overprint | 600. | 600. |
| | v4. *PANAMA* 16mm long | 40.00 | 40.00 |
| | v5. *PANAWA* | 40.00 | 40.00 |
| | v6. *PANAM* | 70.00 | 70.00 |
| | v7. *ANAMA* | 80.00 | 80.00 |
| | v8. *PANAAM* | 950. | 950. |
| | v9. *PAN MA* | 75.00 | 75.00 |
| | v10.*PAMANA* reading up | 75.00 | 75.00 |
| | v11.*PAMANA* reading down | 200. | 200. |
| | v12.right *P* 5mm below bar | 50.00 | 50.00 |
| | v13.*PANAMA* inverted overprint, bar at bottom | 800. | 1000. |
| | v14.*PANAMA* double overprint | 1050. | 850. |

| 13 | | UnFVF | UseFVF |
|---|---|---|---|
| 10¢ | **yellow orange** | 20.00 | 10.00 |
| | v. *CANAL* Type II | 225. | 225. |
| | v1. *CANA L* | 200. | 200. |
| | v2. *ZONE* Type II | 175. | 175. |
| | v3. red brown *PANAMA* overprint | 29.00 | 29.00 |
| | v4. *PANAMA* 16mm long | 75.00 | 75.00 |
| | v5. *PANAWA* | 100. | 100. |
| | v6. *PAMANA* reading down | 200. | 200. |
| | v7. right *P* 5mm below bar | 150. | 150. |
| | v8. left *A* touching bar | 175. | 175. |
| | v9. *PANAMA* double overprint | 600. | 600. |

## 1904-06. CANAL ZONE OVERPRINT ISSUE

**CANAL**  14

**ZONE**

**8 cts**

| 14 | | UnFVF | UseFVF |
|---|---|---|---|
| 8¢ on 50¢deep ochre | | 30.00 | 18.50 |
| | v. *CANA L* | 175. | 175. |
| | v1. *ZONE* Type II | 1150. | 1150. |
| | v2. *CANAL ZONE* inverted overprint | 425. | 400. |
| | v3. right *P* 5mm below bar | 175. | 175. |
| | v4. red brown *PANAMA* overprint | 40.00 | 40.00 |
| | v5. *CANAL* Type II on x4 | 2210. | |
| | v6. *ZONE* Type II on x4 | 2210. | |
| | v7. 8¢ double overprint on x4 | 850. | |
| | v8. omitted *8* on x4 | 4250. | |

## 1904-06. CANAL ZONE ISSUE

| 15 | | UnFVF | UseFVF |
|---|---|---|---|
| 8¢ on 50¢deep ochre, (Sept. 1906) | | 70.00 | 60.00 |
| | v. *CANAL* Type II | 95.00 | 95.00 |
| | v1. *ZONE* Type II | 200. | 200. |
| | v2. *PAMANA* reading up | 120. | 120. |
| | v3. 8¢ omitted | 750. | 750. |
| | v4. 8¢ double overprint | 1500. | |

## 1905-06. CANAL ZONE ISSUE

| 16 | | UnFVF | UseFVF |
|---|---|---|---|
| 8¢ on 50¢deep ochre, overprint 14 | | 3000. | 4250. |
| | v. *CANA L* | 4000. | |
| | v1. *PANAMA* 15mm long | 3250. | 4750. |
| | v2. *PANAMA* reading up & down | 6500. | 6500. |
| | v3. *P NAMA* | 3500. | |

## 1905-06. CANAL ZONE ISSUE

| 17 | | UnFVF | UseFVF |
|---|---|---|---|
| 8¢ on 50¢deep ochre, (Nov. 1905) | | 50.00 | 35.00 |
| | v. *ZONE* Type II | 200. | 200. |
| | v1. *PANAMA* 15mm long | 80.00 | 70.00 |
| | v2. *PANAMA* reading up & down | 100. | 100. |
| | v3. *P NAMA* | 85.00 | |

## 1905-06. CANAL ZONE ISSUE

| 18 | | UnFVF | UseFVF |
|---|---|---|---|
| 8¢ on 50¢deep ochre, (April 23, 1906) | | 67.50 | 60.00 |
| | v. *CANAL* Type II | 200. | 200. |
| | v1. *ZONE* Type II | 200. | 200. |
| | v2. *PANAMA* 15mm long | 80.00 | 70.00 |
| | v3. *PANAMA* reading up & down | 100. | 100. |
| | v4. *P NAMA* | 85.00 | |
| | v5. 8¢ double overprint | 1100. | 1100. |

*Nos. 14, 15, 17, 18 without CANAL ZONE overprint were not regularly issued.*

*The plate used for the CANAL ZONE overprint on Nos. 9-18 was altered 5 times, giving 6 different stages from which printings were made. A full list of the characteristic varieties and all alterations of the plate, with the approximate time they occurred and the stamps upon which the overprint is found, appears in Bartels' Check List of Canal Zone Stamps, second edition, 1908.*

*The Panama overprint was applied by a 50-subject plate to one-half of the sheet at a time and is sometimes misplaced vertically or horizontally. Such misplaced overprints exist on nearly all values. When misplaced vertically the bar may appear at the bottom of the stamp instead of the top, and one row will be left without bar. When misplaced horizontally the word PANAMA may appear once only, twice at either right or left, and three times on the same stamp. In some cased the overprint on two vertical rows of a sheet may overlap giving the appearance of a double overprint. Although of interest to the specialist, such varieties are not worth appreciably more than the normal stamp.*

*Rejection by the Canal Zone authorities of a lot of 1¢ and 2¢ provisionals that Panama had prepared for its own postal needs resulted in alternate offer by Panama of some Department of Panama stock, that had not yet been overprinted. These were accepted and the bars obliterating COLOMBIA and the old values were applied by the Canal Zone authorities at the same time that PANAMA, CANAL ZONE and the new values were added.*

## 1906. CANAL ZONE ISSUE

**PANAMA  CANAL  PANAMA**
**ZONE**
**1 ct.**

19, 20, 21

| 19 | | UnFVF | UseFVF |
|---|---|---|---|
| 1¢ on 20¢slate view, (March 1906) | | 1.75 | 1.50 |

**20**
**1¢ on 20¢slate violet,** (May 1906)

| | UnFVF | UseFVF |
|---|---|---|
| | 1.90 | 1.60 |

**21**
**1¢ on 20¢slate violet,** (Sept. 1906)

| | UnFVF | UseFVF |
|---|---|---|
| | 1.60 | 1.60 |
| v. *C ANAL* | 12.50 | |

22, 23, 24

CANAL
ZONE
2 cts.
PANAMA PANAMA

**22**
**2¢ on 1pbrown lake,** (April 1906)

| | UnFVF | UseFVF |
|---|---|---|
| | 3.00 | 2.25 |

**23**
**2¢ on 1pbrown lake,** (May 1906)

| | UnFVF | UseFVF |
|---|---|---|
| | 3.00 | 2.25 |

**24**
**2¢ on 1pbrown lake,** (Sept. 1906)

| | UnFVF | UseFVF |
|---|---|---|
| | 20.00 | 20.00 |

*Misplaced overprints occur with bars shifted so that both bars appear at top or botton, or occasionally only one bar altogether.*

## 1906-07. PORTRAIT ISSUE

25 *Galboa*

**25**
**1¢    deep blue green and black,** (Jan. 1907)

| | UnFVF | UseFVF |
|---|---|---|
| | 2.50 | 1.25 |
| v. *ANA* for *CANAL* | 70.00 | 70.00 |
| v1. *CAN L* | 80.00 | 80.00 |
| v2. *ONE* for *ZONE* | 80.00 | 80.00 |
| v3. imperforate horizontal, pair | | |
| v4. imperforate between, horizontal pair | | |
| v5. imperforate between, vertical pair | | |
| v6. head & inverted overprint | | |
| v7. overprint reading up | | |
| v8. Pair, 1 not overprint | | |
| v9. double overprint | | |
| v10.double overprint second inverted | | |

**26**
**2¢    scarlet and black,** (Oct. 1906)

| | UnFVF | UseFVF |
|---|---|---|
| | 27.50 | 21.00 |

27 *Córdoba*

**27**
**2¢    scarlet and black,** (Nov. 1906)

| | UnFVF | UseFVF |
|---|---|---|
| | 3.00 | 1.20 |
| a. carmine & black | 3.00 | 1.40 |
| v. *CAN L* | 45.00 | |
| v1. imperforate between, horizontal pair | | |
| v2. head & inverted overprint | | |
| v3. pair, 1 w/o overprint | | |
| v4. double overprint | | |

28 *Arosemena*

**28**
**5¢    blue and black,** (Dec. 1906)

| | UnFVF | UseFVF |
|---|---|---|
| | 7.00 | 2.50 |
| a. light blue & black | 7.00 | 2.50 |
| b. cobalt & black | 3.25 | 1.50 |
| c. dark blue & black | 7.00 | 2.50 |
| v. *CAN L* | 60.00 | |
| v1. *CANAL* only | 35.00 | |
| v2. *CANAL* double overprint | 500. | 350. |

29 *Hurtado*

**29**
**8¢    dark lilac and black,** (Dec. 1906)

| | UnFVF | UseFVF |
|---|---|---|
| | 24.00 | 7.50 |
| v. imperforate between, horizontal pair | | |

30 *Obaldia*

**30**
**10¢    dark violet and black,** (Dec. 1906)

| | UnFVF | UseFVF |
|---|---|---|
| | 25.00 | 7.50 |
| v. double overprint second inverted | | |

*Earlier printings of Nos. 25-30 are on soft and thick, later printings on hard, thin paper. Nos. 25 and 30 exist imperforate between stamp and sheet margin. CA of CANAL spaced 1/2mm farther apart on position 50 of the sheet on later printings of Nos. 25, 27-29.*

*A change of printers resulted in a new series of Panama stamps and again certain denominations were obtained for Canal Zone use. These designs were in use until 1924 and appeared with several styles of overprint.*

## 1909. SECOND PORTRAIT ISSUE

31 *Cordoba*

**31**
**2¢    rose red and black,** (May 29, 1909)

| | UnFVF | UseFVF |
|---|---|---|
| | 15.00 | 6.50 |
| v. Horizontal pair, 1 w/o overprint | | |
| v1. vertical pair, 1 w/o overprint | 1450. | |

32 *Arosemana*

**32**
**5¢    deep blue and black,** (May 28, 1909)

| | UnFVF | UseFVF |
|---|---|---|
| | 55.00 | 12.50 |

33 *Hurtado*

| 33 | | | UnFVF | UseFVF |
|---|---|---|---|---|
| 8¢ | **red violet and black,** (May 25, 1909) | | 50.00 | 12.00 |

*34 Ogaldia*

| 34 | | | UnFVF | UseFVF |
|---|---|---|---|---|
| 10¢ | **red violet and black,** (Jan. 19, 1909) | | 50.00 | 13.50 |
| | v. | horizontal pair, 1 w/o overprint | 1450. | |
| | v1. | vertical pair, 1 w/o overprint | | |

*CA of CANAL widely spaced on position 50 of the sheet of Nos. 31-34.*

*Inquiries developed that stamps could be obtained already overprinted by the manufacturer at no extra cost. The following overprint types I, II, IV and V represent stamps secured in this manner until the use of overprinted Panama stamps was discontinued in 1924. Type III was local emergency issue overprinted by The Panama Canal Press. 1¢ and 2¢ stamps were supplied in booklet form beginning late in 1911.*

### 1909-10. SECOND PORTRAIT ISSUE

*35-39 CANAL ZONE reading up, spaced 10mm (1c) or 8 1/2 mm apart.*

**CANAL ZONE**

| 35 | | | UnFVF | UseFVF |
|---|---|---|---|---|
| 1¢ | **deep green and black** | | 4.00 | 1.60 |
| | v. | head and inverted overprint | | 15000. |
| | v1. | *CANAL* only | 500. | |
| | | Booklet pane of 6 | 750. | |
| 36 | | | UnFVF | UseFVF |
| 2¢ | **scarlet and black** | | 4.50 | 1.65 |
| | v. | pair imperforate horizontal | 1000. | 1000. |
| | v1. | *CANAL* double overprint | 400. | |
| | | Booklet pane of 6 | 1000. | |
| 37 | | | UnFVF | UseFVF |
| 5¢ | **deep blue and black** | | 14.75 | 3.75 |
| | v. | double overprint | 180. | 180. |
| 38 | | | UnFVF | UseFVF |
| 8¢ | **violet and black,** (Mar. 18, 1910) | | 11.00 | 4.75 |
| | v. | vertical pair, 1 w/o overprint | 1500. | |
| 39 | | | UnFVF | UseFVF |
| 10¢ | **violet and black** | | 55.00 | 20.00 |

### 1912-16 PORTRAIT ISSUE

**CANAL ZONE**

*40-43 "C" serif at top only, "O" tilted left.*

| 40 | | | UnFVF | UseFVF |
|---|---|---|---|---|
| 1¢ | **deep green and black,** (July 1913) | | 12.00 | 2.60 |
| | v. | vertical pair, 1 w/o overprint | 1500. | |
| | | margins imperforate | 750. | |
| | | perforate | 1150. | |
| 41 | | | UnFVF | UseFVF |
| 2¢ | **scarlet and black,** (Dec. 1912) | | 10.00 | 1.40 |
| | v. | overprint reading down | 175. | |
| | v1. | head and inverted overprint | 700. | 750. |
| | v2. | horizontal pair, 1 w/o overprint | 1500. | |
| | v3. | *CANAL* only | 1100. | |
| | | margins imperforate | 210. | |
| | | perforate | 1700. | |

| 42 | | | UnFVF | UseFVF |
|---|---|---|---|---|
| 5¢ | **deep blue and black,** (Dec. 1912) | | 42.50 | 3.25 |
| | t. | head of 2¢ | | 8000. |
| 43 | | | UnFVF | UseFVF |
| 10¢ | **red violet and black,** (Feb. 1916) | | 50.00 | 9.00 |

### 1915-20. PORTRAIT ISSUE

**CANAL ZONE**

*44-45 Words spaced 9 1/2 mm apart.*

| 44 | | | UnFVF | UseFVF |
|---|---|---|---|---|
| 1¢ | **deep green and black,** (Dec. 1915) | | 180. | 110. |
| | v. | overprint reading down | 315. | |
| | v1. | double overprint | 300. | |
| | v2. | *ZONE* double overprint | 4250. | |
| 45 | | | UnFVF | UseFVF |
| 2¢ | **scarlet and black,** (Aug. 1920) | | 3000. | 150. |
| 46 | | | UnFVF | UseFVF |
| 5¢ | **deep blue and black,** (Dec. 1915) | | 725. | 200. |

### 1915-20. PORTRAIT ISSUE

*47-49 "C" thick at bottom.*

| 47 | | | UnFVF | UseFVF |
|---|---|---|---|---|
| 1¢ | **deep green and black,** (Jan. 1918) | | 35.00 | 9.50 |
| | v. | overprint reading down | 175. | |
| | | left row w/o overprint | 850. | |
| | | right row w/double overprint | 2500. | |
| 48 | | | UnFVF | UseFVF |
| 2¢ | **scarlet and black,** (Nov. 1918) | | 125. | 9.50 |
| | v. | overprint reading down | 150. | 150. |
| | v1. | horizontal pair, 1 w/o overprint | 2000. | |
| | | left row w/o overprint | 5000. | |
| 49 | | | UnFVF | UseFVF |
| 5¢ | **deep blue and black,** (April 1920) | | 250. | 30.00 |

### 1920-21. CANAL ZONE ISSUE

*50-52 "A" with flat top.*

| 50 | | | UnFVF | UseFVF |
|---|---|---|---|---|
| 1¢ | **deep green and black,** (April 1921) | | 20.00 | 3.50 |
| | v. | overprint reading down | 2.50 | |
| | v1. | horizontal pair, 1 w/o overprint | 1100. | |
| | v2. | *CANAL* double overprint | 1500. | |
| | v3. | *ZONE* only | 2750. | 1400. |
| | | left row w/o overprint | 3250. | |
| 51 | | | UnFVF | UseFVF |
| 2¢ | **scarlet and black,** (Sept. 1920) | | 10.00 | 2.50 |
| | v. | horizontal pair, 1 w/o overprint | 1750. | |
| | v1. | vertical pair, 1 w/o overprint | 1500. | |
| | v2. | double overprint second inverted | 650. | |
| | v3. | double overprint second inverted | 575. | |
| | v4. | *CANAL* double overprint | 1000. | |
| | v5. | *ZONE* double overprint | 1000. | |
| | v6. | *CANAL* only | 2250. | |
| | | left row w/o overprint | 850. | |

**52**
**5¢**    **deep blue and black,** (April 1921)

| | UnFVF | UseFVF |
|---|---|---|
| | 300. | 45.00 |

   v.  horizontal pair, 1 w/o overprint     825.

*Officials Nos. 40-43, 46, 47, 50, 51 with perfin 52; P.*

### 1911-14. CANAL ZONE OVERPRINT ISSUE

     53-54

**53**
**10¢ on 13¢slate,** (Jan. 14, 1911)

| | UnFVF | UseFVF |
|---|---|---|
| | 6.50 | 2.00 |

   v.  *10¢ omitted*     250.
   v1. *10¢ inverted overprint*     300.     250.

**54**
**10¢**    **slate,** (Jan. 6, 1914)

| | UnFVF | UseFVF |
|---|---|---|
| | 55.00 | 12.50 |

*Many stamps offered as No. 53v are No. 53 from which the overprint 10¢ has been removed. This is especially true of used copies.*

*Official; No. 54 with perfin 52,P.*

**1914. POSTAGE DUE OVERPRINT ISSUE** Prior to 1914, regular postage stamps were used to collect amounts due on unpaid matter; some stamps were specially handstamped *Postage Due*. The first set of dues comprised overprinted U.S. stamps notwithstanding the provisions of the *Taft Agreement*.

     55-57 *1914, March Postage Due.*

**55**
**1¢**    **dark carmine,** overprint on USPD

| | UnFVF | UseFVF |
|---|---|---|
| | 65.00 | 15.00 |

**56**
**2¢**    **dark carmine,** overprint on USPD

| | UnFVF | UseFVF |
|---|---|---|
| | 250. | 50.00 |

**57**
**10¢**    **dark carmine,** overprint on USPD

| | UnFVF | UseFVF |
|---|---|---|
| | 735. | 40.00 |

*Many stamps show one or more letters of the overprint out of alignment, principally, E of ZONE.*

### 1915-19. BLUE OVERPRINT ISSUE

     58, 61 *Gate to San Geronimo Castle, Portobelo, erroneously inscribed* San Lorenzo Castle, Chagres.

**58**
**1¢**    **black brown**

| | UnFVF | UseFVF |
|---|---|---|
| | 10.00 | 5.00 |

   v.  overprint 50 reading down     15.50
   v1. overprint 50 reading up        5.00

     59, 62, 63 *Statue of Columbus.*

**59**
**2¢**    **black brown**

| | UnFVF | UseFVF |
|---|---|---|
| | 200. | 17.50 |

     60, 65 *Pedro J Sosa*

**60**
**10¢**    **black brown**

| | UnFVF | UseFVF |
|---|---|---|
| | 50.00 | |

### 1915-19. RED OVERPRINT ISSUE

**61**
**1¢ on 1¢ black brown**

| | UnFVF | UseFVF |
|---|---|---|
| | 100. | 17.50 |

     62, 63

**62**
**2¢ on 2¢ black brown**

| | UnFVF | UseFVF |
|---|---|---|
| | 35.00 | 12.50 |

**63**
**2¢ on 2¢ black brown, overprint 44**

| | UnFVF | UseFVF |
|---|---|---|
| | 35.00 | 14.00 |

**64**
**4¢ on 4¢ black brown, overprint 44**

| | UnFVF | UseFVF |
|---|---|---|
| | 40.00 | 18.00 |

   v.  *ZONE omitted*     7500.
   v1. *4 omitted*     7500.

**65**
**10¢ on 10¢black brown**

| | UnFVF | UseFVF |
|---|---|---|
| | 24.00 | 5.00 |

*Two spacings between 1 and 0 of 10 on No. 65.*

**1915. PANAMA NATIONAL EXPOSITION ISSUE** Honors the 400th anniversary of the European discovery of the Pacific (1513) and the completion of the Canal (1914). Perforated 12.

     66 *Relief map of Panama Canal.*

**66**
**1¢**    **deep blue green and black** *(March 1, 1915)*

| | UnFVF | UseFVF |
|---|---|---|
| | 10.00 | 5.00 |

     67 *Balboa claims the Pacific.*

**67**
**2¢**    **bright rose red and black**

| | UnFVF | UseFVF |
|---|---|---|
| | 11.00 | 6.50 |

     68 *Gatun Locks*

| 68 | | UnFVF | UseFVF |
|---|---|---|---|
| 5¢ | deep blue and black | 12.50 | 6.00 |

69 *Gaillard (Culebra) Cut*

| 69 | | UnFVF | UseFVF |
|---|---|---|---|
| 10¢ | brown orange and black | 22.50 | 10.00 |

## 1917-20. PICTORIALS OF PANAMA ISSUE

70 *SS Panama in Gaillard (Culebra) Cut.*

| 70 | | UnFVF | UseFVF |
|---|---|---|---|
| 12¢ | red violet and black, overprinted blue | 20.00 | 6.00 |

71 *SS Panama in Gaillard (Culebra) cut.*

| 71 | | UnFVF | UseFVF |
|---|---|---|---|
| 15¢ | turquoise blue and black, overprinted blue | 55.00 | 22.00 |

72 *SS Cristobal in Gatun Locks.*

| 72 | | UnFVF | UseFVF |
|---|---|---|---|
| 24¢ | yellow brown and black, overprinted blue | 55.00 | 12.50 |

*Official; No. 72 with perfin 52, P.*

73 *Drydock at Balboa.*

| 73 | | UnFVF | UseFVF |
|---|---|---|---|
| 50¢ | yellow orange and black *(Sept. 4, 1920)* | 300. | 160. |

74 *USS Nereus in Pedro Miquel Locks.*

| 74 | | UnFVF | UseFVF |
|---|---|---|---|
| 1b | black purple and black *(Sept. 4, 1920)* | 160. | 60.00 |

## 1921-24. CENTENERY OF INDEPENDENCE FROM SPAIN ISSUE
Stamps of Panama with black or red overprint.

75, 76 *José Vallarino*

| 75 | | UnFVF | UseFVF |
|---|---|---|---|
| 1¢ | green | 3.75 | 1.20 |
| | v. *CANAL* double inverted | 2750. | |
| | Booklet pane of 6 | 1000. | |
| 76 | | UnFVF | UseFVF |
| 1¢ | green, overprint 44 *(Jan. 28, 1924)* | 525. | 180. |
| | v. *ZONE* only, inverted overprint | 19.00 | |
| | v1. *ZONE CANAL*, inverted overprint | 850. | |

77 *Land Gate, Panama City.*

| 77 | | UnFVF | UseFVF |
|---|---|---|---|
| 2¢ | carmine red | 3.00 | 1.75 |
| | v. Overprint reading down | 225. | |
| | v1. *ZONE* only | 2000. | |
| | v2. Pair, 1 w/o overprint | 3500. | |
| | v3. Double overprint | 900. | |
| | v4. CANAL double overprint | 1900. | |
| | Booklet pane of 6 | 2100. | |

78 *Bolivar's Praise of Independence Movement.*

| 78 | | UnFVF | UseFVF |
|---|---|---|---|
| 5¢ | deep blue, overprinted red | 11.00 | 3.50 |
| | v. overprint reading down | 60.00 | |
| | v1. red overprint 50 | 72.00 | |
| | v2. black overprint 50 | 40.00 | |

79 *Municipal Building 1821 and 1921, Panama City.*

| 79 | | UnFVF | UseFVF |
|---|---|---|---|
| 10¢ | dark red violet | 17.50 | 6.00 |
| | v. Overprint reading down | 100. | |

*Officials; #75, 77-79 with perfin 52, P.*

80 *Statue of Balboa, Panama City.*

| 80 | | UnFVF | UseFVF |
|---|---|---|---|
| 15¢ | light blue | 52.50 | 14.50 |

81 *T. Herrera*

| 81 | | UnFVF | UseFVF |
|---|---|---|---|
| 24¢ | black brown | 77.50 | 20.00 |

82 *J. de Fábrega*

| 82 | | UnFVF | UseFVF |
|---|---|---|---|
| 50¢ | black | 150. | 100. |

**1924. ARMS OF PANAMA ISSUE**

83, 84 *Arms of Panama*

| 83 | | UnFVF | UseFVF |
|---|---|---|---|
| 1¢ | deep blue green | 11.00 | 3.50 |
| **84** | | **UnFVF** | **UseFVF** |
| 2¢ | vermilion | 9.00 | 2.75 |
| **84A** | | **UnFVF** | **UseFVF** |
| 5¢ | | 110. | |
| **84B** | | **UnFVF** | **UseFVF** |
| 10¢ | | 110. | |
| **84C** | | **UnFVF** | **UseFVF** |
| 12¢ | | 110. | |
| **84D** | | **UnFVF** | **UseFVF** |
| 15¢ | | 110. | |
| **84E** | | **UnFVF** | **UseFVF** |
| 24¢ | | 110. | |
| **84F** | | **UnFVF** | **UseFVF** |
| 50¢ | | 110. | |
| **84G** | | **UnFVF** | **UseFVF** |
| $1 | | 110. | |

*Nos. 84A-84G were prepared for use but not issued. 600 sets exist.*

**1924-33. CANAL ZONE OVERPRINT ISSUE** on U.S. Regular Issue Series. All Panama stamps overprinted *CANAL ZONE* were withdrawn from sale June 30, 1924 and were not valid for postage after August 31, 1924. The formal opening of the Panama Canal was proclaimed by President Wilson July 20, 1920, signifying the end of the construction period of the Canal. The executive order comprising the *Taft Agreement* was subsequentley abrogated by President Coolidge, effective June 1, 1924. No change was made in operations until the end of the fiscal year, June 30, 1924. As a temporary measure to replace the overprinted Panama stamps, overprinted U.S. stamps were obtained. These were used until gradually replaced by definitive designs beginning in 1928. As in the case of the Panama issues the Canal Zone authorities were obliged to accept whatever was currently available in the U.S.

85-96 *Flat top "A".*

| 85 | | UnFVF | UseFVF |
|---|---|---|---|
| 1/2¢ | **olive brown,** overprinted red *(April 15, 1925)* | 1.25 | .75 |

86, 112

| 86 | | UnFVF | UseFVF |
|---|---|---|---|
| 1¢ | **green** | 1.40 | .90 |
| | v.  *CANAL* only | 1750. | |
| | v1. *ZONE* inverted overprint | 450. | 450. |
| | v2. *ZONE CANAL* | 450. | |
| | v3. *CANAL ZONE* inverted overprint | 500. | 500. |
| | Booklet pane of 6 | 44.00 | |

87

| 87 | | UnFVF | UseFVF |
|---|---|---|---|
| 1 1/2¢ | **yellow brown** *(April 15, 1925)* | 2.00 | 1.70 |
| **88** | | **UnFVF** | **UseFVF** |
| 2¢ | **carmine** | 7.50 | 1.79 |
| | Booklet pane of 6 | 57.50 | |

89, 99, 116

| 89 | | UnFVF | UseFVF |
|---|---|---|---|
| 5¢ | **prussian blue** | 19.00 | 8.50 |

90, 100, 111, 117

| 90 | | UnFVF | UseFVF |
|---|---|---|---|
| 10¢ | **orange yellow** | 45.00 | 22.50 |

91, 101

| 91 | | UnFVF | UseFVF |
|---|---|---|---|
| 12¢ | **maroon** | 35.00 | 32.50 |
| | v. *ZONE,* inverted overprint | 37.50 | 30.00 |

92, 102, 118

| | | UnFVF | UseFVF |
|---|---|---|---|
| **92** | | | |
| **14¢** | **blue** *(June 27, 1925)* | 30.00 | 22.50 |

93, 103

| | | UnFVF | UseFVF |
|---|---|---|---|
| **93** | | | |
| **15¢** | **gray black** | 50.00 | 35.00 |

94, 106

| | | UnFVF | UseFVF |
|---|---|---|---|
| **94** | | | |
| **30¢** | **olive brown** | 32.50 | 22.50 |

95, 107

| | | UnFVF | UseFVF |
|---|---|---|---|
| **95** | | | |
| **50¢** | **gray lilac** | 70.00 | 45.00 |

96, 108

| | | UnFVF | UseFVF |
|---|---|---|---|
| **96** | | | |
| **$1** | **purple brown** | 250. | 105. |

**1925-28. CANAL ZONE OVERPRINT 2ND ISSUE** perforated 11.

# CANAL

97-108 *Overprint "A" with printed top.*

# ZONE

| | | UnFVF | UseFVF |
|---|---|---|---|
| **97** | | | |
| **2¢** | **carmine** *(May 26, 1926)* | 32.00 | 7.50 |
| | v.  *CANAL* only | 1500. | 1200. |
| | v1. *ZONE CANAL* | 350. | |
| | v2. horizontal pair, 1 w/o overprint | 3500. | |

98, 110, 114

| | | UnFVF | UseFVF |
|---|---|---|---|
| **98** | | | |
| **3¢** | **red violet** *June 27, 1925)* | 4.00 | 3.25 |
| | v.  *ZONE ZONE* | 500. | 500. |
| **99** | | UnFVF | UseFVF |
| **5¢** | **prussian blue** *(Jan. 7, 1926)* | 4.00 | 2.25 |
| | v.  *CANAL* only | 2250. | |
| | v1. *CANAL* inverted overprint | 950. | |
| | v2. *ZONE* only | 2000. | |
| | v3. *ZONE ZONE* | 1100. | |
| | v4. *ZONE CANAL* | 325. | |
| | v5. *CANAL ZONE* inverted overprint | 500. | |
| | v6. horizontal pair, 1 w/o overprint | 3250. | |
| | v7. vertical pair, 1 w/o overprint, 1 w/overprint inverted | 2250. | |
| **100** | | UnFVF | UseFVF |
| **10¢** | **orange yellow** *(Aug. 1925)* | 35.00 | 12.00 |
| | v.  *ZONE* only | 3000. | |
| | v1. *ZONE ZONE* | 3000. | |
| **101** | | UnFVF | UseFVF |
| **12¢** | **maroon** *(Feb. 1926)* | 2.50 | 12.50 |
| | v.  *ZONE ZONE* | 5000. | |
| **102** | | UnFVF | UseFVF |
| **14¢** | **blue** *(Dec. 1928)* | 20.00 | 16.00 |
| **103** | | UnFVF | UseFVF |
| **15¢** | **gray black** *(Jan 1926)* | 6.50 | 4.00 |
| | v.  *ZONE* only | 3200. | |
| | v1. *ZONE ZONE* | 5500. | |
| **104** | | UnFVF | UseFVF |
| **17¢** | **black** *(April 5, 1926)* | 4.00 | 3.25 |
| | v.  *CANAL* only | 1700. | |
| | v1. *ZONE* only | 800. | |
| | v2. *ZONE CANAL* | 200. | |
| **105** | | UnFVF | UseFVF |
| **20¢** | **carmine red** *(April 5, 19260)* | 7.25 | 3.25 |
| | V.  *CANAL* inverted overprint | 3500. | |
| | V1. *ZONE* inverted overprint | 3850. | |
| | V2. *ZONE CANAL* | 3500. | |

106

| | | UnFVF | UseFVF |
|---|---|---|---|
| **106** | | | |
| **30¢** | **olive brown** *(Dec. 1926)* | 5.00 | 4.00 |
| **107** | | UnFVF | UseFVF |
| **50¢** | **gray lilac** *(July 1928)* | 250. | 200. |
| **108** | | UnFVF | UseFVF |
| **$1** | **brown** *(April 1926)* | 125. | 75.00 |

**1927. CANAL ZONE OVERPRINT 3RD ISSUE** perforated 10.

109 *"A" with pointed top.*

| | | UnFVF | UseFVF |
|---|---|---|---|
| **109** | | | |
| **5¢** | **carmine** *(Jan. 1927)* | 42.50 | 11.00 |
| | *CANAL* only | 2000. | |
| | v1. *ZONE* only | 2750. | |
| | v2. Horizontal pair, 1 w/o overprint | 3000. | |
| | Booklet pane of 6 | 650. | |
| **110** | | UnFVF | UseFVF |
| **3¢** | **red violet** *(May 9, 1927)* | 8.00 | 4.25 |
| **111** | | UnFVF | UseFVF |
| **10¢** | **orange yellow** *May 9, 1927)* | 15.00 | 7.25 |

**1927-33. Canal Zone Overprint 4th Issue** perforated 11 x 10 1/2.

112 "A" with pointed top.

| 112 | | UnFVF | UseFVF |
|---|---|---|---|
| 1¢ | green *(June 28, 1927)* | 2.25 | 1.40 |
| | vertical pair, 1 w/o overprint | 3000. | |
| **113** | | UnFVF | UseFVF |
| 2¢ | carmine red *(June 28, 1927)* | 2.50 | 1.00 |
| | Booklet pane of 6 | 70.00 | |
| | *CANAL* double on 2 bottom stamps | 875. | |
| **114** | | UnFVF | UseFVF |
| 3¢ | red violet, No. 477 *(Feb. 1931)* | 4.00 | 3.00 |
| | (handmade) | 925. | |
| **115** | | UnFVF | UseFVF |
| 3¢ | red violet, No. 518 *(Jan. 14, 1933)* | 2.80 | 30.00 |
| | v. *ZONE* only | 1750. | |
| | v. *CANAL* only | 3500. | |
| | (handmade) | 72.00 | |
| **116** | | UnFVF | UseFVF |
| 5¢ | blue *(Dec. 13, 1927)* | 30.00 | 10.00 |
| **117** | | UnFVF | UseFVF |
| 10¢ | orange yellow *(July 1930)* | 17.50 | 10.50 |
| **118** | | UnFVF | UseFVF |
| 14¢ | blue *(Jan. 14, 1933)* | 4.50 | 3.50 |
| | V. *ZONE CANAL* | 1500. | |

Officials; Nos. 85, 86, 88-90, 97, 99, 100, 109, 111-114, 116, 117 with perfin 52, P.

**1924-25. Overprint Postage Due 1st Issue** perforated 11.

119 "A" with flat top.

| 119 | | UnFVF | UseFVF |
|---|---|---|---|
| 1¢ | deep rose | 115. | 25.00 |
| **120** | | UnFVF | UseFVF |
| 2¢ | deep claret | 65.00 | 11.00 |
| **121** | | UnFVF | UseFVF |
| 10¢ | deep claret | 250. | 55.00 |

**1924-25. Overprint Postage Due 2nd Issue** perforated 11.

122 "A" with pointed top.

| 122 | | UnFVF | UseFVF |
|---|---|---|---|
| 1¢ | deep rose | 9.00 | 4.50 |
| | *ZONE ZONE* | 1250. | |
| **123** | | UnFVF | UseFVF |
| 2¢ | deep rose | 18.00 | 5.00 |
| | *ZONE ZONE* | 1500. | |
| **124** | | UnFVF | UseFVF |
| 10¢ | deep rose | 135. | 24.00 |
| | v. Vertical pair, 1 w/o overprint | 1200. | |
| | v1. double overprint | 275. | |

**1925. Overprint Postage Due Issue**

 125

| 125 | | UnFVF | UseFVF |
|---|---|---|---|
| 1¢ | green | 95.00 | 18.00 |
| **126** | | UnFVF | UseFVF |
| 2¢ | carmine, overprinted blue | 22.50 | 75.00 |
| **127** | | UnFVF | UseFVF |
| 10¢ | orange yellow | 50.00 | 12.50 |
| | v. *POSTAGE DUE* double overprint | 450. | |
| | v1. *POSTAG* | 450. | |
| | v2. *POSTAG* double overprint | 3250. | |

**1926. 150th Anniversary Declaration of Independence Issue**

 128 Liberty Bell

| 128 | | UnFVF | UseFVF |
|---|---|---|---|
| 2¢ | carmine red | 3.75 | 3.50 |

**1928-40. First Definitive Issue**

 129 Maj. Gen William C. Gorgas

| 129 | | UnFVF | UseFVF |
|---|---|---|---|
| 1¢ | green *(Oct. 3, 1928)* | .15 | .10 |

 130 Maj. Gen. George W. Goethals

| 130 | | UnFVF | UseFVF |
|---|---|---|---|
| 2¢ | rose red *(Oct. 1, 1928)* | .18 | .12 |
| | Booklet pane of 6 | 7.25 | |

 131 Maj. Gen. George W. Goethals.

| 131 | | UnFVF | UseFVF |
|---|---|---|---|
| 3¢ | red violet *(Aug. 15, 1934)* | .20 | .10 |
| | handmade perforated margins | 100. | |
| | Booklet pane of 6 | 9.00 | |

 132 Gaillard Cut

**132**
**5¢**    **blue** *(June 25, 1929)*

| | UnFVF | UseFVF |
|---|---|---|
| | 1.10 | .35 |

133 *Maj. Gen. Harry F. Hodges*

**133**
**10¢**    **yellow orange** *(Jan. 11, 1932)*

| | UnFVF | UseFVF |
|---|---|---|
| | .50 | .30 |

134 *Lt. Col. David DuB Gaillard*

**134**
**12¢**    **brown purple** *(July 1, 1929)*

| | UnFVF | UseFVF |
|---|---|---|
| | 1.35 | .50 |

135 *Maj. Gen. William L. Sibert*

**135**
**14¢**    **dark blue** *(Sept. 27, 1937)*

| | UnFVF | UseFVF |
|---|---|---|
| | .95 | .70 |

136 *Jackson Smith*

**136**
**15¢**    **gray black** *(Jan. 11, 1932)*

| | UnFVF | UseFVF |
|---|---|---|
| | .70 | .35 |

137 *Rear Adm. Harry H. Rousseau*

**137**
**20¢**    **sepia** *(Jan. 11, 1932)*

| | UnFVF | UseFVF |
|---|---|---|
| | .85 | .35 |

138 *Col. Sydney B. Williamson*

**138**
**30¢**    **black** *(April 15, 1940)*

| | UnFVF | UseFVF |
|---|---|---|
| | 1.50 | 1.25 |

139 *Joseph C.S. Blackburn*

**139**
**50¢**    **red lilac** *(July 1, 1929)*

| | UnFVF | UseFVF |
|---|---|---|
| | 2.00 | .50 |

*Coil: see No. 230.*

*Officials; No.129-134, 136, 137, 139 with perfin 52, P.*

## 1929-31. CANAL ZONE OVERPRINT AIRMAIL ISSUE

**AIR MAIL**    140, 143

**≡10**c

**140**
**10¢ on 50¢red lilac** *(Dec. 31, 1929)*

| | UnFVF | UseFVF |
|---|---|---|
| | 7.75 | 6.50 |

**15**    141 *Flag of 5 with Serif*

**141**
**15¢ on 1¢green, blue overprint** *(April 1. 1029)*

| | UnFVF | UseFVF |
|---|---|---|
| | 8.00 | 5.00 |

**15**    142 *Flag of 5 curved*

**142**
**15¢ on 1¢green, blue overprint** *(March 1931)*

| | UnFVF | UseFVF |
|---|---|---|
| | 125. | 90.00 |

**143**
**20¢ on 2¢rose red** *(Dec. 31, 1929)*
    v.  dropped *2* in overprint

| | UnFVF | UseFVF |
|---|---|---|
| | 3.75 | 2.00 |
| | 90.00 | 75.00 |

144

**144**
**25¢ on 2¢rose red, blue overprint** *(Jan. 11, 1929)*

| | UnFVF | UseFVF |
|---|---|---|
| | 2.40 | 1.75 |

*Officials; No.140, 143, 143v., 144 with perfin 52, P.*

## 1929-30. CANAL ZONE POSTAGE DUE OVERPRINT ISSUE

145 *Postage due overprint.*

**145**
**1¢ on 5¢blue** *(March 20, 1930)*
    V.  W/o *POSTAGE DUE*

| | UnFVF | UseFVF |
|---|---|---|
| | 4.50 | 1.75 |
| | 1250. | |

**146**
**2¢ on 5¢blue** *(Oct. 18, 1930)*

| | UnFVF | UseFVF |
|---|---|---|
| | 7.50 | 2.50 |

**147**
**5¢ on 5¢blue** *(Dec. 1, 1930)*, horizontal bars of
    overprint omitted.

| | UnFVF | UseFVF |
|---|---|---|
| | 7.50 | 2.75 |

**148**
**10¢ on 5¢blue** *(Dec. 16, 1929)*

| | UnFVF | UseFVF |
|---|---|---|
| | 7.50 | 2.75 |

## 1931-49. CANAL ZONE AIRMAIL ISSUE

149

**149**
**4¢**    **rose purple** *(Jan. 3, 1949)*

| | UnFVF | UseFVF |
|---|---|---|
| | .70 | .70 |

| 150 | | UnFVF | UseFVF |
|---|---|---|---|
| 5¢ | light green | .60 | .45 |
| 151 | | UnFVF | UseFVF |
| 6¢ | yellow brown *(Feb. 15, 1946)* | .75 | .35 |
| 152 | | UnFVF | UseFVF |
| 10¢ | orange | 1.00 | .35 |
| 153 | | UnFVF | UseFVF |
| 15¢ | light blue | 1.25 | .30 |

 154

| 154 | | UnFVF | UseFVF |
|---|---|---|---|
| 20¢ | red violet | 2.00 | .30 |
| 155 | | UnFVF | UseFVF |
| 30¢ | carmine lake *(July 15, 1941)* | 3.50 | 1.00 |
| 156 | | UnFVF | UseFVF |
| 40¢ | yellow | 3.50 | 1.00 |
| 157 | | UnFVF | UseFVF |
| $1 | black | 8.25 | 1.80 |

Officials; No.150, 152-154, 156, 157 with perfin 52, P.

## 1932-41. Canal Zone Postage Due Issue

 158-162

| 158 | | UnFVF | UseFVF |
|---|---|---|---|
| 1¢ | claret | .20 | .20 |
| 159 | | UnFVF | UseFVF |
| 2¢ | claret | .20 | .20 |
| 160 | | UnFVF | UseFVF |
| 5¢ | claret | .35 | .35 |
| 161 | | UnFVF | UseFVF |
| 10¢ | claret | 1.40 | 1.50 |
| 162 | | UnFVF | UseFVF |
| 15¢ | claret *(April 21, 1941)* | 1.10 | 1.00 |

## 1939 25th Anniversary of Canal Issue

 163 *Balboa, June 1912. Looking East from Sosa Hill; Administrative Building Site.*

| 163 | | UnFVF | UseFVF |
|---|---|---|---|
| 1¢ | light green | .65 | .35 |

 164 *Balboa, June 1936. View from Sosa, completed Administrative Building and Prado.*

| 164 | | UnFVF | UseFVF |
|---|---|---|---|
| 2¢ | carmine | .65 | .40 |

 165 *Gaillard (Culebra) Cut, June 1913. Deepest excavation in Canal.*

| 165 | | UnFVF | UseFVF |
|---|---|---|---|
| 3¢ | deep violet | .65 | .20 |

 166 *Gaillard (Culebra) Cut, 1921. Gold and Contractor's Hills.*

| 166 | | UnFVF | UseFVF |
|---|---|---|---|
| 5¢ | deep blue | 1.30 | 1.25 |

 167 *Bas Obispo, Jan. 1910. View S from Panama Railroad relocation.*

| 167 | | UnFVF | UseFVF |
|---|---|---|---|
| 6¢ | orange red | 2.75 | 3.00 |

 168 *Bas Obispo, July 11, 1934. USS Houston in completed cut.*

| 168 | | UnFVF | UseFVF |
|---|---|---|---|
| 7¢ | black | 2.50 | 3.00 |

 169 *Gatun Lower Locks, April 15, 1911. View South from north end.*

| 169 | | UnFVF | UseFVF |
|---|---|---|---|
| 8¢ | green | 4.50 | 3.00 |

 170 *Gatun Lower Locks, June 19, 1924. View of new approach.*

| 170 | | UnFVF | UseFVF |
|---|---|---|---|
| 10¢ | bright blue | 3.50 | 3.00 |

 171 *Gaillard (Culebra) cut. May 20, 1913. Pioneer cut.*

| 171 | | UnFVF | UseFVF |
|---|---|---|---|
| 11¢ | blue green | 8.00 | 8.50 |

172 *Gaillard (Culebra) Cut, Aug. 16, 1930. SS Santa Clara.*

| 172 | | UnFVF | UseFVF |
|---|---|---|---|
| 12¢ | lake | 7.50 | 8.00 |

173 *Gamboa, July 1913. Dike, Bas Obispo cut, Rio Chagres Bridge.*

| 173 | | UnFVF | UseFVF |
|---|---|---|---|
| 14¢ | red violet | 7.50 | 8.00 |

174 *Gamboa, Dec. 7, 1922. Ships at Rio Chagres crossing.*

| 174 | | UnFVF | UseFVF |
|---|---|---|---|
| 15¢ | olive green | 10.00 | 6.00 |

175 *Pedro Miquel Locks, June 3, 1912. Construction of gates.*

| 175 | | UnFVF | UseFVF |
|---|---|---|---|
| 18¢ | rose carmine | 10.00 | 8.50 |

176 *Pedro Miquel Locks, July 16, 1927. SS Duchesa d' Aosta, Pres. Polk.*

| 176 | | UnFVF | UseFVF |
|---|---|---|---|
| 20¢ | brown | 12.50 | 7.50 |

177 *Gatun Spillway Dam, Feb. 5, 1913. Crest dam construction.*

| 177 | | UnFVF | UseFVF |
|---|---|---|---|
| 25¢ | orange | 17.50 | 17.50 |

178 *Gatun Spillway Dam, May 1922. Crest Dam in operation.*

| 178 | | UnFVF | UseFVF |
|---|---|---|---|
| 50¢ | brown purple | 22.50 | 6.00 |

*Officials; No. 163-166, 170, 172, 174, 176, 178 with perfin 52, P.*

**1939. AIRMAIL ISSUE** for the 25th anniversary of the Canal opening.

179 *Douglas plane over Sosa Hill.*

| 179 | | UnFVF | UseFVF |
|---|---|---|---|
| 5¢ | greenish black *(July 15, 1939)* | 4.00 | 2.25 |

180 *Planes and map of Central America.*

| 180 | | UnFVF | UseFVF |
|---|---|---|---|
| 10¢ | red violet *(July 15, 1939)* | 3.00 | 2.25 |

181 *Sikorsky S.42 flying boat and scene near Ft. Amador.*

| 181 | | UnFVF | UseFVF |
|---|---|---|---|
| 15¢ | yellow brown *(July 15, 1939)* | 4.25 | 1.25 |

182 *Sikorsky S.42 flying boat at Cristobal Harbor.*

| 182 | | UnFVF | UseFVF |
|---|---|---|---|
| 25¢ | deep blue *(July 15, 1939)* | 12.50 | 8.00 |

183 *Sikorsky S.42 flying boat over Gaillard Cut.*

| 183 | | UnFVF | UseFVF |
|---|---|---|---|
| 30¢ | carmine red *(July 15, 1939)* | 10.50 | 6.75 |

184 *Sikorsky S.42 flying boat landing.*

| 184 | | UnFVF | UseFVF |
|---|---|---|---|
| $1 | green *(July 15, 1939)* | 35.00 | 22.50 |

*Officials; No. 179, 180, 181, 183, 184 with perfin 52, P.*

**1939. PRESIDENTIAL SERIES OVERPRINT ISSUE** perforated 11 x 10 1/2.

185

| 185 | | | UnFVF | UseFVF |
|---|---|---|---|---|
| 1/2¢ | **red orange**, US No. 524, *(Sept. 1, 1939)* | | .15 | .15 |
| 186 | | | UnFVF | UseFVF |
| 1 1/2¢ | **yellow brown**, US No. 526, *(Sept. 1, 1939)* | | .20 | .20 |

**1941. OFFICIAL OVERPRINT ISSUE** Official stamps. Definitive issues overprinted by Panama Canal Press with OFFICIAL PANAMA CANAL in two lines on overprint large, three lines on small stamps. No. 129//139, 187, PANAMA. 10mm long, 5c, large stamp, overprint 194.

 187

| 187 | | MNHVF | UseVF |
|---|---|---|---|
| 1¢ | **green** | 2.25 | .40 |
| 188 | | MNHVF | UseVF |
| 3¢ | **red violet** | 4.00 | .75 |
| 189 | | MNHVF | UseVF |
| 5¢ | **blue** | | 32.50 |
| 190 | | MNHVF | UseVF |
| 10¢ | **yellow orange** | 7.00 | 1.40 |
| 191 | | MNHVF | UseVF |
| 15¢ | **gray black** | 12.50 | 2.25 |
| 192 | | MNHVF | UseVF |
| 20¢ | **sepia** | 15.00 | 2.75 |
| 193 | | MNHVF | UseVF |
| 50¢ | **red lilac** | 37.50 | 5.50 |
| | v. *PANAMA 9mm, (Sept. 22, 1941)* | | 500. |

**1941. OFFICIAL AIRMAIL ISSUE** overprint on No.150-175.

| 194 | | MNHVF | UseVF |
|---|---|---|---|
| 5¢ | **light green** | 5.50 | 1.50 |
| | v. Type II, *(Sept. 22, 1941) (CO8)* | | 180. |
| 195 | | MNHVF | UseVF |
| 6¢ | **yellow brown** *(Nov. 15, 1948)* | 12.50 | 5.00 |
| | v. inverted overprint | | 2500. |

 196

| 196 | | MNHVF | UseVF |
|---|---|---|---|
| 10¢ | **orange** | 8.50 | 2.00 |
| | v. Type II, *Sept. 22, 1941), (CO9)* | | 325. |
| 197 | | MNHVF | UseVF |
| 15¢ | **light blue** | 11.00 | 2.00 |
| 198 | | MNHVF | UseVF |
| 20¢ | **red violet** | 12.50 | 4.00 |
| | v. Type II, *(Sept. 22, 1941), (CO10)* | | 180. |
| 199 | | MNHVF | UseVF |
| 30¢ | **carmine lake** *(May 5, 1942)* | 17.50 | 4.50 |
| | v. Type II, *(Sept. 22, 1941) (CO11)* | | 55.00 |
| 200 | | MNHVF | UseVF |
| 40¢ | **yellow** | 17.50 | 6.25 |
| | v. Type II, *(Sept. 22, 1941), (CO12)* | | 180. |
| 201 | | MNHVF | UseVF |
| $1 | **black** | 20.00 | 10.00 |

*The use of official postage was restricted to departments and divisions of The Panama Canal, the Panama Railroad and certain other U.S. agencies in the Canal Zone. The stamps were used on official corre-spondence which did not enjoy the franking privilege, such as ordinary letters to foreign countries, certain official matter dispatched via parcel post and all airmail except official post office mail. Official stamps were also used to pay return receipt fees on registered official mail. First Class mail was almost always dispatched via airmail and airmail official stamps are therefore not uncommon on cover. Ordinary official post-age, however, was nearly always used on parcel post mail and covers are very rare.*

*Nos. 187-201 and 207 were sold to the public cancelled with Balboa Heights, Canal Zone between wavy lines until Dec. 31, 1951, when use of official stamps was discontinued. Mint stamps were available to the public at face for three months begining Jan. 2, 1952. O prices are for cancelled-to-order stamps; postally used copies are worth more. To fa-cilitate overprinting, all sheet margins were removed and no place num-bers are known to exist.*

**1946-49. ISSUE**

 *202 Maj. Gen. George W. Davis, first govenor.*

| 202 | | MNHVF | UseVF |
|---|---|---|---|
| 1/2¢ | **vermilion** *(Aug. 16, 1948)* | .70 | .15 |

 *203 C. E. Magoon, second govenor.*

| 203 | | MNHVF | UseVF |
|---|---|---|---|
| 1 1/2¢ | **red brown** *(Aug. 16, 1948)* | .70 | .15 |

 *204 T. Roosevelt*

| 204 | | MNHVF | UseVF |
|---|---|---|---|
| 2¢ | **rose** *(Oct. 27, 1949)* | .35 | .15 |

 *205 John F. Stevens*

| 205 | | MNHVF | UseVF |
|---|---|---|---|
| 5¢ | **prussion blue** *(April 25, 1946)* | .60 | .20 |

 *206 John F. Wallace*

| 206 | | MNHVF | UseVF |
|---|---|---|---|
| 25¢ | **yellow green** *(Aug. 16, 1948)* | 1.50 | 1.00 |

*No. 205 may have straight edges.*

*Coil see No. 234.*

## 1947. Official Stamp Issue

207 *No. 205 with overprint 187, OFFICIAL/PANAMA/CANAL.*

| 207 | | MNHVF | UseVF |
|---|---|---|---|
| 5¢ | prussian blue | 7.50 | 3.00 |

*See note after No. 201.*

## 1948. Canal Biological Area Issue celebrating the 25th anniversary of the establishment of the Canal Zone Biological area.

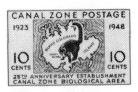

208 *Barro Colorando Island and Costi-Mundi. The Island, declared a biological area by Governor Jay Johnson Morrow in 1923, has been administered by the Smithsonian Institution. The Island is in Gatun Lake, formed by the damming of the Chagres River during the building of the Canal.*

| 208 | | MNHVF | UseVF |
|---|---|---|---|
| 10¢ | black | 1.50 | 1.30 |

## 1949. Gold Rush Centennial Issue

209 *Forty-niners arriving at Chagres.*

| 209 | | MNHVF | UseVF |
|---|---|---|---|
| 3¢ | deep blue | .50 | .30 |

210 *Up the Chagres River by Bungo.*

| 210 | | MNHVF | UseVF |
|---|---|---|---|
| 6¢ | red violet | .60 | .35 |

211 *Las Cruces Trail to Panama City.*

| 211 | | MNHVF | UseVF |
|---|---|---|---|
| 12¢ | blue green | 1.20 | .70 |

212 *Departure for San Francisco.*

| 212 | | MNHVF | UseVF |
|---|---|---|---|
| 18¢ | deep magneta | 3.00 | 1.50 |

## 1951. West Indian Canal Workers Issue

213 *West Indian workers in Gaillard (Culebra) Cut. During the construction period of 1904-14, 31,071 out of 45,107 workers brought to the Isthmus by the Isthmian Canal Commission were from the West Indies and additional thousands came on their own.*

| 213 | | MNHVF | UseVF |
|---|---|---|---|
| 10¢ | carmine *(Aug. 15, 1951)* | 2.90 | 2.00 |

## 1951-63. Airmail Issue perforated 11.

214-224 *Winged Sticker and Globe*

| 214 | | MNHVF | UseVF |
|---|---|---|---|
| 4¢ | rose purple | .75 | .30 |
| 215 | | MNHVF | UseVF |
| 5¢ | yellow green *(Aug. 16, 1958)* | 1.25 | .60 |
| 216 | | MNHVF | UseVF |
| 6¢ | brown | .60 | .30 |
| 217 | | MNHVF | UseVF |
| 7¢ | olive *(Aug. 16, 1958)* | 1.40 | .55 |
| 217A | | MNHVF | UseVF |
| 8¢ | carmine *(Jan. 7, 1963)* | .60 | .30 |
| 218 | | MNHVF | UseVF |
| 10¢ | red orange | .90 | .45 |
| 219 | | MNHVF | UseVF |
| 15¢ | dark purple *(Aug. 18, 1958)* | 4.25 | 2.00 |
| 220 | | MNHVF | UseVF |
| 21¢ | blue | 6.75 | 4.00 |
| 221 | | MNHVF | UseVF |
| 25¢ | orange yellow *(Aug. 16, 1958)* | 9.00 | 2.75 |
| 222 | | MNHVF | UseVF |
| 31¢ | deep carmine | 6.75 | 3.75 |
| | v.  vertical pair | 350. | |
| 223 | | MNHVF | UseVF |
| 35¢ | dark blue *(Aug. 16, 1958)* | 10.25 | 1.50 |
| 224 | | MNHVF | UseVF |
| 80¢ | gray black | 6.50 | 1.80 |

*Beginning June 1954, Canal Zone stamps have been printed by the dry process on pregummed paper instead of the wet intaglio method previously employed. The same plates are used but due to the absence of paper shrinkage and other factors, the size of the sheets is slightly larger than wet process stamps. Stamps printed by the dry process to date are 129, 131, 139, 215 and 217. As additional supplies of other current denominations are ordered they will be printed by the dry process.*

## 1955. Panama Railroad Centennial Issue

225 *Panama Railroad*

| 225 | | MNHVF | UseVF |
|---|---|---|---|
| 3¢ | dark red violet *(Jan. 28, 1955)* | .70 | .50 |

**1957. GORGAS HOSPITAL ISSUE** celebrates the 75th anniversary of the institution. Perforated 11.

226 *Gorgas Hospital Adminstration Building with Ancon Hill in background.*

| 226 | | MNHVF | UseVF |
|---|---|---|---|
| 3¢ | **black on turquoise green** *(Nov. 17, 1957)* | .50 | .40 |

**1958. SS ANCON ISSUE** perforated 11.

227 *SS Ancon Panama Line*

| 227 | | MNHVF | UseVF |
|---|---|---|---|
| 4¢ | **turquoise blue** *(Aug. 30, 1958)* | .40 | .35 |

**1958. ROOSEVELT CENTENNIAL ISSUE** perforated 11.

228 *Theodore Roosevelt medal (reverse and obverse), map of Canal.*

| 228 | | MNHVF | UseVF |
|---|---|---|---|
| 4¢ | **brown** *(Nov. 15, 1958)* | .50 | .40 |

**1960. BSA 50TH ANNIVERSARY ISSUE**

229 *First Class Boy Scout Badge and CANAL Zone Community strip.*

| 229 | | MNHVF | UseVF |
|---|---|---|---|
| 4¢ | **deep blue, carmel and deep ochre** *(Feb. 8, 1960)* | .85 | .70 |

**1960. GOTHALS COIL ISSUE** perforated 10 horizontal.

| 230 | | MNHVF | UseVF |
|---|---|---|---|
| 3¢ | **violet** *(Nov. 1, 1960)* | .75 | .50 |

**1960. ADMINISTRATION BUILDING ISSUE** perforated 11.

231 *Adminstration building*

| 231 | | MNHVF | UseVF |
|---|---|---|---|
| 4¢ | **deep rose lilac** *(Nov. 1, 1960)* | .20 | .15 |

*perforated 11.*

**1960. DEFINITIVE COIL ISSUE** perforated 10 vertically.

| 232 | | MNHVF | UseVF |
|---|---|---|---|
| 4¢ | **dull rose lilac** | .30 | .25 |

**1960. US ARMY CARIBBEAN SCHOOL ISSUE** Airmail, perforated 11.

233 *Emblem*

| 233 | | MNHVF | UseVF |
|---|---|---|---|
| 15¢ | **red and deep blue** *(Nov. 21, 1961)* | 1.50 | .90 |

**1961. JOHN F. STEVENS COIL ISSUE** perforated 10 horizontally.

234 *John F. Stevens*

| 234 | | MNHVF | UseVF |
|---|---|---|---|
| 5¢ | **prussian blue** *(Feb. 10, 1962)* | .40 | .35 |

**1962. GIRL SCOUTS USA 59TH ANNIVERSARY ISSUE** perforated 11.

235 *Badge; tents on Gatun Lake.*

| 235 | | MNHVF | UseVF |
|---|---|---|---|
| 4¢ | **turquoise blue, dark green and ochre** *(Mar. 12, 1962)* | .40 | .30 |

**1962. MALARIA ERADICATION ISSUE** perforated 11.

236

| 236 | | MNHVF | UseVF |
|---|---|---|---|
| 7¢ | **black on lemon** *(Sept. 24, 1962)* | .70 | .50 |

**1962. THATCHER FERRY BRIDGE ISSUE** perforated 11.

Thatcher Ferry Bridge over Panama Canal and map.

| 237 | | MNHVF | UseVF |
|---|---|---|---|
| 4¢ | **black and silver** *(Oct. 12, 1962)* | .35 | .30 |
| t. | bridge omitted | 6500. | |

**1962. ALLIANCE FOR PROGRESS ISSUE** Airmail, perforated 11.

239 *Alliance emblem.*

| 239 | | MNHVF | UseVF |
|---|---|---|---|
| 15¢ | **gray, blue and green** *(Aug. 17, 1963)* | 1.50 | .90 |

**1963. PANAMA CANAL 50TH ANNIVERSARY ISSUE** perforated 11.

240 *Cristobal.*

| | | MNHVF | UseVF |
|---|---|---|---|
| **240** | | | |
| **6¢** | **green** *(Aug. 15, 1964)* | .50 | .35 |

241 *Gatun locks*

| | | MNHVF | UseVF |
|---|---|---|---|
| **241** | | | |
| **8¢** | **carmine** *(Aug. 15, 1964)* | .55 | .35 |

242 *Madden Dam*

| | | MNHVF | UseVF |
|---|---|---|---|
| **242** | | | |
| **15¢** | **blue** *(Aug. 15, 1964)* | 1.00 | .65 |

243 *Gaillard Cut*

| | | MNHVF | UseVF |
|---|---|---|---|
| **243** | | | |
| **20¢** | **reddish purple** *(Aug. 15, 1964)* | 1.30 | .85 |

244 *Miraflores Locks*

| | | MNHVF | UseVF |
|---|---|---|---|
| **244** | | | |
| **30¢** | **chocolate** *(Aug. 15, 1964)* | 2.10 | 1.25 |

245 *Balboa*

| | | MNHVF | UseVF |
|---|---|---|---|
| **245** | | | |
| **80¢** | **bistre** *(Aug. 15, 1964)* | 4.50 | 3.00 |

**1964-74. SEAL AND JET AIRMAIL ISSUE** perforated 11.

246-253 *Canal Zone seal and jet plane.*

| | | MNHVF | UseVF |
|---|---|---|---|
| **246** | | | |
| **6¢** | **green and black** | .30 | .15 |

| | | MNHVF | UseVF |
|---|---|---|---|
| **247** | | | |
| **8¢** | **camine and black** | .35 | .15 |
| **248** | | **MNHVF** | **UseVF** |
| **10¢** | **salmon and black,** *(March 15, 1968)* | .35 | .15 |
| | Booklet pane of 4 | 5.00 | |
| | perforation 11 (2 adjacent sides x) | 1.80 | |
| | *(Feb. 18, 1970)* | 1.80 | |
| **248A** | | **MNHVF** | **UseVF** |
| **11¢** | **drab and black,** *(Sept. 24, 1971)* | .30 | .15 |
| | Booklet pane of 4 | 4.00 | |
| **248B** | | **MNHVF** | **UseVF** |
| **13¢** | **light green and black.** *(Feb. 11, 1974)* | .30 | .15 |
| | Booklet pane of 4 | 6.75 | |
| **249** | | **MNHVF** | **UseVF** |
| **15¢** | **blue and black** | .35 | .18 |
| **250** | | **MNHVF** | **UseVF** |
| **20¢** | **purple and black** | .50 | .25 |
| **251** | | **MNHVF** | **UseVF** |
| **25¢** | **light green and black,** *(March 15, 1968)* | .60 | .30 |
| **252** | | **MNHVF** | **UseVF** |
| **30¢** | **brown and black** | .70 | .35 |
| **253** | | **MNHVF** | **UseVF** |
| **80¢** | **bistre and black** | 1.90 | .95 |

**1965-74. AIRMAIL ISSUE**

255 *Goethals Memorial in in Balboa, Canal Zone.*

| | | MNHVF | UseVF |
|---|---|---|---|
| **255** | | | |
| **6¢** | **green and blue** *(Mar. 15, 1968)* | .30 | .15 |

**1968. ISSUE**

256 *Ruins of Ft. San Lorenzo on bluff overlooking Chagres River at its junction with the Atlantic Ocean.*

| | | MNHVF | UseVF |
|---|---|---|---|
| **256** | | | |
| **8¢** | **multicolored** *(July 14, 1971)* | .35 | .20 |

**1975. COIL ISSUE** perforated 10 vertically.

257

| | | MNHVF | UseVF |
|---|---|---|---|
| **257** | | | |
| **1¢** | **green** *(Feb. 14, 1975)* | .15 | .15 |

258

| | | MNHVF | UseVF |
|---|---|---|---|
| **258** | | | |
| **10¢** | **yellow orange** *(Feb. 14, 1975)* | .70 | .35 |

259

**259**
**25¢** **yellow green** *(Feb. 14, 1975)*

| | MNHVF | UseVF |
|---|---|---|
| | 2.75 | 2.75 |

## 1976. REGULAR ISSUE

260 *Cascadas,* 15 cubic yard dipper dredge built by Bucyrus Co. of New York, joined the digging fleet of Panama Canal on Oct. 31, 1915, established world record for a day's work by excavating machine in hard material Feb. 18, 1916 when she excavated and loaded into dump scows 23,305 cubic yards of rock and sand.

**260**
**13¢** **blue, black and green** *(Feb. 23, 1976*
Booklet pane of 4, *(Apr. 19, 1976)*

| | MNHVF | UseVF |
|---|---|---|
| | .35 | .20 |
| | 2.95 | 2.00 |

## 1976. AIRMAIL ISSUE perforated 11.

 261

**261**
**22¢** **violet and black** *(May 10, 1976)*

| | MNHVF | UseVF |
|---|---|---|
| | 1.00 | .35 |

**262**
**35¢** **red and black** *(May 10, 1976)*

| | MNHVF | UseVF |
|---|---|---|
| | 1.00 | .50 |

## 1977. J.P. STONES ISSUE perforated 11 1/2.

 263

**263**
**5¢** **prussian blue**
v. tagged

| | MNHVF | UseVF |
|---|---|---|
| | .95 | .95 |
| | 10.00 | |

## 1978. REGULAR ISSUE

264 *Towing locomotive ("mule") used to guide ships through the locks.*

**264**
**15¢** **green and blue green** *(Oct. 25, 1978)*

| | MNHVF | UseVF |
|---|---|---|
| | .80 | .60 |

# Cuba

After the sinking of the *USS Maine* at Havana (Feb. 1898) the US intervened, destroyed the Spanish fleet at Santiago, infested the island with land forces and acquired trusteeship of Cuba in the Treaty of Paris. After three years of US military administration (marked chiefly by the eradication of yellow fever), a republic was established May 20, 1902.

## Regular Postal Issues

### 1898-1899. CUBA PUERTO PRINCIPE ISSUE

 201

| 201 | | UnFVF | UseFVF |
|---|---|---|---|
| 1¢ | chestnut | | |
| | inverted overprint | | 130. |

| 202 | | UnFVF | UseFVF |
|---|---|---|---|
| 2¢ on 2mchestnut | | 14.50 | 8.50 |
| v. | inverted overprint | | 48.00 |
| a. | thin 2 overprint | 14.50 | 20.00 |
| av1. | Inverted overprint | 210. | |
| 202 | Inverted overprint | | 130. |
| 202a | Inverted overprint | | 90.00 |

| 203 | | UnFVF | UseFVF |
|---|---|---|---|
| 3¢ on 2mchestnut | | 3000. | |
| a. | Thin 3 | 48.00 | 30.00 |
| | Inverted overprint | | 60.00 |
| | Inverted overprint | | 300. |

| 204 | | UnFVF | UseFVF |
|---|---|---|---|
| 3¢ on 3mchestnut | | 18.00 | 9.00 |
| | Thin 3 | 48.00 | 30.00 |

| 205 | | UnFVF | UseFVF |
|---|---|---|---|
| 5¢ on 1mchestnut | | 325. | 90.00 |
| a. | Thin 5 | 1200. | 325. |
| | Inverted overprint | | 600. |
| | Inverted overprint | | 725. |

| 206 | | UnFVF | UseFVF |
|---|---|---|---|
| 5¢ on 2mchestnut | | 650. | 150. |
| | Thin 5 | 1450. | 440. |

| 207 | | UnFVF | UseFVF |
|---|---|---|---|
| 5¢ on 3mchestnut | | 1025. | 90.00 |
| | Inverted overprint | 1450. | 290. |
| a. | Thin 5 | | 575. |
| | Inverted overprint | | 725. |

| 208 | | UnFVF | UseFVF |
|---|---|---|---|
| 5¢ on 5mchestnut | | | |
| v2. | Double overprint | | 87.50 |
| a. | Thin 5 | 210. | 150. |
| v3. | 208x Double overprint | | |
| a. | Inverted overprint | | 285. |
| a2. | Double overprint | | |
| a3. | 208x Double overprint | | |

### 1898-99. PUERTO PRICIPE RED OVERPRINT ISSUE

 209

| 209 | | UnFVF | UseFVF |
|---|---|---|---|
| 3¢ on 1¢ purple black | | 26.00 | 14.50 |
| a. | thin 3 | 72.00 | 60.00 |
| a1. | Inverted overprint | | 90.00 |
| a3. | Inverted overprint | | 175. |

| 210 | | UnFVF | UseFVF |
|---|---|---|---|
| 5¢ on 1¢ purple black | | 8.75 | 8.75 |
| | Inverted overprint | | 72.00 |
| a. | thin 5 | 20.00 | 17.50 |
| a2. | Overprint sideways | | 600. |
| a3. | Double inverted | 360. | |
| a4. | Inverted overprint | | 285. |
| a5. | 210x overprint sideways | | 720. |
| a6. | Double overprint | 440. | |
| | Inverted overprint | | 150. |

| 211 | | UnFVF | UseFVF |
|---|---|---|---|
| 10¢ on 1¢ | | 20.00 | 20.00 |
| a. | broken 1 | 45.00 | 45.00 |

### 1898-99. PUERTO PRINCIPE BLACK OVERPRINT ISSUE

 212

| 212 | | UnFVF | UseFVF |
|---|---|---|---|
| 1¢ on 1mchestnut | | 24.00 | 15.00 |
| | Inverted overprint | | 130. |
| | broken 1 | 39.00 | 35.00 |
| | Double overprint | | |
| | 212a. double overprint | | 225. |

| 213 | | UnFVF | UseFVF |
|---|---|---|---|
| 3¢ on 1mchestnut | | 265. | 100. |
| a. | thin 3 overprint | 1300. | 440. |
| a2. | Double overprint | | |
| a3. | 213a. double overprint | | |

| 214 | | UnFVF | UseFVF |
|---|---|---|---|
| 5¢ on 1mchestnut | | | |

| 215 | | UnFVF | UseFVF |
|---|---|---|---|
| 5¢ on 5m | | | |

### 1898-99. PUERTO PRINCIPE BLACK OVERPRINT ISSUE

| 216 | | UnFVF | UseFVF |
|---|---|---|---|
| 3¢ on 1mslate green | | 130. | 36.00 |
| | Double overprint | | 90.00 |
| a. | thin 5 overprint | 225. | 42.50 |
| a2. | pair, 1 no overprint | | |
| | Double overprint | | 300. |
| | Inverted overprint | 150. | |

### 1898-99. PUERTO PRINCIPE BLACK OVERPRINT ISSUE

| 217 | | UnFVF | UseFVF |
|---|---|---|---|
| 3¢ on 1mslate green | | 150. | 100. |
| | Inverted overprint | | 225. |
| a. | *eents* | 440. | 225. |
| | Inverted overprint | | 725. |
| a2. | thin 3 overprinted | 360. | 300. |
| | Inverted overprint | | 440. |

### 1898-99. PUERTO PRINCIPE BLACK OVERPRINT ISSUE

| 218 | | UnFVF | UseFVF |
|---|---|---|---|
| 3¢ on 2mslate green | | 650. | 130. |
| | Inverted overprint | | 725. |
| a. | *eents* | 725. | 225. |
| a1. | Inverted overprint | | 1300. |
| a2. | thin 3 overprint | 1150. | 400. |
| | Inverted overprint | | 875. |

| 219 | UnFVF | UseFVF |
|---|---|---|
| 3¢ on 3mslate green | 800. | 130. |
| Inverted overprint | | 300. |
| a. *eents* | 1025. | 225. |
| a1. Inverted overprint | | 875. |
| a2. thin 3 overprint | 1200. | 300. |
| Inverted overprint | | 725. |

| 220 | UnFVF | UseFVF |
|---|---|---|
| 5¢ on 1/2mslate green | 440. | 60.00 |
| a. thin 5 overprint | 360. | |
| 2a. Double overprint | | |

| 221 | UnFVF | UseFVF |
|---|---|---|
| 5¢ on 1mslate green | | 1500. |
| a. *eents* | 2300. | |
| a2. thin 5 overprint | | |

### 1899. CUBA REGULAR ISSUE

226

| 226 | UnFVF | UseFVF |
|---|---|---|
| 1¢ on 1¢ yellow green | 2.25 | .60 |

| 227 | UnFVF | UseFVF |
|---|---|---|
| 2¢ on 2¢ carmine, No.191 | 2.25 | .70 |
| a. orange red, No. 192a | 3.00 | .60 |
| v. CUPA | 72.00 | |
| v1. inverted overprint | 975. | 725. |

| 228 | UnFVF | UseFVF |
|---|---|---|
| 2 1/2 ¢ on 2¢ carmine No. 191 | 3.25 | 3.25 |
| orange red, No. 192a | 1.65 | .95 |

| 229 | UnFVF | UseFVF |
|---|---|---|
| 3¢ on 3¢ dark red violet | 3.50 | 1.50 |
| v. CUBA | 7.50 | 4.25 |

| 230 | UnFVF | UseFVF |
|---|---|---|
| 5¢ on 5¢ dark blue | 3.75 | 1.50 |
| v. CUBA | 27.50 | 11.00 |

| 231 | UnFVF | UseFVF |
|---|---|---|
| 10¢ on 10¢ brown Type I | 10.50 | 6.00 |
| v. on 10¢ Type III, special printing | 2000. | |

*No. 228 was sold and used as 2¢. No. 229, Type I: 3 over P, Type II: 3 to left over P.*

### 1899. CUBA POSTAGE DUE ISSUE

| 232 | UnFVF | UseFVF |
|---|---|---|
| 1¢ on 1¢ brown carmine | 14.50 | 4.40 |

| 233 | UnFVF | UseFVF |
|---|---|---|
| 2¢ on 2¢ brown carmine | 14.50 | 3.60 |
| v. inverted overprint | 975. | |

| 234 | UnFVF | UseFVF |
|---|---|---|
| 5¢ on 5¢ brown carmine | 5.00 | 2.40 |
| v. CUPA | | |

| 235 | UnFVF | UseFVF |
|---|---|---|
| 10¢ on 10¢ brown carmine | 2.75 | 1.30 |

236

| 236 | UnFVF | UseFVF |
|---|---|---|
| 10¢ on 10¢ indigo | 87.50 | 87.50 |
| v. no period after CUBA | 165. | |

### 1899. CUBA PICTORIALS ISSUE

| 237 | UnFVF | UseFVF |
|---|---|---|
| 1¢ | 1.30 | .25 |

| 238 | UnFVF | UseFVF |
|---|---|---|
| 2¢ | 1.15 | .18 |
| Booklet pane of 6 | 150. | |

| 239 | UnFVF | UseFVF |
|---|---|---|
| 3¢ | 1.00 | .35 |

| 240 | UnFVF | UseFVF |
|---|---|---|
| 5¢ | 2.00 | .50 |

| 241 | UnFVF | UseFVF |
|---|---|---|
| 10¢ | 6.50 | 1.10 |

### 1899. CUBA SPECIAL DELIVERY IS

| 242 | UnFVF | UseFVF |
|---|---|---|
| 10¢ | 12.00 | 6.50 |

### 1902. CUBA FOUNDING OF THE REPUBLIC ISSUE

| 243 | UnFVF | UseFVF |
|---|---|---|
| 1¢ on 3¢ | 3.75 | 1.25 |
| v. overprint sideways | | |
| v1. inverted overprint | 28.00 | 28.00 |
| v2. double overprint | 37.50 | 37.50 |

*No. 237 overprinted.*

# Danish West Indies

## Regular Postal Issues

### 1855-66. ISSUE

| | | UnFVF | UseFVF |
|---|---|---|---|
| **1** | | UnFVF | UseFVF |
| 3¢ | **deep carmine red on yellowish** | 165. | 200. |
| **2** | | UnFVF | UseFVF |
| 3¢ | **rose red,** (May 1865) | 55.00 | 50.00 |
| | p.  thick paper | | |
| | v.  privately rouletted 4 1/2 | 250. | 180. |

*No. 1 had to be re-gummed after arrival in St. Croix. New gum was yellow or brown, same price. Original white gum rare.*

### 1872-73. ISSUE

| | | UnFVF | UseFVF |
|---|---|---|---|
| **3** | | UnFVF | UseFVF |
| 3¢ | **brown red** | 75.00 | 125. |
| | p.  thick paper | | |
| **4** | | UnFVF | UseFVF |
| 4¢ | **dull blue,** (Jan. 1, 1873) | 125. | 250. |
| | v.  pair imperforate | 600. | |
| | v1. pair, imperforate vertical | 600. | |

*Control marks. Nos. 1-3: 3 in left bottom square, C in right bottom square; engraver's mark B (A Buntzen) over right bottom square; No. 4: engraver's mark only.*

*No. 1: Many sheets destroyed when bundle with stamps fell into water while being unloaded. Remainders destroyed in 1873: No. 3 (210,000), No. 4 (200,000).*

### 1896-1901. ISSUE

| | | UnFVF | UseFVF |
|---|---|---|---|
| **5** | | UnFVF | UseFVF |
| 1¢ | **bright green and dull lilac,** first printing | 18.00 | 15.00 |
| | v.  frame inverted overprint | 150. | 180. |
| | a.  apple green & dull lilac, second printing | 28.00 | 28.00 |
| | av. frame inverted overprint | 225. | |
| | b.  blue green & deep lilac, third printing | 6.75 | 6.00 |
| | c.  pale green & pale red lilac, thick paper, fourth printing | .85 | .40 |
| | d.  yellowish green & claret, thick paper, fifth printing | 2.25 | .60 |
| | e.  light green & red lilac, thick paper, sixth printing | .60 | .30 |
| | f.  green & red brown, inverted overprint, thick paper, seventh printing | 1.00 | .40 |
| | g.  deep green & deep claret, thick paper, eighth printing | .90 | .40 |
| | h.  yellow green & brown red, inverted overprint, thick paper, ninth printing | .70 | .35 |
| | v2. normal frame, thick paper | 37.50 | 30.00 |

| | | UnFVF | UseFVF |
|---|---|---|---|
| **6** | | UnFVF | UseFVF |
| 3¢ | **blue and rose carmine,** first printing | 20.00 | 12.00 |
| | v.  frame inverted overprint | 130. | 100. |
| | a.  sky blue & carmine rose, second printing | 20.00 | 12.50 |
| | av. frame inverted overprint | 300. | |
| | b.  pale blue & dull rose, third printing | 20.00 | 12.50 |
| | bv. frame inverted overprint | 5.00 | 2.00 |
| | c.  deep blue & carmine lake, thick paper, fourth printing | 1.80 | 2.00 |
| | cv. frame inverted overprint, thick paper | 87.50 | 92.50 |
| | cvp.pair, thick paper | 550. | |
| | d.  gray blue & dull carmine, thick paper, fifth printing | 3.00 | .85 |
| | e.  bright blue & bright carmine, thick paper, sixth printing | .85 | .25 |
| | f.  deep gray blue & lake, inverted overprint, thick paper, seventh printing | .85 | .25 |
| | fv. normal frame, thick paper | 67.50 | 42.50 |
| | g.  greenish blue & carmine red, thick paper, eighth printing | .85 | .25 |
| **7** | | UnFVF | UseFVF |
| 4¢ | **deep brown and deep ultramarine,** first printing | 15.00 | 15.00 |
| | a.  bistre brown and pale blue, second printing | 1.25 | 1.75 |
| | b.  pale brown & dull blue, third printing | 1.25 | 1.75 |
| | v.  frame inverted overprint | 750. | 600. |
| **8** | | UnFVF | UseFVF |
| 5¢ | **pale green and light gray,** (1876) first printing | 18.00 | 15.00 |
| | a.  grass green & gray, second printing | 50.00 | 35.00 |
| | b.  pale green & brownish gray, thick paper, third printing | 12.50 | 8.00 |
| | c.  bright green & deep gray, thick paper, fourth printing | 6.00 | 1.50 |
| | d.  dark green & slate gray, thick paper, fifth printing | 8.00 | 3.00 |
| | e.  deep green & dark brownish gray, thick paper, sixth printing | 8.00 | 3.00 |
| **9** | | UnFVF | UseFVF |
| 7¢ | **pale lilac and orange buff,** (1874) first printing | 25.00 | 28.00 |
| | a.  light violet & orange, second printing | 2.25 | 40.00 |
| | av. frame inverted overprint | 35.00 | 45.00 |
| **10** | | UnFVF | UseFVF |
| 10¢ | **pale ultramarine and yellow brown,** (1876) first printing | 25.00 | 20.00 |
| | a.  pale blue & brown, second printing | 25.00 | 20.00 |
| | b.  deep ultramarine & blackish brown, thick paper, third printing | 20.00 | 12.00 |
| | bv. frame inverted overprint | 120. | 100. |
| | c.  pale ultramarine & yellowish brown, thick paper, fourth printing | 9.25 | 6.00 |
| | d.  bluish gray & pale yellow brown, thick paper, fifth printing | 1.75 | .35 |
| | e.  light blue & black brown, thick paper, sixth printing | 2.25 | .35 |
| | f.  blue & reddish brown, thick paper, seventh printing | 4.25 | .85 |
| **11** | | UnFVF | UseFVF |
| 12¢ | **pale lilac and green,** (1877) first printing | 3750. | 95.00 |
| | a.  red lilac & yellow green, second printing | 3250. | 3750. |
| **12** | | UnFVF | UseFVF |
| 14¢ | **lilac and green,** first printing | 435. | 450. |
| | v.  frame inverted overprint | 1500. | 1750. |
| **13** | | UnFVF | UseFVF |
| 50¢ | **bright purple,** first printing | 72.50 | 87.50 |
| | a.  dull violet, second printing | 725. | 87.50 |
| | b.  gray violet, thick paper, third printing | 100. | 150. |

### 1898. ISSUE

| | | UnFVF | UseFVF |
|---|---|---|---|
| **14** | | UnFVF | UseFVF |
| 1¢ | **pale green and claret,** inverted overprint, (Feb. 1898) | 8.00 | 8.00 |
| | v.  normal frame | 250. | 260. |

## 1896-1901. Issue

| | | UnFVF | UseFVF |
|---|---|---|---|
| **15** | | UnFVF | UseFVF |
| **3¢** | **bright blue and carmine red,** inverted overprint (Mar. 1898) | 7.75 | 7.75 |
| | v. normal frame | 225. | 240. |
| **16** | | UnFVF | UseFVF |
| **4¢** | **ochre and light gray blue,** (Mar. 1901) | 9.00 | 9.00 |
| | v. frame inverted overprint | 60.00 | 60.00 |
| **17** | | UnFVF | UseFVF |
| **5¢** | **green and gray,** inverted overprint (June 1896) | 35.00 | 27.50 |
| | v. normal frame | 300. | 500. |
| **18** | | UnFVF | UseFVF |
| **10¢** | **turquoise blue and brown ochre,** (Feb. 1901) | 65.00 | 72.00 |
| | v. frame inverted overprint | 900. | 1200. |
| | v1. period between *t* & *s* of *cents* | 70.00 | 95.00 |

| | | UnFVF | UseFVF |
|---|---|---|---|
| **19** | | UnFVF | UseFVF |
| **1¢ on 7¢** | **lilac and orange yellow,** overprint 9 (May, 12, 1987) | 50.00 | 75.00 |
| | v. frame inverted overprint | 100. | 110. |
| | v1. double overprint | 225. | 240. |

| | | UnFVF | UseFVF |
|---|---|---|---|
| **20** | | UnFVF | UseFVF |
| **2¢ on 3¢** | **gray blue and rose,** inverted overprint, overprint 6 (Mar. 1902) | 450. | 550. |
| | v. normal frame | 2000. | |
| | v1. *2* w/straight tail | 500. | 425. |
| **21** | | UnFVF | UseFVF |
| **2¢ on 3¢** | **bright blue and carmine red,** inverted overprint, overprint 15 (Mar. 1902) | 8.75 | 14.00 |
| | v. normal frame | 240. | 285. |
| | v1. *2* w/straight tail | 17.50 | 22.50 |
| | v2. dated *1901* | 375. | 450. |

## 1887-1902. Issue.

| | | UnFVF | UseFVF |
|---|---|---|---|
| **22** | | UnFVF | UseFVF |
| **2¢ on 3¢** | **bright blue and carmine red,** inverted overprint green, overprint 15 (1902) | 1250. | |
| | v. normal frame | 6000. | |
| | v1. *2* w/straight tail | 1500. | |
| **23** | | UnFVF | UseFVF |
| **2¢ on 3¢** | **bright blue and carmine red,** overprint 15 (July 1902) | 8.00 | 10.00 |
| | v. normal frame | 240. | |

# 8

# CENTS

## 1902

| | | UnFVF | UseFVF |
|---|---|---|---|
| **24** | | UnFVF | UseFVF |
| **8¢ on 10¢** | **turquoise blue and brown ochre,** overprint 18 (Mar. 1902) | 15.00 | 19.00 |
| | v. frame inverted overprint | 325. | 360. |
| | v1. period between *t* & *s* of *cents* | 20.00 | 22.50 |
| | v2. *2* w/straight tail | 20.00 | 25.00 |
| **25** | | UnFVF | UseFVF |
| **8¢ on 10¢** | **turquoise blue and brown ochre,** overprint 18 (July 1902) | 8.00 | 8.00 |
| | v. frame inverted overprint | 225. | 250. |
| | v1. period between *t* & *s* of *cents* | 12.00 | 14.00 |

| | | UnFVF | UseFVF |
|---|---|---|---|
| **26** | | UnFVF | UseFVF |
| **10¢ on 50¢** | **purple,** overprint 13 (May 1895) | 20.00 | 50.00 |

## 1902-1903. Issue

| | | UnFVF | UseFVF |
|---|---|---|---|
| **27** | | UnFVF | UseFVF |
| **1¢** | **green** | 2.00 | 2.00 |
| **28** | | UnFVF | UseFVF |
| **2¢** | **carmine** (April 1903) | 8.00 | 10.00 |
| **29** | | UnFVF | UseFVF |
| **5¢** | **light blue** | 8.00 | 8.00 |
| **30** | | UnFVF | UseFVF |
| **8¢** | **light brown** (April 1903) | 20.00 | 22.50 |

## 1902. Postage Due Issue

| | | UnFVF | UseFVF |
|---|---|---|---|
| **31** | | UnFVF | UseFVF |
| **1¢** | **deep blue** | 6.00 | 9.25 |
| **32** | | UnFVF | UseFVF |
| **4¢** | **deep blue** | 8.75 | 15.00 |
| **33** | | UnFVF | UseFVF |
| **6¢** | **deep blue** | 25.00 | 50.00 |
| **34** | | UnFVF | UseFVF |
| **10¢** | **deep blue** | 17.50 | 30.00 |

*Nos. 31-34: 5 types of each value.*

## 1905. Issue

| | | UnFVF | UseFVF |
|---|---|---|---|
| **35** | | UnFVF | UseFVF |
| **5b** | **emerald** | 6.50 | 3.75 |
| **36** | | UnFVF | UseFVF |
| **10b** | **orange** | 6.50 | 3.75 |
| **37** | | UnFVF | UseFVF |
| **20b** | **light green and blue** | 11.00 | 11.00 |

| 38 | | | UnFVF | UseFVF |
|----|----|----|-------|--------|
| 25b | ultramarine | | 10.00 | 8.75 |
| 39 | | | UnFVF | UseFVF |
| 40b | red and brown black | | 10.00 | 7.75 |
| 40 | | | UnFVF | UseFVF |
| 50b | yellow and brown black | | 7.50 | 9.00 |

## 1905. ISSUE

| 41 | | UnFVF | UseFVF |
|----|----|-------|--------|
| 5b on 4¢ochre and light gray blue | | 10.00 | 20.00 |
| | v. frame inverted overprint | 32.50 | 42.50 |
| 42 | | UnFVF | UseFVF |
| 5b on 5¢light blue | | 8.00 | 12.00 |
| 43 | | UnFVF | UseFVF |
| 5b on 8¢light brown | | 8.00 | 12.00 |

## 1905. ISSUE

| 44 | | UnFVF | UseFVF |
|----|----|-------|--------|
| 1f | green and blue | 15.00 | 22.50 |
| 45 | | UnFVF | UseFVF |
| 2f | red orange and brown | 30.00 | 45.00 |
| 46 | | UnFVF | UseFVF |
| 5f | yellow and brown | 60.00 | 175. |

## 1905. POSTAGE DUE ISSUE

| 47 | | UnFVF | UseFVF |
|----|----|-------|--------|
| 5b | vermilion and drab gray | 3.75 | 5.50 |
| 48 | | UnFVF | UseFVF |
| 20b | vermilion and drab gray | 11.00 | 13.00 |
| 49 | | UnFVF | UseFVF |
| 30b | vermilion and drab gray | 6.00 | 12.50 |
| 50 | | UnFVF | UseFVF |
| 50b | vermilion and drab gray | 8.00 | 11.25 |
| | v. perforated 14 x 14 1/2, (1913) | 30.00 | 70.00 |
| | v1. perforated 11 1/2 | 400. | |

## 1907-08. ISSUE

| 51 | | UnFVF | UseFVF |
|----|----|-------|--------|
| 5b | deep yellow green | 2.50 | 1.00 |
| 52 | | UnFVF | UseFVF |
| 10b | orange red, (Jan. 1908) | 2.25 | 1.00 |
| 53 | | UnFVF | UseFVF |
| 15b | red purple and chocolate, (Sept. 1908) | 7.00 | 7.00 |
| 54 | | UnFVF | UseFVF |
| 20b | yellow, emerald and blue, (May 1908) | 45.00 | 27.50 |
| 55 | | UnFVF | UseFVF |
| 25b | prussian blue | 3.00 | 2.25 |
| 56 | | UnFVF | UseFVF |
| 30b | claret and slate, (Sept. 1908) | 60.00 | 35.00 |
| 57 | | UnFVF | UseFVF |
| 40b | vermilion and gray (Sept. 1908) | 5.00 | 12.50 |
| 58 | | UnFVF | UseFVF |
| 50b | yellow and brown (Sept. 1908) | 6.00 | 15.00 |

## 1915-16. ISSUE

| 59 | | UnFVF | UseFVF |
|----|----|-------|--------|
| 5b | pale green | 2.25 | 4.00 |
| 60 | | UnFVF | UseFVF |
| 10b | orange red (Mar. 1915) | 2.25 | 32.00 |
| 61 | | UnFVF | UseFVF |
| 15b | red purple and red brown (Mar. 1915) | 2.50 | 32.00 |
| 62 | | UnFVF | UseFVF |
| 20b | yellow emerald and dark blue (Mar. 1915) | 2.50 | 32.00 |
| 63 | | UnFVF | UseFVF |
| 25b | blue and deep blue | 2.50 | 8.00 |
| 64 | | UnFVF | UseFVF |
| 30b | brown red and black (1916) | 2.50 | 37.50 |
| 65 | | UnFVF | UseFVF |
| 40b | orange salmon and gray black (1915) | 3.00 | 37.50 |
| 66 | | UnFVF | UseFVF |
| 50b | yellow and chocolate (Mar. 1915) | 3.00 | 37.50 |

*Since 1917: U.S. stamps have been used.*

# Guam

## Regular Postal Issues

The First Government stamps were put into use early in July 1847. They superseded Postmaster's Provisionals and other stamps which were thereafter not tolerated by the Postmaster General. The 5¢ stamp paid for carrying an ordinary letter up to 300 miles, and the 10¢ value was used for letters requiring higher postage.

Rawdon, Wright, Hatch & Edson of New York engraved the stamps and printed them in sheets of 200 that were cut into panes of 100 before distribution to the post offices. *The stamps were printed on thin, bluish wove paper. They were unwatermarked and imperforate, Intaglio.*

### 1899. OVERPRINT ISSUE

| | | | UnFVF | UseFVF |
|---|---|---|---|---|
| 1 | 1¢ | deep green | 22.50 | 32.50 |
| 2 | 2¢ | ~~carmine,~~ triangle III, No. 191 | 21.50 | 31.50 |
| 3 | 2¢ | red, triangle III, No. 192 | 22.50 | 32.50 |
| 4 | 4¢ | dark red violet | 120. | 145. |
| 5 | 4¢ | chocolate | 125. | 145. |
| | | t.  extra frame line at top (P1 793) | | |
| 6 | 5¢ | dark blue | 27.50 | 37.50 |
| 7 | 6¢ | lake | 120. | 165. |
| 8 | 8¢ | purple brown | 120. | 165. |
| 9 | 10¢ | brown, Type I | 37.50 | 60.00 |
| 10 | 10¢ | orange brown, Type II | 32.50 | |
| 11 | 15¢ | olive green | 125. | 165. |
| 12 | 50¢ | orange | 250. | 300. |
| 13 | $1 | black, Type I, overprinted red | 350. | 450. |
| | | a.  Type II red overprint, special printing | 2250. | |
| 14 | 10¢ | indigo | 130. | 175. |

# Hawaii

## Regular Postal Issues

The First Government stamps were put into use early in July 1847. They superseded Postmaster's Provisionals and other stamps which were thereafter not tolerated by the Postmaster General. The 5¢ stamp paid for carrying an ordinary letter up to 300 miles, and the 10¢ value was used for letters requiring higher postage.

Rawdon, Wright, Hatch & Edson of New York engraved the stamps and printed them in sheets of 200 that were cut into panes of 100 before distribution to the post offices. *The stamps were printed on thin, bluish wove paper. They were unwatermarked and imperforate, Intaglio.*

**1851. HAWAIIAN POSTAGE ISSUE** Numerals inscribed. Nos. 1-3, Type I, "P" of Postage slightly to the right of "H". Type II, "P" is directly under "H".

 1-3

| | | UnFVF | UseFVF |
|---|---|---|---|
| **1** | | | |
| 2¢ | blue | 600000. | 200000. |
| | pelure paper | | |
| **2** | | UnFVF | UseFVF |
| 5¢ | blue | 45000. | 25000. |
| **3** | | UnFVF | UseFVF |
| 13¢ | blue | 20500. | 17500. |

**1852. H.I. & U.S. POSTAGE ISSUE** Numeral inscribed. *Type I 16 1/2mm Long or Type II 17 1/2 mm long.*

| | | UnFVF | UseFVF |
|---|---|---|---|
| **4** | | | |
| 13¢ | blue | 40000. | 27500. |

**1853-61. KAMEHANEHA III ISSUE** Intaglio, imperforate.

No. 5, 8, 9 Kamehameha III (1813-54) was 12 when he succeeded his brother as king. His statement *The life of the land is preserved by righteousness,* is now the motto of Hawaii.

| | | UnFVF | UseFVF |
|---|---|---|---|
| **5** | | | |
| 5¢ | blue | 1250. | 950. |
| | line through *HONOLULU* | 2750. | 3250. |

**1853-61. KAMEHAMEHA III REPRINT ISSUE**

| | | UnFVF | UseFVF |
|---|---|---|---|
| **5** | | | |
| 5¢ | bright blue | 60.00 | |

**1853-61. KAMEHANEHA III ISSUE** Intaglio, imperforate.

on 13c

| | | UnFVF | UseFVF |
|---|---|---|---|
| **6** | | | |
| | dull red | 6500. | 9000. |

 7

| | | UnFVF | UseFVF |
|---|---|---|---|
| **7** | | | |
| 13¢ | dull red | 600. | 900. |

*Thick wove paper; No. 6 with pen-written overprint.*

**1853-61. KAMEHAMEHA III REPRINT ISSUE**

| | | UnFVF | UseFVF |
|---|---|---|---|
| **7** | | | |
| 13¢ | dull rose | 250. | |

**1857-61. KAMEHAMEHA III ISSUE** Thin white wove paper.

| | | UnFVF | UseFVF |
|---|---|---|---|
| **8** | | | |
| 5¢ | light blue, 1851 | 600. | 575. |
| **9** | | UnFVF | UseFVF |
| 5¢ | light blue on bluish, 1861 | 250. | 250. |
| | line through *HONOLULU* | 650. | |
| | Double impression | | |

*Reprints on ordinary white ove paper.*

**1863. INTER ISLAND ISSUE** numerals inscribed at top; type set, imperforate. Thin paper.

| | | UnFVF | UseFVF |
|---|---|---|---|
| **10** | | | |
| 1¢ | blue on bluish | 7000. | 5000. |
| **11** | | UnFVF | UseFVF |
| 2¢ | blue on bluish | 6000. | 3500. |

| | | UnFVF | UseFVF |
|---|---|---|---|
| **12** | | | |
| 2¢ | deep blue on blue | 7500. | 6500. |

**1863. INTER ISLAND REPRINT ISSUE** Color changes, thin paper.

| | | UnFVF | UseFVF |
|---|---|---|---|
| **13** | | | |
| 1¢ | black on grayish, 1863 | 450. | 1000. |
| | tete-beche pair | | |
| **14** | | UnFVF | UseFVF |
| 2¢ | black on grayish, 1863 | 8000. | 600. |
| | *2* near top of frame | 3500. | 3000. |
| | v1. *1 of INTER* omitted | 3000. | 3000. |
| | v. printed on both sides | | |
| **15** | | UnFVF | UseFVF |
| 2¢ | black on greenish blue, (April 1, 1863) | 2750. | 4500. |
| **16** | | UnFVF | UseFVF |
| 2¢ | black on light blue, 1864 | 800. | 600. |

**1864. INTER ISLAND ISSUE** White wove or laid paper.

| | | UnFVF | UseFVF |
|---|---|---|---|
| **17** | | | |
| 1¢ | black | 475. | 1000. |
| **18** | | UnFVF | UseFVF |
| 1¢ | black, | 250. | 2000. |
| | *HA* in left panel | 2500. | |
| | tete-beche pair | 6000. | |

**19**

| | | UnFVF | UseFVF |
|---|---|---|---|
| 2¢ | black | 325. | 475. |

**20**

| | | UnFVF | UseFVF |
|---|---|---|---|
| 2¢ | black, | 250. | 1000. |
| | v. *I* of *INTER* omitted | 2250. | |
| | v1. *PO TAGE* | 1000. | |

**1865. INTER ISLAND ISSUE** Numerals, inscribed INTERISLAND in left panel; type-set imperforate.

**21**

| | | UnFVF | UseFVF |
|---|---|---|---|
| 1¢ | dark blue | 250. | |

**22**

| | | UnFVF | UseFVF |
|---|---|---|---|
| 2¢ | dark blue | 6500. | |

**23**

| | | UnFVF | UseFVF |
|---|---|---|---|
| 5¢ | deep blue on blue | 500. | 750. |
| | tete-beche pair | 5000. | |

**1865. INTER ISLAND ISSUE** *HAWAIIAN POSTAGE* in both left and right panels.

**24**

| | | UnFVF | UseFVF |
|---|---|---|---|
| 5¢ | dark blue on blue | 675. | 475. |
| | tete-beche pair | 7500. | |

*No. 10-23; 10 different types. Gutter pair, tete-beche gutter pair exits.*

**1861-63. KAMEHAMEHA IV ISSUE**

25 *Kamehameha IV*

**25**

| | | UnFVF | UseFVF |
|---|---|---|---|
| 2¢ | pale rose red | 225. | 200. |
| | deep rose red | 1500. | 2000. |
| | p. vertical laid paper | | |

**1869. KAMEHAMEHA IV RE-ISSUE**

**25**

| | | UnFVF | UseFVF |
|---|---|---|---|
| 2¢ | red, 1869 | 48.00 | 90.00 |

*Not issued for postal purposes. Sold at Honolulu Post Office with or without overprint CANCELLED.*

**1861-63. KAMEHAMEHA IV ISSUE**

**26**

| | | UnFVF | UseFVF |
|---|---|---|---|
| 2¢ | pale rose red | 225. | 150. |
| | deep rose red (1863) | 225. | 325. |

**1886-89. KAMEHAMEHA IV REPRINTS ISSUE**

**26**

| | | UnFVF | UseFVF |
|---|---|---|---|
| 2¢ | dull vermilion, 1886, | 165. | 165. |

**26A**

| | | UnFVF | UseFVF |
|---|---|---|---|
| 2¢ | dull scarlet, 1889, | | |

*These 2 reprints were made in order to have complete-sets of Hawaiian stamps for sale. In 1885 original plate could not be found, so a copy of the reissue 2¢ red was sent to the American Bank Note Co., and from it a new plate was engraved and 10,000 stamps (No.N25) printed (5,000 of these overprinted SPECIMEN in blue). Subsequently (1887) the missing plate of the reissue was found, retouched and 37,500 stamps (No. 26) printed from it during 1889-90. In all remaining unsold were overprinted REPRINT.*

**1864-75. PORTRAITS ISSUE** BEP, intaglio, perforated 12.

27 *Princess Victoria*

**27**

| | | UnFVF | UseFVF |
|---|---|---|---|
| 1¢ | purple, 1871 | 8.50 | 5.50 |

28 *Kamehameha IV (1834-63) reigned 1854-63, vainly sought U.S. reciprocal trade agreements, made English the school language.*

**28**

| | | UnFVF | UseFVF |
|---|---|---|---|
| 2¢ | orange red | 14.00 | 7.50 |

29, 36, 37 *David Kalakaua (1836-91), elected king to succeed Lunalilo (No.47) in 1874. 1877 revolution forced from him a constitution guaranteeing responsible government.*

**29**

| | | UnFVF | UseFVF |
|---|---|---|---|
| 2¢ | deep brown, 1875 | 7.50 | 2.50 |

*No. 29 bisected and used with 5¢ stamp to make up 6¢ rate to U.S.*

**30**

| | | UnFVF | UseFVF |
|---|---|---|---|
| 5¢ | deep blue, 1866 | 135. | 21.00 |

*No. 30 traces of frame lines around design.*

**31**

| | | UnFVF | UseFVF |
|---|---|---|---|
| 6¢ | emerald green, 1871 | 26.00 | 7.25 |

32, 44 *Prince William Pitt Leleiohoku, died 1877.*

**32**

| | | UnFVF | UseFVF |
|---|---|---|---|
| 12¢ | black, 1875 | 50.00 | 22.50 |

33 *Mataio Kekuanada, father of Xamehameha.*

**33**

| | | UnFVF | UseFVF |
|---|---|---|---|
| 18¢ | dull carmine red, 1871 | 75.00 | 22.50 |
| | no gum | 17.00 | |

**1882-91. ISSUE** No. T29-32 and new designs; engraved, perforated 12.

34,35 *Princess Likelike (Mrs. Archibald Cleghorn).*

| 34 | | UnFVF | UseFVF |
|---|---|---|---|
| 1¢ | **1882 prussian blue** | 5.00 | 10.00 |

| 35 | | UnFVF | UseFVF |
|---|---|---|---|
| 1¢ | **blue green**, 1883, T34 | 3.25 | 1.80 |

| 36 | | UnFVF | UseFVF |
|---|---|---|---|
| 2¢ | **lilac rose**, 1882 T29 | 120. | 45.00 |

| 37 | | UnFVF | UseFVF |
|---|---|---|---|
| 2¢ | **deep rose**, 1886, T29 | 4.50 | 1.25 |

## 1890-91. Lydia Kamehameha Issue  BEP, intaglio, perforated 12.

38 *Lydia Kamehameha (Mrs. John O Dominis, 1837-1917), sister of Kalakaua, reigned for 2 years as Queen Liliuokalani. Deposed in 1893, she swore allegiance to the republic after an abortive counter-revolution in 1895. She is author of the best-known Hawaiian song, Aloha Oe.*

| 38 | | UnFVF | UseFVF |
|---|---|---|---|
| 2¢ | **deep violet blue**, 1890 | 10.50 | 2.75 |
| | v. horizontal pair, imperforate | 2250. | |

| 39 | | UnFVF | UseFVF |
|---|---|---|---|
| 5¢ | **bright blue**, T30 | 14.00 | 2.70 |
| | v. horizontal pair, imperforate | 2250. | |

| 40 | | UnFVF | UseFVF |
|---|---|---|---|
| 5¢ | **deep blue**, 1891, T30 | 120. | 125. |

## 1882-83. Kalakaua Issue

| 41 | | UnFVF | UseFVF |
|---|---|---|---|
| 10¢ | **black**, 1882 | 30.00 | 16.75 |

| 42 | | UnFVF | UseFVF |
|---|---|---|---|
| 10¢ | **vermilion**, 1883, T41 | 30.00 | 12.00 |

| 43 | | UnFVF | UseFVF |
|---|---|---|---|
| 10¢ | **red brown**, 1884, T41 | 27.50 | 8.00 |

| 44 | | UnFVF | UseFVF |
|---|---|---|---|
| 12¢ | **red purple**, 1883, T32 | 85.00 | 30.00 |

## 1882. Queen Kapiolani Issue

45 *Queen Kapiolani*

| 45 | | UnFVF | UseFVF |
|---|---|---|---|
| 15¢ | **red brown** | 50.00 | 25.00 |

## 1883. Kamehameha the Great Statue Issue

46 *Bronze statue, sculputured by Gould.*

| 46 | | UnFVF | UseFVF |
|---|---|---|---|
| 25¢ | **black violet**, 1883 | 120. | 48.00 |

## 1883. William C. Lunalilo Issue

47 *William C. Lunalilo (1835-74), whom the legislature unanimously elected king in 1873, was liberal, pro-American and beloved, but died within 13 months.*

| 47 | | UnFVF | UseFVF |
|---|---|---|---|
| 50¢ | **orange red**, 1883 | 165. | 72.50 |

## 1883. Queen Emma Kaleleonalani Issue

48 *Dowager Queen Emma Kaleleonalani, widow of Kamehameha IV, lost the 1874 election to Kalakaua, which caused a week's rioting in Honolulu.*

| 48 | | UnFVF | UseFVF |
|---|---|---|---|
| $1 | **rose red**, | 235. | 125. |
| | Maltese cross cancellation | 45.00 | |

## 1893. Provisional Govt. Issue  Overthrow of monarchy; Nos.27-48 overprinted. Nos. 49-60 in red, Nos. 61-69 black.

| 49 | | UnFVF | UseFVF |
|---|---|---|---|
| 1¢ | **purple** | 6.50 | 10.50 |
| | v. double overprint | 180. | |
| | v2. 189 | 400. | |
| | v3. w/o period after *GOVT* | 200. | |

| 50 | | UnFVF | UseFVF |
|---|---|---|---|
| 1¢ | **prussian blue** | 5.00 | 10.00 |
| | v. double overprint | 130. | |
| | v1. w/o period after *GOVT* | 135. | |
| | v2. pair, one w/o overprint | 775. | |

| 51 | | UnFVF | UseFVF |
|---|---|---|---|
| 1¢ | **bright green** | 1.80 | 3.00 |
| | v. double overprint | 600. | 450. |
| | v1. pair, one w/o overprint | 10000. | |

| 52 | | UnFVF | UseFVF |
|---|---|---|---|
| 2¢ | **deep brown** | 8.00 | 16.00 |
| | v. double overprint | 300. | |
| | v1. w/o period after *GOVT* | 300. | |

| 53 | | UnFVF | UseFVF |
|---|---|---|---|
| 2¢ | **slate violet** | 5.25 | 5.25 |
| | v. double overprint | 850. | 650. |
| | v1. inverted overprint | 4000. | 2500. |
| | v2. 18 3 | 600. | 500. |

| 54 | | UnFVF | UseFVF |
|---|---|---|---|
| 5¢ | **bright blue** | 6.00 | 2.50 |
| | v. double overprintd | 5000. | 1250. |
| | v1. inverted overprint | 1250. | |

| 55 | | UnFVF | UseFVF |
|---|---|---|---|
| 5¢ | **indigo** | 10.50 | 25.00 |
| | v. double overprint | 650. | |
| | v1. w/o period after *GOVT* | 225. | |

| 56 | | UnFVF | UseFVF |
|---|---|---|---|
| 6¢ | **emerald green** | 13.00 | 20.00 |
| | v. double overprint | 1250. | |
| | v1. black overprint | 15000. | 30000. |

| 57 | | UnFVF | UseFVF |
|---|---|---|---|
| 10¢ | **black** | 8.50 | 14.00 |
| | v. double overprint | 700. | 300. |

| 57A | | UnFVF | UseFVF |
|---|---|---|---|
| 10¢ | **red brown** | 11000. | 13500. |

| 58 | | UnFVF | UseFVF |
|---|---|---|---|
| 12¢ | **black** | 8.50 | 17.00 |
| | v. double overprint | 2000. | |

| 59 | | UnFVF | UseFVF |
|---|---|---|---|
| 12¢ | **red purple** | 150. | 200. |

| 60 | | UnFVF | UseFVF |
|---|---|---|---|
| 25¢ | **black violet** | 25.00 | 40.00 |
| | v double overprint | 375. | |
| | V1. w/o period after *GOVT* | 250. | |

| 61 | | UnFVF | UseFVF |
|---|---|---|---|
| 2¢ | **orange red** | 60.00 | 70.00 |
| | v. w/o period after *GOVT* | 250. | 250. |

| 62 | | | UnFVF | UseFVF |
|---|---|---|---|---|
| 2¢ | deep rose | | 1.50 | 2.25 |
| | v. | double overprint | 2500. | |
| | v1. | w/o period after *GOVT* | 50.00 | 60.00 |
| **62A** | | | **UnFVF** | **UseFVF** |
| 6¢ | green | | 11000. | 13500. |
| **63** | | | **UnFVF** | **UseFVF** |
| 10¢ | vermilion | | 13.50 | 27.50 |
| | v. | double overprint | 650. | |
| **64** | | | **UnFVF** | **UseFVF** |
| 10¢ | red brown | | 7.50 | 12.50 |
| | v. | red overprint | 15000. | 30000. |
| **65** | | | **UnFVF** | **UseFVF** |
| 12¢ | red purple | | 270. | 500. |
| **66** | | | **UnFVF** | **UseFVF** |
| 15¢ | red brown | | 22.50 | 32.50 |
| | v. | double overprint | 2000. | |
| **67** | | | **UnFVF** | **UseFVF** |
| 18¢ | dull carmine red | | 26.50 | 37.50 |
| | v. | double overprint | 225. | |
| | v1. | 18 3 | 375. | |
| | v2. | w/o period after *GOVT* | 300. | 300. |
| | v3. | pair, one w/o overprint | 2500. | |
| **68** | | | **UnFVF** | **UseFVF** |
| 50¢ | orange red | | 65.00 | 95.00 |
| | v. | double overprint | 325. | |
| | v1. | w/o period after *GOVT* | 400. | |
| **69** | | | **UnFVF** | **UseFVF** |
| $1 | rose red | | 120. | 190. |
| | v. | w/o period after *GOVT* | 425. | 400. |

**1894-99. PICTORIALS ISSUE** BEP, intaglio, perforated 12.

70, 82 *Arms*

| 70 | | UnFVF | UseFVF |
|---|---|---|---|
| 1¢ | orange yellow | 1.80 | 1.50 |

71, 83 *Honolulu*

| 71 | | UnFVF | UseFVF |
|---|---|---|---|
| 2¢ | brown drab | 2.40 | .90 |

72 *Kamehameha I*

| 72 | | UnFVF | UseFVF |
|---|---|---|---|
| 5¢ | carmine red | 4.00 | 1.80 |

73 *Hope of Statehood.*

| 73 | | UnFVF | UseFVF |
|---|---|---|---|
| 10¢ | yellow green | 5.30 | 4.00 |

74 *S.S. Arawa.*

| 74 | | UnFVF | UseFVF |
|---|---|---|---|
| 12¢ | deep blue | 12.00 | 20.00 |

75 *Sanford Ballard Dole (1858-1926), justice of Hawaiian Supreme Court, led 1893 revolution, was 1st Pres. of Hawaii, 1894-98, 1st territorial governor. 1900-03.*

| 75 | | UnFVF | UseFVF |
|---|---|---|---|
| 25¢ | deep blue | 12.00 | 20.00 |

**1896. OFFICIALS ISSUE** BEP, intaglio, perforated 12.

| 76 | | UnFVF | UseFVF |
|---|---|---|---|
| 2¢ | yellow green | 37.50 | 20.00 |
| **77** | | **UnFVF** | **UseFVF** |
| 5¢ | sepia | 37.50 | 20.00 |
| **78** | | **UnFVF** | **UseFVF** |
| 6¢ | ultramarine | 37.50 | 20.00 |
| **79** | | **UnFVF** | **UseFVF** |
| 10¢ | carmine | 37.50 | 20.00 |
| **80** | | **UnFVF** | **UseFVF** |
| 12¢ | orange | 37.50 | 20.00 |
| **81** | | **UnFVF** | **UseFVF** |
| 25¢ | deep violet | 37.50 | 20.00 |

**1899. U.S. GOVERNMENT ISSUE** T70-72 changed colors; No. 84 inscribed CENTS at bottom. BEP, intaglio, perforated 12.

| 82 | | UnFVF | UseFVF |
|---|---|---|---|
| 1¢ | deep blue green | 1.50 | 1.40 |
| **83** | | **UnFVF** | **UseFVF** |
| 2¢ | rose carmine | 1.30 | .85 |
| | v. horizontal pair, imperforate | 1700. | |
| **84** | | **UnFVF** | **UseFVF** |
| 5¢ | deep blue | 5.50 | 3.00 |

*Since 1899: U.S. Stamps have been used in Hawaii.*

# *Puerto Rico*
## Regular Postal Issues

### 1898. PONCE PROVISIONAL ISSUE

191

| | | | UnFVF | UseFVF |
|---|---|---|---|---|
| **191** | | | | |
| **5¢** | **violet,** Handstamp on white or yellowish paper | | 2750. | |

### 1898. COAMO PROVISIONAL ISSUE

CORREOS

**5 CTS.**

COAMO

192 *Coamo provisional issue; type-set in sheet of 10; 4 varieties; imperforate; violet control mark F. Santiago (mayor of Coamo).*

**5 CTS.**    **5 CTS**    **5 CTS.**

| | | UnFVF | UseFVF |
|---|---|---|---|
| **192** | | | |
| **5¢** | **Black Type I** | 300. | 325. |
| | t.   Type II | 310. | 325. |
| | t1.  Type III | 325. | 360. |
| | t2.  Type IV | 360. | 375. |

### 1899. PORTO RICO OVERPRINT ISSUE

193 *No. 193-197 overprint at 25 degree angle.*

| | | UnFVF | UseFVF |
|---|---|---|---|
| **193** | | | |
| **1¢** | **deep green** | | |
| | v1. pair, 36 degree & 25 degree | 2.50 | 1.00 |
| | v2. PORTO RICU ovpt. 36 degrees. | 9.50 | |
| | a.   overprint 36 degree | | |
| | b.   overprint 25 degree | 3.50 | 1.25 |

194 *No. 193-197 overprint at 36 degree angle.*

| | | UnFVF | UseFVF |
|---|---|---|---|
| **194** | | | |
| **2¢** | **carmine** | | |
| | v1. pair, 36 degree & 25 degree overprints | | |
| | av1. PORTO RICU ovpt. 36 degrees. | | |
| | av2. FORTO RICO ovpt. 36 degrees. | | |
| | bv1. PORTU RICO ovpt. 25 degrees. | | |
| | bv2. PURTO RICO ovpt. 25 degrees. | | |

195 *No. 193-197 overprint at 36 degree angle.*

| | UnFVF | UseFVF |
|---|---|---|
| **195** | | |

| | | | UnFVF | UseFVF |
|---|---|---|---|---|
| **5¢** | **dark blue** | | 3.00 | 1.80 |
| **196** | | | UnFVF | UseFVF |
| **8¢** | **purple brown** | | | |
| | a.   ovpt. 36 degrees. | | 12.00 | 9.50 |
| | b.   ovpt. 25 degrees. | | 16.50 | 9.50 |
| | a1. pair, 36 degree & 25 degree overprints | | 32.50 | |
| | av2. FORTO RICO ovpt. 36 degrees. | | 60.00 | 60.00 |
| | av3. PORTO RIC ovpt. 36 degrees. | | | |
| **197** | | | UnFVF | UseFVF |
| **10¢** | **orange brown** | | | |
| | v1. FORTO RICO | | 6.50 | 3.25 |

### 1899. POSTAGE DUE ISSUE

198 *Overprint at 36 or 25 degree angle.*

| | | UnFVF | UseFVF |
|---|---|---|---|
| **198** | | | |
| **1¢** | **brown carmine** | | |
| **199** | | UnFVF | UseFVF |
| **2¢** | **brown carmine** | | |
| **200** | | UnFVF | UseFVF |
| **10¢** | **brown carmine** | | |

### 1900. PUERTO RICO ISSUE

201

| | | UnFVF | UseFVF |
|---|---|---|---|
| **201** | | | |
| **1¢** | | 1.80 | .95 |
| **202** | | UnFVF | UseFVF |
| **2¢** | **carmine** | 1.80 | .85 |
| **203** | | UnFVF | UseFVF |
| **2¢** | **red** | 1.90 | .85 |
| | v.   inverted overprint | 2400. | |

# Ryukyu Islands

## Regular Postal Issues

### 1948-49. FIRST PICTORIAL ISSUE

1, 3 *Edible Cycad Bush*

| **1** | | MNHVF | UseVF |
|---|---|---|---|
| **5s** | purple magenta *(July 1, 1948)* | 6.00 | 5.00 |

2, 5 *Lilly*

| **2** | | MNHVF | UseVF |
|---|---|---|---|
| **10s** | pale green | 4.00 | 3.00 |
| **3** | | MNHVF | UseVF |
| **20s** | pale green | 3.50 | 3.00 |

4, 6 *Trading Junk*

| **4** | | MNHVF | UseVF |
|---|---|---|---|
| **30s** | red | 6.00 | 3.00 |
| **5** | | MNHVF | UseVF |
| **40s** | purple magenta | 125. | 100. |
| **6** | | MNHVF | UseVF |
| **50s** | dull ultramarine | 3.50 | 3.00 |

7 *Farmer and dawn.*

| **7** | | MNHVF | UseVF |
|---|---|---|---|
| **1y** | dull ultramarine | 150. | 90.00 |

### 1949. SECOND PICTORIAL ISSUE

| **7a** | | MNHVF | UseVF |
|---|---|---|---|
| **5¢** | purple magenta *(July 18, 1949)* | 4.50 | 2.50 |
| **7b** | | MNHVF | UseVF |
| **10¢** | pale green | 5.00 | 2.50 |
| **7c** | | MNHVF | UseVF |
| **20¢** | pale green | 5.00 | 2.75 |
| **7d** | | MNHVF | UseVF |
| **30¢** | red | 4.50 | 3.75 |
| **7e** | | MNHVF | UseVF |
| **40¢** | purple magenta | 4.50 | 3.25 |
| **7f** | | MNHVF | UseVF |
| **50¢** | dull ultramarine | 5.00 | 3.50 |
| **7g** | | MNHVF | UseVF |
| **1y** | dull ultramarine | 5.00 | 3.00 |

### 1950-58. PICTORIAL ISSUE

8 *Roof tiles*

| **8** | | | MNHVF | UseVF |
|---|---|---|---|---|
| **50¢** | | carmine rose | .20 | .15 |
| | p. | carmine rose on white paper, *(Sept. 6, 1958)* | .35 | .35 |

9 *Girl*

| **9** | | MNHVF | UseVF |
|---|---|---|---|
| **1y** | blue | 3.00 | .75 |

10 *Shuri Castle*

| **10** | | MNHVF | UseVF |
|---|---|---|---|
| **2y** | purple | 12.50 | 2.50 |

11 *Guardian dragon*

| **11** | | MNHVF | UseVF |
|---|---|---|---|
| **3y** | carmine rose | 25.00 | 6.00 |

12 *Two women*

| **12** | | MNHVF | UseVF |
|---|---|---|---|
| **4y** | dark slate green | 7.50 | 2.50 |

*Sea shells*

| **13** | | MNHVF | UseVF |
|---|---|---|---|
| **5y** | emerald green | 12.50 | 4.00 |

### 1950. AIR MAIL ISSUE

14

| 14 | | | MNHVF | UseVF |
|---|---|---|---|---|
| 8y | blue | | 50.00 | 15.00 |
| 15 | | | MNHVF | UseVF |
| 12y | deep emerald | | 25.00 | 15.00 |
| 16 | | | MNHVF | UseVF |
| 16y | carmine rose | | 25.00 | 12.50 |

## 1950. SPECIAL DELIVERY ISSUE

17 Dragon

| 17 | | MNHVF | UseVF |
|---|---|---|---|
| 5y | bright blue | 30.00 | 12.50 |

## 1951. RYUKYU UNIVERSITY ISSUE

18

| 18 | | | MNHVF | UseVF |
|---|---|---|---|---|
| 3y | chocolate | (Feb. 12, 1951) | 45.00 | 20.00 |

## 1951. ARBOR WEEK ISSUE

| 19 | | MNHVF | UseVF |
|---|---|---|---|
| 3y | emerald green | 42.00 | 20.00 |

## 1951-54. AIRMAIL ISSUE

20 Heavenly maiden

| 20 | | MNHVF | UseVF |
|---|---|---|---|
| 13y | prussian blue Oct.1, 1951) | 2.00 | .50 |
| 21 | | MNHVF | UseVF |
| 18y | light green (Oct. 1, 1951) | 3.50 | 2.00 |
| 22 | | MNHVF | UseVF |
| 30y | bright magenta (Oct. 1, 1951) | 4.50 | 1.25 |
| 23 | | MNHVF | UseVF |
| 40y | purple (Aug. 16, 1954) | 6.50 | 2.00 |
| 24 | | MNHVF | UseVF |
| 50y | yellow orange (Aug. 16, 1954) | 9.00 | 2.50 |

**1952. OVERPRINT ISSUE** Nos. 25, 26 overprinted in sheets of 100 (10x10).

No. 25, types 1-6: 1st printing: narrow bar spacing, top characters small (1), large (2). 2nd printing: wide bar spacing, top characters small (3), large (4) or mixed (5). 3rd printing: wide bar spacing, top characters thin, 10 yen about 7.8mm long (instead of 7mm).

No. 26, types 3-5: top characters small (3), large (4) or mixed (5).

25

| 25 | | MNHVF | UseVF |
|---|---|---|---|
| 10y on 50sT1,2 (Jan. 1) | | 10.00 | 4.00 |
| v. T3, 4 (June 5) | | 20.00 | 10.00 |
| v1.T5 (June 5), T6 (Dec. 8) | | 35.00 | 20.00 |

| 26 | | MNHVF | UseVF |
|---|---|---|---|
| 100y on 2ypurple, T4 (June 16, 1952) | | 1200. | 600. |
| v. T3 | | | |
| v1. T5 | | | |

## 1952. ESTABLISHMENT RYUKYU ISLAND GOVERNMENT ISSUE

27

| 27 | | MNHVF | UseVF |
|---|---|---|---|
| 3y | deep claret (April 1, 1952) | 100. | 20.00 |

## 1952-53. HISTORICAL SITES ISSUE

28

| 28 | | MNHVF | UseVF |
|---|---|---|---|
| 1y | rose red | .20 | .15 |

29 Main hall, Shuri Castle.

| 29 | | MNHVF | UseVF |
|---|---|---|---|
| 2y | deep emerald | .25 | .15 |

30 Shuri Gate

| 30 | | MNHVF | UseVF |
|---|---|---|---|
| 3y | turquoise | .50 | .15 |

31 Stone gate, Soenji Temple.

| 31 | | MNHVF | UseVF |
|---|---|---|---|
| 6y | blue (Jan. 20, 1953) | 4.00 | 2.50 |

32 Benzaiten-do Temple

| 32 | | MNHVF | UseVF |
|---|---|---|---|
| 10y | bright rose red (Jan. 20, 1953) | 1.25 | .35 |

33 Sonohan Utaki, Shuri Castle

| 33 | | MNHVF | UseVF |
|---|---|---|---|
| 30y | olive green (Jan. 20, 1953) | 4.00 | 1.50 |

34 *Tansudum, Shuri*

**34**
**50y**   **rose purple** *(Jan. 20, 1953)*

| | MNHVF | UseVF |
|---|---|---|
| | 7.50 | 1.50 |

35 Stone bridge, Hosho Pond, Enkaku Temple

**35**
**100y**   **brown claret** *(Jan. 20, 1953)*

| | MNHVF | UseVF |
|---|---|---|
| | 15.00 | 1.50 |

**1953. MATHEW PERRY ISSUE**

36 *Reception at Shuri Castle*

**36**
**3y**   **purple magenta**

| | MNHVF | UseVF |
|---|---|---|
| | 14.00 | 5.00 |

27 *Perry and the American fleet.*

**37**
**6y**   **dark cobalt**

| | MNHVF | UseVF |
|---|---|---|
| | 2.25 | 1.50 |

**1953. NEWSPAPER WEEK ISSUE**

38 *Chofu Ota*

**38**
**4y**   **yellow brown** *(Oct. 1, 1953)*

| | MNHVF | UseVF |
|---|---|---|
| | 12.00 | 4.00 |

**1954-55. INDUSTRIAL ARTS ISSUE**

39 *Pottery*

**39**
**4y**   **brown** *(June 25, 1954)*

| | MNHVF | UseVF |
|---|---|---|
| | .75 | .15 |

40 *Lacquerware*

**40**
**15y**   **light scarlet** *(June 20, 1955)*

| | MNHVF | UseVF |
|---|---|---|
| | 2.75 | .35 |

41 *Textiles*

**41**
**20y**   **yellow orange** *(June 20, 1955)*

| | MNHVF | UseVF |
|---|---|---|
| | 3.50 | 1.00 |

**1954. NEWSPAPER WEEK ISSUE**

42 *Shigs Toma*

**42**
**4y**   **blue** *(Oct. 1, 1954)*

| | MNHVF | UseVF |
|---|---|---|
| | 12.00 | 4.00 |

**1955. SWEET POTATO ISSUE** Celebrates the 350th anniversary of the introduction of the sweet potato to the Ryukyu Islands.

43 *Noguni Shrine*

**43**
**4y**   **blue** *(Nov. 26, 1955)*

| | MNHVF | UseVF |
|---|---|---|
| | 11.00 | 4.00 |

**1956. ARBOR WEEK ISSUE**

44

**44**
**4y**   **blue green** *(Feb. 18, 1956)*

| | MNHVF | UseVF |
|---|---|---|
| | 11.00 | 4.00 |

**1956. CEREMONIAL DANCERS ISSUE**

45 *Willow dance*

**45**
**5y**   **rose purple** *(May 1, 1956)*

| | MNHVF | UseVF |
|---|---|---|
| | 1.25 | .50 |

46 *Straw hat dance*

| 46 | | | **MNHVF** | **UseVF** |
|---|---|---|---|---|
| 8y | blue violet | | 1.50 | 1.00 |

47 *Warrior costume*

| 47 | | | **MNHVF** | **UseVF** |
|---|---|---|---|---|
| 14y | dark red brown *(June 8, 1956)* | | 2.75 | 1.50 |

## 1956. TELEPHONE ISSUE

48

| 48 | | | **MNHVF** | **UseVF** |
|---|---|---|---|---|
| 4y | blue violet | | 19.00 | 6.00 |

## 1956. NEW YEAR ISSUE

49 *Pine, Bamboo and Plum*

| 49 | | | **MNHVF** | **UseVF** |
|---|---|---|---|---|
| 2y | multicolored *(Dec. 1, 1956)* | | 2.50 | 1.00 |

## 1957. AIRMAIL ISSUE

50 *Heavenly maiden with flute.*

| 50 | | | **MNHVF** | **UseVF** |
|---|---|---|---|---|
| 15y | blue green *(Aug. 1, 1957)* | | 2.00 | .30 |
| **51** | | | **MNHVF** | **UseVF** |
| 20y | deep carmine | | 6.50 | 2.50 |
| **52** | | | **MNHVF** | **UseVF** |
| 35y | light green | | 12.50 | 2.50 |
| **53** | | | **MNHVF** | **UseVF** |
| 45y | light red brown | | 15.00 | 4.00 |
| **54** | | | **MNHVF** | **UseVF** |
| 60y | violet black | | 20.00 | 5.00 |

## 1957. NEWSPAPER WEEK ISSUE

| 55 | | | **MNHVF** | **UseVF** |
|---|---|---|---|---|
| 4y | deep violet blue *(Oct. 1, 1957)* | | 1.50 | 1.00 |

## 1957. NEW YEAR ISSUE

56 *Phoenix*

| 56 | | | **MNHVF** | **UseVF** |
|---|---|---|---|---|
| 2y | multicolored *(Dec. 1, 1957)* | | .40 | .20 |

**1958. POSTAGE STAMP ISSUE** celebrates the 10th anniversary of Ryukyu stamps.

57

| 57 | | | **MNHVF** | **UseVF** |
|---|---|---|---|---|
| 4y | multicolored | | 1.30 | .30 |

## 1958-61. CHANGE TO U.S. CURRENCY ISSUE

58 *Yen symbol and potter sign.*

| 58 | | | **MNHVF** | **UseVF** |
|---|---|---|---|---|
| 1/2¢ | yellow orange | | .20 | .15 |
| | v. imperforate, pair | | 750. | .15 |
| **59** | | | **MNHVF** | **UseVF** |
| 1¢ | pale green | | .20 | .15 |
| **60** | | | **MNHVF** | **UseVF** |
| 2¢ | dark blue | | .35 | .15 |
| **61** | | | **MNHVF** | **UseVF** |
| 3¢ | dark rose red | | .25 | .15 |
| **62** | | | **MNHVF** | **UseVF** |
| 4¢ | light emerald | | .75 | .20 |
| **63** | | | **MNHVF** | **UseVF** |
| 5¢ | brown salmon | | 2.00 | .20 |
| **64** | | | **MNHVF** | **UseVF** |
| 10¢ | turquoise green | | 5.00 | .25 |
| **65** | | | **MNHVF** | **UseVF** |
| 25¢ | blue violet | | 4.00 | .50 |
| | p. gummed paper *(April 20, 1961)* | | 4.00 | .60 |
| **66** | | | **MNHVF** | **UseVF** |
| 50¢ | gray black | | 7.50 | .75 |
| | p. gummed paper *(April 20, 1961)* | | 6.50 | 1.25 |
| **67** | | | **MNHVF** | **UseVF** |
| $1 | light red violet | | 10.00 | 1.50 |

**1958. RESTORATION OF SHURI MON ISSUE** the Gate of Courtsey is on the road to Shuri City.

68 *Gate of Courtsey.*

| 68 | | | **MNHVF** | **UseVF** |
|---|---|---|---|---|
| 3¢ | multicolored *(Oct. 15, 1958)* | | 2.00 | .35 |

## 1958. NEW YEAR'S ISSUE

69 *Lion Dance*

**69**

| | | MNHVF | UseVF |
|---|---|---|---|
| 1-1/2¢ | multicolored *(Dec. 10. 1958)* | .50 | .25 |

### 1959. ARBOR WEEK ISSUE

70

**70**

| | | MNHVF | UseVF |
|---|---|---|---|
| 3¢ | emerald green, blue and red *(April 30, 1959)* | 1.50 | 1.00 |
| v. | red omitted | | |

### 1959. JAPANESE BIOLOGICAL EDUCATION SOCIETY ISSUE

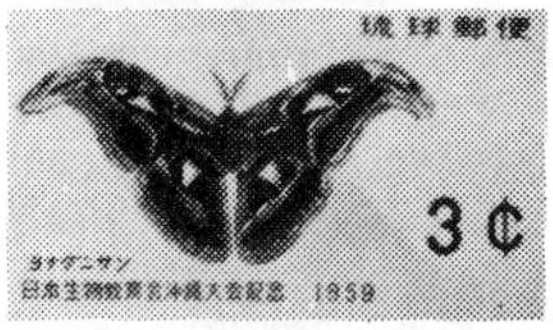

71 *Yonaguni Moth*

**71**

| | | MNHVF | UseVF |
|---|---|---|---|
| 3¢ | multicolored *(July 23, 1959)* | 3.50 | 1.50 |

### 1959. NATIVE FLORA AND FAUNA ISSUE

72 *Hibiscus*

**72**

| | | MNHVF | UseVF |
|---|---|---|---|
| 1/2¢ | multicolored *(Aug. 10, 1959)* | .30 | .15 |

73 *Moorism Idol*

**73**

| | | MNHVF | UseVF |
|---|---|---|---|
| 3¢ | multicolored | 1.25 | .25 |

74 *Sea Shell*

**74**

| | | MNHVF | UseVF |
|---|---|---|---|
| 8¢ | multicolored | 6.00 | 1.25 |

75 *Butterfly*

**75**

| | | MNHVF | UseVF |
|---|---|---|---|
| 13¢ | multicolored | 2.50 | 1.25 |

76 *Jellyfish*

**76**

| | | MNHVF | UseVF |
|---|---|---|---|
| 17¢ | deep violet blue, chestnut and yellow | 17.50 | 5.00 |

### 1959. NEW YEAR'S ISSUE

**77**

| | | MNHVF | UseVF |
|---|---|---|---|
| 1-1/2¢ | multicolored on gold *(Dec. 1, 1959)* | 1.25 | .25 |

### 1959. AIRMAIL OVERPRINT ISSUE

78

**78**

| | MNHVF | UseVF |
|---|---|---|
| 9¢ on 15yblue green *(Dec. 20, 1959)* | 2.50 | .35 |
| v. inverted overprint | 500. | |

**79**

| | MNHVF | UseVF |
|---|---|---|
| 14¢ on 20ydeep carmine | 5.00 | 2.50 |

**80**

| | MNHVF | UseVF |
|---|---|---|
| 19¢ on 35ylight green | 6.00 | 2.75 |

**81**

| | MNHVF | UseVF |
|---|---|---|
| 27¢ on 45ylight red brown | 10.00 | 3.00 |

**82**

| | MNHVF | UseVF |
|---|---|---|
| 35¢ on 60yviolet black | 12.50 | 4.00 |

*Several varieties of overprints exist.*

### 1960. RYUKYU UNIVERSITY ISSUE celebrates it's 10th anniversary.

83

**83**

| | | MNHVF | UseVF |
|---|---|---|---|
| 3¢ | multicolored | 2.00 | 1.25 |

### 1960-61. FLORA AND FANNA REDRAWN ISSUE

83A

**83A**

| | | MNHVF | UseVF |
|---|---|---|---|
| 1/2¢ | multicolored *(Oct. 1961)* | .30 | .15 |

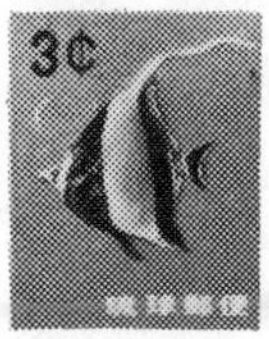

83B

**83B**

| | | MNHVF | UseVF |
|---|---|---|---|
| 3¢ | multicolored *(Aug. 23, 1961)* | 1.75 | .15 |

**84**

| | | MNHVF | UseVF |
|---|---|---|---|
| 84 | | | |
| 8¢ | multicolored *(1961)* | 1.00 | .75 |

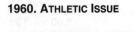

**85**

| | | MNHVF | UseVF |
|---|---|---|---|
| 85 | | | |
| 13¢ | multicolored *(1961)* | 1.50 | .75 |

**86**

| | | MNHVF | UseVF |
|---|---|---|---|
| 86 | | | |
| 17¢ | multicolored *(1961)* | 5.00 | 1.75 |

## 1960. AIRMAIL OVERPRINT ON REGULAR ISSUE

**87**

| | | MNHVF | UseVF |
|---|---|---|---|
| 87 | | | |
| 9¢ on 4y brown #39 *(Aug. 3, 1961)* | | 5.00 | .25 |
| v. inverted overprint | | 3500. | |

**88**

| | | MNHVF | UseVF |
|---|---|---|---|
| 88 | | | |
| 14¢ on 5y rose purple, overprinted brown #45 | | 2.50 | 1.25 |

**89**

| | | MNHVF | UseVF |
|---|---|---|---|
| 89 | | | |
| 19¢ on 15y light claret, overprinted red #40 | | 4.00 | 1.75 |

**90**

| | | MNHVF | UseVF |
|---|---|---|---|
| 90 | | | |
| 27¢ on 14y dark red brown, overprinted blue #47 | | 6.50 | 3.00 |

**91**

| | | MNHVF | UseVF |
|---|---|---|---|
| 91 | | | |
| 35¢ on 20y yellow orange, overprinted green #41 | | 7.50 | 3.00 |

## 1960. DANCES ISSUE

**92**

| | | MNHVF | UseVF |
|---|---|---|---|
| 92 | | | |
| 1¢ | *munjuru (Nov. 1, 1962)* | 2.50 | .50 |

**93**

| | | MNHVF | UseVF |
|---|---|---|---|
| 93 | | | |
| 2-1/2¢ | *inoha* | 1.50 | .50 |

**94**

| | | MNHVF | UseVF |
|---|---|---|---|
| 94 | | | |
| 5¢ | *batoma* | 1.50 | .50 |

**95**

| | | MNHVF | UseVF |
|---|---|---|---|
| 95 | | | |
| 10¢ | *banafu* | 2.00 | .50 |

## 1960. ATHLETIC ISSUE

**96**

| | | MNHVF | UseVF |
|---|---|---|---|
| 96 | | | |
| 3¢ | light blue, deep blue green and orange red *(Nov. 8, 1960)* | 7.50 | 1.75 |

97

**97**
**8¢     orange yellow and blue green**

| | MNHVF | UseVF |
|---|---|---|
| | 1.75 | 1.50 |

## 1960. NEW YEAR'S ISSUE

98

**98**
**1-1/2¢   bistre, blue and brown red** *(Dec. 10, 1960)*

| | MNHVF | UseVF |
|---|---|---|
| | 2.50 | .35 |

## 1960. SECOND NATIONAL CENSUS ISSUE

99 *Egret in flight.*

**99**
**3¢     brown**

| | MNHVF | UseVF |
|---|---|---|
| | 7.25 | 2.00 |

## 1961. ARBOR WEEK ISSUE

100

**100**
**3¢     yellow green, red and blue green** *(May 1, 1961)*

| | MNHVF | UseVF |
|---|---|---|
| | 2.50 | 1.25 |

## 1961. NAHA CITY ISSUE

101

**101**
**3¢     turquoise blue** *(May 20, 1961)*

| | MNHVF | UseVF |
|---|---|---|
| | 3.50 | 1.50 |

## 1961-71. DANCERS ISSUE Country name added in English.

102

**102**
**1¢       *munjuru (Dec. 5, 1961)*

| | MNHVF | UseVF |
|---|---|---|
| | .10 | .05 |

102 A

**102A**
**2-1/2¢    *inoba (June 20, 1962)*

| | MNHVF | UseVF |
|---|---|---|
| | .15 | .08 |

102 B

**102B**
**4¢       *nuwabushi (Nov. 1, 1971)*

| | MNHVF | UseVF |
|---|---|---|
| | .20 | .10 |

102 C

**102C**
**5¢       *batoma (June 20, 1961)*

| | MNHVF | UseVF |
|---|---|---|
| | .25 | .10 |

**102D**
**10¢      *banafu (June 20, 1962)*

| | MNHVF | UseVF |
|---|---|---|
| | .50 | .10 |

**103**
**20¢      *shundun (Jan. 20, 1964)*

| | MNHVF | UseVF |
|---|---|---|
| | 1.25 | .25 |

104

**104**
**25¢      *baodori (Feb. 1, 1962)*

| | MNHVF | UseVF |
|---|---|---|
| | 1.25 | .40 |

105

**105**
**50¢      *nobori-kuduchi (Sept. 1, 1961)*

| | MNHVF | UseVF |
|---|---|---|
| | 2.50 | .40 |

106

| 106 | | MNHVF | UseVF |
|---|---|---|---|
| $1 | *koteibushi (Sept. 1, 1961)* | 5.00 | .75 |

## 1961. Airmail Issue

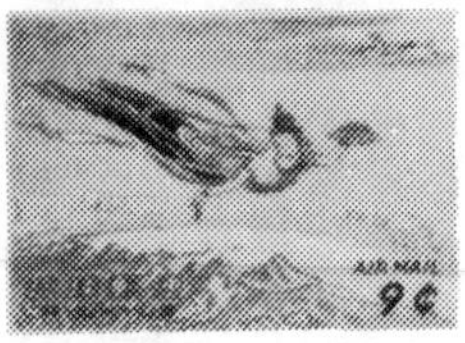

107

| 107 | | MNHVF | UseVF |
|---|---|---|---|
| 9¢ | multicolored, *(Sept. 21, 1961)* | .50 | .10 |

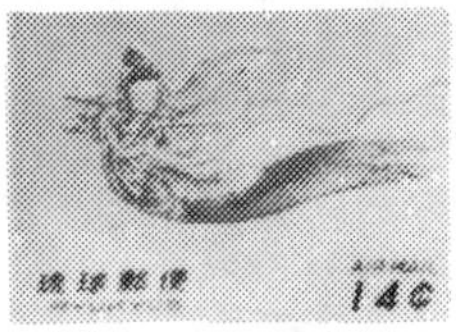

108

| 108 | | MNHVF | UseVF |
|---|---|---|---|
| 14¢ | multicolored | .75 | .40 |

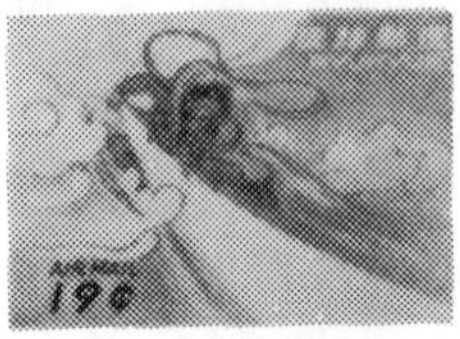

109

| 109 | | MNHVF | UseVF |
|---|---|---|---|
| 19¢ | multicolored | 1.00 | .40 |

110

| 110 | | MNHVF | UseVF |
|---|---|---|---|
| 27¢ | multicolored | 1.50 | .75 |

111

| 111 | | MNHVF | UseVF |
|---|---|---|---|
| 35¢ | multicolored | 2.00 | .75 |

## 1961. Merger of Townships Issue Takammil, Kanegu Shiku and Miwa merged into Itoman.

112 *White Silver Temple*

| 112 | | MNHVF | UseVF |
|---|---|---|---|
| 3¢ | red brown *(Oct. 1, 1961)* | 2.00 | 1.00 |
| | v. horizontal pair, imperforate between | 300. | |
| | v1. vertical pair, imperforate between | 500. | |

## 1961. Book Week Issue

113

| 113 | | MNHVF | UseVF |
|---|---|---|---|
| 3¢ | multicolored *(Nov. 12, 1961)* | 2.00 | 1.00 |

## 1961. New Year's Issue

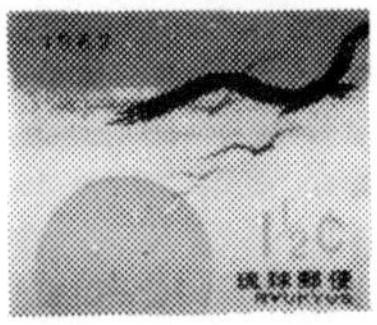

114

| 114 | | MNHVF | UseVF |
|---|---|---|---|
| 1-1/2¢ | gold, vermilion and black *(Dec. 10, 1961)* | 3.50 | .35 |

## 1962. Ryukyu Islands Government Issue

119 *Government Buildings*

| 119 | | MNHVF | UseVF |
|---|---|---|---|
| 1-1/2¢ | multicolored *(April 1, 1962)* | .90 | .50 |
| 120 | | MNHVF | UseVF |
| 3¢ | blue green, red and greenish gray | 1.25 | .75 |

## 1962. Malaria Issue draws attention to the WHO drive to eradicate Malaria.

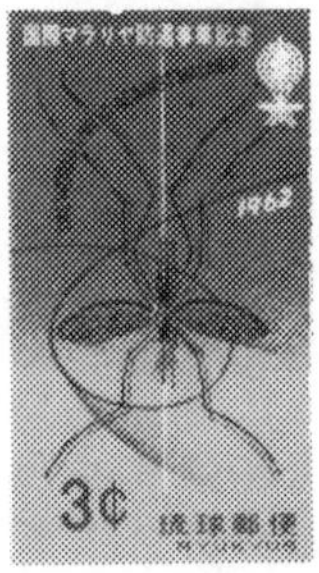

121

| 121 | | MNHVF | UseVF |
|---|---|---|---|
| 3¢ | multicolored *(April 7, 1962)* | 1.00 | .65 |

122

| 122 | | MNHVF | UseVF |
|---|---|---|---|
| 8¢ | deep blue, yellow and red | 2.00 | 1.50 |

**1962. CHILDREN'S DAY ISSUE**

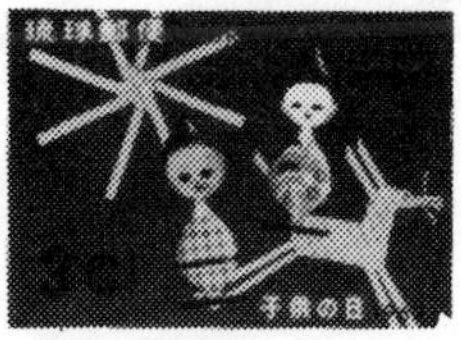

123 *Dolls and toys*

| 123 | | MNHVF | UseVF |
|---|---|---|---|
| 3¢ | multicolored *(May 5, 1962)* | 2.50 | 1.00 |

**1962. FLOWER ISSUE**

124

| 124 | | MNHVF | UseVF |
|---|---|---|---|
| 1/2¢ | *hibiscus tiliacus (June 1, 1962)* | | |

125

| 125 | | MNHVF | UseVF |
|---|---|---|---|
| 3¢ | *eythrila varieta orientalis* | | |

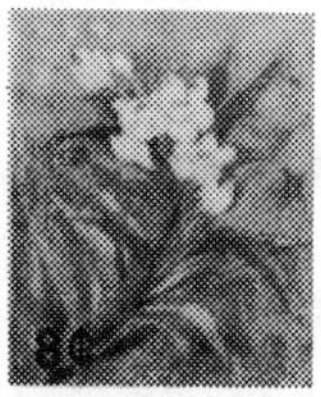

| 126 | | MNHVF | UseVF |
|---|---|---|---|
| 8¢ | *schima superba* | | |

127

| 127 | | MNHVF | UseVF |
|---|---|---|---|
| 13¢ | *impatiens balsamina* | | |

128

| 128 | | MNHVF | UseVF |
|---|---|---|---|
| 17¢ | *alpinia specisa* | | |

*See also Nos. 142, 244, 244A.*

**1962. STAMP WEEK ISSUE**

129

| 129 | | MNHVF | UseVF |
|---|---|---|---|
| 3¢ | multicolored *(July 5, 1962)* | 5.00 | 2.00 |

**1962. JAPAN KENDO MEETING ISSUE**

130

| 130 | | MNHVF | UseVF |
|---|---|---|---|
| 3¢ | multicolored | 6.50 | 1.50 |

**1962. NEW YEAR'S ISSUE**

131 Rabbit near water, textile design.

| 131 | | MNHVF | UseVF |
|---|---|---|---|
| 1-1/2¢ | multicolored *(Dec. 10, 1962)* | 1.25 | .25 |

**1963. ADULT DAY ISSUE**

132 *Stone relief of Man and Woman.*

| 132 | | MNHVF | UseVF |
|---|---|---|---|
| 3¢ | gold, black and blue *(Jan. 15, 1963)* | 1.50 | .75 |

**1963. REFORESTATION ISSUE**

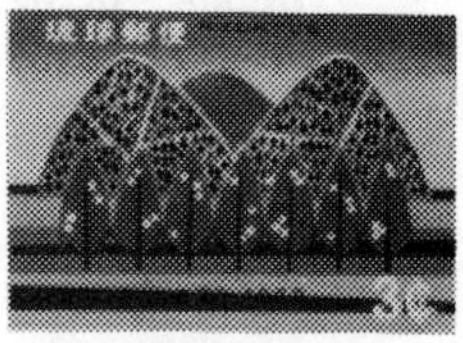

133

| 133 | | MNHVF | UseVF |
|---|---|---|---|
| 3¢ | multicolored *(March 25, 1963)* | 1.50 | .75 |

**1963. DEFINITIVE ISSUE**

134 *Gooseneck cactus*

| 134 | | MNHVF | UseVF |
|---|---|---|---|
| 1-1/2¢ | multicolored *(April 5, 1963)* | .10 | .05 |

## 1963. OPENING OF ROUND ROAD ISSUE

135

| | | MNHVF | UseVF |
|---|---|---|---|
| **135** | | | |
| 3¢ | multicolored *(April 30, 1963)* | 2.00 | .75 |

## 1963. BIRD WEEK ISSUE

136

| | | MNHVF | UseVF |
|---|---|---|---|
| **136** | | | |
| 3¢ | **multicolored** *(May 10, 1963)* | 2.00 | .75 |

## 1963. SHIOYA BRIDGE ISSUE Commemorates opening of bridge over Shioya Bay.

137

| | | MNHVF | UseVF |
|---|---|---|---|
| **137** | | | |
| 3¢ | **multicolored** *(June 5, 1963)* | 2.00 | .75 |

## 1963. STAMP WEEK ISSUE

138 *Tsuikin-wan Lacquerware*

| | | MNHVF | UseVF |
|---|---|---|---|
| **138** | | | |
| 3¢ | **multicolored** *(July 1, 1963)* | 3.75 | 1.25 |

## 1963. AIRMAIL ISSUE

139

| | | MNHVF | UseVF |
|---|---|---|---|
| **139** | | | |
| 5-1/2¢ | **multicolored** *(Aug. 28, 1963)* | .35 | .15 |

140

| | | MNHVF | UseVF |
|---|---|---|---|
| **140** | | | |
| 7¢ | **multicolored** | .40 | .15 |

## 1963. JUNIOR CHAMBER OF COMMERCE ISSUE meeting of the International organization held at Naha Okinawa.

141

| | | MNHVF | UseVF |
|---|---|---|---|
| **141** | | | |
| 3¢ | **multicolored** *(Sept. 16, 1963)* | 1.35 | .65 |

## 1963. DEFINITIVE ISSUE

142

| | | MNHVF | UseVF |
|---|---|---|---|
| **142** | | | |
| 15¢ | *Mamaomoto (Oct. 15, 1963)* | 1.00 | .30 |

## 1963. NATIONAL CULTURAL TREASURES ISSUE

143 *Nakagusuku Castle*

| | | MNHVF | UseVF |
|---|---|---|---|
| **143** | | | |
| 3¢ | **multicolored** *(Nov. 1, 1963)* | 1.35 | .65 |

## 1963. HUMAN RIGHTS ISSUE celebrates the 15th anniversary of the Universal Declaration of Human Rights.

144

| | | MNHVF | UseVF |
|---|---|---|---|
| **144** | | | |
| 3¢ | **multicolored** *(Dec. 10, 1963)* | 1.35 | .65 |

## 1963. NEW YEAR'S ISSUE

145 *Dragon*

| | | MNHVF | UseVF |
|---|---|---|---|
| **145** | | | |
| 1-1/2¢ | **multicolored** *(Dec. 10, 1963)* | .65 | .20 |

## 1964. MOTHER'S DAY ISSUE

147 *Carnation*

**147**

| | | MNHVF | UseVF |
|---|---|---|---|
| 3¢ | multicolored *(May 10, 1964)* | .90 | .35 |

**1964. AGRICULTURAL CENSUS ISSUE**

148

**148**

| | | MNHVF | UseVF |
|---|---|---|---|
| 3¢ | multicolored *(June 1, 1964)* | .75 | .35 |

**1964. PHILATELIC WEEK ISSUE**

149 *Minsah Obi (Sash Woven of Kapok)*

**149**

| | | MNHVF | UseVF |
|---|---|---|---|
| 3¢ | multicolored, rose | .90 | .35 |
| | a. deep carmine | 1.25 | .50 |

**1964. GIRL SCOUT ISSUE** 10th anniversary.

150

**150**

| | | MNHVF | UseVF |
|---|---|---|---|
| 3¢ | multicolored *(Aug. 31, 1964)* | .50 | .35 |

**1964. RYUKYU-JAPAN MICROWAVE SYSTEM ISSUE**

151 *Shuri Relay Tower*

**151**

| | | MNHVF | UseVF |
|---|---|---|---|
| 3¢ | green *(Sept. 1, 1964)* | 1.25 | .75 |
| | v. overprint "1" inverted overprint in date (pos 8) | 25.00 | 20.00 |

152 *Parabolic Antenna*

**152**

| | | MNHVF | UseVF |
|---|---|---|---|
| 8¢ | ultramarine | 2.00 | 1.50 |

*Broken type and inking varieties exits. Shifted overprints are fairly common.*

**1964. OLYMPIC TORCH FLIGHT ISSUE** The Olympic torch reached Okinawa enroute to Tokyo.

153 *Gate of Courtesy*

**153**

| | | MNHVF | UseVF |
|---|---|---|---|
| 3¢ | multicolored *(Sept. 7, 1964)* | .50 | .25 |

**1964-65. KARATE ISSUE**

154 *Naihanchi stance*

**154**

| | | MNHVF | UseVF |
|---|---|---|---|
| 3¢ | multicolored *(Oct. 5, 1964)* | .90 | .25 |

155 *Makiwara*

**155**

| | | MNHVF | UseVF |
|---|---|---|---|
| 3¢ | multicolored *(Feb. 5, 1965)* | .65 | .25 |

156 *Kumite*

**156**

| | | MNHVF | UseVF |
|---|---|---|---|
| 3¢ | multicolored *(June 5, 1965)* | .65 | .25 |

**1964. NATIONAL CULTURAL TREASURES ISSUE**

157 *Miyara Dunchi, 1819*

**157**

| | | MNHVF | UseVF |
|---|---|---|---|
| 3¢ | multicolored *(Nov. 1, 1964)* | .50 | .25 |

## 1964. New Year's Issue

158 *Snake and iris*

| | | MNHVF | UseVF |
|---|---|---|---|
| **158** | | | |
| 1-1/2¢ | **multicolored** *(Dec. 10, 1964)* | .40 | .15 |

## 1965. Boy Scout Issue  10th anniversary Ryukyuan Boy Scouts.

159

| | | MNHVF | UseVF |
|---|---|---|---|
| **159** | | | |
| 3¢ | **multicolored** *(Feb. 6, 1965)* | .85 | .25 |

## 1965. Kin Power Plant Issue

| | | MNHVF | UseVF |
|---|---|---|---|
| **160** | | | |
| 3¢ | **multicolored** *(July 1, 1965)* | .40 | .25 |

## 1965. Onoyama Athletic Facility Issue

161 *Main stadium*

| | | MNHVF | UseVF |
|---|---|---|---|
| **161** | | | |
| 3¢ | **multicolored** *(July 1, 1965)* | .40 | .25 |

## 1965. Philatelic Week Issue

162 *Samisen*

| | | MNHVF | UseVF |
|---|---|---|---|
| **162** | | | |
| 3¢ | **multicolored** *(July 1, 1965)* | .90 | .25 |

## 1965. International Cooperation Year Issue

| | | MNHVF | UseVF |
|---|---|---|---|
| **163** | | | |
| 3¢ | **multicolored** *(July 1, 1965)* | .30 | .20 |

## 1965. Naha City Hall Issue

164

| | | MNHVF | UseVF |
|---|---|---|---|
| **164** | | | |
| 3¢ | **multicolored** *(Sept. 18, 1965)* | .30 | .20 |

## 1965. Turtle Issue

165 *Box Turtle*

| | | MNHVF | UseVF |
|---|---|---|---|
| **165** | | | |
| 3¢ | **brown** *(Oct. 20, 1965)* | .50 | .25 |

166 *Hawks bill turtle*

| | | MNHVF | UseVF |
|---|---|---|---|
| **166** | | | |
| 3¢ | **white** *(Jan. 20, 1966)* | .50 | .25 |

167 *Asian Terrapin*

| | | MNHVF | UseVF |
|---|---|---|---|
| **167** | | | |
| 3¢ | **multicolored** *(April 20, 1966)* | .40 | .25 |

## 1965. New Year's Issue

168 *Horse*

| | | MNHVF | UseVF |
|---|---|---|---|
| **168** | | | |
| 1-1/2¢ | **multicolored** *(Dec. 10, 1965)* | .20 | .15 |
| | v.  gold omitted | 500. | |

## 1966. Wild Life Conservation Issue

169 *Okinawa Woodpecker*

| | | MNHVF | UseVF |
|---|---|---|---|
| **169** | | | |
| 3¢ | **multicolored** *(Feb. 15, 1966)* | .40 | .25 |

170 *Sika Deer*

| | | MNHVF | UseVF |
|---|---|---|---|
| **170** | | | |
| 3¢ | **multicolored** *(March 15)* | .40 | .25 |

171 *Dugong*

| 171 | | MNHVF | UseVF |
|---|---|---|---|
| 3¢ | multicolored *(April 20)* | .40 | .25 |

## 1966. BIRD WEEK ISSUE

172 *Bungalow Swallow*

| 172 | | MNHVF | UseVF |
|---|---|---|---|
| 3¢ | multicolored *(May 10, 1966)* | .25 | .20 |

## 1966. MEMORIAL DAY ISSUE  end of the Battle of Okinawa 1945.

| 173 | | MNHVF | UseVF |
|---|---|---|---|
| 3¢ | multicolored *(June 23, 1966)* | .25 | .20 |

## 1966. UNIVERSITY OF RYUKYUS ISSUE

| 174 | | MNHVF | UseVF |
|---|---|---|---|
| 3¢ | multicolored *(July 1, 1966)* | .25 | .20 |

## 1966. PHILATELIC WEEK ISSUE

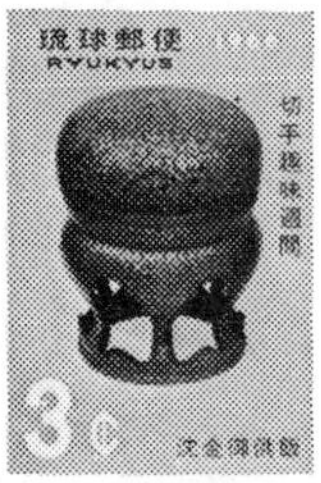

175 *18th Century Lacquerware*

| 175 | | MNHVF | UseVF |
|---|---|---|---|
| 3¢ | multicolored *(August 1966)* | .30 | .20 |

## 1966. 20TH ANNIVERSARY UNESCO ISSUE

176 *Tile-roofed house*

| 176 | | MNHVF | UseVF |
|---|---|---|---|
| 3¢ | multicolored *(Sept. 20, 1966)* | .25 | .20 |

## 1966. MUSEUM ISSUE

177 *Museum building*

| 177 | | MNHVF | UseVF |
|---|---|---|---|
| 3¢ | multicolored *(Oct. 6, 1966)* | .25 | .20 |

## 1966. NATIONAL CULTURAL TREASURES ISSUE

178 *Tomb of Nakasone-Tuimya Genga*

| 178 | | MNHVF | UseVF |
|---|---|---|---|
| 3¢ | multicolored *(Nov. 1, 1966)* | .25 | .20 |

## 1966. NEW YEAR'S ISSUE

179 *Ram in Iris wreath*

| 179 | | MNHVF | UseVF |
|---|---|---|---|
| 1-1/2¢ | multicolored *(Dec. 10, 1966)* | .30 | .15 |

## 1966-67. TROPICAL FISH ISSUE

180

| 180 | | MNHVF | UseVF |
|---|---|---|---|
| 3¢ | *Amphipron frenatus (Dec. 20, 1966)* | .40 | .20 |

181

| 181 | | MNHVF | UseVF |
|---|---|---|---|
| 3¢ | *Ostracion tuberculotus (Jan. 10, 1967)* | .40 | .20 |

182

| 182 | | MNHVF | UseVF |
|---|---|---|---|
| 3¢ | *Forcipiger longirostris (April 10, 1967)* | .40 | .20 |

183

| | | MNHVF | UseVF |
|---|---|---|---|
| **183** | | .40 | .20 |
| **3¢** | *Balistoides (niger) conspicilum* (May 25, 1967) | | |

| | | MNHVF | UseVF |
|---|---|---|---|
| **184** | | .40 | .20 |
| **3¢** | *Chaetodon ephippium* (June 10, 1967) | | |

**1967. PHILATELIC WEEK ISSUE**

186 *Tsuboya Urn*

| | | MNHVF | UseVF |
|---|---|---|---|
| **186** | | .30 | .20 |
| **3¢** | **multicolored** (April 20, 1967) | | |

**1967-68. SEA SHELL ISSUE**

187

| | | MNHVF | UseVF |
|---|---|---|---|
| **187** | | .35 | .20 |
| **3¢** | *Mitra mitra* (July 20, 1967) | | |

188

| | | MNHVF | UseVF |
|---|---|---|---|
| **188** | | .35 | .20 |
| **3¢** | *Murex Aranea triremis* (Aug. 30, 1967) | | |

189

| | | MNHVF | UseVF |
|---|---|---|---|
| **189** | | .50 | .20 |
| **3¢** | *Lambis chiragraz* (Jan. 18, 1968) | | |

190

| | | MNHVF | UseVF |
|---|---|---|---|
| **190** | | .50 | .20 |
| **3¢** | *Turbo mamoratus* (Feb. 20, 1968) | | |

191

| | | MNHVF | UseVF |
|---|---|---|---|
| **191** | | 1.00 | .20 |
| **3¢** | *Euprotomus bulla* (June 5, 1968) | | |

**1967. INTERNATIONAL TOURIST YEAR ISSUE**

192 *Red tiled roofs*

| | | MNHVF | UseVF |
|---|---|---|---|
| **192** | | .30 | .20 |
| **3¢** | **multicolored** (Sept. 11, 1967) | | |

**1967. ANTI-TUBERCULOSIS ISSUE**

193 *Mobile TB unit*

| | | MNHVF | UseVF |
|---|---|---|---|
| **193** | | .30 | .20 |
| **3¢** | **multicolored** (Oct. 13, 1967) | | |

**1967. NATIONAL CULTURAL TREASURES ISSUE**

194 *Hojo Bridge, Enkaku Tempe*

| | | MNHVF | UseVF |
|---|---|---|---|
| **194** | | .30 | .20 |
| **3¢** | **multicolored** | | |

**1967. NEW YEAR'S ISSUE**

195 *Monkey*

**195**
1-1/2¢ multicolored *(Dec. 11, 1967)*

| MNHVF | UseVF |
|---|---|
| .30 | .15 |

**1967. TV STATION ISSUE**

196 *Tower & map*

**196**
3¢ multicolored *(Dec. 22, 1967)*

| MNHVF | UseVF |
|---|---|
| .30 | .20 |

**1968. VACCINATION ISSUE** honors 120th anniversary of first vaccinations in Ryukyu.

197

**197**
3¢ multicolored *(March 15, 1968)*

| MNHVF | UseVF |
|---|---|
| .30 | .20 |

**1968. PHILATELIC WEEK ISSUE**

198 *Pill box*

**198**
3¢ multicolored *(April 18, 1968)*

| MNHVF | UseVF |
|---|---|
| .90 | .20 |

**1968. LIBRARY WEEK ISSUE**

199 *Youth running toward library.*

**199**
3¢ multicolored *(May 13, 1968)*

| MNHVF | UseVF |
|---|---|
| .75 | .20 |

**1968. RYUKYAN POSTAGE ISSUE** celebrates 20th anniversary postage.

200

**200**
3¢ multicolored *(May 13, 1968)*

| MNHVF | UseVF |
|---|---|
| .75 | .20 |

**1968. ENKAKU TEMPLE RECONSTRUCTION ISSUE**

201 *Main gate*

**201**
3¢ multicolored *(July 15, 1968)*

| MNHVF | UseVF |
|---|---|
| .75 | .20 |

**1968. ELDERLY PEOPLE'S DAY ISSUE**

202 *Old man's dance*

**202**
3¢ multicolored *(Sept. 15, 1968)*

| MNHVF | UseVF |
|---|---|
| .75 | .20 |

**1968-69. CRAB ISSUE**

203

**203**
3¢ *Mictyris longicarpus (Oct. 10, 1968)*

| MNHVF | UseVF |
|---|---|
| .75 | .20 |

204

**204**
3¢ *Uoa dubia (Feb. 5, 1969)*

| MNHVF | UseVF |
|---|---|
| .65 | .20 |

205

**205**
3¢ *Baptozius vinosus (March 5, 1969)*

| MNHVF | UseVF |
|---|---|
| .65 | .20 |

206

**206**
3¢ *Cardisoma carnifex (May 15, 1969)*

| MNHVF | UseVF |
|---|---|
| .65 | .20 |

207

**207**
3¢      *Ocypode Ceratophthalma (June 2, 1969)*

| | MNHVF | UseVF |
|---|---|---|
| | .65 | .20 |

### 1968. NATIONAL CULTURAL TREASURES ISSUE

208 *Saraswati Pavilion*

**208**
3¢      multicolored *(Nov. 1, 1968)*

| | MNHVF | UseVF |
|---|---|---|
| | .75 | .20 |

### 1968. ALL-JAPAN SOFTBALL TENNIS TOURNAMENT ISSUE

209 *Tennis player*

**209**
3¢      multicolored *(Nov. 3, 1968)*

| | MNHVF | UseVF |
|---|---|---|
| | .75 | .20 |

### 1968. NEW YEAR'S ISSUE

210 *Cock and iris*

**210**
1-1/2¢  multicolored *(Dec. 10, 1968)*

| | MNHVF | UseVF |
|---|---|---|
| | .25 | .15 |

### 1969. BOXING ISSUE 20th anniversary All-Japan amateur boxing championships.

211 *Boxer*

**211**
3¢      multicolored *(Jan. 3, 1969)*

| | MNHVF | UseVF |
|---|---|---|
| | .75 | .20 |

### 1969. PHILATELIC WEEK ISSUE

212 *Ink slab screen*

**212**
3¢      multicolored *(April 17, 1969)*

| | MNHVF | UseVF |
|---|---|---|
| | .75 | .20 |

### 1969. UHF CIRCUT SYSTEM ISSUE

213 *Box antenna*

**213**
3¢      multicolored *(July 1, 1969)*

| | MNHVF | UseVF |
|---|---|---|
| | .30 | .20 |

### 1969. FORMATIVE EDUCATION CONFERENCE ISSUE

214 *Gate of Courtesy*

**214**
3¢      multicolored *(Aug. 1, 1969)*

| | MNHVF | UseVF |
|---|---|---|
| | .30 | .20 |

### 1969. FOLKLORE & FESTIVAL ISSUE

215

**215**
3¢      *Tug of war festival (Aug. 1, 1969)*

| | MNHVF | UseVF |
|---|---|---|
| | .65 | .20 |

216

**216**
3¢      *Hari boat race (Sept. 5, 1969)*

| | MNHVF | UseVF |
|---|---|---|
| | .65 | .20 |

217

**217**
3¢      *Izaiho ceremony  (Oct. 3, 1969)*

| | MNHVF | UseVF |
|---|---|---|
| | .65 | .20 |

218

**218**
3¢      *Vshideiku (Jan. 20, 1970)*

| | MNHVF | UseVF |
|---|---|---|
| | .65 | .20 |

219

**219**
**3¢**     *Unjiyami (Feb. 27, 1970)*     MNHVF .65     UseVF .20

### 1969. PROVISIONAL ISSUE overprint on No. 125.

220

**220**
**1/2¢ on 3¢multicolored**     MNHVF .25     UseVF .20

### 1969. NATIONAL CULTURAL TREASURES ISSUE

221 *Nakamura-ke farm house*

**221**
**3¢**     **multicolored** *(Nov. 1, 1969)*     MNHVF .30     UseVF .20

### 1969. NEW YEAR'S ISSUE

222 *Dog and flowers*

**222**
**1-1/2¢**     **multicolored** *(Dec. 10, 1969)*     MNHVF .25     UseVF .15

### 1969. EMIGRATION TO HAWAII ISSUE

223 *Kyuzo Toyama statue*

**223**
**3¢**     **multicolored** *(Dec. 5, 1969)*     MNHVF .50     UseVF .20
           v.  overprint *1969* omitted     2000.

### 1970. PHILATELIC WEEK ISSUE

224 *Sake flask*

**224**
**3¢**     **multicolored** *(Dec. 10, 1969)*     MNHVF .40     UseVF .20

### 1970. CLASSIC OPERA ISSUE

225

**225**
**3¢**     **multicolored,** The Bell *(April 28, 1970)*     MNHVF .90     UseVF .25
**225A**
**3¢**     Sheet (4) #225     MNHVF 5.00     UseVF 4.50

226

**226**
**3¢**     **multicolored,** Child and kidnapper *(May 29, 1970)*     MNHVF .75     UseVF .25
**226A**
**3¢**     Sheet (4) #226     MNHVF 5.00     UseVF 4.50

227

**227**
**3¢**     **multicolored** Robe of Feathers *(June 30, 1970)*     MNHVF .90     UseVF .25
**227A**
**3¢**     Sheet (4) #227     MNHVF 5.00     UseVF 4.50

228

**228**
**3¢**     **multicolored,** Vengeance of Two Young Sons *(July 30, 1970)*     MNHVF .75     UseVF .25
**228A**
**3¢**     Sheet (4) #228     MNHVF 5.00     UseVF 4.50

229

**229**
**3¢**     **multicolored,** Virgin and the Dragon *(Aug. 25, 1970)*     MNHVF .75     UseVF .25
**229A**
**3¢**     Sheet (4) #229     MNHVF 5.00     UseVF 4.50

## 1970. UNDERWATER OBSERVATORY ISSUE

230

| | MNHVF | UseVF |
|---|---|---|
| **230** | | |
| 3¢ **multicolored** *(May 22, 1970)* | .30 | .20 |

## 1970-71. GREAT MEN ISSUE

231

| | MNHVF | UseVF |
|---|---|---|
| **231** | | |
| 3¢ **deep carmine,** Noboru Jahana *(Sept. 25, 1970)* | .60 | .20 |

232

| | MNHVF | UseVF |
|---|---|---|
| **232** | | |
| 3¢ **multicolored** Saion Gushichan Bunjaku *(Dec. 22, 1970)* | .60 | .20 |

233

| | MNHVF | UseVF |
|---|---|---|
| **233** | | |
| 3¢ **gray,** Choho Giwan *(Jan. 22, 1971)* | .60 | .20 |

## 1970. CENSUS ISSUE

234

| | MNHVF | UseVF |
|---|---|---|
| **234** | | |
| 3¢ **multicolored** *(Oct. 1, 1970)* | .30 | .20 |

## 1970. NATIONAL CULTURAL TREASURES ISSUE

235

| | MNHVF | UseVF |
|---|---|---|
| **235** | | |
| 3¢ **multicolored** | .40 | .20 |

## 1970. NATIONAL ELECTIONS ISSUE

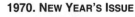

236 *Government Buildings*

| | MNHVF | UseVF |
|---|---|---|
| **236** | | |
| 3¢ **multicolored** *(Nov. 15, 1970)* | 1.50 | .25 |

## 1970. NEW YEAR'S ISSUE

237 *Wild boar and cherry blossoms*

| | MNHVF | UseVF |
|---|---|---|
| **237** | | |
| 1-1/2¢ **multicolored** *(Dec. 10, 1970)* | .20 | .10 |

## 1971. FOLK CRAFT ISSUE

238

| | MNHVF | UseVF |
|---|---|---|
| **238** | | |
| 3¢ *Hand loom (Feb. 16, 1971)* | .60 | .20 |

239

| | MNHVF | UseVF |
|---|---|---|
| **239** | | |
| 3¢ *Filature (March 16, 1971)* | .60 | .20 |

240

| | MNHVF | UseVF |
|---|---|---|
| **240** | | |
| 3¢ *Coat and hat (Apr. 30, 1971)* | .60 | .20 |

241

**241**
**3¢**   *Rice huller (May 20, 1971)*   MNHVF .60   UseVF .20

242

**242**
**3¢**   *Fisherman (June 15, 1971)*   MNHVF .60   UseVF .20

**1971. PHILATELIC WEEK ISSUE**

243 *Taku water carrier*

**243**
**3¢**   **multicolored** *(April 15, 1971)*   MNHVF .60   UseVF .20

**1971. DEFINITIVE ISSUE**

244

**244**
**2¢**   *Lxora chinensis lam (Sept. 30, 1971)*   MNHVF .10   UseVF .10

244A

**244A**
**3¢**   *Caesalpinia Icherrima (May 10, 1971)*   MNHVF .15   UseVF .10

**1971. NAHA CITY ISSUE** 50th anniversary as a municipality.

245

**245**
**3¢**   **multicolored** *(May 20, 1971)*   MNHVF .40   UseVF .20

**1971-72. GOVERNMENT PARK ISSUE**

246 *Mabuni Hill*

**246**
**3¢**   *Mabuni Hill (July 30, 1971)*   MNHVF .30   UseVF .20

247 *Mt. Arashi*

**247**
**3¢**   *Inland Sea (Aug. 30, 1971)*   MNHVF .30   UseVF .20
**248**
**4¢**   *Yabuchai Island (Jan. 20, 1972)*   MNHVF .30   UseVF .20

**1971. DANEER ISSUE**

248A *Dancer*

**248A**
**4¢**   **multicolored** *(Nov. 1, 1971)*   MNHVF .30   UseVF .20

**1971. NATIONAL CULTURAL ISSUE**

249 *Deva King, Torinji Temple*

**249**
**4¢**   **multicolored** *(Dec. 1, 1971)*   MNHVF .30   UseVF .20

**1971. NEW YEAR'S ISSUE**

250 *Rat and Chrysanthemums*

**250**
**2¢**   **multicolored** *(Dec. 10, 1971)*   MNHVF .10   UseVF .10

**1971. NURSES ISSUE** 25th anniversary of nurse's training student nurse.

251

**251**

**251**
**4¢**     **multicolored** *(Dec. 24, 1971)*     MNHVF  UseVF
                                                 .30    .20

**1972. SEASCAPES ISSUE**

 252A

**252A**
**5¢**     Inlet *(1972)*     MNHVF  UseVF
                             .35    .35

 253

**253**
**5¢**     Islands *(March 21, 1972)*     MNHVF  UseVF
                                         .35    .25

254

**254**
**5¢**     Sea Shore *(March 30, 1972)*     MNHVF  UseVF
                                           .35    .25

 255 *Coral Reef*

**255**
**5¢**     *Coral reef (April 14, 1972)*     MNHVF  UseVF
                                            .35    .25

**1972. PHILATELIC WEEK ISSUE**

 256   *Sake Pot*

**256**
**5¢**     **multicolored** *(April 20, 1972)*     MNHVF  UseVF
                                                  .35    .25

**1972. REVERSION OF RYUKYU ISLAND TO JAPAN ISSUE**

257   *US & Japanese Flags*

**257**
**5¢**     **multicolored** *(April 17, 1972)*     MNHVF  UseVF
                                                  .35    .25

*Ryukyu stamps were discontinued and replaced with those of Japan stamps on May 15, 1972 as the Ryukyu Islands reverted to Japanese control.*

# Postage Stamp Envelopes

### By R.B. White

The introduction to these pages gives the background of the financial times preceding the introduction of Fractional Currency. In mid-1862 hard money was fast disappearing from circulation and postage stamps were pressed into service as a means of making small change.

The Postmaster General in his December report of 1862 said: "In the first quarter of the current year, ending September 20th, the number of stamps issued to postmasters was one hundred and four million dollars; there were calls for about two hundred millions, which would have been nearly sufficient to meet the usual demands for the year. This extraordinary demand arose from the temporary use of these stamps as a currency for the public in lieu of the smaller denominations of specie, and ceased with the introduction of the so-called 'postal currency.' "

But stamps were ill-suited for the wear and tear of commerce and at least in the early part of this period, the post office refused to exchange them for new issues. Before Gault produced his encased postage or the die-sinkers had produced their "copperheads" (more commonly now known as Civil War Tokens), a few enterprising printers produced small envelopes, approximately 70 x 35 mm in size, labeled with the value of the stamps contained and usually with an advertising message either for themselves or for some local merchant. This was mainly confined to the larger cities of the east. New York City had by far the most pieces, but Brooklyn, Albany, Cincinnati, Jersey City, and Philadelphia are also represented.

The New York Central Railroad issued a slightly different version. The only example seen being a piece of stiff card with two slots by which the stamp or stamps are captured.

Some of these envelopes have the value of the stamps printed on them, others have blank spaces for hand written values. Occasionally the printed values are changed by hand.

The issues of J. Leach, stationer and printer in New York City, are by far the most common. They have been seen in five distinct types with multiple denominations within the types.

The first listing of Civil War postage stamp envelopes was published by Henry Russell Drowne in the *American Journal of Numismatics* in 1918. That article, primarily based on the Moreau hoard of 77 envelopes, reported that these pieces "were variously printed with black, blue, red and green ink on white, amber, lemon, pink, orange, violet, blue, pale green, buff, manilla and brown paper." Red and blue ink on white paper was the most popular combination. Wood cuts and electrotypes were employed in the manufacture. One single piece bears a picture of Washington. All of the envelopes show evidence of having been hastily made and printed.

In the listings which follow, spaces have been left in the numbering system to accommodate future finds. No claim is made that the list is complete.

These pieces are all extremely rare. The most common probably having no more than half a dozen extant pieces. The pricing thus reflects the rarity of the firm name and the desirability of the design, legend and value. Drowne reported that the 25cts denomination is "by far the most common, about half as many are for 50cts, and a quarter for 10cts and 75cts." All prices are for the envelope only; stamps may be included but there is really no way of knowing that they are original with the envelopes. Any stamps will increase the total value by their own philatelic value. A total of 110 different numbers are listed here; it is doubtful that 500 pieces total of all types still exist.

In the numbering system, a first number is assigned for each firm name or known major design type within that firm. The second number of the system is the stated value of the envelope in cents (blank value shown by 0); "hw" following the second number means the value was hand written. A question mark means that the value of the piece has not been reported. "Vars" means that minor varieties exist.

# POSTAGE STAMP ENVELOPES

| KL# | Name, address and notations | Value |
|---|---|---|
| 1-25 | H. Armstrong, Hosiery, Laces, etc | |
| | 140 6th Ave, (NYC) | 700. |
| 3-? | Arthur, Gregory & Co., Stationer | |
| | 39 Nassau St. NYC | 650. |
| 5-25 | Bergen & Tripp, Stationer | |
| | 114 Nassau St, (NYC) | 650. |
| 7-25 | Berlin & Jones, Stationer | |
| | 134 William St, NYC | 650. |

| KL# | Name, address and notations | Value |
|---|---|---|
| 9-15 | Joseph Bryan, Clothing | |
| | 214 Fulton St, Brooklyn | 725. |
| 9-50 | Same | 650. |
| 11-25 | P.D. Braisted, Jr. Billiards | |
| | 14-16 4th Ave, NYC | 650. |
| 13-50 | G.C. Brown, Tobacco | |
| | 669 Broadway, NYC | 650. |
| 15-25 | John M. Burnett, Stationer | |
| | 51 William St, NYC | 650. |
| 15-25hw50 | | 650. |
| 15-50 | Same | 650. |
| 17-25 | Chas. T. Chickhaus, Tobacco | |
| | 176 Broadway, NYC | 725. |
| 19-? | Clarry & Reilley, Stationer | |
| | 12-14 Spruce St, NYC | 725. |

| KL# | Name, address and notations | Value |
|---|---|---|
| 21-50hw25 | | |
| | B.F. Corlies & Macy, Stationer | |
| | 33 Nassau St, NYC | 725. |
| 23-30 | Crook & Duff, Bar-Lunch-Dining | |
| | 39-40 Park Row, (NYC) | 800. |
| 25-? | Cutter Tower & Co, Stationer | |
| | 128 Nassau St, NYC | 650. |
| 27-25 | Dawley, Stationer & Printer | |
| | 28, 30 & 32 Center St, NYC | 650. |
| 28-50 | T.R. Dawley, Printer | |
| | Cor. Reade & Center Streets, NYC | 650. |
| 29-0hw25 | | |
| | Mad (Ame) A. Doubet, Importer | |
| | 697 & 951 Broadway, (NYC) | 725. |
| 31-25 | Francis Duffy, Oysters & Dining | |
| | 239-241 8th Ave, (NYC) | 725. |
| 33-25 | Embree, Stationer | |
| | 130 Grand St, (NYC) | 650. |
| 34-50 | Jno. C. Force | |
| | Brooklyn | 800. |
| 35-25 | Fox's Old Bowery Theatre | |
| | (NYC) | 800. |
| 37-? | German Opera | |
| | 485 Broadway, NYC | 400. |

## GOULD'S DINING ROOMS,
### 35 Nassau Street,
Opposite Post Office.  NEW YORK.

U. S. POSTAGE STAMPS. **75 cts.**

| KL# | Name, address and notations | Value |
|---|---|---|
| 39-75 | Gould's Dining Rooms | |
| | 35 Nassau St, NYC | 650. |
| 40-50 | Arthur Gregory | |
| | NYC | 800. |

| KL# | Name, address and notations | Value |
|---|---|---|
| 41-25 | Harlem & NY Navigation Co | |
| | Sylvan Shore & Sylvan Grove, (NYC) | |
| | "LEGAL CURRENCY" | 850. |
| 43-5 | Harpel, Printers | |
| | Cincinnati | 725. |
| 45-10 | Irving House, Hotel | |
| | Broadway & 12th St, NYC | 650. |
| 47-25 | James, Hatter | |
| | 525 Broadway, (NYC) | 650. |
| 49-0 | Hamilton Johnston, Stationer | |
| | 545 Broadway, (NYC) | |
| | with Washington portrait | 825. |
| 51-25 | C.O. Jones, Stationer | |
| | 76 Cedar St, NYC | 650. |
| 53-? | Kaiser & Waters, Stationer | |
| | 104 Fulton St, NYC | 650. |
| 55-60 | Kavanagh & Freeman, Billards | |
| | 10th & Broadway, NYC | 725. |
| 57-25 | Lansingh's Gent's Furnishings | |
| 57-50 | Albany | 650. |
| 59-10 | J. Leach, Stationer | |
| | 86 Nassau St, NYC | |
| | Type I, Value in central diamond, most | |
| | common type (vars.) | 575. |
| 59-15 | | 650. |
| 59-20 | | 575. |
| 59-25 | | 575. |
| 59-30 | | 650. |
| 59-50 | | 575. |
| 59-75 | | 700. |

| KL# | Name, address and notations | Value |
|---|---|---|
| 60-15 | As Above | 700. |
| 60-25 | As Above | |
| | Type II, Eagle between "U" and "S" (vars.) | 575. |
| 60-50 | | 575. |
| 61-25 | As above | |
| | Type III, Large central oval with | |
| | denomination (vars.) | 575. |
| 61-50 | As above | 575. |
| | Type V, Denomination in oval, flag left, | |
| | shield right, similar to H. Smith design | 575. |

| KL# | Name, address and notations | Value |
|---|---|---|
| 62-25 | As above | |
| | Type IV, denomination between flags | 575. |
| 63-50 | As above | 575. |
| 71-75 | D.W. Lee, Stationer | |
| | 82 Nassau St, NYC | 575. |
| 72-O | R. Letson, Mercantile | |
| | Dining Room, 256 | |
| | Broadway, NYC | 575. |
| 73-25 | J.W. Lingard, New | |
| | Bowery Theatre, (NYC) | 650. |
| 74-25 | Macoy & Herwig, Stationers | |
| | 112-114 Broadway, (NYC) | 650. |
| 75-20 | Hy Maillards, Confectionery | |
| | 621 Broadway, (NYC) | 650. |
| 75-25 | Same | 650. |
| 77-25 | Frank McElroy, Stationers | |
| | 113 Nassau St, (NYC) | 650. |
| 81-10 | Metropolitan Hotel | |
| | NYC | 650. |
| 83-25 | Miller & Grant, Importers, Laces | |
| | 703 Broadway, NYC | 725. |

| KL# | Name, address and notations | Value |
|---|---|---|
| 85-50 | W.H. Murphy (by D. Murphy's Sons) | |
| | Stationers, 372 Pearl St, NYC | 650. |
| 87-? | Wm. Murphy, Stationer | |
| | 438 Canal St, NYC | 650. |
| 89-25 | National Express Co. | |
| | 74 Broadway, NYC | 800. |
| 93-20 | New York Central Railraod (N.Y.C.R.R.) | |
| | NYC | 725. |
| 95-50 | N.Y. Consolidated Stage Co. | |
| | (NYC) | 725. |

| KL# | Name, address and notations | Value |
|---|---|---|
| 97-25 | Niblos Garden - Wm Wheatley | |
| | (Edwin Forrest) (NYC) | 725. |
| 97-50 | Same except Ravel Troupe | |
| | (NYC) | 725. |
| 101-10 | Nixon's Cremorne Garden, | |
| | Palace of Music | |
| | 14th and 6th Ave, (NYC) | 975. |
| 101-25hw10 | | 725. |

| KL# | Name, address and notations | Value |
|---|---|---|
| 101-25 | Postal type hand stamp appears to | |
| | read "CREMORNE (GARD)EN" | 725. |

| KL# | Name, address and notations | Value |
|---|---|---|
| 103-25 | Chris O'Neills, Liquors | |
| | Hudson Ave, Brooklyn | |
| | "UNCLE SAM'S CHANGE" | 800. |
| 105-? | Oyster Bay House | |
| | 553 Broadway, NYC | 650. |
| 107-25 | The Oyster House | |
| | 604 Broadway, NYC | 650. |
| 109-0 | Pettit & Crook's Dining Rooms | |
| | 136 Water St, NYC | |
| | "UNCLE SAM'S CHANGE" | 800. |

## POMROY'S
### 699 Broadway, New York.
U. S. POSTAGE STAMPS.
**50**

| KL# | Name, address and notations | Value |
|---|---|---|
| 111-50 | Pomroy's | |
| | 699 Broadway, NYC | 650. |
| 113-50 | Power, Bogardus & Co., Steamship Line | |
| | Pier 34, No. River, NYC | 700. |
| 115-50 | S. Raynor, Envelope Manuf'r | |
| | 118 William St, NYC | 650. |

| KL# | Name, address and notations | Value |
|---|---|---|
| 117-25 | Capt. Tom Reeves, Billards 214 Broadway, NYC | 800. |

| KL# | Name, address and notations | Value |
|---|---|---|
| 119-25 | Revere House 604-608 Broadway, NYC | 650. |
| 121-? | Thomas Richardson, Chop Steak & Oyster House 66 Maiden Lane, NYC | 650. |
| 122-50 | E.M. Riggin, Sanford House 336 Delaware Ave., Pine St. Wharf, Philadelphia | 650. |
| 123-25 | Wm Robins, Excelsion Envelope Manufactory 51 Ann St, NYC | 575. |
| 125-25 | R. Scovel, Stationer 26 Nassau St, (NYC) | 650. |
| 126-25 | Reuben Scovel "GOVERNMENT CURRENCY" 26 Nassau St, (NYC) | 650. |
| 126-50 | Same | 650. |

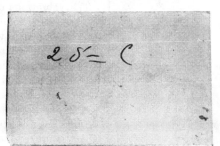

| KL# | Name, address and notations | Value |
|---|---|---|
| 127-25 | C.C. Shelley, Stationer 68 Barclay St, NYC | 650. |
| 128-10 | H. Smith, Stationer 137 Williams St, NYC Type I, denomination in oval, flag left, shield right (vars.) | 575. |
| 128-13 | Same | 575. |
| 128-25 | Same | 575. |
| 128-50 | Same | 575. |
| 129-15hw50 | As above Type II, fancy border, no flag, denomination below postage stamps | 575. |
| 129-50 | Same | 575. |
| 130-25 | Snow & Hapgood 22 Court St., Boston | 650. |
| 131-25 | Sonnebom, Stationer 130 Nassau St., NYC (vars.) | 650. |
| 133-25 | Taylor's Hotel Exchange Place, Jersey City (vars.) | 725. |
| 133-50 | Same | 725. |
| 135-? | Dion Thomas, Stationer 142 Nassau St, NYC | 725. |

| KL# | Name, address and notations | Value |
|---|---|---|
| 137-25 | R.D. Thompson, Stationer 104 Fulton St, NYC (vars.) | 650. |
| 139-25 | G.W. & S. Turney 77 Chatham St, NYC | 650. |
| 140-? | S.C. Upham 403 Chestnut St., Phil. | 650. |
| 141-25 | James Wiley, Wines & Liquors 307 Broadway, NYC | 650. |
| 141-50 | Same | 650. |

## PIECES WITH NO COMPANY NAME

| KL# | Name, address and notations | Value |
|---|---|---|
| 151-25 | Blank - marked by hand Envelope perhaps hand made | 500. |
| 152-10 | U.S. POSTAGE STAMPS 10 CENTS | — |
| 153-20 | U.S. POSTAGE STAMPS 20 CENTS | 500. |
| 155-25 | U.S. POSTAGE STAMPS 25 CENTS (vars.) | 500. |

| KL# | Name, address and notations | Value |
|---|---|---|
| 156-25 | POSTAGE STAMPS 25 CENTS Does not say U.S. postage as others do. | 500. |
| 157-25 | "UNITED STATES POSTAGE STAMPS" in oval | 500. |

| KL# | Name, address and notations | Value |
|---|---|---|
| 157-30 | U.S. POSTAGE STAMPS 30 CENTS | 500. |

| KL# | Name, address and notations | Value |
|---|---|---|
| 159-50 | U.S. POSTAGE STAMPS 50 CENTS (vars.) | 500. |
| 161-75 | U.S. POSTAGE STAMPS 75 CENTS | 500. |

163-75hw90 U.S. POSTAGE STAMPS 90 CENTS
Hand changed from 75 cents.        650.

Envelopes come with various color ink and paper color combinations. Much of this new information became available through the sale of the Moreau hoard by Bowers & Merena. Photo's on this page courtesy of Bowers & Merena.

A single hoard of these pieces consisting of a "cigar box full" is known to exist but it has not been seen or cataloged. A small group is known to have been lost in a fire some years ago. The author is indebted to Jackson Storm and to the Chase Bank Collection for some of the illustrations, and to Gene Hessler for some of the photography.

# Encased Postage Stamps

## By Len Glazer

Encased postage has always been among the most elusive of American numismatic items to collect, and consequently, among the most rewarding. With their natural appeal to numismatists, philatelists, and collectors of antique advertising media, demand has also been strong. This competition for scarce items, especially so in high grades of preservation, has meant a steady upward price progression that also makes Encased Postage Stamps desirable from an investment viewpoint.

While a complete set — by denomination, merchant and major variety — of Encased Postage has never been formed and likely never will be, it is entirely within the grasp of the determined numismatist to assemble a collection that is "complete" within self-set boundries; that is, be denomination, by merchant, by type of merchant (medicinal, dry goods, etc.), by locality of issue, or by any other criteria.

**(Encased Postage Stamp photographs in this section are provided through the courtesy of Kagin's.)**

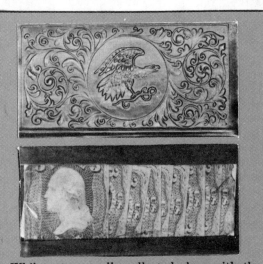

While not generally collected along with the Gault encased postage stamps, the so-called Feuchtwanger rectangular encasement is a contemporary, though unsuccessful, competitor.

Approximately 31x61mm, with a brass frame and no mica cover for the stamps, this item is generally found with a trio of 3-cent postage stamps; a face value of nine cents. The item is also found with other quantities of 3-cent stamps, though the originality of these other denominations is questionable.

Naturally, since the stamps are easily replaced, their condition has little bearing on the value.

| KL# | VF |
|---|---|
| EPS300 | 395.00 |

## Grading

Three factors must be considered in the grading of Encased Postage Stamps: the case itself, the enclosed stamp and the protective mica.

For the listings which follow, generally accepted standards for coin grading have been used to grade the cases. The accepted standards for grading unused U.S. postage stamps have been considered for that element. For the mica, terminology is that which has been in use since the collecting of Encased Postage Stamps began.

In referring to the price listing that follows, it should be made clear that unlike coins or stamps, which are bought and sold on the basis of generally accepted grading standards, Encased Postage Stamps are sold on the individual merits of the piece involved. This is the result of the many and varied states of preservation of each of the three main elements — case, stamp and mica — of these items.

The valuations quoted refer basically to the condition of the case. If the condition of the stamp and mica are consistent in their own way with that of the case, the valuations can be considered accurate at the time of this catalog's issue. If, however, either the stamp or the mica is significantly better or worse than the case, the value of the item as a whole may be more or less than the figure quoted.

Assume, for example, that a piece with a VF case holds a stamp that is Extremely Fine, protected by a piece of mica which is crazed (see mica grading). The stamp is obviously better than the case, and the crazed mica is also quite nice, though not perfect. The value of such a piece is definitely higher than the quoted VF price, and may be closer to the XF valuation.

### Grading of Case

**NEW** — A condition unknown among Encased Postage Stamps. While there do, indeed, exist specimens which show no wear traces of circulation on the case, the condition of the stamp and/or mica will always contain some imperfection which prevents the accurate description of any Encased Postage Stamp as "New."

**ABOUT NEW** — The highest grade in which Encased Postage can practically be collected. Just a touch of rubbing on the case, which may or may not still retain some original silvering, if so issued.

**EXTREMELY FINE** — Higher than average grade, with a bit of noticeable wear on the case; still a very nice piece.

**VERY FINE** — The average grade for collectible Encased Postage Stamps. The case shows definite wear, but little or no flatness of the embossed lettering. Most catalog values are based on this grade.

**FINE** — A worn, but acceptable, piece. Generally the lowest undamaged or collectible grade of untampered Encased Postage, since the items did not circulate long enough to attain any greater degree of wear.

## Grading of Stamp

In their usage with Encased Postage, stamps are generally described in one of the following degrees of brightness. Since the paper was protected by the mica, the only measurement of the state of preservation of the stamp can be the degree to which it was subjected to the fading effects of sunlight or other causes.

**FULLY BRIGHT** — A stamp that is 100% as vivid as the day it was issued.

**NEAR FULL BRIGHT** — Perhaps a spot or two of less than perfect brightness.

**BRIGHT** — A stamp which has lost some of its original color, but is still sharp and always acceptable.

**TONED** — A stamp which has darkened with age or exposure to light and other elements.

**DULL or FADED** — A stamp which has lost much of its color; the lowest generally collectable condition for an undamaged item.

## Grading of Mica

Because it is a natural silicate mineral, mica of flawless, perfect quality probably does not exist in connection with its use in Encased Postage Stamps. Collectors are warned that only "perfect" mica generally encountered is acetate which has been used to repair a damaged Encased Postage Stamp. Upon close examination, some flaw can be found on virtually every mica piece used in this manner.

**NEARLY PERFECT** — The highest degree of preservation for a mica encasement.

**CRAZED** — Fine cracks in the surface on the surface, or between the thin natural layers of mica. Separation beginning in its early stages. None of the crazing fully breaks the mica, exposing the stamp.

**CRACKED** — A break in the mica through to the stamp, but with no piece of the mica missing.

**CHIPPED** — A breaking of only the upper layer or layers of mica, with the chip or chips missing, though the mica beneath remains intact and the stamp protected.

**BROKEN** — A break in all layers of the mica, with some missing and the stamp exposed. The degree of broken or missing mica should be described.

## Other Terms

Two other terms which the collector of Encased Postage will encounter also bear definition.

**RIBBED FRAME** — Some varieties of Encased Postage are known with cases which have fine parallel lines on the face (stamp side) of the metal case.

**SILVERING** — Many Encased Postage Stamps were issued with a thin silver wash on the case, to enhance their resemblance to the disappearing silver coinage of the day. More research is needed to determine which issues came with silvering, which came without and which, if any, were issued both ways. Since the silver wore off very quickly, even many high grade pieces have no traces of the original finish. A piece with a high percentage of silvering remaining is worth a premium, but those with just a trace of silver are not; though it is generally mentioned when describing an item for sale.

## Rarity Ratings

When dealing with the relative rarity of Encased Postage Stamps, the collector must realize that all are scarce in terms of numismatic collectibles. Even the most common variety "Take Ayer's Pills" may not be easy to locate on the market at any given time.

Following years of study of major collections and auction offerings, and conversations with other specialists, the following table of rarity lists each piece in what we believe to be its correct order, and broken into six categories of rarity. While there may be some disagreement as to order within category, we believe most knowledgeable specialists will agree with the listing.

**VERY RARE**
1. Arthur M. Claflin
2. B. F. Miles
3. John W. Norris
4. Pearce, Tolle & Holton

**RARE**
5. White the Hatter
6. Sands' Ale
7. S. Steinfeld
8. Dougan
9. N.G. Taylor & Co.
10. Ellis McAlpin & Co.
11. L.C. Hopkins & Co.
12. Aerated Bread

**VERY SCARCE**
13. F. Buhl & Co.
14. Weir & Larminie
15. Lord & Taylor
16. H.A. Cook
17. Bailey & Co.

**SCARCE**
18. Schapker & Bussing
19. G.G. Evans
20. John Shillito & Co.
21. Mendum's Wine Emporium
22. North America Life Insurance Co.

**COMMON**
23. Tremont House
24. Joseph L. Bates
25. Kirkpatrick & Gault
26. Irving House
27. Brown's Bronchial Troches
28. Burnett's Cocoaine
29. J. Gault
30. Burnett's Cooking Extracts
31. Drake's Plantation Bitters

**MOST COMMON**
32. Take Ayer's Pills
33. Ayer's Cathartic Pills
34. Ayer's Sarsaparilla

## Aerated Bread Co., New York

| KL# | Denom. | Fine | VF | XF |
|---|---|---|---|---|
| EPS1 | 1¢ | 800. | 1250. | 1500. |

## Ayer's Cathartic Pills
### (Long arrows variety)

| KL# | Denom. | Fine | VF | XF |
|---|---|---|---|---|
| EPS2 | 3¢ | 100. | 175. | 250. |
| EPS3 | 5¢ | 125. | 275. | 350. |
| EPS4 | 10¢ | 250. | 500. | 650. |

### (Short arrows variety)

| KL# | Denom. | Fine | VF | XF |
|---|---|---|---|---|
| EPS5 | 1¢ | 150. | 225. | 300. |
| EPS6 | 3¢ | 100. | 175. | 250. |
| EPS7 | 5¢ | 125. | 275. | 350. |
| EPS8 | 10¢ | 200. | 350. | 500. |
| EPS9 | 12¢ | 300. | 550. | 1000. |
| EPS10 | 24¢ | 1200. | 2000. | 3000. |
| EPS11 | 30¢ | 1500. | 3000. | 4000. |

## Take Ayer's Pills

| KL# | Denom. | Fine | VF | XF |
|---|---|---|---|---|
| EPS12 | 1¢ | 150. | 250. | 325. |
| EPS13 | 3¢ | 100. | 150. | 225. |
| EPS14 | 5¢ | 100. | 200. | 300. |
| EPS15 | 10¢ | 175. | 375. | 500. |
| EPS16 | 12¢ | 300. | 550. | 1000. |
| EPS17 | 90¢ | Two known are both suspect as being counterfeit or altered. | | |

## Ayer's Sarsaparilla
### (Small Ayer's)

| KL# | Denom. | Fine | VF | XF |
|---|---|---|---|---|
| EPS18 | 1¢ | 300. | 625. | 925. |
| EPS19 | 3¢ | 350. | 550. | 750. |
| EPS20 | 10¢ | 300. | 625. | 925. |
| EPS21 | 12¢ | 700. | 1400. | 2000. |

### (Medium Ayer's)

| KL# | Denom. | Fine | VF | XF |
|---|---|---|---|---|
| EPS22 | 1¢ | 150. | 225. | 300. |
| EPS23 | 3¢ | 100. | 175. | 225. |
| EPS24 | 5¢ | 150. | 225. | 300. |
| EPS25 | 10¢ | 175. | 300. | 450. |
| EPS26 | 12¢ | 300. | 550. | 1000. |
| EPS27 | 24¢ | 1200. | 2000. | 3000. |
| EPS28 | 30¢ | 1500. | 3000. | 4000. |
| EPS29 | 90¢ | 2500. | 5000. | 9000. |

### (Large Ayer's)

| KL# | Denom. | Fine | VF | XF |
|---|---|---|---|---|
| EPS30 | 3¢ | 275. | 400. | 750. |
| EPS31 | 10¢ | 450. | 700. | 1000. |

## Bailey & Co., Philadelphia

| KL# | Denom. | Fine | VF | XF |
|---|---|---|---|---|
| EPS32 | 1¢ | 375. | 550. | 1000. |
| EPS33 | 3¢ | 375. | 550. | 1000. |
| EPS34 | 5¢ | 400. | 650. | 1300. |
| EPS35 | 10¢ | 400. | 600. | 1250. |
| EPS36 | 12¢ | 1000. | 1500. | 2500. |

## Joseph L. Bates "Fancy Goods," Boston
### Fancygoods One Word

| KL# | Denom. | Fine | VF | XF |
|---|---|---|---|---|
| EPS41 | 1¢ | 150. | 225. | 300. |
| EPS42 | 3¢ | 300. | 450. | 650. |
| EPS43 | 10¢ | 200. | 375. | 600. |

### Joseph L. Bates Fancy Goods Two Words

| KL# | Denom. | Fine | VF | XF |
|---|---|---|---|---|
| EPS37 | 1¢ | 150. | 225. | 300. |
| EPS38 | 3¢ | 350. | 675. | 850. |
| EPS39 | 10¢ | 200. | 375. | 600. |
| EPS40 | 12¢ | 300. | 550. | 1000. |

## Brown's Bronchial Troches

| KL# | Denom. | Fine | VF | XF |
|---|---|---|---|---|
| EPS44 | 1¢ | 225. | 375. | 550. |
| EPS45 | 3¢ | 175. | 300. | 400. |
| EPS46 | 5¢ | 175. | 300. | 400. |
| EPS47 | 10¢ | 250. | 375. | 500. |
| EPS48 | 12¢ | 600. | 1000. | 1400. |

## F. Buhl & Co., Detroit

| KL# | Denom. | Fine | VF | XF |
|---|---|---|---|---|
| EPS49 | 1¢ | 400. | 650. | 1100. |
| EPS50 | 3¢ | 400. | 700. | 1250. |
| EPS51 | 5¢ | 400. | 650. | 1100. |
| EPS52 | 10¢ | 750. | 1000. | 2000. |
| EPS53 | 12¢ | 750. | 1500. | 2000. |

## Burnett's Cocoaine Kalliston

| KL# | Denom. | Fine | VF | XF |
|---|---|---|---|---|
| EPS54 | 1¢ | 150. | 250. | 375. |
| EPS55 | 3¢ | 125. | 175. | 275. |
| EPS56 | 5¢ | 150. | 300. | 425. |
| EPS57 | 10¢ | 200. | 550. | 800. |
| EPS58 | 12¢ | 300. | 550. | 1000. |
| EPS59 | 24¢ | 1500. | 2000. | 3000. |
| EPS60 | 30¢ | 1750. | 3000. | 4000. |
| EPS61 | 90¢ | 2500. | 5000. | 9000. |

## Burnett's Cooking Extracts
### (Plain frame)

| KL# | Denom. | Fine | VF | XF |
|---|---|---|---|---|
| EPS62 | 1¢ | 150. | 250. | 375. |
| EPS63 | 3¢ | 150. | 275. | 425. |
| EPS64 | 5¢ | 150. | 250. | 375. |
| EPS65 | 10¢ | 200. | 375. | 550. |
| EPS66 | 12¢ | 300. | 550. | 1000. |
| EPS67 | 24¢ | 1500. | 2000. | 3000. |
| EPS68 | 30¢ | 1750. | 3000. | 4000. |
| EPS69 | 90¢ | 2500. | 5000. | 9000. |

### (Ribbed frame)

| KL# | Denom. | Fine | VF | XF |
|---|---|---|---|---|
| EPS70 | 10¢ | 350. | 650. | 800. |

## A.M. Claflin, Hopkinton, R.I.

| KL# | Denom. | Fine | VF | XF |
|---|---|---|---|---|
| EPS71 | 1¢ | 3000. | 6250. | 12,750. |
| EPS72 | 3¢ | 3000. | 4000. | 6000. |
| EPS73 | 5¢ | 3000. | 4000. | 6000. |
| EPS74 | 12¢ | 3000. | 5000. | 7500. |

## H.A. Cook, Evansville, Ind.

| KL# | Denom. | Fine | VF | XF |
|---|---|---|---|---|
| EPS75 | 5¢ | 350. | 650. | 1300. |
| EPS76 | 10¢ | 600. | 1200. | 2500. |

## Dougan, New York

| KL# | Denom. | Fine | VF | XF |
|---|---|---|---|---|
| EPS77 | 1¢ | 800. | 1500. | 2500. |
| EPS78 | 3¢ | 800. | 1500. | 2500. |
| EPS79 | 5¢ | 600. | 1000. | 2000. |
| EPS80 | 10¢ | 1000. | 2000. | 3000. |

## Drake's Plantation Bitters, New York

| KL# | Denom. | Fine | VF | XF |
|---|---|---|---|---|
| EPS81 | 1¢ | 175. | 225. | 300. |
| EPS82 | 3¢ | 125. | 275. | 400. |
| EPS83 | 5¢ | 200. | 300. | 400. |
| EPS84 | 10¢ | 225. | 375. | 550. |
| EPS85 | 12¢ | 300. | 550. | 1000. |
| EPS86 | 24¢ | 1500. | 2500. | 3000. |
| EPS87 | 30¢ | 2000. | 3000. | 4000. |
| EPS88 | 90¢ | 2750. | 5500. | 9000. |

## Ellis, McAlpin & Co., Cincinnati

| KL# | Denom. | Fine | VF | XF |
|---|---|---|---|---|
| EPS89 | 1¢ | 600. | 1250. | 1850. |
| EPS90 | 3¢ | 600. | 1250. | 1750. |
| EPS91 | 5¢ | 800. | 1650. | 2300. |
| EPS92 | 10¢ | 600. | 1250. | 1750. |
| EPS93 | 12¢ | 800. | 1500. | 2250. |
| EPS94 | 24¢ | 1200. | 2000. | 3000. |

## G.G. Evans, Philadelphia

| KL# | Denom. | Fine | VF | XF |
|---|---|---|---|---|
| EPS95 | 1¢ | 300. | 600. | 900. |
| EPS96 | 3¢ | 400. | 700. | 1000. |
| EPS97 | 5¢ | 450. | 750. | 1250. |
| EPS98 | 10¢ | 450. | 750. | 1250. |

## J. Gault
### (Plain frame)

| KL# | Denom. | Fine | VF | XF |
|---|---|---|---|---|
| EPS99 | 1¢ | 150. | 225. | 300. |
| EPS100 | 2¢ | — | 12,000. | — |
| | (Three known) | | | |
| EPS101 | 3¢ | 150. | 250. | 350. |
| EPS102 | 5¢ | 150. | 250. | 375. |
| EPS103 | 10¢ | 200. | 300. | 500. |
| EPS104 | 12¢ | 300. | 550. | 1000. |
| EPS105 | 24¢ | 1250. | 2000. | 3000. |
| EPS106 | 30¢ | 1500. | 3000. | 4000. |
| EPS107 | 90¢ | 2500. | 5000. | 9000. |

### (Ribbed frame)

| KL# | Denom. | Fine | VF | XF |
|---|---|---|---|---|
| EPS108 | 1¢ | 400. | 700. | 1000. |
| EPS109 | 3¢ | 400. | 700. | 1000. |
| EPS110 | 5¢ | 275. | 450. | 600. |
| EPS111 | 10¢ | 300. | 550. | 700. |
| EPS112 | 12¢ | 500. | 800. | 1500. |
| EPS113 | 24¢ | 1500. | 2750. | 3500. |
| EPS114 | 30¢ | 1750. | 3000. | 4000. |

## L. C. Hopkins & Co., Cincinnati

| KL# | Denom. | Fine | VF | XF |
|---|---|---|---|---|
| EPS115 | 1¢ | 700. | 1250. | 1750. |
| EPS116 | 3¢ | 600. | 1150. | 1500. |
| EPS117 | 5¢ | 800. | 1500. | 2250. |
| EPS118 | 10¢ | 700. | 1250. | 1750. |

## Irving House, N.Y. (Hunt & Nash)
### (Plain frame)

| KL# | Denom. | Fine | VF | XF |
|---|---|---|---|---|
| EPS119 | 1¢ | 150. | 250. | 350. |
| EPS120 | 3¢ | 150. | 250. | 350. |
| EPS121 | 5¢ | 400. | 700. | 1000. |
| EPS122 | 10¢ | 200. | 300. | 450. |
| EPS123 | 12¢ | 300. | 550. | 1000. |
| EPS124 | 24¢ | 1250. | 2000. | 3000. |
| EPS125 | 30¢ | 1500. | 3000. | 4000. |

### (Ribbed frame)

| KL# | Denom. | Fine | VF | XF |
|---|---|---|---|---|
| EPS126 | 1¢ | 400. | 700. | 1000. |
| EPS127 | 3¢ | 400. | 700. | 1000. |
| EPS128 | 5¢ | 450. | 750. | 1500. |
| EPS129 | 10¢ | 350. | 550. | 750. |
| EPS130 | 12¢ | 500. | 800. | 1500. |
| EPS131 | 24¢ | 1500. | 2750. | 3500. |

## Kirkpatrick & Gault, New York

| KL# | Denom. | Fine | VF | XF |
|---|---|---|---|---|
| EPS132 | 1¢ | 150. | 225. | 300. |
| EPS133 | 3¢ | 125. | 200. | 275. |
| EPS134 | 5¢ | 175. | 350. | 500. |
| EPS135 | 10¢ | 200. | 300. | 500. |
| EPS136 | 12¢ | 300. | 550. | 1000. |
| EPS137 | 24¢ | 1250. | 2000. | 3000. |
| EPS138 | 30¢ | 1500. | 3000. | 4000. |
| EPS139 | 90¢ | 2500. | 5000. | 9000. |

## Lord & Taylor, New York

| KL# | Denom. | Fine | VF | XF |
|---|---|---|---|---|
| EPS140 | 1¢ | 400. | 650. | 1250. |
| EPS141 | 3¢ | 400. | 650. | 1250. |
| EPS142 | 5¢ | 400. | 650. | 1250. |
| EPS143 | 10¢ | 400. | 700. | 1500. |
| EPS144 | 12¢ | 800. | 1500. | 2000. |
| EPS145 | 24¢ | 1500. | 2500. | 3500. |
| EPS146 | 30¢ | 2000. | 4000. | 5000. |
| EPS147 | 90¢ | 4000. | 7500. | 9000. |

## Mendum's Family Wine Emporium, New York
### (Plain frame)

| KL# | Denom. | Fine | VF | XF |
|---|---|---|---|---|
| EPS148 | 1¢ | 250. | 350. | 500. |
| EPS149 | 3¢ | 350. | 500. | 800. |
| EPS150 | 5¢ | 300. | 450. | 600. |
| EPS151 | 10¢ | 300. | 450. | 700. |
| EPS152 | 12¢ | 650. | 1250. | 1750. |

### (Ribbed frame)

| KL# | Denom. | Fine | VF | XF |
|---|---|---|---|---|
| EPS153 | 10¢ | 400. | 700. | 1000. |

## B. F. Miles, Peoria

| KL# | Denom. | Fine | VF | XF |
|---|---|---|---|---|
| EPS154 | 5¢ | 3500. | 7000. | 9000. |

## John W. Norris, Chicago

| KL# | Denom. | Fine | VF | XF |
|---|---|---|---|---|
| EPS155 | 1¢ | 750. | 1000. | 1700. |
| EPS156 | 3¢ | 1000. | 1750. | 3000. |
| EPS157 | 5¢ | 1000. | 1750. | 3000. |
| EPS158 | 10¢ | 1000. | 1750. | 3000. |

## North America Life Insurance Co., New York
### (Straight "Insurance")

| KL# | Denom. | Fine | VF | XF |
|---|---|---|---|---|
| EPS159 | 1¢ | 175. | 250. | 350. |
| EPS160 | 3¢ | 175. | 250. | 350. |
| EPS161 | 10¢ | 200. | 375. | 600. |
| EPS162 | 12¢ | 450. | 1000. | 1500. |

## (Curved "Insurance")
## (Trial Piece)

| KL# | Denom. | Fine | VF | XF |
|---|---|---|---|---|
| EPS163 | 1¢ | 225. | 500. | 1000. |
| EPS164 | 10¢ | 300. | 500. | 750. |

## Pearce, Tolle & Holton, Cincinnati

| KL# | Denom. | Fine | VF | XF |
|---|---|---|---|---|
| EPS165 | 1¢ | 1000. | 1750. | 3000. |
| EPS166 | 3¢ | 800. | 1500. | 2500. |
| EPS167 | 5¢ | 1000. | 1750. | 3000. |
| EPS168 | 10¢ | 1100. | 2000. | 3500. |

## Sands' Ale

| KL# | Denom. | Fine | VF | XF |
|---|---|---|---|---|
| EPS169 | 5¢ | 800. | 1500. | 2500. |
| EPS170 | 10¢ | 1000. | 1750. | 2750. |
| EPS171 | 30¢ | 2000. | 3500. | 5000. |

## Schapker & Bussing, Evansville, Ind.

| KL# | Denom. | Fine | VF | XF |
|---|---|---|---|---|
| EPS172 | 1¢ | 400. | 700. | 1000. |
| EPS173 | 3¢ | 225. | 350. | 600. |
| EPS174 | 5¢ | 450. | 750. | 1250. |
| EPS175 | 10¢ | 450. | 800. | 1250. |
| EPS176 | 12¢ | 500. | 1250. | 1750. |

## John Shillito & Co., Cincinnati

| KL# | Denom. | Fine | VF | XF |
|---|---|---|---|---|
| EPS177 | 1¢ | 400. | 700. | 1000. |
| EPS178 | 3¢ | 250. | 350. | 600. |
| EPS179 | 5¢ | 250. | 450. | 900. |
| EPS180 | 10¢ | 275. | 425. | 750. |
| EPS181 | 12¢ | 500. | 1250. | 1750. |

## S. Steinfeld, New York

| KL# | Denom. | Fine | VF | XF |
|---|---|---|---|---|
| EPS182 | 1¢ | 1000. | 1700. | 2500. |
| EPS183 | 10¢ | 1000. | 1600. | 2500. |
| EPS184 | 12¢ | 1000. | 1750. | 2750. |

## N. G. Taylor & Co., Philadelphia

| KL# | Denom. | Fine | VF | XF |
|---|---|---|---|---|
| EPS185 | 1¢ | 800. | 1250. | 1900. |
| EPS186 | 3¢ | 800. | 1250. | 1750. |
| EPS187 | 5¢ | 800. | 1500. | 2000. |
| EPS188 | 10¢ | 800. | 1250. | 1750. |

## Tremont House (Gage Brothers & Drake), Chicago

| KL# | Denom. | Fine | VF | XF |
|---|---|---|---|---|
| EPS189 | 1¢ | 150. | 225. | 300. |
| EPS190 | 5¢ | 150. | 300. | 375. |
| EPS191 | 10¢ | 200. | 325. | 450. |
| EPS192 | 12¢ | 350. | 600. | 1250. |

## Weir & Larminie, Montreal

| KL# | Denom. | Fine | VF | XF |
|---|---|---|---|---|
| EPS193 | 1¢ | 450. | 750. | 1250. |
| EPS194 | 3¢ | 400. | 700. | 1000. |
| EPS195 | 5¢ | 500. | 800. | 1500. |
| EPS196 | 10¢ | 600. | 900. | 1700. |

## White the Hatter, New York

| KL# | Denom. | Fine | VF | XF |
|---|---|---|---|---|
| EPS197 | 1¢ | 750. | 1000. | 1900. |
| EPS198 | 3¢ | 800. | 1500. | 2500. |
| EPS199 | 5¢ | 900. | 1750. | 3000. |
| EPS200 | 10¢ | 800. | 1500. | 2500. |

# First Issue "Postage Currency"

## 5 CENTS

| KL# | Fr# | Date | Description | VG | VF | Unc |
|-----|-----|------|-------------|-----|-----|-----|
| 3209 | 1228 | 17.7.1862. Brown. One 5 cent Jefferson stamp at center. Perf. edges; ANBC's monogram on back. | | 14.00 | 16.00 | 155. |
| 3210 | 1229 | Perf. edges; back w/o ANBC's monogram. | | 15.00 | 22.00 | 180. |
| 3211 | 1230 | Straight edges; ABNC's monogram on back. | | 14.50 | 16.00 | 50.00 |
| 3212 | 1231 | Straight edges; back w/o ABNC's monogram. | | 15.00 | 21.00 | 150. |

## 10 CENTS

| KL# | Fr# | Date | Description | VG | VF | Unc |
|-----|-----|------|-------------|-----|-----|-----|
| 3213 | 1240 | 17.7.1862. Green. One 10 cent Washington stamp at center. Perf. edges; ABNC's monogram on back. | | 15.00 | 18.50 | 115. |
| 3214 | 1241 | Perf. edges; back w/o ABNC's monogram. | | 15.50 | 30.00 | 130. |
| 3215 | 1242 | Straight edges; ABNC's monogram on back. | | 11.50 | 13.00 | 40.00 |
| 3216 | 1243 | Straight edges; back w/o ABNC's monogram. | | 12.50 | 40.00 | 150. |

## 25 CENTS

| KL# | Fr# | Date | Description | VG | VF | Unc |
|-----|-----|------|-------------|-----|-----|-----|
| 3217 | 1279 | 17.7.1862. Brown. Horizontal row of five 5 cent Jefferson stamps. Perf. edges; ABNC's monogram on back. | | 16.00 | 25.00 | 170. |
| 3218 | 1280 | Perf. edges; back w/o ABNC's monogram. | | 25.00 | 60.00 | 275. |
| 3219 | 1281 | Straight edges; ABNC's monogram on back. | | 11.50 | 15.00 | 75.00 |
| 3220 | 1282 | Straight edges; back w/o ABNC's monogram. | | 13.00 | 60.00 | 300. |

## 50 CENTS

| KL# | Fr# | Date | Description | VG | VF | Unc |
|-----|-----|------|-------------|-----|-----|-----|
| 3221 | 1310 | 17.7.1862. Green. Horizontal row of five 10 cent Washington stamps. #12 perf. edges; ABNC's monogram on back. | | 24.00 | 30.00 | 290. |
| 3222 | 1310-A | #14 perf. edges; ABNC's monogram on back. | | — | Rare | — |
| 3223 | 1311 | Perf. edges; back w/o ABNC's monogram. | | 30.00 | 70.00 | 300. |
| 3224 | 1312 | Straight edges; ABNC's monogram on back. | | 17.00 | 18.50 | 120. |
| 3225 | 1313 | Straight edges; back w/o ABNC's monogram. | | 20.00 | 75.00 | 300. |

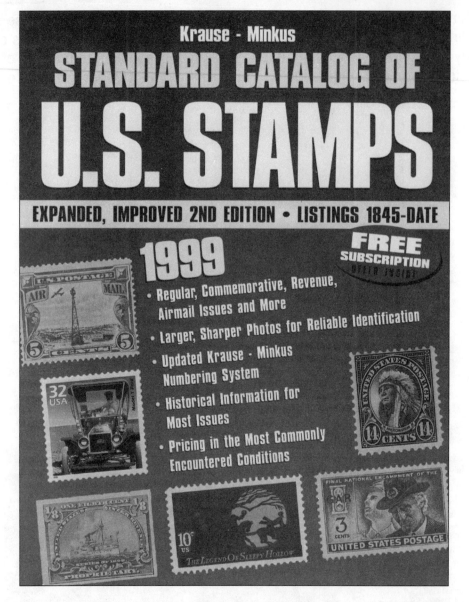